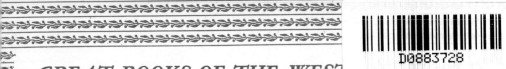

GREAT BOOKS
OF THE WESTERN WORLD

ROBERT MAYNARD HUTCHINS, *EDITOR IN CHIEF*

28.

GILBERT

GALILEO

HARVEY

On the Loadstone and Magnetic Bodies

BY WILLIAM GILBERT

Concerning the Two New Sciences

BY GALILEO GALILEI

On the Motion of the Heart and Blood in Animals. On the Circulation of the Blood. On the Generation of Animals

BY WILLIAM HARVEY

WILLIAM BENTON, *Publisher*

ENCYCLOPÆDIA BRITANNICA, INC.

CHICAGO · LONDON · TORONTO · GENEVA · SYDNEY · TOKYO

On the Loadstone and Magnetic Bodies, translated by P. Fleury Mottelay, is reprinted by arrangement with JOHN WILEY AND SONS, INC.

Dialogues Concerning the Two New Sciences, translated by Henry Crew and Alfonso de Salvio, is reprinted by arrangement with NORTHWESTERN UNIVERSITY STUDIES

THE UNIVERSITY OF CHICAGO

The Great Books
is published with the editorial advice of the faculties
of The University of Chicago

GENERAL CONTENTS

++++++++++++++++++++++

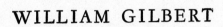

WILLIAM GILBERT

WILLIAM GILBERT

BIOGRAPHICAL NOTE
William Gilbert, 1540–1603

Gilbert was born May 24, 1540, at Colchester in Essex. He came from an ancient Suffolk family and was the eldest of the five sons of Hierome Gilbert, recorder at Colchester. After completing his preliminary education at the town school, Gilbert in 1558 entered St. John's College, Cambridge, where he studied for eleven years. He took his bachelor's degree in 1560, was elected fellow the following year, and proceeded to work for his M.A., which he received in 1564. It was about this time that his interest in science apparently began to attract notice; he was appointed mathematical examiner in 1565 and then turned to the study of medicine, in which he received his doctorate four years later, when he was also elected senior fellow at St. John's College.

Shortly after receiving his degree, Gilbert left Cambridge and apparently made extensive travels on the continent, particularly in Italy. It is probable that he received the degree of Doctor of Physic from a continental university, and he presumably then made the acquaintance of some of the learned men with whom he was later in correspondence. After his return to England he settled in London in 1573, where he practised as a physician with "great success and applause." Admitted to the College of Physicians about 1576, Gilbert held the office of censor from 1581 to 1590; he was treasurer from 1587 to 1592 and again from 1597 to 1599, when he succeeded to the presidency of the college. He served on the committee appointed to superintend the preparation of the *Pharmacopoeia Londinensis*, which was undertaken by the college in 1589 although it did not appear until 1618.

During these years that Gilbert was making a reputation as a physician, he was also becoming known as a savant in chemistry, physics, and cosmology. He appears to have studied these sciences from his youth. He was perhaps the first advocate of Copernican views in England, and he held that the fixed stars were not all at the same distance from the earth. His study of navigation is said to have resulted in the invention of two instruments enabling sailors "to find out the latitude without seeing of sun, moon, or stars." But the main basis of his reputation as a scientist was the publication in 1600, after eighteen years of reading, experiment, and reflection, of his book on the magnet, *De Magnete Magneticisque Corporibus et de Magno Magnete Tellure Physiologia Nova*. It was the first important work in physical science to be published in England, and almost immediately after its publication Gilbert was famous throughout Europe. Kepler paid tribute to its influence upon his own physical speculations. Galileo first turned his attention to magnetism after reading Gilbert and said of him that he was "great to a degree that is enviable." Bacon, though he spoke disparagingly of Gilbert's attempt "to raise a general system upon the magnet," praised him as an experimental philosopher and seems to have taken whole paragraphs of Gilbert's work as his own.

At his London house, where he possessed a large collection of books, globes, instruments, and minerals, Gilbert gathered about him men who were interested in discussing scientific problems. The group, which held regular monthly meetings and constituted a kind of society, is now looked upon as a precursor of the Royal Society. Gilbert presumably took a leading part in these discussions, and he is known to have continued his scientific investigations, but his only other book, a treatise dealing with meteorological subjects, *De Mundo Nostro Sublunari Philosophia Nova*, was edited after his death by his brother.

In 1601 Gilbert was appointed physician to Queen Elizabeth, and it appears that he then moved to the court. Upon the death of the Queen, it was discovered that her only personal legacy was made to Gilbert for the prosecution of his studies. He was immediately reappointed royal physician by James I, but died shortly afterward, probably of the plague, on November 30, 1603, and was buried in the chancel of Holy Trinity church in Colchester. He bequeathed his scientific library and instruments to the College of Physicians, but they were destroyed in the great fire of London.

He left his portrait, which is said to have been painted for that purpose, to Oxford University. In it he is represented as standing, wearing his doctor's robes and holding in his hand a globe on which is written the word *terrella;* as its inscription the painting has, *Gilbert, the first investigator of the powers of the magnet.*

CONTENTS

CONTENTS

On the Loadstone and Magnetic Bodies and on the Great Magnet the Earth

PREFACE

SINCE in the discovery of secret things and in the investigation of hidden causes, stronger reasons are obtained from sure experiments and demonstrated arguments than from probable conjectures and the opinions of philosophical speculators of the common sort; therefore to the end that the noble substance of that great loadstone, our common mother (the earth), still quite unknown, and also the forces extraordinary and exalted of this globe may the better be understood, we have decided first to begin with the common stony and ferruginous matter, and magnetic bodies, and the parts of the earth that we may handle and may perceive with the senses; then to proceed with plain magnetic experiments, and to penetrate to the inner parts of the earth. For after we had, in order to discover the true substance of the earth, seen and examined very many matters taken out of lofty mountains, or the depths of seas, or deepest caverns, or hidden mines, we gave much attention for a long time to the study of magnetic forces—wondrous forces they, surpassing the powers of all other bodies around us, though the virtues of all things dug out of the earth were to be brought together. Nor did we find this our labour vain or fruitless, for every day, in our experiments, novel, unheard-of properties came to light: and our philosophy became so widened, as a result of diligent research, that we have attempted to set forth, according to magnetic principles, the inner constitution of the globe and its genuine substance, and in true demonstrations and in experiments that appeal plainly to the senses, as though we were pointing with the finger to exhibit to mankind earth, mother of all.

And even as geometry rises from certain slight and readily understood foundations to the highest and most difficult demonstrations, whereby the ingenious mind ascends above the æther: so does our magnetic doctrine and science in due order first show forth certain facts of less rare occurrence; from these proceed facts of a more extraordinary kind; at length, in a sort of series, are revealed things most secret and privy in the earth, and the causes are recognized of things that, in the ignorance of those of old or through the heedlessness of the moderns, were unnoticed or disregarded. But why should I, in so vast an ocean of books whereby the minds of the studious are bemuddled and vexed—of books of the more stupid sort whereby the common herd and fellows without a spark of talent are made intoxicated, crazy, puffed up; and are led to write numerous books and to profess themselves philosophers, physicians, mathematicians, and astrologers, the while ignoring and contemning men of learning—why, I say, should I add aught further to this confused world of writings, or why should I submit this noble and (as comprising many things before unheard of) this new and inadmissible philosophy to the judgment of men who have taken oath to follow the opinions of others, to the most senseless corrupters of the arts, to lettered clowns, grammatists, sophists, spouters, and the wrongheaded rabble, to be denounced, torn to tatters and heaped with contumely. To you alone, true philosophers, ingenuous minds, who not only in books but in things themselves look for knowledge, have I dedicated these foundations of magnetic science—a new style of philosophizing. But if any see fit not to agree with the opinions here expressed and not to accept certain of my paradoxes, still let them note the great multitude of experiments and discoveries —these it is chiefly that cause all philosophy to flourish; and we have dug them up and demonstrated them with much pains and sleepless nights and great money expense. Enjoy them you, and, if ye can, employ them for better purposes. I know how hard it is to impart the air of newness to what is old, trimness to what is gone out of fashion; to lighten what is dark; to make that grateful which excites disgust; to win belief for things doubtful; but far more difficult is it to win any standing for or to establish doctrines that are novel, unheard-of, and opposed to everybody's opinions. We care naught, for that, as we have held that philosophy is for the few.

We have set over against our discoveries and experiments larger and smaller asterisks according to their importance and their subtility. Let whosoever would make the same experiments handle the bodies carefully, skilfully, and deftly, not heedlessly and bunglingly; when an experiment fails, let him not in his ignorance condemn our discoveries, for there is naught in these books that has not been investigated and again and again done and repeated under our eyes. Many things in our reasonings and our hypotheses will perhaps seem hard to accept, being at variance with the general opinion; but I have no doubt that hereafter they will win authoritativeness from the demonstrations themselves. Hence the more advanced one is in the science of the loadstone, the more trust he has in the hypotheses, and the greater the progress he makes; nor will one reach anything like certitude in the magnetic philosophy, unless all, or at all events most, of its principles are known to him.

This natural philosophy (*physiologia*) is almost a new thing, unheard of before; a very few writers have simply published some meagre accounts of certain magnetic forces. Therefore we do not at all quote the ancients and the Greeks as our supporters, for neither can paltry Greek argumentation demonstrate the truth more subtilly nor Greek terms more effectively, nor can both elucidate it better. Our doctrine of the loadstone is contradictory of most of the principles and axioms of the Greeks. Nor have we brought into this work any graces of rhetoric, any verbal ornateness, but have aimed simply at treating knotty questions about which little is known in such a style and in such terms as are needed to make what is said clearly intelligible. Therefore we sometimes employ words new and unheard of, not (as alchemists are wont to do) in order to veil things with a pedantic terminology and to make them dark and obscure, but in order that hidden things with no name and up to this time unnoticed may be plainly and fully published.

After the magnetic experiments and the account of the homogenic parts of the earth, we proceed to a consideration of the general nature of the whole earth; and here we decided to philosophize freely, as freely, as in the past, the Egyptians, Greeks, and Latins published their dogmas; for very many of their errors have been handed down from author to author till our own time; and as our sciolists still take their stand on these foundations, they continue to stray about, so to speak, in perpetual darkness. To those men of early times and, as it were, first parents of philosophy, to Aristotle, Theophrastus, Ptolemy, Hippocrates, Galen, be due honour rendered ever, for from them has knowledge descended to those that have come after them: but our age has discovered and brought to light very many things which they too, were they among the living, would cheerfully adopt. Wherefore we have had no hesitation in setting forth, in hypotheses that are provable, the things that we have through a long experience discovered. Farewell.

BOOK FIRST

CHAPTER 1. *Writings of ancient and modern authors concerning the loadstone: various opinions and delusions*

In former times when philosophy, still rude and uncultured, was involved in the murkiness of errors and ignorances, a few of the virtues and properties of things were, it is true, known and understood: in the world of plants and herbs all was confusion, mining was undeveloped, and mineralogy neglected. But when, by the genius and labours of many workers, certain things needful for man's use and welfare were brought to light and made known to others (reason and experience meanwhile adding a larger hope), then did mankind begin to search the forests, the plains, the mountains and precipices, the seas and the depths of the waters, and the inmost bowels of earth, and to investigate all things. And by good luck at last the loadstone was found, as seems probable, by iron-smelters or by miners in veins of iron ore. On being treated by the metallurgists, it quickly exhibited that strong powerful attraction of iron—no latent nor obscure property, but one easily seen of all: one observed and commended with many praises. And after it had come forth as it were out of darkness and out of deep dungeons and been honoured of men on account of its strong and marvellous attraction of iron, then many ancient philosophers and physicians discoursed of it, and briefly (but briefly only) made it matter of record: as, for instance, Plato in the *Ion,* Aristotle only in his first book *On the Soul;* likewise Theophrastus the Lesbian, Dioscorides, Caius Plinius Secundus, Julius Solinus.

These record only that the loadstone attracts iron: its other properties were all hid. But lest the story of the loadstone should be jejune and too brief, to this one sole property then known were appended certain figments and falsehoods which in the early time no less than nowadays were by precocious sciolists and copyists dealt out to mankind to be swallowed. For example, they asserted that a loadstone rubbed with garlic does not attract iron; nor when it is in presence of a diamond. The like of this is found in Pliny and in Ptolemy's *Quadripartitum;* and errors have steadily been spread abroad and been accepted—even as evil and noxious plants ever have the most luxuriant growth—down to our day, being propagated in the writings of many authors who, to the end that their volumes might grow to the desired bulk, do write and copy all sorts about ever so many things of which they know naught for certain in the light of experience. Such fables about the loadstone even Georgius Agricola, a man that has deserved well indeed of letters, has inserted as truthful history in his books *De natura fossilium,* putting his trust in others' writings. Galen, in the ninth book of his *De simplicium medicamentorum facultatibus,* recognizes its medicinal virtue, and its natural power of attracting iron, in the first book of his *On the Natural Faculties;* but he knew not the cause, any more than Dioscorides before him, nor did he seek further. But his translator Matthiolus furbishes again the garlic and diamond story, and further brings in the fable of Mohammed's shrine having an arched roof of magnets so that the people might be fooled by the trick of the coffin suspended in air, as though 'twere some divine miracle. But this is shown to be false by the reports of travellers. Pliny, however, records that the architect Chinocrates began to put an arched roof of loadstone on the temple of Arsinoë at Alexandria, so that her effigy in iron might seem to be suspended in air: in the meantime the architect died, as also Ptolemy, who had ordered the work to be done in honor of his sister.

But little has been written by the ancients about the causes of the attraction of iron: some trifling remarks of Lucretius and others are extant; other authors barely make slight mention of the attraction of iron: all these are berated by Cardan for being so heedless and indifferent about so notable a matter, so broad a field of philosophizing, and for not giving a fuller account or a more developed philosophy; yet Cardan himself in his ponderous volumes has handed down to posterity, beyond a few commonplaces and quotations from other writers and false discoveries, naught that is worthy of a philosopher. Of later authors, some tell only of its efficacy in medicine, as Antonius Musa Brasevolus, Baptista Montanus, Amatus Lusitanus, as did before them Oribasius in Book XIII of the *De facultate metallicorum,* Avicenna, Serapio Mauritanus, Abohali (Hali Abbas), Santes de Ardoniis, Petrus Apponensis, Marcellus, Arnaldus. Only a few points touching the loadstone are very briefly mentioned by Marbodeus Gallus, Albertus, Matthæus Silvaticus, Hermolaus Barbatus, Camillus Leonhardus, Cornelius Agrippa, Fallopius, Joannes Langius, Cardinal de Cusa, Hannibal Roserius Calaber: by all these the subject is handled in the most careless way, while they repeat only the figments and ravings of others. Matthiolus compares the attractive virtues of the loadstone, which pass through iron, to the mischief of the torpedo, whose poison passes through bodies and spreads in an occult way. Gulielmus Puteanus in his *Ratio purgantium medicamentorum* discusses the loadstone briefly and crudely. Thomas Erastus, knowing naught of the nature of the loadstone, draws from it weak arguments against Paracelsus. Georgius Agricola, like Encelius and other writers on metals, simply describes it. Alexander Aphrodiseus, in his *Problemata,* judges the question of the loadstone to be incapable of explication. Lucretius Carus, the Epicurean poet, deems the attraction to be due to this, that as there is from all things an efflux of minutest bodies, so there is from iron efflux of atoms into the space betwixt the iron and the loadstone— a space emptied of air by the loadstone's atoms [seeds]; and when these begin to return to the loadstone, the iron follows, the corpuscles being entangled with each other. Something similar is said by Joannes Costæus, following Plutarch. Thomas Aquinas, in his *Physica,* Book VII, treating briefly of the loadstone, gets at the nature of it fairly well: with his godlike and perspicacious mind he would have developed many a point had he been acquainted with magnetic experiments. Plato holds the magnetic virtue to be divine.

But when, some three or four hundred years ago, the magnetic movement to the north and the south was discovered or recognized anew, many learned men, each according to his own gifts, strove to honour with admiration and praise or to explain with feeble reasonings a property so curious and so necessary for the use of mankind. Of more recent authors, very many have striven to discover the cause of this

direction and movement to north and south, and to understand this so great miracle of nature and lay it open to others: but they wasted oil and labor, because, not being practical in the research of objects in nature, being acquainted only with books, being led astray by certain erroneous physical systems, and having made no magnetical experiments, they constructed certain raciocinations on a basis of mere opinions, and old-womanishly dreamt the things that were not. Marcilius Ficinus chews the cud of ancient opinions, and to give the reason of the magnetic direction seeks its cause in the constellation Ursa: in the loadstone, says he, the potency of Ursa prevails and hence it is transferred into the iron. Paracelsus declares that there are stars which, gifted with the loadstone's power, do attract to themselves iron.

Levinus Lemnius describes and praises the mariner's compass, and on certain grounds infers its antiquity: he does not divulge the hidden miracle which he makes profession to know. The people of Amalfi, in the kingdom of Naples, first, 'tis said, constructed a mariner's compass; and, as Flavius Blondus says, the townsmen do not without reason boast, they were so taught by one Joannes Goia, a fellow-citizen, in the year 1300. This town is in the Kingdom of Naples, not far from Salerno, and near the promontory of Minerva. The sovereignty of the place was conferred by Charles V on Andrea Doria, the great naval commander, in recognition of his splendid achievements. And that nothing ever has been contrived by the art of man nor anything been of greater advantage to the human race than the mariner's compass is certain: but many infer from ancient writings and from certain arguments and conjectures, that the compass was discovered earlier and received among the arts of navigation. Knowledge of the mariner's compass appears to have been brought into Italy by the Venetian Paolo [Marco Polo], who about the year 1260 learned the art of the compass in China; still I do not want to strip the Amalfitani of so great an honour, seeing that by them compasses were first commonly made in Mediterranean lands. Goropius ascribes the invention to the Cimbri or Teutons, on the ground that the thirty-two names of the winds inscribed on the compass are pronounced in German by all mariners, whether they be British or Spaniards, or Frenchmen. But the Italians give them names in their own vernacular. Some think that Solomon, King of Judea, was acquainted with the compass and taught the use of it to his pilots for their long voyages when they brought from the Western Indies such a quantity of gold: hence Arias Montanus holds that the regions in Peru that abound in gold got their name from the Hebrew word *Paruaim*. But it is more probable that the gold came from the coast of lower Ethiopia, or, as others declare, from the region called Cephala. The story seems less true for the reason that the Phœnicians, next neighbours of Judea, most skilful navigators in early times (whose talents, labour, and counsels Solomon employed in building ships and in his expeditions as well as in other ways), were ignorant of magnetic aids, of the use of the mariner's compass: for were it used by them, doubtless the Greeks, the Italians, and all the barbarians would have known of a thing so necessary and so celebrated through common use; nor would things famous, most easily known, and of the highest necessity ever perish in oblivion; on the contrary, the knowledge would have been handed on to posterity, or some memorial in writing would survive.

Sebastian Cabot first discovered that the magnetized iron (needle) varied. Gonzales Oviedo first made mention in his history that in the meridian of the Azores there is no variation. Fernel, in his book *De abditis rerum causis,* says that in the loadstone is a hidden and abstruse cause: elsewhere he says this cause is celestial, and he does but explain the unknown by the more unknown. This search after hidden causes is something ignorant, beggarly, and resultless. The ingenious Fracastorio, a philosopher of no common stamp, asks what gives direction to the loadstone [needle], and imagines the existence of hyperborean magnetic mountains, attracting objects of magnetic iron. This opinion, in some degree accepted by others also, many authors follow in their writings, their geographical maps, their marine charts, and their descriptions of the globe: dreaming magnetic poles and mighty cliffs, apart from the earth's poles. Of date two hundred years or more earlier than Fracastorio is a small work attributed to one Petrus Peregrinus, a pretty erudite book considering the time: many believe it owes its origin to the opinions of Roger Bacon, Englishman of Oxford. In this work the arguments touching the magnetic direction are drawn from the celestial poles and from the heaven itself. From this book of Petrus Peregrinus, Joannes Taisner Hannonius extracted the matter of a little volume, which he published for new. Cardan

makes much of the star in the tail of Ursa Major; the cause of variation he assigns to its rising, thinking that variation is always certain at the rising of the star. But the difference of variation for change of locality, and the mutations in many places—mutations that even in the southern regions are irregular—preclude this exclusive dominance of one star at its northern rising. The College of Coimbra seeks the cause in some region of the heavens nigh to the pole; Scaliger, in the 131st of his *Exercitationes* on Cardan's work *De subtilitate,* brings in a celestial cause to himself unknown, and terrestrial loadstones that have nowhere been discovered; and seeks the cause not in the "siderite mountains" but in that force which formed them, to wit, in the part of the heavens which overhangs that northern point. This opinion the learned author dresses in abundant verbiage and crowns with many subtle observations in the margin: but his reasons are not so subtle. Martinus Cortesius holds that the seat of the attraction is beyond the poles, and that it is the heavens in motion. One Bessard, a Frenchman, studies the pole of the Zodiac, but to as little purpose. Jacobus Severtius, of Paris, after quoting a few observations of others, fashions new errors about loadstones of different regions being different in direction, as also about the eastern and western parts of a loadstone. Robert Norman, an Englishman, posits a point and place toward which the magnet looks (but whereto it is) not drawn: toward which magnetized iron, according to him, is collimated, but which does not attract it. Franciscus Maurolycus discusses a few problems regarding the loadstone, adopting the current opinions of others; he believes that the variation is caused by a certain magnetic island mentioned by Olaus Magnus. Josephus Costa, knowing nothing whatever of the subject, nevertheless pours out empty words about the loadstone. Livio Sanuto, in his *Geography* (written in Italian), discourses at length of the prime magnetic meridian, of the magnetic poles, whether they are terrestrial or celestial; treats also of an instrument for finding the longitude; but as he does not understand the nature of the loadstone, he does but add errors and obscurities to his otherwise excellent treatise. Fortunius Affaitatus has some rather silly philosophizing about attraction of iron and the turning toward the poles. Very recently Baptista Porta, a philosopher of no ordinary note, makes the seventh book of his *Magia naturalis* a very storehouse and repertory of magnetic wonders; but he knows little about the movements of the loadstone, and never has seen much of them; much of what he has learned about its obvious properties, either from Messer Paolo, the Venetian, or through his own studies, is not very accurately noted and observed; the book is full of most erroneous experiments, as will appear in fitting place; still I hold him worthy of praise for that he essayed so great a task (even as he has essayed many another task, and successfully too, and with no inconsiderable results), and that he has given occasion for further researches.

All these philosophers, our predecessors, discoursing of attraction on the basis of a few vague and indecisive experiments and of reasonings from the recondite causes of things; and reckoning among the causes of the direction of the magnet, a region of the sky, celestial poles, stars, asterisms; or mountains, cliffs, vacant space, atoms, attractional or collimational regions beyond the heavens, and other like unproved paradoxes, are world-wide astray from the truth and are blindly wandering. But we do not propose just now to overturn with arguments either these their errors and impotent reasonings, or the other many fables about the loadstone, or the fairy-tales of mountebanks and story-tellers; as, for example, the questions raised by Franciscus Rueus about the loadstone, whether it is an imposture of cacodæmons; or the assertion that a loadstone placed unawares under the head of a sleeping woman drives her out of the bed if she be an adulteress; or that by its fume and vapour the loadstone is of use to thieves, as though the stone were by nature given to promote thefts; or that it withdraws bolts and opens locks, as Serapio insanely imagines; or that iron held by a loadstone's attraction, being placed in a balance, adds nought to the weight of the loadstone, as though the weight of the iron were absorbed by the virtue of the loadstone; or that, as Serapio and the Moors report, there are in Indian seas certain sharp-pointed rocks abounding in loadstone, the which draw every nail out of ships that land alongside them and hold the vessels: this story, Olaus Magnus does not fail to recite: he tells of mountains in the North possessing such power of attraction that ships have to be constructed with wooden pegs, so that as they sail by the magnetic cliffs there be no iron nails to draw out.

Nor will we take the trouble to refute such stories as that a white loadstone may be used as a philter; or that, as Abohali (Hali Abbas) rashly asserts, when held in the hand it cures pains of the feet and cramps; or that, as Pictorius sings, it gives one favour and acceptance with princes or makes one eloquent; that, as Albertus Magnus says, there are two species of loadstones, one pointing north, the other south; or that iron is directed toward the northern stars by a force communicated from the polar stars, even as plants, like the sunflower, follow the sun; or, as the astrologer Lucas Gauricus held, that beneath the tail of Ursa Major is a loadstone; Lucas further assigns the loadstone (as the sardonyx and the onyx) to the planet Saturn, but also to Mars (with the diamond, jasper, and ruby), so that the loadstone, according to him, is ruled by two planets; further, Lucas says that the loadstone belongs to the sign Virgo; and with a veil of mathematical erudition does he cover many similar disgraceful stupidities. Gaudentius Merula advises that on a loadstone be graven the image of a bear, when the moon looks to the north, so that being suspended by an iron thread it may win the virtue of the celestial Bear; Ficinus writes, and Merula copies, that the loadstone draws iron and makes it point north, because it is of higher order than iron in the Bear. Others tell that in daytime the loadstone possesses the power of attracting iron, but that at night this power is feeble or rather null; Ruellius writes that the loadstone's force, when failing or dulled, is restored by the blood of a buck; it has been said that a buck's blood frees the magnet from the diamond's sorcery, giving back its lost power when the magnet is bathed in the blood—this, because of the variance between that blood and the diamond; Arnoldus de Villanova fancies that the loadstone frees women from witchcraft and puts demons to flight; Marbodaeus, a Frenchman, fugleman of vain imaginings, says that it can make husbands agreeable to wives and may restore wives to their husbands; Caelius Calcagninus in his *Relationes* says that a magnet pickled with salt of the sucking-fish has the power of picking up a piece of gold from the bottom of the deepest well. In such-like follies and fables do philosophers of the vulgar sort take delight; with such-like do they cram readers a-hungered for things abstruse, and every ignorant gaper for nonsense. But when the nature of the loadstone shall have been in the discourse following disclosed, and shall have been by our labours and experiments tested, then will the hidden and recondite but real causes of this great effect be brought forward, proven, shown, demonstrated; then, too, will all darkness vanish; every smallest root of error, being plucked up, will be cast away and will be neglected; and the foundations of a grand magnetic science being laid will appear anew, so that high intellects may no more be deluded by vain opinions.

There are other learned men who on long sea voyages have observed the differences of magnetic variation; as that most accomplished scholar Thomas Hariot, Robert Hues, Edward Wright, Abraham Kendall, all Englishmen; others have invented and published magnetic instruments and ready methods of observing, necessary for mariners and those who make long voyages: as William Borough in his little work the *Variation of the Compass,* William Barlo [Barlowe] in his *Supplement,* Robert Norman in his *New Attractive*—the same Robert Norman, skilled navigator and ingenious artificer, who first discovered the dip of the magnetic needle. Many others I pass by of purpose: Frenchmen, Germans, and Spaniards of recent time who in their writings, mostly composed in their vernacular languages, either misuse the teachings of others, and like furbishers send forth ancient things dressed with new names and tricked in an apparel of new words as in prostitutes' finery; or who publish things not even worthy of record; who, pilfering some book, grasp for themselves from other authors, and go a-begging for some patron, or go a-fishing among the inexperienced and the young for a reputation; who seem to transmit from hand to hand, as it were, erroneous teachings in every science and out of their own store now and again to add somewhat of error.

CHAPTER 2. *The Loadstone: what it is: its discovery*

THIS stone is commonly called *magnet,* either after its finder (*not* Pliny's mythical herdsman —copied from Nicander—the hobnails of whose brogues and the point of whose staff were held fast in a magnetic region while he was pasturing his cattle), or after the district Magnesia in Macedonia, abounding in loadstones; or after the City of Magnesia in Ionia of Asia Minor, on the river Maender; hence Lucretius writes, "*Quem Magneta vocant patrio de nomine Graü, Magnetum quia sit patriis in montibus ortus.*[1]" It is called *heracleus* from

[1] Which the Greeks call *magnetes,* from the name of its country, for it had its origin in the native hills of the Magnesians.

the city Heraclea, or after that unconquerable hero Hercules, because of its great strength and its power and dominion over iron which is the subduer of all things; it is also called *sideritis,* as though one should say ferrarius (*ferrarius lapis*—ironstone). It was not unknown to the earliest writers, whether among the Greeks, as Hippocrates and others, or (as I believe) among the Jews and the Egyptians; for in the most ancient iron mines, in particular the most famous mines of Asia, the loadstone, brother uterine of iron, was oft dug out in company with that ore. And if those things be true which are told about the people of China, neither were they in primitive times ignorant of magnetic experiments, for even in their country are seen the most excellent magnets in the world. The Egyptians, as Manetho relates, give it the name of "the bone of Horus," calling the potency that presides over the revolution of the sun Horus, as the Greeks called it Apollo. But later, as Plato declares, Euripides gave to it the name *magnet.* It is mentioned and praised by Plato in the *Ion,* by Nicander of Colophon, Theophrastus, Dioscorides, Pliny, Solinus, Ptolemy, Galen, and other investigators of nature. But considering the great differences of loadstones, their dissimilitude in hardness, softness, heaviness, lightness, density, firmness, friableness: in colour and in all other qualities; these writers have not handed down any sufficient account of it. The history of the magnet was overlooked by them, or, if written, was incompletely given, because in olden time objects of many kinds and foreign products never before seen were not brought in by traders and mariners as they are wont to be brought in now, when all manner of commodities— stones, woods, spices, herbs, metals, and metallic wares—are eagerly sought for all over the earth; neither was mining carried on everywhere in early times as it is now.

The difference between loadstones rests on their respective power: hence one loadstone is male, another female: so the ancients were wont to distinguish many objects of the same species. Pliny quotes from Sotacus five kinds, *viz.*: the loadstones of Ethiopia, Macedonia, Bœotia, Troas, and Asia, respectively, which were the chief sorts known to the ancients. But we recognize as many kinds as there are in the whole world regions differing in soil; for in every clime, in every province, in all kinds of land, either the loadstone is found or lies unknown because of its deep site or its inaccessible situation; or, because of its weaker and less potent virtues, it is not recognized by us the while we see it and touch it.

For the ancients, the differences were based on the colour: The magnets from Magnesia in Macedonia were red and black, those from Bœotia red rather than black, those from the Troad black without strength, those from Asian Magnesia white, without power of attracting iron, and resembling pumice. A strong loadstone and one that under experiment demonstrates its power nowadays generally resembles unpolished iron and usually is found in iron mines: sometimes it is found also forming a continuous vein by itself: such loadstones are imported from the East Indies, China, and Bengal, and they are of the colour of iron, or of a dark blood-red or liver colour. These are the most excellent and often are of great size and weight, as if broken off a great rock; or again they are as if complete in themselves. Some of these, though they may weigh but one pound, will lift four ounces, or half a pound, or even an entire pound of iron. In Arabia are found red loadstones shaped like tiles, not as heavy as those imported from China, yet strong and good. Rather black loadstones are found in Elba, an island of the Etrurian sea; with these occur also white loadstones like those from the mines of Caravaca in Spain: but they are of inferior strength. Black loadstones also are found, and these, too, are rather inferior in strength, for example, those met with in the iron mines of Norway and in the coast region along the Cattegat. Blue-black and dusky-blue loadstones are likewise powerful and highly prized. But there are others of a lead colour, fissile or not fissile, that can be split up like slate; I have also loadstones resembling an ashy-gray marble, mottled like gray marble: these take a high polish. In Germany are loadstones perforated like the honeycomb; these are lighter than the other sorts, yet they are powerful. The metallic loadstones are those which are smelted into the best of iron; the rest are not easily smelted, but are burnt.

There are loadstones that are very heavy, as there are others very light; some are very powerful and carry masses of iron; others are weaker and less powerful; some so faint and void of strength that they can hardly attract ever so small a piece of iron, nor do they repel an opposite magnetized body. Others are firm and tough, nor are they easy to work; others are friable. Again, some are dense and hard like corundum, or light or soft like pumice; porous or solid; smooth and uniform, or irreg-

ular and corroded. Now hard as iron, nay sometimes harder to cut or to file than iron; again as soft as clay. Not all magnets can properly be called stones: some there are that represent rather rocks; others are rather metallic ores; others are like clods of earth. So do they vary and differ from one another, and some possess more, others less, of the peculiar magnetic virtue. For they differ according to the nature of the soil, and the different mixtures of clays and humours; according to the lay of the land and the decay of this highest substance born to earth: decay due to the concurrence of many causes and the never-ceasing vicissitude of rise and decline and the mutations of bodies. Nor is this stone, endowed as it is with such power, a rarity: there is no country wherein it may not be found in one form or other. But were men to seek it more diligently and at greater expense, and could they in the face of difficulties mine it, it might be obtained everywhere, as later we will prove. In many regions are found and are now opened mines of powerful loadstones unknown to ancient authors, in Germany, for example, where none of them ever said that loadstones were mined; and yet since the time within the memory of our fathers when the business of mining began there to be developed, in many parts of Germany powerful loadstones of great virtues have been taken out of the earth, as in the Black Forest near Helceburg: in Mt. Misena not far from Schwarzberg; some of considerable strength from the region betwixt Schneeberg and Annaberg in the Joachimsthal, as was observed by Cordus; also near Pela in Franconia; in Bohemia from the iron mines near Lesse; and in other places, as we are informed by Georgius Agricola and other men learned in the art of mining.

The like is to be said of other countries in our time; for this stone, famous for its virtues, as to-day it is well known throughout the world, so is produced in every land; it is, so to speak, a native of all countries. In East India, in China, in Bengal, along the banks of the Indus, it is plentiful, also in certain marine rocks; in Persia, too, in Arabia and the isles of the Red Sea; in many parts of Ethiopia, as was anciently Zimiri, mentioned by Pliny; in Asia Minor around Alexandria, Bœotia, Italy, the island Elba, Barbary; in Spain, still in many localities as of old; in England quite recently a vast quantity was found in a mine owned by a gentleman, named Adrian Gilbert, as also in Devonshire and in the Forest of Dean; in Ireland too, in Norway, Denmark, Sweden, Lapland, Livonia, Prussia, Poland, Hungary. For albeit the terrestrial globe, various humours and diversities of soils being produced by the perpetual vicissitude of generaton and decay, is ever to a greater and greater depth beneath the surface in the lapse of ages efflorescing, and is being clothed as it were with a diversified and perishable covering and wrappage; still from its interior arises in many places a progeny nigher to the more perfect body, and makes its way into the sunlit air. But the weak loadstones and those of less strength, which thus have been deprived of their virtue by being soaked with humours, are visible everywhere, in every country-side; great masses of these are to be found in every quarter, without tunnelling mountains or sinking mines, and without any of the toils and difficulties of mining, as we will show in the sequel. These we will so manipulate according to a simple process that their languid and dormant properties shall be made manifest.

The magnet is called by the Greeks 'ηράκλειος, as by Theophrastus, and μαγνῆτις and μάγνης, as by Euripides, quoted by Plato in the *Ion;* by Orpheus it is called also μαγνῆοσα and σιδήριτης (*quasi* ironstone); by the Latins it is called *magnes Herculeus;* by the French *aimant,* a corruption of *adamas;* by the Spaniards *piedramant;* by the Italians *calamita;* by the English loadstone and adamant stone; by the Germans *magness* and *siegelstein.* Among the English, French, and Spaniards, it has its common name from *adamas,* and this is probably because at some time those people were led astray by the term *siderites,* which was applied both to the diamond and the magnet. The magnet is called σιδηρίτης because of its property of attracting iron; and the diamond is called σιδηρίτης from the glistening of polished iron. Aristotle merely names the loadstone in his work *On the Soul,* I. [405ᵃ 19]: "Ἔοικε δὲ καὶ Θαλῆς ἐξ ὧν ἀπομνεμονεύονσί, κινητικὸν τι τὴν ψυχὴν ἱπολαμβάνειν, ἔιπερ τὸν λιθὸν ψυχὴν ἔφη ἔχειν, ὅτι τον σιδηρὸν κινεῖ. (Thales, too, seems, from what they relate, to regard the soul as somewhat producing motion, for he said that this stone has a soul, since it moves iron.) The name magnet is also given to another stone differing widely from the siderites, and having the look of silver: in its nature this stone resembles amianth (asbestus), and in form differs from that inasmuch as it consists, like mica, of laminæ; the Germans call it *Katzensilber* and *Talk.*

CHAPTER 3. *The loadstone possesses parts differing in their natural powers, and has poles conspicuous for their properties*

THE many qualities exhibited by the loadstone itself, qualities hitherto recognized yet not well investigated, are to be pointed out in the first place, to the end the student may understand the powers of the loadstone and of iron, and not be confused through want of knowledge at the threshold of the arguments and demonstrations. In the heavens, astronomers give to each moving sphere two poles; thus do we find two natural poles of excelling importance even in our terrestrial globe, constant points related to the movement of its daily revolution, to wit, one pole pointing to Arctos (Ursa) and the north; the other looking toward the opposite part of the heavens. In like manner, the loadstone has from nature its two poles, a northern and a southern; fixed, definite points in the stone, which are the primary termini of the movements and effects, and the limits and regulators of the several actions and properties. It is to be understood, however, that not from a mathematical point does the force of the stone emanate, but from the parts themselves; and all these parts in the whole—while they belong to the whole—the nearer they are to the poles of the stone the stronger virtues do they acquire and pour out on other bodies. These poles look toward the poles of the earth, and move toward them, and are subject to them. The magnetic poles may be found in every loadstone, whether strong and powerful (male, as the term was in antiquity) or faint, weak, and female; whether its shape is due to design or to chance, and whether it be long, or flat, or four-square, or three-cornered, or polished; whether it be rough, broken-off, or unpolished: the loadstone ever has and ever shows its poles. But inasmuch as the spherical form, which, too, is the most perfect, agrees best with the earth, which is a globe, and also is the form best suited for experimental uses, therefore we propose to give our principal demonstrations with the aid of a globe-shaped loadstone, as being the best and the most fitting. Take then a strong loadstone, solid, of convenient size, uniform, hard, without flaw; on a lathe, such as is used in turning crystals and some precious stones, or on any like instrument (as the nature and toughness of the stone may require, for often it is worked only with difficulty), give the loadstone the form of a ball. The stone thus prepared is a true homogeneous offspring of the earth and is of the same shape, having got from art the orbicular form that nature in the beginning gave to the earth, the common mother; and it is a natural little body endowed with a multitude of properties whereby many abstruse and unheeded truths of philosophy, hid in deplorable darkness, may be more readily brought to the knowledge of mankind. To this round stone we give the name μικρόγη [microge] or terrella [earthkin, little earth].

To find, then, poles answering to the earth's poles, take in your hand the round stone, and lay on it a needle or a piece of iron wire: the ends of the wire move round their middle point, and suddenly come to a standstill. Now, with ochre or with chalk, mark where the wire lies still and sticks. Then move the middle or centre of the wire to another spot, and so to a third and a fourth, always marking the stone along the length of the wire where it stands still: the lines so marked will exhibit meridian circles, or circles like meridians on the stone or terrella; and manifestly they will all come together at the poles of the stone. The circles being continued in this way, the poles appear, both the north and the south, and betwixt these, midway, we may draw a large circle for an equator, as is done by the astronomer in the heavens and on his spheres and by the geographer on the terrestrial globe; for the line so drawn on this our terrella is also of much utility in our demonstrations and our magnetic experiments. Poles are also found in the round stone, in a versorium, in a piece of iron touched

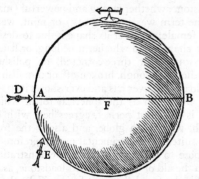

with a loadstone and resting on a needle or point (attached at its base to the terrella), so that it can freely revolve, as in the figure.

On top of the stone *AB* is set the versorium in such a way that its pointer may remain in equilibrium: mark with chalk the direction of the pointer when at rest. Then move the instrument to another spot and again mark the direction in which the pointer looks; repeat

this many times at many different points and you will, from the convergence of the lines of direction, find one pole at the point *A*, the other at *B*. A pointer also indicates the true pole if brought near to the stone, for it eagerly faces the stone at right angles, and seeks the pole itself direct and turns on its axis in a right line toward the centre of the stone. Thus the pointer *D* regards *A* and *F,* the pole and the centre, but the pointer *E* looks not straight either toward the pole *A* or the centre *F*. A bit of fine iron wire as long as a barley-corn is laid on the stone and is moved over the zones and the surface of the stone till it stands perpendicularly erect; for at the poles, whether N. or S., it stands erect; but the farther it is from the poles (towards the equator) the more it inclines. The poles thus found, you are to mark with a sharp file or a gimlet.

CHAPTER 4. *Which pole is the north: how the north pole is distinguished from the south pole*

ONE of the earth's poles is turned toward Cynosura and steadily regards a fixed point in the heavens (save that it is unmoved by the precession of the fixed stars in longitude, which movement we recognize in the earth, as we shall later show); the other pole is turned toward the opposite aspect of the heavens, an aspect unknown to the ancients, but which is adorned with a multitude of stars, and is itself a striking spectacle for those who make long voyages. So, too, the loadstone possesses the virtue and power of directing itself toward the north and the south (the earth itself co-operating and giving to it that power) according to the conformation of nature, which adjusts the movements of the stone to its true locations.

In this manner it is demonstrated: put the magnetic stone (after you have found the poles) in a round wooden vessel—a bowl or a dish; then put the vessel holding the magnet (like a boat with a sailor in it) in a tub of water or a cistern where it may float freely in the middle without touching the rim, and where the air is not stirred by winds (currents) which might interfere with the natural movement of the stone: there the stone, as if in a boat floating in the middle of an unruffled surface of still water, will straightway set itself, and the vessel containing it in motion, and will turn in a circle till its south pole shall face north and its north pole, south. For, from a contrary position, it returns to the poles; and though with its first too strong impetus it passes beyond, still, as it comes back again and again, at last it rests at the poles or in the meridian (save that, according to the place, it diverges a very little from those points, or from the meridional line, the cause of which we will define later). As often as you move it out of its place, so often, by reason of the extraordinary power with which nature has endowed it, does it seek again its fixed and determinate points. Nor does this occur only when the poles of the loadstone in the float are made to lie evenly in the plane of the horizon; it takes place also even though one pole, whether north or south, be raised or depressed 10, 20, 30, 40, or 80 degrees from the plane of the horizon; you shall see the north part of the stone seek the south, and the south part the north; so that if the pole of the stone be but one degree from the zenith and the centre of the heavens, the whole stone revolves until the pole finds its own place; and though the pole does not point exactly to its seat, yet it will incline toward it, and will come to rest in the meridian of its true direction. And it moves with the same impetus whether the north pole be directed toward the upper heavens, or whether the south pole be raised above the horizon. Yet it must always be borne in mind that though there are manifold differences between stones, and one far surpasses another in virtue and efficiency, still all loadstones have the same limits and turn to the same points. Further, it is to be remembered that all who hitherto have written about the poles of the loadstone, all instrument-makers, and navigators, are egregiously mistaken in taking for the north pole of the loadstone the part of the stone that inclines to the north, and for the south pole the part that looks to the south: this we will hereafter prove to be an error. So ill-cultivated is the whole philosophy of the magnet still, even as regards its elementary principles.

CHAPTER 5. *One loadstone appears to attract another in the natural position; but in the opposite position repels it and brings it to rights*

First we have to describe in popular language the potent and familiar properties of the stone; afterward, very many subtile properties, as yet recondite and unknown, being involved in obscurities, are to be unfolded; and the causes of all these (nature's secrets being unlocked) are in their place to be demonstrated in fitting words and with the aid of apparatus. The fact is trite and familiar, that the loadstone attracts iron; in the same way, too, one loadstone attracts another. Take the stone on which you

have designated the poles, N. and S., and put it in its vessel so that it may float; let the poles lie just in the plane of the horizon, or at least in a plane not very oblique to it; take in your hand another stone the poles of which are also known, and hold it so that its south pole shall lie toward the north pole of the floating stone, and near it alongside; the floating loadstone will straightway follow the other (provided it be within the range and dominion of its powers), nor does it cease to move nor does it quit the other till it clings to it, unless, by moving your hand away, you manage skilfully to prevent the conjunction. In like manner, if you oppose the north pole of the stone in your hand to the south pole of the floating one, they come together and follow each other. For opposite poles attract opposite poles. But, now, if in the same way you present N. to N. or S. to S., one stone repels the other; and as though a helmsman were bearing on the rudder it is off like a vessel making all sail, nor stands nor stays as long as the other stone pursues. One stone also will range the other, turn the other around, bring it to right about and make it come to agreement with itself. But when the two come together and are conjoined in nature's order, they cohere firmly. For example, if you present the north pole of the stone in your hand to the Tropic of Capricorn (for so we may distin-

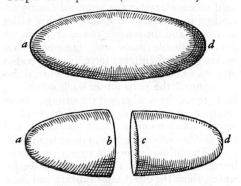

guish with mathematical circles the round stone, or *terrella,* just as we do the globe itself) or to any point between the equator and the south pole: immediately the floating stone turns round and so places itself that its south pole touches the north pole of the other and is most closely joined to it. In the same way you will get like effect at the other side of the equator by presenting pole to pole; and thus by art and contrivance we exhibit attraction and repulsion, and motion in a circle toward the concordant position, and the same movements to avoid hostile meetings. Furthermore, in one same stone we are thus able to demonstrate all this: but also we are able to show how the self-same part of one stone may by division become either north or south. Take the oblong stone *ad* in which *a* is the north pole and *d* the south. Cut the stone in two equal parts, and put part *a* in a vessel and let it float in water.

You will find that *a,* the north point, will turn to the south as before; and in like manner the point *d* will move to the north, in the divided stone, as before division. But *b* and *c,* before connected, now separated from each other, are not what they were before: *b* is now south while *c* is north, *b* attracts *c,* longing for union and for restoration of the original continuity. They are two stones made out of one, and on that account the *c* of one turning toward the *b* of the other, they are mutually attracted, and, being freed from all impediments and from their own weight, borne as they are on the surface of the water, they come together and into conjunction. But if you bring the part or point *a* up to *c* of the other, they repel one another and turn away; for by such a position of the parts nature is crossed and the form of the stone is perverted: but nature observes strictly the laws it has imposed upon bodies: hence the flight of one part from the undue position of the other, and hence the discord unless everything is arranged exactly according to nature. And nature will not suffer an unjust and inequitable peace, or an unjust and inequitable peace and agreement, but makes war and employs force to make bodies acquiesce fairly and justly. Hence, when rightly arranged, the parts attract each other, i.e., both stones, the weaker and the stronger, come together and with all their might tend to union: a fact manifest in all loadstones, and not, as Pliny supposed, only in those from Ethiopia. The Ethiopic stones if strong, and those brought from China, which are all powerful stones, show the effect most quickly and most plainly, attract with most force in the parts nighest the pole, and keep turning till pole looks straight on pole.

The pole of a stone has strongest attraction for that part of another stone which answers to it (the *adverse,* as it is called); *e.g.,* the north pole of one has strongest attraction for, has the most vigorous pull on, the south part of another: so too it attracts iron more powerfully, and iron clings to it more firmly, whether previously magnetized or not. Thus it has been settled by nature, not without reason, that the parts nigher the pole shall have the greatest attractive force; and that in the pole itself shall be the seat, the throne as it were, of a high and splendid power; and that magnetic bodies brought near thereto shall be attracted most powerfully and relinquished with most reluctance. So, too, the poles are readiest to spurn and drive away what is presented to them amiss, and what is inconformable and foreign.

CHAPTER 6. *The loadstone attracts iron ore as well as the smelted metal*

THE most potent virtue of the loadstone and the one valued by the ancients is the attraction for iron; for Plato mentions that the magnet, so called by Euripides, draws to itself iron, and not only attracts iron rings but also endows them with the power of doing as the stone itself, to wit, of attracting other rings, and that thus sometimes a long chain of iron objects, as nails, or rings, is made, the several parts hanging from one another. The best iron (such as that which from its uses is called *acies,* and from the country of the Chalybes, *chalybs*) is most readily and strongly attracted by a good magnet[1]; but inferior iron, iron that is impure, rusty, not well purged of dross, and not worked over in the second furnace is attracted more weakly; and any iron is more faintly attracted if covered and smeared with thick, greasy, tenacious fluids. The loadstone also attracts iron ores—rich ores and those of the colour of iron; poor ores and those without much pure metal it does not attract unless they receive special treatment. The loadstone loses some part of its attractive power, and, as it were, enters on the decline of old age, if it be too long exposed in open air and not kept in a case, with a covering of iron filings or iron scales: hence it must be packed in such material. Nothing withstands this unimpairable virtue, except what destroys the form of the body or corrodes it; no, not a thousand adamants made into one. Nor do I believe in the *theamedes,* or that it has a power the opposite of the loadstone's, albeit Pliny, that eminent author and best of compilers (for he has handed down to posterity the observations and discoveries of others and not always or mainly his own), copies out of other writers the *theamedes* fable, now from repetition become a familiar story among the moderns. The story is that in India are two mountains near the river Indus, and that one of them—consisting

---

[1] See Aristotle's reference to the iron of the Chalybes. See Book 1, Chap. 8, p. 15, below.

of loadstone—possesses the power of holding everything containing iron; while the other, consisting of *theamedes,* repels the same. Hence if you should have iron nails in the soles of your shoes, it would be impossible to lift your foot if you were standing on one of the mountains, and impossible to stand on the other at all. Albertus Magnus writes that in his time a loadstone was found that on one side drew iron to itself and on the other side repelled it. But Albertus's observation was faulty, for every loadstone attracts on one side magnetized iron, on the other repels, and attracts magnetized iron more powerfully than non-magnetized.

CHAPTER 7. *What iron is; what its matter; its use*

HAVING declared the origin and nature of the loadstone, we hold it needful first to give the history of iron also, and to point out properties of iron as yet not known, before we come to the explication of difficulties connected with the loadstone, and to the demonstrations; before we come to the consideration of its uniting and according with iron. Iron is, by all, classed among metals; it is of bluish colour, very hard, grows red hot before fusion, is very hard to fuse, spreads under the hammer, and is resonant. Chemists say that, if fixed earthy sulphur be combined with fixed earthy mercury and these two bodies present not a pure white but a bluish-white colour, if the sulphur prevail, iron results. For those hard masters of the metals, who in many various processes put them to the torture, by crushing, calcining, smelting, subliming, precipitating, distinguish this, on account both of the earthy sulphur and the earthy mercury, as more truly the child of earth than any other metal; for neither gold, nor silver, nor lead, nor tin, nor even copper do they hold to be so earthy; and therefore it is treated only in the hottest furnaces with the help of bellows; and when thus smelted if it becomes hard again it cannot be smelted once more without great labour; and its slag can be fused only with the utmost difficulty. It is the hardest of metals, subduing and breaking them all, because of the strong concretion of the more earthy substance.

Hence we shall better understand what iron is when we shall have developed, in a way different from that of those who have gone before us, what are the causes and the matter of metals. Aristotle supposes their matter to be an exhalation. The chemists in chorus (unison)

declare that sulphur and quicksilver are the prime elements. Gilgil, the Mauretanian, holds the prime element to be ash moistened with water; Georgius Agricola, a mixture of water with earth; and his opinion differs nought from Gilgil's thesis. But our opinion is that metals have their origin and do effloresce in the uppermost parts of the globe, each distinct by its form, as do many other minerals and all the bodies around us. The globe of the earth is not made of ash or of inert dust. Nor is fresh water an element, but only a less complex consistence of the earth's evaporated fluids. Unctuous bodies (*pinguia corpora*), fresh water void of properties, quicksilver, sulphur: these are not the principles of the metals: they are results of another natural process; nor have they a place now or have they had ever, in the process of producing metals. The earth gives forth sundry humours, not produced from water nor from dry earth, nor from mixtures of these, but from the matter of the earth itself: these are not distinguished by opposite qualities or substances. Nor is the earth a simple substance, as the Peripatetics imagine. The humours come from sublimed vapours that have their origin in the bowels of the earth.

And all waters are extractions from the earth and exudations, as it were. Therefore Aristotle is partly in the right when he says that the exhalation which condenses in the earth's veins is the prime matter of metals: for exhalations are condensed in situations less warm than the place of their origin, and owing to the structure of lands and mountains, they are in due time condensed, as it were in wombs, and changed into metals. But they do not of themselves alone constitute the veins of ore; only they flow into and coalesce with solider matter and form metals.

When, therefore, this concreted matter has settled in more temperate cavities, in these moderately warm spaces it takes shape, just as in the warm uterus the seed or the embryo grows. Sometimes the exhalation coalesces only with matter homogeneous throughout, and hence some metals are now and then but not often obtained pure and not needing to be smelted. But other exhalations, being mixed with foreign earths, must be smelted; and thus are treated the ores of all metals, which are freed from all their dross by the action of fire; when smelted into the metallic state they are fluid and then are freed from earthly impurities but not from the true substance of the earth. But that there is gold, or silver, or copper, or that any other metals exist, does not happen from any *quantitas* or proportion of matter nor by any specific virtues of matter, as the chemists fondly imagine; but it happens when, earth cavities and the conformation of the ground concurring with the fit matter, those metals take from universal nature the forms by which they are perfected, just as in the case of all other minerals, all plants and all animals: else the kinds of metals would be vague and undefined; in fact, the varieties are very few, hardly ten in number.

But why nature should be so grudging in the number of metals, or why there should be even so many metals as are recognized by man, were not easy to explain, though simpletons and raving astrologers refer to the several planets their respective metals. But neither do the planets agree with the metals nor the metals with the planets, either in number or in properties. For what is common between Mars and iron, save that, like many other implements, swords and artillery are made of iron? What has copper to do with Venus? Or how does tin, or zinc, relate to Jupiter? These were better dedicated to Venus. But a truce to old wives' talk. Thus exhalations are the remote cause of the generation of metals; the proximate cause is the fluid from the exhalations: like the blood and the semen in the generation of animals. But these exhalations and the fluids produced from them enter bodies often and change them into marchasites[1] and they pass into veins (we find many instances of timber so transformed), into appropriate matrices within bodies, and these metals are formed; oftenest they enter the more interior and more homogeneous matter of the globe, and in time there results a vein of iron, or loadstone is produced, which is nothing but a noble iron ore; and for this reason and also on account of its matter being quite peculiar and distinct from that of all other metals, nature very seldom or never mingles with iron any other metal, though the other metals are very often commingled in some small proportion and are produced together. Now, when these exhalations or fluids happen to meet efflorescences altered from the homogeneous matter of the globe— sundry precipitates, and salts, in suitable matrices (operant forms)—the other metals are produced (a specificating nature operating in that place). For within the globe are hidden the principles of metals and stones, as at the earth's surface are hidden the principles of

[1] The crystallized form of iron pyrites.

herbs and plants. And earth dug from the bottom of a deep pit, where there appears to be no chance of any seed being formed, produces, if strewn on the top of a very high tower, green herbage and unbidden grasses, the sun and the sky brooding over earth; the earth regions produce those things which in each are spontaneous; each region produces its own peculiar herbs and plants, its own metals.

Do you not see how Tmolus sends fragrant saffron, India its ivory, the Sabaens their frankincense, the naked Chalybes iron, Pontus the malodorous castor, Epirus the mares that have won at Olympia? (Virgil, *Georgics,* [i.56-59].)

What the chemists (as Geber and others) call the fixed earthy sulphur in iron is nothing else but the homogenic matter of the globe held together by its own humour, hardened by a second humour: with a minute quantity of earth-substance not lacking humour is introduced the metallic humour. Hence it is said very incorrectly by many authors that in gold is pure earth, in iron impure; as though natural earth and the globe itself were become in some incomprehensible sense impure. In iron, especially in best iron, is earth in its true and genuine nature. In the other metals is not so much earth as, instead of earth and precipitate, condensed and (so to speak) fixed salts, which are efflorescences of the earth, and which also differ in firmness and consistence. In mines they ascend in great volume, with double humour from the exhalations; in the subterranean spaces they are consolidated into metallic ores; so too they are produced together, and in virtue of their place and of the surrounding bodies, they acquire, in natural matrices, their specific forms.

Of the various bodily constitutions of loadstones, their different substances, colours, and properties, we have spoken before: but now after having declared the cause and origin of metals, the matter of iron, not in the smelted metal but in the ore from which that is obtained by smelting, has to be examined. Iron, that from its colour appears pure, is found in the earth; yet it is not exactly metallic iron, not quite suitable for the different uses of iron. Sometimes it is found covered with a white moss-like substance, or with a coating of other stones.

Such ore is often seen in the sands of rivers: such is the ore from Noricum (the region south of the Danube, watered by the Inn and the Drave; mostly comprised in the modern Austria). Iron ore, nearly pure, is often mined in Ireland: from this the smith, without the labor of the furnace, forges in his shop iron implements. From an ore of liver colour is very often obtained in France an iron with bright scales (*bracteæ*); such iron is made in England without the scales; carpenters use it instead of chalk. In Sussex, in England, is a rich ore of dark, and one of pale ashy colour; both of these ores when made red hot for some time, or when kept in a moderate fire, take the colour of liver: in Sussex also is a dark-coloured ore in square masses, with a black rind of harder material. The liver-like ore is often mixed with other stones in various ways, as also with perfect loadstone, which yields the best iron. There is likewise rust-coloured ore, ore of a lead colour mixed with black, simply black, or black mixed with cobalt; there is also an ore with admixture of pyrites or sterile plumbago. One kind of ore resembles jet, another the precious stone *hæmatites*. The stone *smiris* (emery; corundum) used by workers in glass for glass-cutting and called by the English *emerelstone* and by the Germans *smeargel,* is of iron, albeit iron is smelted from it with difficulty; it attracts an unmagnetized needle. It is often found in deep silver and iron mines. Thomas Erastus tells of having been informed by a certain learned man, of iron ores, in colour resembling metallic iron, but quite soft and greasy, capable of being moulded with the fingers like butter; we have seen ores of about the same kind that were found in England: they resemble Spanish soap. Besides the numberless forms of stony ores, there is a substance like iron rust deposited from ferriferous water: it is got from mud, loam, and from ochre. In England, a good deal of iron is obtained in the furnace from sand stones and clayey stones that appear to contain not so much iron as sand, marl, or other mud. In Aristotle's book *De admirandis narrationibus,* we read:

'Tis said the iron of the Chalybes and the Myseni has quite a peculiar origin, being carried in the gravel of the streams. Some say that, after being merely washed, it is smelted in the furnace; others that it is washed repeatedly, and as often the residue treated with fire in the furnace, together with the stone *pyrimachus* (a stone refractory to the action of fire), which occurs there in great abundance. Thus do many sorts of substances contain in themselves strikingly and most plentifully this ferric and telluric element. Many, too, and most plentiful in every soil are the stones and earths and the various bodies and compounds, which contain iron (though not in such abundance) and yield it in the furnace fire, but which are rejected by the metallurgist as not workable with profit; and there are other earths that give evidence of the presence of iron in them; these, being very poor in the metal, are not smelted at all, and not being esteemed they are not known.

The kinds of manufactured iron differ very much from one another. For one kind has great tenacity; and that is the best. There is a medium kind. Another kind is brittle; that is the worst. Sometimes the iron, on account of the excellence of the ore, is made into steel; as in Noricum at present. From the best iron also, worked over and over again, and purged of all impurities, or plunged red-hot into water, is produced what the Greeks call στομωμα and the Latins *acies* and *aciarium* [steel], and which is variously called Syrian, Parthian, Norican, Comese and Spanish; in other places it takes its name from the water in which it is repeatedly immersed, as at Como in Italy, and Bilbao and Tariassone in Spain. Steel sells at a far higher price than iron. And, on account of its superiority, it is in better accord with the magnet. It is often made from powerful loadstone, and it acquires the magnetic virtue readily, retains it a long time unimpaired and fit for all magnetic experiments.

The iron, after it has been smelted in the first furnace, is then treated with various processes in great forges or mills, the metal under mighty blows acquiring toughness, and dropping its impurities. When first smelted it is brittle and by no means perfect. Therefore, here in England, when great cannons are cast, in order that they may be able to withstand the explosive force of the ignited gunpowder, the metal is specially purged of impurities: while fluid it is made to pass a second time through a narrow opening, and thus is freed of recremental substances. Smiths, with the use of certain liquids and hammer-strokes, toughen the iron laminæ from which are made shields and coats of mail not penetrable by any musket-ball. Iron is made harder by skill and tempering; but skill also makes it softer and as pliant as lead. It is made hard by certain waters into which it is plunged at white heat, as in Spain. It is made soft again either by fire alone when, without hammering and without the use of water, it is allowed to grow cool; or by being dipped in grease; or it is variously tempered, to serve the purposes of the different arts, by being smeared with special preparations. This art is described by Baptista Porta in Book XIII of the *Magia naturalis*.

Thus is this ferric and telluric substance contained in and extracted from various kinds of stones, ores, and earths; thus too does it differ in appearance, form, and efficiency; and by various processes of art it is smelted and purified and made to serve man's uses in all sorts of trades and in all sorts of tools, as no other body can serve. One kind of iron is suitable for breastplates, another withstands cannon balls, another protects against swords or the curved blades called scimitars; one kind is used in making swords, another in forging horseshoes. Of iron are made nails, hinges, bolts, saws, keys, bars, doors, folding-doors, spades, rods, pitchforks, heckles, hooks, fish-spears, pots, tripods, anvils, hammers, wedges, chains, manacles, fetters, hoes, mattocks, sickles, hooks for pruning vines, and for cutting rushes, shovels, weeding-hooks, ploughshares, forks, pans, ladles, spoons, roasting-spits, knives, daggers, swords, axes, Celtic and Gallic darts, Macedonian pikes, lances, spears, anchors and many nautical implements; furthermore, bullets, javelins, pikes, corselets, helmets, breastplates, horseshoes, greaves, wire, strings of musical instruments, armchairs, portcullises, bows, catapults, and those pests of humanity, bombs, muskets, cannon-balls, and no end of implements unknown to the Latins.

I have recounted so many uses in order that the reader may know in how many ways this metal is employed. Its use exceeds that of all other metals a hundredfold; it is smelted daily; and there are in every village iron forges. For iron is foremost among metals and supplies many human needs, and they the most pressing: it is also far more abundant in the earth than the other metals, and it is predominant. Therefore it is a vain imagination of chemists to deem that nature's purpose is to change all metals to gold, that being brightest, heaviest, strongest, as though she were invulnerable, would change all stones into diamonds because the diamond surpasses them all in brilliancy and in hardness. Iron ore, therefore, as also manufactured iron, is a metal slightly different from the primordial homogenic telluric body because of the metallic humour it has imbibed; yet not so different but that in proportion as it is purified it takes in more and more of the magnetic virtues, and associates itself with that prepotent form and duly obeys the same.

CHAPTER 8. *In what countries and regions iron is produced*

IRON mines are very numerous everywhere—both the ancient mines mentioned by the earliest writers and the new and modern ones. The first and greatest were, I think, in Asia, for in the countries of Asia, which naturally abound in iron, government and the arts did most flourish; and there were the things needful for man's use first discovered and sought for. It is related that iron existed in the neighbourhood of Andria; in the land of the Chalybes, on the banks of the river Thermodon in Pontus; in the mountains of Palestine on the side toward Arabia; in Carmania. In Africa, there was an iron mine in the island of Meroe. In Europe, iron was found in the hills of Britain, as Strabo writes; in hither Spain, in Cantabria; among the Petrocorii and the Cabi Bituriges in Gaul were smithies in which iron was made. In Germany was a mine near Luna, mentioned by Ptolemy; the Gothinian iron is spoken of by Cornelius Tacitus; and the iron of Noricum is famed in poesy; there was also iron in Crete and in Eubœa. Many other mines, neither meagre nor scant, but of vast extent, were overlooked by writers or were unknown to them. Pliny calls hither Spain and the whole region of the Pyrenees an iron country; and he says that, in the part of Cantabria washed by the ocean, there is a mountain steep and high which (wonderful to tell) is all iron. The earliest mines were iron mines, not mines of gold, silver, copper or lead: for iron is more sought after for the needs of man; besides, iron mines are plainly visible in every country, in every soil, and they are less deep and less encompassed with difficulties than other mines.

But were I simply to enumerate modern iron mines and those worked in our own time, a very large book would have to be written, and paper would fail me before iron: yet each one of these mines could supply a thousand forges. For among minerals there is no other substance so plentiful: all metals and all stones distinct from iron ore are surpassed by ferric and ferruginous substances. For you cannot easily find a district, hardly a township, throughout all Europe, if you search thoroughly, that has not a rich and plentiful vein of iron, or that does not yield an earth either saturated with iron-rust or at least slightly tinctured with it. That this is so, is easily shown by any one versed in metallurgy and chemistry.

Besides iron and its ore, there is another ferric substance, which, however, does not yield the metal, because the thin humour is burnt up by the fierce fires and is converted into dross like that separated from the metal when first smelted. Such is the white clay and argillaceous earth which is seen to make up a great part of our British island; this, if treated with strong heat, either exhibits a ferric and metallic body, or is transformed into a ferric vitrification: this fact can be verified in houses built of brick, for the bricks that in the kiln are laid nearest to the fires, and are there burnt, show ferric vitrification at their other end, which grows black. Furthermore, all those earths when prepared are attracted by the magnet like iron. Lasting and plentiful is the earth's product of iron. Georgius Agricola says that nearly all mountainous regions are full of its ores; and we ourselves know that a rich iron ore is often dug in the lowlands and plains throughout England and Ireland, as Agricola tells of iron being dug in the meadows near the town of Saga out of ditches not more than two feet deep. Nor is iron lacking, as some say, in the West Indies; but, there, the Spaniards, intent on gold, avoid the toilsome manufacture of iron and do not search for rich iron ores and mines. It is probable that nature and the terrestrial globe cannot repress, but is ever sending forth into the light a great quantity of its own native substance, and that this action is not entirely impeded by the pressure of the mingled substances and efflorescences at the circumference.

But iron is produced not only in the common mother (the globe of earth), but sometimes is also in the air, in the uppermost clouds from the earth's vapours. It rained iron in Lucania the year that Marcus Crassus met his death. They tell, too, of a mass of iron, resembling slag, having fallen out of the air in the Nethorian forest near Grina, which is said to have weighed several pounds; and that it could not be carried to that village it was so heavy, and could not be taken on a wagon because there were no roads. This happened before the civil war of the Saxons, waged by the dukes. A similar occurrence is mentioned by Avicenna. In the Torinese, it once rained iron at several points, some three years before that province was conquered by the king. In the year 1510, as Cardan relates in his book *De rerum varietate,* there fell from the sky, upon a field near the river Abdua, 1200 stones, one of which weighed 120, another 30 or 40 pounds, all of them the colour of iron and exceedingly hard. These occurrences, because they happen seldom, seem to be portents, like the earth-rains and stone-showers mentioned in the annals of the Romans. But that it ever rained other metals is not mentioned; for it does not appear that gold, silver, lead, tin, or zinc ever fell from heaven. But copper has sometimes been observed to fall from the clouds—a metal differing not much from iron: and this cloud-gendered iron and copper are seen to be imperfect metals, absolutely infusible and unforgeable. For the earth, in its eminences, abounds in store of iron, and the globe contains great plenty of ferric and magnetic matter. Exhalations of such matter sent forth with some violence may, with the concurrence of powerful agencies, become condensed in the upper regions, and so may be evolved a certain monstrous progeny of iron.

CHAPTER 9. *Iron ore attracts iron ore*

LIKE the other metals, iron is obtained from various substances—stones, earths, and suchlike concretions, called by miners ores, or veins, because they are produced in fissures of the earth. Of the diversity of ores we have already spoken. A piece of crude iron ore of the colour of iron and *rich* as miners say, when floated in a bowl or other vessel in water (as in the case of the loadstone *supra*) is usually attracted by a like piece of ore held in the hand and brought near to it, but it is not attracted strongly and with rapidity as a loadstone is drawn by a loadstone, but slowly and weakly. Stony ores, and those of an ashy, brown, ruddy, etc., colour, neither attract one another nor are attracted even by a powerful loadstone, any more than so much wood or lead or silver or gold would be. Take some pieces of such ores and roast or rather heat them in a moderate fire so that they may not suddenly split or fly to pieces, and retain them ten or twelve hours in the fire, which is to be kept up and moderately increased; then suffer them to cool, according to the method given in Book III, *Of Direction*: these stones so manipulated, the loadstone now attracts; they show mutual sympathy, and, when arranged according to artificial conditions, they come together through the action of their own forces.

CHAPTER 10. *Iron ore has and acquires poles, and arranges itself with reference to the earth's poles*

MEN are deplorably ignorant with respect to natural things, and modern philosophers, as though dreaming in the darkness, must be aroused and taught the uses of things, the dealing with things; they must be made to quit the sort of learning that comes only from books, and that rests only on vain arguments from probability and upon conjectures. For the science of iron (than which nought is more in use among us), as of many other bodies, remains unknown—iron, I say, whose rich ore, by an inborn force, when floated in a vessel on water, assumes, like the loadstone, a north and south direction, coming to a standstill at those points, whence if it be turned away, it goes back to them again in virtue of its inborn activity. But of less perfect ores which, however, under the guise of stone or earth contain a good deal of iron, few possess the power of movement; yet when treated artificially with fire, as told in the foregoing chapter, these acquire polar activity, strength (*verticity,* as we call it); and not only such ores as miners seek, but even earths simply impregnated with ferruginous matter, and many kinds of rock, do in like manner (provided they be skilfully placed), tend and glide toward those positions of the heavens, or rather of the earth, until they reach the point they are seeking: there they eagerly rest.

CHAPTER 11. *Wrought-iron, not magnetized by the loadstone, attracts iron*

IRON is extracted in the first furnace from the ore, which is converted or separated partly into metal, partly into dross, by the action of very great heat continued for eight, ten, or twelve hours. The metal flows out, leaving behind the dross and useless substances, and forms a great long mass, which under the blows of a large hammer is cut into pieces: from these, after being reduced in another furnace and again put on the anvil, the workmen form cubical masses, or more usually bars, which are sold to merchants and blacksmiths: from these blocks or bars are everywhere made in smiths' shops various implements. This we call wrought-iron, and, as every one knows, it is attracted by the loadstone. But we, steadily trying all sorts of experiments, have discovered that mere iron itself, magnetized by no loadstone, nor impregnated with any extraneous force, attracts other iron, though it does not seize the other iron as eagerly nor as suddenly pulls it to itself as would a strong loadstone.

That this is so you may learn from the following experiment: a small piece of cork, round, and the size of a filbert, has an iron wire passed through it to the middle of the wire: float this in still water and approach

(without contact) to one end of that wire, the end of another wire: wire attracts wire, and when the one is withdrawn slowly the other follows, yet this action takes place only within fit limits. In the figure, *A* is the cork holding

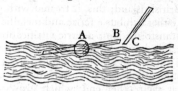

the wire, *B* one end of the wire rising a little out of the water, *C* the end of the second wire, which pulls *B*. You may demonstrate the same thing with a larger mass of iron. Suspend in equilibrium with a slender silken cord a long rod of polished iron, such as are used to support hangings and curtains; bring within the distance of half a finger's length of one end of this as it rests still in the air, some oblong mass of polished iron with suitable end: the balanced rod returns to the mass; then quickly withdraw your hand with the mass in a circular track around the point of equilibrium of the suspended rod, and the cord holding the rod will travel in a circle.

CHAPTER 12. *A long piece of iron, even not magnetized, assumes a north and south direction*

ALL good and perfect iron, if it be drawn out long, acts like a loadstone or like iron rubbed with loadstone: it takes the direction north and south—a thing not at all understood by our great philosophers who have laboured in vain to demonstrate the properties of the loadstone and the causes of the friendship of iron for the loadstone. Experiment can be made either with large or small objects of iron, either in air or in water. A straight rod of iron six feet in length and as thick as one's finger is (as described in the foregoing chapter) suspended in exact equilibrium with a fine but strong silk thread. The thread, however, should be composed of several silk filaments, twisted differently and not all in one direction. Let the experiment be made in a small room with doors and windows all closed, to prevent currents of air in the room: hence it is not well to experiment on windy days or when a storm is brewing. The rod of iron freely acts according to its property and moves slowly until at last coming to a stop at its goals it points north and south, like magnetized iron in a sun-dial, a common magnetic compass, and the mariner's compass. You may, if you are curious of such experiments, suspend at once from slender threads, iron rods, or wires, or knitting-needles: you shall find them all in accord unless there is some flaw in the conduct of this interesting experiment; for unless you make all the preparations precisely and exactly, your labour will be vain. Test the thing in water also: here the result is more sure and more easily obtained. Pass through a round cork an iron wire two or three fingers long, more or less, so that it may just float in water: the moment you put it in the water it turns round on its centre, and one end of the wire travels to the north, the other to the south: the cause of this, you will find later, when we treat of the reasons of the loadstone's directions. And it is well to know and to hold fast in memory, that as a strong loadstone and iron magnetized by the same, point not always toward the true pole, but exactly to the point of variation; likewise will a weaker loadstone and iron that directs itself by its own force, and not by force derived from the impress of any magnet; so, too, all iron ores, and all substances imbued with any ferric matter and duly prepared, turn to the same point in the horizon—to the place of variation of the locality concerned (if variation exist there), and there they remain and rest.

CHAPTER 13. Smelted iron has in itself fixed north and south parts, magnetic activity, verticity, and fixed vertices or poles

IRON takes a direction toward north and south, but not with the same point directed toward either pole; for one end of a piece of iron ore or of an iron wire steadily and constantly points to the north and the other to the south, whether it be suspended in air, or floating in water, and whether the specimens be iron bars or thin wires. Even an iron rod or wire ten, twenty, or more ells in length will point with one extremity to the north, with the other to the south. And if you cut off a part, if the farther end of that piece is boreal (northern), the farther end of the other piece, with which it was before joined, will be austral (southern). And so, if you divide the rod or wire into several pieces, you shall know the poles even before you make an experiment by floating the pieces in water. In all these fragments a boreal end attracts an austral, and repels a boreal, and vice versa, according to magnetic law. But, herein, manufactured iron so differs from loadstone and iron ore, that in a ball of iron of whatever size—e.g., bombs, cannon-balls, cul-

verin balls, falcon balls—polarity (verticity) is less easily acquired and less readily manifested than in the loadstone itself, in ore, and in a round loadstone; but in iron instruments of any length the force is at once seen: the cause of which, as also the modes of acquiring polarity and poles without a loadstone, together with the account of all other recondite facts touching verticity, we will set forth when we come to treat of the movement of direction.

CHAPTER 14. Of other properties of the loadstone and of its medicinal virtue

DIOSCORIDES tells that loadstone blended in water is administered in a dose of three oboli to expel gross humours. Galen writes that it has virtues like those of bloodstone. Others say that loadstone causes mental disturbance and makes people melancholic, and often is fatal. Gartias ab Horto does not think it injurious or unwholesome. The people of East India, he says, declare that loadstone taken in small quantity preserves youthfulness: for this reason the elder King Zeilam (Zeilan) is said to have ordered made of loadstone some pans for cooking his food (victus). "The man who was ordered to do this thing told me," says Gartias. Many are the varieties of loadstone, produced by different mixtures of earths, metals, and humours; therefore are they totally different in their virtues and effects, according to the neighbourhoods of places and the nearness of adhering bodies, and the pits themselves—unclean matrices, as it were. Hence one loadstone is able to purge the bowels, and another loadstone to stay the purging; with a sort of fumes, it can gravely affect the mind; it may corrode the stomach and produce in it serious disease: for such disorders, quacks prescribe gold and emerald, practising the vilest imposture for lucre's sake. Pure loadstone also may be harmless; and not only that, but many correct excessive humours of the bowels and putrescence of the same, and may bring about a better temperature: such loadstones are the Oriental ones from China, the more compact loadstones of Bengal: these kinds of loadstone are not distasteful nor ungrateful to the senses. Plutarch and Caius Ptolemy, and all the copyists that came after them, believe that loadstone rubbed with garlic does not attract iron. Hence some writers conjecture that garlic is of service against the harmful action of loadstone: in this way does many an untrue and vain opinion in philosophy take its rise in fables and falsehoods. Not a few physicians have thought that loadstone has power to extract an iron arrow-head from a human body: but a loadstone attracts when it is whole, not when reduced to powder, deformed, buried in a plaster; for it does not with its matter attract in such case, but serves rather to heal the ruptured tissues by exsiccation, so causing the wound to close and dry up, whereby the arrow-head becomes fixed in the wound. Thus do pretenders to science vainly and preposterously seek for remedies, ignorant of the true causes of things.

Headaches, despite the opinion of many, are no more cured by application of a loadstone, than by putting on the head an iron helmet or a steel hat. Administration of loadstone to dropsical persons is either an error of the ancients or a blundering quotation of their transcribers, albeit a loadstone may be found capable of purging the bowels, after the manner of sundry metallic substances: but the effect would be due to some vice of the stone, not to its magnetic force. Nicolaus puts into his "divine plaster" a good deal of loadstone, as do the Augsburg doctors in their "black plaster" for fresh wounds and stabs; because of the exsiccating effect of the loadstone without corrosion, it becomes an efficacious and useful remedy. Paracelsus, in like manner and for the same end, makes loadstone an ingredient of his plaster for stab-wounds.

CHAPTER 15. *The medicinal power of the iron*
IT will not be alien to our purpose to treat briefly of the medicinal power of iron; for it is beneficial in many diseases of the human system, and by its virtues, both natural and acquired through fit and skilful preparation, it brings about wonderful changes in the human body; so that we may more clearly describe its nature through its medicinal power and by means of a few well-known experiments; to the end that even those prentices of medicine who abuse this most excellent medicinal agent may learn to prescribe it more judiciously, for the curing of patients, not as is too often the case, to their destruction. The best iron, *i.e.,* *stomoma, chalybs, acies,* or *aciarium* [steel], is reduced by filing to a fine powder; this powder has strongest vinegar poured on it, is dried in the sun, again treated with vinegar, and once more dried. Then it is washed in spring water or other water at hand, and dried. It is again pulverized and pounded fine on porphyry, sifted through a fine sieve, and kept for use. It is given chiefly in cases of lax and over-humid liver, and in cases of tumid spleen after suitable evacuations; hence young women of pale, muddy, blotchy complexion are by it restored to soundness and comeliness, for it is highly exsiccative and harmlessly astringent. But some, who in every internal disorder always recognize obstructions of liver and spleen, think it beneficial in such cases, as removing obstructions; and herein they accept the opinions chiefly of certain Arabic writers. Hence in cases of dropsy, schirrus of the liver, of chronic jaundice, and hypochondriac melancholia, or complaints of the œsophagus, they prescribe it, or add it to electuaries, often to the sure destruction of many a patient. Fallopius recommends a preparation of iron of his own for schirrus of the spleen; but he is much mistaken, for though loadstone is exceedingly beneficial where the spleen is lax and tumid on account of humours, so far is it from curing a spleen thickened to a schirrhus, that it makes the mischief far worse; for agents that are greatly siccative and that absorb humours, transform viscera that have been thickened by schirrhus, into the hardness almost of a stone. Some there are who dry it at a high temperature in an oven, burning it till its colour is changed to red: it is then called "saffron of Mars,"[1] and is a very powerful exsiccant and quickly penetrates the intestines. Further, they prescribe violent exercise so that the remedy may enter the heated intestines and reach the part affected. Hence it is reduced to a very fine powder; else it would remain in the œsophagus and in the chyle and would not penetrate to the intestines. Therefore this dry, earthly medicament is proved by the most conclusive tests to be, after due evacuations, a remedy in diseases arising from humour (when the intestines are running and overflowing with morbid fluids). A preparation of steel is indicated for tumid spleen; chalybeate waters also reduce the spleen, albeit, as a rule, iron is of frigid efficiency and a constringent rather than a resolvent; but it does this neither by heat nor by cold, but by its own dryness when mixed with a penetrant fluid; in this way it dissipates humours, thickens the *villi;* strengthens the fibres and when they are lax makes them contract; then the natural warmth in the organs thus strengthened becoming stronger does the rest; but should the liver be indurated and impaired through age or chronic obstruction, or should the spleen be dried up and thickened into a schirrhus, under which complaints the flesh parts of the members become atrophied, and water collects all

[1] See Book II, Chap. XXIII.

over the body under the skin—in such cases the preparation of steel does but hasten a fatal result and makes the mischief worse. Some recent authorities prescribe, as a highly commended and celebrated remedy for dried-up liver, an electuary of iron slag described by Razes (Rhazes—Abu Bekr Arrasi) in book ninth *Ad Almansorem,* or of prepared steel filings: bad and pernicious counsel. But now if they never will learn from our philosophy, at least daily experience and the decline and death of their patients will convince them, slow and sluggish as they are.

Whether iron be warm or cold is a question over which many contend. Manardus, Curtius, Fallopius, and others bring many arguments for both sides: every one judges according to his own way of looking at it. Some will have it cold, saying that iron has the power of refrigeration, since Aristotle in the *Meteorology* declares it to belong to the class of bodies that become concreted through cold by emission of all their warmth. Galen, too, says that iron gets its consistency from cold; further, that it is an earthy body and dense. It is declared to be cold also because it is astringent, and because chalybeate water stills thirst; they mention also the sensation of coolness produced by thermic chalybeate waters. But others hold it to be warm, since Hippocrates says that chalybeate waters issuing from places where iron exists are warm. Galen says that in all metals there is much substance or essence of fire. Razes will have it that iron is warm and dry in the third degree. The Arabs hold that iron opens the spleen and the liver: hence it is warm. Montagnana recommends it for frigid complaints of uterus and œsophagus. And thus do sciolists wrangle with one another, and confuse the minds of learners with their questionable cogitations, and debate over the question of goat's wool, philosophizing about properties illogically inferred and accepted: but these things will appear more plainly when we come to treat of causes, the murky cloud being dispersed that has so long involved all philosophy. Iron filings, iron scales, iron dross, do not, says Avicenna, lack harmful quality (perhaps when they are not properly prepared, or are taken in too large doses), hence they produce violent intestinal pains, roughness in the mouth and on the tongue, marasmus, and drying up of the members. But mistakenly and old womanishly does Avicenna declare that the true antidote of this ferric poison is a drachm of loadstone taken in a draught of the juice of dog's mercury or of beet-root; for load-stone too is of a twofold nature, and often is injurious and fatal in its effects; neither does it withstand iron, for it attracts it; nor is it able to attract when drunk as a powder in liquid; rather does it cause the self-same mischiefs

CHAPTER 16. *That loadstone and iron ore are the same, and that iron is obtained from both, like other metals from their ores; and that all magnetic properties exist, though weaker, both in smelted iron and in iron ore*

So far we have been telling of the nature and properties of loadstone, as also of the properties and nature of iron; it now remains that we point out their mutual affinities—their consanguinity, so to speak—and that we show the two substances to be very nearly allied. In the uppermost part of the terrestrial globe or its superficies of detritus—its rind as it were—these two bodies come into being and are generated in the same matrix, in one bed, like twins. Strong loadstones are mined from separate deposits, and weaker loadstones also have their own beds. Both occur in iron mines. Iron ore occurs usually by itself, unaccompanied by strong loadstone (for the more perfect loadstones occur more rarely). A strong loadstone looks like iron: from it is often made the best iron, which the Greeks call *stomoma,* the Latins *acies,* and the Barbarians, not inappropriately, *aciare* or *aciarium.* This stone attracts and repels other loadstones, and governs their directions; points to the earth's poles, attracts molten iron, and does many other wonderful things, some of which we have already mentioned, but many more remain yet to be pointed out. A weak loadstone will do the same, but less forcefully: and iron ore, and also smelted iron (if they be prepared), show their virtues in all magnetic experiments, no less than do weak magnets; and the inert iron ore, endowed with no magnetic powers, that is taken out of the mine, becomes awake when treated in the furnace and fittingly prepared, and then is a loadstone in power and properties. Sometimes ironstone or iron ore exerts attractive action the moment it comes from the mine, and without being prepared in any way; native iron, also, or ore of iron colour, attracts iron and makes it point to the poles. Thus the form, appearance, and essence are one. For to me there seems to be greater difference and unlikeness between a very strong loadstone and a weak one that is hardly able to attract a single particle of iron filings; between a hard, firm, and metallic loadstone and one that is soft, friable, clayey, with so great a difference between them in colour, substance, qualities and weight; than between the best ore, rich in iron, or iron that from the first is metallic, on the one hand, and the best loadstone on the other. Nay, the two are usually not to be distinguished by any signs, nor can miners tell one from the other, for they agree in all respects.

Further, we see both the finest magnet and iron ore visited as it were by the same ills and diseases, aging in the same way and with the same indications, preserved by the same remedies and protective measures, and so retaining their properties: so, too, the one adds to the other's power and intensifies and increases it, when the two are artificially connected. For they are both impaired by the action of acrid liquids as though by poisons; the *aqua fortis* of the chemists does equal injury to both; exposed for a long time to the action of the atmosphere they both, in equal degree, age as it were and decline; each is saved from impairment by being kept in the *débris* and scrapings of the other, and a suitable piece of steel or iron being applied to its pole, the magnetic power is intensified by the steadfast union. A loadstone is kept in iron filings not as though it fed on iron, or as though it were a living thing needing victual, as Cardan philosophizes; neither because thus it is protected from the injurious action of the atmosphere (wherefore both the loadstone and iron are kept in bran by Scaliger; though Scaliger is mistaken here, for they are not best preserved so, and loadstone and iron in some of their forms last a long time); but because each is kept unimpaired in filings of the other and their extremities do not become weak, but are cherished and preserved. For as in their native sites and mines, similar bodies surrounded by other bodies of the same kind, *e.g.*, the minor interior parts of some great mass, endure for ages whole and undecayed; so loadstone, and iron ore, when buried in a like material, do not part with their native humour, and do not become weak, but retain their original properties. A loadstone packed in iron filings, as also iron ore in scrapings of loadstone, and manufactured iron in the same or in iron filings, lasts longer.

Thus these two associated bodies possess the true, strict form of one species, though, because of their outwardly different aspect and the inequality of the self-same innate potency, they have hitherto been by all held to be different, and by sciolists to be specifically different, for sciolists have not understood that in both substances reside exactly the same potencies, differing however in strength. They are in fact true parts and intimate parts of the globe, retaining nature's primal powers of mutual attraction, of mobility, and of ordering themselves according to the position of the globe itself: these powers they impart to each other, enhancing each other's powers, confirming them, taking them from each other, and holding them. The stronger invigorates the weaker, not as if it imparted of its own substance or parted with aught of its own strength, neither by injecting into that other any physical substance; but the dormant power of one is awakened by the other's without expenditure. For if with one loadstone you magnetize one thousand compass needles for mariners' use that loadstone not less powerfully attracts iron than it did before; with one stone weighing a pound any one can suspend in air 1000 pounds of iron. For if one were to drive into a wall a number of iron nails weighing all together 1000 pounds, and were to apply to them an equal number of other nails properly magnetized by contact with a loadstone, the nails would plainly hang suspended in air through the power of one single stone. Hence this is not the action, work, or outlay of the loadstone solely, for the iron, which is something extracted from loadstone, a transformation of loadstone into metal, and which gains force from the loadstone and (whatever ore it may have been derived from) by its proximity strengthens the loadstone's magnetic power, at the same time enhances its own native force by the proximity of the loadstone and by contact therewith, even though solid bodies intervene between them. Iron touched by loadstone renovates other iron by contact and gives it magnetic direction; and that does the same for a third piece of iron. But if you rub with loadstone any other metal, or wood, or bone, or glass, as they will not move toward a fixed and determinate quarter of the heavens, nor will be attracted by a magnetized body; so they cannot impart by attrition or by infection any magnetic property either to other bodies or to iron itself.

Loadstone differs from iron ore, as also from some weak loadstones, in that when reduced in the furnace to a ferric and metallic molten mass, it does not always assume readily the fluid condition and become changed to metal, but sometimes is burnt into ash in the large furnaces: this, either because of a certain admixture of sulphurous matter, or because of its own excellence and more simple nature; or because of the resemblance it bears to nature, and the form it has in common with that mother of all; for earths, ferruginous stones, and load-stones rich in metal, are much loaded and dis-figured with drossy metallic humours and with foreign earthy admixtures in their substance, like most weak magnets from the mines; hence they are farther removed from the common mother and are degenerate, and in the furnace they are more easily melted and give a softer sort of iron and no good steel. Most loadstones, if they be not unduly burnt, yield in the furnace the best of iron. But in all these prime qualities iron ore agrees with loadstone, for both, being more akin to the earth and more nearly associ-ated to it than any other bodies around us, pos-sess within themselves the magnetic, genuine, homogenic, and true substance of the terres-trial globe, less tainted and impaired by for-eign impurities, and less mixed with the efflo-rescences on the earth's surface and the *débris* of generations of organisms. And on this ground does Aristotle seem, in the fourth book of his *Meteorology,* to distinguish iron from all other metals. Gold, says he, silver, copper, tin, lead, pertain to water; but iron is earthy. Galen, in the fourth book *De facultatibus sim-plicium medicamentorum,* says that iron is an earthy and dense body.

So, according to our reasoning, loadstone is chiefly earthy; next after it comes iron ore or weak loadstone; and thus loadstone is by origin and nature ferruginous, and iron magnetic, and the two are one in species. Iron ore in the fur-nace yields iron; loadstone in the furnace yields iron also, but of far finer quality, which is called steel; and the better sort of iron ore is weak loadstone, just as the best loadstone is the most excellent iron ore in which we will show that grand and noble primary properties in-here. It is only in weaker loadstone, or iron ore, that these properties are obscure, or faint, or scarcely perceptible to the senses.

CHAPTER 17. *That the terrestrial globe is mag-netic and is a loadstone; and just as in our hands the loadstone possesses all the primary powers (forces) of the earth, so the earth by reason of the same potencies lies ever in the same direc-tion in the universe*

BEFORE we expound the causes of the magnetic movements and bring forward our demonstra-tions and experiments touching matters that for so many ages have lain hid—the real foun-dations of terrestrial philosophy—we must for-mulate our new and till now unheard-of view of the earth, and submit it to the judgment of scholars. When it shall have been supported with a few arguments of *prima facie* cogency, and these shall have been confirmed by subse-quent experiments and demonstrations, it will stand as firm as aught that ever was proposed in philosophy, backed by ingenious argumen-tation, or buttressed by mathematical demon-strations. The terrestrial mass which together with the world of waters produces the spheri-cal figure and our globe, inasmuch as it con-sists of firm durable matter, is not easily al-tered, does not wander nor fluctuate with inde-terminate movements like the seas and the flowing streams; but in certain hollows, within certain bounds, and in many veins and arter-ies, as it were, holds the entire volume of liquid matter, nor suffers it to spread abroad and be dissipated. But the solid mass of the earth has the greater volume and holds pre-eminence in the constitution of our globe. Yet the water is associated with it, though only as something supplementary and as a flux emanating from it; and from the beginning it is intimately mixed with the smallest particles of earth and is innate in its substance. The earth growing hot emits it as vapour, which is of the greatest service to the generation of things.

But the strong foundation of the globe, its great mass, is that terrene body, far surpassing in quantity the whole aggregate of fluids and waters whether in combination with earth or free (whatever vulgar philosophers may dream about the magnitudes and proportions of their elements); and this mass makes up most of the globe, constituting nearly its whole inte-rior framework, and of itself taking on the spherical form. For the seas do but fill certain not very deep hollows, having very rarely a depth of a mile, and often not exceeding 100 or 50 fathoms. This appears from the observa-tions of navigators who have with line and sinker explored their bottoms. In view of the earth's dimension, such depressions cannot much impair the spheroidal shape of the globe. Still the portion of the earth that ever comes into view for man or that is brought to the sur-face seems small indeed, for we cannot pene-trate deep into its bowels, beyond the *débris* of its outermost efflorescence, hindered either by the waters that flow as through veins into great mines; or by the lack of wholesome air neces-sary to support the life of the miners; or by the enormous cost of executing such vast undertak-ings, and the many difficulties attending the work. Thus we cannot reach the inner parts of the globe, and if one goes down, as in a few mines, 400 fathoms, or (a very rare thing) 500 fathoms, it is something to make every one wonder. But how small, how almost null, is the proportion of 500 fathoms to the earth's diameter—6872 miles—can be easily understood. So we do only see portions of the earth's circumference, of its prominences; and everywhere these are either loamy, or argillaceous, or sandy; or consist of organic soils or marls; or it is all stones and gravel; or we find rock-salt, or ores, or sundry other metallic substances. In the depths of the ocean and other waters are found by mariners, when they take soundings, ledges and great reefs, or bowlders, or sands, or ooze. The Aristotelian element, earth, nowhere is seen, and the Peripatetics are misled by their vain dreams about elements. But the great bulk of the globe beneath the surface and its inmost parts do not consist of such matters; for these things had not been were it not that the surface was in contact with and exposed to the atmosphere, the waters, and the radiations and influences of the heavenly bodies; for by the action of these are they generated and made to assume many different forms of things, and to change perpetually. Still do they imitate the inner parts and resemble their source, because their matter is of the earth, albeit they have lost the prime qualities and the true nature of terrene matter; and they bear toward the earth's centre and cohere to the globe and cannot be parted from it save by force.

Yet the loadstone and all magnetic bodies—not only the stone but all magnetic, homogenic matter—seem to contain within themselves the potency of the earth's core and of its inmost viscera, and to have and comprise whatever in the earth's substance is privy and inward: the loadstone possesses the actions peculiar to the globe, of attraction, polarity, revolution, of taking position in the universe according to the law of the whole; it contains the supreme excellencies of the globe and orders them: all this is token and proof of a certain eminent combination and of a most accordant nature. For, if among bodies one sees aught that moves and breathes and has senses and is governed and impelled by reason, will he not, knowing and seeing this, say that here is a man or something more like man than a stone or a stalk? The loadstone far surpasses all other bodies around us in the virtues and properties that pertain to the common mother of all; but those properties have been very little understood and noted by philosophers. Toward it, as we see in the case of the earth, magnetic bodies tend from all sides, and adhere to it; it has poles—not mathematical points, but natural points of force that through the co-operation of all its parts excel in prime efficiency; such poles exist also in the same way in the globe, and our forefathers always sought them in the heavens. Like the earth, it has an equator, a natural line of demarkation between the two poles; for of all the lines drawn by mathematicians on the terrestrial globe, the equator (as later will appear) is a natural boundary, and not merely a mathematical circle.

Like the earth, the loadstone has the power of direction and of standing still at north and south; it has also a circular motion to the earth's position, whereby it adjusts itself to the earth's law. It follows the elevations and depressions of the earth's poles, and conforms precisely to them: according to the position of the earth and of the locality, it naturally and of itself elevates its poles above the horizon, or depresses them. The loadstone derives properties from the earth *ex tempore,* and acquires verticity; and iron is affected by the verticity of the globe as it is affected by a loadstone. Magnetic bodies are governed and regulated by the earth, and they are subject to the earth in all their movements. All the movements of the loadstone are in accord with the geometry and form of the earth and are strictly controlled thereby, as will later be proved by conclusive experiments and diagrams; and the greater part of the visible earth is also magnetic, and has magnetic movements, though it is defaced by all sorts of waste matter and by no end of transformations.

Why, then, do we not recognize this primary and homogeneous earth-substance, likest of all substances to the inmost nature, to the very marrow, of the earth itself, and nearest to it? For not any of the other mixed earths—those suitable for agriculture,—not any of the metalliferous veins, no stones, no sands, no other fragments of the globe that come under our notice, possess such stable, such distinctive virtues. Yet we do not hold the whole interior of this our globe to be of rock or of iron, albeit the learned Franciscus Maurolycus deems the earth in its interior to consist throughout of rigid rock. For not every loadstone that we find is a stone, being sometimes like a clod of earth, or like clay, or like iron; consisting of various materials compacted into hardness, or soft, or by heat reduced to the metallic state; and in the earth's surface formations, according to circumstances of place, of the bodies around it, and of its matrix in the mine, a magnetic substance is distinguished by divers qualities and by adventitious accretions, as we see in marl, in some stones, and in iron ores. But the true earth-matter we hold to be a solid body homogeneous with the globe, firmly coherent, endowed with a primordial and (as in the other globes of the universe) an energic form. By being so fashioned, the earth has a fixed verticity, and necessarily revolves with an innate whirling motion: this motion the loadstone alone of all the bodies around us possesses genuine and true, less spoilt by outside interferences, less marred than in other bodies,—as though the motion were an homogeneous part taken from the very essence of our globe. This pure native iron is produced when homogenic portions of the earth's substance coalesce to form a metallic vein; loadstone is produced when they are transformed into metallic stone or a vein of the finest iron or steel; so, too, rather imperfect homogenic material collects to form other iron ores—just as many parts of the earth, even parts that rise above the general circumference, are of homogenic matter, only still more debased. Native iron is iron fused and reduced from homogenic matters, and coheres to earth more tenaciously than the ores themselves.

Such, then, we consider the earth to be in its interior parts; it possesses a magnetic homogenic nature. On this more perfect material (foundation) the whole world of things terrestrial, which, when we search diligently, manifests itself to us everywhere, in all the magnetic metals and iron ores and marls, and multitudinous earths and stones; but Aristotle's "simple element," and that most vain terrestrial phantasm of the Peripatetics,—formless, inert, cold, dry, simple matter, the substratum of all things, having no activity,—never appeared to any one even in dreams, and if it did appear would be of no effect in nature. Our philosophers dreamt only of an inert and simple matter. Cardan thinks the loadstone is not a stone of any species, but that it is, as it were, a perfect portion of a certain kind of earth that is absolute, whereof a proof is its abundance, for there is no place where it is not found. He says that this kind of conceptive, generative earth,

possessed of an affinity like that of the marriage tie, is perfected when it has been placed in contact with, or received the fecundating influence of, the masculine or Herculean stone, it having been, moreover, shown in a previous proposition (*Libro de proportionibus*) that the loadstone is true earth.

A strong loadstone shows itself to be of the inmost earth, and in innumerable experiments proves its claim to the honour of possessing the primal form of things terrestrial, in virtue of which the earth itself remains in its position and is directed in its movements. So a weak loadstone, and all iron ore, all marls and argillaceous and other earths (some more, some less, according to the difference of their humours and the varying degrees in which they have been spoilt by decay), retain, deformed, in a state of degeneration from the primordial form, magnetic properties, powers, that are conspicuous and in the true sense telluric. For not only does metallic iron turn to the poles, not only is one loadstone attracted by another and made to revolve magnetically, but so do (if prepared) all iron ores and even other stones, as slates from the Rhineland, the black slates (*ardoises,* as the French call them) from Anjou, which are used for shingles, and other sorts of fissile stone of different colours; also clays, gravel, and several sorts of rock; and, in short, all of the harder earths found everywhere, provided only they be not fouled by oozy and dank defilements like mud, mire, heaps of putrid matter, or by the decaying remains of a mixture of organic matters, so that a greasy slime oozes from them, as from marl,—they are all attracted by the loadstone, after being prepared simply by the action of fire and freed from their excrementitious humour; and as by the loadstone, so, too, are they magnetically attracted and made to point to the poles by the earth itself, therein differing from all other bodies; and by this innate force they are made to conform to the ordering and planning of the universe and the earth, as later will appear. Thus every separate fragment of the earth exhibits in indubitable experiments the whole impetus of magnetic matter; in its various movements it follows the terrestrial globe and the common principle of motion.

BOOK SECOND

CHAPTER 1. *Of magnetic movements*

OF opinions touching the loadstone and its varieties; of its poles and its recognized faculties; of iron and its properties; of the magnetic substance common to loadstone and iron and the earth itself, we have treated briefly in the foregoing book. Now remain the magnetic movements and their broader philosophy as developed by experiments and demonstrations. These movements are impulsions of homogeneous parts toward one another or toward the primary conformation of the whole earth. Aristotle admits only two simple movements of his elements—from the centre and toward the centre; light objects upward, heavy objects downward: so that in the earth there is but one motion of all its parts toward the centre of the world,—a wild headlong falling. We, however, will elsewhere consider what this "light" may be, and will show how erroneously it is inferred by the Peripatetics from the simple motion of the elements; we shall also inquire what "heavy" means.[1] But now we have to inquire into the causes of the other movements depending on its true form: these we see clearly in all magnetic bodies; these also we find existing in the earth and all its homogenic parts; further, we find that they are in accord with the earth, and are bound up in its forces. Now five movements or differences of movement are perceived by us: COITION[2] (commonly called attraction), an impulsion to magnetic union; DIRECTION[3] toward the earth's poles, and verticity of the earth toward determinate points in the universe, and the standstill there; VARIATION,[4] deflection from the meridian—this we call a perverted motion; DECLINATION[5] (inclination or dip), a descent of the magnetic pole beneath the horizon; and circular movement, or REVOLUTION.[6] Of each of these we will treat separately, and will show how they all proceed from a congregant nature, or from verticity or from volubility. Jofrancus Offusius distinguishes several magnetic movements, the first to the centre, the second to the pole, traversing 77 degrees, the third to iron, the fourth to a loadstone. The first is not always to the centre, for only at the poles is it in a right line to the centre, if the motion is magnetic, otherwise it is only the movement of matter toward its mass and toward the earth. The second, of 77 degrees to the pole, is no movement, but a direction or a variation to the earth's pole. The third and the fourth are magnetic, and are but one movement. Thus this author recognizes no true magnetic movement but coition toward iron or loadstone, commonly known as attraction. There is another movement in the earth as a whole, which does not take place toward the terrella or the parts, *i.e.*, the movement of coacervation and that movement of matter called by philosophers a "right movement": of that elsewhere.

CHAPTER 2. *Of magnetic coition; and, first, of the attraction exerted by amber, or more properly the attachment of bodies to amber*

GREAT has ever been the fame of the loadstone and of amber in the writings of the learned: many philosophers cite the loadstone and also amber whenever, in explaining mysteries, their minds become obfuscated and reason can no farther go. Over-inquisitive theologians, too, seek to light up God's mysteries and things beyond man's understanding by means of the loadstone and amber: just as light-headed metaphysicians, when they utter and teach their vain imaginings, employ the loadstone as a sort of Delphic sword and as an illustration of all sorts of things. Medical men also (at the bidding of Galen), in proving that purgative medicines exercise attraction through likeness of substance and kinships of juices (a silly error and gratuitous!), bring in as a witness the loadstone, a substance of great authority and of noteworthy efficiency, and a body of no common order. Thus in very many affairs persons who plead for a cause the merits of which they cannot set forth, bring in as masked advocates the loadstone and amber. But all these, besides sharing the general misapprehension, are ignorant that the causes of the

[1] See Plato's *Timæus*.   [2] See II, 2, *et seq.*
[3] See III.   [4] See IV.   [5] See V.
[6] See VI, 3, *et seq.*

loadstone's movements are very different from those which give to amber its properties; hence they easily fall into errors, and by their own imaginings are led farther and farther astray. For in other bodies is seen a considerable power of attraction, differing from that of the loadstone,—in amber, for example. Of this substance a few words must be said, to show the nature of the attachment of bodies to it, and to point out the vast difference between this and the magnetic actions; for men still continue in ignorance, and deem that inclination of bodies to amber to be an attraction, and comparable to the magnetic coition. The Greeks call this substance ἤλεκτρον, because, when heated by rubbing, it attracts to itself chaff; whence it is also called ἅρπαξ, and from its golden colour, χρυσοφόρον. But the Moors call it *carabe*, because they used to offer it in sacrifices and in the worship of the gods; for in Arabic *carab* means oblation, not *rapiens paleas* (snatching chaff), as Scaliger would have it, quoting from the Arabic or Persian of Abohali (Hali Abbas). Many call this substance *ambra* (amber) especially that which is brought from India and Ethiopia. The Latin name *succinum* appears to be formed from *succus*, juice. The Sudavienses or Sudini call the substance *geniter*, as though *genitum terra* (produced by the earth). The erroneous opinion of the ancients as to its nature and source being exploded, it is certain that amber comes for the most part from the sea: it is gathered on the coast after heavy storms, in nets and through other means, by peasants, as by the Sudini of Prussia; it is also sometimes found on the coast of our own Britain. But it seems to be produced in the earth and at considerable depth below its surface, like the rest of the bitumens; then to be washed out by the sea-waves, and to gain consistency under the action of the sea and the saltness of its waters. For at first it was a soft and viscous matter, and hence contains, buried in its mass forevermore (*æternis sepulchris relucentes*), but still (shining) visible, flies, grubs, midges, and ants. The ancients as well as moderns tell (and their report is confined by experience) that amber attracts straws and chaff. The same is done by jet, a stone taken out of the earth in Britain, Germany, and many other regions: it is a hard concretion of black bitumen,—a sort of transformation of bitumen to stone. Many modern authors have written about amber and jet as attracting chaff and about other facts unknown to the generality, or have copied from other writers: with the results of their labors booksellers' shops are crammed full. Our generation has produced many volumes about recondite, abstruse, and occult causes and wonders, and in all of them amber and jet are represented as attracting chaff; but never a proof from experiments, never a demonstration do you find in them. The writers deal only in words that involve in thicker darkness subject-matter; they treat the subject esoterically, miracle-mongeringly, abstrusely, reconditely, mystically. Hence such philosophy bears no fruit; for it rests simply on a few Greek or unusual terms—just as our barbers toss off a few Latin words in the hearing of the ignorant rabble in token of their learning, and thus win reputation—bears no fruit, because few of the philosophers themselves are investigators, or have any first-hand acquaintance with things; most of them are indolent and untrained, add nothing to knowledge by their writings, and are blind to the things that might throw a light upon their reasonings. For not only do amber and (gagates or) jet, as they suppose, attract light corpuscles (substances): the same is done by diamond, sapphire, carbuncle, iris stone, opal, amethyst, vincentina, English gem (Bristol stone, *bristola*), beryl, rock crystal. Like powers of attracting are possessed by glass, especially clear, brilliant glass; by artificial gems made of (paste) glass or rock crystal, antimony glass, many fluor-spars, and belemnites. Sulphur also attracts, and likewise mastich, and sealing-wax [of lac], hard resin, orpiment (weakly). Feeble power of attraction is also possessed in favoring dry atmosphere by sal gemma [native chloride of sodium], mica, rock alum. This we may observe when in mid-winter the atmosphere is very cold, clear, and thin; when the electrical effluvia of the earth offer less impediment, and electric bodies are harder: of all this later. These several bodies (electrics) not only draw to themselves straws and chaff, but all metals, wood, leaves, stones, earths, even water and oil; in short, whatever things appeal to our senses or are solid: yet we are told that it attracts nothing but chaff and twigs. Hence Alexander Aphrodiseus incorrectly declares the question of amber to be unsolvable, because that amber does attract chaff, yet not the leaves of basil; but such stories are false, disgracefully inaccurate. Now in order clearly to understand by experience how such attraction takes place, and what those substances may be that so attract other bodies (and in the case of many of these electrical substances, though the bodies influenced by them lean toward them, yet because of the feebleness of the attraction they are not drawn clean up to them, but are easily made to rise), make yourself a rotating-needle (electroscope—*versorium*) of any sort of metal, three or four fingers long, pretty light, and poised on a sharp point after the manner of a magnetic pointer. Bring near to one end of it a

piece of amber or a gem, lightly rubbed, polished and shining: at once the instrument revolves. Several objects are seen to attract not only natural objects, but things artificially prepared, or manufactured, or formed by mixture. Nor is this a rare property possessed by one object or two (as is commonly supposed), but evidently belongs to a multitude of objects, both simple and compound, *e.g.*, sealing-wax and other unctuous mixtures. But why this inclination and what these forces,—on which points a few writers have given a very small amount of information, while the common run of philosophers give us nothing,—these questions must be considered fully. Galen recognizes in all three kinds of attractions in nature: first, the attraction exercised by those bodies which attract by an elemental quality—heat, to wit; secondly, by those which attract by the in-rush into a vacuum; thirdly, by those which attract through a property pertaining to their entire mass: and these three kinds are enumerated by Avicenna and others. This division cannot by any means content us, nor does it define the causes of amber, jet, diamond, and other like substances, which owe to the same virtue the forces they possess; nor of loadstone or of other magnetic bodies, which possess a force altogether different from that of those other bodies, both in its efficiency and in the sources whence it is derived. We must, therefore, find other causes of movements, or must with these stray about as it were in darkness, never at all reaching our goal. Now amber does not attract by heat, for when heated at a fire and brought near to straws, whether it is merely warm, or whether it is hot, even burning hot, or even brought to the flaming point, it has no attraction. Cardan (and Pictorius too) is of opinion that the attraction of amber is much like that seen in the cupping-glass: yet the attractional force of the cupping-glass does not really come from igneous force; but he had already said that a dry body is eager to drink up one that is moist and juicy, and therefore such bodies are drawn to it. These two explications are inconsistent, and

they are without ground in reason also. For were amber to move toward its sustenance, or other bodies to turn to amber, as to their food, the one, being swallowed up, would disappear, while the other would increase in size. And then why seek in amber the attractive force of fire? If fire attracts, why do not many other bodies heated by the fire, the sun, or by friction attract also? Nor can attraction, because of air displaced, occur in open air, though this is the cause Lucretius assigns for magnetic movements; nor in the cupping-glass can heat or fire feeding on the air attract: the air in the cupping-glass rarefied to flame, when again it becomes dense and is compressed into small space, causes the skin and flesh to rise, because nature avoids a vacuum. In open air, heated objects cannot attract, not even metals or stones brought to a very high temperature by fire. For an iron rod at white heat, a flame, a candle, a flaming torch, or a red-hot coal when brought near to straws or to a revolving pointer (*versorium*) does not attract; and yet plainly all these cause the air to come to them in a current, for they consume air as a lamp consumes oil. But of heat, and how very different is the view held by the whole crowd of the philosophers, as to its attractive power in natural bodies and materia medica, from the fact as seen in nature, we will treat elsewhere when we come to explain what heat and cold really are. They are very general properties or close appurtenances of substances, but are not called true causes; and if I may use the expression, they utter certain words, but in fact they show nothing specifically. Nor does the supposed attractive force of amber arise from any peculiar property of its substance or from any special relation between it and other bodies; for in many other substances, if we but search with any diligence, we see the same effect, and, by them, all other bodies, of whatever properties possessed, are attracted. And likeness is not the cause of amber's attracting, for all things that we see on the globe, whether similar or dissimilar, are attracted by amber and such like; hence no strong analogy is to be drawn either from likeness or from identity of substance. Besides, like does not attract like—a stone does not attract a stone, flesh flesh: there is no attraction outside of the class of magnetic and electric bodies. Fracastorio thinks that all bodies that mutually attract are alike, or of the same species, and that, either in their action or in their proper *subjectum*: "Now the proper *subjectum*," says he, "is that from which is emitted that emanational something which attracts, and, in mixed substances, this is not perceptible on account of deformation, whereby they are one thing *actu*, another *potentia*. Hence, perhaps, hairs and twigs are drawn to amber and diamond not because they are hairs, but because there is imprisoned within them either air or some other principle that is first attracted and that has reference and analogy to that which of itself attracts; and herein amber and diamond are as one, in virtue of a principle common to both." So much for Fracastorio. But had he in experiment noted that all bodies are attracted by electrics save those which are afire or flaming, or extremely rarefied, he never would have entertained such views. Men of acute intelligence, without actual knowledge of facts, and in the absence of experiment, easily slip and err. In greater error are they who hold amber, diamond, etc., and the objects attracted by them, to be like one another, but not the same, near to one another in kind, and that therefore like moves toward like, and is by it perfected. But that is reckless speculation; for all bodies are drawn to all electrics, save bodies aflame or too rarefied, as the air which is the universal effluvium of the globe. Plants draw moisture, and thus our crops thrive and grow; but from this analogy Hippocrates in his book *De natura hominis*, I, illogically infers that morbid humour is purged by the specific virtue of a drug. Of the action of purges we will treat elsewhere. Wrongly, too, attraction is postulated to exist in other effects; *e.g.*, when a stoppered bottle of water being covered with a heap of wheat, its liquid is drawn out: for in fact the liquid is reduced to vapour by the spirit of the fermenting wheat, and the wheat takes in that vapour. Nor do elephants' tusks suck up moisture, but transform it into vapour and absorb it. And thus very many bodies are said to attract, whereas the ground of their action is to be sought elsewhere. A large polished lump of amber attracts; a smaller piece, or a piece of impure amber, seems not to attract without friction. But very many electric bodies (as precious stones, etc.) do not attract at all unless they are first rubbed; while sundry other bodies, and among them some gems, have no power of attraction, and cannot be made to attract, even by friction; such bodies are emerald, agate, carnelian, pearls, jasper, chalcedony, alabaster, porphyry, coral, the marbles, lapis lydius (touchstone, basanite), flint, bloodstone, emery or corundum, bone, ivory; the hardest woods, as ebony; some other woods, as cedar, juniper, cypress; metals, as silver, gold, copper, iron.

The loadstone, though it is susceptible of a very high polish, has not the electric attraction. On the other hand, many bodies (already mentioned) that can be polished attract when rubbed. All this we shall understand when we have more closely studied the prime origin of bodies. As is plain to all, the earth's mass or rather the earth's framework and its crust consist of a twofold matter, a matter, to wit, that is fluid and humid, and a matter that is firm and dry. From this twofold matter, or from the simple concretion of one of these matters, come all the bodies around us, which consist in major proportion now of terrene matter, anon of watery. Those that derive their growth mainly from humours, whether watery humour or one more dense; or that are fashioned from these humours by simple concretion, or that were concreted out of them long ages ago; if they possess sufficient firmness, and after being polished are rubbed, and shine after friction, such substances attract all bodies presented to them in the air, unless the said bodies be too heavy. For amber and jet are concretions of water; so too are all shining gems, as rock-crystal, which is a product of limpid water, not always of such water at an extremely low temperature, as some have thought, but sometimes at a more moderate degree of cold, the nature of the ground fashioning them, and the humour or juices being prisoned in definite cavities, just as fluorites are generated in mines. So clear glass is reduced from sand and other substances that have their origin in humid juices. But these substances contain a quantity of impurities of metals, or metals themselves, stones, rocks, wood, earth, or are largely mixed with earth; therefore they do not attract. Rock crystal, mica, glass, and other electric bodies do not attract if they be burned or highly heated, for their primordial humour is destroyed by the heat, is altered, and discharged as vapour. Hence all bodies that derive their origin principally from humours, and that are firmly concreted, and that retain the appearance and property of fluid in a firm, solid mass, attract all substances, whether humid or dry. Such as are parts of the true substance of the earth or differ but little from that, appear to attract also, but in a very different way, and, so to speak, magnetically: of them we are to treat later. But those that consist of mixed water and earth, and that result from equal degradation of both elements—in which the magnetic force of the earth is degraded and lies in abeyance, while the aqueous humour, spoilt by combination with a quantity of earth, does not form a concretion by itself, but mingles with the earthy matter—such bodies are powerless to attract to themselves aught that they are not in actual contact with, or to repel the same. For this reason it is that neither metals, marbles, flints, woods, grasses, flesh, nor various other substances can attract or solicit a body, whether magnetically or electrically (for it pleases us to call electric force that force which has its origin in humours). But bodies consisting mostly of humour and not firmly compacted by nature wherefore they do not stand friction, but either fall to pieces or grow soft, or are sticky, as pitch, soft rosin, camphor, galbanum, ammoniacum, storax, asa, gum benjamin, asphaltum (especially in a warm atmosphere), do not attract corpuscles. For without friction few bodies give out their true natural electric *emanation* and effluvium. Turpentine resin in the liquid state does not attract, because it cannot be rubbed; but when it hardens to a mastic it does attract.

And now, at last, we have to see why corpuscles are drawn toward substances that derive their origin from water, and by what manner of force, by what hands, so to speak, such substances lay hold of matters nigh them.

In all bodies everywhere are presented two causes or principles whereby the bodies are produced, to wit, matter (*materia*) and form (*forma*). Electrical movements come from the *materia*, but magnetic from the prime *forma;* and these two differ widely from each other and become unlike—the one ennobled by many virtues, and prepotent; the other lowly, of less potency, and confined in certain prisons, as it were; wherefore its force has to be awakened by friction till the substance attains a moderate heat, and gives out an effluvium, and its surface is made to shine. Moist air blown upon it from the mouth or a current of humid air from the atmosphere chokes its powers; and if a sheet of paper or a linen cloth be interposed there is no movement. But loadstone, neither rubbed nor heated, and even though it be drenched with liquid, and whether in air or water, attracts magnetic bodies, and that, though solidest bodies or boards, or thick slabs of stone or plates of metal, stand between. A loadstone attracts only magnetic bodies; electrics attract everything. A loadstone lifts great weights; a strong one weighing two ounces lifts half an ounce or one ounce. Electrics attract only light weights; *e.g.*, a piece of amber three ounces in weight lifts only one-fourth of a barleycorn's weight.

But this attraction of amber and of electric bodies must be investigated further; and since it is an acquired state the question arises why amber is rubbed, and what state is brought about by rubbing; also, what causes are evoked that seize all sorts of substances. By friction it is made moderately hot and also smooth; and these conditions must in most cases concur; but a large polished piece of amber or of jet attracts even without friction, though not strongly; yet if it be carefully brought nigh to a flame or a red coal and warmed to the same degree as by friction, it does not attract corpuscles, because it becomes involved in dark fumes from the body of the hot or flaming mass, which emits a hot exhalation; and the vapour from that other body is driven upon it—something quite alien to the nature of the amber. Besides, the exhalation produced in the amber by an alien heat is feeble, for the amber must not have any heat save that produced by friction: its own heat, so to speak,—not heat contributed by other bodies. For as the igneous heat emitted by any flaming matter is useless to procure for electrics their virtue, so, too, heat from the sun's rays does not excite an electric by the right dissolution of its matter—rather dissipates and consumes it (albeit a body that undergoes friction and then is exposed to the solar rays retains its powers longer than it does in shade, because that in shade effluvia are condensed more and more quickly); further, the sun's heat, heightened by means of a burning-glass, imparts no power to amber, for it dissipates and spoils all the electric effluvia. Again, flaming sulphur and burning sealing-wax do not attract, for heat produced by friction dissolves bodies into effluvia, and these are consumed by flame. It is impossible for solid electrics to be resolved into their effluvia otherwise than by attrition, save a few that, because of their native strength, emit effluvia continually. They are to be rubbed with bodies that do not foul the surface, and that cause them to shine, *e.g.*, strong silk, and coarse woollen cloth, scrupulously clean, and the dry palm of the hand. Amber may be rubbed with amber, with diamond, with glass, etc. Thus are electrics made ready for action.

And now what is it that produces the movement? The body itself circumscribed by its contour? Or is it something imperceptible for us flowing out of the substance into the ambient air? (This appears to have been in some sense the opinion of Plutarch, who, in the *Quæstiones Platonicæ*, says that there is in amber something flame-like, or having the nature of the breath, and that this, when the paths are cleared by friction of the surface, is emitted and attracts bodies.) And if it is an effluvium, does the effluvium set the air in current, and is the current then followed by the bodies? or is it the bodies themselves directly that are drawn up? But if the amber attracts the body itself, then supposing its surface is clean and free from adhesions, what need is there of friction? Nor does the force come from the lustre proceeding from the rubbed and polished electric; for the vincentina, the diamond, and pure glass attract when they are rough, but not so strongly nor so readily; because then they are not so easily cleansed of extraneous moisture settled on the surface, nor are they subjected all over to such an equal degree of friction as to be resolved into effluvia. Nor does the sun, with its shining and its rays, which are of vast importance in nature, attract bodies thus; and yet the common run of philosophizers think that liquids are attracted by the sun, whereas only the denser humours are resolved into rarer, (and) into vapour and air; and thus, through the motion given to them by diffusion, they ascend to the upper regions, or, being attenuated exhalations, are lifted by the heavier air. Neither does it seem that the electric attraction is produced by the effluvia rarefying the air so that bodies, impelled by the denser air, are made to move toward the source of the rarefaction: if that were so, then hot bodies and flaming bodies would also attract other bodies; but no lightest straw, no rotating pointer is drawn toward a flame. If there is afflux and appulsion of air, how can a minute diamond of the size of a chick-pea pull to itself so much air as to sweep in a corpuscle of relatively considerable length, the air being pulled toward the diamond only from around a small part of one or other end? Besides, the attracted body must stand still or move more slowly before coming into contact, especially if the attracting body be a broad flat piece of amber, on account of the heaping up of air on the surface, and its rebounding after collision. And if the effluvia go out rare and return dense (as with vapours), then the body would begin to move toward the electric a little after the beginning of its application; yet, when rubbed electrics are suddenly applied to a versorium, instantly the pointer turns, and the nearer it is to the electric the quicker is the attraction. But if rare effluvia rarefy the medium, and therefore the bodies pass from a denser into a rarer medium, then the bodies might be attracted sideways or downward, but not upward, or the attraction

and holding of the bodies would be only for a moment. But jet and amber after one friction strongly and for a length of time solicit and attract bodies, sometimes for as long as five minutes, especially if the weather is fair. But if the mass of amber be large, and its surface polished, it attracts without friction. Flint, on being struck, gives off inflammable matter that turns to sparks and heat. Hence the denser fire-containing effluvia of flint are very different indeed from the electrical effluvia, which, by reason of their extreme tenuity, cannot take fire, nor are they fit matter of flame. They are not a breath, for, when given forth, they do not exert propelling force; they flow forth without any perceptible resistance, and reach bodies. They are exceedingly attenuated humours, much more rarefied than the ambient air; to produce them requires bodies generated of humour and consolidated to considerable hardness. Non-electric bodies are not resolvable into humid effluvia; and such effluvia mingle with the common and general effluvia of the earth, and are not peculiar. In addition to the attracting of bodies, electrics hold them for a considerable time. Hence it is probable that amber exhales something peculiar that attracts the bodies themselves, and not the air. It plainly attracts the body itself in the case of a spherical drop of water standing on a dry surface; for a piece of amber held at suitable distance pulls toward itself the nearest particles and draws them up into a cone; were they drawn by the air the whole drop would come toward the amber. And that amber does not attract the air is thus proved: take a very slender wax candle giving a very small clear flame; bring a broad flat piece of amber or jet, carefully prepared and rubbed thoroughly, within a couple of fingers' distance from it; now an amber that will attract bodies from a considerable radius will cause no motion in the flame, though such motion would be inevitable if the air were moving, for the flame would follow the current of air. The amber attracts from as far as the effluvia are sent out; but as the body comes nearer the amber its motion is quickened, the forces pulling it being stronger, as is the case also in magnetic bodies, and in all natural motion; and the motion is not due to rarefaction of the air or to an action of the air impelling the body to take the vacated place; for in that case the body would be pulled but not held, since, at first, approaching bodies would even be repelled just as the air itself would be: yet in fact the air is not in the least repelled even at the instant that the rubbed amber is brought near after very rapid friction. An effluvium is exhaled by the amber and is sent forth by friction; pearls, carnelian, agate, jasper, chalcedony, coral, metals, and the like, when rubbed are inactive; but is there nought that is emitted from them also by heat and friction? There is indeed; but what is emitted from the denser bodies, and those with considerable admixture of earth matter, is thick and vaporous; and in fact in the case of very many of the electric bodies, if they be violently rubbed, there is but a faint attraction of bodies to them, or none at all; the best method is to use gentle but very rapid friction, for so the finest effluvia are elicited. The effluvia arise from a subtle solution of moisture, not from force applied violently and recklessly; this is true especially of bodies that are of oily substance consolidated, which, when the atmosphere is thin and the wind is from the north, or here in England from the east, produce their effects best and with most certainty; but in a south wind and a humid atmosphere the effect is very slight: so that effluvia that attract but feebly when the weather is clear, produce no motion at all when it is cloudy. And this as well because in thick weather light objects are harder to move, as also (and rather) because the effluvia are stifled, and the surface of the rubbed body is affected by the vaporous air, and the effluvia are stopped at their very origin; hence it is that in amber, jet, and sulphur, because these bodies do not so readily collect the humid air on their surface, and are much more thoroughly resolved, this force is not so easily suppressed as in gems, rock-crystal, glass, and the like, which collect the condensed moist air on their surface. But the question may arise, why amber attracts water, though water existing on a surface annuls its action. That is because it is one thing to suppress the effluvium at its rise, another to destroy it after it is emitted. Thus a certain gauzy texture of silk, commonly called *sarsenet*, when quickly laid over amber immediately after friction, hinders the body's attraction; but if it be interposed midway between the two bodies, it does not altogether annul the attraction. Moisture from steam, a breath from the mouth, water thrown on the amber, instantly check the effluvium. But olive-oil that is light and pure does not prevent it, and even rubbing amber with a warm finger dipped in the oil does not prevent attraction. But if after that friction the amber be drenched with alcohol, or brandy, it does not attract, as the spirit is heavier, denser, than the oil, and when added to the oil sinks below it. For olive-oil is light and rare, and does not oppose the passage of the lightest effluvia. A breath, then, proceeding from a body that is a concretion of moisture or aqueous fluid, reaches the body that is to be attracted, and as soon as it is reached it is united to the attracting electric; and a body in touch with another body by the peculiar radiation of effluvia makes of the two one: united, the two come into most intimate harmony, and that is what is meant by attraction. This unity is, according to Pythagoras, the principle, through participation, in which a thing is said to be one. For as no action can be performed by matter save by contact, these electric bodies do not appear to touch, but of necessity something is given out from the one to the other to come into close contact therewith, and be a cause of incitation to it.

All bodies are united and, as it were, cemented together by moisture, and hence a wet body on touching another body attracts it if the other body be small; and wet bodies on the surface of water attract wet bodies. But the peculiar effluvia of electrics, being the subtilest matter of solute moisture, attract corpuscles. Air, too (the earth's universal effluvium), unites parts that are separated, and the earth, by means of the air, brings back bodies to itself; else bodies would not so eagerly seek the earth from heights. The electric effluvia differ much from air, and as air is the earth's effluvium, so electric bodies have their own distinctive effluvia; and each peculiar effluvium has its own individual power of leading to union, its own movement to its origin, to its fount, and to the body that emits the effluvium. But bodies that give out a thick or a vaporous or an aerial effluvium when rubbed have no effect; for either such effluvia are diverse from humour (unifier of all things), or, being very like the common air, they become blended with the air and one with it: wherefore they have no effect in the air, and do not produce any movements different from those of that universal and common element. Bodies tend to come together and move about on the surface of water like the rod *C*, which dips a little into

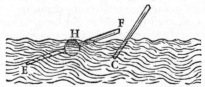

the water. Evidently the rod *EF*, floated by the cork *H* and having only the wetted end *F* above the water's surface, will be attracted by the rod *C*, if *C* be wetted a little above the water's surface. As a drop brought into contact with another drop is attracted, and the two forthwith unite, in the same way a wet object on the surface of water seeks union with another wet object when the surface of the water rises in both: at once, like drops or bubbles of water, they come together; but they are in much higher neighborhood than in the case of electrics, and they unite by their wetted surfaces. But if the whole rod C be dry above the water, it no longer attracts but repels the rod EF. The same is seen in the case of bubbles on water: one is seen to approach another, all the more rapidly the nearer they are. Solids draw to solids through the medium of liquid; e.g., touch the end of a versorium with the end of a rod on which a drop of water stands: the instant the rotating pointer comes in contact with the circumference of the drop it adheres to it with a sudden motion. So do bodies concreted from liquids when melted a little in the air exercise attraction, their effluvia being the means of unition; for the water in humid bodies or in bodies drenched with superficial moisture on the top of water has the force of an effluvium. A clear atmosphere is a good medium for the electric effluvium developed from concreted humour. Wet bodies projecting out of the surface of water come together, if they be near, and unite, for the water's surface rises around wet surfaces. A dry body does not move toward a wet, nor a wet toward a dry, but rather they seem to go away from each other; for if all of the body that is above the water is dry, the nearest water surface does not rise but falls away with subsidence of the surface around the dry object. So, too, a dry body does not run to the dry rim of a vessel containing water; but, on the contrary, a wet object does. In the figure, AB is the water surface; C, D, two rods with

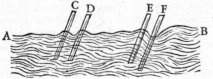

their projecting ends wet. Evidently the surface of the water at C and D rises simultaneously with the rods; hence the rod C, because its water, standing above the general level, seeks equilibrium and union, moves with the water toward D. On the wet rod E the water rises also, but by the dry rod F the water is depressed, and as it strives to depress also the water rising on E, the higher water at E turns away from F, for it refuses to be depressed. All electric attractions are effected by means of moisture, and thus all

things come together because of humour: fluid bodies and aqueous bodies come together on the surface of water, and concreted bodies, if reduced to vapour, come together in the air. And in the air the effluvium of electrics is very rare, that so it may more thoroughly permeate the atmosphere, and yet not give it impulsion by its own motion. For were this effluvium as dense as air, or the winds, or the fumes of burning saltpetre, or as the thick, foul effluvia emitted with much force from other bodies, or as the air from vaporized water rushing forth from a pipe (as in the instrument described by Hero of Alexandria in his book *Spiritualia*): in such case it would repel everything, and not attract. But those thinner effluvia lay hold of the bodies with which they unite, enfold them, as it were, in their arms, and bring them into union with the electrics; and the bodies are led to the electric source, the effluvia having greater force the nearer they are to that. But what is the effluvium from rock-crystal, glass, diamond—substances very hard and very highly compressed? For such effluvium there is no need of any notable or sensible outflow of substance: no need of abrading, or rubbing, or otherwise disfiguring the electric body: odoriferous substances give forth fragrance for many years, exhale continually, yet are not soon consumed. Cypress wood, as long as it remains sound—and it lasts a very long time—is fragrant, as many learned men testify from experience. Such an electric, after only a moment's friction, emits powers subtile and fine, far beyond all odors; but sometimes an odor also is emitted by amber, jet, sulphur, these bodies being more readily resolved. Hence it is that usually they attract after the gentlest friction, or even without friction; and they attract more powerfully and keep hold longer because their effluvia are stronger and more lasting. But diamond, glass, rock-crystal, and very many of the harder and more compacted gems are heated, and then rubbed for a good while at first, after which they, too, attract strongly: they cannot be resolved in any other way. Electrics attract all things save flame and objects aflame, and thinnest air. And as they do not draw to themselves flame, so they have no effect on a versorium if it have very near it on any side the flame of a lamp or of any burning substance; for it is plain that the effluvia are consumed by flame and igneous heat. Therefore electrics do not attract either flame or bodies near flame; for such effluvia have the virtue and analogy of rarefied humour, and they will produce their effect, bringing about unition and continuity, not through the external action of humours, or through heat, or through attenuation of heated bodies, but through the attenuation of the humid substance into its own specific effluvia. Yet they draw to themselves the smoke from an extinguished candle; and the lighter the smoke becomes as it ascends, the less strongly is it attracted, for substances that are too rare do not suffer attraction. At last, when the smoke has nearly vanished, it is not attracted at all, as is plainly seen when the fact is observed toward the light. But when it has passed quite into the air it is not stirred by electrics, as has already been shown. For thin air itself is in no wise attracted, save by reason of its coming into a vacuum, as is seen in furnaces in which air is supplied by means of appliances for drawing it in. Therefore the effluvium called forth by a friction that does not clog the surface—an effluvium not altered by heat, but which is the natural product of the electric body—causes unition and cohesion, seizure of the other body, and its confluence to the electrical source, provided the body to be drawn is not unsuitable by reason either of the circumstances of the bodies or of its own weight. Hence corpuscles are carried to the electrical bodies themselves. The effluvia spread in all directions: they are specific and peculiar, and *sui generis*, different from the common air; generated from humour; called forth by calorific motion and rubbing, and attenuation; they are as it were material rods—hold and take up straws, chaff, twigs, till their force is spent or vanishes; and then these small bodies, being set free again, are attracted by the earth itself and fall to the ground. The difference (distinction) between electric and magnetic bodies is this: all magnetic bodies come together by their joint forces (mutual strength); electric bodies attract the electric only, and the body attracted undergoes no modification through its own native force, but is drawn freely under impulsion in the ratio of its matter (composition). Bodies are attracted to electrics in a right line toward the centre of electricity: a loadstone approaches another loadstone on a line perpendicular to the circumference only at the poles, elsewhere obliquely and transversely, and adheres at the same angles. The electric motion is the motion of coacervation of matter; the magnetic is that of arrangement and order. The matter of the earth's globe is brought together and held together by itself electrically. The earth's globe is directed and revolves magnetically; it both coheres and, to the end it may be solid, is in its interior fast joined.

CHAPTER 3. *Opinions of others concerning magnetic coition, which they call attraction*

HAVING treated of electrics, we have now to set forth the causes of magnetic coition. Coition, we say, not attraction, for the term attraction has wrongfully crept into magnetic philosophy, through the ignorance of the ancients; for where attraction exists, there, force seems to be brought in and a tyrannical violence rules. Hence, if we have at any time spoken of magnetic attraction, what we meant was magnetic coition and primary confluence. But here it will be not unprofitable first to set forth briefly the views of others, both among the ancients and the moderns. Orpheus, in his hymns, tells that iron is drawn by the loadstone as the bride to the embraces of her spouse. Epicurus holds that iron is drawn by the loadstone as straws by amber; and adds a reason: "Atoms," he says, "and indivisible bodies that flow from stone and from iron, agree together in their figures, so that they readily embrace mutually; hence, when they impinge on concretions both of iron and stone, they rebound into the middle space, connected together on the way, and carry the iron with them," This, surely, cannot be, for though solid and very dense bodies, or blocks of marble, stand between, they do not hinder the passage of this potency, though they can separate atoms from atoms; besides, on the hypothesis, the stone and iron would quickly be resolved into atoms, so profuse and incessant would be the atomic outflow. And as the mode of attraction is quite different in amber, there the Epicurean atoms cannot agree in their figures. Thales, as we are told by Aristotle, in Book 1, *On the Soul*, deemed the loadstone endowed with a sort of life, because it possesses the power of moving and attracting iron. Anaxagoras was of the same opinion. The opinion of Plato in the *Timæus*, about the effect of the Herculean stone, is baseless. He says: "With respect to all the motions of water, the fallings of thunder, and the wonderful circumstances observed in the attraction of amber, and the Herculean stone—in all these, no real attraction takes place at all, but, as a vacuum can nowhere be found, the particles are mutually impelled by each other; hence, as they all individually, both in a separate and mingled state, have an attraction for their own proper seats, it is by the mutual intermingling of these affections, that such admirable effects present themselves to the view of the accurate investigator." Galen knows not why Plato should have chosen rather the theory of circumpulsion than of attraction (on this point alone differing from Hippocrates), seeing that circumpulsion harmonizes in fact neither with reason nor with experiment. For neither is air nor anything else circumpelled, and even the bodies that are attracted are not borne to the attracting body in confused fashion or in a circle. The Epicurean poet Lucretius thus presents his master's theory:

Principio fluere e lapide hoc permulta necesset
Semina sive æstum, qui discutit aera plagis;
Inter qui lapidem, ferrumque est, cumque locatus,
Hoc ubi inanitur spatium, multiusque vacefit
In medio locus: extemplo primordia ferri
In vacuum prolapsa cadunt coniuncia; fit ut qui
Anulus ipse sequatur, eatque ita corpore toto, etc.[1]

A similar explication is offered by Plutarch in the *Quæstiones Platonicæ*. He says that the loadstone emits heavy exhalations, whereby the contiguous air, being impelled, makes dense the air in front of it, and that air, driven round in a circle and returning to the part whence the air was displaced, forcibly carries the iron with it. The following theory of the powers of loadstone and amber is propounded by Joannes Costæus of Lodi: Costæus holds that "there is work on both sides, result on both sides, and therefore the motion is produced in part by the loadstone's attraction, in part by the iron's spontaneous movement; for, as we say that the vapours given out by the loadstone do by their own nature haste to attract the iron, so, too, do we say that the air impelled by the vapours, while seeking a place for itself, is turned back, and when turned back impels and transfers the iron, which is picked up, as it were, by it, and which, besides, is exerted on its own account. In this way there is found a certain composite movement, resulting from the attraction, the spontaneous motion, and the impulsion; which composite motion, however, is rightly to be referred to attraction, because the beginning of this motion is invariably from one term, and its end is there too; and that is precisely the distinguishing character of attraction." There is, it is true, mutual action, not mutual work; the loadstone does not thus attract, and there is no impulsion; neither is the principle of the motion found in vapours and their return movements: that is Epicurus's theory, so oft repeated by others. Galen errs in his first book, *On the Natural Faculties*, ch. 14, when he expresses the opinion that whatever agents draw out the venom of serpents or arrows possess the same powers as the loadstone. As for this attraction (if

[1] See *On the Nature of Things*, VI. 1002-8.

attraction it may be called) of medicaments, we will treat of it in another place. Drugs against poisons and arrow-wounds have no relation, no resemblance, to the actions of magnetic bodies. Galen's followers, who teach that purgative medicines attract because of likeness of substance, say that bodies are attracted on account of resemblance, not of identity; therefore, say they, loadstone draws iron, but iron does not draw loadstone. But we say and prove that this takes place in all prime bodies, and in bodies that are allied and especially that are near akin to these, and this on account of identity: wherefore loadstone draws loadstone, and iron draws iron; all true earth substance draws its kind; and iron invigorated by the action of a loadstone within whose sphere of influence it is, draws iron more powerfully than it does loadstone. Cardan asks why no other metal is drawn by any stone; and his answer is, because no other metal is so cold as iron: as if, forsooth, cold were cause of attraction, or iron were much colder than lead, which neither follows the loadstone nor leans toward it. But this is sorry trifling, no better than old wives' gossip. Of the same sort is the belief that the loadstone is a living thing, and that iron is its victual. But how does loadstone feed on iron if the iron filings it is kept in neither are consumed nor become lighter in weight? Cornelius Gemma (*Cosmocrit*, x), declares that loadstone draws iron to itself by means of invisible rods; and to this opinion he tacks on a story of the sucking-fish and the cataclepas. Guilelmus Puteanus deduces the power of the loadstone, not from a property of its whole substance unknown to any one and incapable of demonstration (as Galen held, and after him nearly all physicians), but from "its substantial form as from a prime motor and self-motor, and as from its own most potent nature and its natural temperament, as the instrument which the efficient form of its substance, or the second cause, which is without a medium, employs in its operations. So the loadstone attracts iron not without a physical cause, and for the sake of some good." But nothing like this is done in other bodies by any substantial form unless it be the primary one, and this Puteanus does not recognize. Naught but good is assuredly held out to the loadstone, to be got from the appulsion of the iron (a sort of friendly association), yet the temperament of which he speaks is not to be found, cannot even be imagined as something that is to be the instrument of the form. For of what use can temperament be in magnetic movements that are calculable, definite, constant, comparable to the movements of the stars; at great distance, with thick, dense bodies interposed. In Baptista Porta's opinion, the loadstone seems to be a mixture of stone and iron, *i.e.*, ferruginous stone, or stony iron. "The stone," he says, "is not changed into iron so as to lose its own nature, nor is the iron so merged in the stone but that it retains its own essence; and while each strives to overcome each, from the struggle results attraction of the iron. In the mass (of the loadstone) there is more stone than iron; therefore the iron, lest it should be dependent on (subdued by) the stone, craves the strength and company of iron, to the end that what it cannot procure of itself it may obtain by the help of the other.... The loadstone does not attract stones because it has no need of them there being stone enough in its mass; and if one loadstone attracts another that is not for the sake of the stone, but of the iron shut up in the stone." As though the iron in a loadstone were a distinct body and not one blended with another, like all other metals in their ores. And it is height of absurdity to speak of these substances, thus confounded together, as warring with each other and quarreling, and calling out from the battle for forces to come to their aid. Now, iron itself when touched with loadstone seizes iron with not less force than loadstone itself. These fights, seditions, conspiracies, in a stone, as though it were nursing quarrels as an occasion for calling in auxiliary forces, are the maunderings of a babbling hag, rather than the devices of an accomplished prestigiator. Others have thought that the cause is a sympathy. But even were fellow-feeling there, even so, fellow-feeling is not a cause; for no passion can rightly be said to be an efficient cause. Others again assign as the cause likeness of substance, and still others postulate rods (*radii*)imperceptible to the senses. These, in very many ways, make a sad misuse of a term first employed by mathematicians. In more scholarly fashion, Scaliger declares that iron moves to the loadstone as to its mother's womb, there to be perfected with recondite principles, as the earth tends to the centre. The godlike Thomas,[1] in Book VII of his *Physica*, treating of the causes of motion, says: "A thing can in another sense be said to pull, in that it moves (an object) toward itself, by altering it in any way, by which alteration it comes about that the body altered moves with respect to place; and in this way is the loadstone said to draw iron: for as a generant moves heavy things and light in so far as it gives them the form

[1] Thomas Aquinas.

whereby they are moved to a place; so does the loadstone give to iron some quality through which it is moved to the loadstone." This view, one by no means ill-conceived, this most learned man, proceeds later briefly to corroborate, citing incredible accounts of the loadstone and of the power of garlic over the loadstone.

Nor is what Cardinal de Cusa states to be disregarded. Says he: "Iron hath in the loadstone a certain principle of its efflux, and while the loadstone by its presence excites the heavy and ponderous iron, the iron is, by a wonderful longing, raised above the natural motion (whereby it ought to tend downward according to its weight), and moves upward, uniting in its principle. For were there not in iron some natural foretaste of the loadstone, it would no more move toward that than toward any other stone; and were there not in the loadstone a stronger inclination toward iron than toward copper, that attraction would not exist." Such, as propounded by different writers, are current opinions about the attraction of the loadstone, all of them full of doubt and uncertainty. As for the causes of magnetic movements, referred to in the schools of philosophers to the four elements and to prime qualities, these we leave for roaches and moths to prey upon.

CHAPTER 4. *Of the strength of a loadstone and its form: the cause of coition*

QUITTING the opinions of others about the attraction of the loadstone, we will now show the reason of its coition and the nature of its motion. There are two kinds of bodies that are seen to attract bodies by motions perceptible to our senses —electric bodies, and magnetic. Electrical bodies do this by means of natural effluvia from humour; magnetic bodies by formal efficiencies or rather by primary native strength (*vigor*). This form is unique and peculiar: it is not what the Peripatetics call *causa formalis* and *causa specifica in mixtis* and *secunda forma;* nor is it *causa propagatrix generantium corporum;* but it is the form of the prime and principal globes; and it is of the homogeneous and not altered parts thereof, the proper entity and existence which we may call the primary, radical, and astral form; not Aristotle's prime form, but that unique form which keeps and orders its own globe. Such form is in each globe —the sun, the moon, the stars—one; in earth also 'tis one, and it is that true magnetic potency which we call the primary energy. Hence the magnetic nature is proper to the earth and is implanted in all its real parts according to a primal and admirable proportion. It is not derived from the heavens as a whole, neither is it generated thereby through sympathy, or influence, or other occult qualities: neither is it derived from any special star; for there is in the earth a magnetic strength or energy of its own, as sun and moon have each its own *forma*; and a little fragment of the moon arranges itself, in accordance with lunar laws, so as to conform to the moon's contour and form, or a fragment of the sun to the contour and form of the sun, just as a loadstone does to the earth or to another loadstone, tending naturally toward it and soliciting it. Thus we have to treat of the earth, which is a magnetic body, a loadstone; then, too, of its true, native parts, which are magnetic, and of how they are affected by coition.

A body that is attracted by a magnetic body is not by it altered, but remains unimpaired and unchanged as it was before, neither has it now greater virtue. A loadstone draws magnetic bodies, and they from its energy eagerly draw forces not in their extremities only, but in their inmost parts. For an iron rod held in the hand is magnetized in the end where it is grasped, and the magnetic force travels to the other extremity, not along the surface only, but through the inside, through the middle. Electrical bodies have material, corporeal effluvia. Is any magnetic effluvium emitted, corporeal or incorporeal? Or is nothing at all that subsists emitted? But if the effluvium is a body, it must needs be light and spiritual so as to enter the iron. Is it such as is exhaled from lead when quicksilver, which is liquid and fluid, is by the mere odour and vapour of lead solidified, and remains as a strongly coherent metal? Gold too, which is very solid and dense, is reduced to a powder by the thin vapour of lead. Can it be that as quicksilver can enter gold, so the magnetic odour can enter the substance of iron, changing it by its substantial property, though in the bodies themselves there is no change perceptible by our senses? For without such entering a body is not changed by another body, as the chemists, not without reason, do teach. But if these effects were produced by a material entrance, then were resistant, dense bodies interposed between such bodies; or were the magnetic bodies shut up in the middle of very thick, dense bodies, objects of iron would not be acted on by the loadstone. Nevertheless, these two do strive to come together and are changed. Therefore the magnetic forces have no such conception, no such origin, as this: nor are they due to those most minute particles of loadstone imagined by Baptista Porta

concentrated as it were into hairs, and springing from friction of the loadstone, which parts fastening on to the iron give it the magnetic powers. For the electric effluvia, as they are hindered by the interposition of any dense body, so too are unable to attract through a flame, or if a flame be near by. But iron, which is hindered by no obstacle (from) deriving from the loadstone force and motion, passes through the midst of a flame to join the loadstone. Take a short piece of iron wire, and when you have brought it near to a loadstone it will make its way through the flames to the stone; and a needle turns no less rapidly, no less eagerly, to the loadstone though a flame intervenes than if only air stands between. Hence a flame interposed does not prevent coition. But were the iron itself red-hot, it certainly would not be attracted. Apply a red-hot iron rod to a magnetized needle and the needle stands still, not turning to the iron; but as soon as the temperature has fallen somewhat it at once turns to it. A piece of iron that has been magnetized, if placed in a hot fire until it becomes red-hot, and permitted to remain for a little while, loses the magnetic power. Even loadstone itself loses its native and inborn powers of attracting, and all other magnetic properties, if left long in fire. And though some magnetic ores when roasted exhale a deep-blue or sulphurous and foul-smelling vapour, nevertheless such vapour is not the soul of the loadstone; neither is it the cause of the attraction of iron, as Porta supposes.[1] Nor do all loadstones when roasted or burned smell of sulphur or give out sulphur fumes: that property is something added, a sort of congenital evil which comes from the foul bed or matrix in which the loadstone is produced; nor does the material corporeal cause introduce into the iron anything of the same sort, for iron derives from loadstone the power of attracting and the property of verticity, though glass or gold or another sort of stone stand between, as later, when treating of the magnetic direction, we shall clearly prove. But fire destroys in the loadstone the magnetic qualities, not because it plucks out of it any particular attractional particles, but because the quick, penetrating force of the flame deforms it by breaking its matter up; just as in the human body the soul's primary powers are not burnt, though yet the burnt body remains without faculties. But though the iron remains after perfect ignition, and is not converted into either ash or slag; still, as Cardan not injudiciously remarks, red-hot iron is not iron, but

[1] *Natural Magic*, VII, 2.

something lying outside its own nature, until it returns to itself. For just as, by the cold of the ambient air, water is changed from its own nature into ice, so iron made white-hot by fire has a confused, disordered form, and therefore is not attracted by a loadstone, and even loses its power of attracting, however acquired; it also acquires a different verticity when, as though born anew, it is impregnated by a loadstone or the earth; in other words, when its form, not utterly destroyed, yet confused, is restored. I shall have more to say on this subject when treating of changed verticity (Book III. 10). Hence, Fracastorio finds no confirmation of his opinion that the iron is not altered: "For," says he, "if it were altered by the loadstone's form, the form of the iron would be spoiled." Yet this alteration is not generation, but restitution and re-formation of a confused form.

Hence that is not corporeal which emanates from the loadstone, or which enters the iron, or which is given forth again by the awakened iron; but one loadstone gives portion to another loadstone by its primary form. And a loadstone recalls the cognate substance, iron, to formate energy and gives it position: hence does it leap to the loadstone and eagerly conforms thereto (the forces of both harmoniously working to bring them together); for the coition is not indeterminate and confused, it is not a violent inclination of body to body, not a mad chance confluence. Here no violence is offered to bodies, there are no strifes or discords; but here we have, as the condition of the world holding together, a concerted action—to wit, an accordance of the perfect, homogeneous parts of the world's globes with the whole, a mutual agreement of the chief forces therein for soundness, continuity, position, direction, and unity. In view of this so wonderful effect, this stupendous innate energy—an energy (strength) not existing in other elements—the opinion of Thales the Milesian is, in Scaliger's judgment, not utterly absurd, not a lunatic's fancy. Thales ascribed to the loadstone a soul, for it is incited, directed, and moved in a circle by a force that is entire in the whole and entire in each part, as later will appear, and because it seems most nearly to resemble a soul. For the power of self-movement seems to betoken a soul, and the supernal bodies, which we call celestial, as it were divine, are by some regarded as animated because that they move with wondrous regularity. If two loadstones be set over against each other in their floats on the surface of water, they do not come together forthwith, but first

they wheel round, or the smaller obeys the larger and takes a sort of circular motion; at length, when they are in their natural position they come together, In iron that has not been excited by the loadstone, there is no need of these preliminaries; for iron, though made from the finest loadstone, has no verticity save such as it gets by chance and momentarily; and this is not stable nor fixed, for while it ran liquid in the furnace its parts were thrown into confusion. Such a body instantly receives from the presence of the loadstone verticity and natural conformity to it, being powerfully altered and converted, and absolutely metamorphosed into a perfect magnet: so, like an actual part of the loadstone, it flies to it. For there is naught that the best loadstone can do which cannot be done by iron excited by a loadstone—not magnetized at all, but only placed in the neighbourhood of a loadstone. For as soon as it comes within the loadstone's sphere of influence, though it be at some distance from the loadstone itself, the iron changes instantly, and has its form renewed, which before was dormant and inert, but now is quick and active: all this will appear clearly when we come to present the proofs of magnetic direction (in Book III). Thus the magnetic coition is the act of the loadstone and of the iron, not of one of them alone: it is ἐντελέχεια, not ἔργον; it is συνεντελέχεια and conactus (mutual action) rather than sympathy. There is, properly speaking, no magnetic antipathy; for the flight and turning away of the poles and the wheeling around of the whole is the act of each of the two toward unition, resulting from the συνεντελέχεια and conactus[1] of both. Thus the iron puts on anew its form; and because that is awakened, as also in order more surely to gain its form, it rushes headlong on the loadstone, and not with circlings and wheelings, as in the case of two loadstones. For as, long ages ago, nay at the very beginning of things, there were gendered in the loadstone and therein fixed verticity and the power of coördinating; and since the great mastering form of the earthly globe cannot be readily changed by another magnet, as iron is changed, therefore, the nature of each being constant, neither hath the momentary power of altering the verticity of the other, but the two do but come to agreement with each other. And magnetized iron, in case it is unable for whatever reason to cause the piece of iron in the natural state to turn, as does the pointer of a versorium, is itself seized at either end by

[1] Conactus, i.e., combined or mutual action. See Book V, 12.

a loadstone brought nigh it. For the loadstone, as it imparts so can it alter verticity, and it can in an instant bestow the formal energy in either end. Thus iron may be transformed variously, as that form is adventitious and has not yet abided long in the metal. In iron, because its body is fused when a magnetic or a ferruginous ore is smelted, the virtue of the primal form, which previously existed distinct, is now confused; but a sound loadstone, when brought near, sets up again the primal action: the form, now arranged and ordered again, joins forces with the loadstone, and, each with other, the two come to agreement, after the manner of the loadstone, in all their movements toward union; they enter into alliance, and whether joined by bodily contact or standing within their sphere of influence, are one and the same. For when iron is reduced in the furnace from its ore, or when steel is got from its ore, which is loadstone, the metallic matter is melted and becomes fluid, and the iron and the steel run off, leaving their slag: this slag consists of matter spoilt by the intense heat of the fire, or of useless matter, or of dross, due to some imperfection or to some intermixture in the projecting surface of the earth. Thus the iron or steel is a purified material, wherein the metallic element, all disordered by the smelting (for the forces of that primal form are all confused and unsettled), is brought back again, as it were, to life, to normal form, and to completeness. Its matter is thus awakened, and tends to union, which is the bond of the universe and the necessary condition of the conservation of all things.

For this reason, and because of the purging of the ore and its change into a purer body, the loadstone gives to iron greater power of attracting than exists in itself. For if you put some iron-filings or a nail on a large magnet, a piece of iron joined to the magnet steals the filings and the nail, and holds them as long as it remains alongside the magnet: so, too, iron attracts iron more powerfully than does a loadstone, if the iron be afformed, and remain within the sphere of the form given out to it. Again, a piece of iron nicely adjusted to the pole of a loadstone holds a greater weight than the loadstone does. So, then, iron and steel are the better elements of their ores, purified by the action of fire, and the loadstone impregnates them again with their forms; wherefore to it do they come by spontaneous approach, so soon as they enter the circle of the magnetic forces, for by it are they first possessed, and made continuous, and united with perfect union. Once within that circle they have absolute continuity, and they are joined by reason of their accordance, albeit the bodies themselves be separated. For the iron is not, after the manner of electrics, possessed and pulled by substantial effluvia, but only by the immaterial act of the form or by its incorporeal going forth, which as in a continuous and homogeneous body doth act in the iron *subjectum*, and is received into it; nor has it need of wider paths.

Hence it is that, with the densest bodies interposed, the iron is put in motion throughout and is attracted, and that the iron, in presence of the loadstone thoroughly stirs and attracts the loadstone itself, and that with their mutual forces they make that rush toward union which commonly is called attraction. But these formal forces sally forth and in meeting unite; and the force conceived in the iron, that also forthwith has its efflux. But Julius Scaliger, who, in his 344th disquisition, cites other examples to prove this explanation to be absurd, is far astray. For the virtues of prime bodies are not comparable with those that are derivate and mixed. Were he still among the living, he might now, in the chapter on "Effused Magnetic Spherical Forms," discover what is the nature of effused forms.

But if iron be badly injured by rust it is but little or not at all affected by the loadstone, for when the metal is corroded and marred by external causes or by decay it is spoilt, as has been said of the loadstone, and loses its prime qualities that are conjoined to its form, or, the stone being impaired by age, these qualities are weak and feeble; neither can it be duly informed when once it has suffered decay. But a strong, fresh loadstone pulls all sound clean iron, and the iron (having conceived force) powerfully attracts other iron—as pieces of iron wire, iron nails; and not only these separately and directly but one after another, one at the end of another, thus holding three, four, or five: thus forming as it were a chain, the successive nails sticking to one another and suspended from one another. But the loadstone would not attract the last piece in such a line if there were no nails in the mid-space. Thus a loadstone placed at A pulls

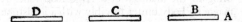

the nail or bar B, and, in like manner, after B pulls C, and after C,D; but at the same distance does not pull aloft D: that is so for the reason that when the nails form an unbroken line the presence of the loadstone A, because of its proper forces, raises the magnetic form of the iron objects *B* and *C*, and makes them as it were its auxiliary forces, while *B* and *C*, like a continuous magnetic body, conduct on to *D* the force whereby it is seized or conformed, yet not so powerfully as *C* is seized by *B*. And these iron nails derive the force from the mere contact, and from the presence of the loadstone without contact, and they retain it in their bodies, as will be shown when we treat of Direction (Book III). For the iron does not assume these powers only while in presence of a loadstone, nor does it hold them of the stone only momentarily as Themistius supposes in his *Physica*, VIII. The best iron (steel) is solicited by the loadstone from a greater distance, a greater weight of it is lifted, it is more powerfully held, and it acquires greater force, than does common, cheaper iron, for it is made of the best ore or of loadstone, and is imbued with superior forces; but iron from impure ores is weaker, and is attracted more feebly. As for what Fracastorio writes, of having seen a bit of loadstone that on one side attracted loadstone but not iron, on another side attracted iron but not loadstone, and on another attracted both—proof, according to him, that in one spot there was more loadstone, in another more iron, in the third the two were present equally; hence the difference in the attraction—all this is utterly erroneous, and the result of mal-observation on the part of Fracastorio, who did not know how to present one loadstone to another properly. Loadstone attracts iron and loadstone if both be properly situated, and free to move and unrestrained. A light object is more readily moved from its position and place than a heavy one, for heavy objects make greater resistance, but a light object bestirs itself to meet a heavy one and is pulled by it.

CHAPTER 5. *In what manner the energy inheres in the loadstone*

THAT the loadstone draws loadstone, iron, and other magnetic bodies was shown in Book I, as also by what forces the magnetic coition is regulated; we have now to inquire how this energy is ordered in magnetic bodies. Here we must bring in the analogy of a large loadstone. A magnetic body unites forcibly with a loadstone if the loadstone is powerful, feebly if it be defective or if it has from any fault become impaired. Loadstone does not attract iron with equal force at every point; in other words, the magnetic body does not tend with the same force to every point of the loadstone; for the

loadstone has points (*i.e.*, true poles) at which its rare energy is most conspicuous. And the regions nearest the poles are the stronger, those remotest are the weaker; yet in all the energy is in some sense equal. In the figure of a terrella,

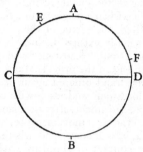

A, *B*, are the poles, *CD* is the equinoctial line; the greatest attractive force is seen at *A* and *B*. At *C* and *D* there is no force that attracts to the body the ends of magnetic objects, for the forces tend toward each of the poles. But the directive force at the equator is strong. *C* and *D* are at equal distances from both poles; hence a piece of iron on the line *CD*, being pulled in contrary directions, does not cling steadily, but it stays and adheres to the stone only when it falls to either side of the line. At *E* the attractive force is greater than at *F*, for *E* is nigher the pole. And this is not for the reason that there is more energy resident at the pole, but because all the parts, being united in the whole, direct their forces to the pole.

By the confluence of the forces from the plane of the equinoctial toward the pole the energy increases poleward, and absolute verticity is seen at the pole so long as the loadstone remains whole; but let it be divided or broken up, and in the separate parts the verticity will find other abiding-places. For with change of

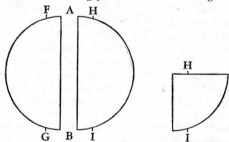

mass always goes change of verticity. Hence, if the terrella be severed along the line *AB* so as to make two stones, the poles in the severed parts will not be *AB*, but *FG* and *HI*. And though these two stones now are so interrelated that F does not tend to H, nevertheless if, before division, A was the north pole, F likewise is now north, as is H also. For the verticity is not reversed, as Baptista Porta erroneously affirms (Porta [*Natural Magic*], VII. 4)[1]; for though F and H are not so related as mutually to attract, yet the two turn to the same point of the horizon. If the hemisphere HI be cut in two quarter spheres, one pole will be at H and the other at I. The integral mass of the stone, as I have said, gives to the vertex or pole a constant place; and any part of the stone, before it was hewed out of the rock might have been the pole or vertex: but of this we shall have more to say under Direction. For the present, the thing to be understood and to be borne steadily in mind is, that the poles are dominant in virtue of the force of the whole, for (the magnetic empire being divided in two by the equi-

curves starting from every point of the equator that divides the sphere into two equal parts: from every point of the superficies from the equator to the north on one side, and from the equator to the south on the other. Hence the verticity is, in each hemisphere, from the equinoctial circle to the pole. This force resides in the whole mass. From A the energy is transmitted to B, from AB to C, from ABC to D, and from them to E, and likewise from G to H; and so on as long as the whole mass is one body. But if the piece AB be cut out, though it be near the equator, nevertheless the effect will be as great on the magnetic action as if CD or DE, equal quantities, had been taken away. For no part has any supereminent value in the whole; whatever it be, that it is because of the parts adjoining, whereby an absolute and perfect whole is produced.

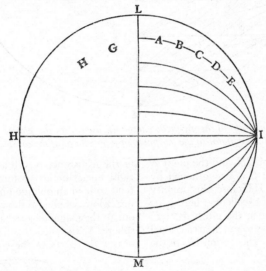

noctial line) all the forces of the hemisphere tend north, and, conversely, all those of the other hemisphere tend south, so long as the parts are united, as appears from the following demonstration. For the whole force tends separately to the two poles along an infinity of

[1] "But the two points we speak of are the end of the right line, running through the middle of the stone from North to South; if any man break the stone, and break this line, those ends of the division will presently be of another property and vertue, and will be enemies one to the other: which is great wonder: for these two points, when they were joined together, had the same force of turning to the pole, but, now being parted asunder, one will turn to the North, the other to the South, keeping the same posture and position they had in the mine where they were bred: and the same happens in the least bits that are seen in the greatest loadstone."

Let HEQ be a terrella, E a pole, M the centre, HMQ the plane of the equinoctial circle. From every point of the equinoctial plane the energy reaches out to the periphery, but differently from each: for from A the formal energy goes toward $CFNE$ and to every point betwixt C and E (the pole), and not toward B; neither from G toward C. The attractive force in the region FGH is not strengthened by the force residing in the region $GMFE$; but FGH increases the energy in the rising curve FE. Thus energy never proceeds from the lines parallel to the axis to points above those parallels, but always internally from the parallels to the pole. From every point of the plane of the equator the energy goes to the pole E; the point F de-

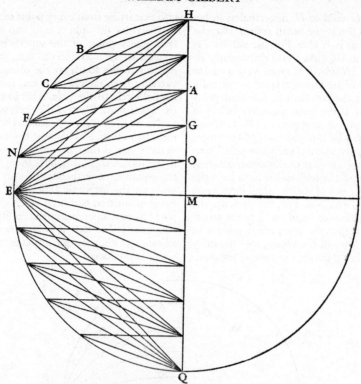

*Diagram of the magnetic energy diffused from the plane
of the equator to the periphery of a terrella or of the earth*

rives its forces only from *GH*, and the point *N*
from *OH*; but the pole *E* is strengthened by
the whole plane *HO*. Therefore this mighty
power has here its chief excellency; here is its
throne, so to speak. But in the intervals at *F*,
for example, there resides so much attractional
energy as can be given by the section *HG* of the
plane.

CHAPTER 6. *How magnetized iron and smaller loadstones conform to the terrella and to the earth itself,
and are governed thereby*

COITION of bodies that are separate from one
another, and that cohere naturally, takes place
by another sort of movement, if they be free
to move. The terrella sends its force abroad in
all directions, according to its energy and its
quality. But whenever iron or other magnetic
body of suitable size happens within its sphere
of influence it is attracted; yet the nearer it is
to the loadstone the greater the force with
which it is borne toward it. Such bodies tend to
the loadstone not as toward a centre nor towards its centre: that they do only at its poles,
i.e., when that which is attracted and the pole

of the loadstone, as well as its centre, are in a
right line. But in the intervals between they
tend to it in an oblique line, as seen in the figure below, wherein is shown how the force goes
out to the magnetic associate bodies within the
sphere. At the poles the line is a right one. The
nearer the parts to the equinoctial circle the

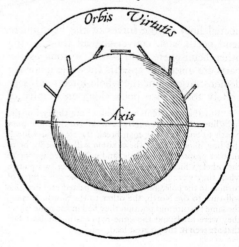

more obliquely do magnetic bodies attract, but the parts nearer the poles attract more directly; at the poles themselves attraction is in a right line. All loadstones alike, whether spherical or oblong, have the self-same mode of turning to the poles of the world; but it is easiest to experiment with oblong ones. For whatever the shape, verticity is present, and there are poles; but owing to imperfect and irregular shape, loadstones are often subject to drawbacks, and are interfered with in their movements. If the loadstone be oblong, with vertices at the extremities and not at the sides, it attracts best at the vertex; for the parts convey to the poles a greater force in right lines than in oblique. Thus do the loadstone and the earth conform magnetic movements.

CHAPTER 7. *Of the potency of the magnetic force, and of its spherical extension*

THE magnetic force is given out in all directions around the body; around the terrella it is given out spherically; around loadstones of other shapes unevenly and less regularly. But the sphere of influence does not persist, nor is the force that is diffused through the air permanent or essential; the loadstone simply excites magnetic bodies situated at convenient distance. And as light—so opticians tell us—arrives instantly in the same way, with far greater instantaneousness, the magnetic energy is present within the limits of its forces; and because its act is far more subtle than light, and it does not accord with non-magnetic bodies, it has no relations with air, water, or other non-magnetic body; neither does it act on magnetic bodies by means of forces that rush upon them with any motion whatever, but being present solicits bodies that are in amicable relations to itself. And as a light impinges on whatever confronts it, so does the loadstone impinge upon a magnetic body and excites it. And as light does not remain in the atmosphere above the vapors and effluvia nor is reflected back by those spaces, so the magnetic ray is caught neither in air nor in water. The forms of things are in an instant taken in by the eye or by glasses; so does the magnetic force seize magnetic bodies. In the absence of light bodies and reflecting bodies, the forms of objects are neither apprehended nor reflected; so, too, in the absence of magnetic objects neither is the magnetic force imbibed nor is it again given back to the magnetic body. But herein does the magnetic energy surpass light,—that it is not hindered by any dense or opaque body, but goes out freely and diffuses its force every

whither. In the case of the terrella and in a spherical loadstone the magnetic energy extends outside the body in a circle; yet in the case of an oblong loadstone it does not extend out in a circle, but into an area of form determined by the shape of the stone, as in the stone A, in the figure, the energy reaches to the limits FCD, everywhere equidistant from the stone A.

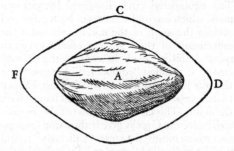

CHAPTER 8. *Of the geography of the earth and the terrella*

WE have next to speak of magnetic circles and magnetic limits, so that what follows later may be better understood. Astronomers, in order to account for and observe the movements of the planets and the revolution of the heavens, as also more accurately to describe the heavenly order of the fixed stars, have drawn in the heavens certain circles and bounds, which geographers also imitate so as to map out the diversified superficies of the globe and to delineate the fairness of the several regions. In a different sense we accept those bounds and circles, for we have discovered many such, both in the terrella and in the earth; but these are determined by nature itself, and are not merely imaginary lines. Geographers make a division of the earth chiefly by defining the equator and the poles; and these bounds are set and defined by nature. Meridians, too, indicate tracks from pole to pole, passing through fixed points in the equator; along such lines the magnetic force proceeds and gives direction. But the tropics and the arctic circles, as also the parallels of latitude, are not natural bounds described on the earth; yet all these parallel circles indicate that a certain conformity between themselves exists among regions of the earth situate in the same latitude or diametrically opposite to them. All these are of service to mathematicians in constructing globes and maps. Thus such circles are of use in the terrella, but they need not be drawn as geographers draw them—on the surface, for the loadstone may be perfectly even and uniform all over. Nor are there any "upper" or "lower" parts, in the terrestrial globe, as there are also none in the terrella, save perhaps that one may choose to call these parts "upper" which are at the periphery and those "lower" which are nigher the centre.

CHAPTER 9. *Of the equinoctial circle of earth and terrella*

THE equinoctial circle imagined by astronomers, which is equidistant from both poles and divides the earth in the middle, measures the movements of their *primum mobile* or tenth sphere,[1] and is called the zone of the *primum mobile*; it is called "equinoctial" because when the sun is in this circle—which must happen twice a year—the days are of equal length with the nights. This circle is designated also *æquidialis*; hence the Greeks give it the name ἰσημερινὸς (which means the same, "equal day"). And it is also well called "equator," for it divides the whole globe of the earth from pole to pole in two equal parts. To the terrella also is justly assigned an equator whereby its power is distributed between two parts. By the plane of this equator, as it passes through the centre, the whole terrella is divided into two parts equal in mass and in verticity, and imbued with equal energy, as though a wall stood betwixt the two verticities.

CHAPTER 10. *The earth's magnetic meridians*

GEOGRAPHERS have devised meridians for the purpose of distinguishing the longitude and latitude of regions. But the magnetic meridians are numberless, and, even as the earth's meridians, they pass through fixed and opposite points in the equator and through the poles. On them also is magnetic latitude measured. By means of them we understand declinations; and along them there is a fixed direction toward the poles, except when the magnetic body for any cause varies, and is jostled out of the right course. The meridian commonly called magnetic is not properly magnetic, neither is it a meridian, but is supposed to pass through the limits of variation in the horizon. Variation is in fact a faulty deviation from the meridian. In various places it is not fixed or constant in any meridian.

CHAPTER 11. *Parallels*

IN parallel circles the same energy and equal potency is seen throughout, when different magnetic bodies are placed on one and the same parallel, either of the earth or of the terrella. For the bodies are at equal distances from the

[1] For *primum mobile*, see Book VI, 3.

poles and have equal changes of declination, and are attracted and held and come together under the action of like forces; just as regions of the earth on the same parallel, though they may differ in longitude, are said to have still the same quantity of daylight and the same climate.

CHAPTER 12. *The magnetic horizon*

AN horizon is a great circle separating the things seen from those that are out of sight, as one half of the heavens is always plainly visible while another half is always hid. So it seems to us by reason of the great distance of the starry sphere; yet the difference is in the ratio of the earth's semi-diameter to the semi-diameter of the starry heavens—a difference not perceived by the senses. But we take the magnetic horizon to be a plane perfectly level throughout, tangent to the earth or to the terrella at the place of the region, with which plane the semi-diameter, whether of the earth or of the terrella, being extended, makes right angles on all sides. Such a plane is to be imagined for the earth, and for the terrella likewise, for the sake of magnetic proofs and demonstrations. For we are considering the bodies themselves, and not the general aspects of the world. Therefore, not with reference to sight—for that varies according to the elevation of regions—we assume in magnetic demonstrations a sensible horizon, not what is called by astronomers the rational horizon.

CHAPTER 13. *Of the magnetic axis and poles*

A LINE drawn through the centre of the earth (or of the terrella) to the poles is called the axis. The poles are so called by the Greeks (πόλοι, ἀπὸ τον πολεῖν—*poloi* from *polein*, to revolve), and by the Latins *cardines* (hinges, pivots) and *vertices* (centres of a whirling motion); and these names were given to signify that the world rotates and is ever whirling. We propose to show that the earth and the terrella are by the magnetic force made to revolve round these poles, whereof that one in the earth which points to Cynosura[2] is called the North, the Boreal, or the Arctic pole; the opposite one is called the South, Austral, or Antarctic pole. And neither in earth nor in terrella do the poles exist merely for the sake of rotation; they are furthermore reference points of direction and of position—on the one hand towards one's destination on the earth, and on the other hand as regards their angular distance.

[2] Cynosura—the constellation of the Lesser Bear (*Ursa Minor*) containing the polar star.

CHAPTER 14. *Why the coition is stronger at the pole than in the parts between equator and pole; and the relative power of coition in different parts of the earth and the terrella*

WE have already shown that the supreme attractional power is at the pole, while the weaker and more sluggish power is in the parts nigh the equator. And as in the declination it is seen that this ordering and rotating force increases as we advance from the equator to the poles, so too does the coition of magnetic bodies grow stronger by the same degrees and in the same proportion. For at points remote from the pole the loadstone does not pull magnetic bodies in a right line toward its centre, but they tend to it obliquely, and obliquely are attracted. For as a very small chord of a circle differs from the diameter, by so much do differ the attractional powers of different parts of the terrella. For inasmuch as the attraction is a coition to a body, and magnetic bodies come together owing to their natural tendency to turn to each other, in the diameter drawn from pole to pole a body impinges on the loadstone in a right line; but not so in other parts. Therefore the less it turns toward the body, the less and the more weak is the coition and the cohesion. Let *ab* be the

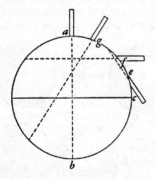

poles. An iron bar or the other magnetic body *c* is attracted at *e*; yet the end that is pulled does not tend toward the centre of the loadstone, but obliquely toward the pole, and a chord drawn from that end obliquely in the direction in which the body is attracted is a short one; the strength of the coition therefore is less, and so too the attracted object turns at a less angle to the terrella. But as from a body at *f* a longer chord proceeds, so the action there is stronger. At *g* the chord is still longer. At *a* (the pole) it is longest of all (for the diameter is the longest line), and thither do all the parts send their forces: there stands, as it were, the citadel, the judgment-seat, of the whole region

—not that the pole holds this eminence in its own right, but because it is the depository of forces contributed to it by all the other parts; it is like soldiers bringing reinforcement to their commander. Hence a rather oblong loadstone attracts better than a spherical one, if its length stretch from pole to pole, and yet the two may be from the same mine, and be of equal size and volume. The way is longer from one pole to the other in the oblong stone, and the forces supplied by the other parts are not so scattered as in a spherical loadstone and the terrella; they are better massed and united, and thus united they are stronger and greater. But a flat or oblong loadstone is much less effective when the length is in the direction of the parallels, and the pole ends neither in a point nor in a circle or sphere, but lies flat on a plane surface so as to be held for something abject and of no account, for its unfit and unadaptable form.

CHAPTER 15. *The magnetic force imparted to iron is more apparent in an iron rod than in an iron sphere or cube, or iron of any other shape*

IT has been already said that an oblong loadstone lifts a greater weight of iron: so in a long piece of iron rubbed with a loadstone the magnetic force is stronger if the poles are at the ends; for the magnetic forces, which are sent to both ends from the poles, are concentrated at the narrow terminals, and not diffused. In square and other angular figures the force is scattered, nor does it proceed in right lines or along suitable arcs. The iron sphere, too, though it hath the figure of the earth, still has less attraction for magnetic bodies for the same reason; hence an excited iron spherule acts with less force on iron than does a magnetized bar of the same weight.

CHAPTER 16. *That motion is produced by the magnetic force through solid bodies interposed: of the interposition of a plate of iron*

AN iron wire passed through a suitable piece of cork, or a needle poised on a point or in a mariner's compass, is set in motion when a loadstone is brought near it or is passed beneath it, though the water, the vessel, or compass-box stand between. No hindrance is offered by thick boards, or by walls of pottery or marble, or even of metals: there is naught so solid as to do away with this force or to check it, save a plate of iron. Whatever substances are interposed, however dense they be, as they do not annul the force nor obstruct its path, so do they in no wise hinder or lessen or retard. Nor is the whole of the force suppressed by a plate of iron, but in part diverted. For when the force enters the middle of an iron plate placed within the sphere of magnetic influence or directly over the pole of the loadstone, that force is distributed chiefly to the extremities, so that the rim of a circular plate of suitable size attracts pieces of iron wire at all points. The same is seen in a long iron rod rubbed with a loadstone in the middle; it has the same verticity at both ends. In the figure, *CD* is a long rod magnetized in the middle by the north pole *E*; *C* is a south end or south pole, and *D* is another south end. But here note the singular fact, that a needle magnetized by that pole turns to that pole, though the round plate stands between, the plate not hindering, but the attraction being only weaker; for the force is scattered to the extremities of the plate, and departs from the straight track, but yet the plate in its middle retains the same verticity with the pole when it is nigh it and alongside

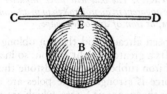

it: hence does the needle magnetized by the same pole tend to the centre of the plate. If the loadstone is a weak one, the needle hardly turns if an iron plate be interposed; for, being diffused out to the extremities of the plate, the load-stone's energy is less able to pass through the centre. But let the plate be magnetized in the middle by the pole, and then let it be removed beyond the loadstone's sphere of influence, and you shall see the point of the same needle go in the contrary direction and quit the centre of the plate, which before it sought: for outside of the sphere of influence the plate has the con-trary verticity, but near the loadstone it has the same; for near the loadstone the plate is as it were part of the loadstone and has the same pole.

Let *A* be an iron plate near a pole; *B* a needle with point tending toward the centre of the plate, which plate has been magnetized by the pole *C* of a loadstone. Now if the same plate be placed outside the sphere of magnetic influ-ence, the point of the needle will not turn to its centre, but only the crotch (the other end) of the same needle. But an iron sphere inter-posed (if it be not too large) attracts the point of the needle at the other side of the stone, for

the verticity of that side is the same as that of the adjoining pole of the loadstone. And this turning of the needle's point (*i.e.*, the end of it magnetized by contact with that pole) and of

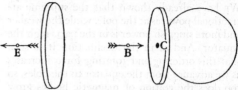

its cross (other end) at a considerable distance takes place with an iron sphere interposed, whereas it would not take place at all were the space between vacant; for the magnetic force travels through bodies and is continued on by them.

Let *A* be a terrella, *B* an iron sphere, *F* a needle between the two bodies, with its point magnetized by the pole *C*. In the second figure *A* is the terrella, *C* a pole, *B* an iron sphere: the needle tends toward *C*, the terrella's pole, through the iron sphere. The needle thus placed between terrella and sphere vibrates more for-cibly toward the pole of the terrella, because the loadstone imparts instantaneous verticity to the opposite sphere. The earth's efficiency is the same, produced by the same cause. For if in a thick box made of gold (the densest of met-als) or glass, or marble, you put a needle free to

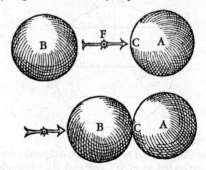

revolve, that needle, in spite of the box, will show that its forces are most closely allied to and unified with those of the earth; of its own accord and instantly, regardless of the box that prisons it, it turns to its desiderated points of north and south. And it does the same though it be shut up in iron vaults sufficiently roomy. Whatever bodies are produced here on the earth or are manufactured from nature's products by art, all consist of the matter of the globe: such bodies do not interfere with the prime poten-cies of nature derived from the primary form; nor can they withstand them, save by contrary forms. But no forms of mixed bodies are inimical to the innate primary form, though some of them oft do not accord among themselves. On the other hand, in all the bodies that have a material cause of attraction (*e.g.*, amber, jet, sulphur) action is hindered by interposition of a body (as paper, leaves, glass, etc.), and the way is obstructed and blocked so that that which is exhaled cannot reach the light body that is to be attracted. But coition and movement of the earth and the loadstone, though corporeal hindrances be interposed, are shown also in the efficiencies of other chief bodies that possess the primary form. The moon, more than the rest of the heavenly bodies, is in accord with the inner parts of the earth because of her nearness and her likeness of form. The moon causes the movement of the waters and the tides of ocean; makes the seashore to be covered and again exposed twice between the time she passes a given point of the heavens and reaches it again in the earth's daily rotation: this movement of the waters is produced and the seas rise and fall no less when the moon is below the horizon and in the nethermost heavens, than when she is high above the horizon. Thus the whole mass of the earth, when the moon is beneath the earth, does not prevent the action of the moon; and thus in certain positions of the heavens, when the moon is beneath the horizon, the seas nearest to our countries are moved, and, being stirred by the lunar power (though not struck by rays nor illumined by light), they rise, approach with great impetus, and recede. Of the reason of this we will treat elsewhere: suffice it here just to have touched the threshold of the question. Hence, here on earth, naught can be held aloof from the magnetic control of the earth and the loadstone, and all magnetic bodies are brought into orderly array by the supreme terrene form, and loadstone and iron sympathize with loadstone though solid bodies stand between.

CHAPTER 17. *Of the iron helmet (cap) of the loadstone, wherewith it is armed at the pole to increase its energy; efficiency of the same*

A CONCAVE hemisphere of thin iron, a finger's width in diameter, is applied to the convex polar superficies of a loadstone and properly fastened; or an iron acorn-shaped ball rising from the base into an obtuse cone, hollowed out a little and fitted to the surface of the stone, is made fast to the pole. The iron must be the best (steel), smooth, polished, and even. Fitted with this contrivance, a loadstone that before lifted only 4 ounces of iron will now lift 12 ounces. But the greatest force of the co-operating or rather unified matter is seen when two loadstones fitted with these projections are so joined as mutually to attract and lift each other: thus may a weight of 20 ounces be lifted, though either stone unarmed would lift only 4 ounces. Iron is held faster by an armed loadstone than by one not armed, and hence it lifts greater weights, because iron clings more strongly to the armed stone: for, by the contiguous presence of the loadstone, the iron of the armature and the iron attracted are bound fast together; and when the armature has imbibed the magnetic energy by reason of the presence of the loadstone, and another piece of iron adjoining at the same time derives force from the presence of a loadstone, the two unite energetically. Hence when two powerful armatures are in contact they cohere strongly. This is proved in Book III. 4, by iron rods cohering, as also where we mention the transformation of steel-filings into a concreted mass. For this reason iron situate near a loadstone takes away from it pieces of iron of suitable weight, provided only it be in contact with them; else, however near they may be, it does not match them. For masses of magnetic iron do not, within the field of a loadstone or near a loadstone, attract more strongly than the loadstone attracts any iron; but once they are in contact with each other they unite more strongly, and become as it were clamped together, though with the same forces at work the substance remains the same.

CHAPTER 18. *An armed loadstone does not endow with greater force magnetized iron than does an unarmed one*

TAKE two pieces of iron, one magnetized with an armed and the other with an unarmed loadstone, and apply to one of them a weight of iron proportioned to its powers: the other loadstone will lift the same weight, and no more. Two needles also turn with the same velocity and constancy toward the poles of the earth, though one needle may have been touched by an armed magnet and the other by one unarmed.

CHAPTER 19. *That unition is stronger with an armed loadstone; heavier weights are thus lifted; the coition is not stronger, but commonly weaker*

THAT an armed loadstone lifts a greater weight is evident to all; but iron is drawn from the same distance, or rather from a greater distance, to the loadstone when the stone is without the iron helmet. This is to be tried with two pieces of iron of the same weight and form at equal distance, or with one and the same needle, tested first with the armed then with the unarmed stone, at equal distances.

CHAPTER 20. *That an armed magnet lifts another, and that one a third: this holds good though there be less energy in the first*

ARMED loadstones duly joined together cohere firmly and form one; and though the first be weak, the second nevertheless clings to it, not alone with the force of the first, but of the second, the stones thus helping each other: to the second a third will often cling, and with strong loadstones a fourth to the third.

CHAPTER 21. *That when paper or other medium is interposed, an armed loadstone does not lift more than one unarmed*

IT has been shown above that an armed loadstone does not attract at a greater distance than an unarmed one, but that it lifts a greater quantity of iron, if it be in contact with the iron and continuous therewith. But put a leaf of paper between, and this intimate coherence is hindered, nor are objects of iron held together by the action of the loadstone.

CHAPTER 22. *That an armed loadstone does not attract iron more than an unarmed one; and that the armed stone is more strongly united to the iron, is shown by means of an armed loadstone and a cylinder of polished iron*

ON a plane surface lay a cylinder too heavy for the unarmed loadstone to lift; then, with paper between, apply at the middle of the cylinder the pole of an armed loadstone: if the cylinder is pulled by the loadstone, it follows after it with rolling motion; but when there is no paper between, the cylinder, joined to the loadstone, is pulled by it, and does not roll at all. But if the same loadstone be unarmed, it pulls the rolling cylinder with the same velocity as does an armed

loadstone with paper between, or wrapped in paper.

Armed loadstones of different weights, force, and shape, but out of the same mine, show an equal degree of strength in adhering to or hanging from iron objects of suitable size and shape. The same is true of unarmed ones. A suitable piece of iron applied to the under side of a loadstone that hangs from a magnetic body heightens the energy of the loadstone, so that it clings with greater force. For a pendent loadstone clings faster to the body above, to which it is attached, when a piece of iron is applied and hangs from it, than when a piece of lead or other nonmagnetic material is fastened to it.

A loadstone, whether armed or not, attached by its proper pole to the pole of another loadstone, armed or not, makes that other lift a greater weight at its opposite end. The same thing is seen when iron is applied to the pole of a loadstone, *viz.*, the opposite pole carries a greater weight of iron: thus, as in the figure, the loadstone with a bar of iron superposed carries the bar below, but cannot carry it if the upper piece be removed. Magnetic bodies in conjunction form one magnetic body; hence, the mass increasing, the magnetic energy increases also.

An armed loadstone, as also an unarmed one, leaps more quickly to a large mass of iron and combines with it more strongly than with a small mass.

CHAPTER 23. *The magnetic force makes motion toward union, and when united connects firmly*

MAGNETIZED objects cohere well and duly to one another according to their forces. Pieces of iron in the presence of a loadstone, though not in contact with it, come together, eagerly seek and seize one another, and when in conjunction are, as it were, glued together. Iron dust or iron reduced to a powder, packed in paper tubes, and placed on the meridian of a loadstone or merely brought near it, coalesces into one mass, and in an instant the many particles come together and combine; and the multitude of united grains acts on a piece of iron and attracts it, as though they formed but one continuous rod of iron, and take the north and south direction when laid on the loadstone. But if they be taken away from the stone to any distance, the particles, resolved again to their original condition, separate, and each stands alone: thus it is that the foundations of the earth are conjoined, connected, held together, magnetically. So let not Ptolemy of Alexandria, and his followers and our philosophers, maintain that the earth will go to pieces, neither let them be alarmed if the earth spins round in a circle.

Iron-filings when made hot are attracted by the loadstone not so strongly nor from as great a distance as if they were not heated. A loadstone subjected to any great heat loses some of its energy; for its humor is dissipated, and so its peculiar nature is marred. So, too, a mass of iron-filings, if roasted in a reverberatory furnace and changed to *crocus Martis*, is not attracted by a loadstone; but if it has not been very highly heated, not quite wasted, it clings to loadstone, though more feebly than iron that has not been put in fire. For *crocus Martis* has nothing of the form of iron left; but metal that has been made hot takes heat from the fire, and in its vitiated substance the magnetic powers are less powerfully awakened by the loadstone, and iron that has quite lost its nature is not attracted by the loadstone.

CHAPTER 24. *That iron within the field of a loadstone hangs suspended in air, if on account of an obstacle it cannot come near*

IRON within the magnetic field tends toward the points of the stone that have the most energy, if it be not hindered by force or by the matter of an intervening body; and this is so whether the iron tends downward to the loadstone, or seeks it from one side and obliquely, or whether it leaps up to it. But if on account of an obstacle it cannot reach the stone, it sticks to the obstacle and there remains, yet is held by a less constant bond, for, owing to the greater intervals and distances, the association (with the loadstone) is less amicable. Fracastorio, in his Chapter 8, *De sympathia*, says that a piece of iron will be suspended in air so that it cannot move either up or down if a loadstone be placed above it that has an attractive force on the iron equal to the force by which the iron tends downward: thus the iron will stand fixed in mid-air. That is ridiculous: for the nearer the loadstone the greater always is its force; and hence the iron that is lifted ever so little above the earth by the loadstone's force must needs be steadily drawn to it, and must cling to it. Baptista Porta

suspends in air a piece of iron (with a loadstone fixed above), and holds back the iron by means of a thin thread fastened to it beneath, so that it shall not rise to the stone—hardly a very brilliant idea. The piece of iron is pulled in a perpendicular line by the loadstone, though the two are not in contact, but only near each other; but, as on account of the greater nearness, the iron mass is stirred by the force that was lifting it, straightway it speeds to the loadstone and clings to it. For the iron, the nearer it comes to the loadstone, the more is excited, and the stronger is the attraction.

CHAPTER 25. *Intensifying the loadstone's forces*

ONE loadstone far surpasses another in energy, for one will snatch up almost its own weight of iron, while another is hardly able to move the smallest particle. All animals and plants that possess life have need of victual of some sort, to the end their powers may last and become firmer and stronger. But iron is not attracted by the loadstone, as Cardan and Alexander Aphrodiseus supposed, so that it may be nourished with morsels of it; neither does the loadstone gain strength from iron-filings as from a nutritious food. Baptista Porta, having his doubts about this view, and wishing to make an experiment, took a loadstone of determinate weight and buried it in iron-filings of a weight not unknown; and, after he had left it there many months, he found the stone heavier, the filings lighter. But the difference was so minute that Porta was uncertain as to the truth. This experiment of Porta's does not prove that the stone devours anything, nor does it show any process of nutrition, for minute quantities of filings are easily lost by handling. So, too, a very small quantity of the iron dust may adhere to some small part of the loadstone and not be noticed, thus adding somewhat to the weight of the stone; but that is a superficial accretion, and can be brushed off without much difficulty. Many think that when weak and sluggish the stone can bring itself back to a better condition, and that a very strong stone can endow a weaker one with the highest degree of force. Is it as when animals gain strength when they feed and are filled? Is a remedy found for the loadstone in addition or subtraction of something? Is there aught that can restore this primary form or give it anew? Surely nothing can do such a thing save what possesses magnetic properties. Magnetic bodies can restore soundness (when not totally lost) to magnetic bodies, and can give to some of them powers greater than they had originally; but to those that are by their nature in the highest degree perfect, it is not possible to give further strength. Hence the more infamous becomes all the charlatanry of Paracelsus, who declares that the loadstone's force and energy may be increased and transformed to tenfold what it is naturally. And the way of doing this is, so to speak, to half-candescify the loadstone, *i.e.*, to make it very hot, yet so that it does not reach white heat, and then immediately to dip it in oil of vitriol made from the best Corynthian steel, letting it become saturated. "In this way," says Paracelsus, "you can give to a loadstone such strength that it will pull a nail out of a wall, and perform many other the like marvels impossible for a common loadstone." But a loadstone so dipped not only acquires no force, but suffers some loss it already hath. A loadstone rubbed and smoothed with steel is made better. When covered with filings of the best iron or pure steel, not rusty, it retains its properties. Sometimes, too, a good strong loadstone gains some strength when rubbed on its opposite pole with the pole of another loadstone: it takes in force. In such experiments it is well to observe the earth's pole, and to lay down in the direction required by the magnetic laws the stone that one wishes to make stronger: this point we will establish hereafter. A strong, large loadstone increases the power of another loadstone, as also the power of iron. If, on the north pole of a loadstone, you place another loadstone, the north pole of the second becomes stronger, and a piece of iron clings like an arrow to the north pole *a*, and not at all to the south pole *b*. And the pole *a*, when it is in a right line above with the axis of both loadstones, they being joined according to the magnetic laws, raises the piece of iron to the perpendicular: this it cannot do if the larger loadstone be moved away, for its strength is insufficient. But as a ball of iron on the pole of the

terrella raises the piece of iron to the perpendicular, so, at the side, the iron is not directed toward the centre, but stands oblique and sticks everywhere; for in the iron ball the pole is ever the point of contact with the terrella's pole, and it is not constant, as it is in the smaller terrella. The parts of the earth, as of all magnetic bodies, are in accord and enjoy neighborhood with each other: there is in them all mutual love, undying good-will. The weaker loadstones are refreshed by the stronger ones, and the less vigorous bring no damage to the more vigorous. Yet a strong loadstone exerts more attraction in another strong one than in one that is feeble, for a vigorous stone contributes forceful action, and itself hastes, flies to the other, and solicits it vehemently; accordingly there is co-operation and a clearer and stronger cohesion.

CHAPTER 26. *Why the love of iron and loadstone appears greater than that of loadstone and loadstone, or iron and iron when nigh a loadstone and within its field*

ONE loadstone does not attract another on all its sides as it does iron, but only at one fixed point: hence the poles of the two must be properly arranged, else they do not duly and powerfully cohere. But this arranging is not easy nor the work of an instant: therefore one loadstone will seem to be refractory toward another, whereas they may be in perfect harmony. Iron, suddenly impressed by a loadstone, is not only attracted by it, but is renovated and its powers enhanced, whereby it pursues and solicits the loadstone with a force not less than its own, and also makes captive other iron objects. Suppose a little iron bar firmly adhering to a loadstone: if you bring near this piece of iron an iron rod, but without touching the loadstone, you shall see the iron instantly follow the rod, relinquishing the loadstone, leaning toward the rod, and, on contact, firmly adhering thereto; for iron in

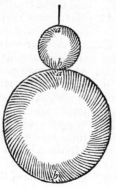

union and contact pulls more vigorously another piece of iron within the field of a loadstone than does the loadstone itself. The natural magnetic force, which in iron lies confined and asleep, is awakened by a loadstone, associates itself with it, and comes into sympathy with it in virtue of the primary form: hence comes the perfect magnetized iron, which is as strong as the loadstone itself; for as the one imparts and arouses, so the other conceives, and, being awakened, endures, and by its very act gives back the force again. But in so much as iron is liker to iron than is loadstone, and in two pieces of iron within the field of a loadstone, the nighness of the latter enhances the powers of both: then, their forces being equal, likeness of substance becomes decisive, and iron gives itself up to iron, and the two pieces are united by their most like (identical) and homogeneous forces. This is effected not only by coition, but by a firmer union; and a steel cap or snout (*glans vel nasus*) properly adjusted to the pole of a loadstone lifts greater weights than can the stone by itself. When steel or iron is made from loadstone or from iron ore, the slag and impurities are separated from the substance by a better fusion: hence usually such iron contains the matter of the earth purged of foreign admixture and dross, and more homogenic and perfect (than before smelting), albeit deformed by fusion. And this matter, when acted on by a loadstone, conceives the magnetic virtue, and within the magnetic field is endowed with force surpassing that of an inferior loadstone, which is seldom without some admixture of impurities.

CHAPTER 27. *That the centre of the magnetic forces in the earth is the centre of the earth; and in the terrella the terrella's centre*

THE rays of magnetic force are dispersed in a circle in all directions; and the centre of this sphere is not in the pole (as Baptista Porta deems, Chap. 22), but in the centre of the stone and of the terrella. So, too, the earth's centre is the centre of the earth's magnetic movements, though magnetic bodies are not borne direct toward the centre in the magnetic movement save when they are attracted by the pole. For as the formal power of loadstone and earth promotes simply unity and conformity between things separate, it follows that every-

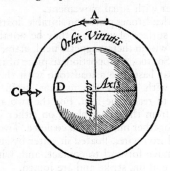

where at equal distance from the centre or from the convex circumference, just as at one point it seems to attract in a right line, so at another it can control and rotate the needle, provided only the loadstone be not of unequal power. For if at the distance C from pole D the stone is able to attract the needle, then at an equal distance A above its equator it can control and rotate the needle. Thus the centre and middle of the terrella is the centre of force, and thence to the circumference of its sphere of influence its magnetic virtues extend (for) equal distances in all directions.

CHAPTER 28. *That a loadstone does not attract to a fixed point or pole only, but to every part of a terrella, except the equinoctial circle*

COITION is always strongest when pole touches pole, for at the poles the force is greatest by concert of the whole: hence one pole seizes the other with greatest force. Points at distances from the poles possess attractional power also, but somewhat weaker and sluggish in the ratio of the distance, so that finally in the equinoctial line they are utterly enervate and faint. The poles, too, do not attract as mathematical points, nor does magnetized iron unite at its poles only with the poles of a loadstone. On the contrary, the coition takes place all over the periphery, north and south, the force emanating from the whole mass. Magnetic bodies, however, are attracted feebly in the parts near the equator, but quickly in the parts near the poles. Wherefore not the poles alone, and not the parts alone that are near the poles, attract and solicit magnetic bodies; but magnetic bodies are controlled and rotated and unite with other magnetic bodies according as parts neighboring and adjoining lend their forces, which forces are ever of the same potency in the same parallel, except when otherwise distributed by causes producing variation.

CHAPTER 29. *Of difference of forces dependent on quantity or mass*

LOADSTONES coming from the same mine, and not intermingled with neighboring metals or ores, have the same potency; yet the stone that is largest exhibits greatest force, as it carries the greatest weight and has a wider sphere of influence. A loadstone weighing an ounce does not lift an iron spike as does one that weighs a pound, nor does its control reach so far, nor does its force extend to such a distance. And if you take from a one-pound stone a part, somewhat of its power will be seen to leave also; for when a part is taken away some of the energy is lost. But when such part is duly applied and united to the stone, though it be not cemented there nor perfectly fitted in by the mere apposition, the original strength is recovered, and the force returns. Sometimes, however, the energy is increased by detachment of a part because of malformation of the stone, as when the force is diffused through awkward corners.

In stones of different sorts the ratio of power is different: one weighing a drachm may have more force than another one of 20 pounds. Many a loadstone is so weak that the force can scarcely be noticed, and such faint magnets are often surpassed by masses prepared of potter's earth. But we may ask: supposing that a stone of a given kind and of definite goodness, and weighing a drachm, carries one drachm, whether one weighing an ounce will carry an ounce, a pound a pound, and so on? So it is, for in proportion to size such loadstone has greater or less strength: so that a loadstone of proportionate size and weight, a drachm weight of which lifts a drachm weight of iron, will, when brought near a suitable great obelisk or enormous pyramid of iron, attract it and pull it to itself, and that with no greater effort of its nature and with no greater pains than when a drachm weight of loadstone seizes a drachm weight of iron. But in all such experiments the power of the loadstones should be equal, the form of the stones should be exactly proportioned: this is true not less of an armed than of a naked loadstone. As an experiment, take a loadstone weighing 8 oz., which when armed lifts 12 oz. of iron; cut off of this stone a part which, when brought to the form of the whole stone as it was before, shall weigh only 2 oz.: such a stone, armed, lifts 3 oz. of iron. In this experiment it is requisite that the form of the 3-oz. piece of iron be the same as that of the 12-oz. piece; if the 12 oz. mass rose in form of a cone, the 3-oz. piece must assume a pyramidal form proportioned to the figure of the original mass.

CHAPTER 30. *The shape and the mass of an iron object are important in magnetic coitions*

It was shown before that the shape and mass of a loadstone are weighty factors in magnetic coitions: similarly, the shape and mass of the iron determine whether its force shall be great or little. Oblong, bacilliform pieces are both more quickly attracted and cling more firmly than spherical or square pieces, and this for the causes we have shown with regard to the loadstone. It is also worthy of note, that when a smaller iron object has attached to it a weight of different material, so that the weight of the two shall equal that of another larger piece whose weight is proportioned to the power of the loadstone, it is not lifted by the loadstone like the larger object; for the smaller piece is not so powerfully attracted by the loadstone, because it gives back less force, and only magnetic matter conceives the magnetic energy: foreign matter appended to such a body cannot take in magnetic force.

CHAPTER 31. *Of oblong and round stones*

Iron bodies are more forcibly attracted by an oblong stone than by a round one, provided only the pole of the stone is at the extreme end of its length. The reason is that in the oblong stone the magnetic body at the extremity is directed straight toward a body wherein the force proceeds in right lines and through a longer diameter. But the oblong stone has only little force on the side; for, plainly, the attraction at *a* and *B* is stronger in a round loadstone at equal distance from the pole, than in *c* and *D*.

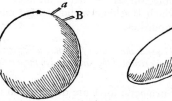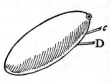

CHAPTER 32. *Some problems and magnetic experiments on the coition, and repulsion, and regular movement, of magnetic bodies*

Loadstones that are equal come together with equal mutual incitation.

Magnetized iron bodies that are in all respects equal do also come together with equal mutual incitation.

Iron bodies not magnetized, if they are equal, and not hindered by their bulk, do also come together with equal movement.

Two loadstones placed on suitable floats apart on the surface of water, if they be suitably arranged within their magnetic field, attract each other. So, too, a proportionate piece of iron on one float hastes to a loadstone with the same speed with which the magnet itself, afloat, strives to reach the iron. For the two are impelled from their own places on either side to come together midway and coalesce. Two magnetized iron wires, floated in water by suitable corks move forward to contact, and, with the proper end on, strike and are joined.

With magnetic bodies that are equal, coition is more vigorous, and quicker than repulsion and separation. That magnetic bodies are more sluggish in repelling than in attracting, is seen

in every magnetic experiment, as when loadstones are borne on suitable floats on water, or
when magnetized iron wire or little bars are
driven through cork and set afloat in water, as
also in experiments with a needle. The reason
is that, since the power of coition is one thing,
the power of conformation and of ordering in
place is another, therefore repulsion and aver-
sation are the act of the force ordering in place;
but the coming together is the result of mutual
attraction to contact as well as of the force that
orders in place; *i.e.,* it is due to a twofold force.

The ordering force is often only the forerun-
ner of coition, so that the bodies shall stand in
due position before the onset: hence they turn
in the direction of the points of coition, if they
be hindered from attaining those points. If a

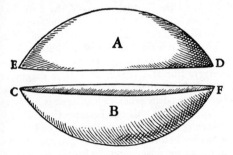

loadstone be cut in two equal parts along the
meridian, the separated parts repel each other,
if the poles be placed at a suitable even distance
from each other; for they mutually repel with
greater velocity than is the case when pole is
wrongly opposed to pole. Thus the half *B* of a
loadstone, placed near the other half *A*, repels *A*
on its float, because *D* withdraws from *F* and *E*
from *C*. But if *B* be again joined exactly with
A, they come together and form one magnetic
body; yet when they are only near each other
they are mutually hostile. And if one half be
turned about so as to bring *C* opposite to *D* and
F to *E*, then *A* follows *B* within the field and becomes joined to it.

South parts of a stone retreat from south
parts, and north parts from north. Nevertheless, if you bring the south end of a piece of iron
near to the south part of the stone, the iron is
seized and the two are held in friendly embrace;
as the verticity fixed in the iron is reversed and
changed by the presence of the more powerful
loadstone, which is more constant in its forces
than the iron. For they come together in accordance with nature, if either by reversal or
change there be produced true conformity and
orderly coition as well as regular direction.

Loadstones of identical shape, size, and strength
attract each other with equal force, and when
in wrong position repel with like energy.

Little rods of unmagnetized iron, though like
and equal, yet act on one another often with
different force; for as there are different grounds
for the acquisition of verticity and also of
strength and vigor, so the particles that are
most strongly excited by the loadstones themselves in turn act with most force.

Pieces of iron that have been magnetized at
one same pole of a loadstone repel one another
at the magnetized ends; and their other extremities are also mutually hostile.

In rotating needles when the points are magnetized but not the crotches, the latter repel
one another, but only feebly and in proportion
to length.

In like rotating needles when the points are
magnetized by the same pole of a loadstone the
crotches attract with equal force.

In a long rotating needle the crotch is attracted feebly by the point of a short needle; the
crotch of a short one is attracted strongly by the
point of a long one, because the crotch of a long
needle has feeble verticity, but the point of a
long needle has strong verticity.

The point of a long needle repels the point
of a short one more strongly than the point of a
short needle repels that of a long one, if one of
them be poised free on a sharp point and the
other held in the hand; for though both have
been equally magnetized by the same loadstone,
still the longer one, by reason of its greater mass,
has greater force at its point.

In unmagnetized iron rods the south end of
one attracts the north end of another, and the
north end the south; the meridional parts, too,
repel meridional parts, and north parts north
parts.

If magnetic bodies be divided or in any way
broken up, each several part hath a north end
and a south end.

A needle is stirred by a loadstone at as great a
distance with an obstacle interposed as in air
and in an open medium.

Rods magnetized by friction with the pole of
a loadstone draw toward that pole and follow it.
Baptista Porta is therefore in error when he
says (Chapter 4) that "if you bring a part nigh
the part that gave it the force, it shudders, and
repels and drives it away, and attracts the converse and opposite part."

The laws of rotation and attraction are the
same as between loadstone and loadstone, loadstone and iron, and iron and iron.

When the parts of a magnetic body that has been broken up by force and cut into pieces are put together again and properly joined, they form one body and their joint force is one; nor have they separate poles.

The separated parts, if division has not been made on the parallels, assume new poles, north and south; if the division is along a parallel, they may retain one pole in the same place as before.

Iron rubbed and excited by a loadstone is seized at the fitting ends by a loadstone more powerfully than iron not magnetized.

If a small iron bar be set erect on the pole of a loadstone, another bar-iron pin in touch with its upper end becomes firmly attached thereto, and if it be moved away pulls the standing bar from the terrella.

If, to the nether end of the erect bar you apply the end of another bar, it does not cohere, nor do they unite.

As a rod of iron pulls iron away from the terrella, so does a small loadstone or a smaller terrella albeit of less force. Here the iron bar C

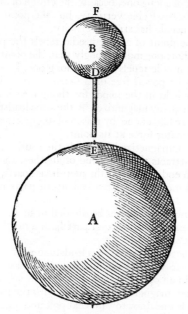

coalesces with the terrella A, and thus its force is enhanced and awakened magnetically both in the end in conjunction and also in the distal end by reason of its contact with the terrella; the distal end furthermore receives energy from the loadstone B, and the pole D of this magnet also gains force by reason of its favourable position and the nearness of the pole E of

the terrella. Hence many causes co-operate to make the bar C, attached to the loadstone B, cling more strongly to that than to the terrella A. The energy called forth in the bar, also the energy called forth in the loadstone B, and B's native energy, all concur; therefore D is magnetically bound more strongly to C than E to C.

But if you turn the pole F to the iron C, then C does not cling to F as it did before to D; for, within the magnetic field, stones so arranged stand in an unnatural order: hence F does not get force from E.

Two loadstones, or two magnetized pieces of iron, duly cohering, fly apart on the coming of a stronger loadstone or a stronger magnetized mass of iron; for the newcomer, presenting the opposite pole, puts one to flight and overmasters it, and the mutual action of the two that before were conjoined ceases. So the forces of one of the bodies are reduced and fail; and were it possible, it would shake off its fellow, and, turning about, would go rolling over to the stronger. For this reason it is that magnetic bodies held pendent in air drop to the ground when the opposite pole of a loadstone is presented to them; and this not because there is any weakening or numbing of the forces of both of the bodies before conjoined, as Baptista Porta maintains, for pole cannot be hostile to both of the ends that cohere, but to one only: this end the newcomer, the stronger loadstone, drives away from itself by presenting its opposite pole, and thus one of the smaller bodies is compelled to give up its friendly association with the other.

CHAPTER 33. *Of the difference in the ratio of strength and movement of coition within the sphere of influence*

IF the greatest weight that is attracted to a loadstone at the nearest distance be divided into a given number of parts, and the radius of the sphere of magnetic attraction into the same number of parts, the parts of the weight will correspond to the intermediate parts of the radius.

The sphere of influence extends farther than the sphere of movement of any magnetic body, for a magnetic body is affected at the outermost edge though it may not move with local motion: that is done when the loadstone is brought nearer. A needle, even a very small one, turns round while remote from a loadstone, though, at the same distance and free to move and in no wise hindered, it does not come to the loadstone.

The velocity of the movement of a magnetic body to a loadstone is in proportion to the strength of the loadstone, or its mass, or its shape, or the nature of the medium, or the distance within the magnetic sphere of action.

A magnetic body approaches with greater velocity a powerful loadstone than a sluggish one, in the ratio of the respective energies of the two loadstones. A smaller mass of iron, as also one rather oblong in shape, is attracted with the greater velocity. The velocity of the movement of a magnetic body to a loadstone varies according to the medium, for bodies move with greater velocity in air than in water, and in a serene atmosphere than in thick and foggy weather.

In the ratio of distance, movement is quicker from anear than from afar. At the outermost edge of a terrella's field magnetic bodies move faintly and slowly. In the immediate neighborhood of the terrella the motor impetus is greatest.

A loadstone that in the outermost verge of its field of force, at the distance of one foot, can hardly stir a rotating needle, will, when connected with a long iron rod, strongly attract and repel (accordingly as its different poles are presented) the needle at the distance of three feet, and this whether the loadstone is armed or unarmed. The iron rod should be of fitting quality, and of the thickness of the little finger.

For the energy of the loadstone awakens verticity in the iron and passes in and through iron to a far greater distance than it extends through air.

The force also passes through a number of pieces of iron conjoined at their extremities, yet not so surely as through one continuous rod.

Steel-filings strewed on paper rise on end and present the appearance of stubby steel hairs when a loadstone is brought near above them; when the loadstone is applied beneath, the hair-like crop rises also.

Steel-filings, when the pole of a loadstone is brought near, coalesce into one body; but when it would come to the loadstone, the body is broken up and rises to the steel in smaller masses that still hold together.

But if the loadstone be beneath the paper, the consolidated mass breaks up as before, and into very many parts, each of which consists of a multitude of grains; and they remain united, like separate bodies; and while the lowermost parts of these eagerly follow the pole of the loadstone beneath, so the separate masses stand like

solid magnetic bodies. In like manner a bit of iron wire one barley-corn or two in length stands on end when a loadstone is applied either beneath or above.

CHAPTER 34. *Why a loadstone is of different power in its poles as well in the north as in the south regions*

THE extraordinary magnetic energy of the earth is beautifully shown in the following neat experiment: Take a terrella of no ordinary power, or an oblong loadstone with equal cones forming its polar ends; but in any figure not exactly spherical it is easy to fall into mistakes, and the experiment is difficult. In northern latitudes raise the true north pole above the horizon straight toward the zenith. Plainly it holds erect on its north pole a larger bar of iron than could the south pole of the same terrella if turned in like manner toward the centre of the sky. The same demonstration is made with a small terrella set atop of a large one.

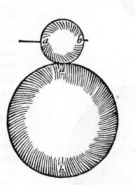

Let *ab* be the earth or a large terrella, and *ab* a small terrella; a larger bar is raised erect by the north pole of the small terrella than the *b* pole of the same, if turned skyward, can raise to the erect position. And the *a* pole of the small terrella derives force from the greater, turning from zenith to the plane of the horizon or to the level. Now if, the smaller terrella having its poles directed as before, you apply a piece of iron to its lower or south pole, that will attract and hold a greater weight than can the south pole if that be turned down. Which is thus shown: Let *A* be the earth or a terrella; *E* the north pole or some point in high latitude; let *B* be a large terrella above the earth, or a small terrella above a larger one; *D* the south pole: it is plain that *D* (south pole) attracts a larger piece of iron, *C*, than can *E* (the north pole), if that pole be turned downward to the position *D*, looking toward the earth or the terrella in their northern regions. Magnetic bodies gain force from other magnetic bodies if they be arranged duly and according to their nature in neighbourhood and within the sphere of influence; and hence, when a terrella is imposed on the earth or on another terrella in such way that the south pole looks toward the north pole and north is turned away from north, the energy and forces of its poles are augmented. Hence the north pole of a terrella in such position lifts a heavier piece of iron than the south pole does if that be turned away. In like manner the south pole, gaining force from the earth or the larger terrella when it is duly placed as nature requires, attracts and holds heavier bars of iron. In the other portion of the terrestrial globe, toward the south, as also in the southern parts of

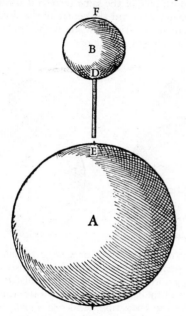

the terrella, the case is reversed, for, there, the south pole of the terrella is strongest when distal, as is the north pole of the terrella when it faces the earth or terrella. The farther a place is from the equinoctial line, whether of the earth or of a terrella, the greater is seen to be the accession of force; but nigh the equator the difference is slight; at the equator it is null; at the poles it is greatest.

CHAPTER 35. *Of a perpetual-motion engine actuated by the attraction of a loadstone, mentioned by authors*

CARDAN writes that out of iron and loadstone may be constructed a perpetual-motion engine —not that he saw such a machine ever; he mere-

ly offers the idea as an opinion, and quotes from the report of Antonius de Fantis, of Treviso; such a machine he describes in Book ix, *De rerum varietate*. But the contrivers of such machines have but little practice in magnetic experiments. For no magnetic attraction can be greater (whatever art, whatever form of instrument you employ) than the force of retention; and objects that are conjoined, and that are near, are held with greater force than objects solicited and set in motion are made to move; and as we have already shown, this motion is a coition of both, not an attraction of one. Such an engine Petrus Peregrinus, centuries ago, either devised or delineated after he had got the idea from others; and Joannes Taysner published this, illustrating it with wretched figures, and copying word for word the theory of it. May the gods damn all such sham, pilfered, distorted works, which do but muddle the minds of students!

CHAPTER 36. *How a strong loadstone may be recognized*

A STRONG loadstone sometimes lifts in air a mass of iron weighing as much as itself; a weak loadstone hardly attracts a bit of fine wire. Those, then, are the stronger loadstones which attract and hold the larger bodies, unless there is some defect of shape, or unless the pole of the stone is not properly applied. Besides, the stronger loadstone, when afloat, more readily turns its poles toward the poles of the earth or the points of variation on the horizon. But the stone that acts sluggishly, betrays some flaw in itself, shows that its force is exhausted. Loadstones are to be all prepared in the same way, shaped alike, and made of the same size; for when they are unlike and unequal, experiments are doubtful. All loadstones are tested for strength in the same way, *viz.*, with a versorium (rotating needle) held at some distance; the stone that at the greatest distance is able to make the needle go round is the best and strongest. Baptista Porta also rightly determines the power of a loadstone by thus weighing in a balance. A piece of loadstone is put in one scale and an equal weight of another substance in the other, so that the scales are balanced. Then some iron lying on a board is brought nigh, so that it shall cleave to the loadstone in the scale, and the two bodies cohere perfectly at their points of attraction; into the opposite scale sand is poured gradually till the scale in which is the loadstone separates from the iron. By weighing the sand the force of the loadstone is ascertained. So, too, we can make experiment and find the stronger stone by weighing sand, if we put in a pair of scales loadstones that balance each other. Such is an experiment given by Cardinal Cusanus in his *Statica*, and from him Porta would seem to have learned the one he cites. The stronger loadstones turn readily toward the poles or the points of variation; so, too, they propel their floats and cause them and other cumbrances, as so much wood, to wheel about. In an inclination or dip instrument the greater power of a loadstone is manifested and there greater power is requisite. Hence loadstones are stronger the more speedily they do their work, and the more rapidly they travel from side to side and return, and the sooner they come to a standstill. Feeble, exhausted loadstones travel more sluggishly, come to a rest more slowly, stick at the pole less decisively, and are easily displaced therefrom.

CHAPTER 37. *Uses of the loadstone as it affects iron*

BY means of magnetic coition we test an iron ore. The ore is roasted in a furnace, is crushed, washed, dried, and so is freed from foreign humours. The loadstone being thrust among the particles collected from the bath attracts the iron dust, which being removed by a feather brush is caught in a crucible; again and again the loadstone is dipped in and the iron dust brushed into the crucible, till nothing remains that it will attract. Then the powdered iron is heated together with halinitro till it is melted and becomes a mass of iron. Now if the loadstone picks up the iron dust readily and easily, we deem the ore to be rich; if slowly, the ore is poor; if the loadstone seems quite to reject it, the ore is judged to have little or no iron. By the same method, iron particles may be separated from particles of any other metal. And many tricks are played by secretly attracting bits of iron to light bodies, or causing a concealed loadstone to attract the iron; to persons who know not the cause, the movements of the objects seem amazing. Any ingenious workman may exhibit a great number of such tricks for sport, with the air of one dealing in incantations and magic.

CHAPTER 38. *Of the attractions of other bodies*

PHILOSOPHIZERS of the vulgar sort and mere copyists oft repeat, from others' memoirs on natural philosophy, opinions and errors with regard to the attractional force of various bodies. They will say, for example, that diamond attracts iron and pulls it away from loadstone; that loadstones differ, some attracting gold, others silver, copper, lead—yea, flesh, water, fish. The flame of sulphur is said to seek iron and stones; so is white naphtha said to draw to itself fire. I have already said that inanimate natural bodies in no other wise attract or are attracted on this terrestrial globe, save either magnetically or electrically. It is therefore not true that there are loadstones that attract gold or other metals; for a magnetic body attracts only a magnetic body. Fracastorio tells of having seen a loadstone attracting silver. If that were true, then it must necessarily have been because some iron had been artificially mixed with the silver and lay hidden therein, or because nature had mixed iron with the silver (as she does sometimes, though very seldom); for iron is now and then mixed with silver by nature, but silver with iron very rarely or never. By false coiners and by avaricious princes, when money is coined, iron is mixed with silver; an instance of this we have in Anthony's denarius, if what Pliny declares be true. So Cardan (led into error, perhaps, by others) says there is a certain kind of loadstone which attracts silver; and he adds a very silly test of the thing: "If," says he, "a thin rod of silver be touched with this and then poised in equilibrium, when it comes to a standstill after being whirled, it will point to silver (especially a large quantity), though the same be buried in the ground; by this means anybody may easily unearth hidden treasures." He adds that "the stone must be of the best," and that he never saw such stone. Nor will he or anybody else ever see such a stone or such an experiment. Cardan cites an attraction, improperly so called, of flesh, which is altogether unlike magnetic attraction; his *magnes creagus* (or flesh-attracting loadstone, so named because it clings to the lips) must be cast out of the company of loadstones and of the whole family of attractional bodies. Lemnian earth, red ochre, and sundry minerals have this action, but it were absurd to say that they attract. Cardan imagines another loadstone, a third species as it were; if a needle be driven into this, it may be thrust into a person's body afterward without being felt. But what has attraction to do with numbing of sense, or what is there in common between stupefaction and the mind of a philosopher while he discourses of attraction? Many are the stones, both of natural origin and artificially compounded, that possess the power of dulling the senses. The flame of sulphur is by some said to attract because that it consumes certain metals by reason of its penetrating force. So does naphtha attract flame because it emits and exhales inflammable vapor, and hence is set aflame at some distance; even as the smudge of a candle that has just been extinguished catches fire again from another flame; for fire creeps to fire through an inflammable medium. Of the sucking-fish or remora, and how it stays ships, philosophers have discoursed variously. It is their custom oft to account with their reasonings for this and many other fables, before ascertaining that the thing is so in fact. Wherefore, approving and indorsing the absurdities of the ancients they published the most blunderous theories and ridiculous theses—*e.g.*, that there are rocks having the power of attraction and that there the remora dwells; and they postulate of the necessity of I know not what vacuum or how produced. Pliny and Julius Solinus tell of the stone *cathochites* and affirm that it attracts flesh and holds one's hand, as loadstone holds iron and amber holds chaff. But that is due solely to its viscosity and its natural glutinousness, for it adheres most readily to a warm hand. The *sagda*, or *sagdo*, is a gem of leek-green color mentioned by Pliny, Solinus, Albertus Magnus, and Euace, who themselves make up or from others copy the story that this stone has the peculiarity of attracting wood. And there are others who utter the nonsense that the wood attracted cannot be pulled off, but has to be cut away; while some tell of a stone of this kind that clings as firmly to ships' bottoms as do the barnacles gathered on a long voyage. But though a stone may cling to a surface, it does not therefore attract; and if it did attract, surely it would draw to itself chips and shavings electrically. A stone of this sort was seen by Encelius in the hands of a certain seaman; a weak stone, it was, hardly able to attract the smallest twigs; and its color was not a true leek-green. Diamond, carbuncle, rock-crystal, and other stones attract in that way. I say nothing of other fabulous stones, of *pantarbes* whereof Philostratus affirms that it attracts to itself other stones; of *amphitane*, said to attract also gold. Pliny, in telling of the discovery of glass, makes the loadstone attract glass as it does iron; for when in speaking of the mode of making glass he describes its nature, he adds this concerning the loadstone: "In time the skill of the workmen, clear sighted and resourceful, was no longer content with mixing in natron; loadstone began to be added because it is believed to attract to itself the liquid glass even as it attracts iron." Georgius Agricola asserts that "A portion of loadstone is added to the in-

gredients of glass (sand and natron), because it is believed in our day as in early times that that force (the magnetic) attracts to itself the molten glass even as it attracts iron, that it purifies it when attracted, and changes it from green or orange-yellow to clear white; but afterward the fire consumes the loadstone." True it is indeed that loadstone of some kind (as the magnesia employed by glass-makers, which has no magnetic powers) is sometimes introduced into and mingled with the material of glass, yet not because that it attracts glass. But a red-hot loadstone does not attract iron at all, nor is iron at white heat attracted by loadstone; and the loadstone is even destroyed by very strong heat and loses its power of attraction. Nor is this work of purifying the function of loadstone alone in the glass furnace, but also of certain pyrites and of readily combustible iron ores; and these alone are used by such of our glass-makers as make clear, fine glass. These materials are mixed with sand, ashes, and natron (just as other materials are mixed with metals when they are smelted), so that, when the contents of the furnace become fluid glass, the well-known green and yellow color may be purged away by the penetrant heat. For no other matter reaches such degree of heat or endures fire for the requisite length of time that the material of the glass may become perfectly fluid, and just then is burnt up by the strong fire. But sometimes it happens that on account of the magnetic stone, or magnesia, or iron ore, or pyrites, the glass hath a dusky tinge, these substances being too resistant to fire and hence not being burnt up, or having been introduced in too great quantity. For this reason, glass-makers procure the right sort of stone and carefully attend to the proportion of ingredients in the mixture. Thus, then, Georgius Agricola and later writers are badly led astray by Pliny's stupid philosophy when they declare that loadstone is needed by glass-makers for its magnetic virtues and attractive force. And Scaliger (*De subtil, ad Cardanum*) strays far from truth when, in treating of magnetic bodies, he speaks of diamond attracting iron; unless he means only that diamond electrically attracts iron as it does bits of wood, straws, and other small bodies of all kinds. Fallopius thinks that quicksilver attracts metals in virtue of an occult property, just as the loadstone does iron, or as amber attracts chaff. But there is no attraction properly so called when quicksilver enters into metals. For metals imbibe quicksilver as clay does water, but not unless the substances are in contact; for quick-silver does not draw to itself gold or lead from a distance, but remains fixed in its place.

CHAPTER 39. *Of mutually repellent bodies*

AUTHORS who have treated of the forces of attracting bodies have discoursed of the powers of repellent bodies also; and in particular those who have classified objects in nature according to sympathy and antipathy. It would seem, therefore, that we must needs say something about the strife of bodies among themselves, lest widespread errors, accepted by all to the ruin of true philosophy, should extend farther. They tell us that as like things attract for conservation's sake, so unlike things and opposites repel and drive each other away, as is seen in the *antiperistasis* (counteraction) of many bodies; but it is most potent in plants and animals, which, as they attract things in affinity and of kin, so do put away things extreme and disadvantageous to themselves. But in other bodies the same reason does not exist for their coming together by mutual attraction when they are separated. Animals take food (as do all things that live), bring it into their inwards, absorb their nourishment by means of certain organs (the vital principle acting and operating). Only things set before them and adjoining them do they enjoy through a natural instinct, not things placed afar; herein there is no exercise of force, no movement on the part of those other things; and therefore animals neither attract bodies nor repel. Water does not repel oil, as some do think, for oil floats on water; nor does water repel mud, because when mixed with water it settles at last. This is a separation of bodies unlike or not perfectly mixed, because of their matter; but after they have been separated, they still remain in conjunction without any natural strife. Thus, in the bottom of a vessel, muddy sediment rests quiet, and oil remains on the top of water, nor is it ordered away. A drop of water remains whole on a dry surface, nor is it chased away by the dry. Wrongly, therefore, do they who discourse of these things impart an antipathy—*antipathia* (*i.e.*, a power of repulsion through opposite passions); for neither is there in them any repellent force, and repulsion comes of action not of passion. But these people dearly love their Greek terms. The question for us is whether there is any body that drives another away to a distance without material impetus, as the loadstone attracts. Now a loadstone does repel another loadstone; for the pole of one is repelled by the pole of another that does not agree naturally with it; driving it, it makes it turn round so that they may come together perfectly according to nature. But if a weak loadstone floating freely in water cannot, on account of obstacles, readily turn about, then it is repelled and driven farther away by the other. All electrics attract objects of every kind; they never repel or propel. What is told of some plants (*e.g.*, of the cucumber, which, when oil is placed beneath it, moves away) is a material change from neighbourhood, not a hidden sympathy. But when they show you a candle's flame that touches a cold solid (as iron) turning to one side, and pretend that here is antipathy, they talk nonsense. The reason of this they will see clearer than light when we come to treat of heat and what it is. As for Fracastorio's belief that a loadstone may be found that shall repel iron, in virtue of some principle latent in it that is opposed to iron, it is without any foundation.

BOOK THIRD

CHAPTER 1. *Of direction*

IN the foregoing books it has been shown that a loadstone has its poles, iron also poles, and rotation, and fixed verticity, and finally that loadstone and iron direct their poles toward the poles of the earth. But now we have to set forth the causes of these things and their wonderful efficiencies known aforetime but not demonstrated. Of these rotations all the writers who went before us have given their opinions with such brevity and indefiniteness that, as it would seem, no one could be persuaded thereby, while the authors themselves could hardly be contented with them. By men of intelligence, all their petty reasonings—as being useless, questionable, and absurd, and based on no proofs or premises—are rejected with the result that magnetic science, neglected more and more and understood by none, has been exiled. The true south pole, and not the north (as before our time all believed), of a loadstone placed on its float in water turns to the north; the south end of a piece of magnetized and of unmagnetized iron also moves to the north. An oblong piece of iron of three or four finger-breadths, properly stroked with a loadstone, quickly turns to north and south. Therefore artificers place such a bar, balanced on a point, in a compass-box or in a sun-dial; or they construct a versorium out of two curved pieces of iron that touch at their extremities so that the movement may be more constant; thus is constructed the mariner's compass, an instrument beneficial, salutary, and fortunate for seamen, showing the way to safety and to port. But it is to be understood at the threshold of their argument, before we proceed farther, that these directions of loadstone or of iron are not ever and always toward the world's true poles, that they do not always seek those fixed and definite points, nor rest on the line of the true meridian, but that at places, more or less far apart, they commonly vary either to the east or to the west; sometimes, too, in certain regions of land or sea, they point to the true poles. This discrepance is known as the variation of the needle and of the loadstone; and as

it is produced by other causes and is, as it were, a sort of perturbation and depravation of the true direction, we propose to treat here only of the true direction of the compass and the magnetic needle, which would all over the earth be the same, toward the true poles and in the true meridian, were not hindrances and disturbing causes present to prevent: in the book next following we will treat of its variation and of the cause of perturbation.

They who aforetime wrote of the world and of natural philosophy, in particular those great elementarian philosophers and all their progeny and pupils down to our day; those, I mean, who taught that the earth is ever at rest, and is, as it were, a dead-weight planted in the centre of the universe at equal distance everywhere from the heavens, of simple uncomplex matter possessing only the qualities of dryness and cold—these philosophers were ever seeking the causes of things in the heavens, in the stars, the planets; in fire, air, water, and in the bodies of compounds; but never did they recognize that the terrestrial globe, besides dryness and cold, hath some principal, efficient, predominant potencies that give to it firmness, direction, and movement throughout its entire mass and down to its inmost depths; neither did they make inquiry whether such things were, and, for this reason, the common herd of philosophizers, in search of the causes of magnetic movements, called in causes remote and far away. Martinus Cortesius, who would be content with no cause whatever in the universal world, dreamt of an attractive magnetic point beyond the heavens, acting on iron. Petrus Peregrinus holds that direction has its rise at the celestial poles. Cardan was of the opinion that the rotation of iron is caused by the star in the tail of Ursa Major. The Frenchman Bessard thinks that the magnetic needle turns to the pole of the zodiac. Marsilius Ficinus will have it that the loadstone follows its Arctic pole, and that iron follows the loadstone, and chaff follows amber: as for amber, why, that, mayhaps, follows the Antarctic pole: emptiest of dreams! Others have come down to rocks and I know not what "magnetic

60

mountains"! So has ever been the wont of man-kind: homely things are vile; things from abroad and things afar are dear to them and the object of longing. As for us, we are habitants of this very earth, and study it as cause of this mighty effect. Earth, the mother of all, hath these causes shut up in her recesses: all mag-netic movements are to be considered with re-spect to her law, position, constitution, verticí-ty, poles, equator, horizon, meridians, centre, periphery, diameter, and to the form of her whole inward substance. So hath the earth been ordered by the Supreme Artificer and by na-ture, that it shall have parts unlike in position, terminal points of an entire and absolute body, and such points dignified by distinct functions, whereby it shall itself take a fixed direction. For like as a loadstone, when in a suitable vessel it is floated on water, or when it is suspended in air by a slender thread, does by its native verticity, according to the magnetic laws, conform its poles to the poles of the common mother, so, were the earth to vary from her natural direc-tion and from her position in the universe, or were her poles to be pulled toward the rising or the setting sun, or other points whatsoever in the visible firmament (were that possible), they would recur again by a magnetic movement to north and south, and halt at the same points where now they stand. But why the terrestrial globe should seem constantly to turn one of its poles toward those points and toward Cynosura, or why her poles should vary from the poles of the ecliptic by 23 deg. 29 min., with some vari-ation not yet sufficiently studied by astronomers, that depends on the magnetic energy. The caus-es of the precession of the equinoxes and of the progression of the fixed stars, as well as of change in the declinations of the sun and the tropics, are traceable to magnetic forces: hence we have no further need of Thebit Bencora's "movement of trepidation," which is at wide variance with observations.[1] A rotating needle turns to conformity with the situation of the earth, and, though it be shaken oft, returns still to the same points. For in far northern climes, in latitude 70 to 80 deg. (whither in the milder season our seamen are wont to penetrate with-out injury from the cold), and in the middle regions, in the torrid zone under the equinoctial line, as also in all maritime regions and lands of the southern hemisphere, at the highest lati-tudes yet known, the magnetic needle ever finds its direction and ever tends in the same way

[1] Abú l'Hasan Thábet Ben Korrah, [Thebitius], born in Mesopotamia A. D. 835-836.

(barring difference of variation) on this side of the equator where we dwell and in the other, the southern part, which, though less known, has been to some extent explored by our sail-ors: and the lily of the mariner's compass ever points north. Of this, we are assured by the most illustrious navigators and by many intel-ligent seamen. The same was pointed out to me and confirmed by our most illustrious Neptune, Francis Drake, and by Thomas Candish [Cav-endish], that other world-explorer.

Our terrella teaches the same lesson. The proposition is demonstrated on a spherical load-stone. Let A, B be the poles; CD, an iron wire placed on the stone, always tends direct in the

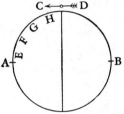

meridian to the poles A, B, whether the centre of the wire be in the middle line or equator of the stone, or whether it be in any other region between equator and poles, as H,G, F, E. So the point of a magnetized needle looks north on this side of the equator: on the other side the crotch is directed to the south; but the point or lily does not turn to the south below the equator, as somebody has thought. Some inexperienced persons, however, who, in distant regions be-low the equator, have at times seen the needle grow sluggish and less prompt, have deemed the distance from the Arctic pole or from the mag-netic rocks to be the cause. But they are very much mistaken, for it has the same power and adjusts itself as quickly to the meridian as the point of variation in southern regions as in nor-thern. Yet at times the movement appears to be slower, the point on which the compass needle is poised becoming in time, during a long voyage, rather blunt, or the magnetized needle itself having lost somewhat of its ac-quired force through age or from rusting. This, too, may be tested experimentally by poising the versorium of a sun-dial on a rather short-pointed needle rising perpendicularly out of the surface of the terrella. The magnetized needle turns to the poles of the terrella, and quits the earth's poles; for a general cause that is remote is overcome by a particular cause that is present and strong. Magnetized bodies incline of their own accord to the earth's position, and they conform to the terrella. Two loadstones of equal weight and force conform to the terrella in accordance with magnetic laws. Iron gets force from the loadstone and is made to conform to the magnetic movements. Therefore true direction is the movement of a magnetized body in the line of the earth's verticity toward the natural position and unition of both, their forms being in accord and supplying the forces. For we have, after many experiments in various ways, found that the disposing and ranging of the magnetized bodies depends on the differences of position, while the force that gives the motion is the one form common to both; also that in all magnetic bodies there is attraction and repulsion. For both the loadstone and the magnetized iron conform themselves, by rotation and by dip, to the common position of nature and the earth. And the earth's energy, with the force inhering in it as a whole, by pulling toward its poles and by repelling, arranges in order all magnetic bodies that are unattached and lying loose. For in all things do all magnetic bodies conform to the globe of earth in accordance with the same laws and in the same ways in which another loadstone or any magnetic body whatsoever conforms to the terrella.

CHAPTER 2. *Directive (or versorial) force, which we call verticity: what it is; how it resides in the loadstone; and how it is acquired when not naturally produced*

THE directive force, which by us is also called verticity, is a force distributed by the innate energy from the equator in both directions to the poles. That energy, proceeding north and south to the poles, produces the movement of direction, and produces also constant and permanent station in the system of nature, and that not in the earth alone but in all magnetic bodies also. Loadstone occurs either in a special vein or in iron mines, for, being a homogenic earth-substance possessing and conceiving a primary form, it becomes converted into or concreted with a stony body which, in addition to the prime virtues of the form, derives from different beds and mines, as from different matrices, various dissimilitudes and differences, and very many secondary qualities and varieties of its substance. A loadstone mined in this *débris* of the earth's surface and of its projections, whether it be (as sometimes found in China) entire in itself, or whether it be part of a considerable vein, gets from the earth its form and imitates the nature of the whole. All the inner

parts of the earth are in union and act in harmony, and produce direction to north and south. Yet the magnetic bodies that in the topmost parts of the earth attract one another are not true united parts of the whole, but are appendages and agnate parts that copy the nature of the whole; hence, when floating free on water, they take the direction they have in the terrestrial order of nature. We once had chiselled and dug out of its vein a loadstone 20 pounds in weight, having first noted and marked its extremities; then, after it had been taken out of the earth, we placed it on a float in water so it could freely turn about; straightway that extremity of it which in the mine looked north turned to the north in water and after a while there abode; for the extremity that in the mine looks north is austral and is attracted by the north parts of earth, just as in the case of iron, which takes verticity from the earth. Of these points we will treat later under the head of "Change of Verticity."

But different is the verticity of the inward parts of the earth that are perfectly united to it and that are not separated from the true substance of the earth by interposition of bodies, as are separated loadstones situated in the outer portion of the globe, where all is defective, spoilt, and irregular. Let *AB* be a loadstone mine, and between it and the uniform earthen globe suppose there are various earths and mixtures that in a manner separate the mine from the true globe of the earth. It is therefore informated by the earth's forces just as *CD*, a mass of iron, is in air; hence the extremity *B* of the mine or of any part thereof moves toward the north pole *G*, just as does *C*, the extremity of the mass of iron, but not *A* nor *D*. But with the part *EF*, which comes into existence continuous with the whole and which is not separated from it by any mixed earthy matter, the case

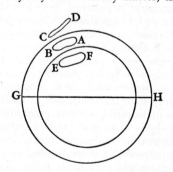

is different. For if the part *EF*, being taken out, were to be floated, it is not *E* that would turn to the north pole, but *F.* Thus, in those bodies which acquire verticity in the air, *C* is the south extremity and is attracted by the north pole *G.* In those which come into existence in the detrital outermost part of the earth, *B* is south, and so goes to the north pole, But these parts which, deep below, are of even birth with the earth, have their verticity regulated differently. For here *F* turns to the north parts of the earth, being a south part; and *E* to the south parts of the earth, being a north part. So the end *C* of the magnetic body *CD,* situate near the earth, turns to the north pole; the end *B* of the agnate body *BA* to the north; the end *E* of the inborn body *EF* to the south pole—as is proved by the following demonstration and as is required by all magnetic laws.

Describe a terrella with poles *A,B;* from its mass separate the small part *EF,* and suspend that by a fine thread in a cavity or pit in the terrella. *E* then does not seek the pole *A* but the pole *B,* and *F* turns to *A,* behaving quite differently from the iron bar *CD;* for, there, *C,* touching a north part of the terrella, becomes magnetized and turns to *A,* not to *B.* But here it is to be remarked that if pole *A* of the terrella were to be turned toward the southern part of the earth, still the end *E* of the solitary part cut

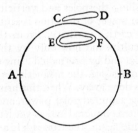

out of the terrella and not brought near the rest of the stone would turn to the south; but the end *C* of the iron bar would, if placed outside the magnetic field, turn to the north. Suppose that in the unbroken terrella the part *EF* gave the same direction as the whole; now break it off and suspend it by a thread, and *E* will turn to *B* and *F* to *A.* Thus parts that when joined with the whole have the same verticity with it, on being separated take the opposite; for opposite parts attract opposite parts, yet this is not a true opposition, but a supreme concordance and a true and genuine conformance of magnetic bodies in nature, if they be but divided and separated; for the parts thus divided must needs be carried away some distance above the whole, as later will appear. Magnetic bodies seek formal unity, and do not so much regard their

own mass. Hence the part *FE* is not attracted into its pit, but the moment it wanders abroad and is away from it, is attracted by the opposite pole. But if the part *FE* be again placed in its pit or be brought near without any media in-

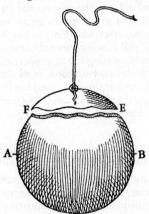

terposed, it acquires the original combination, and, being again a united portion of the whole, co-operates with the whole and readily clings in its pristine position, while *E* remains looking toward *A* and *F* toward *B,* and there they rest unchanging.

The case is the same when we divide a loadstone into two equal parts from pole to pole. In the figure, a spherical stone is divided into two equal parts along the axis *AB;* hence, whether the surface *AB* be in one of the two parts supine (as in the first diagram), or prone in both (as in the second), the end *A* tends to *B.* But it is also to be understood that the point *B* does not always tend sure to *A,* for, after the division, the verticity goes to other points, for example to *F, G,* as is shown in Chapter 14 of this Third Book. *LM,* too, is now the axis of the two halves, and *AB* is no longer the axis; for, once a magnetic body is divided, the sever-

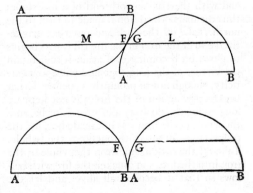

al parts are integral and magnetic, and have vertices proportional to their mass, new poles arising at each end on division. But the axis and poles ever follow the track of a meridian, because the force proceeds along the stone's meridian circles from the equinoctial to the poles invariably, in virtue of an innate energy that belongs to matter, owing to the long and secular position, and bearings toward the earth's poles, of a body possessing the fit properties; and such body is endowed with force from the earth for ages and ages continuously, and has from its first beginning stood firmly and constantly turned toward fixed and determinate points of the same.

CHAPTER 3. *How iron acquires verticity from the loadstone, and how this verticity is lost or altered*

AN oblong piece of iron, on being stroked with a loadstone, receives forces magnetic, not corporeal, nor inhering in or consisting with any body, as has been shown in the chapters on coition. Plainly, a body briskly rubbed on one end with a loadstone, and left for a long time in contact with the stone, receives no property of stone, gains nothing in weight; for if you weigh in the smallest and most accurate scales of a goldsmith a piece of iron before it is touched by the loadstone you will find that after the rubbing it has the same precise weight, neither less nor more. And if you wipe the magnetized iron with cloths, or if you rub it with sand or with a whetstone, it loses naught at all of its acquired properties. For the force is diffused through the entire body and through its inmost parts, and can in no wise be washed or wiped away. Test it, therefore, in fire, that fiercest tyrant of nature. Take a piece of iron the length of your hand and as thick as a goosequill; pass it through a suitable round piece of cork and lay it on the surface of water, and note the end of the bar that looks north. Rub that end with the true smooth end of a loadstone; thus the magnetized iron is made to turn to the north. Take off the cork and put that magnetized end of the iron in the fire till it just begins to glow; on becoming cool again it will retain the virtues of the loadstone and will show verticity, though not so promptly as before, either because the action of the fire was not kept up long enough to do away all its force, or because the whole of the iron was not made hot, for the property is diffused throughout the whole. Take off the cork again, drop the whole of the iron into the fire, and quicken the fire with bellows so that it becomes all alive, and let the

glowing iron remain for a little while. After it has grown cool again (but in cooling it must not remain in one position) put iron and cork once more in water, and you shall see that it has lost its acquired verticity. All this shows how difficult it is to do away with the polar property conferred by the loadstone. And were a small loadstone to remain for as long in the same fire, it too would lose its force. Iron, because it is not so easily destroyed or burnt as very many loadstones, retains its powers better, and after they are lost may get them back again from a loadstone; but a burnt loadstone cannot be restored.

Now this iron, stripped of its magnetic form, moves in a way different from any other iron, for it has lost the polar property; and though before contact with the loadstone it may have had a movement to the north, and after contact toward the south, now it turns to no fixed and determinate point; but afterward, very slowly, after a long time, it turns unsteadily toward the poles, having received some measure of force from the earth. There is, I have said, a twofold cause of direction—one native in the loadstone and in iron, and the other in the earth, derived from the energy that disposes things. For this reason it is that after iron has lost the faculty of distinguishing the poles and verticity, a tardy and feeble power of direction is acquired anew from the earth's verticity. From this we see how difficultly, and how only by the action of intense heat and by protracted firing of the iron till it becomes soft, the magnetic force impressed in it is done away. When this firing has suppressed the acquired polar power, and the same is now quite conquered and as yet has not been called to life again, the iron is left a wanderer, and quite incapable of direction.

But we have to inquire further how it is that iron remains possessed of verticity. It is clear that the presence of a loadstone strongly affects and alters the nature of the iron, also that it draws the iron to itself with wonderful promptness. Nor is it the part rubbed only, but the whole of the iron, that is affected by the friction (applied at one end only), and therefrom the iron acquires a permanent though unequal power, as is thus proved.

Rub with a loadstone a piece of iron wire on one end so as to magnetize it and to make it turn to the north; then cut off part of it, and you shall see it move to the north as before, though weakly. For it is to be understood that the loadstone awakens in the whole mass of the iron a strong verticity (provided the iron rod be not too long), a pretty strong verticity in the shorter piece throughout its entire length, and, as long as the iron remains in contact with the loadstone, one somewhat stronger still. But when the iron is removed from contact it becomes much weaker, especially in the end not touched by the loadstone. And as a long rod, one end of which is thrust into a fire and made red, is very hot at that end, less hot in the parts adjoining and midway, and at the farther end may be held in the hand, that end being only warm—so the magnetic force grows less from the excited end to the other; but it is there in an instant, and is not introduced in any interval of time nor successively, as when heat enters iron, for the moment the iron is touched by the loadstone it is excited throughout. For example, take an unmagnetized iron rod, 4 or 5 inches long: the instant you simply touch with a loadstone either end, the opposite end straightway, in the twinkling of the eye, repels or attracts a needle, however quickly brought to it.

CHAPTER 4. *Why magnetized iron takes opposite verticity; and why iron touched by the true north side of the stone moves to the earth's north, and when touched by the true south side to the earth's south: iron rubbed with the north point of the stone does not turn to the south, nor vice versa, as all writers on the loadstone have erroneously thought*

It has already been shown that the north part of a loadstone does not attract the north part of another stone, but the south part, and that it repels the north end of another stone applied to its north end. That general loadstone, the terrestrial globe, does with its inborn force dispose magnetized iron, and the magnetic iron too does the same with its inborn force, producing movement and determining the direction. For whether we compare together and experiment on two loadstones, or a loadstone and piece of iron, or iron and iron, or earth and loadstone, or earth and iron conformated by the earth or deriving force from the energy of a loadstone, of necessity the forces and movements of each and all agree and harmonize in the same way.

But the question arises, why does iron touched with loadstone take a direction of movement toward the earth's opposite pole and not toward that pole of earth toward which looked the pole of the loadstone with which it was magnetized? Iron and loadstone, we have said, are of the same primary nature: iron when joined to a loadstone becomes as it were one body with it, and not only is one extremity of the iron altered, but the rest of its parts are af-

fected. Let *A* be the north pole of a loadstone to which is attached the tip of an iron pointer: the tip is now the south part of the iron, because it is contiguous to the north part of the stone;

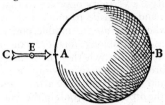

the crotch of the pointer becomes north. For were this contiguous magnetic body separated from the pole of the terrella or the parts nigh the pole, the other extremity (or the end which when there was conjunction was in contact with the north part of the stone) is south, while the other end is north. So, too, if a magnetized needle be divided into any number of parts however minute, those separated parts will take the same direction which they had before division. Hence, as long as the point of the needle remains at *A*, the north pole, it is not austral, but is, as it were, part of a whole; but when it is taken away from the stone it is south, because on being rubbed it tended toward the north parts of the stone, and the crotch (the other end of the pointer) is north. The loadstone and the pointer constitute one body: *B* is the south pole of the whole mass; *C* (the crotch) is the north extremity of the whole. Even divide the needle in two at *E*, and *E* will be south as regards the crotch, *E* will also be north with reference to *B*. *A* is the true north pole of the stone, and is attracted by the south pole of the earth. The end of a piece of iron touched with the true north part of the stone is south, and turns to the north pole of the stone *A* if it be near; if it be at a distance from the stone, it turns to the earth's north. So whenever iron is magnetized it tends (if free and unrestrained) to the portion of the earth opposite the part toward which inclines the loadstone at which it was rubbed. For verticity always enters the iron if only it be magnetized at either

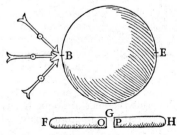

end. Hence all the needle points at B acquire the same verticity after being separated, but it is the opposite verticity to that of the pole B of the stone; and all the crotches in the present figure have a verticity opposite to that of the pole E, and are made to move and are seized by E when they are in suitable position. The case is as in the oblong stone FH, cut in two at G, where F and H, whether the stone be whole or be broken, move to opposite poles of the earth, and O and P mutually attract, one being north, the other south. For if in the whole stone H was south and F north, then in the divided stone P will be north with respect to H and O, south with respect to F; so, too, F and H tend toward connection if they be turned round a little, and at length they come together. But if the division be made meridionally, *i.e.*, along the line of the meridian and not on any parallel circle, then the two parts turn about and A pulls B, and the end B is attracted to A, until, being

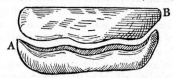

turned round, they form connection and are held together. For this reason, iron bars placed on parallels near the equator of a terrella whose poles are AB, do not combine and do not cohere firmly; but when placed alongside on a

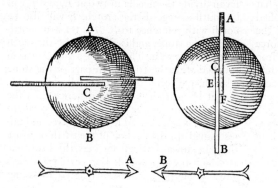

meridian line, at once they become firmly joined, not only on the stone and near it, but at any distance within the magnetic field of the controlling loadstone. Thus they are held fast together at E, but not at C of the other figure. For the opposite ends C and F of the bars, come together and cohere, as the ends A and B of the stone did. But the ends are opposite, because the bars proceed from opposite poles and parts

of the terrella; and C is south as regards the north pole A, and F is north as regards the south pole B. Similarly, too, they cohere if the rod C (not too long) be moved further toward A, and the rod F toward B, and they will be joined on the terrella just as A and B of the divided stone were joined. But now if the magnetized needle point A be north, and if with this you touch and rub the point B of another needle that rotates freely but is not magnetized, B will be north and will turn to the south. But if with the north point B you touch still another new rotary needle on its point, that point again will be south, and will turn to the north: a piece of iron not only takes from the loadstone, if it be a good loadstone, the forces needful for itself, but also, after receiving them, infuses them into another piece, and that into a third, always with due regard to magnetic law.

In all these our demonstrations it is ever to be borne in mind that the poles of the stone as of the iron, whether magnetized or not, are always in fact and in their nature opposite to the pole toward which they tend, and that they are thus named by us, as has been already said. For, everywhere, that is north which tends to the south of the earth or of a terrella, and that is south which turns to the north of the stone. Points that are north are attracted by the south part of the earth, and hence when floated they tend to the south. A piece of iron rubbed with the north end of a loadstone becomes south at the other end and tends always (if it be within the field of a loadstone and near) to the north part of the loadstone, and to the north part of the earth if it be free to move and stand alone at a distance from the loadstone. The north pole A of a loadstone turns to the south of the earth, G; a needle magnetized on its point by the part A follows A, because the point has been made south. But the needle C, placed at a distance from the loadstone, turns its point to the earth's north, F, for that point was made south by contact with the north part of the loadstone. Thus the ends magnetized by the north part of the stone become south, or

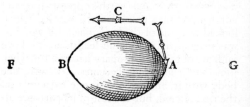

are magnetized southerly, and tend to the earth's north; the ends rubbed with the south pole become north, or are magnetized northerly, and tend to the earth's south.

CHAPTER 5. *Of magnetizing stones of different shapes*

OF a magnetized piece of iron one extemity is north, the other south, and midway is the limit of verticity: such limit, in the globe of the terrella or in a globe of iron, is the equinoctial circle. But if an iron ring be rubbed at one part with a loadstone, then one of the poles is at the point of friction, and the other pole at the opposite side; the magnetic force divides the ring into two parts by a natural line of demarkation, which, though not in form, is in its power and effect equinoctial. But if a straight rod be bent into the form of a ring without welding and unition of the ends, and it be touched in the middle with a loadstone, the ends will be both of the same verticity. Take a ring, whole and unbroken, rubbed with a loadstone at one point; then cut it across at the opposite point and stretch it out straight: again both ends will be of the same verticity, just like an iron rod magnetized in the middle, or a ring not cohering at the joint.

CHAPTER 6. *What seems to be a contrary movement of magnetic bodies is the regular tendence to union*

IN magnetic bodies nature ever tends to union —not merely to confluence and agglomeration, but to agreement, so that the force that causes rotation and bearing toward the poles may not be disordered, as is shown in various ways in the following example. Let *CD* be an unbroken magnetic body, with *C* looking toward *B*, the

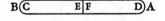

earth's north, *B* and *D* toward *A*, the earth's south. Now cut it in two in the middle, in the equator, and then *E* will tend to *A* and *F* to *B*. For, as in the whole, so in the divided stone, nature seeks to have these bodies united; hence the end *E* properly and eagerly comes together again with *F*, and the two combine, but *E* is never joined to *D* nor *F* to *C*, for, in that case, *C* would have to turn, in opposition, to nature, to *A*, the south, or *D* to *B*, the north—which

were abnormal and incongruous. Separate the halves of the stone and turn *D* toward *C*: they come together nicely and combine. For *D* tends to the south, as before, and *C* to the north; *E* and *F*, which in the mine were connate parts, are now greatly at variance, for they do not come together on account of material affinity, but take movement and tendence from the form. Hence the ends, whether they be conjoined or separate, tend in the same way, in accordance with magnetic law, toward the earth's poles in the first figure of the stone, whether unbroken or divided as in the second figure; and *FE* of the second figure, when the two parts come together and form one body, is as perfect a magnetic mass as was *CD* when first produced in the mine; and *FE*, placed on a float, turn to the earth's poles, and conform thereto in the same way as the unbroken stone.

This agreement of the magnetic form is seen in the shapes of plants. Let *AB* be a branch of osier or other tree that sprouts readily; and let

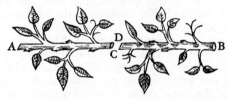

A be the upper part of the branch and *B* the part rootward. Divide the branch at *CD*. Now, the extremity *CD*, if skilfully grafted again on *D*, begins to grow, just as *B* and *A*, when united become consolidated and germinate. But if *D* be grafted in *A*, or *C* on *B*, they are at variance and grow not at all, but one of them dies because of the preposterous and unsuitable apposition, the vegetative force, which tends in a fixed direction, being now forced into a contrary one.

CHAPTER 7. *A determinate verticity and a directive power make magnetic bodies accord, and not an attractional or a repulsative force, nor strong coition alone or unition*

IN the equinoctial circle *A* there is no coition of the ends of a piece of iron wire with the terrella; at the poles the coition is very strong. The greater the distance from the equinoctial the stronger is the coition with the terrella itself, and with any part thereof, not with the pole only. But the pieces of iron are not made to stand because of any peculiar attracting force or any strong combined force, but because of the common energy that gives to them direction, conformity, and rotation. For in the re-

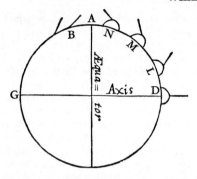

gion *B* not even the minutest bit of iron that weighs almost nothing can be reared to the perpendicular by the strongest of loadstones, but adheres obliquely. And just as the terrella attracts variously, with unlike force, magnetic bodies, so, too, an iron hump (or protuberance —*nasus*) attached to the stone has a different potency according to the latitude: thus the hump *L*, as being strongly adherent, will carry a greater weight than *M*, and *M* a heavier weight than *N*. But neither does the hump rear to perpendicular a bit of iron except at the poles, as is shown in the figure. The hump *L* will hold and lift from the ground two ounces of solid iron, yet it is unable to make a piece of iron wire weighing two grains stand erect; but that would not be the case if verticity arose from strong attraction, or more properly coition, or from unition.

CHAPTER 8. *Of disagreements between pieces of iron on the same pole of a loadstone; how they may come together and be conjoined*

If two pieces of iron wire or two needles above the poles of a terrella adhere, when about to be raised to the perpendicular they repel each other at their upper ends and present a furcate appearance; and if one end be forcibly pushed toward the other, that other retreats and bends back to avoid the association, as shown in the

figure. *A* and *B*, small iron rods, adhere to the pole obliquely because of their nearness to each other: either one alone would stand erect and perpendicular. The reason of the obliquity is that *A* and *B*, having the same verticity, retreat from each other and fly apart. For if *C* be the north pole of a terrella, then the ends *A* and *B* of the rods are also north, while the ends in contact with and held fast by the pole *C* are both south. But let the rods be rather long (say two finger-breadths), and let them be held together by force: then they cohere and stand together like friends, nor can they be separated save by force, for they are held fast to each other magnetically, and are no longer two distinct terminals but one only and one body, like a piece of wire bent double and made to stand erect.

But here we notice another curious fact, *viz.*, that if the rods be rather short, not quite a finger's breadth in length, or as long as a barleycorn, they will not unite on any terms, nor will they stand up together at all, for in short pieces of wire the verticity at the ends farthest from the terrella is stronger and the magnetic strife more intense than in longer pieces. Therefore they do not permit any association, any fellowship. Again, if two light pieces of wire, *A* and *B*, be suspended by a very slender thread of

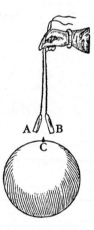

silk filaments not twisted but laid together,[1] and held at the distance of one barley-corn's length from the loadstone, then the opposite ends, *A* and *B*, situate within the sphere of influence above the pole, go a little apart for the same reason, except when they are very near the pole *C* of the stone: in that position the stone attracts them to the one point.

[1] See Book I, 12.

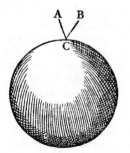

CHAPTER 9. *Directional figures showing the varieties of rotation*

HAVING now sufficiently shown, according to magnetic laws and principles the demonstrable cause of the motion toward determinate points, we have next to show the movements. On a spherical loadstone having the poles *A*, *B*, place a rotating needle whose point has been magnetized by the pole *A*: that point will be directed steadily toward *A* and attracted by *A*,

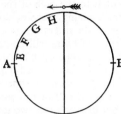

because, having been magnetized by *A*, it accords truly and combines with *A*; and yet it is said to be opposite because when the needle is separated from the stone it moves to the opposite part of earth from that toward which the loadstone's pole *A* moves. For if *A* be the north pole of the terrella, the point of the needle is its south end, and its other end, the crotch, points to *B*: thus *B* is the loadstone's south pole, while the crotch of the needle is the needle's north end. So, too, the point is attracted by *EFGH* and by every part of a meridian from the equator to the pole, because of the power of directing; and when the needle is in those places on the meridian the point is directed toward *A*; for it is not the point *A* but the whole loadstone that makes the needle turn, as does the whole earth in the case of magnetic bodies turning to the earth.

The figure following shows the magnetic directions in the right sphere of a loadstone and in the right sphere of the earth, also the polar directions to the perpendicular of the poles. All the points of the versorium have been magnetized by pole *A*. All the points are directed toward *A* except the one that is repelled by *B*.

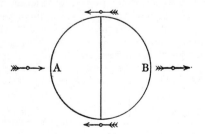

The next figure shows horizontal directions above the body of the loadstone. All the points

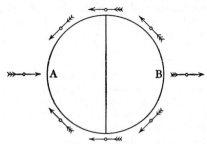

that have been made south by rubbing with the north pole or some point around the north pole *A*, turn to the pole *A* and turn away from the south pole *B*, toward which all the crotches are directed.

I call the direction horizontal because it coincides with the plane of the horizon; for nautical and horological instruments are so constructed that the needle shall be suspended or supported in equilibrium on a sharp point, which prevents the dip of the needle, as we shall explain later. And in this way it best serves man's use, noting and distinguishing all the points of the horizon and all the winds. Otherwise in every oblique sphere (whether terrella or earth) the needle and all magnetized bodies would dip below the horizon, and, at the poles, the directions would be perpendicular, as appears from our account of the dip.

The next figure shows a spherical loadstone cut in two at the equator; all the points of the needles have been magnetized by pole *A*. The points are directed in the centre of the earth and

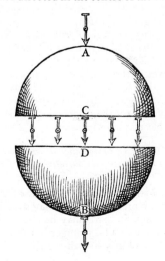

between the two halves of the terrella, divided in the plane of the equator as shown in the diagram. The case would be the same if the division were made through the plane of a tropic and the separation and distance of the two parts were as above, with the division and separation of the loadstone through the plane of the equinoctial. For the points are repelled by *C*, attracted by *D*, and the needles are parallel, the poles or the verticity at both ends controlling them.

The next figure shows half of a terrella by itself, and its directions differing from the directions given by the two parts in the preceding figure, which were placed alongside. All the

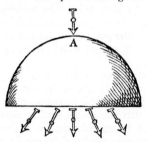

points have been magnetized by *A*; all the crotches below, except the middle one, tend not in a right line but obliquely, to the loadstone, for the pole is in the middle of the plane that before was the plane of the equinoctial. All points magnetized by parts of the loadstone away from the pole move to the pole (just as though they had been magnetized by the pole itself) and not to the place of friction, wherever that may be in the whole stone at any latitude betwixt pole and equator. And for this reason there are only two differences of regions—they are north and south as well in the terrella as in the great globe of earth; and there is no east, no west place, no regions truly eastern or western, but, with respect to each other, east and west are simply terms signifying toward the east or west part of the heavens. Hence Ptolemy seems in the *Quadripartitum* to err in laying out eastern and western divisions, to which he improperly annexes the planets; he is followed by the rabble of philosophasters and astrologers.

CHAPTER 10. *Of the mutation of verticity and magnetic properties, or of the alteration of the force awakened by the loadstone*

IRON excited by the magnetic influx has a verticity that is pretty strong, yet not so stable but that the opposite parts may be altered by the friction not only of a stronger but of the same loadstone, and may lose all their first verticity

and take on the opposite. Procure a piece of iron wire and with the self-same pole of a loadstone rub each end equally; pass the wire through a suitable cork float and put it in the water. Then one end of the wire will look toward a pole of the earth whereto that end of the loadstone does not look. But which end of the wire? It will be just the one that was rubbed last. Now rub with the same pole the other end again, and straightway that end will turn in the opposite direction. Again rub the end that first pointed to the pole of the loadstone, and at once that, having, as it were, obtained its orders, will go in the direction opposite to the one it took last. Thus you will be able to alter again and again the property of the iron, and the extremity of it that is last rubbed is master. And now merely hold for a while the north end of the stone near the north end of the wire that was last rubbed, not bringing the two into contact, but at the distance of one, two, or even three finger-breadths, if the stone be a powerful one; again the iron will change its property and will turn to the opposite direction: so it will, too, though rather more feebly, if the loadstone be four finger-breadths away. The same results are had in all these experiments whether you employ the south or the north part of the stone. Verticity can also be acquired or altered with plates of gold, silver, and glass between the loadstone and the end of the piece of iron or wire, provided the stone be rather powerful, though the plates of metal be touched neither by the stone nor by the iron. And these changes of verticity occur in cast-iron. But what is imparted or excited by one pole of the loadstone is expelled and annulled by the other, which confers new force. Nor is a stronger loadstone needed to make the iron put off the weaker and sluggish force and to put on a new. Neither is the iron "made drunken" (*inebriatur*) by equal forces of loadstone, so that it becomes "undecided and neutral," as Baptista Porta maintains. But by one same loadstone, and by loadstones endowed with equal power and strength, the force is altered, changed, incited, renewed, driven out. The loadstone itself, however, is not robbed, by friction with another bigger or stronger stone, of its property and verticity, nor is it turned, when on a float, to the opposite direction or to another pole different from that toward which, by its own nature and verticity, it tends. For forces that are innate and long implanted inhere more closely, nor do they easily retire from their ancient seats; and what is the growth of a long period of time is not in an instant reduced to nothing unless that in which it inheres perishes. Nevertheless change comes about in a considerable interval of time, *e.g.*, a year or two, sometimes in a few months—to wit, when a weaker loadstone remains applied, in a way contrary to the order of nature, to a stronger, *i.e.*, with the north pole of one touching the north pole of the other, or the south of one touching the other's south. Under such conditions, in the lapse of time the weaker force declines.

CHAPTER 11. *Of friction of iron with the mid parts of a loadstone between the poles, and at the equinoctial circle of a terrella*

TAKE a piece of iron wire not magnetized, three finger-widths long ('twill be better if its acquired verticity be rather weak or deformed by some process); touch and rub it with the equator of the terrella exactly on the equinoctial line along its whole tract and length, only one end, or both ends, or the whole of the iron, being brought into contact. The wire thus rubbed, run through a cork and float it in water. It will go wandering about without any acquired verticity, and the verticity it had before will be disordered. But if by chance it should be borne in its wavering toward the poles, it will be feebly held still by the earth's poles, and finally will be endowed with verticity by the energy of the earth.

the causes of the magnetic virtue existing in manufactured iron not magnetized by the loadstone. The loadstone and iron present and exhibit to us wonderful subtile properties. It has already oft been shown that iron not excited by the loadstone turns to north and south; further, that it possesses verticity, *i.e.*, distinct poles proper and peculiar to itself, even as the loadstone or iron rubbed with the loadstone. This seemed to us at first strange and incredible: the metal, iron, is smelted out of the ore in the furnace, flows out of the furnace, and hardens in a great mass; the mass is cut up in great workshops and drawn out into iron bars, and from these again the smith fashions all sorts of necessary implements and objects of iron. Thus the same mass is variously worked and transformed into many shapes. What, then, is it that preserves the verticity, or whence is it derived? First take a mass of iron as produced in the first iron-works. Get a smith to shape a mass weighing two or three ounces, on the anvil, into an iron bar one palm or nine inches long. Let the smith stand facing the north, with back to the south, so that as he hammers the red-hot iron it may have a motion of extension northward; and so let him complete the task at one or two heatings of the iron (if needed); but ever while he hammers and lengthens it, have him keep the

CHAPTER 12. *How verticity exists in all smelted iron not excited by the loadstone*

HITHERTO we have declared the natural and innate causes and the powers acquired through the loadstone; but now we are to investigate

same point of the iron looking north, and lay the finished bar aside in the same direction. In this way fashion two, three, or more, yea one hundred or four hundred bars: it is plain that all the bars so hammered out toward the north and so laid down while cooling will rotate round their centres and when afloat (being passed through suitable pieces of cork) will move about in water, and, when the end is duly reached, will point north. And as an iron bar takes verticity from the direction in which it lies while being stretched, or hammered, or pulled, so too will iron wire when drawn out toward any point of the horizon between east and south or between south and west, or conversely. Nevertheless, when the iron is directed and stretched rather to a point east or west, it takes almost no verticity, or a very faint verticity. This verticity is acquired chiefly through the lengthening. But when inferior iron ore, in which no magnetic properties are apparent, is put in the fire (its position with reference to the world's poles being noted) and there heated for eight or ten hours, then cooled away from the fire and in the same position with regard to the poles, it acquires verticity according to its position during heating and cooling.

Let a bar of iron be brought to a white heat in a strong fire, in which it lies meridionally, *i.e.*, along the track of a meridian circle; then take it out of the fire and let it cool and return to the original temperature, lying the while in the same position as before: it will come about that, through the like extremities having been directed toward the same poles of the earth, it will acquire verticity; and that the extremity that looked north when the bar, before the firing, was floated in water by means of a cork, if now the same end during the firing and the cooling looked southward, will point to the south. If perchance the turning to the pole should at any time be weak and uncertain, put the bar in the fire again, take it out when it has reached white heat, cool it perfectly as it lies pointing in the direction of the pole from which you wish it to take verticity, and the verticity will be acquired. Let it be heated again, lying in the contrary direction, and while yet white-hot lay it down till it cools; for, from the position in cooling (the earth's verticity acting on it), verticity is infused into the iron and it turns toward points opposite to the former verticity. So the extremity that before looked north now turns to the south. For these reasons and in these ways does the north pole of the earth give to that extremity of the iron which is turned toward it south verticity; hence, too, that extremity is attracted by the north pole. And here it is to be observed that this happens with iron not only when it cools lying in the plane of the horizon, but also at any inclination thereto, even almost up to perpendicular to the centre

of the earth. Thus heated iron more quickly gets energy (strength) and verticity from the earth in the very process of returning to soundness in its renascence, so to speak (wherein it is transformated), than when it simply rests in position. This experiment is best made in winter and in a cold atmosphere, when the metal returns more surely to the natural temperature than in summer and in warm climates.

Let us see also what position alone, without fire and heat, and what mere giving to the iron a direction toward the earth's poles may do. Iron bars that for a long time—twenty years or more—have lain fixed in the north and south position, as bars are often fixed in buildings and in glass windows—such bars, in the lapse of time, acquire verticity, and whether suspended in air or floated by corks on water turn to the pole toward which they used to be directed, and magnetically attract and repel iron in equilibrium; for great is the effect of long-continued direction of a body toward the poles. This, though made clear by plain experiment, gets confirmation for what we find in a letter written in Italian and appended to a work by Master Philip Costa, of Mantua, also in Italian, *Of the Compounding of Antidotes*, which, translated, is as follows: "At Mantua, an apothecary showed to me a piece of iron completely turned to loadstone, so attracting other iron that it might be compared to a loadstone. But this piece of iron, after it had for a long time supported a terra-cotta ornament on the tower of the church of San Agostino at Rimini, was at last bent by the force of the winds and so remained for ten years. The friars, wishing to have it restored to its original shape, gave it to a blacksmith, and in the smithy Master Giulio Cesare, prominent surgeon, discovered that it resembled loadstone and attracted iron. The effect was produced by long-continued lying in the direction of the poles. It is well, therefore, to recall what has already been laid down with regard to alteration of verticity, *viz.*, how that the poles of iron bars are changed when a loadstone simply presents its pole to them and faces them even from some distance. Surely in a like way does that great loadstone the earth affect iron and change verticity. For albeit the iron does not touch the earth's pole nor any magnetic portion of the earth, still the verticity is acquired and altered —not that the earth's pole, that identical point lying thirty-nine degrees of latitude, so great a number of miles, away from this City of London, changes the verticity, but that the entire deeper magnetic mass of the earth which rises between us and the pole, and over which stands the iron—that this, with the energy residing within the field of the magnetic force, the matter of the entire orb conspiring, produces verticity in bodies. For everywhere within the sphere of the magnetic force does the earth's magnetic effluence reign, everywhere does it alter bodies. But those bodies that are most like to it and most closely allied, it rules and controls, as loadstone and iron. For this reason it is not altogether superstitious and silly in many of our affairs and businesses to note the positions and configurations of countries, the points of the horizon and the locations of the stars. For as when the babe is given forth to the light from the mother's womb and gains the power of respiration and certain animal functions, and as the planets and other heavenly bodies, according to their positions in the universe and according to their configuration with the horizon and the earth, do then impart to the newcomer special and peculiar qualities; so a piece of iron, while it is being wrought and lengthened, is affected by the general cause, the earth, to wit; and while it is coming back from the fiery state to its original temperature it becomes imbued with a special verticity according to its position. Long bars have sometimes the same verticity at both ends, and hence they have a wavering and ill-regulated motion on account of their length and of the aforesaid manipulations, just as when an iron wire four feet long is rubbed at both ends with one same pole of a loadstone.

CHAPTER 13. *Why no other bodies save the magnetic are imbued with verticity by friction with a loadstone; and why no body not magnetic can impart and awaken that force*

WOOD floating on water never turns by its own forces toward the poles of the world save by chance: so neither threads of gold, silver, copper, zinc, lead, nor glass, when passed through cork and floated, have ever sure direction; and, therefore, when rubbed with a loadstone they show neither poles nor points of variation; for bodies that do not of their own accord turn toward the poles and are not obedient to the earth are in no wise governed by the loadstone's touch; neither has the energy of the loadstone entrance into their interior, nor are their forms excited magnetically; nor, if the energy did enter in, could it effect aught, for the reason that there are no primary qualities in such bodies, mixed as they are with a variety of efflorescent humours and degenerate from the primal prop-

erty of the globe. On the other hand the properties of iron which are primal are awakened by approach of a loadstone: like brute animals and men when awakened out of sleep, the properties of iron now move and put forth their strength.

Here we must express wonder at a manifest error of Baptista Porta, who, though he properly refuses assent to the inveterate falsehood about a force the opposite of the magnetic, imparts a still falser opinion, to wit that iron rubbed with diamond turns to the north. "If," he writes, "we rub an iron needle on diamond, and then put it in a boat or on a straw or suspend it properly with a thread, at once it turns to the north like iron rubbed on a loadstone, or perhaps a little more sluggishly. Nay—and this is worthy of remark—the opposite part, like the loadstone itself at its south end, repels iron, and when we experimented with a multitude of small iron rods in water, they all stood at equal distances apart and pointed north." Now this is contrary to our magnetic rules; and hence we made the experiment ourselves with seventy-five diamonds in presence of many witnesses, employing a number of iron bars and pieces of wire, manipulating them with the greatest care while they floated in water, supported by corks; yet never was it granted me to see the effect mentioned by Porta. He was led astray by the verticity of the iron in the bars or wires got from the earth (as shown above); the iron of itself tended toward its determinate pole, and Porta, ignorant of this, supposed the thing was done by the diamond. But let searchers of the things of nature beware lest they be further deluded by their own faultily observed experiments, and lest, with errors and blunders, they throw into confusion the republic of letters. Diamond is sometimes called siderite, not because it is ferruginous or that it attracts iron, but on account of its glister, like that of shining iron; this brilliance is possessed by the finest diamonds. On account of this confusion of names many effects are credited to diamond that in fact belong to the loadstone siderite.[1]

CHAPTER 14. *The position of a loadstone, now above, anon beneath, a magnetic body suspended in equilibrium, alters neither the force nor the verticity of the magnetic body*

THIS point we may not rightly pass by, because we must correct an error that has lately arisen out of a faulty observation of Baptista Porta; out of this erroneous judgment, Porta, by vain

[1] See Book I. 2.

repetition, makes three chapters, *viz.*, the eighth, the thirty-first, and the sixty-second. Now, if a loadstone or a piece of iron suspended in equilibrium or floating in water is attracted or controlled by another piece of iron or another loadstone held above it, the stone or the iron does not turn to the opposite direction when you apply the second iron or stone beneath; on the contrary, the ends of the floating loadstone or of the floating iron will ever turn to the same points of the stone, however the loadstone or the iron may be suspended in equilibrium or whether they be mounted on a point so that they may revolve freely. Porta was led into error by the uneven shape of some loadstone or by the fact that he did not manage the experiment aright. Thus he is badly mistaken, thinking it fair to infer that, as the loadstone has a north and a south pole, it has also an east and a west, a superior and an inferior, pole. So do many vain imaginations arise out of mistakes committed and accepted as true judgments.

CHAPTER 15. *The poles, equator, centre, are permanent and stable in the unbroken loadstone; when it is reduced in size and a part taken away, they vary and occupy other positions*

LET *AB* be a terrella, *E* its centre, *DF* its diameter (and also its equinoctial circle). If you cut out a piece (for instance along the Arctic circle) *GH*, it is evident that the pole which before was at *A* now has its seat at *I*. But the centre

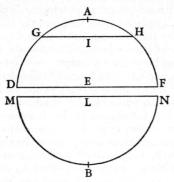

and the equinoctial circle recede only toward *B*, so as always to be in the middle of the mass that remains between the plane of the Arctic circle *GIH* and the Antarctic pole *B*. Thus the segment of the terrella between the plane of the former equinoctial circle *DEF* (that is of the equinoctial circle which existed before the part was cut away) and the newly acquired equator *MLN* will always be equal to one half of the part cut off, *GIHA*. But if the part be

cut from the side *CD* then the poles and the axis will not be in the line *AB* but in *EF*; and the axis is changed in the same proportion as

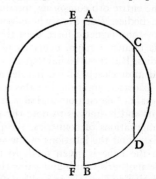

the equator in the previous figure. For these points of forces and of energy, or rather these terminals of forces that flow from the entire form, are moved forward by change of mass or of figure; as all these points result from the joint action of the whole and of all the parts united, and verticity or polarity is not a property innate in the part or in any fixed point, but a tendency of the force to such part. And as a terrella dug out of the earth has no longer the poles and the equator of the earth but special poles and equator of its own, so, too, if the terrella be cut in two again, these points and distinctions of its forms and powers migrate to other parts. But if the loadstone be in any way divided either on the parallels or on the meridians so that in consequence of the change of its shape either the poles or the equator migrate to other seats, then if the part that has been cut off be but set in its natural position and conjoined to the rest, though they be not cemented or otherwise fastened together, the terminal points go back again to the former places as though no part of the body had been cut away. When the body is whole the form remains whole; but when the mass of the body is reduced, a new whole results, and a new wholeness necessarily arises in each minutest piece of loadstone, even in magnetic gravel and fine sand.

CHAPTER 16. *If the south part of a loadstone have a part broken off, somewhat of power is taken away from the north part also*

FOR though the south part of magnetic iron is attracted by the north part of the loadstone, still the south part of the stone does not reduce but increases the power of the north part. Hence if a loadstone be cut and divided at the Arctic circle, or at the tropic of Cancer, or at the equator, the south part does not so powerfully attract at its pole as before; for a new whole arises and the equator leaves its former place and advances poleward, because of the division of the stone. In the former state, inasmuch as the opposite part of the stone beyond the plane of the equator increases the mass, it also strengthens the verticity and the force and the movement toward unition.

CHAPTER 17. *Of the use of rotary needles and their advantages; how the directive iron rotary needles of sundials and the needles of the mariner's compass are to be rubbed with loadstone in order to acquire stronger verticity*

MAGNETIZED versoriums (or magnetized rotary needles) serve so many purposes in the life of man, that it will not be out of place to show the best process for rubbing and magnetically exciting them and the proper method of applying the process. With the aid of a small bar of iron magnetically prepared and suspended in equilibrium, rich iron ores and those containing most metal are recognized, and magnetic stones, clays, and earths, whether crude or prepared, are distinguished. A little iron bar—that soul of the mariner's compass, that wonderful director in sea-voyages, that finger of God, so to speak—points the way and has made known the whole circle of earth, unknown for so many ages. Spaniards (and Englishmen too) have again and again circumnavigated the whole globe on a vast circle by the help of the mariner's compass. They who travel on land or who remain at home have sun-dial horologes. The magnetic needle pursues and searches for veins of iron in mines: with its help mines are driven when cities are besieged; cannons and military engines are trained at night in the desired directions. The needle is of use for topography, for determining the areas and position of buildings, and in constructing underground aqueducts. On it depend the instruments invented for investigating its own dip and its own variation. When iron is to be quickened by the loadstone, let it be clean and neat, not disfigured by rust or dirt, and have it of the best steel. Let the stone be wiped dry so that there shall be no moisture, and scrape it gently with some well-polished iron tool. But beating it with a hammer is of no avail. And let the naked iron be applied to the naked stone and rubbed at it in such a way that they may come into closer contact—not in order that the corporeal matter of the stone may be joined to the stone and stick to it, but the two are slightly worn away by the

friction, and (useless parts being ground off) are united closely: hence arises in the excited iron a grander force. In the figure, *A* shows the best mode of applying the versorium to the stone—its point touches the pole and is directed toward the pole—*B* is a passable mode, for though it is at a little distance from the pole it is directed toward it; so, too, *C* is only a passa-

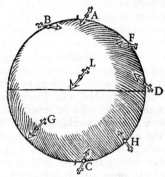

ble mode, the point being turned away from the pole; *D* is a worse mode on account of the greater distance from the pole; *F* is a bad mode because it lies on a parallel across the stone; the magnetic needle *L* that is rubbed on the equator is of no value and plainly is negative and forceless; the oblique indirect mode *G* and the oblique indirect averse *H* are both bad.

The purpose of all this is to show the different powers of a globular loadstone. But the artificers often use a stone rather tending toward the conical form, and, therefore, more powerful, its topmost projection being the pole, at which they rub the needles. Sometimes, also, the stone has at the top and above the very pole an artificial cap or snout of steel to give more strength; on this cap iron versoriums are rubbed, and thereafter they turn to that same pole as though they had been magnetized at that part without the cap.

The stone should be of good size and strong; the versorium, even if it be long, must be pretty thick, not too thin, with moderate-sized point, not too sharp, though the energy is not in the point itself but in the whole needle. Any powerful, large loadstone serves well for rubbing versoriums, though sometimes, owing to its powerfulness, it causes, when the needle is long, some dip and perturbation, so that the needle, that before friction stood in equilibrium in the plane of the horizon, now, after friction and excitation, dips with one end as low as the fulcrum on which it is supported permits. Hence in the case of a long versorium the end that is to be north should be, before friction, a little lighter than the other end, so that it may remain in exact equipoise after friction. But a versorium so prepared performs its function poorly at any considerable distance from the equinoctial circle.

When the versorium has been magnetized, put it back in its box, and do not let it come in contact with other magnetic bodies, nor remain in close neighborhood with them, lest it become unsteady and sluggish through the action of opposite forces, whether potent or feeble. And if you rub the other end of the needle at the opposite pole of the stone, the needle will act with more steadiness, especially if it be rather long. Iron rubbed with loadstone keeps constant and strong, even for several centuries, the magnetic power awakened in it, if it be laid in the natural position, meridionally, not on a parallel, and is not spoilt by rust or any external ill coming from the ambient medium.

Porta seeks amiss a ratio between loadstone and iron: a small mass of iron, saith he, cannot hold a great measure of power, for it is wasted by the mighty energy of the loadstone. Clearly, the iron takes to the full its own virtue, though it weigh only one scruple and the mass of the loadstone more than 100 lbs. It is vain also to make the versorium rather flat at the end that is rubbed in order that it may become a better and stronger magnetic body, and that it may better seize and hold certain magnetic particles, but few of which can adhere to a sharp point; for it was Porta's belief that the energy is transmitted and retained by adhesion of particles of the loadstone, like hairs, whereas these particles are simply scrapings detached by the iron from the softer stone; besides, the magnetized iron points steadily north and south if, after friction, it be scoured with sand or emery or other material, and even though by long-continued friction its outer parts be ground down and worn away. In stroking the loadstone with a versorium each stroke should terminate at one end of the versorium, else, if the stroke is made toward the middle, a less degree of verticity, or none at all, or very little is excited in the iron. For where the contact ends there is the pole and the point of verticity. To produce stronger verticity in iron by friction with a loadstone, it is necessary in northern latitudes to turn the loadstone's true north pole toward the zenith; on such pole that end of the versorium is to be rubbed which afterward will turn to the earth's north; the other end of the versorium must be

rubbed on the south pole of the terrella turned toward the earth; so excited, it will incline to the south. In southern latitudes, below the equator, the case is different, and the cause of the difference is given in Book II. 34, where is shown (by means of a combination of earth and terrella) why the poles of a loadstone are, for diverse reasons, one stronger than the other.

If between the ends of two loadstones in conjunction and equal in power, shape, and mass, you rub a versorium, it acquires no property.

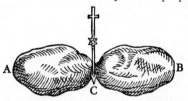

A, B are two loadstones conjoined naturally at their opposite ends; C, the point of a versorium, touched simultaneously by both, is not excited, if the loadstones be equal (though the loadstones are connected with it in the natural way); but if the loadstones be unequal, force is gained from the stronger.

In magnetizing a versorium with a loadstone begin at its middle and so draw it over the stone that one end quits the stone last; finally let the application be continued by a gentle stroking of the stone with the end of the needle for a while, say one or two minutes. The movement from middle to end must not, as is the wont, be repeated, for so the verticity is spoilt. Some delay is needed, for though the energy is infused and the iron is excited instantaneously, still the verticity is more steady and endures more surely in the iron when the versorium is left near the loadstone and abandoned at rest for a proper length of time; although an armed stone lifts a greater weight of iron than an unarmed, still a versorium is not more powerfully magnetized by the armed than by the unarmed stone. Take two pieces of iron wire, of equal length, cut off the same coil of wire, and let one be excited by the armed end, the other by the unarmed end: it will be found that they begin to move and make a perceptible inclination toward the loadstone at the same distances: this can be ascertained by measurement with a long rod. But objects powerfully excited turn quickly to the pole; those that are feebly excited turn slowly and only when brought nearer: the experiment is made in water with corks of equal size.

BOOK FOURTH

CHAPTER 1. *Of variation*

So far we have been treating of direction as if there were no such thing as variation; for we chose to have variation left out and disregarded in the foregoing natural history, just as if in a perfect and absolutely spherical terrestrial globe variation could not exist. But inasmuch as the magnetic direction of the earth, through some fault and flaw, does depart from the right track and the meridian, the occult and hidden cause of variance which has troubled and tormented, but to none effect, the minds of many has to be brought to light by us and demonstrated. They who hitherto have written of the magnetic movements have recognized no difference between direction and variation, but hold that there is one only movement of the magnetized needle. But the true direction is a movement of the magnetic body to the true meridian, and continuance therein, with the ends pointing to the respective poles. Yet very oft it happens, afloat and ashore, that a magnetic needle does not look toward the true pole, but is drawn to a point in the horizon nigh to the meridian, and that there is a deflection not only of the needle and magnetized iron in general and of the mariner's compass, but also of a terrella on its float, of iron ore and ironstone, and of magnetic clays artificially treated; for they often look with their poles toward points different from the meridian. The variation, then, as observed with the aid of instruments or of the mariner's compass, is an arc of the horizon between the intersection of the horizon by the meridian and the term of the deflection on the horizon, or the range of deviation of the magnetized body. This arc varies and is different according to locality. So the terminus of the variation is commonly assigned to a great circle—the circle of variation, as it is called—and a magnetic meridian passing through the zenith and the point of variation on the horizon.

In northern terrestrial latitudes this variation takes place either in the direction from north toward east, or from north toward west; in southern latitudes, in like manner, it is from south toward east, or south toward west. Hence in northern latitudes we must heed the end of the needle that tends north, and in southern latitudes the end looking south: this navigators and sciolists seldom understand, for on both sides of the equator they note only the north point terminal of the compass, or the one that looks north. As we have already said, every movement of loadstone and needle, every turn and dip, and their standing still, are effects of the magnetic bodies themselves and of the earth, mother of all, which is the fount and source and producer of all these forces and properties. Thus, then, the earth is the cause of this variation and tendence to a different point in the horizon; but we have to inquire further how and by what potencies it acts.

Here we must first reject the common opinion of modern writers concerning magnetic mountains or a certain magnetic rock or a distant phantom pole of the world controlling the movement of the compass or of the versorium. This opinion Fracastorio adopted and developed after it had been broached by others; but it does not agree with the experiments at all. For, if it were correct, in different places on land and sea the variation point would in geometrical ratio change to east or to west, and the versorium would always regard the magnetic pole; but experience teaches that there is no determinate pole, no fixed terminus of variation in the globe. For the arc of variation changes in different ways erratically, so that in different meridians and even in the same meridian, and when, according to the opinion of recent writers, the magnetized needle would deviate toward east, suddenly, on a trifling change of place, it goes from north toward west, as in the northern regions near Nova Zembla.[1] In southern latitudes also, and at sea, far away from the equator and toward the Antarctic, and not in northern latitudes near those magnetic mountains, is variation frequent and great.

But still more vain and silly are the imaginations of other writers—Cortesius, for example, who speaks of a motive force beyond the far-

[1] See Book iv. 16.

thest heavens; Marsilius Ficinus, who finds the cause of variation in a star of Ursa; Petrus Peregrinus, who finds it in the pole of the world; Cardan, referring it to the rising of a star in the tail of Ursa; the Frenchman Bessard, to the pole of the zodiac; Livius Sanutus, to a certain magnetic meridian; Franciscus Maurolycus, to a magnetic island; Scaliger, to the heavens and to mountains; the Englishman Robert Norman, to the "respective point."[1]

Quitting, therefore, those opinions that are at odds with every-day experience, or that at least are by no means proven, let us look for the true cause of variation. The Great Loadstone, or the terrestrial globe, gives, as I have said, to iron a north and south direction; magnetized iron readily conforms itself to those points. But as the globe of earth is at its surface broken and uneven, marred by matters of diverse nature, and hath elevated and convex parts that rise to the height of some miles and that are uniform neither in matter nor in constitution but opposite and different, it comes about that this entire earth-energy turns magnetic bodies at its periphery toward stronger massive magnetic parts that are more powerful and that stand above the general level. Wherefore at the outmost superficies of the earth magnetic bodies are turned a little away from the true meridian. And since the earth's surface is diversified by elevations of land and depths of seas, great continental lands, ocean, and seas differing in every way—while the force that produces all magnetic movements comes from the constant magnetic earth-substance, which is strongest in the most massive continent and not where the surface is water or fluid or unsettled—it follows that toward a massive body of land or continent rising to some height in any meridian (passing whether through islands or seas) there is a measurable magnetic leaning from the true pole toward east or west, i.e., toward the more powerful or higher and more elevated magnetic part of the earth's globe. For as the earth's diameter is more than 1700 German miles, these continents may rise above the general superficies to a height equal to the depth of the ocean bed, or more than four miles, and yet the earth keep the spherical shape, albeit slightly uneven at the top. For this reason a magnetic body under the action of the whole earth is attracted toward a great elevated mass of land as toward a stronger body, so far as the perturbed verticity permits or abdicates its right. Yet the variation takes place not so much because of these elevated but less perfect parts

[1] See Book I. 1; Book III. 1; Book IV. 6.

of the earth and these continental lands, as because of the inequality of the magnetic globe and of the true earth-substance which projects farther in continents than beneath sea-depths. We have therefore to inquire how the demonstration of this new natural philosophy may be drawn from unquestionable experiments.

From the coast of Guinea to Cape Verde, the Canaries, and the frontier of the empire of Morocco, thence along the coasts of Spain, France, England, Holland, Germany, Denmark, Norway, the land on the right and to the east is all continent, vast regions forming one mass; on the left, immense seas and the mighty ocean extend far and wide: now we should expect that (as has in fact been observed by diligent investigators) magnetic bodies would deflect a little eastward from the true pole toward those more powerful and extraordinary elevations of the terrestrial globe. Very different is the case on the east coasts of North America, for, from the region of Florida through Virginia and Norumbega[2] to Cape Race and away to the north, the needle turns to the west. But in the mid spaces, so to speak, for example in the western Azores, it regards the true pole. But it is not on account of that meridian or of the coincidence of the meridian with any magnetic pole, as the philosophastric crew suppose, that a magnetic body turns in like manner to the same regions of the world; neither does the variation take place along the entire meridian, for on the same meridian near Brazil the case is very different, as later we will show.

Other things equal, variation is less along the equator, greater in high latitude, save quite nigh the very pole. Hence is it greater off the coast of Norway and Holland than off Morocco or Guinea; greater, too, at Cape Race than in the ports of Norumbega or of Virginia. In the Guinea littoral, the magnetized needle inclines to the east one-third part of a point; in the Cape Verde Islands two thirds; in England, at the mouth of the Thames, one point: the higher the latitude the stronger the moving force, and the masses of land toward the pole exert most influence: all this is easily seen in a terrella. For just as, when the direction is true, magnetic bodies tend toward the pole (i.e., the greater force and the entire earth co-operating), so do they tend a little toward the more powerful elevated parts

[2] Norumbega, "the lost city of New England." Its site was indicated as on the bank of the Penobscot, the province of that name extending from the Kennebec River to the St. Croix River.

under the action of the whole and in virtue of the concurrent action of their iron.

CHAPTER 2. *That variation is due to inequality among the earth's elevations*

THIS very thing is clearly demonstrated on the terrella thus: take a spherical loadstone imperfect in any part or decayed (I once had such a stone crumbled away at a part of its surface and so having a depression comparable to the Atlantic sea or great ocean); lay on it bits of iron wire two barley-corns in length, as in the figure. *AB* is a terrella imperfect in parts and of unequal power on the circumference; the needles *E*, *F* do not vary but regard the pole straight, for they are placed in the middle of the sound and strong part of the terrella at a distance from the decayed part: the surface that is dotted and that is marked with cross-lines is weaker. Neither does the needle *O* vary because it is in the middle line of the decayed part, but turns to the pole just as off the western Azores. *H* and *L* vary, for they incline toward the sound parts.

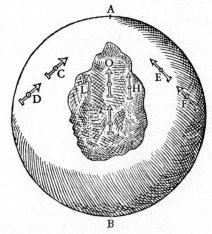

And as this is shown on a terrella whose surface has sensible imperfections, so, too, in terrellas that are whole and perfect, for often one part of a stone is of greater strength on the outside than another, though no difference is plain to sense. With such a terrella variation is demonstrated and the strong points are discovered in the following way: Here *A* is the pole, *B* the place of variation, *G* the more powerful region. The horizontal needle at *B* varies from the pole *C*-ward. So is the variation shown and the regions of greater force recognized. The more powerful surface is found also by means of a slender iron wire two barley-corns long: for

though it will stand upright on the pole of the terrella and in other parts will lean toward the equator, still if on the same parallel circle it stands more nearly erect at one point than at another, the terrella's surface has more power where the needle is the more erect; and also

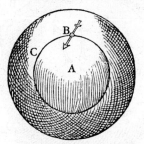

when a piece of iron wire laid on the pole inclines more to one side than the other. For ex-

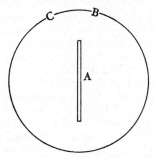

periment take a piece of iron wire three finger-widths long, resting on the pole *A* so that its middle lies over the pole. One of the ends turns toward *G* and will not rest in position toward *B*; yet, in a terrella that is flawless and even all over, it will be at rest on the pole no matter toward what point of the equator it be directed. Or make another experiment: Suppose two meridians meeting at the poles *A*, *B* in equal arcs *DA* and *CA*; at their extremities *D*, and *C*, let pieces of iron wire be reared: at *D* (which is the region of greater force) the wire will be reared more near perpendicular than at *C*, the

region of less force. Thus can we discern the stronger and more powerful part of a loadstone, else not recognizable by the senses. In a terrella that is perfect, even, and alike in all its parts, there is at equal distances from the pole no variation.

Variation may be shown by means of a terrella having a considerable part of its surface

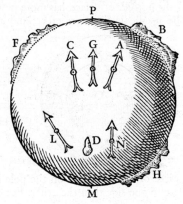

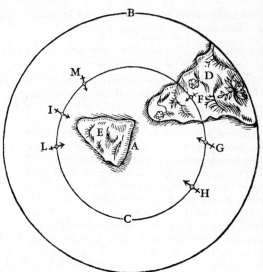

projecting a little above the rest: such terrella, though not decayed nor spoilt, attracts out of the true direction, its whole mass operating. The figure shows a terrella with uneven surface. The demonstration is made with small bars or short needles placed on the terrella: they turn from the terrella toward the projecting mass and the great eminences. In this way is verticity disturbed on the earth by the great continents which mostly rise above the beds of the seas and which at times cause the needle to deviate from the straight track, i.e., from the true meridian. The tip of the versorium A does not point toward the pole P if there be a large projection B on the terrella; so, too, the point G varies from the pole because of the projection F. Midway between the two eminences, the needle G points to the true pole, because, being equidistant from both projections B and F, it deviates to neither but keeps the true meridian, particularly when the energy of the projections is equal. But elsewhere, at N, the needle varies from the pole M toward the eminence H, nor is hindered nor stayed nor checked by the small eminence D on the terrella, which is like some island of the earth in the ocean. But L unhindered tends poleward.

In another mode may variation be shown, whether in a terrella or on the earth. Let A be the earth's pole; B its equator; C a parallel circle at latitude 30 degrees; D an eminence reaching poleward; E another eminence stretching from the pole equatorward. Evidently the versorium F in the middle line of D does not vary; but G deflects very much, C very little as being more remote from D. So, too, the needle I, placed

directly toward E, does not deflect from the pole: but L and M turn from the pole toward the eminence E.

CHAPTER 3. *Variation is constant at a given place*

As the needle hath ever inclined toward east or toward west, so even now does the arc of variation continue to be the same in whatever place or region, be it sea or continent; so, too, will it be forevermore unchanging, save there should be a great break-up of a continent and annihilation of countries, as of the region Atlantis, whereof Plato and ancient writers tell.

The constancy of the variation and the regard of the versorium toward a fixed point of the horizon in each region is shown by laying a very small versorium on a terrella of uneven surface: the needle always diverges from the meridian over an equal arc. It is shown also by the inclination of the needle toward a second loadstone, though in truth this is done by a changed direction of all within the earth and the terrella. Lay upon a plane surface a versorium with its point looking toward A, north; bring alongside

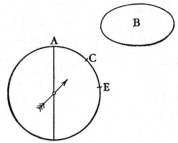

the loadstone, *B* at such distance as to make the versorium turn to *C* and no further. Move the needle of the versorium as often as you will (yet without stirring either its case or the loadstone) and the needle will ever surely return to the point *C*. Thus if you so hold the stone as to make the needle turn to *E*, its point ever returns to *E* and not to any other point of the compass. Just so, by reason of the position of countries and the differing nature of the uppermost parts of the earth's globe (certain more magnetic projections of the terrestrial sphere prevailing), variation is ever fixed in a given place, but it differs and is unequal between one place and another, for the true and polar direction, having its birth in the entire globe of earth, is slightly diverted toward particular eminences of great magnetic force on the broken surface.

CHAPTER 4. *The arc of variation does not differ according to distance between places*

On the broad ocean, while a ship is borne by favouring wind along the same parallel, if the variation be reduced just one degree in a voyage of 100 miles, it does not follow that the next 100 miles will reduce it another degree. For the needle varies according to the position and conformation of the land and the magnetic force; also according to distance. For example, when a ship from the Scilly Islands bound for Newfoundland has proceeded so far that the compass points to the true magnetic pole, then, as she sails on, the borrholybic variation begins, but faintly and with small divergence. But after a while the arc increases in a higher ratio as equal distances are traversed, till the ship comes nigh the continent, when the variation is very great. Yet before she comes quite to land or enters port, while at some distance away, the arc is again lessened a little. But if the ship in her course departs much from that parallel, either to north or south, the needle will vary more or less according to the position of the land and the latitude of the region; for, other things equal, the higher the latitude the greater the variation.

CHAPTER 5. *An island in ocean does not alter the variation; neither do mines of loadstone*

Islands, albeit they are more magnetic than the seas, still do not alter magnetic direction nor variation. For direction being a movement produced by the energy of the entire earth, and not due to the attractive force of any prominence but to the controlling power and verticity of the whole mass, therefore variation (which is a perturbation of the directive force), is a wandering from the true verticity and arises out of the great inequalities of the earth, by reason of which the earth itself, when very large and powerful magnetic bodies are present, has but little power of turning away magnetic bodies that revolve freely. As for the wonders that some do report about the island of Elba: loadstones do there abound, but, nevertheless, the versorium (or the mariner's compass) makes no special inclination toward it when ships sail by in the Tyrrhenian Sea. The reasons already given sufficiently account for this; but, furthermore, a reason may be found in the fact that the energy of minor loadstones reaches of itself but little beyond their own site; for variation is not produced by a pulling to, as they would make it who have thought out magnetic poles. Besides, mines of loadstone are only agnate, not innate, in the true earth-substance, and, therefore, the globe as a whole does not heed them; neither are magnetic bodies borne toward them, as is proved in the diagram of prominences.

CHAPTER 6. *That variation and direction are produced by the controlling force of the earth and the rotatory magnetic nature, not by an attraction or a coition, or by other occult cause*

Inasmuch as the loadstone is deemed by the philosophizers of the vulgar sort to seize and snatch objects away, as it were, and pretenders to science have, in fact, noticed no other properties save this much-lauded force of attraction, therefore they have supposed that the whole movement to north and south is produced by some natural force soliciting bodies. But the Englishman Robert Norman first strove to show that this is not done by attraction; he, therefore, originated the idea of the "respective point" looking, as it were, toward hidden principles, and held that toward this the magnetized needle ever turns, and not toward any attractional point; but he was greatly in error, albeit he exploded the ancient false opinion about attraction. Norman proves his theory as follows: take a round vessel full of water; on the mid surface of the water float a small bit of iron wire sup-

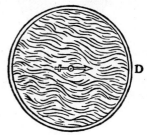

ported by just so much cork as will keep it afloat while the water is in equilibrium; the wire must have been first magnetized so as to show plainly the variation point *D*. Let it remain in the water for a while. Clearly the wire with its cork does not move toward the rim *D* of the vessel, as it would do if attraction came to the iron from *D*, and the cork would move from its place. This assertion of the Englishman Robert Norman is demonstrable, and it does seem to do away with attraction, inasmuch as the iron remains in the still water both in the direction toward the very pole (if the direction be true) and in variation and irregular direction; and it revolves on its iron centre, and is not borne toward the vessel's rim. Yet the direction is not produced by attraction, but by a disposing and conversory power existing in the earth as a whole, not in a pole or any attrahent part of the stone, neither in any mass projecting beyond the circle of the periphery, so that the variation should result because of the attraction of that mass. Besides, the directive force of the stone and of iron, and their natural power of revolving on their centre, produce the movement of direction and of collimation, in which is included also the motion of dip or inclination. Nor does the earth's pole attract as though the force of the globe resided in the pole only: the magnetic force exists in the whole, but in the pole it is preeminent and surpassing. Therefore that the cork abides quietly in the midst, and that the magnetic needle does not move toward the rim of the vessel, is a fact in accord and agreement with the loadstone's nature, as is shown with the aid of a terrella. Here a little iron bar, placed on the stone at *C*, clings there, nor is it pulled farther away by the pole *A* or by the parts near the pole. So, too, it continues at *D* and takes direction toward the pole *A*, but it sticks at *D*, and dips also toward

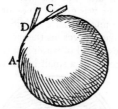

D in virtue of its power of rotation whereby it conforms itself to the terrella. On this point we shall treat further when we consider inclination or the dip of the compass.

CHAPTER 7. *Why the variation due to this lateral cause is not greater than hitherto it has been observed to be, seldom appearing to amount to two points of the compass, except near the pole*

THE earth, by reason of lateral elevations of the more energic globe, causes iron and loadstone to diverge a few degrees from the true pole or true meridian. For example, here in England, at London, it varies 11⅓ degrees; in some other places the variation is somewhat greater, yet in no region does the end of the needle diverge very many degrees more from the meridian. For as the needle always gets its direction from the true verticity of the earth, so the polar nature of a continent tends poleward, even as does that of the whole globe of earth; and though the mass of a continent may turn magnetic bodies away from the meridian, still the verticity of that same land (as of the whole earth also) controls and di-

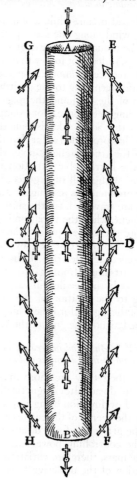

rects those bodies so that they shall not turn eastward in too large an arc. It were not easy to determine according to any general method how great the arc of variation is in every place, nor how many degrees and minutes it covers on the horizon, because it becomes greater or less according to divers causes. For we must take account of the force of true verticity of each place and of the elevated regions, also of the distances of those regions from the place under consideration and from the world's poles; and these distances are to be compared—a thing that cannot be done with precision. Still, by our method, the variation is ascertained in such way that no serious error is left to perturb the course of a sea-voyage. Were the positions of masses of land uniform, if the land lay on a meridian line, and did not present a broken and indented contour, the variations near the land would be without complexity, as in the figure.

This is demonstrated with the aid of a long loadstone whose poles are at the ends A, B: the middle of the loadstone and the equinoctial is CD; and the lines GH and EF are meridians on which are arranged versoriums, the deviations of which are greater the greater their distance from the equator. But the inequalities of the seaboard parts of the habitable globe, the great promontories, the wide gulfs, the mountainous and the more elevated regions, and the more uneven and precipitous regions make the variations more difficult of determination, and in high latitudes less certain and more irregular.

CHAPTER 8. *Of the construction of the common mariner's compass, and of the different compasses of various nations*

IN a round wooden box (bowl), having its top covered over with glass, a fly-card (versorium) rests on a pretty long pin fixed in the middle. The glass cover keeps out wind and draughts of air produced by outer causes. All that is within can be distinctly seen through the glass. The versorium (rotating part) is circular, made of light material, as pasteboard, to the under side of which is attached the magnetized iron or needle. On the upper side 32 spaces (points as they are called) are distributed to as many mathematical intervals in the horizon, or *winds*, which are distinguished by certain marks and by a lily indicating the north. The compass-box is suspended in equilibrium in the plane of the horizon, within a ring of brass, which is also pivoted (equilibrated) in another ring suspended in a roomy stand, a leaden weight being attached to the box so that it shall remain in the plane of

the horizon though the ship may be tossed by the sea in all directions. There are either two magnetized-iron bars (with ends united) or one piece of a rather oval shape with the ends projecting: this style is the surer and quicker of the two in performing its function. This is to be so fitted to the pasteboard disk (or card of the compass) that the centre of the disk shall be in the middle of the magnetized iron. But as variation begins in the horizon from the point where the meridian intersects it at right angles, therefore, on account of the variation, instrument makers in different countries and cities inscribe the compass variously, and have different ways of attaching the magnetized iron to the card whereon are marked the bounds of the 32 spaces or points.

There are in general use in Europe four different constructions and forms of compass. First, the form adopted throughout the Mediterranean, and in Sicily, Genoa, and the Venetian republic. In all of these compasses the pieces of iron are so attached beneath to the rotating card that (where there is no variation) they turn to the true points of north and south. Hence the mark for north, designated by a lily, always indicates exactly the point of variation: for the point of the lily on the card, together with the ends of the pieces of magnetized iron beneath, come to a standstill at the point of variation. Another form of compass is that of Danzig, employed in the Baltic Sea and in the Netherlands. Here the magnetized iron underneath diverges three-fourths of one point eastward from the lily; for a voyage to Russia the divergence (recognized difference) is two-thirds. But the compasses made at Seville, Lisbon, La Rochelle, Bordeaux, Rouen, as well as throughout all England, have an interval of one-half of a point.

Out of these differences have grown very serious errors in seafaring and in the science of navigation. For, after the directional positions of sea-coasts, of promontories, ports, islands, have been found by the aid of the compass, and the tides of the seas or the times of full sea have been determined from the moon's position above one or another point of the compass (as the phrase is), we have still to inquire in what country or according to what country's usage the compass was constructed by which the directions of said places and the times of the marine tides were observed and determined. For the mariner, who, using British compass, should follow the directions of the Mediterranean marine charts, must needs stray far from his true course; so, one who should use an Italian compass in the North Sea, the German Sea, or the Baltic, in connection with the marine charts commonly used in those parts, would oft stray from the right direction. These differences were introduced by reason of the unlike variations, that navigators might escape grave errors in those parts of the world. Yet Petrus Nonius seeks the meridian with a mariner's compass or versorium (the Spaniards call it a needle), taking no account of variation; and he brings forward many geometric proofs that rest on utterly vicious foundations: for he had small acquaintance or experience of things magnetic. In like manner Pedro de Medina, who does not accept variation, has with many errors disgraced the art of navigation.

CHAPTER 9. *Whether terrestrial longitude can be found from variation*

THAT were a welcome service to mariners and would advance geography very much. But Porta (VII. 38) is deluded by a vain hope and by a baseless theory. For he thinks that, in moving along a meridian, the needle observes order and proportion, so that the nearer it is to east the more it will deviate eastward, and, according as you advance west, the needle takes a westerly direction: all of which is false as false can be. Porta thinks he has found a true index of longitude; but he is mistaken. Taking, however, and assuming for true these premises, he constructs a large compass showing degrees and minutes for observing these proportional changes of the needle. But his principles are erroneous and illogically taken and very poorly studied; for a versorium does not vary more to the east because it is carried to the east; and though in the countries of western Europe and the seas adjoining the variation is to the east, and beyond the Azores it is changed a little toward the west, nevertheless variation is in divers ways ever uncertain, both because of latitude and longitude and because of approach to great masses of land, also because of the altitude of dominant terrestrial elevation; but it does not follow the rule of any meridian, as we have already shown. Livius Sanutus sorely tortures himself and his readers with like vanities. As for the opinion of the common run of philosophizers and mariners, that the meridian which passes through the Azores is the limit of variation, so that on the opposite side of that meridian a magnetic body will point to the poles exactly as at the Azores—an opinion held also by Joannes Baptista Benedictus and sundry other writers on the art of navigation —it is in no wise true. Stevinus (quoted by Hugo Grotius), in his *Portuum inveniendarum*

ratione, distinguishes variation according to meridians. "In the island of Corvo,"[1] says he, "the magnetic pointer indicates the true north, but the farther one advances thence toward the east the more will he see the needle 'easting', till he comes to within one mile of Plymouth on the east, where the variation, reaching maximum, is 13 deg. 24 min. Then the anatolism (easting) begins to grow less as far as Helmshud, which place is not far from North Cape in Finmark: there the north is pointed to again. There are 60 degrees of longitude between Corvo and Helmshud, but the variation is greatest at Plymouth, whose longitude is 30 degrees." But though these statements are in part true, still along the entire meridian of the island of Corvo the compass does by no means point due north. Neither in the whole meridian of Plymouth at other places is the variation 13 deg. 24 min., nor in other parts of the meridian of Helmshud does the needle point to the true pole. For, on the meridian passing through Plymouth at lat. 60 deg., the north by east variation is greater; in lat. 40 deg. it is much less; in lat. 20 deg. it is very small indeed. On the meridian of Corvo, though the variation near the island is nil, yet in lat. 55 deg. the variation north by west is about $\frac{1}{2}$; in lat. 20 deg. the variation is $\frac{1}{4}$ of a point toward the east. Hence the bounds of variation are not properly defined by great meridian circles, and far less are the ratios of increase or decrease toward a given region of the heavens investigated by that method. Therefore the rules of *clattumen* (declining) or *auxanomen* (increasing), anatolism (easting) or dysism (westing), cannot possibly be found by that device. The grounds of variation in the southern regions of the earth, which Stevinus thereafter searches into in the same way, are utterly vain and absurd; they have been put forth by some Portuguese mariners, but they do not agree with investigations: equally absurd are sundry observations wrongly accepted as correct. But the method of finding the port on long voyages to distant parts by means of accurate knowledge of the variation (a method invented by Stevinus and recorded by Grotius) is of great importance, if only fit instruments be at hand wherewith the deviation may positively be ascertained at sea.

CHAPTER 10. *Why in various places near the pole the variations are much ampler than in lower latitudes*

ON the equator or near it, the variation of a needle is often trifling; not unusually it is null. In higher latitudes, as 60, 70, 80 degrees, the

[1] One of the Azores, the northernmost of the whole group, lying ten miles north of Flores.

variations are not infrequently very great. The reason of this is found partly in the nature of the earth, partly in the position of the versorium. The earth causes magnetic bodies to rotate and directs them poleward strongly at the equator; at the poles there is no direction, but only fast coition of terminals that agree. Hence direction is weaker at the poles, because the versorium, by reason of its tendency to turn to the pole, dips greatly, and is but feebly directed; but the force of the lands and eminences is strong, with an energy proceeding from the entire earth, and, besides, the causes of variation are nearer: therefore the versorium deflects more to those eminences. It must be known also that the direction of a versorium poised on a needle toward the plane of the horizon is much stronger at the equator than anywhere else by reason of the lie of the versorium; and in proportion as latitude increases the direction is less strong, for at the equator the versorium is directed naturally toward the plane of the horizon, but in other places it is forced to be in equilibrium and remains in equilibrium because of an external force: by its nature it dips under the horizon as the latitude increases, as will be shown in the Book on Inclination or Dip. Wherefore direction becomes weaker and at the pole itself is null. For this reason a weak direction is easily overcome by powerful causes of variation, and near the pole the needle deflects more from the meridian. This is demonstrated with a terrella, on which is put an iron wire of two finger-breadths: the wire is quickly and strongly directed toward the poles on a meridian, but in the intervals between equator and pole it is directed weakly; herein we may see the great tendency to variation near the poles.

CHAPTER 11. *Cardan's error in seeking to determine the distance of the earth's centre from the centre of the world by means of the loadstone* (*in his* De proportionibus, v)

How very easy it is to make mistakes and errors in the absence of trustworthy experiments, while investigating the hidden causes of things, is well shown by a gross blunder of Cardan, who thinks he has discovered the distances of the centres of the earth and the world through the variation of the magnetic needle over nine degrees; for he believed that

the variation point in the horizon is everywhere distant eastward nine degrees from due north: on this basis he establishes a demonstrative ratio of the different centres.

CHAPTER 12. *Of finding the amount of the variation; what the quantity is of the arc of the horizon from its arctic or antarctic intersection by a meridian to the point toward which the needle turns*

THE true meridian is the principal basis of the whole question; when that is surely known it is easy, with the mariner's compass (when you know its construction and how the iron bars are fixed in it), or with any large horizontal versorium, to show the arc of variation on the horizon. A variation compass of good size, after you have made two observations of the sun before and after noon, shows the variation by the shadow:

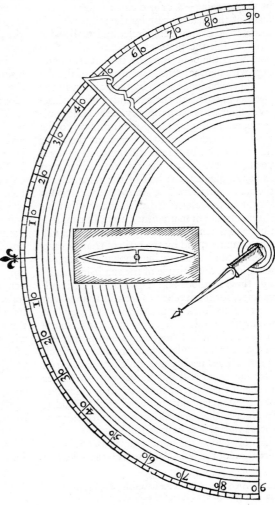

the sun's altitude is observed with a *radius*[1] or with a large quadrant. On account of the greater size of the instrument, there is an easier and surer way of finding the variation on shore. Get a thick plank of suitable timber, two feet long, sixteen inches broad; on it describe several semicircles, as in the accompanying plate, but more numerous. In the centre erect perpendicularly a brass stilus; let there be also a rotatory pointer reaching from the centre to the outermost semicircle, and a magnetized versorium in a box with glass cover. Then when the plank is placed accurately to the level of the horizon by the plane instrument with its perpendicular, turn the extremity of the pointer toward the north, so that the versorium shall rest just on the midline of its case, which regards the point of variation in the horizon. Afterwards, at some convenient hour in the morning—8 or 9 o'clock—observe the point of the shadow cast by the stilus when it reaches the nearest semicircle, and mark with chalk or ink the place of the shadow's point; now bring the pointer round to that mark and note with another mark the number of the degree in the horizon shown by the pointer. In the afternoon, see when the extremity of the shadow again reaches the periphery of the same semicircle, and, bringing the pointer around to the tip of the shadow, find the degree at the other side of the lily. From the difference in degrees, you find the variation: the less being substracted from the greater, the half of the remainder is the arc of variation. The amount of variation is sought to be determined with many other instruments and in many other ways, in conjunction with the mariner's compass—by means of a globe, number, and by the ratio of triangles and of sines, the latitude being known and one observation of the altitude of the sun being made. But these methods and means are of little advantage, for it is useless to seek in roundabout ways and by intricate paths what you may find more quickly and more surely by taking a shorter road. The whole trick consists in proper use of the instruments by which the sun's position is ascertained readily and quickly (as the sun does not stand still but moves on), for either the hand trembles, or the eyesight is defective, or the instrument does not work aright. Besides, to observe the sun's altitude on both sides of the meridian, is as easy as to observe it on one side only and at the same time to ascertain the elevation of the pole. And he who can take one

altitude with an instrument can take another, and if the one is doubtful, the whole work with globe, number, sines, and triangles is thrown away. Nevertheless, these exercises of mathematical minds are praiseworthy. It is easy for anyone who stands on the land, by means of accurate observations and with the use of fit instruments, to ascertain the variation, especially in a rather right sphere; but at sea, in view of the motion and the turning of the waters, experiments cannot be made with exactness as to degrees and minutes, and, in fact, with the instruments in common use, hardly within one third or one half of a point, particularly in high latitude: hence so many incorrect and faulty records of observations by navigators. As for us, we have contrived a method of finding the variation, by means of a convenient, handy instrument, from the rising of certain stars, the rising or setting of the sun, in northern regions, from the pole-star; for, at sea, when the ship is tossed by the waves, even the skilled observer determines the variation more surely with the aid of a simple instrument and one of no great precision. Such an instrument is constructed as follows:

After the pattern of a true and meridional mariner's compass (with a bare versorium or with a versorium fastened to a card circle), make an instrument at least one foot in diameter; divide its rim into four quarters, each subdivided into 90 degrees. Let the movable compass-box be balanced below (*subtus librata*) with a heavy weight of 16 pounds. On the edge of the suspended box at beginnings opposite quadrants, a semicircle rising in the middle to a point (*conum*) is to be erected (the feet of the semicircle at both sides being fastened in holes on the margin) so that the top of the *conum* shall be perpendicular to the plane of the compass; on its top a rule sixteen digits long is to be fastened at its middle over the central axis, as it were (of the compass-box), like the beam of a balance, with such a joint that it may move. At the ends of the rule are small sights with holes through which we may observe the sun and stars. By means of the rising or the setting sun at the equinoxes, the variation can be taken very well and very readily with this instrument. When the sun is in other parts of the zodiac, the variation can also be determined when we have the altitude of the pole: that known, any one may find, with a globe, or maps, or with the instrument, the amplitude (of the sun or star) on the horizon and the distance from the true east as well of the sun as of the following fixed stars.

[1] *Radius astronomicus*—measuring-rod, same as radiometer. An old instrument for measuring angles; the crossstaff; Jacob's-staff; a kind of astrolabe.

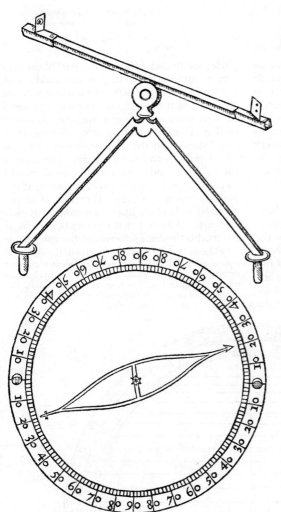

Then, having counted the degrees and minutes of the ortive amplitude (time of rising) from the true east, we readily find the variation. Observe the foremost star of the three in Orion's belt when first it appears on the horizon; direct the instrument toward it, and observe the versorium, for as that star rises in the true east, generally one degree toward the south, we can see how far the versorium diverges from the meridian, allowance made for that one degree. You may also observe the Artic pole-star when it is on the meridian or at greatest distance from the meridian (about 3 degrees: according to the observations of Tycho Brahe the pole-star is 2 deg. 55 min. from the pole), and with the aid of the instrument you may determine the variation scientifically, by adding or subtracting the *due prostaphæresis*[1] of the star's distance from the meridian (if it is not in the meridian). You will find when the pole-star is in the meridian, the sun's place and the hour of the night being known: even the practised observer will easily know that without much error, by the visible inclination of the asterism —as we do not care for a matter of a few minutes, as some do, who while striving to get at the minutes at sea often miss by a whole point. The experienced observer will allow somewhat for refraction in noting the rise of the sun or stars, so that his calculation may be more exact.

[1] Prostaphæresis (*Gr.* previous subtraction). (1) The reduction to bring the apparent place of a planet or moving point to the mean place. (2) A method of computing by means of a table of natural trigonometrical functions without multiplying.

List of bright, brilliant stars not far from the equator, that can be observed in rising or in setting from the altitude of the pole and the declination of the stars, the ortive amplitude on the horizon being ascertained on a globe, or map, or the instrument whence the variation is determined by artful calculation.

		Right Ascension deg. min.		Declination deg. min.		
Aldebaran	Eye of Taurus	62	55	15	53	N.
Bellatrix	Left shoulder of Orion	72	24	4	5	N.
Betelgeuze	Right shoulder of Orion	83	30	6	19	N.
Mintaka	Foremost star in belt of Orion	77	46	1	16	S.
Sirius	Canis Major	97	10	15	55	S.
Procyon	Canis Minor	109	41	5	55	N.
Alphard	Bright star in Hydra	137	10	5	3	S.
Pollux	South head of Gemini	110	21	28	30	N.
Castor	North head of Gemini	107	4	32	10	N.
Regulus	Heart of Leo	146	8	13	47	N.
Denebola	Tail of Leo	171	38	16	30	N.
Spica	Spica Virginis	195	44	8	34	S.

		Eight Ascension deg. min.		Declination deg. min.		
Arcturus and Boötæ		29	13	21	54	N.
Altair	Heart of Aquila	291	56	7	35	N.

An instrument for finding the ortive amplitude on the horizon. Describe the periphery of a circle and divide it into quarters by two diameters intersecting at right angles. One of the diameters indicates the equinoctial circle, the other the axis of the world. Divide the four quarters in the usual way, each into 90 degrees, and to every fifth or every tenth degree from each end of the two diameters in both directions assign numbers on the two margins (outside of this periphery) provided for the purpose. Then from each degree draw a right line parallel to the equator. Next make a rule, or alidade, of the same length as the diameter of the circle and divided into the same parts exactly as the diameter which represents the axis of the world. In the middle of this rule let a small projecting piece be left attached whereby the middle of the *linea fiducialis*[1] of the rule may be connected with the centre of the circle; and to each fifth or tenth part of the rule give a number, beginning in the middle and numbering right and left. The circle represents the plane of the meridian; its centre represents the very point of rising or setting, *i.e.*, the intersection of horizon and equator. All these lines equidistant from the equator, represent parallels of the sun and stars; the *linea fiducialis* of the rule or alidade represents the horizon, and its parts degrees of the horizon, beginning at the point of rising or setting. Therefore, if to the given latitude of the place, as numbered at each end of the diameter that represents the axis of the world, the *linea fiducialis* of the rule be ap-

[1] Fiducial line: (1) The straight edge of the alidade of a plane table. (2) The initial line of a graduated circle or vernier. (3) Any line which is intended to be taken as a standard straight line. The term fiducial, in *physics*, denotes a fixed position or character, and hence is used as a basis of reference or comparison.

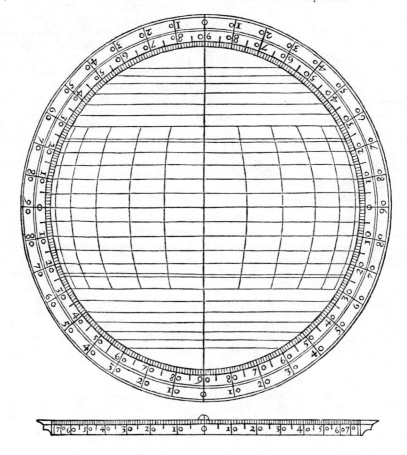

plied; and if the given declination (less the complement of the latitude of the station) of sun or any star from the equator be found on the rim of the instrument, then a section of a parallel drawn from the point of this declination in the horizon, or in the *linea fiducialis*, will show the ortive amplitude of the given star or of the sun at the stated latitude of the place.

CHAPTER 13. *Observations made by seamen commonly vary and are untrustworthy, partly through mistakes and want of knowledge and the imperfectness of the instruments, and partly because the sea is seldom so calm but shadows or lights may rest on the instruments*

FROM the time when first the variation of the needle was noticed, many alert navigators have in sundry ways striven to investigate the difference in the direction of the mariner's compass; but this has not been done with the exactness that was requisite, much to the disadvantage of the art of navigation. For, either, being unlearned, they knew of no sure method, or they used ill-constructed and unsuitable instruments, or they adopted some conjecture based merely on the false hypothesis of some prime meridian or magnetic pole; while many copy others' writings and pass off for their own the observations of earlier writers: and these early authors, however stupid the writings in which they entered their observations, are held in high respect just because of their antiquity; and their posterity hold it to be not safe to differ from them. Hence on long voyages, especially to the East Indies, the inexact records of variation of the compass kept by the Portuguese are prized; but whoever reads what the Portuguese have written will quickly see that in very many respects they are mistaken, and that they did not rightly understand the construction and the use, in taking the variation of the compass of Portugal (in which the lily points one-half point west from the magnetized needle). Hence while they exhibit the variation of the compass in different places, it is not certain whether they measure the deviation with a true meridional compass or with some other kind, in which the magnetized iron points away from the lily. The Portuguese (as is seen in their writings) employ the compass of Portugal, in which the magnetized iron is one-half of a point to the east of the lily.

Even expert navigators find it very difficult to observe the variation at sea on account of the ship's motions and her tossing in every direction, though they may employ the best instruments yet devised and in use. Hence have arisen various opinions about magnetic deviation. For example, the Portuguese navigator Roderigues de Lazos takes it to be one-half point off the island of St. Helena; the Dutch, in their nautical journal, make it one point there; Kendall, an expert English navigator, makes it only one-sixth of a point, using a true meridional compass. Diego Alfonso finds no variation at a point a little southeast of Cape Agulhas,[1] and by the astrolabe shows that the compass stands in the true meridian; but Roderigues declares that the compass points due north and south at Cape Agulhas if it be of the Portuguese style, in which the variation is one-half point to the southeast. There is the same degree of confusion, carelessness, and falsity in most of the other records.

CHAPTER 14. *Of the variation under the equinoctial line and near by*

IN northern regions the compass varies because of the northern eminences; in southern regions because of the southern eminences; on the equator, if the eminences on both sides were equal, there would be no variation. But because this seldom happens, therefore oftimes variation is observed under the equator; and even at some distance from the equator, three or four degrees, variation may be produced by austral eminences, if extensive and potent austral continents lie near on one side.

CHAPTER 15. *The variation of the magnetized needle in the great sea, Ethiopic and American, below the equator*

WE have already spoken of the mode and reason of variation in the great Altantic Sea; but below the equator, on the east coast of Brazil, the needle swerves toward the continent; with the end that looks south: thus, at that end, it declines from the true meridian, toward the west; this is noticed by navigators as a movement of the point of the needle, and so they think that the variation is to the east. But, over the whole route from the first eastern promontory of Brazil, past Cape São Agostino to Cape Frio and as far as the mouth of the Strait of Magellan, the variation is always from south to west, the crotch of the needle tending to the Antartic pole. For it always turns with the proper end toward a continent. Yet the variation takes place not only on the coast itself, but at some distance from the land—over a space of 50 or 60 German miles or more.

But at a great distance from the land the arc begins to grow less, for the needle turns less to-

[1] Southernmost point of Africa.

ward distant prominences; and it is not made to diverge much by such prominences when present and on the spot, for it then shares with them. On the island of St. Helena (whose longitude is less than it is usually given in maps) the compass varies one or perhaps two degrees. The Portuguese, and others who have learnt of them, in sailing beyond the Cape of Good Hope to the Indies, in order to have favorable winds, shape their course toward the islands of Tristan de Cunha, and on the first half of the voyage find no considerable difference of variation; but near those islands the difference is greater than anywhere else in the entire voyage. For the great promontory of the southerly continent which lies to the southwest pulls and solicits that end of the versorium which points south (and at that end is the principal cause of the variation). But as the ship approaches the Cape of Good Hope the variation grows steadily less. In the prime meridian, at latitude 45 degrees, the needle points southeast by south; and so, too, he who sails along the coast from Manicongo to the tropic and a little beyond will find the needle tending from the south to the southeast, but not much. At Cape Agulhas it still keeps a little of the variation it showed near the islands of Tristan de Cunha, but it is much diminished owing to the remoteness from the cause of the variation; and the south end of the needle does not yet point due south.

CHAPTER 16. *Of the variation in Nova Zembla*

THE variations are greatest in regions nigh to the poles, as has been proved, and there, too, the changes of variation are sudden, as Dutch observers noted some years ago, though their observations were not exact; yet the inexactitude can be excused, for, with the ordinary instruments, it is hard to get at the truth in such high latitudes—about 80 degrees. But now the variation of the compass gives the clear evidence of the existence of an open passage eastward through the North Sea—Arctic Ocean—for, since the compass has so great an arc of variation to the west, it is evident that no continent stretches for any great distance along that whole route eastward. Therefore we can strive and explore more hopefully for a passage to the Moluccas by the northeast than by the northwest.

CHAPTER 17. *Variation in the South Sea*

AFTER passing through the Strait of Magellan, the variation off the Peruvian coast is to the southeast; and a like deflection continues all along the coast of Peru to the equator. In higher latitude, up to 45 degrees, the variation is greater than near the equator; and, just as on the eastern coast of South America, the deflection was from south toward west, so now it is to the southeast. From the equator northward the variation is very small or null till you reach New Galicia; thence along the whole coast as far as Quivira the inclination is from the north to the east.

CHAPTER 18. *Of the variation in the Mediterranean Sea*

SICILIAN and Italian mariners declare that in the Sicilian sea and eastward to the meridian of Peloponnesus (as Francis Maurolycus relates) the needle grecizes, *i.e.*, is diverted from the pole toward the wind called Græcus (Greek), or north wind; that on the coast of Peloponnesus it points to the true pole; but that when you proceed farther, then it mistralizes, inclining from the pole to the mistral or northwest wind: this is in accordance with our rule of the variation. For, as the Mediterranean Sea stretches away from that meridian toward the west, so, on the side toward the east, there is open sea as far as Palestine, and toward the north and east is the whole archipelago, and hard by the Black Sea. From Peloponnesus to the north pole, that meridian passes through the largest and most elevated regions of all Europe: through Achaia, Macedonia, Hungary, Transylvania, Lithuania, Livonia, Novgorod, Karelia, and Biarmia.[1]

CHAPTER 19. *The variation in the interior of the great continents*

GREAT seas usually have great variations; in some parts, however, there is no variation, but true direction poleward. On the continents, too, the needle often deflects from the meridian, as on the margin of the land and the confines, but the arc of variation is wont to be small: in the middle regions of great continents there is no variation. Hence in the heart of northern Europe and of Asia, in the interior of Africa, Peru, and of North or Mexican America, the versorium rests in the meridian.

CHAPTER 20. *The variation in the Eastern Ocean*

THE variation in the Eastern Ocean, all the way to Goa and the Moluccas, is noted by the Portuguese, but they are mistaken in very many points, for they follow the first observers who set down the variations for sundry places, ascertained by

[1] The name given by Scandinavian writers to that section of northeastern Russia bordering upon the White Sea.

the use of unfit instruments, or by inaccurate observations, or by conjecture. Thus in the island of Brandö[1] they make the compass vary 22 degrees to the northwest. Now, in no region, in no place on earth that has not a higher latitude than that, is the variation so much as 22 degrees: in fact the deviation on that island is trifling. So, when they say that in Mozambique the compass varies to the northwest one point, they are in error even though the compass they use is that of Portugal; for, without a doubt, the needle varies in Mozambique to the southwest one quarter of a point or more. Again, they are all wrong in holding that beyond the equator, on the route toward Goa, the compass varies westward one point and one half; better had they said that in the first part of the route the compass of Portugal inclines one point, but that a true or meridional compass varies only one-half point. Yet to determine the amount of the variation in the Eastern Ocean according to our rules, we need a more exact and correct reconnoissance of the austral continent, which stretches farther from the south toward the equinoctial than it is described in current charts and globes.

CHAPTER 21. *How the deviation of the needle is greater or less according to the distances of places*

In the heart of great continents there is no variation; so, too, in the midst of great seas. On the edge of such lands and seas the variation is often large, but not as great as it is a little out at sea: thus off Cape São Agostino there is variation, but 50 miles away to the east there is a larger variation; still larger 80 miles away and 100 miles away. But from 100 miles distance the reduction of the deviation is slower as you approach the continent than from the distance of 80 miles, and from 80 miles than from 50; for the deviation is changed and reduced somewhat more quickly as you come toward the shore from anear then from afar. So, for mariners approaching Newfoundland, the change of the variation is quicker (*i.e.*, a degree of variation is lost in a less arc of the route on a parallel) when they are not

[1] Brandö lies in the Gulf of Bothnia, close to the east coast of Sweden.

far from land than when they are 100 miles away; but when they journey inland the changes are more tardy at first than when they come farther into the interior.

The figure shows the ratio of the arcs on a parallel circle while a versorium is brought toward a continent that reaches to the pole; the ratio answers to the degrees of the variation. Let *A* be the pole, *B* the elevation of a great mass of land. At *C* there is no variation caused by *B*, which is too distant; at *D* the variation is greatest, because there the needle is attracted or is made by the whole earth to turn to the projecting land *B*; nor is the needle hindered, nor

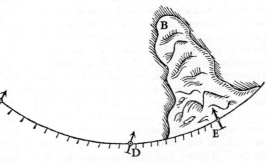

checked, nor led toward the pole by the verticity of this land, but, tending to the pole, it is nevertheless deflected therefrom, because of the site or position and convenient distance of the overmastering elevations of land.

But, now, from *C* to *D* the variation grows, yet the versorium does not deviate so quickly in the first stages as it does when near *D*. But you sail more miles on the parallel circle *CD* as long as you are near *C*, to register one degree of variation, than you sail when near *D*; so, too, in travelling from *D* toward *E* you must make a greater number of miles when near *D* than when near *E*. Thus there are equal deviations for unequal distances sailed, both for rising and falling variation, yet it falls within a less space than it rises. There are, however several other incidental cases that confuse this ratio.

BOOK FIFTH

CHAPTER 1. *Of the dip of the magnetic needle*

We come at last to that fine experiment, that wonderful movement of magnetic bodies as they dip beneath the horizon in virtue of their natural verticity; after we have mastered this, the wondrous combination, harmony, and concordant interaction of the earth and the loadstone (or magnetized iron), being made manifest by our theory, stand revealed. This motion we have so illustrated and demonstrated with many experiments, and purpose in what follows so to point out the causes and reasons, that no one endowed with reason and intelligence may justly contemn, or refute, or dispute our chief magnetic principles. Direction, as also variation, is demonstrated on the plane of the horizon whenever a magnetic needle poised in equilibrium comes to a rest in any fixed point of it. But inclination (dip) is seen to be the motion of the iron bar, first balanced on its axis and then excited by a loadstone, from that point in the horizon, one end or pole tending toward the earth's centre. And we have found that this inclination differs in the ratio of the latitude of each region. Now this movement is produced not by any motion away from the horizon toward the earth's centre, but by the turning of the whole of the magnetic body to the whole of the earth, as later we will show. Nor does the needle descend below the horizon in the ratio of the degrees of the elevation of the pole in the given region, and with an equal arc of the quadrant in any oblique sphere, as later will be seen. But how much the needle dips in every horizon can now first be ascertained by means of an instrument (which, however, is not very easily constructed), just as in sun-dials when the needle returns to points in the horizon, or as in the mariner's compass. Get a circular planed board with diameter at least six finger-lengths, which is to be fastened to one face of an upright square post and to rest on a wooden base. Divide the periphery of the instrument into four quadrants, and then each quadrant into ninety degrees. In the centre of the instrument drive a brass nail, and in the centre of its head bore a

small hole well reamed and smoothed. Adjust to the instrument a circle or ring of brass about two finger-breadths wide, with a transverse plate or flat bar of the same metal fastened across the middle of the ring and serving for horizon. In the middle of this horizon bar bore another hole which shall be exactly opposite to the centre of the instrument, in which a hole was already bored. Next get a steel wire such as is used for compass needles, and at the exact middle of it and at right angles to it pass a very thin iron axis through it so that the middle of the axis and the middle of the needle shall exactly meet; let this inclination (dipping) needle, the ends of the axis having been inserted into the holes, be suspended so that it may move freely and evenly on itself in most exact equilibrium, and so accurately that it may not turn away from any one degree or point marked on the circumference more than from any other, but may rest easily at any one point. Have the instrument fastened upright to the face of the post, and on the edge of the base set a very small magnetized versorium. The needle thus nicely balanced, now rub skilfully at both ends with the opposite poles of a loadstone, but do this with the greatest care lest the wire be in the least bent; for unless you do all this with great skill and dexterity, you will reach no result. Next get a second brass ring, a little larger than the first, so as to go round it, and to one rim fit a cover of glass or of very thin mica; this, when placed over the other ring, encloses the whole space, and the needle is protected from dust and currents of air. The instrument being now complete, set it up perpendicularly with the small versorium on the base, so that when thus erected exactly upright it may tend to the true point of the magnetic direction. Then that one of the needle's ends which in northern latitudes looks to the north dips below the horizon; but in southern latitudes the end of the needle that looks south tends toward the earth's centre in a certain ratio (afterward to be explained) of the latitude of the region in question from the equator on either side. But the needle must be rubbed with a powerful loadstone, else it does

Dip instrument

not dip at the true point or goes beyond it and is not always at rest in it. A larger instrument can also be employed, of ten or twelve finger-lengths diameter, but in that case there is more trouble in balancing the needle exactly. Care must be taken to have the needle of steel, also that it be straight, and that the sharp points of the axis on both ends be at right angles with the needle itself, and that it pass through the very centre.

As in other magnetic movements there is strict agreement and a clearly visible, sensible accordance between the earth and the loadstone in our demonstration, so in this inclination is the accordance of the globe of the earth and the loadstone positive and manifest. The true and definite cause of this great and hitherto unknown effect is as follows: The loadstone

moves and revolves until one of its poles, being impelled toward the north, comes to rest in its predetermined point on the horizon; the pole that comes to a stand looking north is (as appears from the foregoing rules and demonstrations) southern, not northern, though till now every one has supposed it to be northern because it turns to the north. An iron wire or versorium touched with this pole of the stone turns south, and is made northern because rubbed at the south end of the stone; just as when the point of a versorium is magnetized in that way it will be directed toward the earth's south pole and to that will turn, while the other end, the crotch, will be southern and will turn to the northern regions of the earth (the earth itself causing the motion), for thus does direction re-

sult from the bearings of the stone and the needle, and from the earth's verticity. But inclination (dip) is when the needle turns to the body
of the earth, its south end pointed to the north,
in any latitude away from the equator. For it
is a fixed and unchanging law that exactly beneath the celestial equator, or rather on the
equator of the terrestrial globe, the magnetic
inclination or dip of the needle is *nil;* and in
whatever way it may have been excited or
rubbed, it rests exactly on the plane of the horizon in the inclination instrument, provided it
be first duly balanced. The reason of this is, that
the needle, being at equal distance from the two
poles, does not in its rotation dip toward either,
but stands balanced, pointing to the level of
the equator, as it does when mounted on a
sharp point or floating free and unhindered on
water.

But when the needle is in any latitude from
the equator, or when one of the earth's poles
is raised (I do not say raised above the visible
horizon, like what is commonly reputed to be
the pole of the revolving world in the heavens,
but raised above the horizon of the centre or
above its own diameter, equidistant from the
plane of the visible horizon, which is the true
elevation of the earth's pole), then inclination
appears and the needle dips in its meridian towards the body of the earth. Thus, let *AB* be the
visible horizon of a region; *CD* the earth's horizon, dividing the earth into equal parts; *EF* the
earth's axis; *G* a place within the region: plainly
the north pole *E* rises above the point *C* by as
much as *G* is distant from the equator; therefore, since at *E* the magnetized needle is raised
to perpendicular just by its turning (to the
north), as has already been shown, so now at
G there is a sort of beginning of such a turning,
proportioned to the latitude (the magnetized
body departing from the plane of the horizon),
and the needle intersects at unequal angles the
horizon and shows dip beneath the horizon; for
this reason, if the dipping needle be placed at

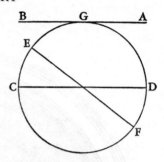

G, its south end (that which points north) descends below the plane of the visible horizon
AB. Thus there is very great difference between
a right and a polar or parallel sphere, in which
the pole is in the true zenith. For in a right
sphere the needle is parallel to the plane of the
horizon. But when the celestial pole is in the
vertical point, or when the earth's pole is itself
the place in question, then the needle is perpendicular to the horizon. This is shown on a terrella; suspend in air, like the beam of a balance,
a small dip needle of only two fingers-width
rubbed at a loadstone, and carefully bring the
terrella under it, and first let the terrella stand
properly as in a right sphere, and, as in the first
of the figures following, the needle will now remain in equilibrium. But in an oblique position
of the terrella, as in an oblique sphere and in
the second figure, the needle dips at one end
obliquely toward the neighbouring pole, but does
not rest on the pole, nor is its dip governed by
the pole, but by the whole body and mass; for
the dipping needle in a higher latitude sinks—
passes—beyond the pole. But in the third position of the terrella the needle is perpendicular,
because the pole of the stone is uppermost, and
the needle tending straight toward the body
attains the pole. The crotch in the foregoing
figures always turns toward the north pole of
the terrella, having been touched with its north
pole; the point having been touched by the
south pole of the terrella tends toward its south

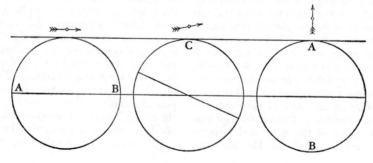

pole. Thus may we see the level, the oblique, and the perpendicular position of the needle on a terrella.

CHAPTER 2. *Diagram showing dip of the magnetic needle in different positions of a sphere and horizons of the earth in which there is no variation of dip*

LET *AB* be the equator, *C* the Arctic and *D* the Antarctic pole, *E*, *G* dipping needles in northern regions, and *H*, *F* in southern regions of the earth or the terrella. All the needles have been touched with the true Arctic pole of the terrella.

The figure shows the needles in horizontal position at *A* and *B*, the earth's and the terrella's equator; they are perpendicular at the poles *C* and *D*; but in the mid spaces, at distances of 45 degrees, the crotches dip toward the south, but the points look toward the north at the same angle.

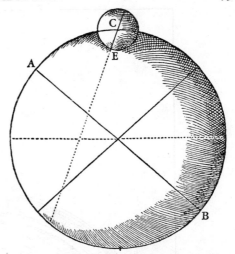

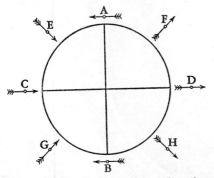

Diagram showing the direction and dip of a terrella representing the earth relative to the standard representation of the globe of the earth, at north latitude 50 degrees.

A is the north pole of the earth or of the large terrella; *B* its south pole, *C* is the smaller terrella, and *E* the south pole of the smaller terrella that dips toward the north region (of the larger). Its centre *C* is placed on the superficies of the larger terrella, because the smaller terrella varies a little on account of the length of the axis, but in the earth the variation is very little. As the needle dips in the latitude of a region of 50 degrees, so, too, the axis of the stone—which is spherical—is depressed beneath the horizon, and its south pole, which is within the circumference of the larger terrella dips, while in the south (of the larger terrella) its (the smaller terrella's) north pole is raised toward the zenith. And a flat circular piece of iron carefully magnetized at opposite points of its circumference acts in the same way; but these magnetic experiments are less striking because in iron disks the magnetic force is rather sluggish. The figure below shows, with bits of iron, the differences in dip at various latitudes in the terrella.

Below is shown the dip of the needle on a terrella by means of a number of bits of iron wire of equal size, one barley-corn in length, and placed in a meridian. At the equator the bits of iron are directed toward the poles, and lie upon the body of the terrella in the plane of its horizon. The nearer they are placed to the poles the more do they rise from the horizontal by reason of their turning poleward; at the poles they tend straight to the centre. But bits of iron will not stand up aright, save on a good loadstone, if they be too long.

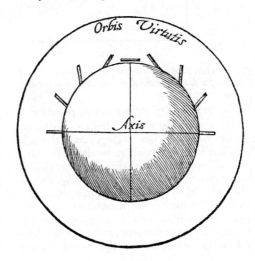

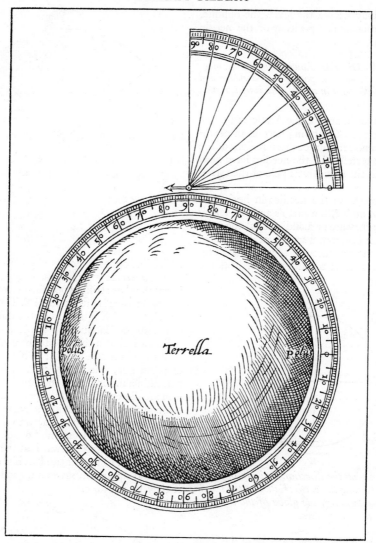

CHAPTER 3. *An instrument for showing by the action of a loadstone the degree of dip below the horizon in any latitude*

Description of the instrument; its uses

MAKE a perfectly round terrella of a superior strong loadstone, one homogeneous throughout, not injured anywhere by decay or corrosion, of proper size, so that its diameter shall be six or seven finger-breadths. Having, by the method heretofore given, found the poles, mark them with some iron instrument, also mark the equinoctial circle. Next, in a squared block of wood, one foot in diameter, make a hemispherical cavity to hold half of the terrella, so that just one half of the terrella shall rise above the block. Where the limb of the terrella is nearest the rim of this cavity draw a circle around it for a meridian, and then divide it into four equal parts or quadrants, and the quadrants each into 90 degrees. Let one end of the quadrants on the limb be near the centre of a quadrant on the block, and divide this also into 90 degrees. At that centre, place a small short versorium having one of its ends sharp and longer than the other, for use as a pointer, and let it be poised on a fitting sharp fulcrum. Evidently, whenever the poles of the terrella are at the beginnings (zero) of the quadrants, then the versorium will lie in a right line on the terrella as in equilibrium. But, if the terrella be moved so that one of the poles rises on the left, then the needle elevates itself in the meridian according to the latitude, just as a piece of magnetized iron rises; and the needle indicates upon the quadrant described on the block the degrees of the dip. The rim of the cavity in the block represents a meridian circle, and to it answers some meridian circle of the terrella, for the poles on both sides are upon the inner circumference of the rim. This is precisely what takes place on the earth itself where there is no variation; but when there is variation either of direction or of dip, *i.e.*, a disordering of the proper magnetic revolution for causes later to be set forth, then there is some difference. The quadrant described on the block must be near the limb of the terrella, or its centre must be at the limb itself, and the needle must be very short so as not to touch the terrella; for there is error when the needle is long or placed at a distance, as it has a truly proportionate movement only at the superficies of the terrella. But were the quadrant—being remote from the terrella—to be moved into its sphere of influence toward the pole on a circle concentric with the terrella, then the needle would indicate on the quadrant the degrees of dip in ratio and symmetry with that circle, not with the terrella.

CHAPTER 4. *Of a suitable length of needle on the terrella for showing the dip*

WHEN it is sought to define the dip by means of a dip-indicating instrument on the earth itself, we may use either a short versorium or one ever so long, provided only the magnetic property of the loadstone with which it has been stroked is able to pervade its whole substance and length. For the greatest length of a versorium, as compared with the earth's diameter, is insignificant and has no ratio perceptible by sense. But on a terrella, or on a plane nigh a meridian of a terrella, a short needle is required, one barley-corn's length; for longer versoria (because they reach farther), in the first degrees of dip, descend suddenly and irregularly, and turn to the body of the terrella. For example,

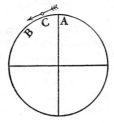

as soon as the long versorium in the figure is moved onward from the equator *A* to *C*, it lays hold of the stone with its point *C* as though with a long outspread wing, when the point reaches the parts around *B*, which give it a greater revolution than those at *C*. And the ends of rather long pieces of wire or little rods are also made to rotate irregularly, just as pieces of iron wire and iron balls and other spherical loadstones are made to rotate irregularly by an oblong loadstone not rounded into a ball. Yet magnetic bodies or pieces of iron on the surface of a terrella should not have a long but a very short axis, so that they may dip true and naturally; for a long versorium situated near a terrella does not easily stand in a right sphere on the horizon, and wavers and suddenly dips to one side or the other, especially its magnetized end, or, if both ends are magnetized, then the end magnetized last.

CHAPTER 5. *That dip is not caused by the attraction of a loadstone, but by its power of giving direction and rotation*

THROUGHOUT nature we have to recognize that wondrous work of the Maker whereby the principal bodies are restricted within particular localities and, as it were, hedged round with fences, nature so ordering. Hence it is that heavenly bodies do not get confused in their motions and in their progressions beyond each other. Similarly are the magnetic revolutions produced by the force of a greater and dominant body as well as by that of a lesser and subject body, though that be of very small volume. For the work is not done by attraction but by incitation on the part of both, and that with a proportionate movement toward fixed points beyond which there is no further motion. For did the versorium dip under the action of an attractive force, then a terrella fashioned out of a very powerful loadstone would pull it to itself more than would one made of an indifferent loadstone, and iron stroked by a strong loadstone would have greater dip; but that is never so. Further, a piece of iron attached to and projecting from the terrella at any latitude does not cause a little iron bar to rise more to perpendicular than does the unarmed stone, though when so armed the stone does seize and lift far heavier weights. But if a loadstone be somewhat fashioned to a point at one end, and rather obtuse at the other, the acute end or pole solicits with greater force magnetized iron, the obtuse, thick end makes the iron turn to itself more powerfully; but a spherical stone makes it turn to itself powerfully and in true direction according to magnetic laws and the form of spheres; while a loadstone of some length from pole to pole stirs the versorium unequally, for in such a stone the pole of the versorium always is pointed toward the pole of the loadstone itself. So, too, if the loadstone take a disk shape, with the poles in the circumference, but with the body plane and not spherical, when the plane is brought near to the versorium, the versorium does not move with the regular magnetic movement as with a terrella, but turns round always pointing toward the pole of the loadstone situated in the circumference of the plane. Besides, if the stone caused the versorium to revolve by attraction, then in the first degrees of latitude it would attract toward the mass of the terrella itself the end of a short versorium; but it does not so attract as to bring the two together and into coition— the versorium simply revolves so far as nature demands, as is shown in the following instance.

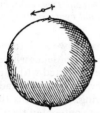

For here the point of a versorium in a low latitude neither touches the stone nor comes into coition with it, only inclines toward it. Further, when the versorium rotates as it dips, the pole of the versorium is not stayed nor held by the pole of the earth or the terrella, but revolves regularly, nor remains in any point or terminus nor looks straight to the pole toward which the centre of the versorium advances, save at the pole itself, and that only once between the pole and the equator; but the inclination goes on according as the change in the site of the centre produces a dip in conformity to magnetic laws. The dip of the needle in water, demonstrated in the sequel, is also constant: the needle does not dip toward the bottom of the vessel, but stands in mid direction poised on its centre according to its due dip; yet this would not be the case if the earth or its poles by attraction made the extremity of the needle to dip.

CHAPTER 6. *Of the ratio of dip to latitude and the causes thereof*

WE have spoken of the construction of the instrument for determining the dip, of the causes and modes of the dip, and of the different inclinations of the needle for different localities; of the inclination of the loadstone, too, and of an instrument for showing the power of the stone at any latitude, as well as of the demonstrated rotation (by erection) of pieces of iron on a meridian of the stone, according to latitude. We have now to treat more at length of the causes of this proportionate inclination. A loadstone and a piece of iron wire, when moved in a meridian from the equator to the pole, turn toward a spherical loadstone, and toward the earth also, with a circular motion. In a right horizon (as also upon the equinoctial circle of the stone) the axis of the iron, which is its middle, is a line parallel with the earth's axis. When that axis reaches the pole, which is its centre, it stands still in the same right line with the earth's axis. The same end of the iron that at the equator points south turns to the north; for it is not a movement of centre to centre, but of one magnetic body to another, and a natural turning of the axis of the body to the axis of the terrella, not caused by the pole's attraction, so that the iron should regard the earth's polar point. On the equator the magnetic iron stands in horizontal equilibrium, but toward the pole on either side of the equator, at every latitude from the beginning of the first degree even to the 90th, it dips; yet, not in ratio to the number of degrees or the arc of the latitude does the magnetic needle dip so many degrees or over a like arc; but over a very different one, for this movement is in truth not a dipping movement, but really a revolution movement, and it describes an arc of revolution proportioned to the arc of latitude. Hence the magnetic body *A*, while it

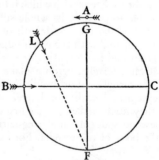

passes round the earth, or an earthkin or terrella, from the equinoctial circle *G* toward *B* (the pole), rotates on its centre, and, midway in its progress from the equator to pole *B*, points to the equator *F* as the mean of the two poles: therefore ought the versorium to rotate much more quickly than the centre travels in order to regard the point *F* in a right line by rotating. For this reason the movement of this rotation is quick in the first degrees from the equator, from *A* to *L*, but slower in the subsequent degrees, from *L* to *B*, that is, with reference to the equatorial point *F*, toward *C*. But were dip equal to the latitude, *i.e.*, always so many degrees from the horizon as the centre of the versorium has gone away from the equator, then the magnetic needle would obey the potency and the peculiar virtue of the centre as a point operating of itself; but it obeys the whole and its mass and outer limits, the powers of both co-operating, to wit, those of the magnetized versorium and of the earth.

CHAPTER 7. *Explanation of the diagram of the rotation of magnetized iron*

LET *ACDL* be the body of the earth or of a terrella, *M* the centre, *AD* the equator, *CL* the axis, *AB* the horizon, which changes according to the locality. From the point *F* in the horizon,

at a distance from the equator *A* equal to the semi-diameter *CM* of earth or terrella, is described an arc to *H* as terminus of the quadrants of dip: for all quadrants of dip that belong (*inserviunt*) to the parts between *A* and *C* begin at that arc and terminate in the earth's centre, *M*. The semi-diameter of this arc is a chord drawn from the equator *A* to the pole *C*. And a line equal to that chord, drawn in the horizon to *B*,

gives the starting point of the arc of the termini of the arcs of revolution and rotation, which arc is continued on to *G*. For as the quadrant of a circle around the earth's centre (the starting-point of it being in the horizon, at a distance from the equator equal to the earth's semi-diameter) is the terminus of all the quadrants of dip produced from every horizon to the centre, so a circle round the centre from the starting point of the first arc of rotation *B* to *G* is the terminus of the arcs of rotation. Between the arc of rotation *BL* and *BG* are intermediate arcs of revolution and rotation of the magnetic needle. The centre of the arc is the region or place where the observation is obtained; the beginning of the arc is taken from the circle that is terminus of the revolutions, and it ends at the opposite pole, as from *O* to *L*, in 45 degrees latitude. Divide any arc of revolution into 90 equal parts from the terminus of the arcs of revolution to the pole; for whatever the degree of latitude of the place, that part of the arc of revolution is to be reckoned as cognominal to it which the magnetic pole in rotating upon or around terrella or earth regards: in the large diagram that follows, this is indicated by the right lines. In the middle latitude of 45 degrees the magnetic rotation is directed to the equator, and there also the arc from its terminus to the pole is the quadrant of a circle; but at latitudes above this (*i.e.*, nearer the equator) all the arcs of revolution are greater than a quadrant; in latitudes below this (*i.e.*, higher, farther from the equator) they are less: in the former the needle rotates quickly; in the latter it gradually rotates more slowly. Each region has its own arc of revolution, in which is, according to the number of the degree of latitude of the place, the terminus toward which the needle turns; so that a right line drawn from the region to a point in that arc cognominal to the number of the degree of latitude indicates the magnetic direction, and shows the degree of the inclination at the intersection of the quadrant of dip that belongs to the given region. Take away the arc of the quadrant of dip from the centre to the line of magnetic direction, and what remains is the arc of dip beneath the horizon. Thus, in the rotation of the versorium *N*, whose line of magnetic direction extends to *D*, take away from the quadrant of dip *SM* its arc *RM*, and what remains will be the arc of dip, that is, it shows how much the needle dips in latitude 45 degrees.

CHAPTER 8. *Diagram of the rotation of magnetized iron, showing the magnetic dip in all latitudes, and showing the latitude from the rotation and dip*

IN the foregoing diagram, around the body of the earth or of the terrella are drawn a circle of rotation and a circle of dip, together with a first, a last, and a middle arc of rotation and dip. Now from each one fifth part of that arc which terminates all the arcs of rotation (and each of which also is supposed to be divided into 90 equal parts) are drawn arcs to the pole, and from every fifth degree of the arc terminating the quadrants of dip are drawn quadrants to the centre, and at the same time is drawn a spiral line indicating (by the aid of a movable quadrant) the dip in every latitude. Right lines of magnetic direction are drawn from the degrees marked on the meridian of earth or terrella to their proper arcs and to the parts answering to those arcs.

How to ascertain the elevation of the pole, or the latitude of any place, by means of the following diagram, turned into a magnetic instrument, in any part of the world, without the help of the heavenly bodies, sun, planets, or fixed stars, and in foggy weather as well as in darkness

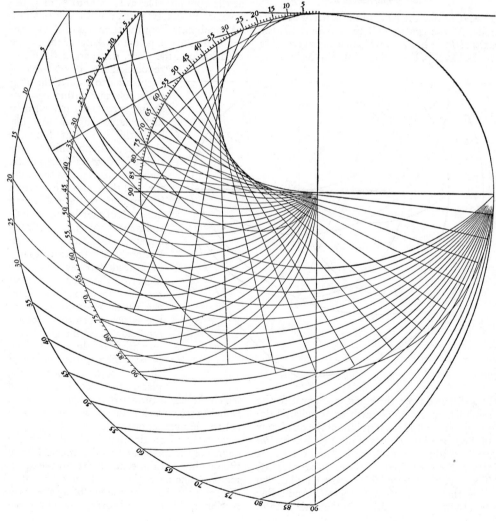

We can see how far from idle is the magnetic philosophy; on the contrary, how delightful, how beneficial, how divine! Seamen tossed by the waves and vexed with incessant storms, while they cannot learn even from the heavenly luminaries aught as to where on earth they are, may with the greatest ease gain comfort from an insignificant instrument, and ascertain the latitude of the place where they happen to be. With a dip instrument an observation is taken of the degree of the needle's dip beneath the horizon; that degree is noted on the inside

arc of the quadrant, and the quadrant is turned round at the centre of the instrument until that degree on the quadrant touches the spiral line: then in the open space B, at the centre of the quadrant, the latitude of the region on the periphery of the globe is found by the *linea fiduciæ AB*. Draw the diagram on a suitable planed board, and to its centre attach the centre of the angle of the quadrant A, so that the quadrant may rotate on that centre. But it must be remembered also that in some places there is variation in dip for the causes aforesaid (albeit the variation is not great): this variation also it will be well to study, and to account for on some probable hypothesis, and it will be of very great interest to observe it in different localities, for this variation of dip seems to present more difficulty than the variation of direction; but it is readily understood with dip instruments when

it disagrees either by plus or by minus with the diagram.

Observing the magnetic dip at sea

Place the dip instrument upon our variation instrument, a wooden ball being put between the round movable compass-box and the dip instrument; but first remove the versorium, lest it interfere with the dip instrument. In this way, when the sea is in commotion the compass-box will remain erect on the level of the horizon. The dip compass is to be directed, by means of a small versorium at its base, to the point of the variation, to the greater circle of which (commonly called the magnetic meridian) the plane of the upright compass conforms; thus the dip instrument, in virtue of its property of rotating, shows the degree of the dip.

In a dip instrument the magnetic needle which when on a meridian circle descends, hangs perpendicular when it lies on a parallel.

The magnetic needle, in due position, while it conforms itself to the earth in virtue of its rotatory property, dips in an oblique sphere to a certain extent. But when the plane of the instrument is removed from the plane of the meridian, the needle (which tends poleward) no longer remains in the degree of its dip, but inclines more toward the centre, for the directional force is greater than that of the dip; and all power of dip is taken away if the plane of the instrument be on a parallel. For then the needle, its axis being transverse, cannot take its due position, and so tends perpendicular to earth, and remains only in its own meridian, or in what is commonly called the magnetic meridian.

CHAPTER 9. *Demonstration of direction, or of variation from the true direction, together with dip, simply by the movement in water, due to the power of controlling and rotating*

Pass through a round cork three finger-breadths of thin iron wire, so that the cork may support the iron in water. Let the water be contained in a vase or large goblet of glass. With a very sharp knife pare the cork away gradually (still preserving its rotundity) till it will stand a finger-breadth or two under the surface motionless, with the wire evenly balanced. Then stroke one

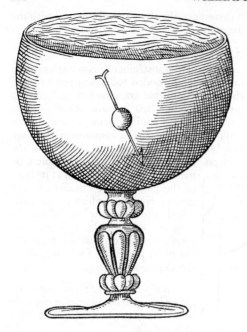

end of the wire on the north pole of a loadstone, the other end on the south pole (very carefully, so that the cork may not be moved ever so little out of its place), and put the instrument again in the water. The wire will dip with a circular movement on its centre below the plane of the horizon, according to the latitude of the place, and even as it dips will show (the true direction being disordered) the point of variation. The loadstone with which it is rubbed should be a powerful one, such as is required in all magnetic demonstrations. When the wire having been thus put in the water, and treated with the loadstone, comes to a standstill in the line of the dip, its lower end remains in the point of variation in an arc of a great circle, or meridian, passing through the zenith and the point of variation in the horizon, and through that lowermost point of the heavens called nadir: all this is demonstrated by bringing a rather long magnetized needle near the vessel on one side. This is a demonstration of the absolute conforming of a magnetic body to unity with the earth's body; here in the natural way is manifested direction with variation thereof and dip. But it is to be understood that delicate and difficult as this experiment is, so it does not continue, for the apparatus does not remain in the midst of the water, but at last sinks to the bottom when the cork has taken in too much water.

CHAPTER 10. *Of variation of dip*

WE have already spoken of direction and of variation as a sort of derangement of direction. Now we observe a like irregular movement in the dip, when it descends beneath the limits or when, as sometimes happens, it does not reach its due bounds. Thus the variation of the dip is an arc of the magnetic meridian betwixt the true and the apparent dip. For as, because of elevations of the earth magnetized bodies are pulled to one side, so, too, the needle (its rotation being a little increased) dips beyond the due measure. And as variation is a deviation in direction, so, for the same reason, there is some error of dip, albeit usually a trifling one. Sometimes, too, though there be no variation of direction on the horizon, there may nevertheless be a variation of the dip, to wit, when either in a direct meridian line, *i.e.*, on the meridian itself, there projects some magnetically powerful earthmass, or when such elevations have less force than is called for by the general constitution of the globe, or when the energy is over-concentrated in one part, and in another is diffused, as we may see in the Atlantic Ocean. And this discrepancy of constitution, this variance of effect, we easily recognize in certain parts of every spherical loadstone. The inequality of force in the various regions of a terrella is shown by the conclusive experiment described in Chapter 2 of this Book. And the effect is clearly shown by the demonstrational instrument, an account of which is contained in Chapter 3 of the same Book.

CHAPTER 11. *Of the formal magnetic act spherically effused*

REPEATEDLY we have spoken of the poles of earth and terrella and of the equinoctial circle; last we treated of the dip of magnetized bodies earthward and terrellaward, and the causes thereof. But having with divers and manifold contrivances laboured long and hard to get at the cause of this dip, we have by good fortune discovered a new and admirable science of the spheres themselves—a science surpassing the marvels of all the virtues magnetical. For such is the property of magnetic spheres that their force is poured forth and diffused beyond their superficies spherically, the form being exalted above the bounds of corporeal nature; and the mind that has diligently studied this natural philosophy will discover the definite causes of the movements and revolutions. The potencies of a terrella, too, are of the same kind throughout the whole sphere of its influence, and the spheres (of influence) themselves, at whatever distance from the body of the terrella, have, in the ratio of their diameter and the quantity of their superficies, termini of their forces, or, in other words, there are points whereat magnetic bodies turn toward them; and these bodies do not regard the same part or point of the terrella at every distance whatever therefrom (unless they be in the axis of the spheres and the terrella), but ever do tend toward those points of the spheres (of influence) which are equal arcs distant from their common axis. Thus in the following diagram we show the body of a terrella,

the air or water took them on or were by them informated; for the forms are only effused and really subsist when magnetic bodies are present: hence the magnetic body within the forces and limits of the spheres is taken hold of, and in the several spheres magnetic bodies control other bodies magnetical and excite them even as though the spheres of influence were solid materiate loadstones; for the magnetic force does not proceed through the whole of the medium, nor exists really as in a continuous body; and so the spheres are magnetical, and yet are not real spheres existing by themselves.

AB is the axis of a terrella and its spheres; *CD*

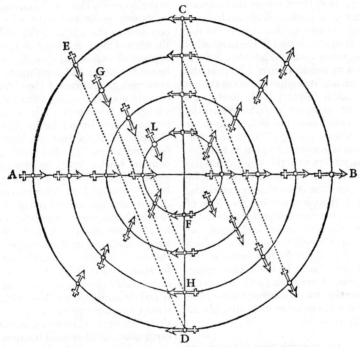

Diagram of the movements in the magnetic spheres.

with its poles and equator; also a magnetic needle in three other concentric spheres around the terrella and at some distance therefrom. In these spheres (and they may be imagined as infinite) the magnetic needle or versorium regards its own sphere in which it is placed and its diameter, poles, and equator, not those of the terrella; and it is by these and in accordance with the magnitude of these that it is made to rotate and is directed, both while its centre stands still and while it advances in any arc whatever of that sphere. Still we do not mean that the magnetic forms and spheres exist in the air, or water, or any other medium not magnetical, as though

the equator. In all the spheres, as on the terrella, at the equator the versorium lies in the plane of the horizon; in the axis it everywhere regards the centre perpendicularly; in the mid spaces, *E* regards *D*, and *G* regards *H*, not *F*, which is regarded by the versorium *L* on the superficies of the terrella. But as is the proportion of *L* to *F* on the terrella's superficies, such is that of *G* to *H* in its own sphere, and of *E* to *D* in its own sphere; so all the revolutions in the spheres to the termini of the spheres are such as are the revolutions at the surface of the terrella or to its termini. But if in the more distant spheres there is now and then some error, that is to be charged to the inertia of the loadstone or to weakened power, because of the too great distance of the spheres from the terrella.

Demonstration

Upon the instrumental diagram above described, place a small board or a strong disk of brass or tin on which are inscribed the magnetic spheres, as in the diagram; and in the middle make a hole proportioned to the size of the terrella, so that the board may lie evenly on the middle of it along the meridian circle above the wood. Then in one of the spheres of influence place a small versorium one barley-corn long; the versorium, as it there moves into various positions in the same circle, will always have regard to the dimensions of that sphere and not those of the terrella, as is seen in the diagram of the effused magnetic forms. While some writers posit as causes of the wonderful effects of the loadstone occult and recondite virtues of things, and others regard a property of the loadstone's substance as the cause, we have discovered the primary substantial form not in some more or less probable foreshadowing of truth or in reasons that admit of controversy; but as in many other demonstrations, so in this most indisputable diagram of the forces magnetical effused by the form, we grasp the true efficient cause. And this (the form), though it is subject to none of our senses and is therefore less perceptible to the intellect, now appears manifest and visible before our very eyes through this formal act, which proceeds from it as light proceeds from a source of light. And here it is to be noted that a magnetic needle moved over the earth, or over a terrella, or over the effused spheres, rotates completely twice in one circuit of its centre, like an epicycle round its circle.

CHAPTER 12. *The magnetic force is animate, or imitates a soul; in many respects it surpasses the human soul while that is united to an organic body*

WONDERFUL is the loadstone shown in many experiments to be, and, as it were, animate. And this one eminent property is the same which the ancients held to be a soul in the heavens, in the globes, and in the stars, in sun and moon. For they deemed that not without a divine and animate nature could movements so diverse be produced, such vast bodies revolve in fixed times, or potencies so wonderful be infused into other bodies; whereby the whole world blooms with most beautiful diversity through this primary form of the globes themselves. The ancient philosophers, as Thales, Heraclitus, Anaxagoras

Archelaus, Pythagoras, Empedocles, Parmenides, Plato and all the Platonists—nor Greek philosophers alone, but also the Egyptian and Chaldean—all seek in the world a certain universal soul, and declare the whole world to be endowed with a soul. Aristotle held that not the universe is animate, but the heavens only; his elements he made out to be inanimate; but the stars were for him animate. As for us, we find this soul only in the globes and in their homogenic parts, and albeit this soul is not in all globes the same (for that in the sun or in certain stars is much superior to that in other less noble globes). Still in very many globes the souls agree in their powers. Thus, each homogenic part tends to its own globe and inclines in the direction common to the whole world, and in all globes the effused forms reach out and are projected in a sphere all round, and have their own bounds—hence the order and regularity of all the motions and revolutions of the planets, and their circuits, not pathless, but fixed and determinate, wherefore Aristotle concedes to the spheres and heavenly orbs (which he imagines) a soul, for the reason that they are capable of circular motion and action and that they move in fixed, definite, tracks. And I wonder much why the globe of earth with its effluences should have been by him and his followers condemned and driven into exile and cast out of all the fair order of the glorious universe, as being brute and soulless. In comparison with the whole creation 'tis a mere mite, and amid the mighty host of many thousands is lowly, of small account, and deformate. And to it the Aristotelians add allied elements that by like ill-fortune are also beggarly and despicable. Thus Aristotle's world would seem to be a monstrous creation, in which all things are perfect, vigorous, animate, while the earth alone, luckless small fraction, is imperfect, dead, inanimate, and subject to decay. On the other hand, Hermes, Zoroaster, Orpheus, recognize a universal soul. As for us, we deem the whole world animate, and all globes, all stars, and this glorious earth, too, we hold to be from the beginning by their own destinate souls governed and from them also to have the impulse of self-preservation. Nor are the organs required for organic action lacking, whether implanted in the homogenic nature or scattered through the homogenic body, albeit these organs are not made up of viscera as animal organs are, nor consist of definite members; indeed in some plants and shrubs the organs are hardly recognizable, nor are visible organs essential for life in all cases. Neither in any of the stars, nor in the sun, nor in the planets that are most operant in the world, can organs be distinguished or imagined by us; nevertheless, they live and endow with life small bodies at the earth's elevated points. If there is aught of which man may boast, that of a surety is soul, is mind; and the other animals, too, are ennobled by soul; even God, by whose rod all things are governed, is soul. But who shall assign organs to the divine intellects, seeing that they are superior to all organ-structure, nor are comprised in material organs? But in the bodies of the several stars the inborn energy works in ways other than in that divine essence which presides over nature; and in the stars, the sources of all things, in other ways than in animals; finally, in animals in other ways than in plants. Pitiable is the state of the stars, abject the lot of earth, if this high dignity of soul is denied them, while it is granted to the worm, the ant, the roach, to plants and morels; for in that case worms, roaches, moths, were more beauteous objects in nature and more perfect, inasmuch as nothing is excellent, nor precious, nor eminent, that hath not soul. But since living bodies spring from earth and sun and by them are animate, and since in the earth herbage springs up without sowing of seeds (*e.g.*, when soil is taken out of the bowels of the earth and carried to some great elevation or to the top of a lofty tower and there exposed to the sunshine, after a little while a miscellaneous herbage springs up in it unbidden), it is not likely that they (sun and earth) can do that which is not in themselves; but they awaken souls, and consequently are themselves possessed of souls. Therefore the bodies of the globes, as being the foremost parts of the universe, to the end they might be in themselves and in their state endure, had need of souls to be conjoined to them, for else there were neither life, nor prime act, nor movement, nor unition, nor order, nor coherence, nor *conactus*, nor *sympathia*, nor any generation, nor alternation of seasons, and no propagation; but all were in confusion and the entire world lapse into chaos, and, in fine, the earth were void and dead and without any use. But only on the superficies of the globes is plain-ly seen the host of souls and of animate existences, and in their great and delightful diversity the Creator taketh pleasure. But the souls (in the interior of the globes) confined, as it were, by prison bars send not forth their effused immaterial forms beyond the limits of the body, nor are bodies put in motion by them without labour and exertion; a breath carries and bears them forth; but if that breath be fouled or stilled by mischance, the bodies lie like the world's recrement or as the waste matter of the globes. But the globes themselves remain and endure, rotate and move in orbits, and without wasting or weariness run their courses. The human soul uses reason, sees many things, investigates many more; but, however well equipped, it gets light and the beginnings of knowledge from the outer senses, as from beyond a barrier—hence the very many ignorances and foolishnesses whereby our judgments and our life-actions are confused, so that few or none do rightly and duly order their acts. But the earth's magnetic force and the formate soul or animate form of the globes, that are without senses, but without error and without the injuries of ills and diseases, exert an unending action, quick, definite, constant, directive, motive, imperant, harmonious, through the whole mass of matter; thereby are the generation and the ultimate decay of all things on the superficies propagated. For if it were not for the movement whereby the daily revolution is accomplished, all things here on earth were wild and disordered, and worse than desert and unused would they ever remain. Yet these movements in nature's founts are not produced by thoughts or reasonings or conjectures, like human acts, which are contingent, imperfect, and indeterminate, but connate in them are reason, knowledge, science, judgment, whence proceed acts positive and definite from the very foundations and beginnings of the world: these, because of the weakness of our soul, we cannot comprehend. Wherefore, not without reason, Thales, as Aristotle reports in his book *On the Soul*, declares the loadstone to be animate, a part of the animate mother earth and her beloved offspring.

BOOK SIXTH

CHAPTER 1. *Of the globe of earth as a loadstone*

HITHERTO we have spoken of the loadstone and magnetic bodies, how they conspire together and act on each other, and how they conform themselves to the terrella and to the earth. Now we have to treat of the globe of earth itself separately. All the experiments that are made on the terrella, to show how magnetic bodies conform themselves to it, may—at least the principal and most striking of them—be shown on the body of the earth; to the earth, too, all magnetized bodies are associate. And first, on the terrella the equinoctial circle, the meridians, parallels, the axis, the poles, are natural limits: similarly on the earth these exist as natural and not merely mathematical limits. As on the periphery of a terrella a loadstone or the magnetic needle takes direction to the pole, so on the earth there are revolutions special, manifest, and constant, from both sides of the equator: iron is endowed with verticity by being stretched toward the pole of the earth as toward the pole of a terrella; again, by being laid down and suffered to grow cool lying toward the earth's pole, after its prior verticity has been destroyed by fire, it acquires new verticity conformed to the position earthward. And iron rods that have for a long time lain in the poleward direction acquire verticity simply by regarding the earth; just as the same rods, if they be pointed toward the pole of a loadstone, though not touching it, receive polar force. There is no magnetic body that draws nigh in any way to a loadstone which does not in like manner obey the earth. As a loadstone is more powerful at one end and at one side of the equator, so the same thing is shown with a small terrella on a large one. According to the difference in amount and mode of friction in magnetizing a piece of iron at a terrella, it will be powerful or weak in performing its functions. In movements toward the body of the earth, just as on a terrella, variation is produced by unlikeness and inequality of prominences and by imperfections of the surface; and all variation of the versorium or the mariner's compass all over the earth and every-

where at sea—a thing that has so bewildered men's minds—is found and recognized through the same causes. The dip of the magnetic needle (that wonderful turning of magnetic bodies to the body of the terrella by formal progression) is seen also in the earth most clearly. And that one experiment reveals plainly the grand magnetic nature of the earth, innate in all the parts thereof and diffused throughout. The magnetic energy, therefore, exists in the earth just as in the terrella, which is a part of the earth and homogenic in nature with it, but by art made spherical so it might correspond to the spherical body of the earth and be in agreement with the earth's globe for the capital experiments.

CHAPTER 2. *The magnetic axis of the earth remains invariable*

THE earth's magnetic axis, just as it passed through the midearth in the very beginnings of the moving world, so to-day tends through the centre to the same points of the superficies, the equinoctial line and plane also persisting the same. For not, save with a vast demolition of the terrestrial mass, may these natural bounds be altered, as is easily shown by magnetic demonstrations. Wherefore the opinion held by Dominicus Maria of Ferrara, a man of rare ability, and who was the preceptor of Nicolaus Copernicus, is to be rejected. It was based on certain observations, and was as follows: "Some years ago," he writes, "while considering Ptolemy's geography, I found the elevations of the north pole given by him for the several regions to fall short by one degree and ten minutes of what they are in our time, which difference can by no means be referred to an error of the table, for it is not credible that the whole book should be throughout equally wrong in the figures contained in the tables; therefore we must suppose the north pole brought toward the vertical point. Thus a protracted observation began to disclose to us things hid from our ancestors—not through any sloth on their part, but because they lacked observation of a long period by their predecessors. For very few places before Ptolemy's time were observed in elevations of the pole, as he himself testifies in the beginning of his *Cosmographia*: 'Hipparchus alone,' he writes, 'hath handed down to us the latitudes of a few places; but many latitudes of distances, especially of distances to east and west, have been fixed on a basis of general tradition, and this is not from any indolence of writers, but because they were unacquaint with a more accurate mathematic.' Hence it is no wonder if our predecessors have not noted the very slow movement, seeing that in 1700 years it has advanced about one degree toward the uttermost point of human habitation. This is shown at the Straits of Gibraltar, where in Ptolemy's day the north pole was raised 36¼ degrees above the horizon, while now it is 37²/₅ degrees. A like difference is shown by Leucopetra (Capo dell' Armi) in Calabria and sundry other places in Italy, namely, places that have not changed from Ptolemy's time to ours. Thus, in consequence of this movement, places that now are inhabited will one day be deserted, while those that now are scorched by the tropic sun will, albeit after a long time, be reduced to our temperature. For this very slow movement will be completed in 395,000 years."

Thus, according to Dominicus Maria's observations, the north pole is raised higher and the latitudes of places are greater now than in the past: from this he infers a change of latitudes. But Stadius, holding the directly opposite opinion, proves by observations that the latitudes have grown less. "The latitude of Rome," says he, "is given in the *Geographica* of Ptolemy as 41²/₃ degrees; and lest any one should say that some error has crept into the text of Ptolemy, Pliny relates, and Vitruvius in his Ninth Book testifies, that at Rome on the day of the equinox the ninth part of the gnomon's shadow is lacking. But recent observation (as Erasmus Rheinhold states) gives the latitude of Rome in our age as 41¹/₆ degrees; so that you are in doubt whether one half of a degree has been lost in the centre of the world, or whether it is the result of an obliquation of the earth." From this we may see how, on the basis of inexact observations, men conceive new and contrary opinions as to the earth's mechanism, and postulate absurd motions. For, as Ptolemy simply took from Hipparchus a few latitudes and did not himself observe them in many places, it is likely that, knowing the position of the countries, he made a conjectural estimate of the latitude of cities, and set such conjectures down in his tables. So, here, in Britain, the latitudes of cities vary two or three degrees, as we know by experience.

Hence no new movement is to be postulated on the ground of these miscalculations, nor is the grand magnetic nature of the earth to be deformed for the sake of a judgment so rashly arrived at. And these errors have crept into geography all the more easily because the magnetic force was quite unknown to authors. Besides, observations of latitudes cannot be made with exactitude save by experts, with the help of large instruments, and by taking account of refraction of lights.

CHAPTER 3. *Of the daily magnetic revolution of the globes, as against the time-honored opinion of a* primum mobile: *a probable hypothesis*

AMONG the ancients, Heraclides of Pontus, and Ecphantus, the Pythagoreans Nicetas of Syracuse and Aristarchus of Samos, and, as it seems, many others, held that the earth moves, that the stars set through the interposition of the earth, and that they rise through the earth's giving way: they do give the earth motion, and the earth being, like a wheel, supported on its axis, rotates upon it from west to east. The Pythagorean Philolaus would have the earth to be one of the stars, and to turn in an oblique circle toward the fire, just as the sun and moon have their paths: Philolaus was an illustrious mathematician and a very experienced investigator of nature. But when philosophy had come to be handled by many, and had been given out to the public, then theories adapted to the capacity of the vulgar herd or supported with sophistical subtleties found entrance into the minds of the many, and, like a torrent, swept all before them, having gained favor with the multitude. Then were many fine discoveries of the ancients rejected and discredited—at the least were no longer studied and developed. First, therefore, Copernicus among moderns (a man most worthy of the praise of scholarship) undertook, with new hypotheses, to illustrate the *phænomena* of bodies in motion; and these demonstrations of reasons, other authors, men most conservent with all manner of learning, either follow, or, the more surely to discover the alleged "symphony" of motion, do observe. Thus the suppositions and purely imaginary spheres postulated by Ptolemy and others for finding the times and periods of movements, are not of necessity to be accepted in the physical lectures of philosophers.

It is then an ancient opinion, handed down from the olden time, but now developed by great thinkers, that the whole earth makes a diurnal rotation in the space of twenty-four hours. But since we see the sun, the moon, and the other planets, and the whole heavenly host, within the term of one day come and depart, then either the earth whirls in daily motion from west to east, or the whole heavens and all the rest of the universe of things necessarily speeds about from east to west. But in the first place, it is not probable that the highest heaven and all those visible splendors of the fixed stars are swept round in this rapid headlong career. Besides, what genius ever has found in one same (Ptolemaic) sphere those stars which we call fixed, or ever has given rational proof that there are any such adamantine spheres at all? No man hath shown this ever; nor is there any doubt that even as the planets are at various distances from earth, so, too, are those mighty and multitudinous luminaries ranged at various heights and at distances most remote from earth: they are not set in any sphæric framework or firmament (as is supposed), nor in any vaulted structure. As for the intervals (between the spheres) imagined by some authors, they are matters of speculation, not of fact; those other intervals do far surpass them and are far more remote; and, situated as they are in the heavens, at various distances, in thinnest æther, or in that most subtile fifth essence, or in vacuity—how shall the stars keep their places in the mighty swirl of these enormous spheres composed of a substance of which no one knows aught? Astronomers have observed 1022 stars; besides these, innumerable other stars appear minute to our senses; as regards still others, our sight grows dim, and they are hardly discernible save by the keenest eye; nor is there any man possessing the best power of vision that will not, while the moon is below the horizon and the atmosphere is clear, feel that there are many more indeterminable and vacillating by reason of their faint light, obscured because of the distance. Hence, that these are many and that they never can be taken in by the eye, we may well believe. What, then, is the inconceivably great space between us and these remotest fixed stars? and what is the vast immeasurable amplitude and height of the imaginary sphere in which they are supposed to be set? How far away from earth are those remotest of the stars: they are beyond the reach of eye, or man's devices, or man's thought. What an absurdity is this motion (of spheres).

It is evident, therefore, that all the heavenly bodies, being, as it were, set down in their destined places, in them are conglobed whatever elements bear to their own centres, and around

them are assembled all their parts. But if they have a motion, it will be motion of each round its proper centre, like the earth's rotation; or it will be by a progression in an orbit, like that of the moon; in so multitudinous a scattered flock there will be no circular motion. And of the stars, those situate nigh the equator would seem to be borne around with greatest rapidity, while others nigher the pole have a rather less rapid movement; and others still, as though motionless, have but a small revolution. Yet no differences in the light, the mass, or the colors of the light are perceptible for us; for they are as brilliant, as clear, as resplendent, or as faint (sombre, *fuscæ*) toward the poles as nigh the equator and the zodiac; and in their seats do they remain and there are they placed, nor are they suspended from aught, nor fastened nor secured in any vault. Far more extravagant yet is the idea of the whirling of the supposititious *primum mobile*, which is still higher, deeper, more immeasurable; and yet this incomprehensible *primum mobile* would have to be of matter, of enormous altitude, and far surpassing all the creation below in mass, for else it could not make the whole universe down to the earth revolve from east to west, and we should have to accept a universal force, an unending despotism, in the governance of the stars, and a hateful tyranny. This *primum mobile* presents no visible body, is in no wise recognizable; it is a fiction believed in by some philosophers, and accepted by weaklings who wonder more at this terrestrial mass here than at those distant mighty bodies that baffle our comprehension.

But there cannot be diurnal motion of infinity or of an infinite body, nor, therefore, of this immeasurable *primum mobile*. The moon, neighbor of earth, makes her circuit in twenty-seven days; Mercury and Venus have a tardy movement; Mars completes his period in two years, Jupiter in twelve, Saturn in thirty. And the astronomers who ascribe motion to the fixed stars hold that it is completed, according to Ptolemy, in 36,000 years, or, according to Copernicus' observations, in 25,816 years; thus in larger circles the motion and the completion of the course are ever more slow; and yet this *primum mobile*, surpassing all else in height and depth, immeasurable, has a diurnal revolution. Surely that is superstition, a philosophic fable, now believed only by simpletons and the unlearned; it is beneath derision; and yet in times past it was supported by calculation and comparison of movements, and was generally accepted by mathematicians, while the importunate rabble of philophasters egged them on.

The motions of the heavenly bodies (*i.e.*, of the planets) seem all to be eastward, and according to the succession of the zodiacal signs; and mathematicians and philosophers of the vulgar sort do also believe that the fixed stars progress in the same way with a very slow movement: to these stars they must needs, through their ignorance of the truth, add a ninth sphere. But now this inadmissible *primum mobile*, this fiction, this something not comprehensible by any reasoning and evidenced by no visible star, but purely a product of imagination and mathematical hypothesis, accepted and believed by philosophers, and reared into the heavens and far beyond all the stars, this must needs by a contrary incitation wheel from east to west, counter to the tendence of all the rest of the universe.

Whatever in nature moves naturally, the same is impelled by its own forces and by a consentient compact of other bodies. Such is the motion of the parts to a whole, of the globes and stars throughout the universe with each other accordant; such is the circular propulsion of the planets' bodies, each the other's career observing and inciting. But as regards this *primum mobile* with its contrary and most rapid career, where are the bodies that incite it, that propel it? Where is the nature conspiring with it? and what mad force lies beyond the *primum mobile?* —for the agent force abides in bodies themselves, not in space, not in the interspaces.

But he who supposes that all these bodies are idle and inactive, and that all the force of the universe pertains to those spheres, is as foolish as the one who, entering a man's residence, thinks it is the ceilings and the floors that govern the household, and not the thoughtful and provident good-man of the house. So, then, not by the firmament are they borne, not from the firmament have they movement or position; and far less are those multitudes of stars whirled round *en masse* by the *primum mobile*, and taken up at random and swept along in a reversed direction at highest velocity.

Ptolemy of Alexandria, it seems to me, was over-timid and scrupulous in apprehending a break-up of this nether world were earth to move in a circle. Why does he not apprehend universal ruin, dissolution, confusion, conflagration, and stupendous celestial and supercelestial calamities from a motion that surpasses all imagination, all dreams and fables and poetic licenses—a motion ineffable and inconceivable? So, then, we are borne round and round by the earth's daily rotation—a more congruous sort of motion; and as a boat glides over the water, so are we whirled round with the earth, the while we think we stand still and are at rest. This seems to some philosophers wonderful and incredible, because of the ingrained belief that the mighty mass of the earth makes an orbital movement in twenty-four hours: it were more incredible that the moon should in the space of twenty-four hours traverse her orbit or complete her course; more incredible that the sun and Mars should do so; still more that Jupiter and Saturn; more than wonderful would be the velocity of the fixed stars and firmament; and let them imagine as best they may the wonders that confront them in the ninth sphere. But it is absurd to imagine a *primum mobile*, and, when imagined, to give to it a motion that is completed in twenty-four hours, denying that motion to the earth within the same space of time. For a great circle of earth, as compared to the circuit of the *primum mobile* is less than a stadium[1] as compared to the whole earth. And if the rotation of the earth seems headlong and not to be permitted by nature because of its rapidity, then worse than insane, both as regards itself and the whole universe, is the motion of the *primum mobile*, as being in harmony or proportion with no other motion. Ptolemy and the Peripatetics think that all nature must be thrown into confusion, and the whole structure and configuration of this our globe destroyed by the earth's so rapid rotation. The diameter of the earth is 1718 German miles; the greatest elongation of the new moon is 65, the least 55, semi-diameters of the earth; but probably its orbit is still larger. The sun at his greatest eccentricity is distant 1142 semi-diameters from earth; Mars, Jupiter, Saturn, as they are slow in movement, so are far more distant from the earth. The best mathematicians regard the distances of the firmament and the fixed stars as indeterminable; to say nothing of the ninth sphere, if the convexity of the *primum mobile* be fairly estimated in its proportion to the rest, it must travel over as much space in one hour as might be comprised within three thousand great circles of the earth, for on the convexity of the firmament it would travel over more than eighteen hundred such circles: but what structure of iron can be imagined so strong, so tough, that it would not be wrecked and shattered to pieces by such mad and unimaginable velocity?

[1] Ancient measure of length, equal to 600 Greek or 625 Roman feet, or 125 Roman paces, or to 606 feet 9 inches English.

The Chaldees believed the heavens to be light. But in light there is no such firmness, neither in the fire-firmament of Plotinus, nor in the fluid or watery heavens of God-inspired Moses, nor in the supremely tenuous and transparent firmament that stands between our eye and the lights of the stars, but does not intercept the same. Hence we must reject the deep-seated error about this mad, furious velocity, and this forceful retardation of the rest of the heavens. Let the theologues reject and erase these old wives' stories of a so rapid revolution of the heavens which they have borrowed from certain shallow philosophers. The sun is not swept round by Mars' sphere (if sphere he have) and its motion, nor Mars by Jupiter's sphere, nor Jupiter by Saturn's: the sphere of the fixed stars too, seems moderate enough, save that movements are attributed to the heavens that really are earth movements, and these produce a certain change in the phenomena. The higher do not tyrannize over the lower, for the heaven both of the philosopher and of the divine must be gentle, happy, tranquil, and not subject to changes; neither will the violence, fury, velocity, and rapidity of the *primum mobile* bear sway. That fury descends through all the celestial spheres and heavenly bodies, enters the elements of the philosophers, sweeps the fire along, whirls the air around, or at least the greater part thereof; leads in its train the universal ether, and causes it to whirl round as though it were a solid and firm body, whereas it is a most tenuous substance, that neither offers resistance nor is ductile; and leads captive the fires of the upper heavens. O wondrous steadfastness of the globe of earth, that alone is unconquered! And yet the earth is holden nor stayed in its place by any chains, by no heaviness of its own, by no contiguity of a denser or a more stable body, by no weights. The substance of the terrestrial globe withstands and resists universal nature.

Aristotle imagines a philosophy of motions simple or complex, holds that the heavens move with a simple circular motion, and his elements with motion in a right line; that the parts of the earth tend to the earth in right lines; that they impinge upon it at the superficies at right angles and seek its centre, and there always rest; and that hence the whole earth stands in its place, held together and compacted by its own weight. This coherence of parts and this consolidation of matter exists in the sun, the moon, the planets, the fixed stars—in short, in all those spherical bodies whose parts cohere and seek their several centres; else would the heavens rush to destruction and their grand order disappear. But these heavenly bodies have a circular motion, and hence the earth, too, may have its motion, for this motion is not, as some suppose, adverse to cohesion nor to production. For, inasmuch as this motion is intrinsic in the earth and natural, and as there is nothing without that may convulse it or with contrary motions impede it, it revolves untroubled by any ill or peril; it moves on under no external compulsion; there is nought to make resistance, nothing to give way before it, but the path is open. For since it revolves in a space void of bodies, the incorporeal æther, all atmosphere, all emanations of land and water, all clouds and suspended meteors, rotate with the globe: the space above the earth's exhalations is a vacuum; in passing through vacuum even the lightest bodies and those of least coherence are neither hindered nor broken up. Hence the entire terrestrial globe, with all its appurtenances, revolves placidly and meets no resistance. Causelessly, therefore, and superstitiously, do certain faint-hearts apprehend collisions, in the spirit of Lucius Lactantius, who, like the most unlearned of the vulgar, or like an uncultured bumpkin, treats with ridicule the mention of antipodes and of a round globe of earth.

From these arguments, therefore, we infer, not with mere probability, but with certainty, the diurnal rotations of the earth; for nature ever acts with fewer rather than with many means; and because it is more accordant to reason that the one small body, the earth, should make a daily revolution than that the whole universe should be whirled around it. I pass by the earth's other movements, for here we treat only of the diurnal rotation, whereby it turns to the sun and produces the natural day (of twenty-four hours) which we call *nycthemeron*. And, indeed, nature would seem to have given a motion quite in harmony with the shape of the earth, for the earth being a globe, it is far easier and far more fitting that it should revolve on its natural poles, than that the whole universe, whose bounds we know not nor can know, should be whirled round; easier and more fitting than that there should be fashioned a sphere of the *primum mobile*—a thing not received by the ancients, and which even Aristotle never thought of or admitted as existing beyond the sphere of the fixed stars; finally, which the holy Scriptures do not recognize, as neither do they recognize a revolution of the whole firmament.

CHAPTER 4. *That the earth hath a circular motion*

AND now, though philosophers of the vulgar sort imagine, with an absurdity unspeakable, that the whole heavens and the world's vast magnitude are in rotation, it remains that the earth daily makes one revolution; for in no third mode can the apparent revolutions be accounted for. The day, therefore, which we call the natural day is the revolution of a meridian of the earth from sun to sun. And it makes a complete revolution from a fixed star to the same fixed star again. Bodies that by nature move with a motion circular, equable, and constant, have in their different parts various metes and bounds. Now the earth is not a chaos nor a chance medley mass, but through its astral property has limits agreeable to the circular motion, to wit, poles that are not merely mathematical expressions, an equator that is not a mere fiction, meridians, too, and parallels; and all these we find in the earth, permanent, fixed, and natural; they are demonstrated with many experiments in the magnetic philosophy. For in the earth are poles set at fixed points, and at these poles the verticity from both sides of the plane of the equator is manifested with greatest force through the co-operation of the whole; and with these poles the diurnal rotation coincides. But no revolutions of bodies, no movements of planets, show any sensible, natural poles in the firmament or in any *primum mobile;* neither does any argument prove their existence; they are the product of imagination. We, therefore, having directed our inquiry toward a cause that is manifest, sensible, and comprehended by all men, do know that the earth rotates on its own poles, proved by many magnetical demonstrations to exist. For not in virtue only of its stability and its fixed permanent position does the earth possess poles and verticity; it might have had another direction, as eastward or westward, or toward any other quarter. By the wonderful wisdom of the Creator, therefore, forces were implanted in the earth, forces primarily animate, to the end the globe might, with steadfastness, take direction, and that the poles might be op- posite, so that on them, as at the extremities of an axis, the movement of diurnal rotation might be performed. Now the steadfastness of the poles is controlled by the primary soul. Thus it is for the good of the earth that the collimations of the verticities do not continually regard a fixed point in the firmament and in the visible heavens. For the changes of the equinoxes are caused by a certain inflection of the earth's axis, yet in this inflection the earth hath from her own forces a steadfastness in her motion. In her rotation the earth bears on her own poles; for since the verticity is fixed in A and B, and the axis horizontal, at C and D (equinoctial line) the parts are free, all the forces being diffused on both sides

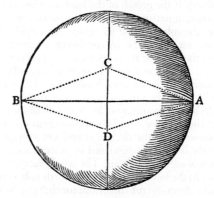

from the plane of the equator toward the poles in the æther, which is without resistance, or in vacuum; and, A and B remaining constant, C revolves toward D both by natural conformity and fitness, as also for the sake of a necessary good and avoidance of ill, but most of all because the effused spheres of solar influence and of solar light do impel. And it revolves not in a new track or one assigned from without, but, in the general trend of all the rest of the planets, tends from west to east. For all planets have a like movement to the east, in accordance with the succession of the zodiacal signs, whether it be Mercury or Venus within the sun's orbit, or whether they revolve round the sun. That the

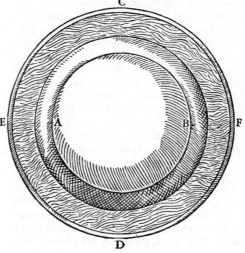

earth is fitted for circular movement is proved
by its parts, which, when separated from the
whole, do not simply travel in a right line, as
the Peripatetics taught, but rotate also. A loadstone placed in a wooden vessel is put in water
so that it may float freely, rotate, and move
about. If the pole *B* of the loadstone be made to
point, unnaturally, toward the south *F*, the terrella revolves round its centre in a circular motion on the plane of the horizon toward the
north *E*, where it comes to a rest, and not at *C*
or at *D*. So acts a small stone weighing only four
ounces; and a powerful loadstone of 100 pounds
will make the same movement as quickly; and
the largest mountain of loadstone would revolve
in the same way were it to be set afloat on a wide
stream or in the deep sea; and yet a magnetic
body is far more hindered by water than is the
whole earth by the air. The whole earth would
act in the same way, were the north pole turned
aside from its true direction; for that pole would
go back, in the circular motion of the whole,
toward Cynosura.

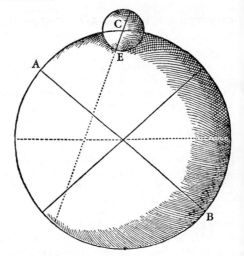

Yet this motion is nothing by that circular
motion wherewith the parts naturally tend to
their own places. The whole earth regards Cynosura by its steadfast nature; and similarly each
true part of the earth seeks a like place in the
world, and turns with circular motion to that
position. The natural movements of the whole
and of the parts are alike: hence, since the parts
move in a circle, the whole, too, hath the power
of circular motion. A spherical loadstone, when
floated in water, moves circularly on its centre
to become (as it seems) conformed to the earth
on the plane of the equator. Thus, too, would it
move on any other great circle if it were free to
move, so that in the dip compass there is circular movement on the meridian (if there be no
variation), or, if there is variation, on a great
circle drawn from the zenith through the variation point in the horizon. And this circular movement of the loadstone to its true and natural
position shows that the whole earth is fitted,
and by its own forces adapted for a diurnal circular motion. I omit what Petrus Peregrinus so
stoutly affirms, that a terrella poised on its poles
in the meridian moves circularly with a complete revolution in twenty-four hours. We have
never chanced to see this: nay, we doubt if there
is such movement, both because of the weight
of the stone itself, and also because the whole
earth, as it moves of itself, so is propelled by the
other stars; but this does not occur proportionately in any part of the earth, a terrella for example. The earth moves by its primary form

and natural desire, for the conservation, perfecting, and beautifying of its parts, toward the
more excellent things: this is more probable than
that those fixed luminous orbs, and the planets
and the sun, foremost of all and divine, while
they get no aid of any sort from earth, no refreshment, no force whatever, should vainly circle round it, and that the whole host of heaven
should make everlasting rounds about the earth,
without any profit whatever to those stars
themselves.

The earth therefore rotates, and by a certain
law of necessity, and by an energy that is innate,
manifest, conspicuous, revolves in a circle toward the sun; through this motion it shares in
the solar energies and influences; and its verticity holds it in this motion lest it stray into every
region of the sky. The sun (chief inciter of action in nature), as he causes the planets to advance in their courses, so, too, doth bring about
this revolution of the globe by sending forth the
energies of his spheres—his light being effused.

And were not the earth to revolve with diurnal rotation, the sun would ever hang with its
constant light over a given part, and, by long
tarrying there, would scorch the earth, reduce
it to powder, and dissipate its substance, and the
uppermost surface of earth would receive griev-
ous hurt: nothing of good would spring from
earth, there would be no vegetation; it could not
give life to the animate creation, and man would
perish. In other parts all would be horror, and
all things frozen stiff with intense cold: hence
all its eminences would be hard, barren, inaccessible, sunk in everlasting shadow and unending night. And as the earth herself cannot endure so pitiable and so horrid a state of things

on either side, with her astral magnetic mind she moves in a circle, to the end there may be, by unceasing change of light, a perpetual vicissitude, heat and cold, rise and decline, day and night, morn and even, noonday and deep night. So the earth seeks and seeks the sun again, turns from him, follows him, by her wondrous magnetical energy.

And not only from the sun would ill impend, were the earth to stand still and be deprived of the benefit of his rays; from the moon also great dangers would threaten. For we see how the ocean swells and comes to flood under certain positions of the moon. But if by the daily rotation of the earth the moon did not quickly pass, the sea would rise unduly at some parts and many coasts would be overwhelmed by mighty tides. Lest the earth, then, should in divers ways perish and be destroyed, she rotates in virtue of her magnetic and primary energy. And such are the movements in the rest of the planets, the motion and light of other bodies especially urging. For the moon also turns round during its menstrual circuit that it may on all its parts successively receive the sun's light, which it enjoys, with which it is refreshed like the earth itself; nor could the moon without grave ill and sure destruction stand the unceasing incidence of the light on one of its sides only.

Thus each of the moving globes has circular motion, either in a great circular orbit or on its own axis or in both ways. But that all the fixed stars, and the planets, and all the higher heavens, still revolve simply for the earth's sake is for the mind of a philosopher a ridiculous supposition. The earth then revolves, and not the whole heavens; and this movement brings growth and decay, gives occasion for the generation of animated things, and arouses the internal heat to productiveness. Hence does matter vegetate to receive forms, and from this primary revolution of the earth natural bodies have prime incitation and original act. The motion of the whole earth, therefore, is primary, astral, circular about its poles, whose verticity rises on both sides from the plane of the equator, and the energy is infused into the opposite ends, so that the globe by a definite rotation might move to the good, sun and stars inciting. But the simple right-downward motion assumed by the Peripatetics is the movement of weight, of coacervation, of separated parts, in the ratio of their matter, by right lines toward the earth's centre, these tending to the centre by the shortest route. The motions of separate magnetical parts of the earth are, besides that of coacervation, those of coition, revolution, and direction of the parts to the whole, into harmony and agreement of the form.

CHAPTER 5. *Arguments of those who deny the earth's motion; and refutation thereof*

It will not be superfluous to weigh also the arguments of those who deny that the earth moves, to the end we may the better satisfy the herd of philosophers who deem the steadfastness and immobility of the globe to be proved by incontrovertible arguments. Aristotle does not allow that the earth moves circularly, for, says he, then every part thereof would take the same motion; but inasmuch as all separated parts tend to the middle point in right lines, that circular motion were something imposed by force, were contrary to nature, were not perpetual. But we have already proven that all true parts of the earth do move circularly, and that all magnetic bodies (when fitly arranged) are borne round in a circle. But they tend to the earth's centre in a right line (if the way is open) by the motion of coacervation, as to their origin; they move with various motions to conformation of the whole; a terrella moves circularly by its inborn forces. "Besides," says Aristotle, "all things that move in a circle seem afterward to lose the first movement and to be carried on by several motions other than the first. The earth, too, whether situate in the middle or near the middle of the world, must needs have two movements; and were that the case there must needs be progressions and retrogressions of the fixed stars: no such thing is seen, however, but evermore the same stars are rising and setting in the same places." Yet it by no means follows that a twofold motion is attributed to the earth. And if there be but the one diurnal motion of the earth round its poles, every one sees that the stars must always rise and set in the same way, at the same points of the horizon, even though there be another movement for which we are not contending; because the changes in the smaller sphere produce in the fixed stars no variation of aspect on account of the great distance, unless the earth's axis changes position: of this we treat in the chapter treating of the cause of the precession of the equinoxes.

In this reasoning (of Aristotle's) are many flaws. For if the earth rotates, that, as we have shown, must be due not to the action of the first sphere, but to its own native forces. And if the motion were produced by the first sphere, there would be no alternations of days and nights, for the globe would then make her revolution along with the *primum mobile*. And it does not follow, because the rest of the heavenly bodies move with a twofold motion, that the earth has a two-fold motion when it rotates round its centre. Then, too, Aristotle does not clearly apprehend the reason of the case, nor do his translators either: τούτον δὲ συμβαίνοντος, ἀναγκαῖον γίγνεσ-θαι παρόδους καὶ τροπὰς τῶν ἐνδεδεμένων ἄστρων (*On the Heavens*, Ch. 14)—*i.e.*, if that be so, there must needs be mutations and regressions of the fixed stars. Some translate τροπὰς "regressions" or "retrogressions," others "diversions": these terms can in no wise be understood of axial motion unless Aristotle means that the earth is whirled by the *primum mobile* round other poles different even from those of the first sphere—which is quite absurd.

More recent writers hold that the Eastern Ocean must needs, in consequence of this motion, so be driven toward the regions to the west that parts of the earth which are dry and water-less would of necessity be daily submerged beneath the waters. But the ocean gets no impulsion from this motion, as there is no resistance, and even the whole atmosphere is carried round also; for this reason, in the rapid revolution of the earth, things in the air around are not left behind nor do they have the appearance of moving westward; the clouds stand motionless in the atmosphere, save when impelled by the force of the winds; and objects thrown up into the air fall back again to their places. But they are dullards who think that steeples, churches, and other edifices must necessarily be shaken and topple down if the earth moves: antipodes might fear lest they should slip over to the other side of the globe; navigators might dread lest in making the circle of the whole globe they might, once they had descended below the plane of our horizon, drop down into the opposite part of the sky. But these are old-wives' imaginings and ravings of philosophasters who, when they undertake to discourse of great things and the fabric of the world and attempt aught, are unable to understand hardly anything *ultra crepidam*. The earth they hold to be the centre of a circle and to stand motionless in the general revolution. But the stars or the planetary globes do not move in a circle round the centre of the earth; nor is the earth the centre—if it be in the centre—but a body around the centre.

And it is inconsistent that the Peripatetics' heavenly bodies should rest on so frail, so perishable, a thing as the earth's centre.

Now generation results from motion, and without motion all nature would be torpid. The sun's motions, the moon's motions, produce changes; the earth's motion awakens the inner life of the globe; animals themselves live not without motion and incessant working of the heart and the arteries. As for the single motion in a right line to the centre, that this is the only movement in the earth, and that the movement of an individual body is one and single, the arguments for it have no weight, for that motion in a right line is but the inclination toward their origin, not only of the earth, but also of the parts of the sun, the moon, and all the other globes; but these move in a circle also. Joannes Costeus, who is in doubt as to the cause of the earth's motion, regards the magnetic energy to be intrinsic, active, and controlling; the sun he holds to be an extrinsic promovent cause; nor is the earth so mean and vile a body as it is commonly reputed to be. Hence, according to him, the diurnal motion is produced by the earth, for the earth's sake and for the earth's behoof.

They (if such there be) who assert that this movement of the earth takes place not only in longitude but also in latitude, speak nonsense; for nature has set in the earth definite poles and has established definite and not confused revolutions. Thus the moon turns round to the sun in its monthly course, the while ever regarding with definite poles definite parts of the heavens. It were absurd to suppose that the atmosphere moves the earth; for the air is but exhalation and the effluvium of the earth given out in every direction; winds, too, are only motions of the exhalation here and there along the earth's surface; the depth of the air current is trifling, and there are in every region various winds from different and opposite points. Some authors, not finding the cause of the revolution in the earth's matter—for there they say they find only solidity and consistence—maintain that it is not to be found in the form, and will admit as qualities of the earth only cold and dryness, which cannot produce the earth's motion. The Stoics attribute to the earth a soul, and hence they declare, amid the derision of the learned, that the earth is an animal. This magnetical form, be it energy or be it soul, is astral. Let the learned lament and weep for that neither the early Peripatetics, nor the common run of philosophasters, nor Joannes Costeus, who mocks at this sort of thing, were capable of appreciating this grand and most extraordinary fact of nature. As for the objection that the superficial unevenness produced by mountains and valleys would prevent diurnal revolution, it is of no weight; for mountains do not mar the rotundity of the earth

—as compared with the entire earth, mountains are but trifling excrescences: besides, the earth does not rotate without carrying along with it its effluences. Beyond the effluences there is no resistance. The earth's motion is performed with as little labor as the motions of the other heavenly bodies: neither is it inferior in dignity to some of these. To say that it is folly to suppose the earth is more eager for the face of the sun than the sun for the face of the earth, is mere wilfulness and ignorance. Of the cause of the rotation I have oft spoken. If any one were to look for the cause of the rotation or any other tendency of the earth on the globe-encircling ocean, or in the movement of the atmosphere, or in the heaviness of the earth's mass, he would reason as stupidly as do those who obstinately cling to an opinion because it was held by the ancients. Ptolemy's arguments are of no account: for our true principles once laid down, the truth is visible, and it is useless to refute Ptolemy. So let Costeus and the philosophers recognize how unprofitable and vain a thing it is to take their stand on the doctrines and unproved theories of certain ancient writers. Many persons cannot see how it is (if the earth rotates) that a ball of iron or lead dropped from a very high tower falls exactly on the spot right below; or how cannon-balls fired from a large culverin with equal charges of gunpowder of the same quality, and with the gun pointed at the same angle with the horizon, have exactly the same range to eastward and to westward, the earth moving to the east. But they who urge such arguments are mistaken through not understanding the nature of primary globes and the combination of parts with their globes, albeit not conjoined thereto with bonds of solid matter. But the earth in its diurnal revolution does not so move that its more solid circumference is separated from the bodies circumfused; on the contrary, all the circumfused effluences, and all heavy bodies therein, howsoever shot thereinto, advance simultaneously and uniformly with the earth because of the general coherence. This is the case in all primary bodies—the sun, moon, earth—the parts betaking themselves to their origin and founts, whereunto they are attached with the same appetence with which what we call heavy bodies are attached to earth. Thus lunar bodies tend to the moon, solar to the sun, within the respective spheres of their effluences. These effluences cohere through continuity of substance; and heavy bodies, too, are united to earth by their heaviness and advance with it in the general movement, especially when no resistance

of bodies hinders. And, for this reason, the diurnal revolution of the earth does not sweep bodies along nor retard them: they neither outstrip the earth's motion nor fall behind when shot with force, whether to east or to west. Let *EFG* be the earth, *A* the centre, *LE* the ascend-

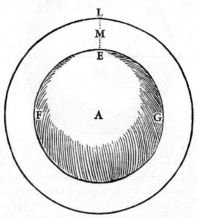

ing effluences. As the sphere of the effluences moves with the earth, so the part of the sphere on the right line *LE* proceeds undisturbed in the general rotation. In *LE* the heavy body *M* falls perpendicularly to *E*, the shortest route centreward; nor is this right motion of *M* a composite motion, *i.e.*, resultant of a motion of coacervation and a circular motion, but simple and direct, never going out of the line *LE*. And an object shot with equal force from *E* toward *F*, and from *E* toward *G*, has the same range in both directions, though the diurnal rotation of the earth goes on—even as twenty steps taken by one man cover the same distance eastward as westward. Hence the diurnal revolution of the earth is not at all refuted by the illustrious Tycho Brahe through such arguments as these.

The tendence to its centre (called by philosophers, weight) works no resistance to the diurnal revolution, neither does it give direction to the earth, nor keep in place the parts of the earth, which have no weight when resting in the earth's solid substance: there they have no longer any tendence, but are at rest in its mass. If there be a flaw in the mass, a cavity of 1000 fathoms for example, a homogenic part of the earth or compacted terrestrial matter descends through that space, be it filled with water or with air, to a more definite centre than air or water, and seeks the solid globe. But the centre of the earth, as also the whole earth itself, has no weight: separated parts tend to their *principium*, and this tendence we call weight: parts in union are at rest, and even if they had weight, they would cause no impediment to the diurnal revolution. For if around the axis *AB* a weight be at *C*, it is balanced by *E*: at *F* it is balanced by *G*;

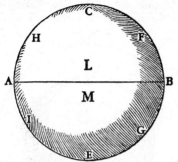

if at *H*, by *I*. And, similarly, if it is at *L*, it is balanced by *M*. Thus the whole globe, having a natural axis, is balanced in equilibrium and is set in motion easily by the slightest cause, but chiefly for the reason that the earth, in its own place, is in no wise heavy nor needs any balancing. Hence no weight hinders the diurnal revolution, and no weight gives to the earth direction or continuance in its place. It is therefore plain that no argument of sufficient force has yet been formed by philosophers to refute the earth's motion.

CHAPTER 6. *Of the cause of the definite time of the total revolution of the earth*

THE causes of the diurnal motion are to be found in the magnetic energy and in the alliance of bodies: that is to say, why a revolution of the earth is performed in the term of 24 hours. For no ingenious artifice, whether of clepsydra, or of hour-glasses, or of time-pieces with toothed wheels and driven by the tension of a steel plate, can show any difference of time. But the diurnal revolution once accomplished comes on again. Now we will take a day to mean a complete revolution of a meridian of the earth from sun to sun. This is a little less than the total revolution; for in 365¼ turnings of a meridian to the sun a year is completed. Because of this fixed and constant motion of the earth the number and time of 365 days 5 hours 55 minutes are always fixed and settled, barring that for other causes there are certain trifling differences. Thus the earth revolves, not fortuitously nor by chance, nor with a headlong motion, but evenly, with a certain high intelligence and with a wonderful steadiness, even like the rest of the movable stars which have fixed periods for their movements.

Thus, inasmuch as the sun itself is the mover and inciter of the universe, the other planets

that are situate within the sphere of his forces, being impelled and set in motion, do also with their own forces determine their own courses and revolve in their own periods, according to the amplitude of their greater rotation and the differences of the forces effused and the perception of a greater good. Hence it is that Saturn, having a greater course to run, revolves in a longer time, while Venus revolves in nine months, and Mercury in 80 days, according to Copernicus; and the moon makes the circuit of the earth in 29 days, 12 hours, 44 minutes. We have asserted that the earth turns on its centre, making one day in its revolution sunward. The moon goes round the earth in a monthly course, and when after its prior conjunction with the sun it comes to conjunction again, it constitutes one month, or one lunar day. The mean distance of the moon's orbit, according to the calculations of Copernicus and other later astronomers, is distant from the earth's centre about 29⅚ diameters of the earth. A solar revolution of the moon in her orbit takes 29 days 12 hours 44 minutes. We reckon her periodic time by her return to the same position relatively to the sun, making the moon's *solar* revolution, not by her return to the same absolute position, making the complete or stellar revolution, just as one day on earth is reckoned as the planets return to the same position relatively to the sun, and not absolutely; because the sun is the cause of both the earth's and the moon's motions. Also, because (as more recent astronomers suppose) the month, as measured between solar conjunctions, is really the full period of revolution, because of the earth's motion in her great orbit. Diameters bear a constant ratio to circumferences. And the moon's orbit is a little more than twice 29½ times the length of great circles on the earth.

Thus the moon and the earth agree in a twofold ratio of motion, and the earth rotates in its diurnal motion in the space of 24 hours; because the moon has a motion proportioned to the earth, and the earth has a motion agreeing in a twofold proportion with the moon's motion. There is some difference in minutes, for the distances of the stars are not sufficiently determined in minutes, nor are astronomers agreed thereupon. So, then, the earth rotates in the space of 24 hours, even as the moon does in her monthly course, by a magnetical compact of both, the globes being impelled forward according to the ratio of their orbits, as Aristotle admits (*On the Heavens*, II. 10). "It comes about," says he, "that the motions of each are performed in a ratio, to wit, in the same intervals whereby some are quicker, others slower." But as between the moon and the earth, it is more reasonable to believe that they are in agreement, because, being neighbor bodies, they are very like in nature and substance, and because the moon has a more manifest effect on the earth than have any of the other stars, except the sun; also the moon alone of all planets directs its movements as a whole toward the earth's centre, and is near of kin to earth, and as it were held by ties to earth.

Such, then, is the symmetry and harmony of the moon's and the earth's movements, very different from the oft-mentioned harmony of the celestial motions, which requires that the nearer any sphere is to the *primum mobile* and to the imaginary and fictitious rapid first motion, the less it opposes it and the more slowly it is borne by its own motion from west to east; but that the farther it is away the more rapidly and the more freely it performs its motion, and hence that the moon (being farthest from the *primum mobile*) revolves with greatest rapidity. These absurdities have been accepted for the sake of the *primum mobile*, and so that it might seem to have some effect in retarding the movements of the nether heavens; as though the motion of the stars was due to retardation, and was not inborn and natural to them, and as though the rest of the heavens (the *primum mobile* alone excepted) were ever driven by a mighty force with a mad impulsion. Far more probable is it that the stars revolve symmetrically, with a certain mutual concert and harmony.

CHAPTER 7. *Of the earth's primary magnetic nature, whereby her poles are made different from the poles of the ecliptic*

HAVING shown the nature and causes of the earth's diurnal revolution, produced partly by the energy of the magnetic property and partly by the superiority of the sun and his light, we have now to treat of the distance of the earth's poles from those of the ecliptic—a condition very necessary for man's welfare. For if the poles of the world or the earth were fixed at the poles of the zodiac, then the equator would lie exactly under the line of the ecliptic, and there would be no change of seasons—neither winter, nor summer, nor spring, nor fall—but the face of things would persist forever unchanging. Hence (for the everlasting good of man) the earth's axis declined from the pole of the zodiac just enough to suffice for generation and diversification. Thus the declination of the tropics and the inclinations of the earth's pole always stand in the 24th degree, but is at present only 23 deg.

28 min., or, according to others, 29 minutes; but formerly the declination was 23 deg. 52 min., and that is the uttermost limit of declination so far observed. This has been wisely ordered by nature and settled by the earth's primary eminency. For were those poles—those of the earth and the ecliptic—to be much farther apart, then as the sun approached the tropic all things would be waste and ruin, in any high latitude of the other and neglected portion of the globe, because of the protracted absence of the sun. But now all things are so disposed that the entire globe of earth has its own changes in due succession, its own fitting and needful seasons, either through a more direct radiation from overhead or by a longer tarrying of the sun above the horizon.

Around these poles of the ecliptic the bearing of the earth's poles rotates, and because of this motion we have the precession of the equinoxes.

CHAPTER 8. *Of the precession of the equinoxes by reason of the magnetic movement of the earth's poles in the arctic and antarctic circle of the zodiac*

THE early astronomers, not noting the inequality of years, made no distinction between the equinoctial or solstitial revolving year and the year determined from a fixed star. They also deemed the Olympian years, which were reckoned from the rising of the Dog Star, or Sirius to be the same as those reckoned from the solstice. Hipparchus the Rhodian was the first to notice that there is a difference between the two, and found another year, calculated from fixed stars, of greater length than the equinoctial or solstitial: hence he supposed that the stars too have a consequent motion, though a very slow one, nor readily noticeable. After Hipparchus, Menelaus, a Roman geometer, then Ptolemy, and a long time afterward, Machometes Aracensis and several others, in all their writings have held that the fixed stars and the whole firmament have a consequent forward movement (*in consequentia procedere*), for they contemplated the heavens and not the earth, and knew nothing of the magnetic inclination. But we will prove that this motion proceeds from a certain revolution of the earth's axis, and that the eighth sphere, so called, the firmament, or *aplanes*, with its ornament of innumerable globes and stars (the distances of which from earth have never been by any man demonstrated, nor ever can be), does not revolve. And surely it must seem more probable that the appearances of the heavens should be produced by a deflection and inclination of the small body, the earth, than by a whirling of the whole system of the universe—especially as this movement is ordered for the good of the earth alone, and is of no benefit at all to the fixed stars or the planets. For by this motion the rising and setting of stars in all horizons are changed, as also their culminations in the zenith, so that stars that once were vertical are now some degrees distant from the zenith. Provision has been made by nature for the earth's soul or its magnetic energy—just as in attempering, receiving, and diverting the sun's rays and light in fitting seasons, it was necessary that the bearings of the earth's pole should be 23 degrees and more distant from the poles of the ecliptic; so that now in regulating and in receiving in due order and succession the luminous rays of the fixed stars, the earth's poles should revolve at the same distance from the ecliptic in the arctic circle of the ecliptic, or rather that they should creep with slow gait, because the actions of the stars do not always persist in the same parallel circles, but have a slower change; for the influences of the stars are not so powerful that the desired course should be more rapid. So the axis is inflected slowly, and the rays of the stars are changed in such length of time as the diameter of the arctic or polar circle extends; hence the star in the extremity of the tail of Cynosura, which once (*i.e.*, in the time of Hipparchus) was 12 degrees 24 minutes distant from the pole of the world or from the point which the earth's pole regarded, now is distant from it only 2 degrees 52 minutes; hence from its nearness to the pole it is called by the moderns the Pole Star. It will not be only ½ degree from the pole, but thereafter will begin to recede till it reaches a distance of 48 degrees; that, according to the Prutenic tables,[1] will be A.D. 15,000. So the bright star (which for us here, in southern Britain, now almost culminates) will in time come within five degrees of the world's pole. Thus do all the stars change their light rays at the earth's surface, because of this admirable magnetic inflection of the earth's axis. Hence the ever new changes of the seasons; hence are regions more or less fruitful, more or less sterile; hence changes in the character and the manners of nations, in governments and in laws, according to the power of the fixed stars, the strength thence derived or lost, and according to the individual and specific nature of the fixed stars as they culminate; or the

[1] The Prutenic (Prussian) Astronomical Tables based upon the observations of Copernicus, Hipparchus, and Ptolemy, were the result of seven years' labour on part of the German astronomer Erasmus Reinhold, who named the work after his benefactor, Albert, Duke of Prussia.

effects may be due to their risings and settings or to new conjunctions in the meridian.

The precession of the equinoxes from the equal motion of the earth's pole in the zodiacal circle is here demonstrated. Let *ABCD* be the eclip-

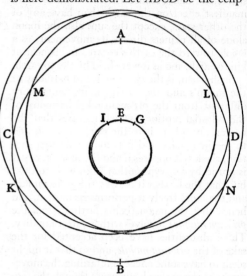

tic; *IEG* the Arctic zodiacal circle. Now if the earth's pole looks toward *E*, then the equinoxes are at *D*, *C*. Suppose this to be in the time of Metho,[2] when the horns of Aries were in the equinoctial colure.[3] But if the earth's pole has advanced to *I*, then *K*, *L* will be the equinoxes, and stars in the ecliptic *C* will seem to have moved forward over the whole arc *KC*, following the signs; *L* advances by precession over the arc *DL*, counter to the order of the signs; but the opposite would be the case if the point *G* were to regard the earth's poles, and the motion be from *E* toward *G*; for then *M*, *N* would be the equinoxes, and the fixed stars would anticipate at *C* and *D*, counter to the order of the signs.

CHAPTER 9. *Of the anomaly of the precession of the equinoxes and of the obliquity of the zodiac*

THE change in the equinoxes is not always equal, but becomes sometimes more rapid, sometimes more slow; for the earth's poles travel unequally

[2] The celebrated astronomer Meton flourished at Athens 432-430 B. C. The mean length of the Metonic Cycle, or Metonic year, was 6939¾ days, which coincides with 19 Julian Years and nearly corresponds to 235 lunations. An improvement on the Metonic Cycle was proposed by Calippus of Cyzicus, a disciple of Plato. The Calippic Period consisted of 76 years, representing four Metonic Cycles, or about 940 complete lunations, 1020 nodal and 1016 complete sidereal revolutions.

[3] The colure is one of two great circles which intersect at right angles in the poles of the equator.

in the Arctic and in the Antarctic zodiacal circle, and recede from the middle line on both sides; hence the obliquity of the zodiac seems to change to the equator. And when this became known through protracted observations, it was apparent that the true equinoctial points were elongated from the mean equinoctial points 70 minutes to one side or the other in the greatest *prostaphæresi*; while the solstices either approach the equator equally by 12 minutes or recede to the same extent; so that the nearest approach is 23 deg. 28 min. and the greatest elongation 23 deg. 52 min. Astronomers in accounting for this inequality of precession and of declination of the tropics have offered various theories. Thebitius,[1] to establish a law for these great inequalities in the movements of the stars, held that the eighth sphere does not advance by continued motion from west to east, but that it has a sort of tremulous motion whereby the leading stars in Aries and in Libra of the eighth heavens describe around the leading stars of Aries and Libra of the ninth sphere certain small circles with diameters equal to about nine degrees. But as this "motion of trepidation" is full of absurdities and impossible motions, this movement has gone out of fashion. Other astronomers, therefore, are compelled to ascribe motion to the eighth sphere, and atop of this to construct a ninth heaven, nay a tenth and an eleventh. We must pardon slips in mathematicians, for one may be permitted in the case of movements difficult to account for to offer any hypotheses whatever in order to establish a law and to bring in a rule that will make the facts agree. But the philosopher never can admit such enormous and monstrous celestial constructions.

   Now though we see in all this how loath these mathematicians are to ascribe any motion to the earth, which is a very small body, nevertheless they drive and whirl the heavens, which are vast and immense beyond human comprehension and human imagination: they construct three heavens, postulate three inconceivable monstrosities, to account for a few unexplained motions. Ptolemy, comparing with his own observations those of Timochares and Hippar-

[1] See note, Book III, I.

chus, of whom the one lived 260 years before his day and the other 460 years, deemed this to be the motion of the eighth sphere and of the whole firmament, and proved it with many phenomena on the poles of the zodiac; and, still thinking its motion to be equal, he held that the fixed stars in 100 years travel only one degree beneath the *primum mobile*. Seven hundred and fifty years after him, Abitegnius found that one degree is travelled over in 66 years, so that the whole period would be 23,760 years. Alphonsus would have this motion still slower—1 degree 28 minutes in 200 years; and thus would the course of the fixed stars proceed, but unequally. At last Copernicus, through his own observations and those of Timochares, Aristarchus the Samian, Menelaus, Ptolemy, Machometes Aracensis and Alphonsus, discovered the anomalies of the motion of the earth's axis; though I have no doubt that other anomalies also will appear some centuries hence, for it is difficult, save in periods of many ages, to note so slow a movement, wherefore we still are ignorant of the mind of nature, what she is aiming at through this inequality of motion. Let *A* be the pole of the ecliptic, *BC* the ecliptic, *D* the equator; when the earth's pole regards the point *M* near the arctic circle of

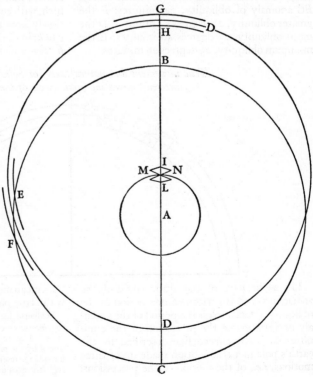

the zodiac let the anomaly of the precession of the equinox be at *F*, but when it regards *N*, let the anomaly of the precession be at *E*. So long as it regards *I* directly there is observed the maximum obliquity *G* in the solstitial colure; but while it regards *L*, then there is minimum obliquity *H* in the colure of the solstices.

and of the anomaly of the precessions, and of obliquity. The period of the precession of the equinoxes is 25,816 Egyptian years; the period of the obliquity of the zodiac is 3434 years and a little more; the period of the anomaly of the precession of the equinoxes is 1717 years and a little more. If we divide the whole time of the

Copernicus's intorta corolla in the arctic zodiacal circle

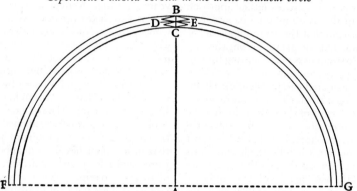

FGB is one half of an arctic circle described around the pole of the zodiac; *ABC* is the colure of the solstices; *A* the pole of the zodiac; *DE* the anomaly of longitude 140 minutes on either side, with twofold terminus (*duplici termino*); *BC* anomaly of obliquity, 24 minutes; *B* the greater obliquity, 23 degrees 52 minutes; *D* the mean obliquity, 23 degrees 40 minutes; *C* the minimum obliquity, 23 degrees 28 minutes.

motion from *a* to *i* into eight equal parts, in the first eighth part the pole travels faster from *a* to *b*; in the second more slowly from *b* to *c*; in the third, with the same slowness from *c* to *d*; in the fourth, more rapidly again from *d* to *e*; in the fifth, with equal rapidity from *e* to *f*; again more slowly from *f* to *g*; with the same slowness from *g* to *h*; in the last eighth again more rapidly from *h* to *i*, and this is Copernicus's *intorta corolla*[1]

True movement and natural axis (or poles) of the earth directed toward the arctic circle of the zodiac

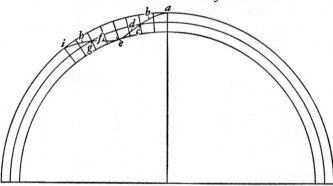

Let *ai* be part of the arctic circle of the zodiac in which is performed one period of the obliquity. From *a* to *e* is the period of the anomaly or variation of the precession of the equinoxes. *ai* is the curved line described by the earth's pole in a true motion made up of three motions, *i.e.*, of the motion of the precessions,

with mean motion fused into a curved line, which is the true path of the motion. And so the pole

[1] Copernicus, *Revolutions of the Heavenly Spheres*, 66, 67: the *intorta corolla* is not an inverted but an irregular crown: a figure representing the successive positions produced by the projection of the earth's pole upon the stellar sphere, resembling a crown, but distorted by the irregularities of motion.

reaches the extreme limit of variation of the precession of the equinoxes twice, but the limit of inclination or obliquity once only. Thus do the moderns, and in particular Copernicus, restorer of astronomy, describe the variations of the movement of the earth's axis, so far as the same is made possible by the observations of the ancients down to our day; but we still lack many and more exact observations to fix anything positively as to the anomaly of the movement of the precessions, as also of the obliquity of the zodiac. For since the time when in various observations this anomaly was first noted, only one half of a period of obliquity has passed. Hence all these points touching the unequal movement of precession and obliquity are undecided and undefined, and so we cannot assign with certainty any natural causes for the motion.

Wherefore we here bring to an end and conclusion our arguments and experiments magnetical.

GALILEO GALILEI

BIOGRAPHICAL NOTE
GALILEO, 1564–1642

GALILEO GALILEI was born at Pisa, February 15, 1564, the eldest of seven children. His father, who belonged to a noble but impoverished Florentine family, was a cloth merchant highly reputed for his skill in mathematics and music. At the age of twelve or thirteen Galileo was sent to school at the monastery of Vallombrosa, where he studied the Latin classics and acquired a fair command of Greek. He seems to have been a novice for a short time, but his father then withdrew him from the charge of the monks.

In 1581 Galileo was sent to the University of Pisa to study medicine. His father apparently hoped to prevent him from following either mathematics or music, whose unremunerative character he had experienced. The young Galileo was already known for his proficiency in music; his judgment in painting was highly esteemed, and Ludovico Cigoli accredited him with the success of his paintings; but mathematics soon had an overwhelming attraction for him. In his first year at the university Galileo discovered the isochronism of the pendulum, to which his attention had been drawn by a swinging lamp in the cathedral, and he applied the principle in a machine for measuring the pulse known as the *pulsilogia*. Although compelled to leave school in 1585 for want of funds, Galileo continued his investigations. He shortly afterwards published an essay describing his invention of the hydrostatic balance. During 1587 and 1588 he delivered two papers before the Florentine Academy on the site and dimensions of Dante's Inferno. A treatise written at this time on the center of gravity in solids won him the title of "the Archimedes of his time."

Despite his growing fame, Galileo was unable to find a means of earning his living until 1589. He tried several times unsuccessfully to obtain a teaching position, and he had even planned to seek his fortune in the East before he was called to the honorable but not lucrative post of mathematical lecturer at the University of Pisa. During the ensuing two years, 1589-91, he conducted experiments on the motion of falling bodies. His lectures on the im-

port of his discoveries alienated the Aristotelian members of the faculty, and he further aroused the anger of the authorities by a burlesque in which he ridiculed the university regulations. In 1591 Galileo found it prudent to resign, and shortly afterwards, he secured the chair of mathematics at the University of Padua.

Galileo taught at Padua for eighteen years, from 1592 to 1610, and during that time established a European reputation as a scientist and inventor. His lectures, which were attended by persons of the highest distinction from all parts of Europe, proved so popular they were given in a hall that held two thousand persons. He wrote numerous treatises, which were circulated among his pupils, dealing with military architecture, gnomonics, the sphere, accelerated motion, and special problems in mechanics. His more notable inventions at Padua included a machine for raising water, a geometrical compass, and an air thermometer. But perhaps his most famous discovery came in 1609, when, upon learning that the Dutch were beginning to manufacture magnifying glasses, he put together a telescope and turned it for the first time towards the heavens. In his *Sidereus Nuncius*, published early in 1610, Galileo gave the first results of this new method of investigation; he noted the mountainous surface of the moon, the fact that the Milky Way consists of stars, and the observation of four of Jupiter's satellites, which he named the "Medicean Stars" in honor of the Grand Duke of Tuscany. Almost immediately, Galileo was nominated philosopher and mathematician extraordinary to the grand duke at a large salary and with unlimited leisure for research.

Galileo did not actively defend the Copernican doctrine until after he had begun to use the telescope. Although he wrote Kepler as early as 1597 that he had "become a convert to the opinions of Copernicus many years ago," he continued to teach the Ptolemaic system throughout his stay at Padua. But with the discovery of the moons of Jupiter and the phases of Venus he came to the conclusion that "all my life and being henceforth depends" on the establishment of the new theory. Galileo's astronomical discoveries brought him great honor, and in 1611 he traveled to Rome, where he gave a highly successful demonstration of the telescope to the ecclesiastical authorities. But as soon as he tried to maintain that the Copernican theory could be reconciled with Scriptures, he began to encounter opposition from the theologians.

The first ecclesiastical attack upon Galileo occurred in 1614 when he was denounced from the pulpit in Florence for holding the new astronomical doctrine. Galileo replied by issuing his *Letter to the Grand Duchess Christine of Lorraine*, in which he strongly supported the words of Cardinal Baronius that the "Holy Spirit intended to teach us in the Bible how to go to Heaven, not how the heavens go." This letter was at once laid before the Inquisition, and in 1615 Galileo was informed by an ecclesiastical friend in Rome: "You can write as a mathematician and hypothetically, as Copernicus is said to have done, and you can write freely so long as you keep out of the sacristy." But early in 1616 the Holy Office condemned two fundamental Copernican propositions selected from Galileo's work *On the Sun Spots*, and he was summoned before Cardinal Bellarmine and warned not to hold or defend the Copernican theory. Dismayed by the slanders regarding him, Galileo obtained from the Cardinal a certificate explaining that he had not been made to abjure his opinions nor enjoined to perform salutary penance.

Galileo maintained silence until 1627. In that year he published *Il Saggiatore*, in which he contended that the new astronomical discoveries were more in accord with the Copernican than the Ptolemaic system; he added that, since the one theory was condemned by the Church and the other by reason, a third system would have to be sought. The book was dedicated to Urban VIII. It was well received by both ecclesiastical and scientific authorities, and in the course of two months Galileo had six audiences with the pope. Encouraged by this reception, he devoted the next eight years to writing his *Dialogue of the Two Principal Systems of the World* (1632). Upon its publication Galileo was denounced by the ecclesiastical authorities and summoned for trial before the Holy Office. He was accused on three charges: that he had broken his agreement of 1616, that he had taught the Copernican theory as a truth and not a hypothesis, and that he inwardly believed the truth of a doctrine condemned by the Church. In the trial of 1633 he was found guilty on the first two charges, but on his assertion that it was never his intention to believe the truth of the Copernican doctrine after its condemnation, he was denounced only as "vehemently suspected of heresy" and sentenced to punishment at the will of the court. Galileo submitted and made the required recantation.

On being allowed to leave Rome, Galileo went to Siena and resided for several months in the house of the archbishop. In December, 1633, he was permitted to return to his villa at Arcetri, near Florence, where he spent the remainder of his life in retirement according to the conditions of his release. Here he completed the *Dialogue of the Two New Sciences*, in which he turned back to the scientific investigations of his youth. The work, which was printed by the Elzevirs at Leyden in 1638, was considered by Galileo to be "superior to everything else of mine hitherto published." His last telescopic discovery—that of the moon's diurnal and monthly librations—was made in 1637, only a few months before he became blind. But blindness was not allowed to interrupt his scientific correspondence and investigation. He worked out the application of the pendulum to the clock, which Huygens was to apply successfully several years later, and was engaged in dictating to his disciples, Viviani and Torricelli, his latest ideas on the theory of impact when he was seized with fever. He died January 8, 1642, and was buried in the chapel of Santa Croce in Florence.

CONTENTS

Dialogues Concerning the
Two New Sciences

TO THE MOST ILLUSTRIOUS LORD COUNT OF NOAILLES
COUNSELLOR OF HIS MOST CHRISTIAN MAJESTY, KNIGHT OF THE ORDER OF THE HOLY GHOST, FIELD MARSHAL AND COMMANDER, SENESCHAL AND GOVERNOR OF ROUERGUE, AND HIS MAJESTY'S LIEUTENANT IN AUVERGNE, MY LORD AND WORSHIPFUL PATRON

MOST ILLUSTRIOUS LORD:

In the pleasure which you derive from the possession of this work of mine, I recognize your Lordship's magnanimity. The disappointment and discouragement I have felt over the ill-fortune which has followed my other books are already known to you. Indeed, I had decided not to publish any more of my work. And yet in order to save it from complete oblivion, it seemed to me wise to leave a manuscript copy in some place where it would be available at least to those who follow intelligently the subjects which I have treated. Accordingly, I chose first to place my work in your Lordship's hands, asking no more worthy depository, and believing that, on account of your affection for me, you would have at heart the preservation of my studies and labours. Therefore, when you were returning home from your mission to Rome, I came to pay my respects in person as I had already done many times before by letter. At this meeting I presented to your Lordship a copy of these two works which at that time I happened to have ready. In the gracious reception which you gave these I found assurance of their preservation. The fact of your carrying them to France and showing them to friends of yours who are skilled in these sciences gave evidence that my silence was not to be interpreted as complete idleness. A little later, just as I was on the point of sending other copies to Germany, Flanders, England, Spain, and possibly to some places in Italy, I was notified by the Elzevirs that they had these works of mine in press, and that I ought to decide upon a dedication and send them a reply at once. This sudden and unexpected news led me to think that the eagerness of your Lord-ship to revive and spread my name by passing these works on to various friends was the real cause of their falling into the hands of printers who, because they had already published other works of mine, now wished to honour me with a beautiful and ornate edition of this work. But these writings of mine must have received additional value from the criticism of so excellent a judge as your Lordship, who by the union of many virtues has won the admiration of all. Your desire to enlarge the renown of my work shows your unparalleled generosity and your zeal for the public welfare which you thought would thus be promoted. Under these circumstances it is eminently fitting that I should, in unmistakable terms, gratefully acknowledge this generosity on the part of your Lordship, who has given to my fame wings that have carried it into regions more distant than I had dared to hope. It is, therefore, proper that I dedicate to your Lordship this child of my brain. To this course I am constrained not only by the weight of obligation under which you have placed me, but also, if I may so speak, by the interest which I have in securing your Lordship as the defender of my reputation against adversaries who may attack it while I remain under your protection.

And now, advancing under your banner, I pay my respects to you by wishing that you may be rewarded for these kindnesses by the achievement of the highest happiness and greatness.

I am your Lordship's
Most devoted Servant,
GALILEO GALILEI

Arcetri, 6 *March*, 1638

FIRST DAY

INTERLOCUTORS: SALVIATI, SAGREDO AND SIMPLICIO

SALVIATI. The constant activity which you Venetians display in your famous arsenal suggests to the studious mind a large field for investigation, especially that part of the work which involves mechanics; for in this department all types of instruments and machines are constantly being constructed by many artisans, among whom there must be some who, partly by inherited experience and partly by their own observations, have become highly expert and clever in explanation.

SAGR. You are quite right. Indeed, I myself, being curious by nature, frequently visit this place for the mere pleasure of observing the work of those who, on account of their superiority over other artisans, we call "first rank men." Conference with them has often helped me in the investigation of certain effects including not only those which are striking, but also those which are recondite and almost incredible. At times also I have been put to confusion and driven to despair of ever explaining something for which I could not account, but which my senses told me to be true. And notwithstanding the fact that what the old man told us a little while ago is proverbial and commonly accepted, yet it seemed to me altogether false, like many another saying which is current among the ignorant; for I think they introduce these expressions in order to give the appearance of knowing something about matters which they do not understand.

SALV. You refer, perhaps, to that last remark of his when we asked the reason why they employed stocks, scaffolding, and bracing of larger dimensions for launching a big vessel than they do for a small one; and he answered that they did this in order to avoid the danger of the ship parting under its own heavy weight, a danger to which small boats are not subject?

SAGR. Yes, that is what I mean; and I refer especially to his last assertion which I have always regarded as false, though current, opinion; namely, that in speaking of these and other similar machines one cannot argue from the small to the large, because many devices which succeed on a small scale do not work on a large scale. Now, since mechanics has its foundation in geometry, where mere size cuts no figure, I do not see that the properties of circles, triangles, cylinders, cones, and other solid figures will change with their size. If, therefore, a large machine be constructed in such a way that its parts bear to one another the same ratio as in a smaller one, and if the smaller is sufficiently strong for the purpose for which it was designed, I do not see why the larger also should not be able to withstand any severe and destructive tests to which it may be subjected.

SALV. The common opinion is here absolutely wrong. Indeed, it is so far wrong that precisely the opposite is true, namely, that many machines can be constructed even more perfectly on a large scale than on a small; thus, for instance, a clock which indicates and strikes the hour can be made more accurate on a large scale than on a small. There are some intelligent people who maintain this same opinion, but on more reasonable grounds, when they cut loose from geometry and argue that the better performance of the large machine is owing to the imperfections and variations of the material. Here I trust you will not charge me with arrogance if I say that imperfections in the material, even those which are great enough to invalidate the clearest mathematical proof, are not sufficient to explain the deviations observed between machines in the concrete and in the abstract. Yet I shall say it and will affirm that, even if the imperfections did not exist and matter were absolutely perfect, unalterable, and free from all accidental variations, still the mere fact that it is matter makes the larger machine, built of the same material and in the same proportion as the smaller, correspond with exactness to the smaller in every respect except that it will not be so strong or so resistant against violent treatment; the larger the machine, the greater its weakness. Since I assume matter to be unchangeable and always the same, it is clear that we are no less able to treat this constant and invariable property in a rigid manner than if it belonged to simple and pure mathematics. Therefore, Sagredo, you would do well to change the opinion which you, and perhaps also many other students of mechanics, have entertained concerning the ability of machines and structures to resist external disturbances, thinking that when they are built of the same material and maintain the same ratio between parts, they are able equally, or rather proportionally, to resist or yield to such external disturbances and blows. For we can demonstrate by geometry that the large machine is not proportionately stronger than the small. Finally, we may say that, for every machine and structure, whether artificial or natural, there is set a necessary limit beyond which neither art nor nature can pass; it is here understood, of course, that the material is the same and the proportion preserved.

SAGR. My brain already reels. My mind, like a cloud momentarily illuminated by a lightning-flash, is for an instant filled with an unusual light, which now beckons to me and which now suddenly mingles and obscures strange, crude ideas. From what you have said it appears to me impossible to build two similar structures of the same material, but of different sizes and have them proportionately strong; and if this were so, it would not be possible to find two single poles made of the same wood which shall be alike in strength and resistance but unlike in size.

SALV. So it is, Sagredo. And to make sure that we understand each other, I say that if we take a wooden rod of a certain length and size, fitted, say, into a wall at right angles, i.e., parallel to the horizon, it may be reduced to such a length that it will just support itself; so that if a hair's breadth be added to its length it will break under its own weight and will be the only rod of the kind in the world. Thus if, for instance, its length be a hundred times its breadth, you will not be able to find another rod whose length is also a hundred times its breadth and which, like the former, is just able to sustain its own weight and no more: all the larger ones will break while all the shorter ones will be strong enough to support something more than their own weight. And this which I have said about the ability to support itself must be understood to apply also to other tests; so that if a piece of scantling will carry the weight of ten similar to itself, a beam having the same proportions will not be able to support ten similar beams.

Please observe, gentlemen, how facts which at first seem improbable will, even on scant explanation, drop the cloak which has hidden them and stand forth in naked and simple beauty. Who does not know that a horse falling from a height of three or four cubits will break his bones, while a dog falling from the same height or a cat from a height of eight or ten cubits will suffer no injury? Equally harmless would be the fall of a grasshopper from a tower or the fall of an ant from the distance of the moon. Do not children fall with impunity from heights which would cost their elders a broken leg or perhaps a fractured skull? And just as smaller animals are proportionately stronger and more robust than the larger, so also smaller plants are able to stand up better than larger. I am certain you both know that an oak two hundred cubits high would not be able to sustain its own branches if they were distributed as in a tree of ordinary size; and that nature cannot produce a horse as large as twenty ordinary horses or a giant ten times taller than an ordinary man unless by miracle or by greatly altering the proportions of his limbs and especially of his bones, which would have to be considerably enlarged over the ordinary. Likewise the current belief that, in the case of artificial machines the very large and the small are equally feasible and lasting is a manifest error. Thus, for example, a small obelisk or column or other solid figure can certainly be laid down or set up without danger of breaking, while the very large ones will go to pieces under the slightest provocation, and that purely on account of their own weight. And here I must relate a circumstance which is worthy of your attention as indeed are all events which happen contrary to expectation, especially when a precautionary measure turns out to be a cause of disaster. A large marble column was laid out so that its two ends rested each upon a piece of beam; a little later it occurred to a mechanic that, in order to be doubly sure of its not breaking in the middle by its own weight, it would be wise to lay a third support midway; this seemed to all an excellent idea; but the sequel showed that it was quite the opposite, for not many months passed before the column was found cracked and broken exactly above the new middle support.

SIMP. A very remarkable and thoroughly unexpected accident, especially if caused by placing that new support in the middle.

SALV. Surely this is the explanation, and the moment the cause is known our surprise vanishes; for when the two pieces of the column were placed on level ground it was observed that one of the end beams had, after a long while, become decayed and sunken, but that the middle one remained hard and strong, thus causing one half of the column to project in the air without any support. Under these circumstances the body therefore behaved differently from what it would have done if supported only upon the first beams; because no matter how much they might have sunken the column would have gone with them. This is an accident which could not possibly have happened to a small column, even though made of the same stone and having a length corresponding to its thickness, i. e., preserving the ratio between thickness and length found in the large pillar.

SAGR. I am quite convinced of the facts of the case, but I do not understand why the strength and resistance are not multiplied in the same proportion as the material; and I am the more puzzled because, on the contrary, I have noticed in other cases that the strength and resistance against breaking increase in a larger ratio than the amount of material. Thus, for instance, if two nails be driven into a wall, the one which is twice as big as the other will support not only twice as much weight as the other, but three or four times as much.

SALV. Indeed you will not be far wrong if you say eight times as much; nor does this phenomenon contradict the other even though in appearance they seem so different.

SAGR. Will you not then, Salviati, remove these difficulties and clear away these obscurities if possible: for I imagine that this problem of resistance opens up a field of beautiful and useful ideas; and if you are pleased to make this the subject of to-day's discourse you will place Simplicio and me under many obligations.

SALV. I am at your service if only I can call to mind what I learned from our Academician[1] who had thought much upon this subject and according to his custom had demonstrated everything by geometrical methods so that one might fairly call this a new science. For, although some of his conclusions had been reached by others, first of all by Aristotle, these are not the most beautiful and, what is more important, they had not been proven in a rigid manner from fundamental principles. Now, since I wish to convince you by demonstrative reasoning rather than to persuade you by mere probabilities, I shall suppose that you are familiar with present-day mechanics so far as it is needed in our discussion. First of all it is necessary to consider what happens when a

piece of wood or any other solid which coheres firmly is broken; for this is the fundamental fact, involving the first and simple principle which we must take for granted as well known.

To grasp this more clearly, imagine a cylinder or prism, AB, made of wood or other solid coherent material. Fasten the upper end, A, so that the cylinder hangs vertically. To the lower end, B, attack the weight C. It is clear that however great they may be, the tenacity and coherence between the parts of this solid, so long as they are not infinite, can be overcome by the pull of the weight C, a weight which can be increased indefinitely until finally the solid breaks like a rope. And as in the case of the rope whose strength we know to be derived from a multitude of hemp threads which compose it, so in the case of the wood, we observe its fibres and filaments run lengthwise and render it much stronger than a hemp rope of the same thickness. But in the case of a stone or metallic cylinder where the coherence seems to be still greater the cement which holds the parts together must be something other than filaments and fibres; and yet even this can be broken by a strong pull.

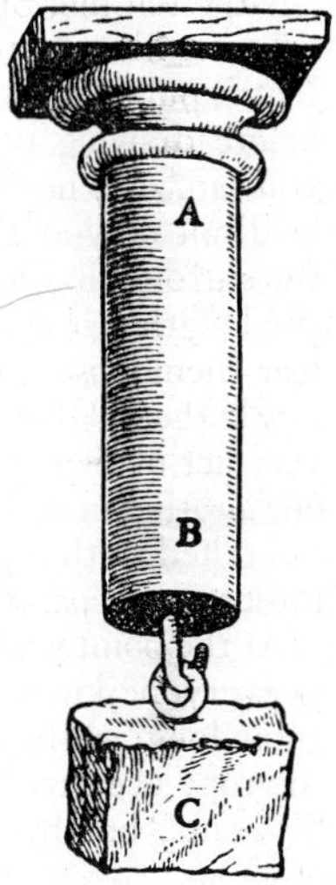

SIMP. If this matter be as you say I can well understand that the fibres of the wood, being as long as the piece of wood itself, render it strong and resistant against large forces tending to break it. But how can one make a rope one hundred cubits long out of hempen fibres which are not more than two or three cubits long, and still give it so much strength? Besides, I should be glad to hear your opinion as to the manner in which the parts of metal, stone, and other materials not showing a filamentous structure are put together; for, if I mistake not, they exhibit even greater tenacity.

Fig. 1

SALV. To solve the problems which you raise it will be necessary to make a digression into subjects which have little bearing upon our present purpose.

SAGR. But if, by digressions, we can reach new truth, what harm is there in making one now, so that we may not lose this knowledge, remembering that such an opportunity, once omitted, may not return; remembering also that we are not tied down to a fixed and brief method but that we meet solely for our own entertainment? Indeed, who knows but that we may thus frequently discover something more interesting and beautiful than the solution originally sought? I beg of you, therefore, to grant the request of Simplicio, which is also mine; for I am no less curious and desirous than he to learn what is the binding material which holds together the parts of solids so that they can scarcely be separated. This information is also needed to understand the coherence of the parts of fibres themselves of which some solids are built up.

SALV. I am at your service, since you desire it. The first question is, How are fibres, each not more than two or three cubits in length, so tightly bound together in the case of a rope one hundred cubits long that great force is required to break it?

Now tell me, Simplicio, can you not hold a hempen fibre so tightly between your fingers that I, pulling by the other end, would break it before drawing it away from you? Certainly you can. And now when the fibres of hemp are held not only at the ends, but are grasped by the surrounding medium throughout their entire length is it not manifestly more difficult to tear them loose from what holds them than to break them? But in the case of the rope the very act of twisting causes the threads to bind one another in such a way that when the rope is stretched with a great force the fibres break rather than separate from each other.

At the point where a rope parts the fibres are, as everyone knows, very short, nothing like a cubit long, as they would be if the parting of the rope occurred, not by the breaking of the filaments, but by their slipping one over the other.

SAGR. In confirmation of this it may be remarked that ropes sometimes break not by a lengthwise pull but by excessive twisting. This, it seems to me, is a conclusive argument because the threads bind one another so tightly that the compressing fibres do not permit those which are compressed to lengthen the spirals even that little bit by which it is necessary for them to lengthen in order to surround the rope which, on twisting, grows shorter and thicker.

SALV. You are quite right. Now see how one fact suggests another. The thread held between the fingers does not yield to one who wishes to draw it away even when pulled with considerable force, but resists because it is held back by a double compression, seeing that the upper finger presses against the lower as hard as the lower against the upper. Now, if we could retain only one of these pressures there is no doubt that only half the original resistance would remain; but since we are not able, by lifting, say, the upper finger, to remove one of these pressures without also removing the other, it becomes necessary to preserve one of them by means of a new device which causes the thread to press itself against the finger or against some other solid body upon which it rests; and thus it is brought

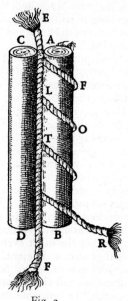

Fig. 2

about that the very force which pulls it in order to snatch it away compresses it more and more as the pull increases. This is accomplished by wrapping the thread around the solid in the manner of a spiral; and will be better understood by means of a figure. Let *AB* and *CD* be two cylinders between which is stretched the thread *EF:* and for the sake of greater clearness we will imagine it to be a small cord. If these two cylinders be pressed strongly together, the cord *EF*, when drawn by the end *F*, will undoubtedly stand a considerable pull before it slips between the two compressing solids. But if we remove one of these cylinders the cord, though remaining in contact with the other, will not thereby be prevented from slipping freely. On the other hand, if one holds the cord loosely against the top of the cylinder *A*, winds it in the spiral form *AFLOTR*, and then pulls it by the end *R*, it is evident that the cord will begin to bind the cylinder; the greater the number of spirals the more tightly will the cord be pressed against the cylinder by any given pull. Thus as the number of turns increases, the line of contact becomes longer and in consequence more resistant; so that the cord slips and yields to the tractive force with increasing difficulty.

Is it not clear that this is precisely the kind of resistance which one meets in the case of a thick hemp rope where the fibres form thousands and thousands of similar spirals? And, indeed, the binding effect of these turns is so great that a few short rushes woven together into a few interlacing spirals form one of the strongest of ropes which I believe they call pack rope.

Sagr. What you say has cleared up two points which I did not previously understand. One fact is how two, or at most three, turns of a rope around the axle of a windlass cannot only hold it fast, but can also prevent it from slipping when pulled by the immense force of the weight which it sustains; and moreover how, by turning the windlass, this same axle, by mere friction of the rope around it, can wind up and lift huge stones while a mere boy is able to handle the slack of the rope. The other fact has to do with a simple but clever device, invented by a young kinsman of mine, for the purpose of descending from a window by means of a rope without lacerating the palms of his hands, as had happened to him shortly before and greatly to his discomfort. A small sketch will make this clear. He took a wooden cylinder, *AB*, about as thick as a walking stick and about one span long: on this he cut a spiral channel of about one turn and a half, and large enough to just receive the rope which he wished to use. Having introduced the rope at the end *A* and led it out again at the end *B*, he enclosed both the cylinder and the rope in a case of wood or tin, hinged along the side so that it could be easily opened and closed. After he had fastened the rope to a firm support above, he could, on grasping and squeezing the case with both hands, hang by his arms. The pressure on the rope, lying between the case and the cylinder, was such that he could, at will, either grasp the case more tightly and hold himself from slipping, or slacken his hold and descend as slowly as he wished.

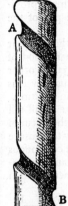

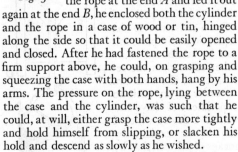

Fig. 3

Salv. A truly ingenious device! I feel, however, that for a complete explanation other considerations might well enter; yet I must not now digress upon this particular topic since you are waiting to hear what I think about the breaking strength of other materials which, unlike ropes and most woods, do not show a filamentous structure. The coherence of these bodies is, in my estimation, produced by other causes which may be grouped under two heads. One is that much-talked-of repugnance which nature exhibits towards a vacuum; but this horror of a vacuum not being sufficient, it is necessary to introduce another cause in the form of a gluey or viscous substance which binds firmly together the component parts of the body.

First I shall speak of the vacuum, demonstrating by definite experiment the quality and quantity of its force. If you take two highly polished and smooth plates of marble, metal, or glass and place them face to face, one will slide over the other with the greatest ease, showing conclusively that there is nothing of a viscous nature between them. But when you attempt to separate them and keep them at a constant distance apart, you find the plates exhibit such a repugnance to separation that the upper one will carry the lower one with it and keep it lifted indefinitely, even when the latter is big and heavy.

This experiment shows the aversion of nature for empty space, even during the brief moment required for the outside air to rush in and fill up the region between the two plates. It is also observed that if two plates are not thoroughly polished, their contact is imperfect so that when you attempt to separate them slowly the only resistance offered is that of weight; if, however, the pull be sudden, then the lower plate rises, but quickly falls back, having followed the upper plate only for that very short interval of time required for the expansion of the small amount of air remaining between the plates, in consequence of their not fitting, and for the entrance of the surrounding air. This resistance which is exhibited between the two plates is doubtless likewise present between the parts of a solid, and enters, at least in part, as a concomitant cause of their coherence.

Sagr. Allow me to interrupt you for a moment, please; for I want to speak of something which just occurs to me, namely, when I see how the lower plate follows the upper one and how rapidly it is lifted, I feel sure that, contrary to the opinion of many philosophers, including perhaps even Aristotle himself, motion in a vacuum is not instantaneous. If this were so the two plates mentioned above would separate without any resistance whatever, seeing that the same instant of time would suffice for their separation and for the surrounding medium to rush in and fill the vacuum between them. The fact that the lower plate follows the upper one allows us to infer, not only that motion in a vacuum is not instantaneous, but also that, between, the two plates, a vacuum really exists, at least for a very short time, sufficient to allow the surrounding medium to rush in and fill the vacuum; for if there were no vacuum there would be no need of any motion in the medium. One must admit then that a vacuum is sometimes produced by violent motion or contrary to the laws of nature, (although in my opinion nothing occurs contrary to nature except the impossible, and that never occurs).

But here another difficulty arises. While experiment convinces me of the correctness of this conclusion, my mind is not entirely satisfied as to the cause to which this effect is to be attributed. For the separation of the plates precedes the formation of the vacuum which is produced as a consequence of this separation; and since it appears to me that, in the order of nature, the cause must precede the effect, even though it appears to follow in point of time, and since every positive effect must have a positive cause, I do not see how the adhesion of two plates and their resistance to separation—actual facts—can be referred to a vacuum as cause when this vacuum is yet to follow. According to the infallible maxim of the Philosopher, the non-existent can produce no effect.

SIMP. Seeing that you accept this axiom of Aristotle, I hardly think you will reject another excellent and reliable maxim of his, namely, Nature undertakes only that which happens without resistance; and in this saying, it appears to me, you will find the solution of your difficulty. Since nature abhors a vacuum, she prevents that from which a vacuum would follow as a necessary consequence. Thus it happens that nature prevents the separation of the two plates.

SAGR. Now admitting that what Simplicio says is an adequate solution of my difficulty, it seems to me, if I may be allowed to resume my former argument, that this very resistance to a vacuum ought to be sufficient to hold together the parts either of stone or of metal or the parts of any other solid which is knit together more strongly and which is more resistant to separation. If for one effect there be only one cause, or if, more being assigned, they can be reduced to one, then why is not this vacuum which really exists a sufficient cause for all kinds of resistance?

SALV. I do not wish just now to enter this discussion as to whether the vacuum alone is sufficient to hold together the separate parts of a solid body; but I assure you that the vacuum which acts as a sufficient cause in the case of the two plates is not alone sufficient to bind together the parts of a solid cylinder of marble or metal which, when pulled violently, separates and divides. And now if I find a method of distinguishing this well known resistance, depending upon the vacuum, from every other kind which might increase the coherence, and if I show you that the aforesaid resistance alone is not nearly sufficient for such an effect, will you not grant that we are bound to introduce another cause? Help him, Simplicio, since he does not know what reply to make.

SIMP. Surely, Sagredo's hesitation must be owing to another reason, for there can be no doubt concerning a conclusion which is at once so clear and logical.

SAGR. You have guessed rightly, Simplicio. I was wondering whether, if a million of gold each year from Spain were not sufficient to pay the army, it might not be necessary to make provision other than small coin for the pay of the soldiers.

But go ahead, Salviati; assume that I admit your conclusion and show us your method of separating the action of the vacuum from other causes; and by measuring it show us how it is not sufficient to produce the effect in question.

SALV. Your good angel assist you. I will tell you how to separate the force of the vacuum from the others, and afterwards how to measure it. For this purpose let us consider a continuous substance whose parts lack all resistance to separation except that derived from a vacuum, such as is the case with water, a fact fully demonstrated by our Academician in one of his treatises. Whenever a cylinder of water is subjected to a pull and offers a resistance to the separation of its parts this can be attributed to no other cause than the resistance of the vacuum. In order to try such an experiment I have invented a device which I can better explain by means of a sketch than by mere words. Let *CABD* represent the cross section of a cylinder either of met-

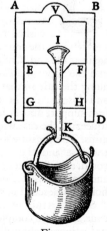

Fig. 4

al or, preferably, of glass, hollow inside and accurately turned. Into this is introduced a perfectly fitting cylinder of wood, represented in cross section by *EGHF*, and capable of up-and-down motion. Through the middle of this cylinder is bored a hole to receive an iron wire, carrying a hook at the end *K*, while the upper end of the wire, *I*, is provided with a conical head. The wooden cylinder is countersunk at the top so as to receive, with a perfect fit, the conical head *I* of the wire, *IK*, when pulled down by the end *K*.

Now insert the wooden cylinder *EH* in the hollow cylinder *AD*, so as not to touch the upper end of the latter but to leave free a space of two or three finger-breadths; this space is to be filled with water by holding the vessel with the mouth *CD* upwards, pushing down on the stopper *EH*, and at the same time keeping the conical head of the wire, *I*, away from the hollow portion of the wooden cylinder. The air is thus allowed to escape alongside the iron wire (which does not make a close fit) as soon as one presses down on the wooden stopper. The air having been allowed to escape and the iron wire having been drawn back so that it fits snugly against the conical depression in the wood, invert the vessel, bringing it mouth downwards, and hang on the hook *K* a vessel which can be filled with sand or any heavy material in quantity sufficient to finally separate the upper surface of the stopper, *EF*, from the lower surface of the water to which it was attached only by the resistance of the vacuum. Next weigh the stopper and wire together with the attached vessel and its contents; we shall then have the force of the vacuum. If one attaches to a cylinder of marble or glass a weight which, together with the weight of the marble or glass itself, is just equal to the sum of the weights before mentioned, and if breaking occurs we shall then be justified in saying that the vacuum alone holds the parts of the marble and glass together; but if this weight does not suffice and if breaking occurs only after adding, say, four times this weight, we shall then be compelled to say that the vacuum furnishes only one fifth of the total resistance.

SIMP. No one can doubt the cleverness of the device; yet it presents many difficulties which make me doubt its reliability. For who will assure us that the air does not creep in between the glass and stopper even if it is well packed with tow or other yielding material? I question also whether oiling with wax or turpentine will suffice to make the cone, I, fit snugly on its seat. Besides, may not the parts of the water expand and dilate? Why may not the air or exhalations or some other more subtile substances penetrate the pores of the wood, or even of the glass itself?

SALV. With great skill indeed has Simplicio laid before us the difficulties; and he has even partly suggested how to prevent the air from penetrating the wood or passing between the wood and glass. But now let me point out that, as our experience increases, we shall learn whether or not these alleged difficulties really exist. For if, as is the case with air, water is by nature expansible, although only under severe treatment, we shall see the stopper descend; and if we put a small excavation in the upper part of the glass vessel, such as indicated by *V*, then the air or any other tenuous and gaseous substance, which might penetrate the pores of glass or wood, would pass through the water and collect in this receptacle *V*. But if these things do not happen we may rest assured that our experiment has been performed with proper caution; and we shall discover that water does not dilate and that glass does not allow any material, however tenuous, to penetrate it.

SAGR. Thanks to this discussion, I have learned the cause of a certain effect which I have long wondered at and despaired of understanding. I once saw a cistern which had been provided with a pump under the mistaken impression that the water might thus be drawn with less effort or in greater quantity than by means of the ordinary bucket. The stock of the pump carried its sucker and valve in the upper part so that the water was lifted by attraction and not by a push as is the case with pumps in which the sucker is placed lower down. This pump worked perfectly so long as the water in the cistern stood above a certain level; but below this level the pump failed to work. When I first noticed this phenomenon I thought the machine was out of order; but the workman whom I called in to repair it told me the defect was not in the pump but in the water which had fallen too low to be raised through such a height; and he added that it was not possible, either by a pump or by any other machine working on the principle of attraction, to lift water a hair's breadth above eighteen cubits; whether the pump be large or small this is the extreme limit of the lift. Up to this time I had been so thoughtless that, although I knew a rope, or rod of wood, or of iron, if sufficiently long, would break by its own weight when held by the upper end, it never occurred to me that the same thing would happen, only much more easily, to a column of water. And really is not that thing which is attracted in the pump a column of water attached at the upper end and stretched more and more until finally a point is reached where it breaks, like a rope, on account of its excessive weight?

Salv. That is precisely the way it works; this fixed elevation of eighteen cubits is true for any quantity of water whatever, be the pump large or small or even as fine as a straw. We may therefore say that, on weighing the water contained in a tube eighteen cubits long, no matter what the diameter, we shall obtain the value of the resistance of the vacuum in a cylinder of any solid material having a bore of this same diameter. And having gone so far, let us see how easy it is to find to what length cylinders of metal, stone, wood, glass, etc., of any diameter can be elongated without breaking by their own weight.

Take for instance a copper wire of any length and thickness; fix the upper end and to the other end attach a greater and greater load until finally the wire breaks; let the maximum load be, say, fifty pounds. Then it is clear that if fifty pounds of copper, in addition to the weight of the wire itself which may be, say, $\frac{1}{8}$ ounce, is drawn out into wire of this same size we shall have the greatest length of this kind of wire which can sustain its own weight. Suppose the wire which breaks to be one cubit in length and $\frac{1}{8}$ ounce in weight; then since it supports 50 lbs. in addition to its own weight, i. e., 4800 eighths-of-an-ounce, it follows that all copper wires, independent of size, can sustain themselves up to a length of 4801 cubits and no more. Since then a copper rod can sustain its own weight up to a length of 4801 cubits it follows that that part of the breaking strength which depends upon the vacuum, comparing it with the remaining factors of resistance, is equal to the weight of a rod of water, eighteen cubits long and as thick as the copper rod. If, for example, copper is nine times as heavy as water, the breaking strength of any copper rod, in so far as it depends upon the vacuum, is equal to the weight of two cubits of this same rod. By a similar method one can find the maximum length of wire or rod of any material which will just sustain its own weight, and can at the same time discover the part which the vacuum plays in its breaking strength.

Sagr. It still remains for you to tell us upon what depends the resistance to breaking, other than that of the vacuum; what is the gluey or viscous substance which cements together the parts of the solid? For I cannot imagine a glue that will not burn up in a highly heated furnace in two or three months, or certainly within ten or a hundred. For if gold, silver and glass are kept for a long while in the molten state and are removed from the furnace, their parts, on cooling, immediately reunite and bind themselves together as before. Not only so, but whatever difficulty arises with respect to the cementation of the parts of the glass arises also with regard to the parts of the glue; in other words, what is that which holds these parts together so firmly?

Salv. A little while ago, I expressed the hope that your good angel might assist you. I now find myself in the same straits. Experiment leaves no doubt that the reason why two plates cannot be separated, except with violent effort, is that they are held together by the resistance of the vacuum; and the same can be said of two large pieces of a marble or bronze column. This being so, I do not see why this same cause may not explain the coherence of smaller parts and indeed of the very smallest particles of these materials. Now, since each effect must have one true and sufficient cause and since I find no other cement, am I not justified in trying to discover whether the vacuum is not a sufficient cause?

Simp. But seeing that you have already proved that the resistance which the large vacuum offers to the separation of two large parts of a solid is really very small in comparison with that cohesive force which binds together the most minute parts, why do you hesitate to regard this latter as something very different from the former?

Salv. Sagredo has already answered this question when he remarked that each individual soldier was being paid from coin collected by a general tax of pennies and farthings, while even a million of gold would not suffice to pay the entire army. And who knows but that there may be other extremely minute vacua which affect the smallest particles so that that which binds together the contiguous parts is throughout of the same mintage? Let me tell you something which has just occurred to me and which I do not offer as an absolute fact, but rather as a passing thought, still immature and calling for more careful consideration. You may take of it what you like; and judge the rest as you see fit. Sometimes when I have observed how fire winds its way in between the most minute particles of this or that metal and, even though these are solidly cemented together, tears them apart and separates them, and when I have observed that, on removing the fire, these particles reunite with the same tenacity as at first, without any loss of quantity in the case of gold and with little loss in the case of other metals, even though these parts have been separated for a long while, I have thought that the explanation might lie in the fact that the extremely fine particles of fire, penetrating the slender pores of the metal (too small to admit even the finest particles of air or of many other fluids), would fill the small intervening vacua and would set free these small particles from the attraction which these same vacua exert upon them and which prevents their separation. Thus the particles are able to move freely so that the mass becomes fluid and remains so as long as the particles of fire remain inside; but if they depart and leave the former vacua then the original attraction returns and the parts are again cemented together.

In reply to the question raised by Simplicio, one may say that although each particular vacuum is exceedingly minute and therefore easily overcome, yet their number is so extraordinarily great that their combined resistance is, so to speak, multiplied almost without limit. The nature and the amount of force which results from adding together in immense number of small forces is clearly illustrated by the fact that a weight of millions of pounds, suspended by great cables, is overcome and lifted, when the south wind carries innumerable atoms of water, suspended in thin mist, which moving through the air penetrate between the fibres of the tense ropes in spite of the tremendous force of the hanging weight. When these particles enter the narrow pores they swell the ropes, thereby shorten them, and perforce lift the heavy mass.

SAGR. There can be no doubt that any resistance, so long as it is not infinite, may be overcome by a multitude of minute forces. Thus a vast number of ants might carry ashore a ship laden with grain. And since experience shows us daily that one ant can easily carry one grain, it is clear that the number of grains in the ship is not infinite, but falls below a certain limit. If you take another number four or six times as great, and if you set to work a corresponding number of ants they will carry the grain ashore and the boat also. It is true that this will call for a prodigious number of ants, but in my opinion this is precisely the case with the vacua which bind together the least particles of a metal.

SALV. But even if this demanded an infinite number would you still think it impossible?

SAGR. Not if the mass of metal were infinite; otherwise....

SALV. Otherwise what? Now since we have arrived at paradoxes let us see if we cannot prove that within a finite extent it is possible to dis-

cover an infinite number of vacua. At the same time we shall at least reach a solution of the most remarkable of all that list of problems which Aristotle himself calls wonderful; I refer to his *Questions in Mechanics*. This solution may be no less clear and conclusive than that which he himself gives and quite different also from that so cleverly expounded by the most learned Monsignor di Guevara.

First it is necessary to consider a proposition, not treated by others, but upon which depends the solution of the problem and from which, if I mistake not, we shall derive other new and remarkable facts. For the sake of clearness let us draw an accurate figure. About G as a centre describe an equiangular and equilateral polygon of any number of sides, say the hexagon ABC-DEF. Similar to this and concentric with it, describe another smaller one which we shall call HIKLMN. Prolong the side AB, of the larger hexagon, indefinitely toward S; in like manner prolong the corresponding side HI of the smaller hexagon, in the same direction, so that the line HT is parallel to AS; and through the centre draw the line GV parallel to the other two. This done, imagine the larger polygon to roll upon the line AS, carrying with it the smaller polygon. It is evident that, if the point B, the end of the side AB, remains fixed at the beginning of the rotation, the point A will rise and the point C will fall describing the arc CQ until the side BC coincides with the line BQ, equal to BC. But during this rotation the point I, on the smaller polygon, will rise above the line IT because IB is oblique to AS; and it will not again return to the line IT until the point C shall have reached the position Q. The point I, having described the arc IO above the line HT, will reach the position O at the same time the side IK assumes the position OP; but in the meantime the centre G has traversed a path above GV and does not return to it until it has completed the arc GC. This step having been taken, the larger polygon has been brought to rest with its side BC coinciding with the line BQ while the side IK of the smaller polygon has been made to coincide with the line OP, having passed over the portion IO without touching it; also the centre G will have reached the position C after having traversed all its course above the parallel line GV. And finally the entire figure will assume a position similar to the first, so that if we continue the rotation and come to the next step, the side DC of the larger polygon will coincide with the portion QX and the side KL of the smaller polygon, having first skipped the arc

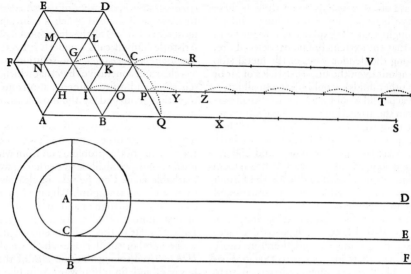

Fig. 5

PY, will fall on *YZ*, while the centre still keeping above the line *GV* will return to it at *R* after
having jumped the interval *CR*. At the end of
one complete rotation the larger polygon will
have traced upon the line *AS*, without break,
six lines together equal to its perimeter; the
lesser polygon will likewise have imprinted six
lines equal to its perimeter, but separated by
the interposition of five arcs, whose chords represent the parts of *HT* not touched by the polygon: the centre *G* never reaches the line *GV* except at six points. From this it is clear that the
space traversed by the smaller polygon is almost
equal to that traversed by the larger, that is, the
line *HT* approximates the line *AS*, differing from
it only by the length of one chord of one of these
arcs, provided we understand the line *HT* to include the five skipped arcs.

Now this exposition which I have given in the
case of these hexagons must be understood to be
applicable to all other polygons, whatever the
number of sides, provided only they are similar,
concentric, and rigidly connected, so that when
the greater one rotates the lesser will also turn
however small it may be. You must also understand that the lines described by these two are
nearly equal provided we include in the space
traversed by the smaller one the intervals which
are not touched by any part of the perimeter of
this smaller polygon.

Let a large polygon of, say, one thousand sides
make one complete rotation and thus lay off a
line equal to its perimeter; at the same time the
small one will pass over an approximately equal

distance, made up of a thousand small portions
each equal to one of its sides, but interrupted
by a thousand spaces which, in contrast with
the portions that coincide with the sides of the
polygon, we may call empty. So far the matter
is free from difficulty or doubt.

But now suppose that about any centre, say
A, we describe two concentric and rigidly connected circles; and suppose that from the points
C and *B*, on their radii, there are drawn the tangents *CE* and *BF* and that through the centre *A*
the line *AD* is drawn parallel to them, then if
the large circle makes one complete rotation
along the line *BF*, equal not only to its circumference but also to the other two lines *CE* and
AD, tell me what the smaller circle will do and
also what the centre will do. As to the centre it
will certainly traverse and touch the entire line
AD while the circumference of the smaller circle will have measured off by its points of contact the entire line *CE*, just as was done by the
above mentioned polygons. The only difference
is that the line *HT* was not at every point in
contact with the perimeter of the smaller polygon, but there were left untouched as many vacant spaces as there were spaces coinciding with
the sides. But here in the case of the circles the
circumference of the smaller one never leaves
the line *CE*, so that no part of the latter is left
untouched, nor is there ever a time when some
point on the circle is not in contact with the
straight line. How now can the smaller circle
traverse a length greater than its circumference
unless it go by jumps?

SAGR. It seems to me that one may say that just as the centre of the circle, by itself, carried along the line *AD* is constantly in contact with it, although it is only a single point, so the points on the circumference of the smaller circle, carried along by the motion of the larger circle, would slide over some small parts of the line *CE*.

SALV. There are two reasons why this cannot happen. First because there is no ground for thinking that one point of contact, such as that at *C*, rather than another, should slip over certain portions of the line *CE*. But if such slidings along *CE* did occur they would be infinite in number since the points of contact (being mere points) are infinite in number: an infinite number of finite slips will however make an infinitely long line, while as a matter of fact the line *CE* is finite. The other reason is that as the greater circle, in its rotation, changes its point of contact continuously the lesser circle must do the same because *B* is the only point from which a straight line can be drawn to *A* and pass through *C*. Accordingly the small circle must change its point of contact whenever the large one changes: no point of the small circle touches the straight line *CE* in more than one point. Not only so, but even in the rotation of the polygons there was no point on the perimeter of the smaller which coincided with more than one point on the line traversed by that perimeter; this is at once clear when you remember that the line *IK* is parallel to *BC* and that therefore *IK* will remain above *IP* until *BC* coincides with *BQ*, and that *IK* will not lie upon *IP* except at the very instant when *BC* occupies the position *BQ;* at this instant the entire line *IK* coincides with *OP* and immediately afterwards rises above it.

SAGR. This is a very intricate matter. I see no solution. Pray explain it to us.

SALV. Let us return to the consideration of the above mentioned polygons whose behavior we already understand. Now in the case of polygons with 100000 sides, the line traversed by the perimeter of the greater, *i.e.*, the line laid down by its 100000 sides one after another, is equal to the line traced out by the 100000 sides of the smaller, provided we include the 100000 vacant spaces interspersed. So in the case of the circles, polygons having an infinitude of sides, the line traversed by the continuously distributed infinitude of sides is in the greater circle equal to the line laid down by the infinitude of sides in the smaller circle but with the exception that these latter alternate with empty spaces; and since the sides are not finite in number, but infinite, so also are the intervening empty spaces

not finite but infinite. The line traversed by the larger circle consists then of an infinite number of points which completely fill it; while that which is traced by the smaller circle consists of an infinite number of points which leave empty spaces and only partly fill the line. And here I wish you to observe that after dividing and resolving a line into a finite number of parts, that is, into a number which can be counted, it is not possible to arrange them again into a greater length than that which they occupied when they formed a *continuum* and were connected without the interposition of as many empty spaces. But if we consider the line resolved into an infinite number of infinitely small and indivisible parts, we shall be able to conceive the line extended indefinitely by the interposition, not of a finite, but of an infinite number of infinitely small indivisible empty spaces.

Now this which has been said concerning simple lines must be understood to hold also in the case of surfaces and solid bodies, it being assumed that they are made up of an infinite, not a finite, number of atoms. Such a body once divided into a finite number of parts it is impossible to reassemble them so as to occupy more space than before unless we interpose a finite number of empty spaces, that is to say, spaces free from the substance of which the solid is made. But if we imagine the body, by some extreme and final analysis, resolved into its primary elements, infinite in number, then we shall be able to think of them as indefinitely extended in space, not by the interposition of a finite, but of an infinite number of empty spaces. Thus one can easily imagine a small ball of gold expanded into a very large space without the introduction of a finite number of empty spaces, always provided the gold is made up of an infinite number of indivisible parts.

SIMP. It seems to me that you are travelling along toward those vacua advocated by a certain ancient philosopher.

SALV. But you have failed to add, "who denied Divine Providence," an inapt remark made on a similar occasion by a certain antagonist of our Academician.

SIMP. I noticed, and not without indignation, the rancor of this ill-natured opponent; further references to these affairs I omit, not only as a matter of good form, but also because I know how unpleasant they are to the good tempered and well ordered mind of one so religious and pious, so orthodox and God-fearing as you.

But to return to our subject, your previous discourse leaves with me many difficulties which

I am unable to solve. First among these is that, if the circumferences of the two circles are equal to the two straight lines, *CE* and *BF*, the latter considered as a *continuum*, the former as interrupted with an infinity of empty points, I do not see how it is possible to say that the line *AD* described by the centre, and made up of an infinity of points, is equal to this centre which is a single point. Besides, this building up of lines out of points, divisibles out of indivisibles, and finites out of infinites, offers me an obstacle difficult to avoid; and the necessity of introducing a vacuum, so conclusively refuted by Aristotle, presents the same difficulty.

SALV. These difficulties are real; and they are not the only ones. But let us remember that we are dealing with infinities and indivisibles both of which transcend our finite understanding, the former on account of their magnitude, the latter because of their smallness. In spite of this, men cannot refrain from discussing them, even though it must be done in a roundabout way.

Therefore I also should like to take the liberty to present some of my ideas which, though not necessarily convincing, would, on account of their novelty, at least, prove somewhat startling. But such a diversion might perhaps carry us too far away from the subject under discussion and might therefore appear to you inopportune and not very pleasing.

SAGR. Pray let us enjoy the advantages and privileges which come from conversation between friends, especially upon subjects freely chosen and not forced upon us, a matter vastly different from dealing with dead books which give rise to many doubts but remove none. Share with us, therefore, the thoughts which our discussion has suggested to you; for since we are free from urgent business there will be abundant time to pursue the topics already mentioned; and in particular the objections raised by Simplicio ought not in any wise to be neglected.

SALV. Granted, since you so desire. The first question was, How can a single point be equal to a line? Since I cannot do more at present I shall attempt to remove, or at least diminish, one improbability by introducing a similar or a greater one, just as sometimes a wonder is diminished by a miracle.[1]

And this I shall do by showing you two equal surfaces, together with two equal solids located upon these same surfaces as bases, all four of which diminish continuously and uniformly in

[1] Cf. p. 143 below.—TRANS.

such a way that their remainders always preserve equality among themselves, and finally both the surfaces and the solids terminate their previous constant equality by degenerating, the one solid and the one surface into a very long line, the other solid and the other surface into a single point; that is, the latter to one point, the former to an infinite number of points.

SAGR. This proposition appears to me wonderful, indeed; but let us hear the explanation and demonstration.

SALV. Since the proof is purely geometrical we shall need a figure. Let *AFB* be a semicircle with centre at *C;* about it describe the rectangle *ADEB* and from the centre draw the straight lines *CD* and *CE* to the points *D* and *E*. Imagine the radius *CF* to be drawn perpendicular to either of the lines *AB* or *DE*, and the entire figure to rotate about this radius as an axis. It is clear that the rectangle *ADEB* will thus describe a cylinder, the semicircle *AFB* a hemisphere, and the triangle *CDE*, a cone. Next let us remove the hemisphere but leave the cone and the rest of the cylinder, which, on account of its shape, we will call a "bowl." First we shall prove that the bowl and the cone are equal; then we shall show that a plane drawn parallel to the circle which forms the base of the bowl and which has the line *DE* for diameter and *F* for a centre —a plane whose trace is *GN*—cuts the bowl in the points *G, I, O, N*, and the cone in the points *H, L*, so that the part of the cone indicated by *CHL* is always equal to the part of the bowl whose profile is represented by the triangles *GAI* and *BON*. Besides this we shall prove that the base of the cone, *i.e.*, the circle whose diameter is *HL*, is equal to the circular surface which

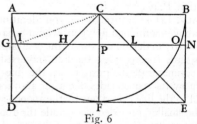

Fig. 6

forms the base of this portion of the bowl, or as one might say, equal to a ribbon whose width is *GI*. (Note by the way the nature of mathematical definitions which consist merely in the imposition of names or, if you prefer, abbreviations of speech established and introduced in order to avoid the tedious drudgery which you and I now experience simply because we have not agreed to call this surface a "circular band" and that sharp solid portion of the bowl a "round razor.") Now call them by what name you please, it suffices to understand that the plane, drawn at any height whatever, so long as it is parallel to the base, *i.e.*, to the circle whose diameter is *DE*, always cuts the two solids so that the portion *CHL* of the cone is equal to the upper portion of the bowl; likewise the two areas which are the bases of these solids, namely the band and the circle *HL*, are also equal. Here we have the miracle mentioned above; as the cutting plane approaches the line *AB* the portions of the solids cut off are always equal, so also the areas of their bases. And as the cutting plane comes near the top, the two solids (always equal) as well as their bases (areas which are also equal) finally vanish, one pair of them degenerating into the circumference of a circle, the other into a single point, namely, the upper edge of the bowl and the apex of the cone. Now, since as these solids diminish equality is maintained between them up to the very last, we are justified in saying that, at the extreme and final end of this diminution, they are still equal and that one is not infinitely greater than the other. It appears therefore that we may equate the circumference of a large circle to a single point. And this which is true of the solids is true also of the surfaces which form their bases; for these also preserve equality between themselves throughout their diminution and in the end vanish, the one into the circumference of a circle, the other into a single point. Shall we not then call them equal seeing that they are the last traces and remnants of equal magnitudes? Note also that, even if these vessels were large enough to contain immense celestial hemispheres, both their upper edges and the apexes of the cones therein contained would always remain equal and would vanish, the former into circles having the dimensions of the largest celestial orbits, the latter into single points. Hence in conformity with the preceding we may say that all circumferences of circles, however different, are equal to each other, and are each equal to a single point.

SAGR. This presentation strikes me as so clever and novel that, even if I were able, I would not be willing to oppose it; for to deface so beautiful a structure by a blunt pedantic attack would be nothing short of sinful. But for our complete satisfaction pray give us this geometrical proof that there is always equality between these solids and between their bases; for it cannot, I think, fail to be very ingenious, seeing how subtle is the philosophical argument based upon this result.

SALV. The demonstration is both short and easy. Referring to the preceding figure, since *IPC* is a right angle the square of the radius *IC* is equal to the sum of the squares on the two sides *IP*, *PC*; but the radius *IC* is equal to *AC* and also to *GP*, while *CP* is equal to *PH*. Hence the square of the line *GP* is equal to the sum of the squares of *IP* and *PH*, or multiplying through by 4, we have the square of the diameter *GN* equal to the sum of the squares on *IO* and *HL*. And, since the areas of circles are to each other as the squares of their diameters, it follows that the area of the circle whose diameter is *GN* is equal to the sum of the areas of circles having diameters *IO* and *HL*, so that if we remove the common area of the circle having *IO* for diameter the remaining area of the circle *GN* will be equal to the area of the circle whose diameter is *HL*. So much for the first part. As for the other part, we leave its demonstration for the present, partly because those who wish to follow it will find it in the twelfth proposition of the second book of *De centro gravitatis solidorum* by the Archimedes of our age, Luca Valerio, who made use of it for a different object, and partly because, for our purpose, it suffices to have seen that the above-mentioned surfaces are always equal and that, as they keep on diminishing uniformly, they degenerate, the one into a single point, the other into the circumference of a circle larger than any assignable; in this fact lies our miracle.

SAGR. The demonstration is ingenious and the inferences drawn from it are remarkable. And now let us hear something concerning the other difficulty raised by Simplicio, if you have anything special to say, which, however, seems to me hardly possible, since the matter has already been so thoroughly discussed.

SALV. But I do have something special to say, and will first of all repeat what I said a little while ago, namely, that infinity and indivisibility are in their very nature incomprehensible to us; imagine then what they are when combined. Yet if we wish to build up a line out of indivisible points, we must take an infinite number of them, and are, therefore, bound to understand both the infinite and the indivisible at the same time. Many ideas have passed through my mind concerning this subject, some of which, possibly the more important, I may not be able to recall on the spur of the moment; but in the course of our discussion it may happen that I shall awaken in you, and especially in Simplicio, objections and difficulties which in turn will bring to memory that which, without such stimulus, would have lain dormant in my mind. Allow me therefore the customary liberty of introducing some of our human fancies, for indeed we may so call them in comparison with supernatural truth which furnishes the one true and safe recourse for decision in our discussions and which is an infallible guide in the dark and dubious paths of thought.

One of the main objections urged against this building up of continuous quantities out of indivisible quantities is that the addition of one indivisible to another cannot produce a divisible, for if this were so it would render the indivisible divisible. Thus if two indivisibles, say two points, can be united to form a quantity, say a divisible line, then an even more divisible line might be formed by the union of three, five, seven, or any other odd number of points. Since however these lines can be cut into two equal parts, it becomes possible to cut the indivisible which lies exactly in the middle of the line. In answer to this and other objections of the same type we reply that a divisible magnitude cannot be constructed out of two or ten or a hundred or a thousand indivisibles, but requires an infinite number of them.

SIMP. Here a difficulty presents itself which appears to me insoluble. Since it is clear that we may have one line greater than another, each containing an infinite number of points, we are forced to admit that, within one and the same class, we may have something greater than infinity, because the infinity of points in the long line is greater than the infinity of points in the short line. This assigning to an infinite quantity a value greater than infinity is quite beyond my comprehension.

SALV. This is one of the difficulties which arise when we attempt, with our finite minds, to discuss the infinite, assigning to it those properties which we give to the finite and limited; but this I think is wrong, for we cannot speak of infinite quantities as being the one greater or less than or equal to another. To prove this I have in mind an argument which, for the sake of clearness, I shall put in the form of questions to Simplicio who raised this difficulty.

I take it for granted that you know which of the numbers are squares and which are not.

SIMP. I am quite aware that a squared number is one which results from the multiplication of another number by itself; thus 4, 9, etc., are squared numbers which come from multiplying 2, 3, etc., by themselves.

SALV. Very well; and you also know that just as the products are called squares so the factors are called sides or roots; while on the other hand those numbers which do not consist of two equal factors are not squares. Therefore if I assert that all numbers, including both squares and non-squares, are more than the squares alone, I shall speak the truth, shall I not?

SIMP. Most certainly.

SALV. If I should ask further how many squares there are one might reply truly that there are as many as the corresponding number of roots, since every square has its own root and every root its own square, while no square has more than one root and no root more than one square.

SIMP. Precisely so.

SALV. But if I inquire how many roots there are, it cannot be denied that there are as many as there are numbers because every number is a root of some square. This being granted we must say that there are as many squares as there are numbers because they are just as numerous as their roots, and all the numbers are roots. Yet at the outset we said there are many more numbers than squares, since the larger portion of them are not squares. Not only so, but the proportionate number of squares diminishes as we pass to larger numbers. Thus up to 100 we have 10 squares, that is, the squares constitute 1/10 part of all the numbers; up to 10000, we find only 1/100 part to be squares; and up to a million only 1/1000 part; on the other hand in an infinite number, if one could conceive of such a thing, he would be forced to admit that there are as many squares as there are numbers all taken together.

SAGR. What then must one conclude under these circumstances?

SALV. So far as I see we can only infer that the totality of all numbers is infinite, that the number of squares is infinite, and that the number of their roots is infinite; neither is the number of squares less than the totality of all numbers, nor the latter greater than the former; and finally the attributes "equal," "greater," and "less," are not applicable to infinite, but only to finite, quantities. When therefore Simplicio introduces several lines of different lengths and asks me how it is possible that the longer ones do not contain more points than the shorter, I answer him that one line does not contain more or less or just as many points as another, but that each line contains an infinite number. Or if I had replied to him that the points in one line were equal in number to the squares; in another, greater than the totality of numbers; and in the little one, as many as the number of cubes, might I not, indeed, have satisfied him by thus placing more points in one line than in another and yet maintaining an infinite number in each? So much for the first difficulty.

SAGR. Pray stop a moment and let me add to what has already been said an idea which just occurs to me. If the preceding be true, it seems to me impossible to say either that one infinite number is greater than another or even that it is greater than a finite number, because if the infinite number were greater than, say, a million it would follow that on passing from the million to higher and higher numbers we would be approaching the infinite; but this is not so; on the contrary, the larger the number to which we pass, the more we recede from infinity, because the greater the numbers the fewer are the squares contained in them; but the squares in infinity cannot be less than the totality of all the numbers, as we have just agreed; hence the approach to greater and greater numbers means a departure from infinity.

SALV. And thus from your ingenious argument we are led to conclude that the attributes "larger," "smaller," and "equal" have no place either in comparing infinite quantities with each other or in comparing infinite with finite quantities.

I pass now to another consideration. Since lines and all continuous quantities are divisible into parts which are themselves divisible without end, I do not see how it is possible to avoid the conclusion that these lines are built up of an infinite number of indivisible quantities because a division and a subdivision which can be carried on indefinitely presupposes that the parts are infinite in number, otherwise the subdivision would reach an end; and if the parts are infinite in number, we must conclude that they are not finite in size, because an infinite number of finite quantities would give an infinite magnitude. And thus we have a continuous quantity built up of an infinite number of indivisibles.

SIMP. But if we can carry on indefinitely the division into finite parts what necessity is there then for the introduction of non-finite parts?

SALV. The very fact that one is able to continue, without end, the division into finite parts makes it necessary to regard the quantity as composed of an infinite number of immeasurably small elements. Now in order to settle this matter I shall ask you to tell me whether, in your opinion, a *continuum* is made up of a finite or of an infinite number of finite parts.

SIMP. My answer is that their number is both infinite and finite; potentially infinite but actually finite; that is to say, potentially infinite before division and actually finite after division; because parts cannot be said to exist in a body which is not yet divided or at least marked out; if this is not done we say that they exist potentially.

SALV. So that a line which is, for instance, twenty spans long is not said to contain actually twenty lines each one span in length except after division into twenty equal parts; before division it is said to contain them only potentially. Suppose the facts are as you say; tell me then whether, when the division is once made, the size of the original quantity is thereby increased, diminished, or unaffected.

SIMP. It neither increases nor diminishes.

SALV. That is my opinion also. Therefore the finite parts in a *continuum*, whether actually or potentially present, do not make the quantity either larger or smaller; but it is perfectly clear that, if the number of finite parts actually contained in the whole is infinite in number, they will make the magnitude infinite. Hence the number of finite parts, although existing only potentially, cannot be infinite unless the magnitude containing them be infinite; and conversely if the magnitude is finite it cannot contain an infinite number of finite parts either actually or potentially.

SAGR. How then is it possible to divide a *continuum* without limit into parts which are themselves always capable of subdivision?

SALV. This distinction of yours between actual and potential appears to render easy by one method what would be impossible by another. But I shall endeavor to reconcile these matters in another way; and as to the query whether the finite parts of a limited *continuum* are finite or infinite in number I will, contrary to the opinion of Simplicio, answer that they are neither finite nor infinite.

SIMP. This answer would never have occurred to me since I did not think that there existed any intermediate step between the finite and the infinite, so that the classification or distinction which assumes that a thing must be either finite or infinite is faulty and defective.

SALV. So it seems to me. And if we consider discrete quantities I think there is, between finite and infinite quantities, a third intermediate term which corresponds to every assigned number; so that if asked, as in the present case, whether the finite parts of a *continuum* are finite or infinite in number the best reply is that they are neither finite nor infinite but correspond to every assigned number. In order that this may be possible, it is necessary that those parts should not be included within a limited number, for in that case they would not correspond to a number which is greater; nor can they be infinite in number since no assigned number is infinite; and thus at the pleasure of the questioner we may, to any given line, assign a hundred finite parts, a thousand, a hundred thousand, or indeed any number we may please so long as it be not infinite. I grant, therefore, to the philosophers, that the *continuum* contains as many finite parts as they please and I concede also that it contains them, either actually or potentially, as they may like; but I must add that just as a line ten fathoms in length contains ten lines each of one fathom and forty lines each of one cubit and eighty lines each of half a cubit, etc., so it contains an infinite number of points; call them actual or potential, as you like, for as to this detail, Simplicio, I defer to your opinion and to your judgment.

SIMP. I cannot help admiring your discussion; but I fear that this parallelism between the points and the finite parts contained in a line will not prove satisfactory, and that you will not find it so easy to divide a given line into an infinite number of points as the philosophers do to cut it into ten fathoms or forty cubits; not only so, but such a division is quite impossible to realize in practice, so that this will be one of those potentialities which cannot be reduced to actuality.

SALV. The fact that something can be done only with effort or diligence or with great expenditure of time does not render it impossible; for I think that you yourself could not easily divide a line into a thousand parts, and much less if the number of parts were 937 or any other large prime number. But if I were to accomplish this division which you deem impossible as readily as another person would divide the line into forty parts would you then be more willing, in our discussion, to concede the possibility of such a division?

SIMP. In general I enjoy greatly your method; and replying to your query, I answer that it would be more than sufficient if it prove not more difficult to resolve a line into points than to divide it into a thousand parts.

SALV. I will now say something which may perhaps astonish you; it refers to the possibility of dividing a line into its infinitely small elements by following the same order which one

employs in dividing the same line into forty, sixty, or a hundred parts, that is, by dividing it into two, four, etc. He who thinks that, by following this method, he can reach an infinite number of points is greatly mistaken; for if this process were followed to eternity there would still remain finite parts which were undivided.

Indeed by such a method one is very far from reaching the goal of indivisibility; on the contrary, he recedes from it and while he thinks that, by continuing this division and by multiplying the multitude of parts, he will approach infinity, he is, in my opinion, getting farther and farther away from it. My reason is this. In the preceding discussion we concluded that, in an infinite number, it is necessary that the squares and cubes should be as numerous as the totality of the natural numbers, because both of these are as numerous as their roots which constitute the totality of the natural numbers. Next we saw that the larger the numbers taken the more sparsely distributed were the squares, and still more sparsely the cubes; therefore it is clear that the larger the numbers to which we pass the farther we recede from the infinite number; hence it follows that, since this process carries us farther and farther from the end sought, if on turning back we shall find that any number can be said to be infinite, it must be unity. Here indeed are satisfied all those conditions which are requisite for an infinite number; I mean that unity contains in itself as many squares as there are cubes and natural numbers.

SIMP. I do not quite grasp the meaning of this.

SALV. There is no difficulty in the matter because unity is at once a square, a cube, a square of a square and all the other powers, nor is there any essential peculiarity in squares or cubes which does not belong to unity; as, for example, the property of two square numbers that they have between them a mean proportional; take any square number you please as the first term and unity for the other, then you will always find a number which is a mean proportional. Consider the two square numbers, 9 and 4; then 3 is the mean proportional between 9 and 1; while 2 is a mean proportional between 4 and 1; between 9 and 4 we have 6 as a mean proportional. A property of cubes is that they must have between them two mean proportional numbers; take 8 and 27; between them lie 12 and 18; while between 1 and 8 we have 2 and 4 intervening; and between 1 and 27 there lie 3 and 9. Therefore we conclude that unity is the only infinite number. These are

some of the marvels which our imagination cannot grasp and which should warn us against the
serious error of those who attempt to discuss
the infinite by assigning to it the same properties which we employ for the finite, the natures
of the two having nothing in common.

With regard to this subject I must tell you of
a remarkable property which just now occurs
to me and which will explain the vast alteration
and change of character which a finite quantity would undergo in passing to infinity. Let
us draw the straight line AB of arbitrary length
and let the point C divide it into two unequal
parts; then I say that, if pairs of lines be drawn,
one from each of the terminal points A and B,
and if the ratio between the lengths of these
lines is the same as that between AC and CB,
their points of intersection will all lie upon the
circumference of one and the same circle. Thus,
for example, AL and BL drawn from A and B,
meeting at the point L, bearing to one another
the same ratio as AC to BC, and the pair AK

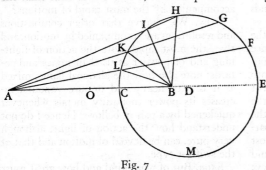

Fig. 7

and BK meeting at K also bearing to one another the same ratio, and likewise the pairs AI,
BI, AH, BH, AG, BG, AF, BF, AE, BE, have
their points of intersection L, K, I, H, G, F, E,
all lying upon the circumference of one and the
same circle. Accordingly if we imagine the point
C to move continuously in such a manner that
the lines drawn from it to the fixed terminal
points, A and B, always maintain the same ratio between their lengths as exists between the
original parts, AC and CB, then the point C
will, as I shall presently prove, describe a circle.
And the circle thus described will increase in
size without limit as the point C approaches the
middle point which we may call O; but it will
diminish in size as C approaches the end B. So
that the infinite number of points located in
the line OB will, if the motion be as explained
above, describe circles of every size, some
smaller than the pupil of the eye of a flea, others
larger than the celestial equator. Now if we

move any of the points lying between the two
ends O and B they will all describe circles, those
nearest O, immense circles; but if we move the
point O itself, and continue to move it according to the aforesaid law, namely, that the lines
drawn from O to the terminal points, A and B,
maintain the same ratio as the original lines AO
and OB, what kind of a line will be produced?
A circle will be drawn larger than the largest of
the others, a circle which is therefore infinite.
But from the point O a straight line will also be
drawn perpendicular to BA and extending to
infinity without ever turning, as did the others,
to join its last end with its first; for the point C,
with its limited motion, having described the
upper semicircle, CHE, proceeds to describe
the lower semicircle EMC, thus returning to
the starting point. But the point O having
started to describe its circle, as did all the other
points in the line AB, (for the points in the
other portion OA describe their circles also, the
largest being those nearest the point O) is unable to return to its starting point because
the circle it describes, being the largest of
all, is infinite; in fact, it describes an infinite
straight line as circumference of its infinite
circle. Think now what a difference there is
between a finite and an infinite circle since
the latter changes character in such a manner that it loses not only its existence but
also its possibility of existence; indeed, we
already clearly understand that there can
be no such thing as an infinite circle; similarly there can be no infinite sphere, no infinite body, and no infinite surface of any
shape. Now what shall we say concerning this
metamorphosis in the transition from finite to
infinite? And why should we feel greater repugnance, seeing that, in our search after the
infinite among numbers we found it in unity?
Having broken up a solid into many parts, having reduced it to the finest of powder and having resolved it into its infinitely small indivisible atoms why may we not say that this solid
has been reduced to a single *continuum* perhaps
a fluid like water or mercury or even a liquified
metal? And do we not see stones melt into glass
and the glass itself under strong heat become
more fluid than water?

SAGR. Are we then to believe that substances
become fluid in virtue of being resolved into
their infinitely small indivisible components?

SALV. I am not able to find any better means
of accounting for certain phenomena of which
the following is one. When I take a hard substance such as stone or metal and when I reduce

it by means of a hammer or fine file to the most minute and impalpable powder, it is clear that its finest particles, although when taken one by one are, on account of their smallness, imperceptible to our sight and touch, are nevertheless finite in size, possess shape, and capability of being counted. It is also true that when once heaped up they remain in a heap; and if an excavation be made within limits the cavity will remain and the surrounding particles will not rush in to fill it; if shaken the particles come to rest immediately after the external disturbing agent is removed; the same effects are observed in all piles of larger and larger particles, of any shape, even if spherical, as is the case with piles of millet, wheat, lead shot, and every other material. But if we attempt to discover such properties in water we do not find them; for when once heaped up it immediately flattens out unless held up by some vessel or other external retaining body; when hollowed out it quickly rushes in to fill the cavity; and when disturbed it fluctuates for a long time and sends out its waves through great distances.

Seeing that water has less firmness than the finest of powder, in fact has no consistence whatever, we may, it seems to me, very reasonably conclude that the smallest particles into which it can be resolved are quite different from finite and divisible particles; indeed the only difference I am able to discover is that the former are indivisible. The exquisite transparency of water also favors this view; for the most transparent crystal when broken and ground and reduced to powder loses its transparency; the finer the grinding the greater the loss; but in the case of water where the attrition is of the highest degree we have extreme transparency. Gold and silver when pulverized with acids more finely than is possible with any file still remain powders, and do not become fluids until the finest particles of fire or of the rays of the sun dissolve them, as I think, into their ultimate, indivisible, and infinitely small components.

SAGR. This phenomenon of light which you mention is one which I have many times remarked with astonishment. I have, for instance, seen lead melted instantly by means of a concave mirror only three hands in diameter. Hence I think that if the mirror were very large, well-polished and of a parabolic figure, it would just as readily and quickly melt any other metal, seeing that the small mirror, which was not well polished and had only a spherical shape, was able so energetically to melt lead and burn every combustible substance. Such effects as these render credible to me the marvels accomplished by the mirrors of Archimedes.

SALV. Speaking of the effects produced by the mirrors of Archimedes, it was his own books (which I had already read and studied with infinite astonishment) that rendered credible to me all the miracles described by various writers. And if any doubt had remained, the book which Father Buonaventura Cavalieri[1] has recently published on the subject of the burning glass and which I have read with admiration would have removed the last difficulty.

SAGR. I also have seen this treatise and have read it with pleasure and astonishment; and knowing the author I was confirmed in the opinion which I had already formed of him, that he was destined to become one of the leading mathematicians of our age. But now, with regard to the surprising effect of solar rays in melting metals, must we believe that such a furious action is devoid of motion or that it is accompanied by the most rapid of motions?

SALV. We observe that other combustions and resolutions are accompanied by motion, and that, the most rapid; note the action of lightning and of powder as used in mines and petards; note also how the charcoal flame, mixed as it is with heavy and impure vapours, increases its power to liquify metals whenever quickened by a pair of bellows. Hence I do not understand how the action of light, although very pure, can be devoid of motion and that of the swiftest type.

SAGR. But of what kind and how great must we consider this speed of light to be? Is it instantaneous or momentary or does it like other motions require time? Can we not decide this by experiment?

SIMP. Everyday experience shows that the propagation of light is instantaneous; for when we see a piece of artillery fired, at great distance, the flash reaches our eyes without lapse of time; but the sound reaches the ear only after a noticeable interval.

SAGR. Well, Simplicio, the only thing I am able to infer from this familiar bit of experience is that sound, in reaching our ear, travels more slowly than light; it does not inform me whether the coming of the light is instantaneous or whether, although extremely rapid, it still oc-

[1] One of the most active investigators among Galileo's contemporaries; a Jesuit, first to introduce the use of logarithms into Italy and first to derive the expression for the focal length of a lens having unequal radii of curvature. TRANS.

cupies time. An observation of this kind tells us nothing more than one in which it is claimed that "As soon as the sun reaches the horizon its light reaches our eyes"; but who will assure me that these rays had not reached this limit earlier than they reached our vision?

SALV. The small conclusiveness of these and other similar observations once led me to devise a method by which one might accurately ascertain whether illumination, *i.e.*, the propagation of light, is really instantaneous. The fact that the speed of sound is as high as it is, assures us that the motion of light cannot fail to be extraordinarily swift. The experiment which I devised was as follows:

Let each of two persons take a light contained in a lantern, or other receptacle, such that by the interposition of the hand, the one can shut off or admit the light to the vision of the other. Next let them stand opposite each other at a distance of a few cubits and practice until they acquire such skill in uncovering and occulting their lights that the instant one sees the light of his companion he will uncover his own. After a few trials the response will be so prompt that without sensible error the uncovering of one light is immediately followed by the uncovering of the other, so that as soon as one exposes his light he will instantly see that of the other. Having acquired skill at this short distance let the two experimenters, equipped as before, take up positions separated by a distance of two or three miles and let them perform the same experiment at night, noting carefully whether the exposures and occultations occur in the same manner as at short distances; if they do, we may safely conclude that the propagation of light is instantaneous; but if time is required at a distance of three miles which, considering the going of one light and the coming of the other, really amounts to six, then the delay ought to be easily observable. If the experiment is to be made at still greater distances, say eight or ten miles, telescopes may be employed, each observer adjusting one for himself at the place where he is to make the experiment at night; then although the lights are not large and are therefore invisible to the naked eye at so great a distance, they can readily be covered and uncovered since by aid of the telescopes, once adjusted and fixed, they will become easily visible.

SAGR. This experiment strikes me as a clever and reliable invention. But tell us what you conclude from the results.

SALV. In fact I have tried the experiment only at a short distance, less than a mile, from which I have not been able to ascertain with certainty whether the appearance of the opposite light was instantaneous or not; but if not instantaneous it is extraordinarily rapid—I should call it momentary; and for the present I should compare it to motion which we see in the lightning flash between clouds eight or ten miles distant from us. We see the beginning of this light—I might say its head and source—located at a particular place among the clouds; but it immediately spreads to the surrounding ones, which seems to be an argument that at least some time is required for propagation; for if the illumination were instantaneous and not gradual, we should not be able to distinguish its origin—its centre, so to speak—from its outlying portions. What a sea we are gradually slipping into without knowing it! With vacua and infinities and indivisibles and instantaneous motions, shall we ever be able, even by means of a thousand discussions, to reach dry land?

SAGR. Really these matters lie far beyond our grasp. Just think; when we seek the infinite among numbers we find it in unity; that which is ever divisible is derived from indivisibles; the vacuum is found inseparably connected with the plenum; indeed the views commonly held concerning the nature of these matters are so reversed that even the circumference of a circle turns out to be an infinite straight line, a fact which, if my memory serves me correctly, you, Salviati, were intending to demonstrate geometrically. Please therefore proceed without further digression.

SALV. I am at your service; but for the sake of greater clearness let me first demonstrate the following problem:

Given a straight line divided into unequal parts which bear to each other any ratio whatever, to describe a circle such that two straight lines drawn from the ends of the given line to any point on the circumference will bear to each other the same ratio as the two parts of the given line, thus making those lines which are drawn from the same terminal points homologous.

Let *AB* represent the given straight line divided into any two unequal parts by the point *C;* the problem is to describe a circle such that two straight lines drawn from the terminal points, *A* and *B*, to any point on the circumference will bear to each other the same ratio as the part *AC* bears to *BC*, so that lines drawn from the same terminal points are homologous. About *C* as centre describe a circle having the shorter part CB of the given line, as radius. Through A draw a straight line AD which shall be tangent to the circle at D and indefinitely prolonged toward E. Draw the radius CD which will be perpendicular to AE. At B erect a perpendicular to AB; this perpendicular will

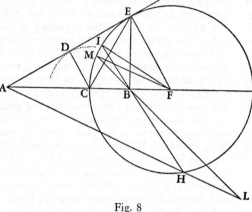

Fig. 8

intersect AE at some point since the angle at A is acute; call this point of intersection, E, and from it draw a perpendicular to AE which will intersect AB prolonged in F. Now I say the two straight lines FE and FC are equal. For if we join E and C, we shall have two triangles, DEC and BEC, in which the two sides of the one, DE and EC, are equal to the two sides of the other, BE and EC, both DE and EB being tangents to the circle DB while the bases DC and CB are likewise equal; hence the two angles, DEC and BEC, will be equal. Now since the angle BCE differs from a right angle by the angle CEB, and the angle CEF also differs from a right angle by the angle CED, and since these differences are equal, it follows that the angle FCE is equal to CEF; consequently the sides FE and FC are equal. If we describe a circle with F as centre and FE as radius it will pass through the point C; let CEG be such a circle. This is the circle sought, for if we draw lines from the terminal points A and B to any point on its circumference they will bear to each other the same ratio as the two portions AC and BC which meet at the point C. This is manifest in the case of the two lines AE and BE, meeting at the point E, because the angle E of the triangle AEB is bisected by the line CE, and therefore $AC : CB = AE : BE$. The same may be proved of the two lines AG and BG terminating in the point G. For since the triangles AFE and EFB are similar, we have $AF : FE = EF : FB$, or $AF : FC = CF : FB$, and

dividendo $AG : CF = CB : BF$, or $AC : FG = CB : BF$; also componendo we have both $AB : BG = CB : BF$ and $AG : GB = CF : FB = AE : EB = AC : BC$.   Q. E. D.

Take now any other point in the circumference, say H, where the two lines AH and BH intersect; in like manner we shall have $AC : CB = AH : HB$. Prolong HB until it meets the circumference at I and join IF; and since we have already found that $AB : BG = CB : BF$ it follows that the rectangle $AB \cdot BF$ is equal to the rectangle $CB \cdot BG$ or $IB \cdot BH$. Hence $AB : BH = IB : BF$. But the angles at B are equal and therefore $AH : HB = IF : FB = EF : FB = AE : EB$.

Besides, I may add, that it is impossible for lines which maintain this same ratio and which are drawn from the terminal points, A and B, to meet at any point either inside or outside the circle, CEG. For suppose this were possible; let AL and BL be two such lines intersecting at the point L outside the circle: prolong LB till it meets the circumference at M and join MF. If $AL : BL = AC : BC = MF : FB$, then we shall have two triangles ALB and MFB which have the sides about the two angles proportional, the angles at the vertex, B, equal, and the two remaining angles, FMB and LAB, less than right angles (because the right angle at M has for its base the entire diameter CG and not merely a part BF: and the other angle at the point A is acute because the line AL, the homologue of AC, is greater than BL, the homologue of BC). From this it follows that the triangles ABL and MBF are similar and therefore $AB : BL = MB : BF$, making the rectangle $AB \cdot BF = MB \cdot BL$; but it has been demonstrated that the rectangle $AB \cdot BF$ is equal to $CB \cdot BG$; whence it would follow that the rectangle $MB \cdot BL$ is equal to the rectangle $CB \cdot BG$ which is impossible; therefore the intersection cannot fall outside the circle. And in like manner we can show that it cannot fall inside; hence all these intersections fall on the circumference.

But now it is time for us to go back and grant the request of Simplicio by showing him that it is not only not impossible to resolve a line into an infinite number of points but that this is quite as easy as to divide it into its finite parts. This I will do under the following condition which I am sure, Simplicio, you will not deny me, namely, that you will not require me to separate the points, one from the other, and show them to you, one by one, on this paper; for I should be content that you, without separating the four or six parts of a line from one another, should show me the marked divisions or at most that you should fold them at angles forming a square or a hexagon: for, then, I am certain you would consider the division distinctly and actually accomplished.

Simp. I certainly should.

Salv. If now the change which takes place when you bend a line at angles so as to form now a square, now an octagon, now a polygon of forty, a hundred or a thousand angles, is sufficient to bring into actuality the four, eight, forty, hundred, and thousand parts which, according to you, existed at first only potentially in the straight line, may I not say, with equal right, that, when I have bent the straight line into a polygon having an infinite number of sides, i. e., into a circle, I have reduced to actuality that infinite number of parts which you claimed, while it was straight, were contained in it only potentially? Nor can one deny that the division into an infinite number of points is just as truly accomplished as the one into four parts when the square is formed or into a thousand parts when the millagon is formed; for in such a division the same conditions are satisfied as in the case of a polygon of a thousand or a hundred thousand sides. Such a polygon laid upon a straight line touches it with one of its sides, i. e., with one of its hundred thousand parts; while the circle which is a polygon of an infinite number of sides touches the same straight line with one of its sides which is a single point different from all its neighbors and therefore separate and distinct in no less degree than is one side of a polygon from the other sides. And just as a polygon, when rolled along a plane, marks out upon this plane, by the successive contacts of its sides, a straight line equal to its perimeter, so the circle rolled upon such a plane also traces by its infinite succession of contacts a straight line equal in length to its own circumference. I am willing, Simplicio, at the outset, to grant to the Peripatetics the truth of their opinion that a continuous quantity is divisible only into parts which are still further divisible so that however far the division and subdivision be continued no end will be reached; but I am not so certain that they will concede to me that none of these divisions of theirs can be a final one, as is surely the fact, because there always remains "another"; the final and ultimate division is rather one which resolves a continuous quantity into an infinite number of indivisible quantities, a result which I grant can never be reached by successive division into

an ever-increasing number of parts. But if they employ the method which I propose for separating and resolving the whole of infinity, at a single stroke (an artifice which surely ought not to be denied me), I think that they would be contented to admit that a continuous quantity is built up out of absolutely indivisible atoms, especially since this method, perhaps better than any other, enables us to avoid many intricate labyrinths, such as cohesion in solids, already mentioned, and the question of expansion and contraction, without forcing upon us the objectional admission of empty spaces which carries with it the penetrability of bodies. Both of these objections, it appears to me, are avoided if we accept the above-mentioned view of indivisible constituents.

Simp. I hardly know what the Peripatetics would say since the views advanced by you would strike them as mostly new, and as such we must consider them. It is however, not unlikely that they would find answers and solutions for these problems which I, for want of time and critical ability, am at present unable to solve. Leaving this to one side for the moment, I should like to hear how the introduction of these indivisible quantities helps us to understand contraction and expansion avoiding at the same time the vacuum and the penetrability of bodies.

Sagr. I also shall listen with keen interest to this same matter which is far from clear in my mind; provided I am allowed to hear what, a moment ago, Simplicio suggested we omit, namely, the reasons which Aristotle offers against the existence of the vacuum and the arguments which you must advance in rebuttal.

Salv. I will do both. And first, just as, for the production of expansion, we employ the line described by the small circle during one rotation of the large one—a line greater than the circumference of the small circle—so, in order to explain contraction, we point out that, during each rotation of the smaller circle, the larger one describes a straight line which is shorter than its circumference.

For the better understanding of this we proceed to the consideration of what happens in the case of polygons. Employing a figure similar to the earlier one, construct the two hexagons, ABC and HIK, about the common centre L, and let them roll along the parallel lines HOM and ABc. Now holding the vertex I fixed, allow the smaller polygon to rotate until the side IK lies upon the parallel, during which motion the point K will describe the arc KM, and the side *KI* will coincide with *IM*. Let us see what, in the meantime, the side *CB* of the larger polygon has been doing. Since the rotation is about the point *I*, the terminal point *B*, of the line *IB*, moving backwards, will describe the arc *Bb* underneath the parallel *cA* so that when the side *KI* coincides with the line *MI*, the side *BC* will coincide with *bc*, having advanced only through the distance *Bc*, but having retreated through a portion of the line *BA* which subtends the arc *Bb*. If we allow the rotation of the smaller polygon to go on it will traverse and describe along its parallel a line equal to its perimeter; while the larger one will traverse and describe a line less than its perimeter by as many times the length *bB* as there are sides less one; this line is approximately equal to that described by the smaller polygon exceeding it only by the distance *bB*. Here now we see, without any difficulty, why the larger polygon, when carried by the smaller, does not measure off with its sides a line longer than that traversed by the smaller one; this is because a portion of each side is superposed upon its immediately preceding neighbour.

Let us next consider two circles, having a common centre at A, and lying upon their respective parallels, the smaller being tangent to its parallel at the point *B*; the larger, at the point

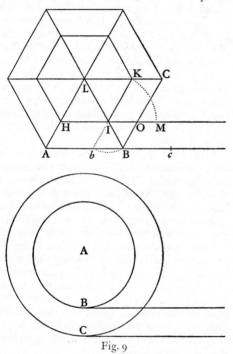

Fig. 9

C. Here when the small circle commences to roll the point *B* does not remain at rest for a while so as to allow *BC* to move backward and carry with it the point *C*, as happened in the case of the polygons, where the point *I* remained fixed until the side *KI* coincided with *MI* and the line *IB* carried the terminal point *B* backward as far as *b*, so that the side *BC* fell upon *bc*, thus superposing upon the line *BA*, the portion *Bb*, and advancing by an amount *Bc*, equal to *MI*, that is, to one side of the smaller polygon. On account of these superpositions, which are the excesses of the sides of the larger over the smaller polygon, each net advance is equal to one side of the smaller polygon and, during one complete rotation, these amount to a straight line equal in length to the perimeter of the smaller polygon.

But now reasoning in the same way concerning the circles, we must observe that whereas the number of sides in any polygon is comprised within a certain limit, the number of sides in a circle is infinite; the former are finite and divisible; the latter infinite and indivisible. In the case of the polygon, the vertices remain at rest during an interval of time which bears to the period of one complete rotation the same ratio which one side bears to the perimeter; likewise, in the case of the circles, the delay of each of the infinite number of vertices is merely instantaneous, because an instant is such a fraction of a finite interval as a point is of a line which contains an infinite number of points. The retrogression of the sides of the larger polygon is not equal to the length of one of its sides but merely to the excess of such a side over one side of the smaller polygon, the net advance being equal to this smaller side; but in the circle, the point or side *C*, during the instantaneous rest of *B*, recedes by an amount equal to its excess over the side *B*, making a net progress equal to *B* itself. In short the infinite number of indivisible sides of the greater circle with their infinite number of indivisible retrogressions, made during the infinite number of instantaneous delays of the infinite number of vertices of the smaller circle, together with the infinite number of progressions, equal to the infinite number of sides in the smaller circle—all these, I say, add up to a line equal to that described by the smaller circle, a line which contains an infinite number of infinitely small superpositions, thus bringing about a thickening or contraction without any overlapping or interpenetration of finite parts. This result could not be obtained in the case of a line divided into finite parts such as is the perimeter of any polygon, which when laid out in a straight line cannot be shortened except by the overlapping and interpenetration of its sides. This contraction of an infinite number of infinitely small parts without the interpenetration or overlapping of finite parts and the previously mentioned expansion of an infinite number of indivisible parts by the interposition of indivisible vacua is, in my opinion, the most that can be said concerning the contraction and rarefaction of bodies, unless we give up the impenetrability of matter and introduce empty spaces of finite size. If you find anything here that you consider worth while, pray use it; if not regard it, together with my remarks, as idle talk; but this remember, we are dealing with the infinite and the indivisible.

SAGR. I frankly confess that your idea is subtle and that it impresses me as new and strange; but whether, as a matter of fact, nature actually behaves according to such a law I am unable to determine; however, until I find a more satisfactory explanation I shall hold fast to this one. Perhaps Simplicio can tell us something which I have not yet heard, namely, how to explain the explanation which the philosophers have given of this abstruse matter; for, indeed, all that I have hitherto read concerning contraction is so dense and that concerning expansion so thin that my poor brain can neither penetrate the former nor grasp the latter.

SIMP. I am all at sea and find difficulties in following either path, especially this new one; because according to this theory an ounce of gold might be rarefied and expanded until its size would exceed that of the earth, while the earth, in turn, might be condensed and reduced until it would become smaller than a walnut, something which I do not believe; nor do I believe that you believe it. The arguments and demonstrations which you have advanced are mathematical, abstract, and far removed from concrete matter; and I do not believe that when applied to the physical and natural world these laws will hold.

SALV. I am not able to render the invisible visible, nor do I think that you will ask this. But now that you mention gold, do not our senses tell us that that metal can be immensely expanded? I do not know whether you have observed the method employed by those who are skilled in drawing gold wire, of which really only the surface is gold, the inside material being silver. The way they draw it is as follows: they take a cylinder or, if you please, a rod of

silver, about half a cubit long and three or four times as wide as one's thumb; this rod they cover with gold-leaf which is so thin that it almost floats in air, putting on not more than eight or ten thicknesses. Once gilded they begin to pull it, with great force, through the holes of a draw-plate; again and again it is made to pass through smaller and smaller holes, until, after very many passages, it is reduced to the fineness of a lady's hair, or perhaps even finer; yet the surface remains gilded. Imagine now how the substance of this gold has been expanded and to what fineness it has been reduced.

SIMP. I do not see that this process would produce, as a consequence, that marvellous thinning of the substance of the gold which you suggest: first, because the original gilding consisting of ten layers of gold-leaf has a sensible thickness; secondly, because in drawing out the silver it grows in length but at the same time diminishes proportionally in thickness; and, since one dimension thus compensates the other, the area will not be so increased as to make it necessary during the process of gilding to reduce the thinness of the gold beyond that of the original leaves.

SALV. You are greatly mistaken, Simplicio, because the surface increases directly as the square root of the length, a fact which I can demonstrate geometrically.

SAGR. Please give us the demonstration not only for my own sake but also for Simplicio provided you think we can understand it.

SALV. I'll see if I can recall it on the spur of the moment. At the outset, it is clear that the original thick rod of silver and the wire drawn out to an enormous length are two cylinders of the same volume, since they are the same body of silver. So that, if I determine the ratio between the surfaces of cylinders of the same volume, the problem will be solved. I say then,

The areas of cylinders of equal volumes, neglecting the bases, bear to each other a ratio which is the square root of the ratio of their lengths.

Take two cylinders of equal volume having the altitudes *AB* and *CD*, between which the line *E* is a mean proportional. Then I claim that, omitting the bases of each cylinder, the surface of the cylinder *AB* is to that of the cylinder *CD* as the length *AB* is to the line *E*, that is, as the square root of *AB* is to the square root of *CD*. Now cut off the cylinder *AB* at *F* so that the altitude *AF* is equal to *CD*. Then since the bases of cylinders of equal volume bear to one another the inverse ratio of their heights, it follows that the area of the circular base of the cylinder *CD* will be to the area of the circular base of *AB* as the altitude *BA* is to *DC*: moreover, since circles are to one another as the squares of their diameters, the said squares will be to each other as *BA* is to *CD*. But *BA* is to *CD* as

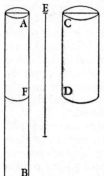

Fig. 10

the square of *BA* is to the square of *E*: and, therefore, these four squares will form a proportion; and likewise their sides; so the line *AB* is to *E* as the diameter of circle *C* is to the diameter of the circle *A*. But the diameters are proportional to the circumferences and the circumferences are proportional to the areas of cylinders of equal height; hence the line *AB* is to *E* as the surface of the cylinder *CD* is to the surface of the cylinder *AF*. Now since the height *AF* is to *AB* as the surface of *AF* is to the surface of *AB*; and since the height *AB* is to the line *E* as the surface *CD* is to *AF*, it follows, *ex æquali in proportione perturbata*[1], that the height *AF* is to *E* as the surface *CD* is to the surface *AB*, and *convertendo*, the surface of the cylinder *AB* is to the surface of the cylinder *CD* as the line *E* is to *AF*, *i. e.*, to *CD*, or as *AB* is to *E* which is the square root of the ratio of *AB* to *CD*.   Q. E. D.

If now we apply these results to the case in hand, and assume that the silver cylinder at the time of gilding had a length of only half a cubit and a thickness three or four times that of one's thumb, we shall find that, when the wire has been reduced to the fineness of a hair and has been drawn out to a length of twenty thousand cubits (and perhaps more), the area of its surface will have been increased not less than two hundred times. Consequently the ten leaves of gold which were laid on have been extended over a surface two hundred times greater, assuring us that the thickness of the gold which now covers the surface of so many cubits of wire cannot be greater than one twentieth that of an ordinary leaf of beaten gold. Consider now what degree of fineness it must have and whether one could conceive it to happen in any other way than by enormous expansion of parts; consider also whether this experiment does not suggest that physical bodies are composed of infinitely small indivisible particles, a view which is supported by other more striking and conclusive examples.

SAGR. This demonstration is so beautiful that,

[1] See Euclid, v. 20.

even if it does not have the cogency originally intended,—although to my mind, it is very forceful—the short time devoted to it has nevertheless been most happily spent.

SALV. Since you are so fond of these geometrical demonstrations, which carry with them distinct gain, I will give you a companion theorem which answers an extremely interesting query. We have seen above what relations hold between equal cylinders of different height or length; let us now see what holds when the cylinders are equal in area but unequal in height, understanding area to include the curved surface, but not the upper and lower bases. The theorem is:

The volumes of right cylinders having equal curved surfaces are inversely proportional to their altitudes.

Let the surfaces of the two cylinders, *AE* and *CF*, be equal but let the height of the latter, *CD*, be greater than that of the former, *AB*: then I say that the volume of the cylinder *AE* is to that of the cylinder *CF* as the height *CD* is to *AB*. Now since the surface of *CF* is equal to the surface of *AE*, it follows that the volume of *CF* is less than that of *AE*; for, if they were equal, the surface of *CF* would, by the preceding proposition, exceed that of *AE*, and the excess would be so much the greater if the volume of the cylinder *CF* were greater than that of *AE*. Let us now take a cylinder *ID* having a volume equal to that of *AE*; then, according to the preceding theorem, the surface of the cylinder *ID* is to the surface of *AE* as the altitude *IF* is to the mean proportional between *IF* and *AB*. But since one

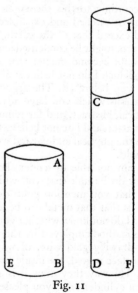

Fig. 11

datum of the problem is that the surface of AE is equal to that of CF, and since the surface ID is to the surface CF as the altitude IF is to the altitude CD, it follows that CD is a mean proportional between IF and AB. Not only so, but since the volume of the cylinder ID is equal to that of AE, each will bear the same ratio to the volume of the cylinder CF; but the volume ID is to the volume CF as the altitude IF is to the altitude CD; hence the volume of AE is to the volume of CF as the length IF is to the length CD, that is, as the length CD is to the length AB. Q. E. D.

This explains a phenomenon upon which the common people always look with wonder, namely, if we have a piece of stuff which has one side longer than the other, we can make from it a cornsack, using the customary wooden base, which will hold more when the short side of the cloth is used for the height of the sack and the long side is wrapped around the wooden base, than with the alternative arrangement. So that, for instance, from a piece of cloth which is six cubits on one side and twelve on the other, a sack can be made which will hold more when the side of twelve cubits is wrapped around the wooden base, leaving the sack six cubits high than when the six cubit side is put around the base making the sack twelve cubits high. From what has been proven above we learn not only the general fact that one sack holds more than the other, but we also get specific and particular information as to how much more, namely, just in proportion as the altitude of the sack diminishes the contents increase and *vice versa*. Thus if we use the figures given which make the cloth twice as long as wide and if we use the long side for the seam, the volume of the sack will be just one-half as great as with the opposite arrangement. Likewise if we have a piece of matting which measures 7 x 25 cubits and make from it a basket, the contents of the basket will, when the seam is lengthwise, be seven as compared with twenty-five when the seam runs endwise.

SAGR. It is with great pleasure that we continue thus to acquire new and useful information. But as regards the subject just discussed, I really believe that, among those who are not already familiar with geometry, you would scarcely find four persons in a hundred who would not, at first sight, make the mistake of believing that bodies having equal surfaces would be equal in other respects. Speaking of areas, the same error is made when one attempts, as often happens, to determine the sizes of various cities by measuring their boundary lines, forgetting that the circuit of one may be equal to the circuit of another while the area of the one is much greater than that of the other. And this is true not only in the case of irregular, but also of regular surfaces, where the polygon having the greater number of sides always contains a larger area than the one with the less number of sides, so that finally the circle which is a polygon of an infinite number of sides contains the largest area of all polygons of equal perimeter. I remember with particular pleasure having seen this demonstration when I was studying the sphere of Sacrobosco[1] with the aid of a learned commentary.

SALV. Very true! I too came across the same passage which suggested to me a method of showing how, by a single short demonstration, one can prove that the circle has the largest content of all regular isoperimetric figures; and that, of other figures, the one which has the larger number of sides contains a greater area than that which has the smaller number.

SAGR. Being exceedingly fond of choice and uncommon propositions, I beseech you to let us have your demonstration.

SALV. I can do this in a few words by proving the following theorem:

The area of a circle is a mean proportional between any two regular and similar polygons of which one circumscribes it and the other is isoperimetric with it. In addition, the area of the circle is less than that of any circumscribed polygon and greater than that of any isoperimetric polygon. And further, of these circumscribed polygons, the one which has the greater number of sides is smaller than the one which has a less number; but, on the other hand, that isoperimetric polygon which has the greater number of sides is the larger.

Let A and B be two similar polygons of which A circumscribes the given circle and B is isoperimetric with it. The area of the circle will then be a mean proportional between the areas of the polygons. For if we indicate the radius of the circle by AC and if we remember that the area of the circle is equal to that of a right-angled triangle in which one of the sides about the right angle is equal to the radius, AC, and the other to the circumference; and if likewise we remember that the area of the polygon A is equal to the area of a right-angled triangle one of whose sides about the right angle has the same length as AC and the other is equal to the perimeter of the polygon itself; it is then manifest

[1] John of Holywood, English mathematician, was known as Johannes de Sacro Bosco.—ED.

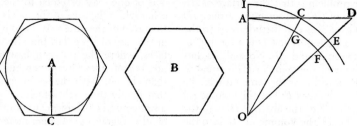

Fig. 12

that the circumscribed polygon bears to the circle the same ratio which its perimeter bears to the circumference of the circle, or to the perimeter of the polygon B which is, by hypothesis, equal to the circumference of the circle. But since the polygons A and B are similar their areas are to each other as the squares of their perimeters; hence the area of the circle A is a mean proportional between the areas of the two polygons A and B. And since the area of the polygon A is greater than that of the circle A, it is clear that the area of the circle A is greater than that of the isoperimetric polygon B, and is therefore the greatest of all regular polygons having the same perimeter as the circle.

We now demonstrate the remaining portion of the theorem, which is to prove that, in the case of polygons circumscribing a given circle, the one having the smaller number of sides has a larger area than one having a greater number of sides; but that on the other hand, in the case of isoperimetric polygons, the one having the more sides has a larger area than the one with less sides. To the circle which has O for centre and OA for radius draw the tangent AD; and on this tangent lay off, say, AD which shall represent one-half of the side of a circumscribed pentagon and AC which shall represent one-half of the side of a heptagon; draw the straight lines OGC and OFD; then with O as a centre and OC as radius draw the arc ECI. Now since the triangle DOC is greater than the sector EOC and since the sector COI is greater than the triangle COA, it follows that the triangle DOC bears to the triangle COA a greater ratio than the sector EOC bears to the sector COI, that is, than the sector FOG bears to the sector GOA. Hence, *componendo et permutando*, the triangle DOA bears to the sector FOA a greater ratio than that which the triangle COA bears to the sector GOA, and also 10 such triangles DOA bear to 10 such sectors FOA a greater ratio than 14 such triangles COA bear to 14 such sectors GOA, that is to say, the circumscribed penta-

gon bears to the circle a greater ratio than does the heptagon. Hence the pentagon exceeds the heptagon in area.

But now let us assume that both the heptagon and the pentagon have the same perimeter as that of a given circle. Then I say the heptagon will contain a larger area than the pentagon. For since the area of the circle is a mean proportional between areas of the circumscribed and of the isoperimetric pentagons, and since likewise it is a mean proportional between the circumscribed and isoperimetric heptagons, and since also we have proved that the circumscribed pentagon is larger than the circumscribed heptagon, it follows that this circumscribed pentagon bears to the circle a larger ratio than does the heptagon, that is, the circle will bear to its isoperimetric pentagon a greater ratio than to its isoperimetric heptagon. Hence the pentagon is smaller than its isoperimetric heptagon.   Q. E. D.

SAGR. A very clever and elegant demonstration! But how did we come to plunge into geometry while discussing the objections urged by Simplicio, objections of great moment, especially that one referring to density which strikes me as particularly difficult?

SALV. If contraction and expansion consist in contrary motions, one ought to find for each great expansion a correspondingly large contraction. But our surprise is increased when, every day, we see enormous expansions taking place almost instantaneously. Think what a tremendous expansion occurs when a small quantity of gun-powder flares up into a vast volume of fire! Think too of the almost limitless expansion of the light which it produces! Imagine the contraction which would take place if this fire and this light were to reunite, which, indeed, is not impossible since only a little while ago they were located together in this small space. You will find, upon observation, a thousand such expansions for they are more obvious than contractions since dense matter is more palpable and accessible to our senses. We can take wood and see it go up in fire and light, but we do not see them recombine to form wood; we see fruits and flowers and a thousand other solid bodies dissolve largely into odours, but we do not observe these fragrant atoms coming together to form fragrant solids. But where the senses fail us reason must step in; for it will enable us to understand the motion involved in the condensation of extremely rarefied and tenuous substances just as clearly as that involved in the expansion and dissolution of solids. Moreover we are trying to find out how it is possible to produce expansion and contraction in bodies which are capable of such changes without introducing vacua and without giving up the impenetrability of matter; but this does not exclude the possibility of there being materials which possess no such properties and do not, therefore, carry with them consequences which you call inconvenient and impossible. And finally, Simplicio, I have, for the sake of you philosophers, taken pains to find an explanation of how expansion and contraction can take place without our admitting the penetrability of matter and introducing vacua, properties which you deny and dislike; if you were to admit them, I should not oppose you so vigorously. Now either admit these difficulties or accept my views or suggest something better.

SAGR. I quite agree with the peripatetic philosophers in denying the penetrability of matter. As to the vacua I should like to hear a thorough discussion of Aristotle's demonstration in which he opposes them, and what you, Salviati, have to say in reply. I beg of you, Simplicio, that you give us the precise proof of the Philosopher and that you, Salviati, give us the reply.

SIMP. So far as I remember, Aristotle inveighs against the ancient view that a vacuum is a necessary prerequisite for motion and that the latter could not occur without the former. In opposition to this view Aristotle shows that it is precisely the phenomenon of motion, as we shall see, which renders untenable the idea of a vacuum. His method is to divide the argument into two parts. He first supposes bodies of different weights to move in the same medium; then supposes, one and the same body to move in different media. In the first case, he supposes bodies of different weight to move in one and the same medium with different speeds which stand to one another in the same ratio as the weights; so that, for example, a body which is ten times as heavy as another will move ten

times as rapidly as the other. In the second case, he assumes that the speeds of one and the same body moving in different media are in inverse ratio to the densities of these media; thus, for instance, if the density of water were ten times that of air, the speed in air would be ten times greater than in water. From this second supposition, he shows that, since the tenuity of a vacuum differs infinitely from that of any medium filled with matter however rare, any body which moves in a plenum through a certain space in a certain time ought to move through a vacuum instantaneously; but instantaneous motion is an impossibility; it is therefore impossible that a vacuum should be produced by motion.

SALV. The argument is, as you see, *ad hominem*, that is, it is directed against those who thought the vacuum a prerequisite for motion. Now, if I admit the argument to be conclusive and concede also that motion cannot take place in a vacuum, the assumption of a vacuum considered absolutely and not with reference to motion, is not thereby invalidated. But to tell you what the ancients might possibly have replied and in order to better understand just how conclusive Aristotle's demonstration is, we may, in my opinion, deny both of his assumptions. And as to the first, I greatly doubt that Aristotle ever tested by experiment whether it be true that two stones, one weighing ten times as much as the other, if allowed to fall, at the same instant, from a height of, say, 100 cubits, would so differ in speed that when the heavier had reached the ground, the other would not have fallen more than 10 cubits.

SIMP. His language would seem to indicate that he had tried the experiment, because he says: *We see the heavier*; now the word *see* shows that he had made the experiment.

SAGR. But I, Simplicio, who had made the test can assure you that a cannon ball weighing one or two hundred pounds, or even more, will not reach the ground by as much as a span ahead of a musket ball weighing only half a pound, provided both are dropped from a height of 200 cubits.

SALV. But, even without further experiment, it is possible to prove clearly, by means of a short and conclusive argument, that a heavier body does not move more rapidly than a lighter one provided both bodies are of the same material and in short such as those mentioned by Aristotle. But tell me, Simplicio, whether you admit that each falling body acquires a definite speed fixed by nature, a velocity which cannot be increased or diminished except by the use of force or resistance.

SIMP. There can be no doubt but that one and the same body moving in a single medium has a fixed velocity which is determined by nature and which cannot be increased except by the addition of momentum or diminished except by some resistance which retards it.

SALV. If then we take two bodies whose natural speeds are different, it is clear that on uniting the two, the more rapid one will be partly retarded by the slower, and the slower will be somewhat hastened by the swifter. Do you not agree with me in this opinion?

SIMP. You are unquestionably right.

SALV. But if this is true, and if a large stone moves with a speed of, say, eight while a smaller moves with a speed of four, then when they are united, the system will move with a speed less than eight; but the two stones when tied together make a stone larger than that which before moved with a speed of eight. Hence the heavier body moves with less speed than the lighter; an effect which is contrary to your supposition. Thus you see how, from your assumption that the heavier body moves more rapidly than the lighter one, I infer that the heavier body moves more slowly.

SIMP. I am all at sea because it appears to me that the smaller stone when added to the larger increases its weight and by adding weight I do not see how it can fail to increase its speed or, at least, not to diminish it.

SALV. Here again you are in error, Simplicio, because it is not true that the smaller stone adds weight to the larger.

SIMP. This is, indeed, quite beyond my comprehension.

SALV. It will not be beyond you when I have once shown you the mistake under which you are labouring. Note that it is necessary to distinguish between heavy bodies in motion and the same bodies at rest. A large stone placed in a balance not only acquires additional weight by having another stone placed upon it, but even by the addition of a handful of hemp its weight is augmented six to ten ounces according to the quantity of hemp. But if you tie the hemp to the stone and allow them to fall freely from some height, do you believe that the hemp will press down upon the stone and thus accelerate its motion or do you think the motion will be retarded by a partial upward pressure? One always feels the pressure upon his shoulders when he prevents the motion of a load resting upon him; but if one descends just as

rapidly as the load would fall how can it gravitate or press upon him? Do you not see that this would be the same as trying to strike a man with a lance when he is running away from you with a speed which is equal to, or even greater, than that with which you are following him? You must therefore conclude that, during free and natural fall, the small stone does not press upon the larger and consequently does not increase its weight as it does when at rest.

SIMP. But what if we should place the larger stone upon the smaller?

SALV. Its weight would be increased if the larger stone moved more rapidly; but we have already concluded that when the small stone moves more slowly it retards to some extent the speed of the larger, so that the combination of the two, which is a heavier body than the larger of the two stones, would move less rapidly, a conclusion which is contrary to your hypothesis. We infer therefore that large and small bodies move with the same speed provided they are of the same specific gravity.

SIMP. Your discussion is really admirable; yet I do not find it easy to believe that a birdshot falls as swiftly as a cannon ball.

SALV. Why not say a grain of sand as rapidly as a grindstone? But, Simplicio, I trust you will not follow the example of many others who divert the discussion from its main intent and fasten upon some statement of mine which lacks a hair's-breadth of the truth and, under this hair, hide the fault of another which is as big as a ship's cable. Aristotle says that "an iron ball of one hundred pounds falling from a height of one hundred cubits reaches the ground before a one-pound ball has fallen a single cubit." I say that they arrive at the same time. You find, on making the experiment, that the larger outstrips the smaller by two finger-breadths, that is, when the larger has reached the ground, the other is short of it by two finger-breadths; now you would not hide behind these two fingers the ninety-nine cubits of Aristotle, nor would you mention my small error and at the same time pass over in silence his very large one. Aristotle declares that bodies of different weights, in the same medium, travel (in so far as their motion depends upon gravity) with speeds which are proportional to their weights; this he illustrates by use of bodies in which it is possible to perceive the pure and unadulterated effect of gravity, eliminating other considerations, for example, figure as being of small importance, influences which are greatly dependent upon the medium which modifies the single effect of gravity alone. Thus we observe that gold, the densest of all substances, when beaten out into a very thin leaf, goes floating through the air; the same thing happens with stone when ground into a very fine powder. But if you wish to maintain the general proposition you will have to show that the same ratio of speeds is preserved in the case of all heavy bodies, and that a stone of twenty pounds moves ten times as rapidly as one of two; but I claim that this is false and that, if they fall from a height of fifty or a hundred cubits, they will reach the earth at the same moment.

SIMP. Perhaps the result would be different if the fall took place not from a few cubits but from some thousands of cubits.

SALV. If this were what Aristotle meant you would burden him with another error which would amount to a falsehood; because, since there is no such sheer height available on earth, it is clear that Aristotle could not have made the experiment; yet he wishes to give us the impression of his having performed it when he speaks of such an effect as one which we see.

SIMP. In fact, Aristotle does not employ this principle, but uses the other one which is not, I believe, subject to these same difficulties.

SALV. But the one is as false as the other; and I am surprised that you yourself do not see the fallacy and that you do not perceive that if it were true that, in media of different densities and different resistances, such as water and air, one and the same body moved in air more rapidly than in water, in proportion as the density of water is greater than that of air, then it would follow that any body which falls through air ought also to fall through water. But this conclusion is false inasmuch as many bodies which descend in air not only do not descend in water, but actually rise.

SIMP. I do not understand the necessity of your inference; and in addition I will say that Aristotle discusses only those bodies which fall in both media, not those which fall in air but rise in water.

SALV. The arguments which you advance for the Philosopher are such as he himself would have certainly avoided so as not to aggravate his first mistake. But tell me now whether the density of the water, or whatever it may be that retards the motion, bears a definite ratio to the density of air which is less retardative; and if so fix a value for it at your pleasure.

SIMP. Such a ratio does exist; let us assume it to be ten; then, for a body which falls in both

these media, the speed in water will be ten times slower than in air.

SALV. I shall now take one of those bodies which fall in air but not in water, say a wooden ball, and I shall ask you to assign to it any speed you please for its descent through air.

SIMP. Let us suppose it moves with a speed of twenty.

SALV. Very well. Then it is clear that this speed bears to some smaller speed the same ratio as the density of water bears to that of air; and the value of this smaller speed is two. So that really if we follow exactly the assumption of Aristotle we ought to infer that the wooden ball which falls in air, a substance ten times less-resisting than water, with a speed of twenty would fall in water with a speed of two, instead of coming to the surface from the bottom as it does; unless perhaps you wish to reply, which I do not believe you will, that the rising of the wood through the water is the same as its falling with a speed of two. But since the wooden ball does not go to the bottom, I think you will agree with me that we can find a ball of another material, not wood, which does fall in water with a speed of two.

SIMP. Undoubtedly we can; but it must be of a substance considerably heavier than wood.

SALV. That is it exactly. But if this second ball falls in water with a speed of two, what will be its speed of descent in air? If you hold to the rule of Aristotle you must reply that it will move at the rate of twenty; but twenty is the speed which you yourself have already assigned to the wooden ball; hence this and the other heavier ball will each move through air with the same speed. But now how does the Philosopher harmonize this result with his other, namely, that bodies of different weight move through the same medium with different speeds—speeds which are proportional to their weights? But without going into the matter more deeply, how have these common and obvious properties escaped your notice? Have you not observed that two bodies which fall in water, one with a speed a hundred times as great as that of the other, will fall in air with speeds so nearly equal that one will not surpass the other by as much as one hundredth part? Thus, for example, an egg made of marble will descend in water one hundred times more rapidly than a hen's egg, while in air falling from a height of twenty cubits the one will fall short of the other by less than four finger-breadths. In short, a heavy body which sinks through ten cubits of water in three hours will traverse ten cubits of air in one or two pulse-beats; and if the heavy body be a ball of lead it will easily traverse the ten cubits of water in less than double the time required for ten cubits of air. And here, I am sure, Simplicio, you find no ground for difference or objection. We conclude, therefore, that the argument does not bear against the existence of a vacuum; but if it did, it would only do away with vacua of considerable size which neither I nor, in my opinion, the ancients ever believed to exist in nature, although they might possibly be produced by force as may be gathered from various experiments whose description would here occupy too much time.

SAGR. Seeing that Simplicio is silent, I will take the opportunity of saying something. Since you have clearly demonstrated that bodies of different weights do not move in one and the same medium with velocities proportional to their weights, but that they all move with the same speed, understanding of course that they are of the same substance or at least of the same specific gravity; certainly not of different specific gravities, for I hardly think you would have us believe a ball of cork moves with the same speed as one of lead; and again since you have clearly demonstrated that one and the same body moving through differently resisting media does not acquire speeds which are inversely proportional to the resistances, I am curious to learn what are the ratios actually observed in these cases.

SALV. These are interesting questions and I have thought much concerning them. I will give you the method of approach and the result which I finally reached. Having once established the falsity of the proposition that one and the same body moving through differently resisting media acquires speeds which are inversely proportional to the resistances of these media, and having also disproved the statement that in the same medium bodies of different weight acquire velocities proportional to their weights (understanding that this applies also to bodies which differ merely in specific gravity), I then began to combine these two facts and to consider what would happen if bodies of different weight were placed in media of different resistances; and I found that the differences in speed were greater in those media which were more resistant, that is, less yielding. This difference was such that two bodies which differed scarcely at all in their speed through air would, in water, fall the one with a speed ten times as great as that of the other. Further, there are bodies which will fall rapidly in air, whereas if

placed in water not only will not sink but will remain at rest or will even rise to the top: for it is possible to find some kinds of wood, such as knots and roots, which remain at rest in water but fall rapidly in air.

SAGR. I have often tried with the utmost patience to add grains of sand to a ball of wax until it should acquire the same specific gravity as water and would therefore remain at rest in this medium. But with all my care I was never able to accomplish this. Indeed, I do not know whether there is any solid substance whose specific gravity is, by nature, so nearly equal to that of water that if placed anywhere in water it will remain at rest.

SALV. In this, as in a thousand other operations, men are surpassed by animals. In this problem of yours one may learn much from the fish which are very skillful in maintaining their equilibrium not only in one kind of water, but also in waters which are notably different either by their own nature or by some accidental muddiness or through salinity, each of which produces a marked change. So perfectly indeed can fish keep their equilibrium that they are able to remain motionless in any position. This they accomplish, I believe, by means of an apparatus especially provided by nature, namely, a bladder located in the body and communicating with the mouth by means of a narrow tube through which they are able, at will, to expel a portion of the air contained in the bladder: by rising to the surface they can take in more air; thus they make themselves heavier or lighter than water at will and maintain equilibrium.

SAGR. By means of another device I was able to deceive some friends to whom I had boasted that I could make up a ball of wax that would be in equilibrium in water. In the bottom of a vessel I placed some salt water and upon this some fresh water; then I showed them that the ball stopped in the middle of the water, and that, when pushed to the bottom or lifted to the top, would not remain in either of these places but would return to the middle.

SALV. This experiment is not without usefulness. For when physicians are testing the various qualities of waters, especially their specific gravities, they employ a ball of this kind so adjusted that, in certain water, it will neither rise nor fall. Then in testing another water, differing ever so slightly in specific gravity, the ball will sink if this water be lighter and rise if it be heavier. And so exact is this experiment that the addition of two grains of salt to six pounds of water is sufficient to make the ball rise to the surface from the bottom to which it had fallen. To illustrate the precision of this experiment and also to clearly demonstrate the non-resistance of water to division, I wish to add that this notable difference in specific gravity can be produced not only by solution of some heavier substance, but also by merely heating or cooling; and so sensitive is water to this process that by simply adding four drops of another water which is slightly warmer or cooler than the six pounds one can cause the ball to sink or rise; it will sink when the warm water is poured in and will rise upon the addition of cold water. Now you can see how mistaken are those philosophers who ascribe to water viscosity or some other coherence of parts which offers resistance to separation of parts and to penetration.

SAGR. With regard to this question I have found many convincing arguments in a treatise by our Academician; but there is one great difficulty of which I have not been able to rid myself, namely, if there be no tenacity or coherence between the particles of water how is it possible for those large drops of water to stand out in relief upon cabbage leaves without scattering or spreading out?

SALV. Although those who are in possession of the truth are able to solve all objections raised, I would not arrogate to myself such power; nevertheless my inability should not be allowed to becloud the truth. To begin with let me confess that I do not understand how these large globules of water stand out and hold themselves up, although I know for a certainty, that it is not owing to any internal tenacity acting between the particles of water; whence it must follow that the cause of this effect is external. Beside the experiments already shown to prove that the cause is not internal, I can offer another which is very convincing. If the particles of water which sustain themselves in a heap, while surrounded by air, did so in virtue of an internal cause then they would sustain themselves much more easily when surrounded by a medium in which they exhibit less tendency to fall than they do in air; such a medium would be any fluid heavier than air, as, for instance, wine: and therefore if some wine be poured about such a drop of water, the wine might rise until the drop was entirely covered, without the particles of water, held together by this internal coherence, ever parting company. But this is not the fact; for as soon as the wine touches the water, the latter without waiting to be covered scatters and spreads out underneath the wine if it be red. The cause of this effect is therefore external

and is possibly to be found in the surrounding air. Indeed there appears to be a considerable antagonism between air and water as I have observed in the following experiment. Having taken a glass globe which had a mouth of about the same diameter as a straw, I filled it with water and turned it mouth downwards; nevertheless, the water, although quite heavy and prone to descend, and the air, which is very light and disposed to rise through the water, refused, the one to descend and the other to ascend through the opening, but both remained stubborn and defiant. On the other hand, as soon as I apply to this opening a glass of red wine, which is almost inappreciably lighter than water, red streaks are immediately observed to ascend slowly through the water while the water with equal slowness descends through the wine without mixing, until finally the globe is completely filled with wine and the water has all gone down into the vessel below. What then can we say except that there exists, between water and air, a certain incompatibility which I do not understand, but perhaps. . . .

SIMP. I feel almost like laughing at the great antipathy which Salviati exhibits against the use of the word antipathy; and yet it is excellently adapted to explain the difficulty.

SALV. Alright, if it please Simplicio, let this word antipathy be the solution of our difficulty. Returning from this digression, let us again take up our problem. We have already seen that the difference of speed between bodies of different specific gravities is most marked in those media which are the most resistant: thus, in a medium of quicksilver, gold not merely sinks to the bottom more rapidly than lead but it is the only substance that will descend at all; all other metals and stones rise to the surface and float. On the other hand, the variation of speed in air between balls of gold, lead, copper, porphyry, and other heavy materials is so slight that in a fall of 100 cubits a ball of gold would surely not outstrip one of copper by as much as four fingers. Having observed this I came to the conclusion that in a medium totally devoid of resistance all bodies would fall with the same speed.

SIMP. This is a remarkable statement, Salviati. But I shall never believe that even in a vacuum, if motion in such a place were possible, a lock of wool and a bit of lead can fall with the same velocity.

SALV. A little more slowly, Simplicio. Your difficulty is not so recondite nor am I so imprudent as to warrant you in believing that I have not already considered this matter and found the proper solution. Hence for my justification and for your enlightenment hear what I have to say. Our problem is to find out what happens to bodies of different weight moving in a medium devoid of resistance, so that the only difference in speed is that which arises from inequality of weight. Since no medium except one entirely free from air and other bodies, be it ever so tenuous and yielding, can furnish our senses with the evidence we are looking for, and since such a medium is not available, we shall observe what happens in the rarest and least resistant media as compared with what happens in denser and more resistant media. Because if we find as a fact that the variation of speed among bodies of different specific gravities is less and less according as the medium becomes more and more yielding, and if finally in a medium of extreme tenuity, though not a perfect vacuum, we find that, in spite of great diversity of specific gravity, the difference in speed is very small and almost inappreciable, then we are justified in believing it highly probable that in a vacuum all bodies would fall with the same speed. Let us, in view of this, consider what takes place in air, where for the sake of a definite figure and light material imagine an inflated bladder. The air in this bladder when surrounded by air will weigh little or nothing, since it can be only slightly compressed; its weight then is small being merely that of the skin which does not amount to the thousandth part of a mass of lead having the same size as the inflated bladder. Now, Simplicio, if we allow these two bodies to fall from a height of four or six cubits, by what distance do you imagine the lead will anticipate the bladder? You may be sure that the lead will not travel three times, or even twice, as swiftly as the bladder, although you would have made it move a thousand times as rapidly.

Simp. It may be as you say during the first four or six cubits of the fall; but after the motion has continued a long while, I believe that the lead will have left the bladder behind not only six out of twelve parts of the distance but even eight or ten.

Salv. I quite agree with you and doubt not that, in very long distances, the lead might cover one hundred miles while the bladder was traversing one; but, my dear Simplicio, this phenomenon which you adduce against my proposition is precisely the one which confirms it. Let me once more explain that the variation of speed observed in bodies of different specific gravities is not caused by the difference of specific gravity but depends upon external circumstances and, in particular, upon the resistance of the medium, so that if this is removed all bodies would fall with the same velocity; and this result I deduce mainly from the fact which you have just admitted and which is very true, namely, that, in the case of bodies which differ widely in weight, their velocities differ more and more as the spaces traversed increase, something which would not occur if the effect depended upon differences of specific gravity. For since these specific gravities remain constant, the ratio between the distances traversed ought to remain constant whereas the fact is that this ratio keeps on increasing as the motion continues. Thus a very heavy body in a fall of one cubit will not anticipate a very light one by so much as the tenth part of this space; but in a fall of twelve cubits the heavy body would outstrip the other by one-third, and in a fall of one hundred cubits by 90/100, etc.

Simp. Very well: but, following your own line of argument, if differences of weight in bodies of different specific gravities cannot produce a change in the ratio of their speeds, on the ground that their specific gravities do not change, how is it possible for the medium, which also we suppose to remain constant, to bring about any change in the ratio of these velocities?

Salv. This objection with which you oppose my statement is clever; and I must meet it. I begin by saying that a heavy body has an inherent tendency to move with a constantly and uniformly accelerated motion toward the common center of gravity, that is, toward the center of our earth, so that during equal intervals of time it receives equal increments of momentum and velocity. This, you must understand, holds whenever all external and accidental hindrances have been removed; but of these there is one which we can never remove, namely, the medium which must be penetrated and thrust aside by the falling body. This quiet, yielding, fluid medium opposes motion through it with a resistance which is proportional to the rapidity with which the medium must give way to the passage of the body; which body, as I have said, is by nature continuously accelerated so that it meets with more and more resistance in the medium and hence a diminution in its rate of gain of speed until finally the speed reaches such a point and the resistance of the medium becomes so great that, balancing each other, they prevent any further acceleration and reduce the motion of the body to one which is uniform and which will thereafter maintain a constant value. There is, therefore, an increase in the resistance of the medium, not on account of any change in its essential properties, but on account of the change in rapidity with which it must yield and give way laterally to the passage of the falling body which is being constantly accelerated.

Now seeing how great is the resistance which the air offers to the slight momentum of the bladder and how small that which it offers to the large weight of the lead, I am convinced that, if the medium were entirely removed, the advantage received by the bladder would be so great and that coming to the lead so small that their speeds would be equalized. Assuming this principle, that all falling bodies acquire equal speeds in a medium which, on account of a vacuum or something else, offers no resistance to the speed of the motion, we shall be able accordingly to determine the ratios of the speeds of both similar and dissimilar bodies moving either through one and the same medium or through different space-filling, and therefore resistant, media. This result we may obtain by observing how much the weight of the medium detracts from the weight of the moving body, which weight is the means employed by the falling body to open a path for itself and to push aside the parts of the medium, something which does not happen in a vacuum where, therefore, no difference is to be expected from a difference of specific gravity. And since it is known that the effect of the medium is to diminish the weight of the body by the weight of the medium displaced, we may accomplish our purpose by diminishing in just this proportion the speeds of the falling bodies, which in a non-resisting medium we have assumed to be equal.

Thus, for example, imagine lead to be ten thousand times as heavy as air while ebony is only one thousand times as heavy. Here we have two substances whose speeds of fall in a medium devoid of resistance are equal: but, when air is the medium, it will subtract from the speed of the lead one part in ten thousand, and from the speed of the ebony one part in one thousand, *i. e.* ten parts in ten thousand. While therefore, lead and ebony would fall from any given height in the same interval of time, provided the retarding effect of the air were removed, the lead will, in air, lose in speed one part in ten thousand; and the ebony, ten parts in ten thousand. In other words, if the elevation from which the bodies start be divided into ten thousand parts, the lead will reach the ground leaving the ebony behind by as much as ten, or at least nine, of these parts. Is it not clear then that a leaded ball

allowed to fall from a tower two hundred cubits high will outstrip an ebony ball by less than four inches? Now ebony weighs a thousand times as much as air but this inflated bladder only four times as much; therefore air diminishes the inherent and natural speed of ebony by one part in a thousand; while that of the bladder which, if free from hindrance, would be the same, experiences a diminution in air amounting to one part in four. So that when the ebony ball, falling from the tower, has reached the earth, the bladder will have traversed only three-quarters of this distance. Lead is twelve times as heavy as water; but ivory is only twice as heavy. The speeds of these two substances which, when entirely unhindered, are equal will be diminished in water, that of lead by one part in twelve, that of ivory by half. Accordingly, when the lead has fallen through eleven cubits of water the ivory will have fallen through only six. Employing this principle we shall, I believe, find a much closer agreement of experiment with our computation than with that of Aristotle.

In a similar manner we may find the ratio of the speeds of one and the same body in different fluid media, not by comparing the different resistances of the media, but by considering the excess of the specific gravity of the body above those of the media. Thus, for example, tin is one thousand times heavier than air and ten times heavier than water; hence, if we divide its unhindered speed into 1000 parts, air will rob it of one of these parts so that it will fall with a speed of 999, while in water its speed will be 900, seeing that water diminishes its weight by one part in ten while air by only one part in a thousand.

Again take a solid a little heavier than water, such as oak, a ball of which will weigh let us say 1000 drachms; suppose an equal volume of water to weigh 950, and an equal volume of air, 2; then it is clear that if the unhindered speed of the ball is 1000, its speed in air will be 998, but in water only 50, seeing that the water removes 950 of the 1000 parts which the body weighs, leaving only 50.

Such a solid would therefore move almost twenty times as fast in air as in water, since its specific gravity exceeds that of water by one part in twenty. And here we must consider the fact that only those substances which have a specific gravity greater than water can fall through it—substances which must, therefore, be hundreds of times heavier than air; hence when we try to obtain the ratio of the speed in air to that in water, we may, without appreciable error, assume that air does not, to any considerable extent, diminish the free weight, and consequently the unhindered speed of such substances. Having thus easily found the excess of the weight of these substances over that of water, we can say that their speed in air is to their speed in water as their free weight is to the excess of this weight over that of water. For example, a ball of ivory weighs 20 ounces; an equal volume of water weighs 17 ounces; hence the speed of ivory in air bears to its speed in water the approximate ratio of 20:3.

SAGR. I have made a great step forward in this truly interesting subject upon which I have long laboured in vain. In order to put these theories into practice we need only discover a method of determining the specific gravity of air with reference to water and hence with reference to other heavy substances.

SIMP. But if we find that air has levity instead of gravity what then shall we say of the foregoing discussion which, in other respects, is very clever?

SALV. I should say that it was empty, vain, and trifling. But can you doubt that air has weight when you have the clear testimony of Aristotle affirming that all the elements have weight including air, and excepting only fire? As evidence of this he cites the fact that a leather bottle weighs more when inflated than when collapsed.

SIMP. I am inclined to believe that the increase of weight observed in the inflated leather bottle or bladder arises, not from the gravity of the air, but from the many thick vapours mingled with it in these lower regions. To this I would attribute the increase of weight in the leather bottle.

SALV. I would not have you say this, and much less attribute it to Aristotle; because, if speaking of the elements, he wished to persuade me by experiment that air has weight and were to say to me: "Take a leather bottle, fill it with heavy vapours and observe how its weight increases," I would reply that the bottle would weigh still more if filled with bran; and would then add that this merely proves that bran and thick vapours are heavy, but in regard to air I should still remain in the same doubt as before. However, the experiment of Aristotle is good and the proposition is true. But I cannot say as much of a certain other consideration, taken at face value; this consideration was offered by a philosopher whose name slips me; but I know I have read his argument which is that air exhibits greater gravity than levity, because it carries heavy bodies downward more easily than it does light ones upward.

SAGR. Fine indeed! So according to this theory air is much heavier than water, since all heavy bodies are carried downward more easily through air than through water, and all light bodies buoyed up more easily through water than through air; further there is an infinite number of heavy bodies which fall through air but ascend in water and there is an infinite number of substances which rise in water and fall in air. But, Simplicio, the question as to whether the weight of the leather bottle is owing to thick vapours or to pure air does not affect our problem which is to discover how bodies move through this vapour-laden atmosphere of ours. Returning now to the question which interests me more, I should like, for the sake of more complete and thorough knowledge of this matter, not only to be strengthened in my belief that air has weight but also to learn, if possible, how great its specific gravity is. Therefore, Salviati, if you can satisfy my curiosity on this point pray do so.

SALV. The experiment with the inflated leather bottle of Aristotle proves conclusively that air possesses positive gravity and not, as some have believed, levity, a property possessed possibly by no substance whatever; for if air did possess this quality of absolute and positive levity, it should on compression exhibit greater levity and, hence, a greater tendency to rise; but experiment shows precisely the opposite.

As to the other question, namely, how to determine the specific gravity of air, I have employed the following method. I took a rather large glass bottle with a narrow neck and attached to it a leather cover, binding it tightly about the neck of the bottle: in the top of this cover I inserted and firmly fastened the valve of a leather bottle, through which I forced into the glass bottle, by means of a syringe, a large quantity of air. And since air is easily condensed one can pump into the bottle two or three times its own volume of air. After this I took an accurate balance and weighed this bottle of compressed air with the utmost precision, adjusting the weight with fine sand. I next opened the valve and allowed the compressed air to escape; then replaced the flask upon the balance and found it perceptibly lighter: from the sand which had been used as a counterweight I now removed and laid aside as much as was necessary to again secure balance. Under these conditions there can be no doubt but that the weight of the sand thus laid aside represents the weight of the air which had been forced into the flask and had afterwards escaped. But after all this experiment tells me merely that the weight of the compressed air is the same as that of the sand removed from the balance; when however it comes to knowing certainly and definitely the weight of air as compared with that of water or any other heavy substance, this I cannot hope to do without first measuring the volume [*quantità*] of compressed air; for this measurement I have devised the two following methods.

According to the first method one takes a bottle with a narrow neck similar to the previous one; over the mouth of this bottle is slipped a leather tube which is bound tightly about the neck of the flask; the other end of this tube embraces the valve attached to the first flask and is tightly bound about it. This second flask is provided with a hole in the bottom through which an iron rod can be placed so as to open, at will, the valve above mentioned and thus permit the surplus air of the first to escape after it has once been weighed: but his second bottle must be filled with water. Having prepared everything in the manner above described, open the valve with the rod; the air will rush into the flask containing the water and will drive it through the hole at the bottom, it being clear that the volume of water thus displaced is equal to the volume of air escaped from the other vessel. Having set aside this displaced water, weigh the vessel from which the air has escaped (which is supposed to have been weighed previously while containing the compressed air), and remove the surplus of sand as described above; it is then manifest that the weight of this sand is precisely the weight of a volume of air equal to the volume of water displaced and set aside; this water we can weigh and find how many times its weight contains the weight of the removed sand, thus determining definitely how many times heavier water is than air; and we shall find, contrary to the opinion of Aristotle, that this is not 10 times, but, as our experiment shows, more nearly 400 times.

The second method is more expeditious and can be carried out with a single vessel fitted up as the first was. Here no air is added to that which the vessel naturally contains but water is forced into it without allowing any air to escape; the water thus introduced necessarily compresses the air. Having forced into the vessel as much water as possible, filling it, say, three-fourths full, which does not require any extraordinary effort, place it upon the balance and weigh it accurately; next hold the vessel mouth up, open the valve, and allow the air to escape; the volume of the air thus escaping is precisely equal to the volume of water contained in the flask. Again weigh the vessel which will have diminished in weight on account of the escaped air; this loss in weight represents the weight of a volume of air equal to the volume of water contained in the vessel.

SIMP. No one can deny the cleverness and ingenuity of your devices; but while they appear to give complete intellectual satisfaction they confuse me in another direction. For since it is undoubtedly true that the elements when in their proper places have neither weight nor levity, I cannot understand how it is possible for that portion of air, which appeared to weigh, say, 4 drachms of sand, should really have such a weight in air as the sand which counterbalances it. It seems to me, therefore, that the experiment should be carried out, not in air, but in a medium in which the air could exhibit its property of weight if such it really has.

SALV. The objection of Simplicio is certainly to the point and must therefore either be unanswerable or demand an equally clear solution. It is perfectly evident that that air which, under compression, weighed as much as the sand, loses this weight when once allowed to escape into its own element, while, indeed, the sand retains its weight. Hence for this experiment it becomes necessary to select a place where air as well as sand can gravitate; because, as has been often remarked, the medium diminishes the weight of any substance immersed in it by an amount equal to the weight of the displaced medium; so that air in air loses all its weight. If therefore this experiment is to be made with accuracy, it should be performed in a vacuum where every heavy body exhibits its momentum without the slightest diminution. If then, Simplicio, we were to weigh a portion of air in a vacuum would you then be satisfied and assured of the fact?

SIMP. Yes truly: but this is to wish or ask the impossible.

SALV. Your obligation will then be very great if, for your sake, I accomplish the impossible. But I do not want to sell you something which I have already given you; for in the previous experiment we weighed the air in vacuum and not in air or other medium. The fact that any fluid medium diminishes the weight of a mass immersed in it, is due, Simplicio, to the resistance which this medium offers to its being opened up, driven aside, and finally lifted up. The evidence for this is seen in the readiness with which the fluid rushes to fill up any space formerly occupied by the mass; if the medium were not affected by such an immersion then it would not react against the immersed body. Tell me now, when you have a flask, in air, filled with its natural amount of air and then proceed to pump into the vessel more air, does this extra charge in any way separate or divide or change the circumambient air? Does the vessel perhaps expand so that the surrounding medium is displaced in order to give more room? Certainly not. Therefore, one is able to say that this extra charge of air is not immersed in the surrounding medium for it occupies no space in it, but is, as it were, in a vacuum. Indeed, it is really in a vacuum; for it diffuses into the vacuities which are not completely filled by the original and uncondensed air. In fact I do not see any difference between the enclosed and the surrounding media: for the surrounding medium does not press upon the enclosed medium, and, *vice versa*, the enclosed medium exerts no pressure against the surrounding one; this same relationship exists in the case of any matter in a vacuum, as well as in the case of the extra charge of air compressed into the flask. The weight of this condensed air is therefore the same as that which it would have if set free in a vacuum. It is true of course that the weight of the sand used as a counterpoise would be a little greater *in vacuo* than in free air. We must, then, say that the air is slightly lighter than the sand required to counterbalance it, that is to say, by an amount equal to the weight *in vacuo* of a volume of air equal to the volume of the sand.

At this point in an annotated copy of the original edition the following note by Galileo is found:

SAGR. A very clever discussion, solving a wonderful problem, because it demonstrates briefly and concisely the manner in which one may find the weight of a body *in vacuo* by simply weighing it in air. The explanation is as follows: when a heavy body is immersed in air it loses in weight an amount equal to the weight of a volume of air equivalent to the volume of the body itself. Hence if one adds to a body, without expanding it, a quantity of air equal to that which it displaces and weighs it, he will obtain its absolute weight *in vacuo*, since, without increasing it in size, he has increased its weight by just the amount which it lost through immersion in air.

When, therefore, we force a quantity of water into a vessel which already contains its normal amount of air, without allowing any of this air to escape it is clear that this normal quantity of air will be compressed and condensed into a smaller space in order to make room for the water which is forced in: it is also clear that the volume of air thus compressed is equal to the volume of water added. If now the vessel be weighed in air in this condition, it is manifest that the weight of the water will be increased by that of an equal volume of air; the total weight of

water and air thus obtained is equal to the weight of the water alone *in vacuo*.

Now record the weight of the entire vessel and then allow the compressed air to escape; weigh the remainder; the difference of these two weights will be the weight of the compressed air which, in volume, is equal to that of the water. Next find the weight of the water alone and add to it that of the compressed air; we shall then have the water alone *in vacuo*. To find the weight of the water we shall have to remove it from the vessel and weigh the vessel alone; subtract this weight from that of the vessel and water together. It is clear that the remainder will be the weight of the water alone in air.

SIMP. The previous experiments, in my opinion, left something to be desired: but now I am fully satisfied.

SALV. The facts set forth by me up to this point and, in particular, the one which shows that difference of weight, even when very great, is without effect in changing the speed of falling bodies, so that as far as weight is concerned they all fall with equal speed: this idea is, I say, so new, and at first glance so remote from fact, that if we do not have the means of making it just as clear as sunlight, it had better not be mentioned; but having once allowed it to pass my lips I must neglect no experiment or argument to establish it.

SAGR. Not only this but also many other of your views are so far removed from the commonly accepted opinions and doctrines that if you were to publish them you would stir up a large number of antagonists; for human nature is such that men do not look with favor upon discoveries—either of truth or fallacy—in their own field, when made by others than themselves. They call him an innovator of doctrine, an unpleasant title, by which they hope to cut those knots which they cannot untie, and by subterranean mines they seek to destroy structures which patient artisans have built with customary tools. But as for ourselves who have no such thoughts, the experiments and arguments which you have thus far adduced are fully satisfactory; however if you have any experiments which are more direct or any arguments which are more convincing, we will hear them with pleasure.

SALV. The experiment made to ascertain whether two bodies differing greatly in weight will fall from a given height with the same speed, offers some difficulty; because, if the height is considerable, the retarding effect of the medium, which must be penetrated and thrust aside by the falling body, will be greater in the case of the small momentum of the very light body than in the case of the great force of the heavy body; so that, in a long distance, the light body will be left behind; if the height be small, one may well doubt whether there is any difference; and if there be a difference it will be inappreciable.

It occurred to me, therefore, to repeat many times the fall through a small height in such a way that I might accumulate all those small intervals of time that elapse between the arrival of the heavy and light bodies respectively at their common terminus, so that this sum makes an interval of time which is not only observable, but easily observable. In order to employ the slowest speeds possible and thus reduce the change which the resisting medium produces upon the simple effect of gravity, it occurred to me to allow the bodies to fall along a plane slightly inclined to the horizontal. For in such a plane, just as well as in a vertical plane, one may discover how bodies of different weight behave: and besides this, I also wished to rid myself of the resistance which might arise from contact of the moving body with the aforesaid inclined plane. Accordingly, I took two balls, one of lead and one of cork, the former more than a hundred times heavier than the latter, and suspended them by means of two equal fine threads, each four of five cubits long. Pulling each ball aside from the perpendicular, I let them go at the same instant, and they, falling along the circumferences of circles having these equal strings for semi-diameters, passed beyond the perpendicular and returned along the same path. This free vibration repeated a hundred times showed clearly that the heavy body maintains so nearly the period of the light body that neither in a hundred swings nor even in a thousand will the former anticipate the latter by as much as a single moment, so perfectly do they keep step. We can also observe the effect of the medium which, by the resistance which it offers to motion, diminishes the vibration of the cork more than that of the lead, but without altering the frequency of either; even when the arc traversed by the cork did not exceed five or six degrees while that of the lead was fifty or sixty, the swings were performed in equal times.

SIMP. If this be so, why is not the speed of the lead greater than that of the cork, seeing that the former traverses sixty degrees in the same interval in which the latter covers scarcely six?

SALV. But what would you say, Simplicio, if both covered their paths in the same time when the cork, drawn aside through thirty degrees, traverses an arc of sixty, while the lead pulled aside only two degrees traverses an arc of four? Would not then the cork be proportionately

swifter? And yet such is the experimental fact. But observe this: having pulled aside the pendulum of lead, say through an arc of fifty degrees, and set it free, it swings beyond the perpendicular almost fifty degrees, thus describing an arc of nearly one hundred degrees; on the return swing it describes a little smaller arc; and after a large number of such vibrations it finally comes to rest. Each vibration, whether of ninety, fifty, twenty, ten, or four degrees occupies the same time: accordingly, the speed of the moving body keeps on diminishing since in equal intervals of time, it traverses arcs which grow smaller and smaller.

Precisely the same things happen with the pendulum of cork, suspended by a string of equal length, except that a smaller number of vibrations is required to bring it to rest, since on account of its lightness it is less able to overcome the resistance of the air; nevertheless the vibrations, whether large or small, are all performed in time-intervals which are not only equal among themselves, but also equal to the period of the lead pendulum. Hence it is true that, if while the lead is traversing an arc of fifty degrees the cork covers one of only ten, the cork moves more slowly than the lead; but on the other hand, it is also true that the cork may cover an arc of fifty while the lead passes over one of only ten or six; thus, at different times, we have now the cork, now the lead, moving more rapidly. But if these same bodies traverse equal arcs in equal times we may rest assured that their speeds are equal.

SIMP. I hesitate to admit the conclusiveness of this argument because of the confusion which arises from your making both bodies move now rapidly, now slowly and now very slowly, which leaves me in doubt as to whether their velocities are always equal.

SAGR. Allow me, if you please, Salviati, to say just a few words. Now tell me, Simplicio, whether you admit that one can say with certainty that the speeds of the cork and the lead are equal whenever both, starting from rest at the same moment and descending the same slopes, always traverse equal spaces in equal times?

SIMP. This can neither be doubted nor gainsaid.

SAGR. Now it happens, in the case of the pendulums, that each of them traverses now an arc of sixty degrees, now one of fifty, or thirty or ten or eight or four or two, etc.; and when they both swing through an arc of sixty degrees they do so in equal intervals of time; the same thing happens when the arc is fifty degrees or thirty or ten or any other number; and therefore we conclude that the speed of the lead in an arc of sixty degrees is equal to the speed of the cork when the latter also swings through an arc of sixty degrees; in the case of a fifty-degree arc these speeds are also equal to each other; so also in the case of other arcs. But this is not saying that the speed which occurs in an arc of sixty is the same as that which occurs in an arc of fifty; nor is the speed in an arc of fifty equal to that in one of thirty, etc.; but the smaller the arcs, the smaller the speeds; the fact observed is that one and the same moving body requires the same time for traversing a large arc of sixty degrees as for a small arc of fifty or even a very small arc of ten; all these arcs, indeed, are covered in the same interval of time. It is true therefore that the lead and the cork each diminish their speed in proportion as their arcs diminish; but this does not contradict the fact that they maintain equal speeds in equal arcs.

My reason for saying these things has been rather because I wanted to learn whether I had correctly understood Salviati, than because I thought Simplicio had any need of a clearer explanation than that given by Salviati which like everything else of his is extremely lucid, so lucid, indeed, that when he solves questions which are difficult not merely in appearance, but in reality and in fact, he does so with reasons, observations and experiments which are common and familiar to everyone.

In this manner he has, as I have learned from various sources, given occasion to a highly esteemed professor for undervaluing his discoveries on the ground that they are commonplace, and established upon a mean and vulgar basis; as if it were not a most admirable and praiseworthy feature of demonstrative science that it springs from and grows out of principles well-known, understood, and conceded by all.

But let us continue with this light diet; and if Simplicio is satisfied to understand and admit that the gravity inherent in various falling bodies has nothing to do with the difference of speed observed among them, and that all bodies, in so far as their speeds depend upon it, would move with the same velocity, pray tell us, Salviati, how you explain the appreciable and evident inequality of motion; please reply also to the objection urged by Simplicio—an objection in which I concur—namely, that a cannon ball falls more rapidly than a bird-shot. From my point of view, one might expect the difference of speed to be small in the case of bodies of the same substance moving through any single medium,

whereas the larger ones will descend, during a single pulse-beat, a distance which the smaller ones will not traverse in an hour, or in four, or even in twenty hours; as for instance in the case of stones and fine sand and especially that very fine sand which produces muddy water and which in many hours will not fall through as much as two cubits, a distance which stones not much larger will traverse in a single pulse-beat.

SALV. The action of the medium in producing a greater retardation upon those bodies which have a less specific gravity has already been explained by showing that they experience a diminution of weight. But to explain how one and the same medium produces such different retardations in bodies which are made of the same material and have the same shape, but differ only in size, requires a discussion more clever than that by which one explains how a more expanded shape or an opposing motion of the medium retards the speed of the moving body. The solution of the present problem lies, I think, in the roughness and porosity which are generally and almost necessarily found in the surfaces of solid bodies. When the body is in motion these rough places strike the air or other ambient medium. The evidence for this is found in the humming which accompanies the rapid motion of a body through air, even when that body is as round as possible. One hears not only humming, but also hissing and whistling, whenever there is any appreciable cavity or elevation upon the body. We observe also that a round solid body rotating in a lathe produces a current of air. But what more do we need? When a top spins on the ground at its greatest speed do we not hear a distinct buzzing of high pitch? This sibilant note diminishes in pitch as the speed of rotation slackens, which is evidence that these small rugosities on the surface meet resistance in the air. There can be no doubt, therefore, that in the motion of falling bodies these rugosities strike the surrounding fluid and retard the speed; and this they do so much the more in proportion as the surface is larger, which is the case of small bodies as compared with greater.

SIMP. Stop a moment please, I am getting confused. For although I understand and admit that friction of the medium upon the surface of the body retards its motion and that, if other things are the same, the larger surface suffers greater retardation, I do not see on what ground you say that the surface of the smaller body is larger. Besides if, as you say, the larger surface suffers greater retardation the larger solid should move more slowly, which is not the fact. But this objection can be easily met by saying that, although the larger body has a larger surface, it has also a greater weight, in comparison with which the resistance of the larger surface is no more than the resistance of the small surface in comparison with its smaller weight; so that the speed of the larger solid does not become less. I therefore see no reason for expecting any difference of speed, so long as the driving weight diminishes in the same proportion as the retarding power of the surface.

SALV. I shall answer all your objections at once. You will admit, of course, Simplicio, that if one takes two equal bodies, of the same material and same figure, bodies which would therefore fall with equal speeds, and if he diminishes the weight of one of them in the same proportion as its surface (maintaining the similarity of shape) he would not thereby diminish the speed of this body.

SIMP. This inference seems to be in harmony with your theory which states that the weight of a body has no effect in either accelerating or retarding its motion.

SALV. I quite agree with you in this opinion from which it appears to follow that, if the weight of a body is diminished in greater proportion than its surface, the motion is retarded to a certain extent; and this retardation is greater and greater in proportion as the diminution of weight exceeds that of the surface.

SIMP. This I admit without hesitation.

SALV. Now you must know, Simplicio, that it is not possible to diminish the surface of a solid body in the same ratio as the weight, and at the same time maintain similarity of figure. For since it is clear that in the case of a diminishing solid the weight grows less in proportion to the volume, and since the volume always diminishes more rapidly than the surface, when the same shape is maintained, the weight must therefore diminish more rapidly than the surface. But geometry teaches us that, in the case of similar solids, the ratio of two volumes is greater than the ratio of their surfaces; which, for the sake of better understanding, I shall illustrate by a particular case.

Take, for example, a cube two inches on a side so that each face has an area of four square inches and the total area, i.e., the sum of the six faces, amounts to twenty-four square inches; now imagine this cube to be sawed through three times so as to divide it into eight smaller cubes, each one inch on the side, each face one inch square, and the total surface of each cube six square inches instead of twenty-four as in the case of the larger cube. It is evident therefore, that the surface of the little cube is only one-fourth that of the larger, namely, the ratio of six to twenty-four; but the volume of the solid cube itself is only one-eighth; the volume, and hence also the weight, diminishes therefore much more rapidly than the surface. If we again divide the little cube into eight others we shall have, for the total surface of one of these, one and one-half square inches, which is one-sixteenth of the surface of the original cube; but its volume is only one-sixty-fourth part. Thus, by two divisions, you see that the volume is diminished four times as much as the surface. And, if the subdivision be continued until the original solid be reduced to a fine powder, we shall find that the weight of one of these smallest particles has diminished hundreds and hundreds of times as much as its surface. And this which I have illustrated in the case of cubes holds also in the case of all similar solids, where the volumes stand in sesquialteral ratio to their surfaces. Observe then how much greater the resistance, arising from contact of the surface of the moving body with the medium, in the case of small bodies than in the case of large; and when one considers that the rugosities on the very small surfaces of fine dust particles are perhaps no smaller than those on the surfaces of larger solids which have been carefully polished, he will see how important it is that the medium should be very fluid and offer no resistance to being thrust aside, easily yielding to a small force. You see, therefore, Simplicio, that I was not mistaken when, not long ago, I said that the surface of a small solid is comparatively greater than that of a large one.

SIMP. I am quite convinced; and, believe me, if I were again beginning my studies, I should follow the advice of Plato and start with mathematics, a science which proceeds very cautiously and admits nothing as established until it has been rigidly demonstrated.

SAGR. This discussion has afforded me great pleasure; but before proceeding further I should like to hear the explanation of a phrase of yours which is new to me, namely, that similar solids are to each other in the sesquialteral ratio of their surfaces; for although I have seen and understood the proposition in which it is demonstrated that the surfaces of similar solids are in the duplicate ratio of their sides, and also the proposition which proves that the volumes are in the triplicate ratio of their sides, yet I have not so much as heard mentioned the ratio of the volume of a solid to its surface.

SALV. You yourself have suggested the answer to your question and have removed every doubt. For if one quantity is the cube of something of which another quantity is the square does it not follow that the cube is the sesquialteral of the square? Surely. Now if the surface varies as the square of its linear dimensions while the volume varies as the cube of these dimensions, may we not say that the volume stands in sesquialteral ratio to the surface?

SAGR. Quite so. And now although there are still some details, in connection with the subject under discussion, concerning which I might ask questions yet, if we keep making one digression after another, it will be long before we reach the main topic which has to do with the variety of properties found in the resistance which solid bodies offer to fracture; and, therefore, if you please, let us return to the subject which we originally proposed to discuss.

SALV. Very well; but the questions which we have already considered are so numerous and so varied, and have taken up so much time that there is not much of this day left to spend upon our main topic which abounds in geometrical demonstrations calling for careful consideration. May I, therefore, suggest that we postpone the meeting until to-morrow, not only for the reason just mentioned but also in order that I may bring with me some papers in which I have set down in an orderly way the theorems and propositions dealing with the various phases of this subject, matters which, from memory alone, I could not present in the proper order.

SAGR. I fully concur in your opinion and all the more willingly because this will leave time to-day to take up some of my difficulties with the subject which we have just been discussing. One question is whether we are to consider the resistance of the medium as sufficient to destroy the acceleration of a body of very heavy material, very large volume, and spherical figure. I say *spherical* in order to select a volume which is contained within a minimum surface and therefore less subject to retardation.

Another question deals with the vibrations of pendulums which may be regarded from several viewpoints; the first is whether all vibrations, large, medium, and small, are performed in exactly and precisely equal times: another is to find the ratio of the times of vibration of pendulums supported by threads of unequal length.

SALV. These are interesting questions: but I fear that here, as in the case of all other facts, if we take up for discussion any one of them, it will carry in its wake so many other facts and

curious consequences that time will not remain to-day for the discussion of all.

SAGR. If these are as full of interest as the foregoing, I would gladly spend as many days as there remain hours between now and nightfall; and I dare say that Simplicio would not be wearied by these discussions.

SIMP. Certainly not; especially when the questions pertain to natural science and have not been treated by other philosophers.

SALV. Now taking up the first question, I can assert without hesitation that there is no sphere so large, or composed of material so dense but that the resistance of the medium, although very slight, would check its acceleration and would, in time reduce its motion to uniformity; a statement which is strongly supported by experiment. For if a falling body, as time goes on, were to acquire a speed as great as you please, no such speed, impressed by external forces, can be so great but that the body will first acquire it and then, owing to the resisting medium, lose it. Thus, for instance, if a cannon ball, having fallen a distance of four cubits through the air and having acquired a speed of, say, ten units were to strike the surface of the water, and if the resistance of the water were not able to check the momentum of the shot, it would either increase in speed or maintain a uniform motion until the bottom were reached: but such is not the observed fact; on the contrary, the water when only a few cubits deep hinders and diminishes the motion in such a way that the shot delivers to the bed of the river or lake a very slight impulse. Clearly then if a short fall through the water is sufficient to deprive a cannon ball of its speed, this speed cannot be regained by a fall of even a thousand cubits. How could a body acquire, in a fall of a thousand cubits, that which it loses in a fall of four? But what more is needed? Do we not observe that the enormous momentum, delivered to a shot by a cannon, is so deadened by passing through a few cubits of water that the ball, so far from injuring the ship, barely strikes it? Even the air, although a very yielding medium, can also diminish the speed of a falling body, as may be easily understood from similar experiments. For if a gun be fired downwards from the top of a very high tower the shot will make a smaller impression upon the ground than if the gun had been fired from an elevation of only four or six cubits; this is clear evidence that the momentum of the ball, fired from the top of the tower, diminishes continually from the instant it leaves the barrel until it reaches the ground. Therefore, a fall from ever so great an altitude will not suffice to give to a body that momentum which it has once lost through the resistance of the air, no matter how it was originally acquired. In like manner, the destructive effect produced upon a wall by a shot fired from a gun at a distance of twenty cubits cannot be duplicated by the fall of the same shot from any altitude however great. My opinion is, therefore, that under the circumstances which occur in nature, the acceleration of any body falling from rest reaches an end and that the resistance of the medium finally reduces its speed to a constant value which is thereafter maintained.

SAGR. These experiments are in my opinion much to the purpose; the only question is whether an opponent might not make bold to deny the fact in the case of bodies which are very large and heavy or to assert that a cannon ball, falling from the distance of the moon or from the upper regions of the atmosphere, would deliver a heavier blow than if just leaving the muzzle of the gun.

SALV. No doubt many objections may be raised not all of which can be refuted by experiment: however in this particular case the following consideration must be taken into account, namely, that it is very likely that a heavy body falling from a height will, on reaching the ground, have acquired just as much momentum as was necessary to carry it to that height; as may be clearly seen in the case of a rather heavy pendulum which, when pulled aside fifty or sixty degrees from the vertical, will acquire precisely that speed and force which are sufficient to carry it to an equal elevation, save only that small portion which it loses through friction on the air. In order to place a cannon ball at such a height as might suffice to give it just that momentum which the powder imparted to it on leaving the gun, we need only fire it vertically upwards from the same gun; and we can then observe whether on falling back it delivers a blow equal to that of the gun fired at close range; in my opinion it would be much weaker. The resistance of the air would, therefore, I think, prevent the muzzle velocity from being equalled by a natural fall from rest at any height whatsoever.

We come now to the other questions, relating to pendulums, a subject which may appear to many exceedingly arid, especially to those philosophers who are continually occupied with the more profound questions of nature. Nevertheless, the problem is one which I do not scorn. I am encouraged by the example of Aristotle whom I admire especially because he did not fail to discuss every subject which he thought in any degree worthy of consideration.

Impelled by your queries I may give you some of my ideas concerning certain problems in music, a splendid subject, upon which so many eminent men have written: among these is Aristotle himself who has discussed numerous interesting acoustical questions. Accordingly, if on the basis of some easy and tangible experiments, I shall explain some striking phenomena in the domain of sound, I trust my explanations will meet your approval.

SAGR. I shall receive them not only gratefully but eagerly. For, although I take pleasure in every kind of musical instrument and have paid considerable attention to harmony, I have never been able to fully understand why some combinations of tones are more pleasing than others, or why certain combinations not only fail to please but are even highly offensive. Then there is the old problem of two stretched strings in unison; when one of them is sounded, the other begins to vibrate and to emit its note; nor do I understand the different ratios of harmony and some other details.

SALV. Let us see whether we cannot derive from the pendulum a satisfactory solution of all these difficulties. And first, as to the question whether one and the same pendulum really performs its vibrations, large, medium, and small, all in exactly the same time, I shall rely upon what I have already heard from our Academician. He has clearly shown that the time of descent is the same along all chords, whatever the arcs which subtend them, as well along an arc of 180° (i.e., the whole diameter) as along one of 100°, 60°, 10°, 2°, ½°, or 4′. It is understood, of course, that these arcs all terminate at the lowest point of the circle, where it touches the horizontal plane.

If now we consider descent along arcs instead of their chords then, provided these do not exceed 90°, experiment shows that they are all traversed in equal times; but these times are greater for the chord than for the arc, an effect which is all the more remarkable because at first glance one would think just the opposite to be true. For since the terminal points of the two motions are the same and since the straight line included between these two points is the shortest distance between them, it would seem reasonable that motion along this line should be executed in the shortest time; but this is not the case, for the shortest time—and therefore the most rapid motion—is that employed along the arc of which this straight line is the chord.

As to the times of vibration of bodies suspended by threads of different lengths, they bear to each other the same proportion as the square roots of the lengths of the thread; or one might say the lengths are to each other as the squares of the times; so that if one wishes to make the vibration-time of one pendulum twice that of another, he must make its suspension four times as long. In like manner, if one pendulum has a suspension nine times as long as another, this second pendulum will execute three vibrations during each one of the first; from which it follows that the lengths of the suspending cords bear to each other the [inverse] ratio of the squares of the number of vibrations performed in the same time.

SAGR. Then, if I understand you correctly, I can easily measure the length of a string whose upper end is attached at any height whatever even if this end were invisible and I could see only the lower extremity. For if I attach to the lower end of this string a rather heavy weight and give it a to-and-fro motion, and if I ask a friend to count a number of its vibrations, while I, during the same time-interval, count the number of vibrations of a pendulum which is exactly one cubit in length, then knowing the number of vibrations which each pendulum makes in the given interval of time one can determine the length of the string. Suppose, for example, that my friend counts 20 vibrations of the long cord during the same time in which I count 240 of my string which is one cubit in length; taking the squares of the two numbers, 20 and 240, namely 400 and 57600, then, I say, the long string contains 57600 units of such length that my pendulum will contain 400 of them; and since the length of my string is one cubit, I shall divide 57600 by 400 and thus obtain 144. Accordingly, I shall call the length of the string 144 cubits.

SALV. Nor will you miss it by as much as a hand's breadth, especially if you observe a large number of vibrations.

SAGR. You give me frequent occasion to admire the wealth and profusion of nature when, from such common and even trivial phenomena, you derive facts which are not only striking and new but which are often far removed from what we would have imagined. Thousands of times I have observed vibrations especially in churches where lamps, suspended by long cords, had been inadvertently set into motion; but the most which I could infer from these observations was that the view of those who think that such vibrations are maintained by the medium is highly improbable: for, in that case, the air must needs have considerable judgment and little else to do but kill time by pushing to and fro a pendent weight with perfect regularity. But I never dreamed of learning that one and the same body, when suspended from a string a hundred cubits long and pulled aside through an arc of 90° or even 1° or $\frac{1}{2}$°, would employ the same time in passing through the least as through the largest of these arcs; and, indeed, it still strikes me as somewhat unlikely. Now I am waiting to hear how these same simple phenomena can furnish solutions for those acoustical problems—solutions which will be at least partly satisfactory.

SALV. First of all one must observe that each pendulum has its own time of vibration so definite and determinate that it is not possible to make it move with any other period than that which nature has given it. For let any one take in his hand the cord to which the weight is attached and try, as much as he pleases, to increase or diminish the frequency of its vibrations; it will be time wasted. On the other hand, one can confer motion upon even a heavy pendulum which is at rest by simply blowing against it; by repeating these blasts with a frequency which is the same as that of the pendulum one can impart considerable motion. Suppose that by the first puff we have displaced the pendulum from the vertical by, say, half an inch; then if, after the pendulum has returned and is about to begin the second vibration, we add a second puff, we shall impart additional motion; and so on with other blasts provided they are applied at the right instant, and not when the pendulum is coming toward us, since in this case the blast would impede rather than aid the motion. Continuing thus with many impulses we impart to the pendulum such momentum that a greater impulse than that of a single blast will be needed to stop it.

SAGR. Even as a boy, I observed that one man alone by giving these impulses at the right instant was able to ring a bell so large that when four, or even six, men seized the rope and tried to stop it they were lifted from the ground, all of them together being unable to counterbalance the momentum which a single man, by properly-timed pulls, had given it.

SALV. Your illustration makes my meaning clear and is quite as well fitted, as what I have just said, to explain the wonderful phenomenon of the strings of the cittern or of the spinet, namely, the fact that a vibrating string will set another string in motion and cause it to sound not only when the latter is in unison but even when it differs from the former by an octave or a fifth. A string which has been struck begins to vibrate and continues the motion as long as one hears the sound; these vibrations cause the immediately surrounding air to vibrate and quiver; then these ripples in the air expand far into space and strike not only all the strings of the same instrument but even those of neighboring instruments. Since that string which is tuned to unison with the one plucked is capable of vibrating with the same frequency, it acquires, at the first impulse, a slight oscillation; after receiving two, three, twenty, or more impulses, delivered at proper intervals, it finally accumulates a vibratory motion equal to that of the plucked string, as is clearly shown by equality of amplitude in their vibrations. This undulation expands through the air and sets into vibration not only strings, but also any other body which happens to have the same period as that of the plucked string. Accordingly if we attach to the side of an instrument small pieces of bristle or other flexible bodies, we shall observe that, when a spinet is sounded, only those pieces respond that have the same period as the string which has been struck; the remaining pieces do not vibrate in response to this string, nor do the former pieces respond to any other tone.

If one bows the base string on a viola rather smartly and brings near it a goblet of fine, thin glass having the same tone as that of the string, this goblet will vibrate and audibly resound. That the undulations of the medium are widely dispersed about the sounding body is evinced by the fact that a glass of water may be made to emit a tone merely by the friction of the finger-tip upon the rim of the glass; for in this water is produced a series of regular waves. The same phenomenon is observed to better advantage by fixing the base of the goblet upon the bottom of a rather large vessel of water filled nearly to the edge of the goblet; for if, as before, we sound the glass by friction of the finger, we shall see ripples spreading with the utmost regularity and with high speed to large distances about the glass. I have often remarked, in thus sounding a rather large glass nearly full of water, that at first the waves are spaced with great uniformity, and when, as sometimes happens, the tone of the glass jumps an octave higher I have noted that at this moment each of the aforesaid waves divides into two; a phenomenon which shows clearly that the ratio involved in the octave is two.

SAGR. More than once have I observed this same thing, much to my delight and also to my profit. For a long time I have been perplexed about these different harmonies, since the explanations hitherto given by those learned in music impress me as not sufficiently conclusive. They tell us that the diapason, i.e., the octave, involves the ratio of two, that the diapente which we call the fifth involves a ratio of 3:2, etc.; because if the open string of a monochord be sounded and afterwards a bridge be placed in the middle and the half length be sounded one hears the octave; and if the bridge be placed at $1/3$ the length of the string, then on plucking first the open string and afterwards $2/3$ of its length the fifth is given; for this reason they say that the octave depends upon the ratio of two to one and the fifth upon the ratio of three to two. This explanation does not impress me as sufficient to establish 2 and 3/2 as the natural ratios of the octave and the fifth; and my reason for thinking so is as follows. There are three different ways in which the tone of a string may be sharpened, namely, by shortening it, by stretching it, and by making it thinner. If the tension and size of the string remain constant one obtains the octave by shortening it to one-half, i.e., by sounding first the open string and then one-half of it; but if length and size remain constant and one attempts to produce the octave by stretching, he will find that it does not suffice to double the stretching weight; it must be quadrupled; so that, if the fundamental note is produced by a weight of one pound, four will be required to bring out the octave.

And finally if the length and tension remain constant, while one changes the size of the string, he will find that in order to produce the octave the size must be reduced to $1/4$ that which gave the fundamental. And what I have said concerning the octave, namely, that its ratio as derived from the tension and size of the string is the square of that derived from the length, applies equally well to all other musical intervals. Thus if one wishes to produce a fifth by changing the length he finds that the ratio of the lengths must be sesquialteral, in other words he sounds first the open string, then two-thirds of it; but if he wishes to produce this same result by stretching or thinning the string then it becomes necessary to square the ratio 3/2 that is by taking $9/4$; accordingly, if the fundamental requires a weight of 4 pounds, the higher note will be produced not by 6, but by 9 pounds; the same is true in regard to size, the string which gives the fundamental is larger than that which yields the fifth in the ratio of 9 to 4.

In view of these facts, I see no reason why those wise philosophers should adopt 2 rather than 4 as the ratio of the octave, or why in the case of the fifth they should employ the sesquialteral ratio, 3/2, rather than that of 9/4. Since it is impossible to count the vibrations of a sounding string on account of its high frequency, I should still have been in doubt as to whether a string, emitting the upper octave, made twice as many vibrations in the same time as one giving the fundamental, had it not been for the following fact, namely, that at the instant when the tone jumps to the octave, the waves which constantly accompany the vibrating glass divide up into smaller ones which are precisely half as long as the former.

SALV. This is a beautiful experiment enabling us to distinguish individually the waves which are produced by the vibrations of a sonorous body, which spread through the air, bringing to the tympanum of the ear a stimulus which the mind translates into sound. But since these waves in the water last only so long as the friction of the finger continues and are, even then, not constant but are always forming and disappearing, would it not be a fine thing if one had the ability to produce waves which would persist for a long while, even months and years, so as to easily measure and count them?

SAGR. Such an invention would, I assure you, command my admiration.

SALV. The device is one which I hit upon by accident; my part consists merely in the observation of it and in the appreciation of its value as a confirmation of something to which I had given profound consideration; and yet the device is, in itself, rather common. As I was scraping a brass plate with a sharp iron chisel in order to remove some spots from it and was running the chisel rather rapidly over it, I once or twice, during many strokes, heard the plate emit a rather strong and clear whistling sound; on looking at the plate more carefully, I noticed a long row of fine streaks parallel and equidistant from one another. Scraping with the chisel over and over again, I noticed that it was only when the plate emitted this hissing noise that any marks were left upon it; when the scraping was not accompanied by this sibilant note there was not the least trace of such marks. Repeating the trick several times and making the stroke, now with greater now with less speed, the whistling followed with a pitch which was correspondingly higher and lower. I noted also that the marks made when the tones were

higher were closer together; but when the tones were deeper, they were farther apart. I also observed that when, during a single stroke, the speed increased toward the end the sound became sharper and the streaks grew closer together, but always in such a way as to remain sharply defined and equidistant. Besides, whenever the stroke was accompanied by hissing I felt the chisel tremble in my grasp and a sort of shiver run through my hand. In short, we see and hear in the case of the chisel precisely that which is seen and heard in the case of a whisper followed by a loud voice; for, when the breath is emitted without the production of a tone, one does not feel either in the throat or mouth any motion to speak of in comparison with that which is felt in the larynx and upper part of the throat when the voice is used, especially when the tones employed are low and strong.

At times I have also observed among the strings of the spinet two which were in unison with two of the tones produced by the aforesaid scraping; and among those which differed most in pitch I found two which were separated by an interval of a perfect fifth. Upon measuring the distance between the markings produced by the two scrapings it was found that the space which contained 45 of one contained 30 of the other, which is precisely the ratio assigned to the fifth.

But now, before proceeding any farther, I want to call your attention to the fact that, of the three methods for sharpening a tone, the one which you refer to as the fineness of the string should be attributed to its weight. So long as the material of the string is unchanged, the size and weight vary in the same ratio. Thus in the case of gut-strings, we obtain the octave by making one string 4 times as large as the other; so also in the case of brass one wire must have 4 times the size of the other; but if now we wish to obtain the octave of a gut-string, by use of brass wire, we must make it, not four times as large, but four times as heavy as the gut-string: as regards size, therefore, the metal string is not four times as big but four times as heavy. The wire may therefore be even thinner than the gut, notwithstanding the fact that the latter gives the higher note. Hence if two spinets are strung, one with gold wire the other with brass, and if the corresponding strings each have the same length, diameter, and tension, it follows that the instrument strung with gold will have a pitch about one-fifth lower than the other because gold has a density almost twice that of brass. And here it is to be noted that it is the weight rather than the size of a moving body which offers resistance to change of motion, contrary to what one might at first glance think. For it seems reasonable to believe that a body which is large and light should suffer greater retardation of motion in thrusting aside the medium than would one which is thin and heavy, yet here exactly the opposite is true.

Returning now to the original subject of discussion, I assert that the ratio of a musical interval is not immediately determined either by the length, size, or tension of the strings but rather by the ratio of their frequencies, that is, by the number of pulses of air waves which strike the tympanum of the ear, causing it also to vibrate with the same frequency. This fact established, we may possibly explain why certain pairs of notes, differing in pitch produce a pleasing sensation, others a less pleasant effect, and still others a disagreeable sensation. Such an explanation would be tantamount to an explanation of the more or less perfect consonances and of dissonances. The unpleasant sensation produced by the latter arises, I think, from the discordant vibrations of two different tones which strike the ear out of time. Especially harsh is the dissonance between notes whose frequencies are incommensurable; such a case occurs when one has two strings in unison and sounds one of them open, together with a part of the other which bears the same ratio to its whole length, as the side of a square bears to the diagonal; this yields a dissonance similar to the augmented fourth or diminished fifth.

Agreeable consonances are pairs of tones which strike the ear with a certain regularity; this regularity consists in the fact that the pulses delivered by the two tones, in the same interval of time, shall be commensurable in number, so as not to keep the ear drum in perpetual torment, bending in two different directions in order to yield to the ever-discordant impulses.

The first and most pleasing consonance is, therefore, the octave since, for every pulse given to the tympanum by the lower string, the sharp string delivers two; accordingly, at every other vibration of the upper string, both pulses are delivered simultaneously so that one-half the entire number of pulses are delivered in unison. But when two strings are in unison their vibrations always coincide and the effect is that of a single string; hence we do not refer to it as consonance. The fifth is also a pleasing interval since for every two vibrations of the lower string the upper one gives three, so that considering the entire number of pulses from

the upper string one-third of them will strike in unison, i.e., between each pair of concordant vibrations there intervene two single vibrations; and when the interval is a fourth, three single vibrations intervene. In case the interval is a second where the ratio is 9/8 it is only every ninth vibration of the upper string which reaches the ear simultaneously with one of the lower; all the others are discordant and produce a harsh effect upon the recipient ear which interprets them as dissonances.

SIMP. Won't you be good enough to explain this argument a little more clearly?

SALV. Let AB denote the length of a wave emitted by the lower string and CD that of a higher string which is emitting the octave of AB; divide AB in the middle at E. If the two strings begin their motions at A and C, it is clear that when the sharp vibration has reached the end D, the other vibration will have travelled only as far as E, which, not being a terminal point, will emit no pulse; but there is a blow delivered at D. Accordingly, when the one wave comes back from D to C, the other passes on from E to B; hence the two pulses from B and C strike the drum of the ear simultaneously Seeing that these vibrations are repeated again and again in the same manner, we conclude that each alternate pulse from CD falls in unison with one from AB. But each of the pulsations at the terminal points, A and B, is constantly accompanied by one which leaves always from C or always from D. This is clear because if we suppose the waves to reach A and C at the same instant, then, while one wave travels from A to B, the other will proceed from C to D and back to C, so that waves strike at C and B simultaneously; during the passage of the wave from B back to A the disturbance at C goes to D and again returns to C, so that once more the pulses at A and C are simultaneous.

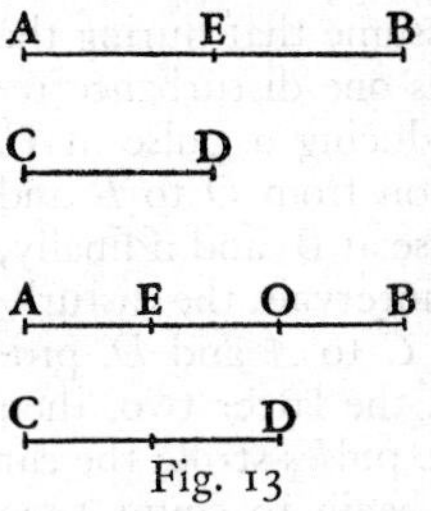

Fig. 13

Next let the vibrations AB and CD be separated by an interval of a fifth, that is, by a ratio of 3/2; choose the points E and O such that they will divide the wave length of the lower string into three equal parts and imagine the vibrations to start at the same instant from each of the terminals A and C. It is evident that when the pulse has been delivered at the terminal D, the wave in AB has travelled only as far as O; the drum of the ear receives, therefore, only the pulse from D. Then during the return of the one vibration from D to C, the other will pass from O to B and then back to O, producing an isolated pulse at B—a pulse which is out of time but one which must be taken into consideration.

Now since we have assumed that the first pulsations started from the terminals A and C at the same instant, it follows that the second pulsation, isolated at D, occurred after an interval of time equal to that required for passage from C to D or, what is the same thing, from A to O; but the next pulsation, the one at B, is separated from the preceding by only half this interval, namely, the time required for passage from O to B. Next while the one vibration travels from O to A, the other travels from C to D, the result of which is that two pulsations occur simultaneously at A and D. Cycles of this kind follow one after another, i.e., one solitary pulse of the lower string interposed between two solitary pulses of the upper string. Let us now imagine time to be divided into very small equal intervals; then if we assume that, during the first two of these intervals, the disturbances which occurred simultaneously at A and C have travelled as far as O and D and have produced a pulse at D; and if we assume that during the third and fourth intervals one disturbance returns from D to C, producing a pulse at C, while the other, passing on from O to B and back to O, produces a pulse at B; and if finally, during the fifth and sixth intervals, the disturbances travel from O and C to A and D, producing a pulse at each of the latter two, then the sequence in which the pulses strike the ear will be such that, if we begin to count time from any instant where two pulses are simultaneous, the ear drum will, after the lapse of two of the said intervals, receive a solitary pulse; at the end of the third interval, another solitary pulse; so also at the end of the fourth interval; and two intervals later, i.e., at the end of the sixth interval, will be heard two pulses in unison. Here ends the cycle—the anomaly, so to speak—which repeats itself over and over again.

Sagr. I can no longer remain silent; for I must express to you the great pleasure I have in hearing such a complete explanation of phenomena with regard to which I have so long been in darkness. Now I understand why unison does not differ from a single tone; I understand why the octave is the principal harmony, but so like unison as often to be mistaken for it and also why it occurs with the other harmonies. It

resembles unison because the pulsations of strings in unison always occur simultaneously, and those of the lower string of the octave are always accompanied by those of the upper string; and among the latter is interposed a solitary pulse at equal intervals and in such a manner as to produce no disturbance; the result is that such a harmony is rather too much softened and lacks fire. But the fifth is characterized by its displaced beats and by the interposition of two solitary beats of the upper string and one solitary beat of the lower string between each pair of simultaneous pulses; these three solitary pulses are separated by intervals of time equal to half the interval which separates each pair of simultaneous beats from the solitary beats of the upper string. Thus the effect of the fifth is to produce a tickling of the ear drum such that its softness is modified with sprightliness, giving at the same moment the impression of a gentle kiss and of a bite.

Salv. Seeing that you have derived so much pleasure from these novelties, I must show you a method by which the eye may enjoy the same game as the ear. Suspend three balls of lead, or other heavy material, by means of strings of different length such that while the longest makes two vibrations the shortest will make four and the medium three; this will take place when the longest string measures 16, either in hand breadths or in any other unit, the medium 9 and the shortest 4, all measured in the same unit.

Now pull all these pendulums aside from the perpendicular and release them at the same instant; you will see a curious interplay of the threads passing each other in various manners but such that at the completion of every fourth vibration of the longest pendulum, all three will arrive simultaneously at the same terminus, whence they start over again to repeat the same cycle. This combination of vibrations, when produced on strings is precisely that which yields the interval of the octave and the intermediate fifth. If we employ the same disposition of apparatus but change the lengths of the threads, always however, in such a way that their vibrations correspond to those of agreeable musical intervals, we shall see a different crossing of these threads but always such that, after a definite interval of time and after a definite number of vibrations, all the threads, whether three or four, will reach the same terminus at the same instant, and then begin a repetition of the cycle.

If however the vibrations of two or more strings are incommensurable so that they never complete a definite number of vibrations at the same instant, or if commensurable they return only after a long interval of time and after a large number of vibrations, then the eye is confused by the disorderly succession of crossed threads. In like manner the ear is pained by an irregular sequence of air waves which strike the tympanum without any fixed order.

But, gentlemen, whither have we drifted during these many hours lured on by various problems and unexpected digressions? The day is already ended and we have scarcely touched the subject proposed for discussion. Indeed we have deviated so far that I remember only with difficulty our early introduction and the little progress made in the way of hypotheses and principles for use in later demonstrations.

SAGR. Let us then adjourn for to-day in order that our minds may find refreshment in sleep and that we may return tomorrow, if so please you, and resume the discussion of the main question.

SALV. I shall not fail to be here to-morrow at the same hour, hoping not only to render you service but also to enjoy your company.

SECOND DAY

SAGREDO. While Simplicio and I were awaiting your arrival we were trying to recall that last consideration which you advanced as a principle and basis for the results you intended to obtain; this consideration dealt with the resistance which all solids offer to fracture and depended upon a certain cement which held the parts glued together so that they would yield and separate only under considerable pull. Later we tried to find the explanation of this coherence, seeking it mainly in the vacuum; this was the occasion of our many digressions which occupied the entire day and led us far afield from the original question which, as I have already stated, was the consideration of the resistance that solids offer to fracture.

SALV. I remember it all very well. Resuming the thread of our discourse, whatever the nature of this resistance which solids offer to large tractive forces there can at least be no doubt of its existence; and though this resistance is very great in the case of a direct pull, it is found, as a rule, to be less in the case of bending forces. Thus, for example, a rod of steel or of glass will sustain a longitudinal pull of a thousand pounds while a weight of fifty pounds would be quite sufficient to break it if the rod were fastened at right angles into a vertical wall. It is this second type of resistance which we must consider, seeking to discover in what proportion it is found in prisms and cylinders of the same material, whether alike or unlike in shape, length, and thickness. In this discussion I shall take for granted the well-known mechanical principle which has been shown to govern the behaviour of a bar, which we call a lever, namely, that the force bears to the resistance the inverse ratio of the distances which separate the fulcrum from the force and resistance respectively.

SIMP. This was demonstrated first of all by Aristotle, in his *Mechanics*.

SALV. Yes, I am willing to concede him priority in point of time; but as regards rigour of demonstration the first place must be given to Archimedes, since upon a single proposition proved in his book on *Equilibrium*[1] depends not only

[1] See Archimedes, *Equilibrium of Planes*, p. 502-19.

the law of the lever but also those of most other mechanical devices.

SAGR. Since now this principle is fundamental to all the demonstrations which you propose to set forth would it not be advisable to give us a complete and thorough proof of this proposition, unless possibly it would take too much time?

SALV. Yes, that would be quite proper, but it is better I think to approach our subject in a manner somewhat different from that employed by Archimedes, namely, by first assuming merely that equal weights placed in a balance of equal arms will produce equilibrium—a principle also assumed by Archimedes—and then proving that it is no less true that unequal weights produce equilibrium when the arms of the steelyard have lengths inversely proportional to the weights suspended from them; in other words, it amounts to the same thing whether one places equal weights at equal distances or unequal weights at distances which bear to each other the inverse ratio of the weights.

In order to make this matter clear imagine a prism or solid cylinder, *AB*, suspended at each end to the rod *HI*, and supported by two threads *HA* and *IB*; it is evident that if I attach a thread, *C*, at the middle point of the balance beam *HI*, the entire prism *AB* will, according to the principle assumed, hang in equilibrium since one-half its weight lies on one side, and the other half on the other side, of the point of suspension *C*. Now suppose the prism to be divided into unequal parts by a plane through the line *D*, and let the part *DA* be the larger and *DB* the smaller: this division having been made, imagine a thread *ED*, attached at the point *E* and supporting the parts *AD* and *DB*, in order that these parts may remain in the same position relative to line *HI*: and since the relative position of the prism and the beam *HI* remains unchanged, there can be no doubt but that the prism will maintain its former state of equilibrium. But circumstances would remain the same if that part of the prism which is now held up, at the ends, by the threads *AH* and *DE* were supported at the middle by a single thread *GL*; and likewise the other part *DB* would not

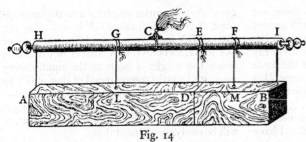

Fig. 14

figure whatever and if G and F were retained as points of suspension, that they would remain in equilibrium about the point C, for it is only too evident that change of figure does not produce change of weight so long as the mass does not vary. From this we may derive the general conclusion that any two heavy bodies are in equilibrium at distances which are inversely proportional to their weights.

change position if held by a thread FM placed at its middle point. Suppose now the threads HA, ED, and IB to be removed, leaving only the two GL and FM, then the same equilibrium will be maintained so long as the suspension is at C. Now let us consider that we have here two heavy bodies AD and DB hung at the ends G and F, of a balance beam GF in equilibrium about the point C, so that the line CG is the distance from C to the point of suspension of the heavy body AD, while CF is the distance at which the other heavy body, DB, is supported. It remains now only to show that these distances bear to each other the inverse ratio of the weights themselves, that is, the distance GC is to the distance CF as the prism DB is to the prism DA—a proposition which we shall prove as follows: Since the line GE is the half of EH, and since EF is the half of EI, the whole length GF will be half of the entire line HI, and therefore equal to CI; if now we subtract the common part CF the remainder GC will be equal to the remainder FI, that is, to FE, and if to each of these we add CE we shall have GE equal to CF: hence GE:EF = FC:CG. But GE and EF bear the same ratio to each other as do their doubles HE and EI, that is, the same ratio as the prism AD to DB. Therefore, by equating ratios we have, *convertendo*, the distance GC is to the distance CF as the weight BD is to the weight DA, which is what I desired to prove.

If what precedes is clear, you will not hesitate, I think, to admit that the two prisms AD and DB are in equilibrium about the point C since one-half of the whole body AB lies on the right of the suspension C and the other half on the left; in other words, this arrangement is equivalent to two equal weights disposed at equal distances. I do not see how any one can doubt, if the two prisms AD and DB were transformed into cubes, spheres, or into any other

This principle established, I desire, before passing to any other subject, to call your attention to the fact that these forces, resistances, moments, figures, etc., may be considered either in the abstract, dissociated from matter, or in the concrete, associated with matter. Hence the properties which belong to figures that are merely geometrical and non-material must be modified when we fill these figures with matter and therefore give them weight. Take, for example, the lever BA which, resting upon the support E, is used to lift a heavy stone D. The principle just demonstrated makes it clear that a force applied at the extremity B will just suffice to equilibrate the resistance offered by the heavy body D, provided this force bears to the force at D the same ratio as the distance AC bears to the distance CB; and this is true so long as we consider only the moments of the single force at B and of the resistance at D, treating the lever as an immaterial body devoid of weight. But if we take into account the weight of the lever itself—an instrument which may be made either of wood or of iron—it is manifest that, when this weight has been added to

Fig. 15

the force at B, the ratio will be changed and must therefore be expressed in different terms. Hence, before going further let us agree to distinguish between these two points of view; when we consider an instrument in the abstract, i.e., apart from the weight of its own material, we shall speak of "taking it in an absolute sense"; but if we fill one of these simple and absolute figures with matter and thus give it weight, we shall refer to such a material figure as a "moment" or "compound force."

SAGR. I must break my resolution about not leading you off into a digression; for I cannot concentrate my attention upon what is to follow until a certain doubt is removed from my mind, namely, you seem to compare the force at *B* with the total weight of the stone *D*, a part of which—possibly the greater part—rests upon the horizontal plane: so that . . .

SALV. I understand perfectly: you need go no further. However, please observe that I have not mentioned the total weight of the stone; I spoke only of its force at the point *A*, the extremity of the lever *BA*, which force is always less than the total weight of the stone, and varies with its shape and elevation.

SAGR. Good: but there occurs to me another question about which I am curious. For a complete understanding of this matter, I should like you to show me, if possible, how one can determine what part of the total weight is supported by the underlying plane and what part by the end *A* of the lever.

SALV. The explanation will not delay us long and I shall therefore have pleasure in granting your request. In the accompanying figure, let us understand that the weight having its center of gravity at *A* rests with the end *B* upon the horizontal plane and with the other end upon the lever *CG*. Let *N* be the fulcrum of a lever to which the force is applied at *G*. Let fall the perpendiculars, *AO* and *CF*, from the center *A* and the end *C*. Then I say, the magnitude of the entire weight bears to the magnitude of the force at *G* a ratio compounded of the ratio between the two distances *GN* and *NC* and the ratio between *FB* and *BO*. Lay off a distance *X* such

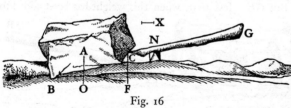

Fig. 16

that its ratio to *NC* is the same as that of *BO* to *FB*; then, since the total weight *A* is counterbalanced by the two forces at *B* and at *C*, it follows that the force at *B* is to that at *C* as the distance *FO* is to the distance *OB*. Hence, *componendo*, the sum of the forces at *B* and *C*, that is, the total weight *A*, is to the force at *C* as the line *FB* is to the line *BO*, that is, as *NC* is to *X*: but the force applied at *C* is to the force applied at *G* as the distance *GN* is to the distance *NC*; hence it follows, *ex æquali in proportione pertur-*

bata,[1] that the entire weight *A* is to the force applied at *G* as the distance *GN* is to *X*. But the ratio of *GN* to *X* is compounded of the ratio of *GN* to *NC* and of *NC* to *X*, that is, of *FB* to *BO*; hence the weight *A* bears to the equilibrating force at *G* a ratio compounded of that of *GN* to *NC* and of *FB* to *BO*: which was to be proved.

Let us now return to our original subject; then, if what has hitherto been said is clear, it will be easily understood that,

PROPOSITION I

A prism or solid cylinder of glass, steel, wood, or other breakable material which is capable of sustaining a very heavy weight when applied longitudinally is, as previously remarked, easily broken by the transverse application of a weight which may be much smaller in proportion as the length of the cylinder exceeds its thickness.

Let us imagine a solid prism *ABCD* fastened into a wall at the end *AB*, and supporting a weight *E* at the other end; understand also that the wall is vertical and that the prism or cylinder is fastened at right angles to the wall. It is clear that, if the cylinder breaks, fracture will occur at the point *B* where the edge of the mortise acts as a fulcrum for the lever *BC*, to which the force is applied; the thickness of the solid *BA* is the other arm of the lever along which is located the resistance. This resistance opposes the separation of the part *BD*, lying outside the wall, from that portion lying inside. From the preceding, it follows that the magnitude of the force applied at *C* bears to the magnitude of the resistance, found in the thickness of the prism, *i. e.*, in the attachment of the base *BA* to its contiguous parts, the same ratio which the length *CB* bears to half the length *BA*; if now we define absolute resistance to fracture as that offered to a longitudinal pull (in which case the stretching force acts in the same direction as that through which the body is moved), then it follows that the absolute resistance of the prism *BD* is to the breaking load placed at the end of the lever *BC* in the same ratio as the length *BC* is to the half of *AB* in the case of a prism, or the semidiameter in the case of a cylinder. This is our first proposition. Observe that in what has here been said the weight of the solid *BD* itself has been left out of consideration, or rather, the prism has been assumed to be devoid of weight. But if the weight of the prism is to be taken account of in conjunction

[1] See Euclid, v. 20.

Fig. 17

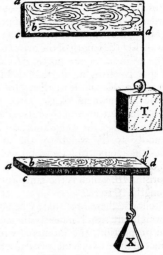

Fig. 18

Salv. Precisely so, and a fact worth remembering. Now we can readily understand

PROPOSITION II

How and in what proportion a rod, or rather a prism, whose width is greater than its thickness offers more resistance to fracture when the force is applied in the direction of its breadth than in the direction of its thickness.

For the sake of clearness, take a ruler ad whose width is ac and whose thickness, cb, is much less than its width. The question now is why will the ruler, if stood on edge, as in the first figure, withstand a great weight T, while, when laid flat, as in the second figure, it will not support the weight X which is less than T. The answer is evident when we remember that in the one case the fulcrum is at the line bc, and in the other case at ca, while the distance at which the force is applied is the same in both cases, namely, the length bd but in the first case the distance of the resistance from the fulcrum—half the line ca— is greater than in the other case where it is only half of bc. Therefore the weight T is greater than X in the same ratio as half the width ca is greater than half the thickness bc, since the former acts as a lever arm for ca, and the latter for cb, against the same resistance, namely, the strength of all the fibres in the cross-section ab. We conclude, therefore, that any given ruler, or prism, whose width exceeds its thickness, will offer greater resistance to fracture when standing on edge than

with the weight E, we must add to the weight E one half that of the prism BD: so that if, for example, the latter weighs two pounds and the weight E is ten pounds we must treat the weight E as if it were eleven pounds.

Simp. Why not twelve?

Salv. The weight E, my dear Simplicio, hanging at the extreme end C acts upon the lever BC with its full moment of ten pounds: so also would the solid BD if suspended at the same point exert its full moment of two pounds; but, as you know, this solid is uniformly distributed throughout its entire length, BC, so that the parts which lie near the end B are less effective than those more remote.

Accordingly, if we strike a balance between the two, the weight of the entire prism may be considered as concentrated at its center of gravity which lies midway of the lever BC. But a weight hung at the extremity C exerts a moment twice as great as it would if suspended from the middle: therefore, if we consider the moments of both as located at the end C, we must add to the weight E one-half that of the prism.

Simp. I understand perfectly; and moreover, if I mistake not, the force of the two weights BD and E, thus disposed, would exert the same moment as would the entire weight BD together with twice the weight E suspended at the middle of the lever BC.

when lying flat, and this in the ratio of the width to the thickness.

PROPOSITION III

Considering now the case of a prism or cylinder growing longer in a horizontal direction, we must find out in what ratio the moment of its own weight increases in comparison with its resistance to fracture. This moment I find increases in proportion to the square of the length. In order to prove this let AD be a prism or cylinder lying horizontal with its end A firmly fixed in a wall. Let the length of the prism be increased by the addition of the portion BE. It is clear that merely changing the length of the lever from AB to AC will, if we disregard its weight, increase the moment of the force tending to produce fracture at A in the ratio of CA to BA. But, besides this, the weight of the solid portion BE, added to the weight of the solid AB increases the moment of the total weight in the ratio of the weight of the prism AE to that of the prism AB, which is the same as the ratio of the length AC to AB.

It follows, therefore, that, when the length and weight are simultaneously increased in any given proportion, the moment, which is the product of these two, is increased in a ratio which is the square of the preceding proportion. The conclusion is then that the bending moments due to the weight of prisms and cylinders which have the same thickness but different lengths, bear to each other a ratio which is the square of the ratio of their lengths, or, what is the same thing, the ratio of the squares of their lengths.

We shall next show in what ratio the resistance to fracture, in prisms and cylinders, increases with increase of thickness while the length remains unchanged. Here I say that

PROPOSITION IV

In prisms and cylinders of equal length, but of unequal thicknesses, the resistance to fracture increases in the same ratio as the cube of the diameter of the thickness, i. e., of the base.

Let A and B be two cylinders of equal lengths DG, FH; let their bases be circular but unequal, having the diameters CD and EF. Then I say that the resistance to fracture offered by the cylinder B is to that offered by A as the cube of the diameter FE is to the cube of the diameter DC. For, if we consider the resistance to fracture by longitudinal pull as dependent upon the bases, *i.e.*, upon the circles EF and DC, no one can doubt that the strength of the cylinder B is greater than that of A in the same proportion in which the area of the circle EF exceeds that of CD; because it is precisely in this ratio that the number of fibres binding the parts of the solid together in the one cylinder exceeds that in the other cylinder.

But in the case of a force acting transversely it must be remembered that we are employing two levers in which the forces are applied at distances DG, FH, and the fulcrums are located at the points D and F; but the resistances are applied at distances which are equal to the radii of the circles DC and EF, since the fibres distributed over these entire cross-sections act as if concentrated at the centres. Remembering this and remembering also that the arms, DG and FH, through which the forces G and H act are equal, we can understand that the resistance, located at the centre of the base EF, acting against the force at H, is more effective than the resistance at the centre of the base CD opposing the force G, in the ratio of the radius FE to the radius DC. Accordingly, the resistance to fracture offered by the cylinder B is greater than that of the cylinder A in a ratio which is

Fig. 19

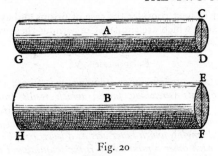

Fig. 20

compounded of that of the area of the circles *EF* and *DC* and that of their radii, *i.e.*, of their diameters; but the areas of circles are as the squares of their diameters. Therefore the ratio of the resistances, being the product of the two preceding ratios, is the same as that of the cubes of the diameters. This is what I set out to prove. Also since the volume of a cube varies as the third power of its edge we may say that the resistance [strength] of a cylinder whose length remains constant varies as the third power of its diameter.

From the preceding we are able to conclude that

COROLLARY

The resistance of a prism or cylinder of constant length varies in the sesquialteral ratio of its volume.

This is evident because the volume of a prism or cylinder of constant altitude varies directly as the area of its base, *i.e.*, as the square of a side or diameter of this base; but, as just demonstrated, the resistance varies as the cube of this same side or diameter. Hence the resistance varies in the sesquialteral ratio of the volume—consequently also of the weight—of the solid itself.

SIMP. Before proceeding further I should like to have one of my difficulties removed. Up to this point you have not taken into consideration a certain other kind of resistance which, it appears to me, diminishes as the solid grows longer, and this is quite as true in the case of bending as in pulling; it is precisely thus that in the case of a rope we observe that a very long one is less able to support a large weight than a short one. Whence, I believe, a short rod of wood or iron will support a greater weight than if it were long, provided the force be always applied longitudinally and not transversely, and provided also that we take into account the weight of the rope itself which increases with its length.

SALV. I fear, Simplicio, if I correctly catch your meaning, that in this particular you are making the same mistake as many others; that is if you mean to say that a long rope, one of perhaps 40 cubits, cannot hold up so great a weight as a shorter length, say one or two cubits, of the same rope.

SIMP. That is what I meant, and as far as I see the proposition is highly probable.

SALV. On the contrary, I consider it not merely improbable but false; and I think I can easily convince you of your error. Let *AB* represent the rope, fastened at the upper end *A*: at the lower end attach a weight *C* whose force is just sufficient to break the rope. Now, Simplicio, point out the exact place where you think the break ought to occur.

SIMP. Let us say *D*.

SALV. And why at *D*?

SIMP. Because at this point the rope is not strong enough to support, say, 100 pounds, made up of the portion of the rope *DB* and the stone *C*.

SALV. Accordingly, whenever the rope is stretched with the weight of 100 pounds at *D* it will break there.

SIMP. I think so.

SALV. But tell me, if instead of attaching the weight at the end of the rope, *B*, one fastens it at a point nearer *D*, say, at *E*: or if, instead of fixing the upper end of the rope at *A*, one fastens it at some point *F*, just above *D*, will not the rope, at the point *D*, be subject to the same pull of 100 pounds?

SIMP. It would, provided you include with the stone *C* the portion of rope *EB*.

SALV. Let us therefore suppose that the rope is stretched at the point *D* with a weight of 100 pounds, then according to your own admission it will break; but *FE* is only a small portion of *AB*; how can you therefore maintain that the long rope is weaker than the short one? Give up then this erroneous view which you share with many very intelligent people, and let us proceed.

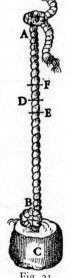

Fig. 21

Now having demonstrated that, in the case of prisms and cylinders of constant thickness, the moment of force tending to produce fracture varies as the square of the length; and having likewise shown that, when the length is constant and the thickness varies, the resistance to fracture varies as the cube of the side, or diameter, of the base, let us pass to the investigation of the case of solids which simultaneously vary in both length and thickness. Here I observe that,

PROPOSITION V

Prisms and cylinders which differ in both length and thickness offer resistances to fracture which are directly proportional to the cubes of the diameters of their bases and inversely proportional to their lengths.

Let *ABC* and *DEF* be two such cylinders; then the resistance of the cylinder *AC* bears to the resistance of the cylinder *DF* a ratio which is the product of the cube of the diameter *AB* divided by the cube of the diameter *DE*, and of

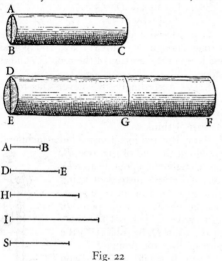

Fig. 22

the length *EF* divided by the length *BC*. Make *EG* equal to *BC*: let *H* be a third proportional to the lines *AB* and *DE*; let *I* be a fourth proportional, $[AB/DE = H/I]$: and let $I:S = EF:BC$.

Now since the resistance of the cylinder *AC* is to that of the cylinder *DG* as the cube of *AB* is to the cube of *DE*, that is, as the length *AB* is to the length I; and since the resistance of the cylinder *DG* is to that of the cylinder *DF* as the length *FE* is to *EG*, that is, as I is to S, it follows that the length *AB* is to S as the resistance of the cylinder *AC* is to that of the cylinder *DF*. But the line *AB* bears to S a ratio which is the product of AB/I and I/S. Hence the resistance of the cylinder *AC* bears to the resistance of the cylinder *DF* a ratio which is the product of AB/I (that is, AB^3/DE^3) and of I/S (that is, EF/BC): which is what I meant to prove.

This proposition having been demonstrated,

let us next consider the case of prisms and cylinders which are similar. Concerning these we shall show that,

PROPOSITION VI

In the case of similar cylinders and prisms, the moments [stretching forces] which result from multiplying together their weight and length [i.e. from the moments produced by their own weight and length], which latter acts as a lever-arm, bear to each other a ratio which is the sesquialteral of the ratio between the resistances of their bases.

In order to prove this let us indicate the two similar cylinders by *AB* and *CD*: then the magnitude of the force in the cylinder *AB*, opposing the resistance of its base *B*, bears to the magnitude of the force at *CD*, opposing the resistance of its base *D*, a ratio which is the sesquialteral of the ratio between the resistance of the base *B* and the resistance of the base *D*. And

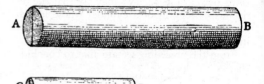

Fig. 23

since the solids *AB* and *CD*, are effective in opposing the resistances of their bases *B* and *D*, in proportion to their weights and to the mechanical advantages of their lever arms respectively, and since the advantage of the lever arm *AB* is equal to the advantage of the lever arm *CD* (this is true because in virtue of the similarity of the cylinders the length *AB* is to the radius of the base *B* as the length *CD* is to the radius of the base *D*), it follows that the total force of the cylinder *AB* is to the total force of the cylinder *CD* as the weight alone of the cylinder *AB* is to the weight alone of the cylinder *CD*, that is, as the volume of the cylinder *AB* is to the volume *CD*: but these are as the cubes of the diameters of their bases *B* and *D*; and the resistances of the bases, being to each other as their areas, are to each other consequently as the squares of their diameters. Therefore, the forces of the cylinders are to each other in the sesquialteral ratio of the resistance of their bases.

SIMP. This proposition strikes me as both new and surprising: at first glance it is very different from anything which I myself should have guessed: for since these figures are similar in all other respects, I should have certainly thought that the forces and the resistances of these cylinders would have borne to each other the same ratio.

Sagr. This is the proof of the proposition to which I referred, at the very beginning of our discussion, as one imperfectly understood by me.

Salv. For a while, Simplicio, I used to think, as you do, that the resistances of similar solids were similar; but a certain casual observation showed me that similar solids do not exhibit a strength which is proportional to their size, the larger ones being less fitted to undergo rough usage, just as tall men are more apt than small children to be injured by a fall. And, as we remarked at the outset, a large beam or column falling from a given height will go to pieces when under the same circumstances a small scantling or small marble cylinder will not break. It was this observation which led me to the investigation of the fact which I am about to demonstrate to you: it is a very remarkable thing that, among the infinite variety of solids which are similar one to another there are no two of which the forces and the resistances of these solids are related in the same ratio.

Simp. You remind me now of a passage in Aristotle's *Questions in Mechanics* in which he tries to explain why it is that a wooden beam becomes weaker and can be more easily bent as it grows longer, notwithstanding the fact that the shorter beam is thinner and the longer one thicker: and, if I remember correctly, he explains it in terms of the simple lever.

Salv. Very true: but, since this solution seemed to leave room for doubt, Bishop di Guevara, whose truly learned commentaries have greatly enriched and illuminated this work, indulges in additional clever speculations with the hope of thus overcoming all difficulties; nevertheless, even he is confused as regards this particular point, namely ,whether, when the length and thickness of these solid figures increase in the same ratio, their strength and resistance to fracture, as well as to bending, remain constant. After much thought upon this subject, I have reached the following result. First I shall show that,

Proposition VII

Among heavy prisms and cylinders of similar figure, there is one and only one which under the stress of its own weight lies just on the limit between breaking and not breaking: so that every larger one is unable to carry the load of its own weight and

breaks; while every smaller one is able to withstand some additional force tending to break it.

Let AB be a heavy prism, the longest possible that will just sustain its own weight, so that if it be lengthened the least bit it will break. Then, I say, this prism is unique among all similar prisms—infinite in number—in occupying that boundary line between breaking and not breaking; so that every larger one will break under its own weight, and every smaller one will not break, but will be able to withstand some force in addition to its own weight.

Let the prism CE be similar to, but larger than, AB: then, I say, it will not remain intact but will break under its own weight. Lay off the portion CD, equal in length to AB. And, since, the resistance of CD is to that of AB as the cube of the thickness of CD is to the cube of the thickness of AB, that is, as the prism CE is to the similar prism AB, it follows that the weight of CE is the utmost load which a prism of the length CD can sustain; but the length of CE is greater; therefore the prism CE will break. Now

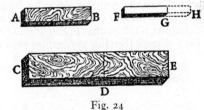

Fig. 24

take another prism FG which is smaller than AB. Let FH equal AB, then it can be shown in a similar manner that the resistance [bending strength] of FG is to that of AB as the prism FG is to the prism AB provided the distance AB that is FH, is equal to the distance FG; but AB is greater than FG, and therefore the moment of the prism FG applied at G is not sufficient to break the prism FG.

Sagr. The demonstration is short and clear; while the proposition which, at first glance, appeared improbable is now seen to be both true and inevitable. In order therefore to bring this prism into that limiting condition which separates breaking from not breaking, it would be necessary to change the ratio between thickness and length either by increasing the thickness or by diminishing the length. An investigation of this limiting state will, I believe, demand equal ingenuity.

Salv. Nay, even more; for the question is more difficult; this I know because I spent no small amount of time in its discovery which I now wish to share with you.

Proposition VIII

Given a cylinder or prism of the greatest length consistent with its not breaking under its own weight; and having given a greater length, to find the diameter of another cylinder or prism of this greater length which shall be the only and largest one capable of withstanding its own weight.

Let BC be the largest cylinder capable of sustaining its own weight; and let DE be a length greater than AC: the problem is to find the diameter of the cylinder which, having the length DE, shall be the largest one just able to withstand its own weight. Let I be a third proportional to the lengths DE and AC; let the diameter FD be to the diameter BA as DE is to I; draw the cylinder FE; then, among all cylinders having the same proportions, this is the largest and only one just capable of sustaining its own weight.

Let M be a third proportional to DE and I: also let O be a fourth proportional to DE, I, and M; lay off FG equal to AC. Now since the diameter FD is to the diameter AB as the length DE is to I, and since O is a fourth proportional to DE, I and M, it follows that $\overline{FD}^3:\overline{BA}^3 = DE:O$. But the resistance [bending strength] of the cyl-

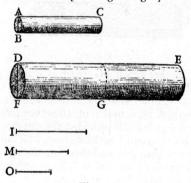

I ├────────────┤

M ├──────────┤

O ├────────┤

Fig. 25

inder DG is to the resistance of the cylinder BG as the cube of FD is to the cube of BA: hence the resistance of the cylinder DG is to that of cylinder BC as the length DE is to O. And since the moment of the cylinder BC is held in equilibrium by its resistance, we shall accomplish our end (which is to prove that the moment of the cylinder FE is equal to the resistance located at FD), if we show that the moment of the cylinder FE is to the moment of the cylinder BC as the resistance DF is to the resistance BA, that is, as the cube of FD is to the cube of BA, or as the length DE is to O. The moment of the cylinder FE is to the moment of the cylinder DG

as the square of DE is to the square of AC, that is, as the length DE is to I; but the moment of the cylinder DG is to the moment of the cylinder BC, as the square of DF is to the square of BA, that is, as the square of DE is to the square of I, or as the square of I is to the square of M, or, as I is to O. Therefore by equating ratios, it results that the moment of the cylinder FE is to the moment of the cylinder BC as the length DE is to O, that is, as the cube of DF is to the cube of BA, or as the resistance of the base DF is to the resistance of the base BA; which was to be proven.

Sagr. This demonstration, Salviati, is rather long and difficult to keep in mind from a single hearing. Will you not, therefore, be good enough to repeat it?

Salv. As you like; but I would suggest instead a more direct and a shorter proof: this will, however, necessitate a different figure.

Sagr. The favor will be that much greater: nevertheless, I hope you will oblige me by putting into written form the argument just given so that I may study it at my leisure.

Salv. I shall gladly do so. Let A denote a cylinder of diameter DC and the largest capable of sustaining its own weight: the problem is to determine a larger cylinder which shall be at once the maximum and the unique one capable of sustaining its own weight.

Let E be such a cylinder, similar to A, having the assigned length, and having a diameter KL. Let MN be a third proportional to the two

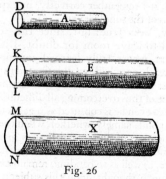

Fig. 26

lengths DC and KL: let MN also be the diameter of another cylinder, X, having the same length as E: then, I say, X is the cylinder sought. Now since the resistance of the base DC is to the resistance of the base KL as the square of DC is to the square of KL, that is, as the square of KL is to the square of MN, or, as the cylinder E is to the cylinder X, that is, as the moment E is to the moment X; and since also the resistance of the base *KL* is to the resistance of the base *MN* as the cube of *KL* is to the cube of *MN*, that is, as the cube of *DC* is to the cube of *KL*, or, as the cylinder *A* is to the cylinder *E*, that is, as the moment of *A* is to the moment of *E*; hence it follows, *ex æquali in proportione perturbata*, that the moment of *A* is to the moment of *X* as the resistance of the base *DC* is to the resistance of the base *MN*; therefore moment and resistance are related to each other in prism *X* precisely as they are in prism *A*.

Let us now generalize the problem; then it will read as follows:

Given a cylinder AC *in which moment and resistance are related in any manner whatsoever; let* DE *be the length of another cylinder; then determine what its thickness must be in order that the relation between its moment and resistance shall be identical with that of the cylinder* AC.

Using Fig. 25 in the same manner as above, we may say that, since the moment of the cylinder *FE* is to the moment of the portion *DG* as the square of *ED* is to the square of *FG*, that is, as the length *DE* is to *I*; and since the moment of the cylinder *FG* is to the moment of the cylinder *AC* as the square of *FD* is to the square of *AB*, or, as the square of *ED* is to the square of *I*, or, as the square of *I* is to the square of *M*, that is, as the length *I* is to *O*; it follows, *ex æquali*, that the moment of the cylinder *FE* is to the moment of the cylinder *AC* as the length *DE* is to *O*, that is, as the cube of *DE* is to the cube of *I*, or, as the cube of *FD* is to the cube of *AB*, that is, as the resistance of the base *FD* is to the resistance of the base *AB*; which was to be proven.

From what has already been demonstrated, you can plainly see the impossibility of increasing the size of structures to vast dimensions either in art or in nature; likewise the impossibility of building ships, palaces, or temples of enormous size in such a way that their oars, yards, beams, iron-bolts, and, in short, all their other parts will hold together; nor can nature produce trees of extraordinary size because the branches would break down under their own weight; so also it would be impossible to build up the bony structures of men, horses, or other animals so as to hold together and perform their normal functions if these animals were to be increased enormously in height; for this increase in height can be accomplished only by employing a material which is harder and stronger than usual, or by enlarging the size of the bones, thus changing their shape until the form and appearance of the animals suggest a

monstrosity. This is perhaps what our wise Poet had in mind, when he says, in describing a huge giant:

> *Impossible it is to reckon his height*
> *So beyond measure is his size.*[1]

To illustrate briefly, I have sketched a bone whose natural length has been increased three times and whose thickness has been multiplied until, for a correspondingly large animal, it would perform the same function which the small bone performs for its small animal. From the figures here shown you can see how out of proportion the enlarged bone appears. Clearly then if one wishes to maintain in a great giant the same proportion of limb as that found in an

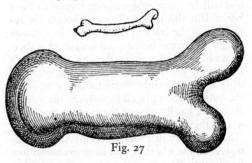

Fig. 27

ordinary man he must either find a harder and stronger material for making the bones, or he must admit a diminution of strength in comparison with men of medium stature; for if his height be increased inordinately he will fall and be crushed under his own weight. Whereas, if the size of a body be diminished, the strength of that body is not diminished in the same proportion; indeed the smaller the body the greater its relative strength. Thus a small dog could probably carry on his back two or three dogs of his own size; but I believe that a horse could not carry even one of his own size.

SIMP. This may be so; but I am led to doubt it on account of the enormous size reached by certain fish, such as the whale which, I understand, is ten times as large as an elephant; yet they all support themselves.

SALV. Your question, Simplicio, suggests another principle, one which had hitherto escaped my attention and which enables giants and other animals of vast size to support themselves and to move about as well as smaller animals do. This result may be secured either by increasing the strength of the bones and other parts intended to carry not only their weight but also the superincumbent load; or, keeping the pro-

[1] ARIOSTO, *Orlando Furioso*, XVII. 30.

portions of the bony structure constant, the skeleton will hold together in the same manner or even more easily, provided one diminishes, in the proper proportion, the weight of the bony material, of the flesh, and of anything else which the skeleton has to carry. It is this second principle which is employed by nature in the structure of fish, making their bones and muscles not merely light but entirely devoid of weight.

SIMP. The trend of your argument, Salviati, is evident. Since fish live in water which on account of its density or, as others would say, heaviness diminishes the weight of bodies immersed in it, you mean to say that, for this reason, the bodies of fish will be devoid of weight and will be supported without injury to their bones. But this is not all; for although the remainder of the body of the fish may be without weight, there can be no question but that their bones have weight. Take the case of a whale's rib, having the dimensions of a beam; who can deny its great weight or its tendency to go to the bottom when placed in water? One would, therefore, hardly expect these great masses to sustain themselves.

SALV. A very shrewd objection! And now, in reply, tell me whether you have ever seen fish stand motionless at will under water, neither descending to the bottom nor rising to the top, without the exertion of force by swimming?

SIMP. This is a well-known phenomenon.

SALV. The fact then that fish are able to remain motionless under water is a conclusive reason for thinking that the material of their bodies has the same specific gravity as that of water; accordingly, if in their make-up there are certain parts which are heavier than water there must be others which are lighter, for otherwise they would not produce equilibrium.

Hence, if the bones are heavier, it is necessary that the muscles or other constituents of the body should be lighter in order that their buoyancy may counterbalance the weight of the bones. In aquatic animals therefore, circumstances are just reversed from what they are with land animals inasmuch as, in the latter, the bones sustain not only their own weight but also that of the flesh, while in the former it is the flesh which supports not only its own weight but also that of the bones. We must therefore cease to wonder why these enormously large animals inhabit the water rather than the land, that is to say, the air.

SIMP. I am convinced and I only wish to add that what we call land animals ought really to be called air animals, seeing that they live in

the air, are surrounded by air, and breathe air.

SAGR. I have enjoyed Simplicio's discussion including both the question raised and its answer. Moreover, I can easily understand that one of these giant fish, if pulled ashore, would not perhaps sustain itself for any great length of time, but would be crushed under its own mass as soon as the connections between the bones gave way.

SALV. I am inclined to your opinion; and, indeed, I almost think that the same thing would happen in the case of a very big ship which floats on the sea without going to pieces under its load of merchandise and armament, but which on dry land and in air would probably fall apart. But let us proceed and show how:

Given a prism or cylinder, also its own weight and the maximum load which it can carry, it is then possible to find a maximum length beyond which the cylinder cannot be prolonged without breaking under its own weight.

Let *AC* indicate both the prism and its own weight; also let *D* represent the maximum load which the prism can carry at the end *C* without fracture; it is required to find the maximum to which the length of the said prism can be increased without breaking. Draw *AH* of such a length that the weight of the prism *AC* is to the sum of *AC* and twice the weight *D* as the length *CA* is to *AH*; and let *AG* be a mean proportional between *CA* and *AH*; then, I say, *AG* is the length sought. Since the moment of the weight *D* attached at the point *C* is equal to the moment of a weight twice as large as *D* placed at the middle point *AC*, through which the weight

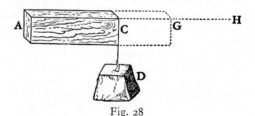

Fig. 28

of the prism *AC* acts, it follows that the moment of the resistance of the prism *AC* located at *A* is equivalent to twice the weight *D* plus the weight of *AC*, both acting through the middle point of *AC*. And since we have agreed that the moment of the weights thus located, namely, twice *D* plus *AC*, bears to the moment of *AC* the same ratio which the length *HA* bears to *CA* and since *AG* is a mean proportional between these two lengths, it follows that the moment of twice *D* plus *AC* is to the moment of *AC* as the square of GA is to the square of CA. But the moment arising from the weight of the prism GA is to the moment of AC as the square of GA is to the square of CA; thence AG is the maximum length sought, that is, the length up to which the prism AC may be prolonged and still support itself, but beyond which it will break.

Hitherto we have considered the moments and resistances of prisms and solid cylinders fixed at one end with a weight applied at the other end; three cases were discussed, namely, that in which the applied force was the only one acting, that in which the weight of the prism itself is also taken into consideration, and that in which the weight of the prism alone is taken into consideration. Let us now consider these same prisms and cylinders when supported at both ends or at a single point placed somewhere between the ends. In the first place, I remark that a cylinder carrying only its own weight and having the maximum length, beyond which it will break, will, when supported either in the middle or at both ends, have twice the length of one which is mortised into a wall and supported only at one end. This is very evident because, if we denote the cylinder by ABC and if we assume that one-half of it, AB, is the greatest possible length capable of supporting its own weight with one end fixed at B, then, for the same reason, if the cylinder is carried on the point G, the first half will be counterbalanced by the other half BC. So also in the case of the cylinder DEF, if its length be

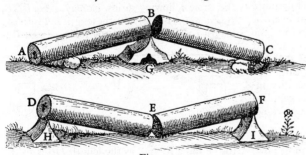

Fig. 29

such that it will support only one-half this length when the end D is held fixed, or the other half when the end F is fixed, then it is evident that when supports, such as H and I, are placed under the ends D and F respectively the moment of any additional force or weight placed at E will produce fracture at this point.

A more intricate and difficult problem is the following: neglect the weight of a solid such as the preceding and find whether the same force or weight which produces fracture when applied at the middle of a cylinder, supported at both ends, will also break the cylinder when applied at some other point nearer one end than the other.

Thus, for example, if one wished to break a stick by holding it with one hand at each end and applying his knee at the middle, would the same force be required to break it in the same manner if the knee were applied, not at the middle, but at some point nearer to one end?

SAGR. This problem, I believe, has been touched upon by Aristotle in his *Questions in Mechanics*.

SALV. His inquiry however is not quite the same; for he seeks merely to discover why it is that a stick may be more easily broken by taking hold, one hand at each end of the stick, that is, far removed from the knee, than if the hands were closer together. He gives a general explanation, referring it to the lengthened lever arms which are secured by placing the hands at the ends of the stick. Our inquiry calls for something more: what we want to know is whether, when the hands are retained at the ends of the stick, the same force is required to break it wherever the knee be placed.

SAGR. At first glance this would appear to be so, because the two lever arms exert, in a certain way, the same moment, seeing that as one grows shorter the other grows correspondingly longer.

SALV. Now you see how readily one falls into error and what caution and circumspection are required to avoid it. What you have just said appears at first glance highly probable, but on closer examination it proves to be quite far from true; as will be seen from the fact that whether the knee —the fulcrum of the two levers— be placed in the middle or not makes such a difference that, if fracture is to be produced at any other point than the middle, the breaking force at the middle, even when multiplied four, ten, a hundred, or a thousand times would not suffice. To begin with we shall offer some general considerations and then pass to the determination of the ratio in which the breaking force must change in order to produce fracture at one point rather than another.

Let AB denote a wooden cylinder which is to be broken in the middle, over the supporting point C, and let DE represent an identical cylinder which is to be broken just over the supporting point F which is not in the middle. First of all it is clear that, since the distances AC and CB are equal, the forces applied at the extremities B and A must also be equal. Secondly since the distance DF is less than the distance AC the moment of any force acting at D is less than the moment of the same force at A, that is, applied at the distance CA; and the moments are less in the ratio of the length DF to AC; consequently it is necessary to increase the force at D in order to overcome, or even to balance, the resistance at F; but in comparison with the length AC the distance DF can be diminished indefinitely: in order therefore to counterbalance the resistance at F it will be necessary to increase indefinitely the force ap-

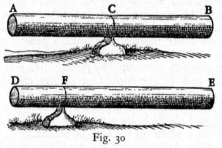

Fig. 30

plied at D. On the other hand, in proportion as we increase the distance FE over that of CB, we must diminish the force at E in order to counterbalance the resistance at F; but the distance FE, measured in terms of CB, cannot be increased indefinitely by sliding the fulcrum F toward the end D; indeed, it cannot even be made double the length CB. Therefore the force required at E to balance the resistance at F will always be more than half that required at B. It is clear then that, as the fulcrum F approaches the end D, we must of necessity indefinitely increase the sum of the forces applied at E and D in order to balance, or overcome, the resistance at F.

SAGR. What shall we say, Simplicio? Must we not confess that geometry is the most powerful of all instruments for sharpening the wit and training the mind to think correctly? Was not Plato perfectly right when he wished that his pupils should be first of all well grounded in mathematics? As for myself, I quite understood the property of the lever and how, by increasing or diminishing its length, one can increase or diminish the moment of force and of resistance; and yet, in the solution of the present problem I was not slightly, but greatly, deceived.

SIMP. Indeed I begin to understand that while logic is an excellent guide in discourse, it does not, as regards stimulation to discovery, compare with the power of sharp distinction which belongs to geometry.

SAGR. Logic, it appears to me, teaches us how to test the conclusiveness of any argument or demonstration already discovered and completed; but I do not believe that it teaches us to discover correct arguments and demonstrations. But it would be better if Salviati were to show us in just what proportion the forces must be increased in order to produce fracture as the fulcrum is moved from one point to another along one and the same wooden rod.

SALV. The ratio which you desire is determined as follows:

If upon a cylinder one marks two points at which fracture is to be produced, then the resistances at these two points will bear to each other the inverse ratio of the rectangles formed by the distances from the respective points to the ends of the cylinder.

Let A and B denote the least forces which will bring about fracture of the cylinder at C; likewise E and F the smallest forces which will break it at D. Then, I say, that the sum of the forces A and B is to the sum of the forces E and F as the area of the rectangle $AD.DB$ is to the area of the rectangle $AC.CB$. Because the sum of the forces A and B bears to the sum of the forces E and F a ratio which is the product of the three following ratios, namely, $(A+B)/B$, B/F, and $F/(F+E)$; but the length BA is to the length CA as the sum of the forces A and B is

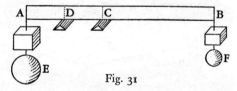

Fig. 31

to the force B; and, as the length DB is to the length CB, so is the force B to the force F; also as the length AD is to AB, so is the force F to the sum of the forces F and E.

Hence it follows that the sum of the forces A and B bears to the sum of the forces E and F a ratio which is the product of the three following ratios, namely, BA/CA, BD/BC, and AD/AB. But DA/CA is the product of DA/BA and BA/CA. Therefore the sum of the forces A and B bears to the sum of the forces E and F a ratio which is the product of $DA:CA$ and $DB:CB$.

But the rectangle $AD.DB$ bears to the rectangle $AC.CB$ a ratio which is the product of DA/CA and DB/CB. Accordingly, the sum of the forces A and B is to the sum of the forces E and F as the rectangle $AD.DB$ is to the rectangle $AC.CB$, that is, the resistance to fracture at C is to the resistance to fracture at D as the rectangle $AD.DB$ is to the rectangle $AC.CB$.   Q. E. D.

Another rather interesting problem may be solved as a consequence of this theorem, namely,

Given the maximum weight which a cylinder or prism can support at its middle-point where the resistance is a minimum, and given also a larger weight, find that point in the cylinder for which this larger weight is the maximum load that can be supported.

Let that one of the given weights which is larger than the maximum weight supported at the middle of the cylinder AB bear to this maximum weight the same ratio which the length E bears to the length F. The problem is to find that point in the cylinder at which this larger weight becomes the maximum that can be supported. Let G be a mean proportional between the lengths E and F. Draw AD and S so that they bear to each other the same ratio as E to G; accordingly S will be less than AD.

Let AD be the diameter of a semicircle AHD, in which take AH equal to S; join the points H and D and lay off DR equal to HD. Then, I say, R is the point sought, namely, the point at which the given weight, greater than the maximum supported at the middle of the cylinder D, would become the maximum load.

On AB as diameter draw the semicircle ANB: erect the perpendicular RN and join the points N and D. Now since the sum of the squares on NR and RD is equal to the square of ND, that is, to the square of AD, or to the sum of the squares of AH and HD; and, since the square of HD is equal to the square of DR, it follows that the square of NR, that is, the rectangle $AR.RB$, is equal to the square of AH, also therefore to the square of S; but the square of S is to the square of AD as the length F is to the length E, that is, as the maximum weight supported at D is to the larger of the two given weights. Hence the latter will be the maximum load which can be carried at the point R; which is the solution sought.

SAGR. Now I understand thoroughly; and I am thinking that, since the prism AB grows constantly stronger and more resistant to the pressure of its load at points which are more

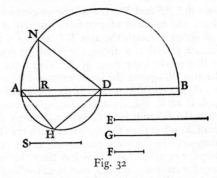

Fig. 32

and more removed from the middle, we could in the case of large heavy beams cut away a considerable portion near the ends which would notably lessen the weight, and which, in the beam work of large rooms, would prove to be of great utility and convenience.

It would be a fine thing if one could discover the proper shape to give a solid in order to make it equally resistant at every point, in which case a load placed at the middle would not produce fracture more easily than if placed at any other point.

SALV. I was just on the point of mentioning an interesting and remarkable fact connected with this very question. My meaning will be clearer if I draw a figure. Let DB represent a prism; then, as we have already shown, its resistance to fracture at the end AD, owing to a load placed at the end B, will be less than the resistance at CI in the ratio of the length CB to AB. Now imagine this same prism to be cut through diagonally along the line FB so that the opposite faces will be triangular; the side facing us will be FAB. Such a solid will have properties different from those of the prism; for, if the load remain at B, the resistance against fracture [bending strength] at C will be less than that at A in the ratio of the length CB to the length AB. This is easily proved: for if CNO represents a cross-section parallel to AFD, then the length FA bears to the length CN, in

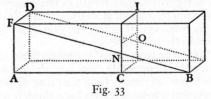

Fig. 33

the triangle FAB, the same ratio which the length AB bears to the length CB. Therefore, if we imagine A and C to be the points at which the fulcrum is placed, the lever arms in the two cases BA, AF and BC, CN will be proportional. Hence the moment of any force applied at B and acting through the arm BA, against a resistance placed at a distance AF will be equal to that of the same force at B acting through the arm BC against the same resistance located at a distance CN. But now, if the force still be applied at B, the resistance to be overcome when the fulcrum is at C, acting through the arm CN, is less than the resistance with the fulcrum at A in the same proportion as the rectangular cross-section CO is less than the rectangular cross-section AD, that is, as the length CN is less than AF, or CB than BA.

Consequently the resistance to fracture at C, offered by the portion OBC, is less than the resistance to fracture at A, offered by the entire block DAB, in the same proportion as the length CB is smaller than the length AB.

By this diagonal saw-cut we have now removed from the beam, or prism DB, a portion, *i.e.*, a half, and have left the wedge, or triangular prism, FBA. We thus have two solids possessing opposite properties; one body grows stronger as it is shortened while the other grows weaker. This being so it would seem not merely reasonable, but inevitable, that there exists a line of section such that, when the superfluous material has been removed, there will remain a solid of such figure that it will offer the same resistance at all points.

SIMP. Evidently one must, in passing from greater to less, encounter equality.

SAGR. But now the question is what path the saw should follow in making the cut.

SIMP. It seems to me that this ought not to be a difficult task: for if by sawing the prism along the diagonal line and removing half of the material, the remainder acquires a property just the opposite to that of the entire prism, so that at every point where the latter gains strength the former becomes weaker, then it seems to me that by taking a middle path, *i.e.*, by removing half the former half, or one-quarter of the whole, the strength of the remaining figure will be constant at all those points where, in the two previous figures, the gain in one was equal to the loss in the other.

SALV. You have missed the mark, Simplicio. For, as I shall presently show you, the amount which you can remove from the prism without weakening it is not a quarter but a third. It now remains, as suggested by Sagredo, to discover the path along which the saw must travel: this, as I shall prove, must be a parabola. But it is first necessary to demonstrate the following lemma:

If the fulcrums are so placed under two levers or balances that the arms through which the forces act are to each other in the same ratio as the squares of the arms through which the resistances act, and if these resistances are to each other in the same ratio as the arms, through which they act, then the forces will be equal.

Let AB and CD represent two levers whose lengths are divided by their fulcrums in such a

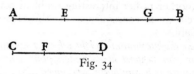

Fig. 34

way as to make the distance EB bear to the distance FD a ratio which is equal to the square of the ratio between the distances EA and FC. Let the resistances located at A and C be to each other as EA is to FC. Then, I say, the forces which must be applied at B and D in order to hold in equilibrium the resistances at A and C are equal. Let EG be a mean proportional between EB and FD. Then we shall have $BE:EG = EG:FD = AE:CF$. But this last ratio is precisely that which we have assumed to exist between the resistances at A and C. And since $EG:FD = AE:CF$, it follows, *permutando*, that $EG:AE = FD:CF$. Seeing that the distances DC and GA are divided in the same ratio by the points F and E, it follows that the same force which, when applied at D, will equilibrate the resistance at C, would if applied at G equilibrate at A a resistance equal to that found at C.

But one datum of the problem is that the resistance at A is to the resistance at C as the distance AE is to the distance CF, or as BE is to EG. Therefore the force applied at G, or rather at D, will, when applied at B, just balance the resistance located at A. Q. E. D.

This being clear draw the parabola FNB in the face FB of the prism DB. Let the prism be sawed along this parabola whose vertex is at B. The portion of the solid which remains will be included between the base AD, the rectangular plane AG, the straight line BG and the surface $DGBF$, whose curvature is identical with that of the parabola FNB. This solid will have, I say, the same strength at every point. Let the solid be cut by a plane CO parallel to the plane AD. Imagine the points A and C to be the fulcrums of two levers of which one will have the arms BA and AF; the other BC and CN. Then since in the parabola FBA, we have $BA:BC = \overline{AF}^2:\overline{CN}^2$, it is clear that the arm BA of one lever is

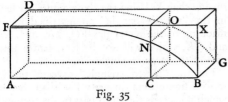

Fig. 35

to the arm BC of the other lever as the square of the arm AF is to the square of the other arm CN. Since the resistance to be balanced by the lever BA is to the resistance to be balanced by the lever BC in the same ratio as the rectangle DA is to the rectangle OC, that is as the length AF is to the length CN, which two lengths are the other arms of the levers, it follows, by the lemma just demonstrated, that the same force which, when applied at BG will equilibrate the resistance at DA, will also balance the resistance at CO. The same is true for any other section. Therefore this parabolic solid is equally strong throughout.

It can now be shown that, if the prism be sawed along the line of the parabola FNB, one-third part of it will be removed; because the rectangle FB and the surface $FNBA$ bounded by the parabola are the bases of two solids included between two parallel planes, *i.e.*, between the rectangles FB and DG; consequently the volumes of these two solids bear to each other the same ratio as their bases. But the area of the rectangle is one and a half times as large as the area $FNBA$ under the parabola; hence by cutting the prism along the parabola we remove one-third of the volume. It is thus seen how one can diminish the weight of a beam by as much as thirty-three per cent without diminishing its strength; a fact of no small utility in the construction of large vessels, and especially in supporting the decks, since in such structures lightness is of prime importance.

SAGR. The advantages derived from this fact are so numerous that it would be both wearisome and impossible to mention them all; but leaving this matter to one side, I should like to learn just how it happens that diminution of weight is possible in the ratio above stated. I can readily understand that, when a section is made along the diagonal, one-half the weight is removed; but, as for the parabolic section removing one-third of the prism, this I can only accept on the word of Salviati who is always reliable; however, I prefer first-hand knowledge to the word of another.

SALV. You would like then a demonstration of the fact that the excess of the volume of a prism over the volume of what we have called the parabolic solid is one-third of the entire prism. This I have already given you on a previous occasion; however I shall now try to recall the demonstration in which I remember having used a certain lemma from Archimedes' book *On Spirals*,[1] namely, Given any number of lines, differing in length one from another by a common difference which is equal to the shortest of these lines; and given also an equal number of lines each of which has the same length as the longest of the first-mentioned series; then the sum of the squares of the lines of this second group will be less than three times the sum of the squares of the lines in the first group. But the sum of the squares of the second group will be greater than three times the sum of the squares of all excepting the longest of the first group.

Assuming this, inscribe in the rectangle $ACBP$ the parabola AB. We have now to prove that the mixed triangle BAP whose sides are BP and PA, and whose base is the parabola BA, is a third part of the entire rectangle CP. If this is not true it will be either greater or less than a third. Suppose it to be less by an area which is represented by X. By drawing lines parallel to the sides BP and CA, we can divide the rectangle CP into equal parts; and if the process be continued we shall finally reach a division into parts so small that each of them will be smaller

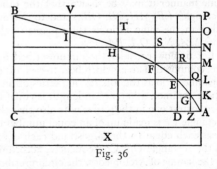

Fig. 36

than the area X; let the rectangle OB represent one of these parts and, through the points where the other parallels cut the parabola, draw lines parallel to AP. Let us now describe about our "mixed triangle" a figure made up of rectangles such as BO, IN, HM, FL, EK, and GA; this figure will also be less than a third part of the rectangle CP because the excess of this figure above the area of the "mixed triangle" is much smaller than the rectangle BO which we have already made smaller than X.

[1] See Archimedes, *On Spirals*, p. 482.

SAGR. More slowly, please; for I do not see how the excess of this figure described about the "mixed triangle" is much smaller than the rectangle BO.

SALV. Does not the rectangle BO have an area which is equal to the sum of the areas of all the little rectangles through which the parabola passes? I mean the rectangles BI, IH, HF, FE, EG, and GA of which only a part lies outside the "mixed triangle." Have we not taken the rectangle BO smaller than the area X? Therefore if, as our opponent might say, the triangle plus X is equal to a third part of this rectangle CP, the circumscribed figure, which adds to the triangle an area less than X, will still remain smaller than a third part of the rectangle, CP. But this cannot be, because this circumscribed figure is larger than a third of the area. Hence it is not true that our "mixed triangle" is less than a third of the rectangle.

SAGR. You have cleared up my difficulty; but it still remains to be shown that the circumscribed figure is larger than a third part of the rectangle CP, a task which will not, I believe, prove so easy.

SALV. There is nothing very difficult about it. Since in the parabola $\overline{DE}^2:\overline{ZG}^2 = DA:AZ =$ rectangle KE: rectangle AG, seeing that the altitudes of these two rectangles, AK and KL, are equal, it follows that $\overline{ED}^2:\overline{ZG}^2 = \overline{LA}^2:\overline{AK}^2 =$ rectangle KE: rectangle KZ. In precisely the same manner it may be shown that the other rectangles LF, MH, NI, OB, stand to one another in the same ratio as the squares of the lines MA, NA, OA, PA.

Let us now consider the circumscribed figure, composed of areas which bear to each other the same ratio as the squares of a series of lines whose common difference in length is equal to the shortest one in the series; note also that the rectangle CP is made up of an equal number of areas each equal to the largest and each equal to the rectangle OB. Consequently, according to the lemma of Archimedes, the circumscribed figure is larger than a third part of the rectangle CP; but it was also smaller, which is impossible. Hence the "mixed triangle" is not less than a third part of the rectangle CP.

Likewise, I say, it cannot be greater. For, let us suppose that it is greater than a third part of the rectangle CP and let the area X represent the excess of the triangle over the third part of the rectangle CP; subdivide the rectangle into equal rectangles and continue the process until one of these subdivisions is smaller than the area X. Let BO represent such a rectangle

smaller than X. Using the above figure, we have in the "mixed triangle" an inscribed figure, made up of the rectangles VO, TN, SM, RL, and QK, which will not be less than a third part of the large rectangle CP.

For the "mixed triangle" exceeds the inscribed figure by a quantity less than that by which it exceeds the third part of the rectangle CP; to see that this is true we have only to remember that the excess of the triangle over the third part of the rectangle CP is equal to the area X, which is less than the rectangle BO, which in turn is much less than the excess of triangle over the inscribed figure. For the rectangle BO is made up of the small rectangles AG, GE, EF, FH, HI, and IB; and the excess of the triangle over the inscribed figure is less than half the sum of these little rectangles. Thus since the triangle exceeds the third part of the rectangle CP by an amount X, which is more than that by which it exceeds the inscribed figure, the latter will also exceed the third part of the rectangle, CP. But, by the lemma which we have assumed, it is smaller. For the rectangle CP, being the sum of the largest rectangles, bears to the component rectangles of the inscribed figure the same ratio which the sum of all the squares of the lines equal to the longest bears to the squares of the lines which have a common difference, after the square of the longest has been subtracted.

Therefore, as in the case of squares, the sum total of the largest rectangles, *i.e.*, the rectangle CP, is greater than three times the sum total of those having a common difference minus the largest; but these last make up the inscribed figure. Hence the "mixed triangle" is neither greater nor less than the third part of rectangle CP; it is therefore equal to it.

SAGR. A fine, clever demonstration; and all the more so because it gives us the quadrature of the parabola, proving it to be four-thirds of the inscribed triangle, a fact which Archimedes demonstrates by means of two different, but admirable, series of many propositions. This same theorem has also been recently established by Luca Valerio, the Archimedes of our age; his demonstration is to be found in his book dealing with the centres of gravity of solids.

SALV. A book which, indeed, is not to be placed second to any produced by the most eminent geometers either of the present or of the past; a book which, as soon as it fell into the hands of our Academician, led him to abandon his own researches along these lines; for he saw how happily everything had been treated and demonstrated by Valerio.

SAGR. When I was informed of this event by the Academician himself, I begged of him to show the demonstrations which he had discovered before seeing Valerio's book; but in this I did not succeed.

SALV. I have a copy of them and will show them to you; for you will enjoy the diversity of method employed by these two authors in reaching and proving the same conclusions; you will also find that some of these conclusions are explained in different ways, although both are in fact equally correct.

SAGR. I shall be much pleased to see them and will consider it a great favor if you will bring them to our regular meeting. But in the meantime, considering the strength of a solid formed from a prism by means of a parabolic section, would it not, in view of the fact that this result promises to be both interesting and useful in many mechanical operations, be a fine thing if you were to give some quick and easy rule by which a mechanician might draw a parabola upon a plane surface?

SALV. There are many ways of tracing these curves; I will mention merely the two which are the quickest of all. One of these is really remarkable; because by it I can trace thirty or forty parabolic curves with no less neatness and precision, and in a shorter time than another man can, by the aid of a compass, neatly draw four or six circles of different sizes upon paper. I take a perfectly round brass ball about the size of a walnut and project it along the surface of a metallic mirror held in a nearly upright position, so that the ball in its motion will press slightly upon the mirror and trace out a fine sharp parabolic line; this parabola will grow longer and narrower as the angle of elevation increases. The above experiment furnishes clear and tangible evidence that the path of a projectile is a parabola; a fact first observed by our friend and demonstrated by him in his book on motion which we shall take up at our next meeting. In the execution of this method, it is advisable to slightly heat and moisten the ball by rolling in the hand in order that its trace upon the mirror may be more distinct.

The other method of drawing the desired curve upon the face of the prism is the following: Drive two nails into a wall at a convenient height and at the same level; make the distance between these nails twice the width of the rectangle upon which it is desired to trace the semiparabola. Over these two nails hang a light chain of such a length that the depth of its sag is equal to the length of the prism. This chain will assume the form of a parabola,[1] so that if this form be marked by points on the wall we shall have described a complete parabola which can be divided into two equal parts by drawing a vertical line through a point midway between the two nails. The transfer of this curve to the two opposing faces of the prism is a matter of no difficulty; any ordinary mechanic will know how to do it.

By use of the geometrical lines drawn upon our friend's compass, one may easily lay off those points which will locate this same curve upon the same face of the prism.

Hitherto we have demonstrated numerous conclusions pertaining to the resistance which solids offer to fracture. As a starting point for this science, we assumed that the resistance offered by the solid to a straight-away pull was known; from this base one might proceed to the discovery of many other results and their demonstrations; of these results the number to be found in nature is infinite. But, in order to bring our daily conference to an end, I wish to discuss the strength of hollow solids, which are employed in art—and still oftener in nature—in a thousand operations for the purpose of greatly increasing strength without adding to weight; examples of these are seen in the bones of birds and in many kinds of reeds which are light and highly resistant both to bending and breaking. For if a stem of straw which carries a head of wheat heavier than the entire stalk were made up of the same amount of material in solid form it would offer less resistance to bending and breaking. This is an experience which has been verified and confirmed in practice, where it is found that a hollow lance or a tube of wood or metal is much stronger than would be a solid one of the same length and weight, one which would necessarily be thinner; men have discovered, therefore, that in order to make lances strong as well as light they must make them hollow. We shall now show that:

In the case of two cylinders, one hollow the other solid but having equal volumes and equal lengths, their resistances are to each other in the ratio of their diameters.

Let AE denote a hollow cylinder and IN a solid one of the same weight and length; then, I say, that the resistance against fracture exhibited by the tube AE bears to that of the solid cylinder IN the same ratio as the diameter AB to the

[1] It is now known that this curve is not a parabola but a catenary. TRANS.

diameter *IL*. This is very evident; for since the tube and the solid cylinder *IN* have the same

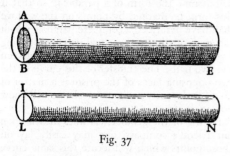

Fig. 37

volume and length, the area of the circular base *IL* will be equal to that of the annulus *AB* which is the base of the tube *AE*. (By annulus is here meant the area which lies between two concentric circles of different radii.) Hence their resistances to a straight-away pull are equal; but in producing fracture by a transverse pull we employ, in the case of the cylinder *IN*, the length *LN* as one lever arm, the point *L* as a fulcrum, and the diameter *LI*, or its half, as the opposing lever arm: while in the case of the tube, the length *BE* which plays the part of the first lever arm is equal to *LN*, the opposing lever arm beyond the fulcrum, *B*, is the diameter *AB*, or its half. Manifestly then the resistance of the tube exceeds that of the solid cylinder in the proportion in which the diameter *AB* exceeds the diameter *IL* which is the desired result. Thus the strength of a hollow tube exceeds that of a solid cylinder in the ratio of their diameters whenever the two are made of the same material and have the same weight and length.

It may be well next to investigate the general case of tubes and solid cylinders of constant length, but with the weight and the hollow portion variable. First we shall show that:

Given a hollow tube, a solid cylinder may be determined which will be equal to it.

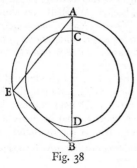

Fig. 38

The method is very simple. Let *AB* denote the external and *CD* the internal diameter of the tube. In the larger circle lay off the line *AE* equal in length to the diameter *CD*; join the points *E* and *B*. Now since the angle at *E* inscribed in a semicircle, *AEB*, is a right-angle, the area of the circle whose diameter is *AB* is equal to the sum of the areas of the two circles whose respective diameters are *AE* and *EB*. But *AE* is the diameter of the hollow portion of the tube. Therefore the area of the circle whose diameter is *EB* is the same as the area of the annulus *ACBD*. Hence a solid cylinder of circular base having a diameter *EB* will have the same volume as the walls of the tube of equal length.

By use of this theorem, it is easy: *To find the ratio between the resistance of any tube and that of any cylinder of equal length.* Let *ABE* denote a tube and *RSM* a cylinder of equal length: it is required to find the ratio between their resistances. Using the preceding proposition, determine a cylinder *ILN* which shall have the

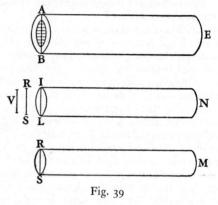

Fig. 39

same volume and length as the tube. Draw a line *V* of such a length that it will be related to *IL* and *RS* (diameters of the bases of the cylinders *IN* and *RM*), as follows: $V:RS=RS:IL$. Then, I say, the resistance of the tube *AE* is to that of the cylinder *RM* as the length of the line *AB* is to the length *V*. For, since the tube *AE* is equal both in volume and length, to the cylinder *IN*, the resistance of the tube will bear to the resistance of the cylinder the same ratio as the line *AB* to *IL*; but the resistance of the cylinder *IN* is to that of the cylinder *RM* as the cube of *IL* is to the cube of *RS*, that is, as the length *IL* is to length *V*: therefore, *ex æquali*, the resistance of the tube *AE* bears to the resistance of the cylinder *RM* the same ratio as the length *AB* to *V*.   Q. E. D.

THIRD DAY

CHANGE OF POSITION

My purpose is to set forth a very new science dealing with a very ancient subject. There is, in nature, perhaps nothing older than motion, concerning which the books written by philosophers are neither few nor small; nevertheless, I have discovered by experiment some properties of it which are worth knowing and which have not hitherto been either observed or demonstrated. Some superficial observations have been made, as, for instance, that the free motion of a heavy falling body is continuously accelerated; but to just what extent this acceleration occurs has not yet been announced; for so far as I know, no one has yet pointed out that the distances traversed, during equal intervals of time, by a body falling from rest, stand to one another in the same ratio as the odd numbers beginning with unity.

It has been observed that missiles and projectiles describe a curved path of some sort; however, no one has pointed out the fact that this path is a parabola. But this and other facts, not few in number or less worth knowing, I have succeeded in proving; and what I consider more important, there have been opened up to this vast and most excellent science, of which my work is merely the beginning, ways and means by which other minds more acute than mine will explore its remote corners.

This discussion is divided into three parts; the first part deals with motion which is steady or uniform; the second treats of motion as we find it accelerated in nature; the third deals with the so-called violent motions and with projectiles.

UNIFORM MOTION

In dealing with steady or uniform motion, we need a single definition which I give as follows:

DEFINITION

By steady or uniform motion, I mean one in which the distances traversed by the moving particle during any equal intervals of time, are themselves equal.

CAUTION

We must add to the old definition (which defined steady motion simply as one in which equal distances are traversed in equal times) the word "any," meaning by this, all equal intervals of time; for it may happen that the moving body will traverse equal distances during some equal intervals of time and yet the distances traversed during some small portion of these time-intervals may not be equal, even though the time-intervals be equal.

From the above definition, four axioms follow, namely:

AXIOM I

In the case of one and the same uniform motion, the distance traversed during a longer interval of time is greater than the distance traversed during a shorter interval of time.

AXIOM II

In the case of one and the same uniform motion, the time required to traverse a greater distance is longer than the time required for a less distance.

AXIOM III

In one and the same interval of time, the distance traversed at a greater speed is larger than the distance traversed at a less speed.

AXIOM IV

The speed required to traverse a longer distance is greater than that required to traverse a shorter distance during the same time-interval.

THEOREM I, PROPOSITION I

If a moving particle, carried uniformly at a constant speed, traverses two distances the time-intervals required are to each other in the ratio of these distances.

Let a particle move uniformly with constant speed through two distances AB, BC, and let the time required to traverse AB be represented by DE; the time required to traverse BC, by EF; then I say that the distance AB is to the distance BC as the time DE is to the time EF.

Let the distances and times be extended on

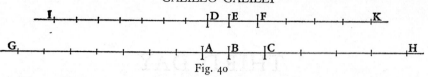

Fig. 40

both sides towards G, H and I, K; let AG be divided into any number whatever of spaces each equal to AB, and in like manner lay off in DI exactly the same number of time-intervals each equal to DE. Again lay off in CH any number whatever of distances each equal to BC; and in FK exactly the same number of time-intervals each equal to EF; then will the distance BG and the time EI be equal and arbitrary multiples of the distance BA and the time ED; and likewise the distance HB and the time KE are equal and arbitrary multiples of the distance CB and the time FE.

And since DE is the time required to traverse AB, the whole time EI will be required for the whole distance BG, and when the motion is uniform there will be in EI as many time-intervals each equal to DE as there are distances in BG each equal to BA; and likewise it follows that KE represents the time required to traverse HB.

Since, however, the motion is uniform, it follows that if the distance GB is equal to the distance BH, then must also the time IE be equal to the time EK; and if GB is greater than BH, then also IE will be greater than EK; and if less, less.[1] There are then four quantities, the first AB, the second BC, the third DE, and the fourth EF; the time IE and the distance GB are arbitrary multiples of the first and the third, namely of the distance AB and the time DE.

But it has been proved that *both* of these latter quantities are either equal to, greater than, or less than the time EK and the space BH, which are arbitrary multiples of the second and the fourth. Therefore the first is to the second, namely the distance AB is to the distance BC, as the third is to the fourth, namely the time DE is to the time EF.   Q. E. D.

THEOREM II, PROPOSITION II

If a moving particle traverses two distances in equal intervals of time, these distances will bear to each other the same ratio as the speeds. And conversely if the distances are as the speeds then the times are equal.

Referring to Fig. 40, let AB and BC represent the two distances traversed in equal time-intervals, the distance AB for instance with the velocity DE, and the distance BC with the ve-

[1]See Euclid, V. 5.

locity EF. Then, I say, the distance AB is to the distance BC as the velocity DE is to the velocity EF. For if equal multiples of both distances and speeds be taken, as above, namely, GB and IE of AB and DE respectively, and in like manner HB and KE of BC and EF, then one may infer, in the same manner as above, that the multiples GB and IE are either less than, equal to, or greater than equal multiples of BH and EK. Hence the theorem is established.

THEOREM III, PROPOSITION III

In the case of unequal speeds, the time-intervals required to traverse a given space are to each other inversely as the speeds.

Let the larger of the two unequal speeds be indicated by A; the smaller, by B; and let the motion corresponding to both traverse the given space CD. Then, I say, the time required to trav-

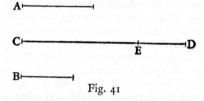

Fig. 41

erse the distance CD at speed A is to the time required to traverse the same distance at speed B, as the speed B is to the speed A. For let CD be to CE as A is to B; then, from the preceding, it follows that the time required to complete the distance CD at speed A is the same as the time necessary to complete CE at speed B; but the time needed to traverse the distance CE at speed B is to the time required to traverse the distance CD at the same speed as CE is to CD; therefore, the time in which CD is covered at speed A is to the time in which CD is covered at speed B as CE is to CD, that is, as speed B is to speed A.   Q. E. D.

THEOREM IV, PROPOSITION IV

If two particles are carried with uniform motion, but each with a different speed, the distances covered by them during unequal intervals of time bear to each other the compound ratio of the speeds and time intervals.

Let the two particles which are carried with uniform motion be E and F and let the ratio of the speed of the body E be to that of the body F as A is to B; but let the ratio of the time consumed by the motion of E be to the time consumed by the motion of F as C is to D. Then, I say, that the distance covered by E, with speed A in time C, bears to the space traversed by F with speed B in time D a ratio which is the product of the ratio of the speed A to the speed B by the ratio of the time C to the time D. For if G is the distance traversed by E at speed A

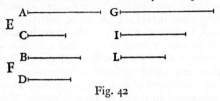

Fig. 42

during the time-interval C, and if G is to I as the speed A is to the speed B; and if also the time-interval C is to the time-interval D as I is to L, then it follows that I is the distance traversed by F in the same time that G is traversed by E since G is to I in the same ratio as the speed A to the speed B. And since I is to L in the same ratio as the time-intervals C and D, if I is the distance traversed by F during the interval C, then L will be the distance traversed by F during the interval D at the speed B.

But the ratio of G to L is the product of the ratios G to I and I to L, that is, of the ratios of the speed A to the speed B and of the time-interval C to the time-interval D.   Q. E. D.

Theorem V, Proposition V

If two particles are moved at a uniform rate, but with unequal speeds, through unequal distances, then the ratio of the time-intervals occupied will be the product of the ratio of the distances by the inverse ratio of the speeds.

Let the two moving particles be denoted by

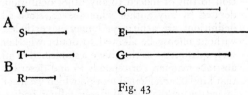

Fig. 43

A and B, and let the speed of A be to the speed of B in the ratio of V to T; in like manner let the distances traversed be in the ratio of S to R; then, I say, that the ratio of the time-interval during which the motion of A occurs to the time-interval occupied by the motion of B is

the product of the ratio of the speed T to the speed V by the ratio of the distance S to the distance R.

Let C be the time-interval occupied by the motion of A, and let the time-interval C bear to a time-interval E the same ratio as the speed T to the speed V.

And since C is the time-interval during which A, with speed V, traverses the distance S, and since T, the speed of B, is to the speed V, as the time-interval C is to the time-interval E, then E will be the time required by the particle B to traverse the distance S. If now we let the time-interval E be to the time-interval G as the distance S is to the distance R, then it follows that G is the time required by B to traverse the space R. Since the ratio of C to G is the product of the ratios C to E and E to G (while also the ratio of C to E is the inverse ratio of the speeds of A and B respectively, *i.e.*, the ratio of T to V); and since the ratio of E to G is the same as that of the distances S and R respectively, the proposition is proved.

Theorem VI, Proposition VI

If two particles are carried at a uniform rate, the ratio of their speeds will be the product of the ratio of the distances traversed by the inverse ratio of the time-intervals occupied.

Let A and B be the two particles which move at a uniform rate; and let the respective dis-

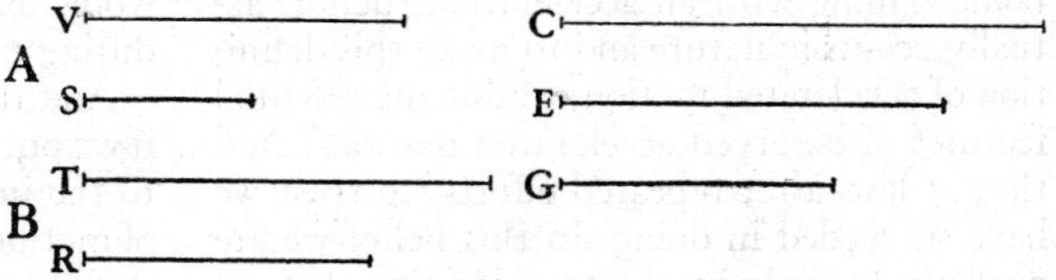

Fig. 44

tances traversed by them have the ratio of V to T, but let the time-intervals be as S to R. Then, I say, the speed of A will bear to the speed of B a ratio which is the product of the ratio of the distance V to the distance T and the time-interval R to the time-interval S.

Let C be the speed at which A traverses the distance V during the time-interval S; and let the speed C bear the same ratio to another speed E as V bears to T; then E will be the speed at which B traverses the distance T during the time-interval S. If now the speed E is to another speed G as the time-interval R is to the time-interval S, then G will be the speed at which the particle B traverses the distance T during the time-interval R. Thus we have the speed C at which the particle A covers the distance V during the time S and also the speed G at which the particle B traverses the distance T during the time R. The ratio of C to G is the product of the ratio C to E and E to G; the ratio of C to E is by definition the same as the ratio of the distance V to distance T; and the ratio of E to G is the same as the ratio of R to S. Hence follows the proposition.

SALV. The preceding is what our Author has written concerning uniform motion. We pass now to a new and more discriminating consideration of naturally accelerated motion, such as that generally experienced by heavy falling bodies; following is the title and introduction.

NATURALLY ACCELERATED MOTION

The properties belonging to uniform motion have been discussed in the preceding section; but accelerated motion remains to be considered.

And first of all it seems desirable to find and explain a definition best fitting natural phenomena. For anyone may invent an arbitrary type of motion and discuss its properties; thus, for instance, some have imagined helices and conchoids as described by certain motions which are not met with in nature, and have very commendably established the properties which these curves possess in virtue of their definitions; but we have decided to consider the phenomena of bodies falling with an acceleration such as actually occurs in nature and to make this definition of accelerated motion exhibit the essential features of observed accelerated motions. And this, at last, after repeated efforts we trust we have succeeded in doing. In this belief we are confirmed mainly by the consideration that experimental results are seen to agree with and exactly correspond with those properties which have been, one after another, demonstrated by us. Finally, in the investigation of naturally accelerated motion we were led, by hand as it were, in following the habit and custom of nature herself, in all her various other processes, to employ only those means which are most common, simple and easy.

For I think no one believes that swimming or flying can be accomplished in a manner simpler or easier than that instinctively employed by fishes and birds.

When, therefore, I observe a stone initially at rest falling from an elevated position and continually acquiring new increments of speed, why should I not believe that such increases take place in a manner which is exceedingly simple and rather obvious to everybody? If now we examine the matter carefully we find no addition or increment more simple than that which repeats itself always in the same manner. This we readily understand when we consider the intimate relationship between time and motion; for just as uniformity of motion is defined by and conceived through equal times and equal spaces (thus we call a motion uniform when equal distances are traversed during equal time-intervals), so also we may, in a similar manner, through equal time-intervals, conceive additions of speed as taking place without complication; thus we may picture to our mind a motion as uniformly and continuously accelerated when, during any equal intervals of time whatever, equal increments of speed are given to it. Thus, if any equal intervals of time whatever have elapsed, counting from the time at which the moving body left its position of rest and began to descend, the amount of speed acquired during the first two time-intervals will be double that acquired during the first time-interval alone; so the amount added during three of these time-intervals will be treble; and that in four, quadruple that of the first time-interval. To put the matter more clearly, if a body were to continue its motion with the same speed which it had acquired during the first time-interval and were to retain this same uniform speed, then its motion would be twice as slow as that which it would have if its velocity had been acquired during *two* time-intervals.

And thus, it seems, we shall not be far wrong if we put the increment of speed as proportional to the increment of time; hence the definition of motion which we are about to discuss may be stated as follows: A motion is said to be uniformly accelerated, when starting from rest, it acquires, during equal time-intervals, equal increments of speed.

SAGR. Although I can offer no rational objection to this or indeed to any other definition, devised by any author whomsoever, since all definitions are arbitrary, I may nevertheless without offense be allowed to doubt whether such a definition as the above, established in an abstract manner, corresponds to and describes that kind of accelerated motion which we meet in nature in the case of freely falling bodies. And since the Author apparently maintains that the motion described in his definition is that of freely falling bodies, I would like to clear my mind of certain difficulties in order that I may later apply myself more earnestly to the propositions and their demonstrations.

SALV. It is well that you and Simplicio raise these difficulties. They are, I imagine, the same which occurred to me when I first saw this treatise, and which were removed either by discussion with the Author himself, or by turning the matter over in my own mind.

SAGR. When I think of a heavy body falling from rest, that is, starting with zero speed and gaining speed in proportion to the time from the beginning of the motion; such a motion as would, for instance, in eight beats of the pulse acquire eight degrees of speed; having at the end of the fourth beat acquired four degrees; at the end of the second, two; at the end of the first, one: and since time is divisible without limit, it follows from all these considerations that if the earlier speed of a body is less than its present speed in a constant ratio, then there is no degree of speed however small (or, one may say, no degree of slowness however great) with which we may not find this body travelling after starting from infinite slowness, i.e., from rest. So that if that speed which it had at the end of the fourth beat was such that, if kept uniform, the body would traverse two miles in an hour, and if keeping the speed which it had at the end of the second beat, it would traverse one mile an hour, we must infer that, as the instant of starting is more and more nearly approached, the body moves so slowly that, if kept on moving at this rate, it would not traverse a mile in an hour, or in a day, or in a year or in a thousand years; indeed, it would not traverse a span in an even greater time; a phenomenon which baffles the imagination, while our senses show us that a heavy falling body suddenly acquires great speed.

SALV. This is one of the difficulties which I also at the beginning, experienced, but which I shortly afterwards removed; and the removal was effected by the very experiment which creates the difficulty for you. You say the experiment appears to show that immediately after a heavy body starts from rest it acquires a very considerable speed: and I say that the same experiment makes clear the fact that the initial motions of a falling body, no matter how heavy, are very slow and gentle. Place a heavy body upon a yielding material, and leave it there without any pressure except that owing to its own weight; it is clear that if one lifts this body a cubit or two and allows it to fall upon the same material, it will, with this impulse, exert a new and greater pressure than that caused by its mere weight; and this effect is brought about by the falling body together with the velocity acquired during the fall, an effect which will be greater and greater according to the height of the fall, that is according as the velocity of the falling body becomes greater. From the quality and intensity of the blow we are thus enabled to accurately estimate the speed of a falling body. But tell me, gentlemen, is it not true that if a block be allowed to fall upon a stake from a height of four cubits and drives it into the earth, say, four finger-breadths, that coming from a height of two cubits it will drive the stake a much less distance, and from the height of one cubit a still less distance; and finally if the block be lifted only one finger-breadth how much more will it accomplish than if merely laid on top of the stake without percussion? Certainly very little. If it be lifted only the thickness of a leaf, the effect will be altogether imperceptible. And since the effect of the blow depends upon the velocity of this striking body, can any one doubt the motion is very slow and the speed more than small whenever the effect is imperceptible? See now the power of truth; the same experiment which at first glance seemed to show one thing, when more carefully examined, assures us of the contrary.

But without depending upon the above experiment, which is doubtless very conclusive, it seems to me that it ought not to be difficult to establish such a fact by reasoning alone. Imagine a heavy stone held in the air at rest; the support is removed and the stone set free; then since it is heavier than the air it begins to fall, and not with uniform motion but slowly at the beginning and with a continuously accelerated motion. Now since velocity can be increased and diminished without limit, what reason is there to believe that such a moving body starting with infinite slowness, that is, from rest, immediately acquires a speed of ten degrees rather than one of four, or of two, or of one, or of a half, or of a hundredth; or, indeed, of any of the infinite number of small values? Pray listen. I hardly think you will refuse to grant that the gain of speed of the stone falling from rest follows the same sequence as the diminution and loss of this same speed when, by some impelling force, the stone is thrown to its former elevation: but even if you do not grant this, I do not see how you can doubt that the ascending stone, diminishing in speed, must before coming to rest pass through every possible degree of slowness.

SIMP. But if the number of degrees of greater and greater slowness is limitless, they will never be all exhausted, therefore such an ascending heavy body will never reach rest, but will continue to move without limit always at a slower rate; but this is not the observed fact.

SALV. This would happen, Simplicio, if the moving body were to maintain its speed for any length of time at each degree of velocity; but it merely passes each point without delaying more than an instant: and since each time-interval however small may be divided into an infinite number of instants, these will always be sufficient to correspond to the infinite degrees of diminished velocity.

That such a heavy rising body does not remain for any length of time at any given degree of velocity is evident from the following: because if, some time-interval having been assigned, the body moves with the same speed in the last as in the first instant of that time-interval, it could from this second degree of elevation be in like manner raised through an equal height, just as it was transferred from the first elevation to the second, and by the same reasoning would pass from the second to the third and would finally continue in uniform motion forever.

SAGR. From these considerations it appears to me that we may obtain a proper solution of the problem discussed by philosophers, namely, what causes the acceleration in the natural motion of heavy bodies? Since, as it seems to me, the force impressed by the agent projecting the body upwards diminishes continuously, this force, so long as it was greater than the contrary force of gravitation, impelled the body upwards; when the two are in equilibrium the body ceases to rise and passes through the state of rest in which the impressed impetus is not destroyed, but only its excess over the weight of the body has been consumed—the excess which caused the body to rise. Then as the diminution of the outside impetus continues, and gravitation gains the upper hand, the fall begins, but slowly at first on account of the opposing impetus, a large portion of which still remains in the body; but as this continues to diminish it also continues to be more and more overcome by gravity, hence the continuous acceleration of motion.

SIMP. The idea is clever, yet more subtle than sound; for even if the argument were conclusive, it would explain only the case in which a natural motion is preceded by a violent motion, in which there still remains active a portion of the external force; but where there is no such remaining portion and the body starts from an antecedent state of rest, the cogency of the whole argument fails.

SAGR. I believe that you are mistaken and that this distinction between cases which you make is superfluous or rather nonexistent. But, tell me, cannot a projectile receive from the projector either a large or a small force such as will throw it to a height of a hundred cubits, and even twenty or four or one?

SIMP. Undoubtedly, yes.

SAGR. So therefore this impressed force may exceed the resistance of gravity so slightly as to raise it only a finger-breadth; and finally the force of the projector may be just large enough to exactly balance the resistance of gravity so that the body is not lifted at all but merely sustained. When one holds a stone in his hand does he do anything but give it a force impelling it upwards equal to the power of gravity drawing it downwards? And do you not continuously impress this force upon the stone as long as you hold it in the hand? Does it perhaps diminish with the time during which one holds the stone?

And what does it matter whether this support which prevents the stone from falling is furnished by one's hand or by a table or by a rope from which it hangs? Certainly nothing at all. You must conclude, therefore, Simplicio, that it makes no difference whatever whether the fall of the stone is preceded by a period of rest which is long, short, or instantaneous provided only the fall does not take place so long as the stone is acted upon by a force opposed to its weight and sufficient to hold it at rest.

SALV. The present does not seem to be the proper time to investigate the cause of the acceleration of natural motion concerning which various opinions have been expressed by various philosophers, some explaining it by attraction to the centre, others to repulsion between the very small parts of the body, while still others attribute it to a certain stress in the surrounding medium which closes in behind the falling body and drives it from one of its positions to another. Now, all these fantasies, and others too, ought to be examined; but it is not really worthwhile. At present it is the purpose of our Author merely to investigate and to demonstrate some of the properties of accelerated motion (whatever the cause of this acceleration may be)—meaning thereby a motion, such that the momentum of its velocity goes on increasing after departure from rest, in simple proportionality to the time, which is the same as saying that in equal time-intervals the body receives equal increments of velocity; and if we find the properties which will be demonstrated later are realized in freely falling and accelerated bodies, we may conclude that the assumed definition includes such a motion of falling bodies and that their speed goes on increasing as the time and the duration of the motion.

Sagr. So far as I see at present, the definition might have been put a little more clearly perhaps without changing the fundamental idea, namely, uniformly accelerated motion is such that its speed increases in proportion to the space traversed; so that, for example, the speed acquired by a body in falling four cubits would be double that acquired in falling two cubits and this latter speed would be double that acquired in the first cubit. Because there is no doubt but that a heavy body falling from the height of six cubits has, and strikes with, a momentum double that it had at the end of three cubits, triple that which it would have if it had fallen from two, and sextuple that which it would have had at the end of one.

Salv. It is very comforting to me to have had such a companion in error; and moreover let me tell you that your proposition seems so highly probable that our Author himself admitted, when I advanced this opinion to him, that he had for some time shared the same fallacy. But what most surprised me was to see two propositions so inherently probable that they commanded the assent of everyone to whom they were presented, proven in a few simple words to be not only false, but impossible.

Simp. I am one of those who accept the proposition, and believe that a falling body acquires force in its descent, its velocity increasing in proportion to the space, and that the momentum of the falling body is doubled when it falls from a doubled height; these propositions, it appears to me, ought to be conceded without hesitation or controversy.

Salv. And yet they are as false and impossible as that motion should be completed instantaneously; and here is a very clear demonstration of it. If the velocities are in proportion to the spaces traversed, or to be traversed, then these spaces are traversed in equal intervals of time; if, therefore, the velocity with which the falling body traverses a space of eight feet were double that with which it covered the first four feet (just as the one distance is double the other), then the time-intervals required for these passages would be equal. But for one and the same body to fall eight feet and four feet in the same time is possible only in the case of instantaneous motion; but observation shows us that the motion of a falling body occupies time, and less of it in covering a distance of four feet than of eight feet; therefore it is not true that its velocity increases in proportion to the space.

The falsity of the other proposition may be shown with equal clearness. For if we consider a single striking body the difference of momentum in its blows can depend only upon difference of velocity; for if the striking body falling from a double height were to deliver a blow of double momentum, it would be necessary for this body to strike with a doubled velocity; but with this doubled speed it would traverse a doubled space in the same time-interval; observation however shows that the time required for fall from the greater height is longer.

Sagr. You present these recondite matters with too much evidence and ease; this great facility makes them less appreciated than they would be had they been presented in a more abstruse manner. For, in my opinion, people esteem more lightly that knowledge which they acquire with so little labor than that acquired through long and obscure discussion.

Salv. If those who demonstrate with brevity and clearness the fallacy of many popular beliefs were treated with contempt instead of gratitude the injury would be quite bearable; but on the other hand, it is very unpleasant and annoying to see men, who claim to be peers of anyone in a certain field of study, take for granted certain conclusions which later are quickly and easily shown by another to be false. I do not describe such a feeling as one of envy, which usually degenerates into hatred and anger against those who discover such fallacies; I would call it a strong desire to maintain old errors, rather than accept newly discovered truths. This desire at times induces them to unite against these truths, although at heart believing in them, merely for the purpose of lowering the esteem in which certain others are held by the unthinking crowd. Indeed, I have heard from our Academician many such fallacies held as true but easily refutable; some of these I have in mind.

Sagr. You must not withhold them from us, but, at the proper time, tell us about them even though an extra session be necessary. But now, continuing the thread of our talk, it would seem that up to the present we have established the definition of uniformly accelerated motion which is expressed as follows:

A motion is said to be equally or uniformly accelerated when, starting from rest, its momentum receives equal increments in equal times.

Salv. This definition established, the Author makes a single assumption, namely,

The speeds acquired by one and the same body moving down planes of different inclinations are equal when the heights of these planes are equal.

By the height of an inclined plane we mean the perpendicular let fall from the upper end of the plane upon the horizontal line drawn through the lower end of the same plane. Thus, to illustrate, let the line AB be horizontal, and let the planes CA and CD be inclined to it; then the Author calls the perpendicular CB the "height" of the planes CA and CD; he supposes that the speeds acquired by one and the same body, descending along the planes CA and CD to the terminal points A and D are equal since the heights of these planes are the same, CB; and also it must be understood that this speed is that which would be acquired by the same body falling from C to B.

SAGR. Your assumption appears to me so reasonable that it ought to be conceded without question, provided of course there are no chance or outside resistances, and that the planes are hard and smooth, and that the figure of the moving body is perfectly round, so that

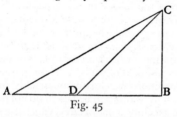

Fig. 45

neither plane nor moving body is rough. All resistance and opposition having been removed, my reason tells me at once that a heavy and perfectly round ball descending along the lines CA, CD, CB would reach the terminal points A, D, B, with equal momenta.

SALV. Your words are very plausible; but I hope by experiment to increase the probability to an extent which shall be little short of a rigid demonstration.

Imagine this page to represent a vertical wall, with a nail driven into it; and from the nail let there be suspended a lead bullet of one or two ounces by means of a fine vertical thread, AB, say from four to six feet long, on this wall draw a horizontal line DC, at right angles to the vertical thread AB, which hangs about two finger-breadths in front of the wall. Now bring the thread AB with the attached ball into the position AC and set it free; first it will be observed to descend along the arc CBD, to pass the point B, and to travel along the arc BD, till it almost reaches the horizontal CD, a slight shortage being caused by the resistance of the air and the string; from this we may rightly in-

fer that the ball in its descent through the arc CB acquired a momentum on reaching B, which was just sufficient to carry it through a similar arc BD to the same height. Having repeated this experiment many times, let us now drive a nail into the wall close to the perpendicular AB, say at E or F, so that it projects out some five or six finger-breadths in order that the thread, again carrying the bullet through the arc CB, may strike upon the nail E when the bullet reaches B, and thus compel it to traverse the arc BG, described about E as centre. From this we can see what can be done by the same momentum which previously starting at the same point B carried the same body through the arc BD to the horizontal CD. Now, gentlemen, you will observe with pleasure that the ball swings to the point G in the horizontal, and you would see the same thing happen if the obstacle were placed at some lower point, say at F, about which the ball would

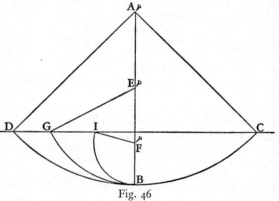

Fig. 46

describe the arc BI, the rise of the ball always terminating exactly on the line CD. But when the nail is placed so low that the remainder of the thread below it will not reach to the height CD (which would happen if the nail were placed nearer B than to the intersection of AB with the horizontal CD), then the thread leaps over the nail and twists itself about it.

This experiment leaves no room for doubt as to the truth of our supposition; for since the two arcs CB and DB are equal and similarly placed, the momentum acquired by the fall through the arc CB is the same as that gained by fall through the arc DB: but the momentum acquired at B, owing to fall through CB, is able to lift the same body through the arc BD; therefore, the momentum acquired in the fall BD is equal to that which lifts the same body through the same arc from B to D; so, in general, every momentum acquired by fall through an arc is equal to that which can lift the same body through the same arc. But all these momenta which cause a rise through the arcs BD, BG, and BI are equal, since they are produced by the same momentum, gained by fall through CB, as experiment shows. Therefore all the momenta gained by fall through the arcs DB, GB, IB are equal.

SAGR. The argument seems to me so conclusive and the experiment so well adapted to establish the hypothesis that we may, indeed, consider it as demonstrated.

SALV. I do not wish, Sagredo, that we trouble ourselves too much about this matter, since we are going to apply this principle mainly in motions which occur on plane surfaces, and not upon curved, along which acceleration varies in a manner greatly different from that which we have assumed for planes.

So that, although the above experiment shows us that the descent of the moving body through the arc CB confers upon it momentum just sufficient to carry it to the same height through any of the arcs BD, BG, BI, we are not able, by similar means, to show that the event would be identical in the case of a perfectly round ball descending along planes whose inclinations are respectively the same as the chords of these arcs. It seems likely, on the other hand, that, since these planes form angles at the point B, they will present an obstacle to the ball which has descended along the chord CB, and starts to rise along the chord BD, BG, BI.

In striking these planes some of its momentum will be lost and it will not be able to rise to the height of the line CD; but this obstacle, which interferes with the experiment, once removed, it is clear that the momentum (which gains in strength with descent) will be able to carry the body to the same height. Let us then, for the present, take this as a postulate, the absolute truth of which will be established when we find that the inferences from it correspond to and agree perfectly with experiment. The Author having assumed this single principle passes next to the propositions which he clearly demonstrates; the first of these is as follows:

THEOREM I, PROPOSITION I

The time in which any space is traversed by a body starting from rest and uniformly accelerated, is equal to the time in which that same space would be traversed by the same body moving at a uniform speed whose value is the mean of the highest speed and the speed just before acceleration began.

Let us represent by the line AB the time in which the space CD is traversed by a body which starts from rest at C and is uniformly accelerated; let the final and highest value of the speed gained during the interval AB be represented by the line EB drawn at right angles to AB; draw the line AE, then all lines drawn from equidistant points on AB and parallel to BE will represent the increasing values of the speed, beginning with the instant A. Let the point F bisect the line EB; draw FG parallel to BA, and GA parallel to FB, thus forming a parallelogram $AGFB$ which will be equal in area to the triangle AEB, since the side GF bisects the side AE at the point I; for if the parallel lines in the triangle AEB are extended to GI, then the sum of all the parallels contained in the quadrilateral is equal to the sum of those contained in the triangle AEB; for those in the triangle IEF are equal to those contained in the triangle GIA, while those included in the trapezium $AIFB$ are common. Since each and every instant of time in the time-interval AB has its corresponding point on the line AB, from which points parallels drawn in and limited by the triangle AEB represent the increasing values of the growing velocity, and since parallels contained within the rectangle represent the values of a speed which is not increasing, but constant, it appears, in like manner, that the momenta assumed by the moving body may also be represented, in the case of the accelerated motion, by the increasing parallels of the triangle AEB, and, in the case of the uniform motion, by the parallels of the rectangle GB. For, what the momenta may lack in the first part of the accelerated motion (the deficiency of the momenta being represented by the parallels of the triangle AGI) is made up by the momenta represented by the parallels of the triangle IEF.

Hence it is clear that equal spaces will be traversed in equal times by two bodies, one of which, starting from rest, moves with a uniform acceleration, while the momentum of the other, moving with uniform speed, is one-half its maximum momentum under accelerated motion. Q. E. D.

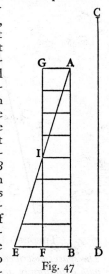

Fig. 47

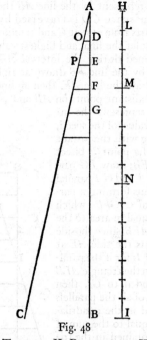

Fig. 48

THEOREM II, PROPOSITION II

The spaces described by a body falling from rest with a uniformly accelerated motion are to each other as the squares of the time-intervals employed in traversing these distances.

Let the time beginning with any instant *A* be represented by the straight line *AB* in which are taken any two time-intervals *AD* and *AE*. Let *HI* represent the distance through which the body, starting from rest at *H*, falls with uniform acceleration. If *HL* represents the space traversed during the time-interval *AD*, and *HM* that covered during the interval *AE*, then the space *MH* stands to the space *LH* in a ratio which is the square of the ratio of the time *AE* to the time *AD*; or we may say simply that the distances *HM* and HL are related as the squares of *AE* and *AD*.

Draw the line *AC* making any angle whatever with the line *AB*; and from the points *D* and *E*, draw the parallel lines *DO* and *EP*; of these two lines, *DO* represents the greatest velocity attained during the interval *AD*, while *EP* represents the maximum velocity acquired during the interval *AE*. But it has just been proved that so far as distances traversed are concerned it is precisely the same whether a body falls from rest with a uniform acceleration or whether it falls during an equal time-interval with a constant speed which is one-

half the maximum speed attained during the accelerated motion. It follows therefore that the distances *HM* and *HL* are the same as would be traversed, during the time-intervals *AE* and *AD*, by uniform velocities equal to one-half those represented by *DO* and *EP* respectively. If, therefore, one can show that the distances *HM* and *HL* are in the same ratio as the squares of the time-intervals *AE* and *AD*, our proposition will be proven.

But in the fourth proposition of the first book [p. 198 above] it has been shown that the spaces traversed by two particles in uniform motion bear to one another a ratio which is equal to the product of the ratio of the velocities by the ratio of the times. But in this case the ratio of the velocities is the same as the ratio of the time-intervals (for the ratio of *AE* to *AD* is the same as that of ½ *EP* to ½*DO* or of *EP* to *DO*). Hence the ratio of the spaces traversed is the same as the squared ratio of the time-intervals. Q. E. D.

Evidently then the ratio of the distances is the square of the ratio of the final velocities, that is, of the lines *EP* and *DO*, since these are to each other as *AE* to *AD*.

COROLLARY I

Hence it is clear that if we take any equal intervals of time whatever, counting from the beginning of the motion, such as *AD*, *DE*, *EF*, *FG*, in which the spaces *HL*, *LM*, *MN*, *NI* are traversed, these spaces will bear to one another the same ratio as the series of odd numbers, 1, 3, 5, 7; for this is the ratio of the differences of the squares of the lines, differences which exceed one another by equal amounts, this excess being equal to the smallest line: or we may say of the differences of the squares of the natural numbers beginning with unity.

While, therefore, during equal intervals of time the velocities increase as the natural numbers, the increments in the distances traversed during these equal time-intervals are to one another as the odd numbers beginning with unity.

SAGR. Please suspend the discussion for a moment since there just occurs to me an idea which I want to illustrate by means of a diagram in order that it may be clearer both to you and to me.

Let the line *AI* represent the lapse of time measured from the initial instant *A*; through *A* draw the straight line *AF* making any angle whatever; join the terminal points *I* and *F*; divide the time *AI* in half at *C*; draw *CB* par-

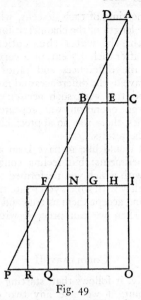

Fig. 49

allel to *IF*. Let us consider *CB* as the maximum value of the velocity which increases from zero at the beginning, in simple proportionality to the intercepts on the triangle *ABC* of lines drawn parallel to *BC*; or what is the same thing, let us suppose the velocity to increase in proportion to the time; then I admit without question, in view of the preceding argument, that the space described by a body falling in the aforesaid manner will be equal to the space traversed by the same body during the same length of time travelling with a uniform speed equal to *EC*, the half of *BC*. Further let us imagine that the body has fallen with accelerated motion so that, at the instant *C*, it has the velocity *BC*. It is clear that if the body continued to descend with the same speed *BC*, without acceleration, it would in the next time-interval *CI* traverse double the distance covered during the interval *AC*, with the uniform speed *EC* which is half of *BC*; but since the falling body acquires equal increments of speed during equal increments of time, it follows that the velocity *BC*, during the next time-interval *CI* will be increased by an amount represented by the parallels of the triangle *BFG* which is equal to the triangle *ABC*. If, then, one adds to the velocity *GI* half of the velocity *FG*, the highest speed acquired by the accelerated motion and determined by the parallels of the triangle *BFG*, he will have the uniform velocity with which the same space would have been described in the time *CI*; and since this speed *IN* is three times as great as *EC* it follows that

the space described during the interval *CI* is three times as great as that described during the interval *AC*. Let us imagine the motion extended over another equal time-interval *IO*, and the triangle extended to *APO*; it is then evident that if the motion continues during the interval *IO*, at the constant rate *IF* acquired by acceleration during the time *AI*, the space traversed during the interval *IO* will be four times that traversed during the first interval *AC*, because the speed *IF* is four times the speed *EC*. But if we enlarge our triangle so as to include *FPQ* which is equal to *ABC*, still assuming the acceleration to be constant, we shall add to the uniform speed an increment *RQ*, equal to *EC*; then the value of the equivalent uniform speed during the time-interval *IO* will be five times that during the first time-interval *AC*; therefore the space traversed will be quintuple that during the first interval *AC*. It is thus evident by simple computation that a moving body starting from rest and acquiring velocity at a rate proportional to the time, will, during equal intervals of time, traverse distances which are related to each other as the odd numbers beginning with unity, 1, 3, 5; or considering the total space traversed, that covered in double time will be quadruple that covered during unit time; in triple time, the space is nine times as great as in unit time. And in general the spaces traversed are in the duplicate ratio of the times, *i.e.*, in the ratio of the squares of the times.

SIMP. In truth, I find more pleasure in this simple and clear argument of Sagredo than in the Author's demonstration which to me appears rather obscure; so that I am convinced that matters are as described, once having accepted the definition of uniformly accelerated motion. But as to whether this acceleration is that which one meets in nature in the case of falling bodies, I am still doubtful; and it seems to me, not only for my own sake but also for all those who think as I do, that this would be the proper moment to introduce one of those experiments—and there are many of them, I understand—which illustrate in several ways the conclusions reached.

SALV. The request which you, as a man of science, make, is a very reasonable one; for this is the custom—and properly so—in those sciences where mathematical demonstrations are applied to natural phenomena, as is seen in the case of perspective, astronomy, mechanics, music, and others where the principles, once established by well-chosen experiments, become the foundations of the entire superstructure. I hope therefore it will not appear to be a waste of time if we discuss at considerable length this first and most fundamental question upon which hinge numerous consequences of which we have in this book only a small number, placed there by the Author, who has done so much to open a pathway hitherto closed to minds of speculative turn. So far as experiments go they have not been neglected by the Author; and often, in his company, I have attempted in the following manner to assure myself that the acceleration actually experienced by falling bodies is that above described.

A piece of wooden moulding or scantling, about 12 cubits long, half a cubit wide, and three finger-breadths thick, was taken; on its edge was cut a channel a little more than one finger in breadth; having made this groove very straight, smooth, and polished, and having lined it with parchment, also as smooth and polished as possible, we rolled along it a hard, smooth, and very round bronze ball. Having placed this board in a sloping position, by lifting one end some one or two cubits above the other, we rolled the ball, as I was just saying, along the channel, noting, in a manner presently to be described, the time required to make the descent. We repeated this experiment more than once in order to measure the time with an accuracy such that the deviation between two observations never exceeded one-tenth of a pulse-beat. Having performed this operation and having assured ourselves of its reliability, we now rolled the ball only one-quarter the length of the channel; and having measured the time of its descent, we found it precisely one-half of the former. Next we tried other distances, comparing the time for the whole length with that for the half, or with that for two-thirds, or three-fourths, or indeed for any fraction; in such experiments, repeated a full hundred times, we always found that the spaces traversed were to each other as the squares of the times, and this was true for all inclinations of the plane, i.e., of the channel, along which we rolled the ball. We also observed that the times of descent, for various inclinations of the plane, bore to one another precisely that ratio which, as we shall see later, the Author had predicted and demonstrated for them.

For the measurement of time, we employed a large vessel of water placed in an elevated position; to the bottom of this vessel was soldered a pipe of small diameter giving a thin jet of water, which we collected in a small glass during the time of each descent, whether for the whole length of the channel or for a part of its length; the water thus collected was weighed, after each descent, on a very accurate balance; the differences and ratios of these weights gave us the differences and ratios of the times, and this with such accuracy that although the operation was repeated many, many times, there was no appreciable discrepancy in the results.

SIMP. I would like to have been present at these experiments; but feeling confidence in the care with which you performed them, and in the fidelity with which you relate them, I am satisfied and accept them as true and valid.

SALV. Then we can proceed without discussion.

COROLLARY II

Secondly, it follows that, starting from any initial point, if we take any two distances, traversed in any time-intervals whatsoever, these time-intervals bear to one another the same ratio as one of the distances to the mean proportional of the two distances.

For if we take two distances ST and SY measured from the initial point S, the mean proportional of which is SX, the time of fall through ST is to the time of fall through SY as ST is to SX; or one may say the time of fall through SY is to the time of fall through ST as SY is to SX. Now since it has been shown that the spaces traversed are in the same ratio as the squares of the times; and since, moreover, the ratio of the space SY to the space ST is the square of the ratio SY to SX, it follows that the ratio of the times of fall through SY and ST is the ratio of the respective distances SY and SX.

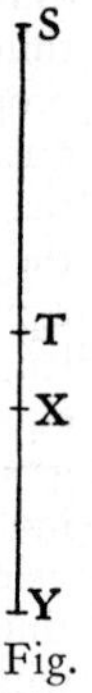

Fig. 50

SCHOLIUM

The above corollary has been proven for the case of vertical fall; but it holds also for planes inclined at any angle; for it is to be assumed that along these planes the velocity increases in the same ratio, that is, in proportion to the time, or, if you prefer, as the series of natural numbers.

[The dialogue which intervenes between this Scholium and the following theorem was elaborated by Viviani, at the suggestion of Galileo. TRANS.]

SALV. Here, Sagredo, I should like, if it be not too tedious to Simplicio, to interrupt for a moment the present discussion in order to make some additions on the basis of what has already been proved and of what mechanical principles we have already learned from our Academician. This addition I make for the better establishment on logical and experimental grounds, of the principle which we have above considered; and what is more important, for the purpose of deriving it geometrically, after first demonstrating a single lemma which is fundamental in the science of motion.

SAGR. If the advance which you propose to make is such as will confirm and fully establish these sciences of motion, I will gladly devote to it any length of time. Indeed, I shall not only be glad to have you proceed, but I beg of you at once to satisfy the curiosity which you have awakened in me concerning your proposition; and I think that Simplicio is of the same mind.

SIMP. Quite right.

SALV. Since then I have your permission, let us first of all consider this notable fact, that the momenta or speeds of one and the same moving body vary with the inclination of the plane.

The speed reaches a maximum along a vertical direction, and for other directions diminishes as the plane diverges from the vertical. Therefore the impetus, ability, energy, or, one might say, the momentum of descent of the moving body is diminished by the plane upon which it is supported and along which it rolls.

For the sake of greater clearness erect the line AB perpendicular to the horizontal AC; next draw AD, AE, AF, etc., at different inclinations to the horizontal. Then I say that all the momentum of the falling body is along the vertical and is a maximum when it falls in that direction; the momentum is less along DA and still less along EA, and even less yet along the more inclined plane FA. Finally on the

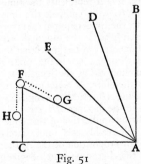

Fig. 51

horizontal plane the momentum vanishes altogether; the body finds itself in a condition of indifference as to motion or rest; has no inherent tendency to move in any direction, and offers no resistance to being set in motion. For just as a heavy body or system of bodies cannot of itself move upwards, or recede from the common centre toward which all heavy things tend, so it is impossible for any body of its own accord to assume any motion other than one which carries it nearer to the aforesaid common centre. Hence, along the horizontal, by which we

understand a surface, every point of which is equidistant from this same common centre, the body will have no momentum whatever.

This change of momentum being clear, it is here necessary for me to explain something which our Academician wrote when in Padua, embodying it in a treatise on mechanics prepared solely for the use of his students, and proving it at length and conclusively when considering the origin and nature of that marvellous machine, the screw. What he proved is the manner in which the momentum varies with the inclination of the plane, as for instance that of the plane FA, one end of which is elevated through a vertical distance FC. This direction FC is that along which the momentum of a heavy body becomes a maximum; let us discover what ratio this momentum bears to that of the same body moving along the inclined plane FA. This ratio, I say, is the inverse of that of the aforesaid lengths. Such is the lemma preceding the theorem which I hope to demonstrate a little later.

It is clear that the impelling force acting on a body in descent is equal to the resistance or least force sufficient to hold it at rest. In order to measure this force and resistance I propose to use the weight of another body. Let us place upon the plane FA a body G connected to the weight H by means of a cord passing over the point F; then the body H will ascend or descend, along the perpendicular, the same distance which the body G ascends or descends along the inclined plane FA; but this distance will not be equal to the rise or fall of G along the vertical in which direction alone G, as other bodies, exerts its force. This is clear. For if we consider the motion of the body G, from A to F, in the triangle AFC to be made up of a horizontal component AC and a vertical component CF, and remember that this body experiences no resistance to motion along the horizontal (because by such a motion the body neither gains nor loses distance from the common centre of heavy things), it follows that resistance is met only in consequence of the body rising through the vertical distance CF. Since then the body G in moving from A to F offers resistance only in so far as it rises through the vertical distance CF, while the other body H must fall vertically through the entire distance FA, and since this ratio is maintained whether the motion be large or small, the two bodies being inextensibly connected, we are able to assert positively that, in case of equilibrium (bodies at rest) the momenta, the velocities, or their tendency to motion i.e., the spaces which would be traversed by them in equal times, must be in the inverse ratio to their weights. This is what has been demonstrated in every case of mechanical motion. So that, in order to hold the weight G at rest, one must give H a weight smaller in the same ratio as the distance CF is smaller than FA. If we do this, $FA:FC =$ weight G : weight H; then equilibrium will occur, that is, the weights H and G will have the same impelling forces, and the two bodies will come to rest.

And since we are agreed that the impetus, energy, momentum or tendency to motion of a moving body is as great as the force or least resistance sufficient to stop it, and since we have found that the weight H is capable of preventing motion in the weight G, it follows that the less weight H whose entire force is along the perpendicular, FC, will be an exact measure of the component of force which the larger weight G exerts along the plane FA. But the measure of the total force on the body G is its own weight, since to prevent its fall it is only necessary to balance it with an equal weight, provided this second weight be free to move vertically; therefore the component of the force on G along the inclined plane FA will bear to the maximum and total force on this same body G along the perpendicular FC the same ratio as the weight H to the weight G. This ratio is, by construction, the same which the height FC, of the inclined plane bears to the length FA. We have here the lemma which I proposed to demonstrate and which, as you will see, has been assumed by our Author in the second part of the sixth proposition of the present treatise.

SAGR. From what you have shown thus far, it appears to me that one might infer, arguing *ex æquali con la proportione perturbata,* that the tendencies of one and the same body to move along planes differently inclined, but having the same vertical height, as FA and FI, are to each other inversely as the lengths of the planes.

SALV. Perfectly right. This point established, I pass to the demonstration of the following theorem:

If a body falls freely along smooth planes inclined at any angle whatsoever, but of the same height, the speeds with which it reaches the bottom are the same.

First we must recall the fact that on a plane of any inclination whatever a body starting from rest gains speed or momentum in direct proportion to the time, in agreement with the definition of naturally accelerated motion given by the Author. Hence, as he has shown in the preceding proposition, the distances traversed are proportional to the squares of the times and therefore to the squares of the speeds. The speed relations are here the same as in the motion first studied, since in each case the gain of speed is proportional to the time.

Let AB be an inclined plane whose height above the level BC is AC. As we have seen above the force impelling a body to fall along the vertical AC is to

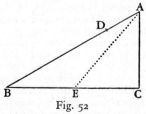

Fig. 52

the force which drives the same body along the inclined plane AB as AB is to AC. On the incline AB, lay off AD a third proportional to AB and AC; then

the force producing motion along AC is to that along AB (*i.e.,* along AD) as the length AC is to the length AD. And therefore the body will traverse the space AD, along the incline AB, in the same time which it would occupy in falling the vertical distance AC, (since the forces are in the same ratio as these distances); also the speed at C is to the speed at D as the distance AC is to the distance AD. But, according to the definition of accelerated motion, the speed at B is to the speed of the same body at D as the time required to traverse AB is to the time required for AD; and, according to the last corollary of the second proposition, the time of passing through the distance AB bears to the time of passing through AD the same ratio as the distance AC (a mean proportional between AB and AD) to AD. Accordingly the two speeds at B and C each bear to the speed at D the same ratio, namely, that of the distances AC and AD; hence they are equal. This is the theorem which I set out to prove.

From the above we are better able to demonstrate the following third proposition of the Author in which he employs the following principle, namely, the time required to traverse an inclined plane is to that required to fall through the vertical height of the plane in the same ratio as the length of the plane to its height.

For, according to the second corollary of the second proposition, if BA represents the time required to pass over the distance BA, the time required to pass the distance AD will be a mean proportional between these two distances and will be represented by the line AC; but if AC represents the time needed to traverse AD it will also represent the time required to fall through the distance AC, since the distances AC and AD are traversed in equal times; consequently, if AB represents the time required for AB then AC will represent the time required for AC. Hence the times required to traverse AB and AC are to each other as the distances AB and AC.

In like manner, it can be shown that the time required to fall through AC is to the time required for any other incline AE as the length AC is to the length AE; therefore, *ex æquali,* the time of fall along the incline AB is to that along AE as the distance AB is to the distance AE, etc.

One might by application of this same theorem, as Sagredo will readily see, immediately demonstrate the sixth proposition of the Author; but let us here end this digression which Sagredo has perhaps found rather tedious, though I consider it quite important for the theory of motion.

SAGR. On the contrary, it has given me great satisfaction, and indeed I find it necessary for a complete grasp of this principle.

SALV. I will now resume the reading of the text.

THEOREM III, PROPOSITION III

If one and the same body, starting from rest, falls along an inclined plane and also along a vertical, each having the same height, the times of descent will be to each other as the lengths of the inclined plane and the vertical.

Let *AC* be the inclined plane and *AB* the perpendicular, each having the same vertical height above the horizontal, namely, *BA*; then, I say, the time of descent of one and the same body along the plane *AC* bears a ratio to the time of fall along the perpendicular *AB*, which is the same as the ratio of the length *AC* to the length *AB*. Let *DG*, *EI* and *LF* be any lines parallel

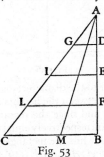

Fig. 53

to the horizontal *CB*; then it follows from what has preceded that a body starting from *A* will acquire the same speed at the point *G* as at *D*, since in each case the vertical fall is the same; in like manner the speeds at *I* and *E* will be the same; so also those at *L* and *F*. And in general the speeds at the two extremities of any parallel drawn from any point on *AB* to the corresponding point on *AC* will be equal.

Thus the two distances *AC* and *AB* are traversed at the same speed. But it has already been proved that if two distances are traversed by a body moving with equal speeds, then the ratio of the times of descent will be the ratio of the distances themselves; therefore, the time of descent along *AC* is to that along *AB* as the length of the plane *AC* is to the vertical distance *AB*.

Q. E. D.

SAGR. It seems to me that the above could have been proved clearly and briefly on the basis of a proposition already demonstrated, namely, that the distance traversed in the case of accelerated motion along *AC* or *AB* is the same as that covered by a uniform speed whose value is one-half the maximum speed, *CB*; the two distances *AC* and *AB* having been traversed at the same uniform speed it is evident, from Proposition I, that the times of descent will be to each other as the distances.

COROLLARY

Hence we may infer that the times of descent along planes having different inclinations, but the same vertical height stand to one another

in the same ratio as the lengths of the planes. For consider any plane *AM* extending from *A* to the horizontal *CB*; then it may be demonstrated in the same manner that the time of descent along *AM* is to the time along *AB* as the distance *AM* is to *AB*; but since the time along *AB* is to that along *AC* as the length *AB* is to the length *AC*, it follows, *ex æquali*, that as *AM* is to *AC* so is the time along *AM* to the time along *AC*.

THEOREM IV, PROPOSITION IV

The times of descent along planes of the same length but of different inclinations are to each other in the inverse ratio of the square roots of their heights.

From a single point *B* draw the planes *BA* and *BC*, having the same length but different inclinations; let *AE* and *CD* be horizontal lines drawn to meet the perpendicular *BD*; and let *BE* represent the height of the plane *AB*, and *BD* the height of *BC*; also let *BI* be a mean proportional to *BD* and *BE*; then the ratio of *BD*

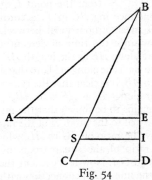

Fig. 54

to *BI* is equal to the square root of the ratio of *BD* to *BE*. Now, I say, the ratio of the times of descent along *BA* and *BC* is the ratio of *BD* to *BI*; so that the time of descent along *BA* is related to the height of the other plane *BC*, namely *BD* as the time along *BC* is related to the height *BI*. Now it must be proved that the time of descent along *BA* is to that along *BC* as the length *BD* is to the length *BI*.

Draw *IS* parallel to *DC*; and since it has been shown that the time of fall along *BA* is to that along the vertical *BE* as *BA* is to *BE*; and also that the time along *BE* is to that along *BD* as *BE* is to *BI*; and likewise that the time along *BD* is to that along *BC* as *BD* is to *BC*, or as *BI* to *BS*; it follows, *ex æquali*, that the time along *BA* is to that along *BC* as *BA* to *BS*, or *BC* to *BS*. However, *BC* is to *BS* as *BD* is to *BI*; hence follows our proposition.

THEOREM V, PROPOSITION V

The times of descent along planes of different length, slope and height bear to one another a ratio which is equal to the product of the ratio of the lengths by the square root of the inverse ratio of their heights.

Draw the planes AB and AC, having different inclinations, lengths, and heights. My theorem then is that the ratio of the time of descent along AC to that along AB is equal to the product of the ratio of AC to AB by the square root of the inverse ratio of their heights.

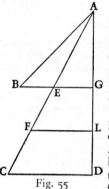

Fig. 55

For let AD be a perpendicular to which are drawn the horizontal lines BG and CD; also let AL be a mean proportional to the heights AG and AD; from the point L draw a horizontal line meeting AC in F; accordingly AF will be a mean proportional between AC and AE. Now since the time of descent along AC is to that along AE as the length AF is to AE; and since the time along AE is to that along AB as AE is to AB, it is clear that the time along AC is to that along AB as AF is to AB.

Thus it remains to be shown that the ratio of AF to AB is equal to the product of the ratio of AC to AB by the ratio of AG to AL, which is the inverse ratio of the square roots of the heights DA and GA. Now it is evident that, if we consider the line AC in connection with AF and AB, the ratio of AF to AC is the same as that of AL to AD, or AG to AL which is the square root of the ratio of the heights AG and AD; but the ratio of AC to AB is the ratio of the lengths themselves. Hence follows the theorem.

THEOREM VI, PROPOSITION VI

If from the highest or lowest point in a vertical circle there be drawn any inclined planes meeting the circumference the times of descent along these chords are each equal to the other.

On the horizontal line GH construct a vertical circle. From its lowest point—the point of tangency with the horizontal—draw the diameter FA and from the highest point, A, draw inclined planes to B and C, any points whatever on the circumference; then the times of descent along these are equal. Draw BD and CE

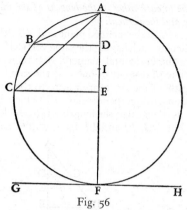

Fig. 56

perpendicular to the diameter; make AI a mean proportional between the heights of the planes, AE and AD; and since the rectangles $FA.AE$ and $FA.AD$ are respectively equal to the squares of AC and AB, while the rectangle $FA.AE$ is to the rectangle $FA.AD$ as AE is to AD, it follows that the square of AC is to the square of AB as the length AE is to the length AD. But since the length AE is to AD as the square of AI is to the square of AD, it follows that the squares on the lines AC and AB are to each other as the squares on the lines AI and AD, and hence also the length AC is to the length AB as AI is to AD. But it has previously been demonstrated that the ratio of the time of descent along AC to that along AB is equal to the product of the two ratios AC to AB and AD to AI; but this last ratio is the same as that of AB to AC. Therefore, the ratio of the time of descent along AC to that along AB is the product of the two ratios, AC to AB and AB to AC. The ratio of these times is therefore unity. Hence follows our proposition.

By use of the principles of mechanics one may obtain the same result, namely, that a falling body will require equal times to traverse the distances CA and DA, indicated in the following figure. Lay off BA equal to DA, and let fall the perpendiculars BE and DF; it follows from the principles of mechanics that the component of the momentum acting along the inclined plane ABC is to the total momentum as BE is to BA; in like manner the momentum along the plane AD is to its total momentum as DF is to DA, or to BA. Therefore the momentum of this same weight along the plane DA is to that along the plane ABC as the length DF is to the length BE; for this reason, this same weight will in equal times according to the second proposition of the first book, traverse spaces

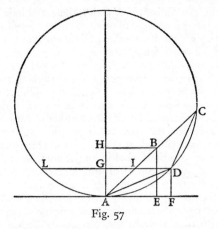

Fig. 57

cumference; then, I say, a body will occupy the same time in falling along the plane DF as along the diameter DC. For draw FG parallel to AB and perpendicular to DC; join FC; and since the time of fall along DC is to that along DG as the mean proportional between CD and GD is to GD itself; and since also DF is a mean proportional between DC and DG, the angle DFC inscribed in a semicircle being a right-angle, and FG being perpendicular to DC, it follows that the time of fall along DC is to that along DG as the length FD is to GD. But it has already been demonstrated that the time of descent along DF is to that along DG as the length DF is to DG; hence the times of descent along DF and DC each bear to the time of fall along DG the same ratio; consequently they are equal.

In like manner it may be shown that if one draws the chord CE from the lower end of the diameter, also the line EH parallel to the horizon, and joins the points E and D, the time of descent along EC, will be the same as that along the diameter, DC.

along the planes CA and DA which are to each other as the lengths BE and DF. But it can be shown that CA is to DA as BE is to DF. Hence the falling body will traverse the two paths CA and DA in equal times.

Moreover the fact that CA is to DA as BE is to DF may be demonstrated as follows: Join C and D; through D, draw the line DGL parallel to AF and cutting the line AC in I; through B draw the line BH, also parallel to AF. Then the angle ADI will be equal to the angle DCA, since they subtend equal arcs LA and DA, and since the angle DAC is common, the sides of the triangles, CAD and DAI, about the common angle will be proportional to each other; accordingly as CA is to DA so is DA to IA, that is as BA is to IA, or as HA is to GA, that is as BE is to DF.   Q. E. D.

The same proposition may be more easily demonstrated as follows: On the horizontal line AB draw a circle whose diameter DC is vertical. From the upper end of this diameter draw any inclined plane, DF, extending to meet the cir-

Corollary I

From this it follows that the times of descent along all chords drawn through either C or D are equal one to another.

Corollary II

It also follows that, if from any one point there be drawn a vertical line and an inclined one along which the time of descent is the same, the inclined line will be a chord of a semicircle of which the vertical line is the diameter.

Corollary III

Moreover, the times of descent along inclined planes will be equal when the vertical heights of equal lengths of these planes are to each other as the lengths of the planes themselves; thus it is clear that the times of descent along CA and DA, in the figure just before the last, are equal, provided the vertical height of AB (AB being equal to AD), namely, BE, is to the vertical height DF as CA is to DA.

SAGR. Please allow me to interrupt the lecture for a moment in order that I may clear up an idea which just occurs to me; one which, if it involve no fallacy, suggests at least a freakish and interesting circumstance, such as often occurs in nature and in the realm of necessary consequences.

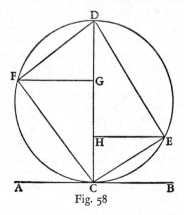

Fig. 58

If, from any point fixed in a horizontal plane, straight lines be drawn extending indefinitely in all directions, and if we imagine a point to move along each of these lines with constant speed, all starting from the fixed point at the same instant and moving with equal speeds, then it is clear that all of these moving points will lie upon the circumference of a circle which grows larger and larger, always having the aforesaid fixed point as its centre; this circle spreads out in precisely the same manner as the little waves do in the case of a pebble allowed to drop into quiet water, where the impact of the stone starts the motion in all directions, while the point of impact remains the centre of these ever-expanding circular waves. But imagine a vertical plane from the highest point of which are drawn lines inclined at every angle and extending indefinitely; imagine also that heavy particles descend along these lines each with a naturally accelerated motion and each with a speed appropriate to the inclination of its line. If these moving particles are always visible, what will be the locus of their positions at any instant? Now the answer to this question surprises me, for I am led by the preceding theorems to believe that these particles will always lie upon the circumference of a single circle, ever increasing in size as the particles recede farther and farther from the point at which their motion began. To be more definite, let A be the fixed point from which are drawn the lines AF and AH inclined at any angle whatsoever. On the perpendicular AB take any two points C and D about which, as centres, circles are described passing through the point A, and cutting the inclined lines at the points F, H, B, E, G, I. From the preceding theorems it

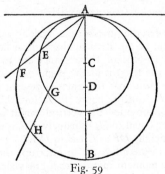

Fig. 59

is clear that, if particles start, at the same instant, from A and descend along these lines, when one is at E another will be at G and another at I; at a later instant they will be found

simultaneously at F, H and B; these, and indeed an infinite number of other particles travelling along an infinite number of different slopes will at successive instants always lie upon a single ever-expanding circle. The two kinds of motion occurring in nature give rise therefore to two infinite series of circles, at once resembling and differing from each other; the one takes its rise in the centre of an infinite number of concentric circles; the other has its origin in the contact, at their highest points, of an infinite number of eccentric circles; the former are produced by motions which are equal and uniform; the latter by motions which are neither uniform nor equal among themselves, but which vary from one to another according to the slope.

Further, if from the two points chosen as origins of motion, we draw lines not only along horizontal and vertical planes but in all directions then just as in the former cases, beginning at a single point ever-expanding circles are produced, so in the latter case an infinite number of spheres are produced about a single point, or rather a single sphere which expands in size without limit; and this in two ways, one with the origin at the centre, the other on the surface of the spheres.

SALV. The idea is really beautiful and worthy of the clever mind of Sagredo.

SIMP. As for me, I understand in a general way how the two kinds of natural motions give rise to the circles and spheres; and yet as to the production of circles by accelerated motion and its proof, I am not entirely clear; but the fact that one can take the origin of motion either at the inmost centre or at the very top of the sphere leads one to think that there may be some great mystery hidden in these true and wonderful results, a mystery related to the creation of the universe (which is said to be spherical in shape), and related also to the seat of the first cause.

SALV. I have no hesitation in agreeing with you. But profound considerations of this kind belong to a higher science than ours. We must be satisfied to belong to that class of less worthy workmen who procure from the quarry the marble out of which, later, the gifted sculptor produces those masterpieces which lay hidden in this rough and shapeless exterior. Now, if you please, let us proceed.

THEOREM VII, PROPOSITION VII

If the heights of two inclined planes are to each other in the same ratio as the squares of their lengths, bodies starting from rest will traverse these planes in equal times.

Take two planes of different lengths and different inclinations, AE and AB, whose heights are AF and AD: let AF be to AD as the square

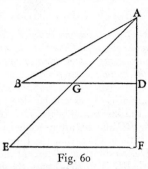

Fig. 60

of AE is to the square of AB; then, I say, that a body, starting from rest at A, will traverse the planes AE and AB in equal times. From the vertical line, draw the horizontal parallel lines EF and DB, the latter cutting AE at G. Since $FA : DA = \overline{EA}^2 : \overline{BA}^2$, and since $FA : DA = EA : GA$, it follows that $EA : GA = \overline{EA}^2 : \overline{BA}^2$. Hence BA is a mean proportional between EA and GA. Now since the time of descent along AB bears to the time along AG the same ratio which AB bears to AG and since also the time of descent along AG is to the time along AE as AG is to a mean proportional between AG and AE, that is, to AB, it follows, *ex æquali*, that the time along AB is to the time along AE as AB is to itself. Therefore the times are equal. Q. E. D.

THEOREM VIII, PROPOSITION VIII

The times of descent along all inclined planes which intersect one and the same vertical circle, either at its highest or lowest point, are equal to the time of fall along the vertical diameter; for those planes which fall short of this diameter the times

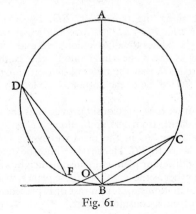

Fig. 61

are shorter; for planes which cut this diameter, the times are longer.

Let AB be the vertical diameter of a circle which touches the horizontal plane. It has already been proven that the times of descent along planes drawn from either end, A or B, to the circumference are equal. In order to show that the time of descent along the plane DF which falls short of the diameter is shorter, we may draw the plane DB which is both longer and less steeply inclined than DF; whence it follows that the time along DF is less than that along DB and consequently along AB. In like manner, it is shown that the time of descent along CO which cuts the diameter is greater: for it is both longer and less steeply inclined than CB. Hence follows the theorem.

THEOREM IX, PROPOSITION IX

If from any point on a horizontal line two planes, inclined at any angle, are drawn, and if they are cut by a line which makes with them angles alternately equal to the angles between these planes and the horizontal, then the times required to traverse those portions of the plane cut off by the aforesaid line are equal.

Through the point C on the horizontal line X, draw two planes CD and CE inclined at any angle whatever: at any point in the line CD lay off the angle CDF equal to the angle XCE; let the line DF cut CE at F so that the angles CDF and CFD are alternately equal to XCE and LCD; then, I say, the times of descent over CD

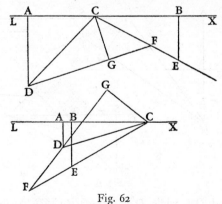

Fig. 62

and CF are equal. Now since the angle CDF is equal to the angle XCE by construction, it is evident that the angle CFD must be equal to the angle DCL. For if the common angle DCF be subtracted from the three angles of the triangle CDF, together equal to two right angles, (to which are also equal all the angles which can be described about the point C on the lower side of the line LX) there remain in the triangle two angles, CDF and CFD, equal to the two angles XCE and LCD; but, by hypothesis, the angles CDF and XCE are equal; hence the remaining angle CFD is equal to the remainder DCL. Take CE equal to CD; from the points D and E draw DA and EB perpendicular to the horizontal line XL; and from the point C draw CG perpendicular to DF. Now since the angle CDG is equal to the angle ECB and since DGC and CBE are right angles, it follows that the triangles CDG and CBE are equiangular; consequently $DC : CG = CE : EB$. But DC is equal to CE, and therefore CG is equal to EB. Since also the angles at C and at A, in the triangle DAC, are equal to the angles at F and G in the triangle CGF, we have $CD : DA = FC : CG$ and, *permutando*, $DC : CF = DA : CG = DA : BE$. Thus the ratio of the heights of the equal planes CD and CE is the same as the ratio of the lengths DC and CF. Therefore, by Corollary I of Prop. VI, the times of descent along these planes will be equal. Q. E. D.

An alternative proof is the following: Draw FS perpendicular to the horizontal line AS. Then, since the triangle CSF is similar to the triangle DGC, we have $SF : FC = GC : CD$; and since the triangle CFG is similar to the triangle DCA, we have $FC : CG = CD : DA$. Hence, *ex æquali*, $SF : CG = CG : DA$. Therefore CG is a mean proportional between SF

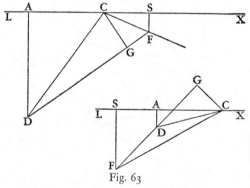

Fig. 63

and DA, while $DA : SF = \overline{DA}^2 : \overline{CG}^2$. Again since the triangle ACD is similar to the triangle CGF, we have $DA : DC = GC : CF$ and, *permutando*, $DA : CG = DC : CF$: also $\overline{DA}^2 : \overline{CG}^2 = \overline{DC}^2 : \overline{CF}^2$. But it has been shown that $\overline{DA}^2 : \overline{CG}^2 = DA : SF$. Therefore $\overline{DC}^2 : \overline{CF}^2 = DA : FS$. Hence from the above Prop. VII, since the heights DA and FS of the planes CD

and CF are to each other as the squares of the lengths of the planes, it follows that the times of descent along these planes will be equal.

Theorem X, Proposition X

The times of descent along inclined planes of the same height, but of different slope, are to each other as the lengths of these planes; and this is true whether the motion starts from rest or whether it is preceded by a fall from a constant height.

Let the paths of descent be along ABC and ABD to the horizontal plane DC so that the falls along BD and BC are preceded by the fall along AB; then, I say, that the time of descent along BD is to the time of descent along BC as the length BD is to BC. Draw the horizontal line AF and extend DB until it cuts this line at F; let FE be a mean proportional between DF and FB; draw EO parallel to DC; then AO will be a mean proportional between CA and AB. If now we represent the time of fall along AB by the length AB, then the time of descent along FB will be represented by the distance FB; so also the time of fall through the entire distance AC will be represented by the mean proportional AO : and for the entire distance FD by FE. Hence the time of fall along the remainder, BC, will be represented by BO, and

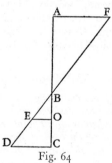

Fig. 64

that along the remainder, BD, by BE; but since $BE : BO = BD : BC$, it follows, if we allow the bodies to fall first along AB and FB, or, what is the same thing, along the common stretch AB, that the times of descent along BD and BC will be to each other as the lengths BD and BC.

But we have previously proven that the time of descent, from rest at B, along BD is to the time along BC in the ratio which the length BD bears to BC. Hence the times of descent along different planes of constant height are to each other as the lengths of these planes, whether the motion starts from rest or is preceded by a fall from a constant height. Q. E. D.

THEOREM XI, PROPOSITION XI

If a plane be divided into any two parts and if motion along it starts from rest, then the time of descent along the first part is to the time of descent along the remainder as the length of this first part is to the excess of a mean proportional between this first part and the entire length over this first part.

Let the fall take place, from rest at A, through the entire distance AB which is divided at any point C; also let AF be a mean proportional between the entire length BA and the first part AC; then CF will denote the excess of the mean proportional FA over the first part AC. Now, I say, the time of descent along AC will be to the time of subsequent fall through CB as the length AC is to CF. This is evident, because the time along AC is to the time along the entire distance AB as AC is to the mean proportional AF. Therefore, *dividendo*, the time along AC will be to the time along the remainder CB as AC is to CF. If we agree to represent the time along AC by the length AC then the time along CB will be represented by CF.   Q. E. D.

In case the motion is not along the straight line ACB but along the broken line ACD to the

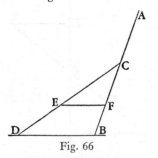

Fig. 66

horizontal line BD, and if from F we draw the horizontal line FE, it may in like manner be proved that the time along AC is to the time along the inclined line CD as AC is to CE. For the time along AC is to the time along CB as AC is to CF; but it has already been shown that the time along CB, after the fall through the distance AC, is to the time along CD, after descent through the same distance AC, as CB is to CD, or, as CF is to CE; therefore, *ex æquali*, the time along AC will be to the time along CD as the length AC is to the length CE.

THEOREM XII, PROPOSITION XII

If a vertical plane and any inclined plane are limited by two horizontals, and if we take mean pro-

portionals between the lengths of these planes and those portions of them which lie between their point of intersection and the upper horizontal, then the time of fall along the perpendicular bears to the time required to traverse the upper part of the perpendicular plus the time required to traverse the lower part of the intersecting plane the same ratio which the entire length of the vertical bears to a length which is the sum of the mean proportional on the vertical plus the excess of the entire length of the inclined plane over its mean proportional.

Let AF and CD be two horizontal planes limiting the vertical plane AC and the inclined plane DF; let the two last-mentioned planes intersect at B. Let AR be a mean proportional between the entire vertical AC and its upper part AB; and let FS be a mean proportional between FD and its upper part FB. Then, I say, the time of fall along the entire vertical path

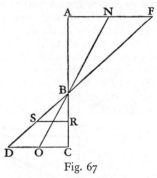

Fig. 67

AC bears to the time of fall along its upper portion AB plus the time of fall along the lower part of the inclined plane, namely, BD, the same ratio which the length AC bears to the mean proportional on the vertical, namely, AR, plus the length SD which is the excess of the entire plane DF over its mean proportional FS.

Join the points R and S giving a horizontal line RS. Now since the time of fall through the entire distance AC is to the time along the portion AB as CA is to the mean proportional AR it follows that, if we agree to represent the time of fall through AC by the distance AC, the time of fall through the distance AB will be represented by AR; and the time of descent through the remainder, BC, will be represented by RC. But, if the time along AC is taken to be equal to the length AC, then the time along FD will be equal to the distance FD; and we may likewise infer that the time of descent along BD, when preceded by a fall along FB or AB, is numerically equal to the distance DS.

Therefore the time required to fall along the path AC is equal to AR plus RC; while the time of descent along the broken line ABD will be equal to AR plus SD.   Q. E. D.

The same thing is true if, in place of a vertical plane, one takes any other plane, as for instance NO; the method of proof is also the same.

PROBLEM I, PROPOSITION XIII

Given a perpendicular line of limited length, it is required to find a plane having a vertical height equal to the given perpendicular and so inclined that a body, having fallen from rest along the perpendicular, will make its descent along the inclined plane in the same time which it occupied in falling through the given perpendicular.

Let AB denote the given perpendicular: prolong this line to C making BC equal to AB, and draw the horizontal lines CE and AG. It is required to draw a plane from B to the horizontal line CE such that after a body starting from rest at A has fallen through the distance AB, it will complete its path along this plane in an equal time. Lay off CD equal to BC, and draw the line BD. Construct the line BE equal to the sum of BD and DC; then, I say, BE is the required plane. Prolong EB till it intersects the horizontal AG at G. Let GF be a mean propor-

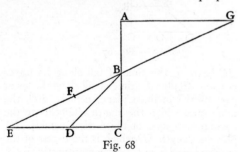

Fig. 68

tional between GE and GB; then $EF : FB = EG : GF$, and $\overline{EF}^2 : \overline{FB}^2 = \overline{EG}^2 : \overline{GF}^2 = EG : GB$. But EG is twice GB; hence the square of EF is twice the square of FB; so also is the square of DB twice the square of BC. Consequently $EF : FB = DB : BC$, and *componendo et permutando*, $EB : DB + BC = BF : BC$. But $EB = DB + BC$; hence $BF = BC = BA$. If we agree that the length AB shall represent the time of fall along the line AB, then GB will represent the time of descent along GB, and GF the time along the entire distance GE; therefore BF will represent the time of descent along the difference of these paths, namely, BE, after fall from G or from A.   Q. E. F.

PROBLEM II, PROPOSITION XIV

Given an inclined plane and a perpendicular passing through it, to find a length on the upper part of the perpendicular through which a body will fall from rest in the same time which is required to traverse the inclined plane after fall through the vertical distance just determined.

Let AC be the inclined plane and DB the perpendicular. It is required to find on the vertical AD a length which will be traversed by a body, falling from rest, in the same time which is needed by the same body to traverse the plane AC after the aforesaid fall. Draw the horizontal CB; lay off AE such that $BA+2AC : AC = AC : AE$, and lay off AR such that $BA : AC = EA : AR$. From R draw RX perpendicular to DB; then, I say, X is the point sought. For since $BA+2AC : AC = AC : AE$, it follows, *dividendo*, that $BA+AC : AC = CE : AE$. And since $BA : AC = EA : AR$, we have, *componendo*, $BA+AC : AC = ER : RA$. But $BA+CA : AC = CE : AE$, hence $CE : EA = ER : RA =$ sum of the antecedents: sum of the consequents $= CR : RE$. Thus RE is seen to be

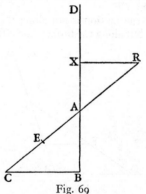

Fig. 69

a mean proportional between CR and RA. Moreover, since it has been assumed that $BA : AC = EA : AR$, and since by similar triangles we have $BA : AC = XA : AR$, it follows that $EA : AR = XA : AR$. Hence EA and XA are equal. But if we agree that the time of fall through RA shall be represented by the length RA, then the time of fall along RC will be represented by the length RE which is a mean proportional between RA and RC; likewise AE will represent the time of descent along AC after descent along RA or along AX. But the time of fall through XA is represented by the length XA, while RA represents the time through RA. But it has been shown that XA and AE are equal.   Q. E. F.

PROBLEM III, PROPOSITION XV

Given a vertical line and a plane inclined to it, it is required to find a length on the vertical line below its point of intersection which will be traversed in the same time as the inclined plane, each of these motions having been preceded by a fall through the given vertical line.

Let *AB* represent the vertical line and *BC* the inclined plane; it is required to find a length on the perpendicular below its point of intersection, which after a fall from *A* will be traversed in the same time which is needed for *BC* after an identical fall from *A*. Draw the horizontal *AD*, intersecting the prolongation of *CB* at *D*; let *DE* be a mean proportional between *CD* and *DB*; lay off BF equal to *BE*; also let *AG* be a third proportional to *BA* and *AF*. Then, I say, *BG* is the distance which a body, after falling through *AB*, will traverse in the

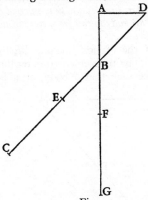

Fig. 70

same time which is needed for the plane *BC* after the same preliminary fall. For if we assume that the time of fall along *AB* is represented by *AB*, then the time for *DB* will be represented by *DB*. And since *DE* is a mean proportional between *BD* and *DC*, this same *DE* will represent the time of descent along the entire distance *DC* while *BE* will represent the time required for the difference of these paths, namely, *BC*, provided in each case the fall is from rest at *D* or at *A*. In like manner, we may infer that *BF* represents the time of descent through the distance *BG* after the same preliminary fall; but *BF* is equal to *BE*. Hence the problem is solved.

THEOREM XIII, PROPOSITION XVI

If a limited inclined plane and a limited vertical line are drawn from the same point, and if the time required for a body, starting from rest, to

traverse each of these is the same, then a body falling from any higher altitude will traverse the inclined plane in less time than is required for the vertical line.

Let *EB* be the vertical line and *CE* the inclined plane, both starting from the common point *E*, and both traversed in equal times by a body starting from rest at *E*; extend the vertical line upwards to any point *A*, from which falling bodies are allowed to start. Then, I say, that after the fall through *AE*, the inclined plane *EC* will be traversed in less time than the perpendicular *EB*. Join *CB*, draw the horizontal *AD*, and prolong *CE* backwards until it meets the latter in *D*; let *DF* be a mean proportional between *CD* and *DE* while *AG* is made a mean proportional between *BA* and *AE*. Draw *FG* and *DG*; then since the times of descent along *EC* and *EB*, starting from rest at *E*, are equal, it follows, according to Corollary II of Proposi-

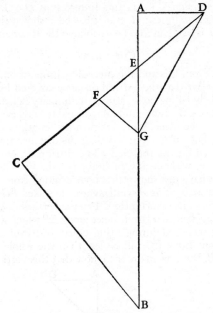

Fig. 71

tion VI that the angle at *C* is a right angle; but the angle at *A* is also a right angle and the angles at the vertex *E* are equal; hence the triangles *AED* and *CEB* are equiangular and the sides about the equal angles are proportional; hence $BE : EC = DE : EA$. Consequently the rectangle $BE.EA$ is equal to the rectangle $CE.ED$; and since the rectangle $CD.DE$ exceeds the rectangle $CE.ED$ by the square of *ED*, and since the rectangle $BA.AE$ exceeds the rectangle $BE.EA$ by the square of *EA*, it follows that the excess of the rectangle $CD.DE$ over the rectangle $BA.AE$, or what is the same thing, the excess of the square of FD over the square of AG, will be equal to the excess of the square of DE over the square of AE, which excess is equal to the square of AD. Therefore $\overline{FD^2} = \overline{GA^2} + \overline{AD^2} = \overline{GD^2}$. Hence DF is equal to DG, and the angle DGF is equal to the angle DFG while the angle EGF is less than the angle EFG, and the opposite side EF is less than the opposite side EG. If now we agree to represent the time of fall through AE by the length AE, then the time along DE will be represented by DE. And since AG is a mean proportional between BA and AE, if follows that AG will represent the time of fall through the total distance AB, and the difference EG will represent the time of fall, from rest at A, through the difference of path EB.

In like manner EF represents the time of descent along EC, starting from rest at D or falling from rest at A. But it has been shown that EF is less than EG; hence follows the theorem.

COROLLARY

From this and the preceding proposition, it is clear that the vertical distance covered by a freely falling body, after a preliminary fall, and during the time-interval required to traverse an inclined plane, is greater than the length of the inclined plane, but less than the distance traversed on the inclined plane during an equal time, without any preliminary fall. For since we have just shown that bodies falling from an elevated point A will traverse the plane EC in Fig. 71 in a shorter time than the vertical EB, it is evident that the distance along EB which will be traversed during a time equal to that of descent along EC will be less than the whole of EB. But now in order to show that this vertical

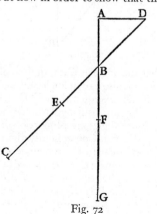

Fig. 72

distance is greater than the length of the inclined plane EC, we reproduce Fig. 70 of the preceding theorem in which the vertical length BG is traversed in the same time as BC after a preliminary fall through AB. That BG is greater than BC is shown as follows: since BE and FB are equal while BA is less than BD, it follows that FB will bear to BA a greater ratio than EB bears to BD; and, *componendo*, FA will bear to BA a greater ratio than ED to DB; but $FA : AB = GF : FB$ (since AF is a mean proportional between BA and AG) and in like manner $ED : BD = CE : EB$. Hence GB bears to BF a greater ratio than CB bears to BE; therefore GB is greater than BC.

PROBLEM IV, PROPOSITION XVII

Given a vertical line and an inclined plane, it is required to lay off a distance along the given plane which will be traversed by a body, after fall along the perpendicular, in the same time-interval which is needed for this body to fall from rest through the given perpendicular.

Let AB be the vertical line and BE the inclined plane. The problem is to determine on BE a distance such that a body, after falling

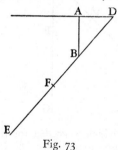

Fig. 73

through AB, will traverse it in a time equal to that required to traverse the perpendicular AB itself, starting from rest.

Draw the horizontal AD and extend the plane until it meets this line in D. Lay off FB equal to BA; and choose the point E such that $BD : FD = DF : DE$. Then, I say, the time of descent along BE, after fall through AB, is equal to the time of fall, from rest at A, through AB. For, if we assume that the length AB represents the time of fall through AB, then the time of fall through DB will be represented by the time DB; and since $BD : FD = DF : DE$, it follows that DF will represent the time of descent along the entire plane DE while BF represents the time through the portion BE starting from rest at D; but the time of descent along BE after the preliminary descent along DB is the same as that after a preliminary fall through *AB*. Hence the time of descent along *BE* after *AB* will be *BF* which of course is equal to the time of fall through *AB* from rest at *A*.   Q. E. F.

PROBLEM V, PROPOSITION XVIII

Given the distance through which a body will fall vertically from rest during a given time-interval, and given also a smaller time-interval, it is required to locate another [equal] vertical distance which the body will traverse during this given smaller time-interval.

Let the vertical line be drawn through *A*, and on this line lay off the distance *AB* which is traversed by a body falling from rest at *A*, during a time which may also be represented by *AB*. Draw the horizontal line *CBE*, and on it lay off *BC* to represent the given interval of

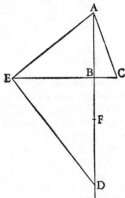

Fig. 74

time which is shorter than *AB*. It is required to locate, in the perpendicular above mentioned, a distance which is equal to *AB* and which will be described in a time equal to *BC*. Join the points *A* and *C*; then, since *BC* < *BA*, it follows that the angle *BAC* < angle *BCA*. Construct the angle *CAE* equal to *BCA* and let *E* be the point where *AE* intersects the horizontal line; draw *ED* at right angles to *AE*, cutting the vertical at *D*; lay off *DF* equal to *BA*. Then, I say, that *FD* is that portion of the vertical which a body starting from rest at *A* will traverse during the assigned time-interval *BC*. For, if in the right-angled triangle *AED* a perpendicular be drawn from the right-angle at *E* to the opposite side *AD*, then *AE* will be a mean proportional between *DA* and *AB* while *BE* will be a mean proportional between *BD* and *BA*, or between *FA* and *AB* (seeing that *FA* is equal to *DB*); and since it has been agreed to represent the time of fall through *AB* by the distance *AB*, it follows

that *AE*, or *EC*, will represent the time of fall through the entire distance *AD*, while *EB* will represent the time through *AF*. Consequently the remainder *BC* will represent the time of fall through the remaining distance *FD*.   Q. E. F.

PROBLEM VI, PROPOSITION XIX

Given the distance through which a body falls in a vertical line from rest and given also the time of fall, it is required to find the time in which the same body will, later, traverse an equal distance chosen anywhere in the same vertical line.

On the vertical line *AB*, lay off *AC* equal to the distance fallen from rest at *A*, also locate at random an equal distance *DB*. Let the time of

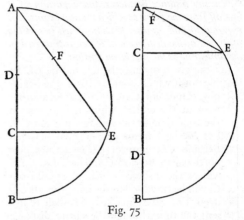

Fig. 75

fall through *AC* be represented by the length *AC*. It is required to find the time necessary to traverse *DB* after fall from rest at *A*. About the entire length *AB* describe the semicircle *AEB*; from *C* draw *CE* perpendicular to *AB*; join the points *A* and *E*; the line *AE* will be longer than *EC*; lay off *EF* equal to *EC*. Then, I say, the difference *FA* will represent the time required for fall through *DB*. For since *AE* is a mean proportional between *BA* and *AC* and since *AC* represents the time of fall through *AC*, it follows that *AE* will represent the time through the entire distance *AB*. And since *CE* is a mean proportional between *DA* and *AC* (seeing that *DA* = *BC*) it follows that *CE*, that is, *EF*, will represent the time of fall through *AD*. Hence the difference *AF* will represent the time of fall through the difference *DB*.   Q. E. D.

COROLLARY

Hence it is inferred, that if the time of fall from rest through any given distance is represented by that distance itself, then the time of fall, after the given distance has been increased

S by a certain amount, will be represented by the excess of the mean proportional between the increased distance and the original distance over the mean proportional

A between the original distance and the increment. Thus, for instance, if we agree that AB represents the time of fall, from rest at A, through the distance AB, and that AS is the increment, the time required to traverse AB, after fall through SA, will be

B the excess of the mean proportional between SB and BA over the mean proportional between BA and AS.

Fig. 76

PROBLEM VII, PROPOSITION XX

Given any distance whatever and a portion of it laid off from the point at which motion begins, it is required to find another portion which lies at the other end of the distance and which is traversed in the same time as the first given portion.

Let the given distance be CB and let CD be

C that part of it which is laid off from the beginning of motion. It is required to find another part, at the end B, which is traversed in the same time as the assigned portion CD.

D Let BA be a mean proportional between BC and CD; also let CE be a third proportional to BC and CA. Then, I say, EB will be the distance which, after fall from C, will be traversed in the same time as CD

E itself. For if we agree that CB shall represent the time through the entire distance CB, then BA (which, of course, is a mean

A proportional between BC and CD) will represent the time along CD; and since CA is a mean proportional between BC and CE, it follows that CA will be the time through

B CE; but the total length CB represents the

Fig. 77 time through the total distance CB. Therefore the difference of distances BA will be the time along the difference of distances, EB, after falling from C; but this same BA was the time of fall through CD. Consequently the distances CD and EB are traversed, from rest at A, in equal times. Q. E. F.

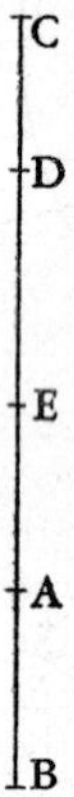

THEOREM XIV, PROPOSITION XXI

If, on the path of a body falling vertically from rest, one lays off a portion which is traversed in any time you please and whose upper terminus coincides with the point where the motion begins, and if this fall is followed by a motion deflected along any inclined plane, then the space traversed along the inclined plane, during a time-interval equal to that occupied in the previous vertical fall, will be greater than twice, and less than three times, the length of the vertical fall.

Let AB be a vertical line drawn downwards from the horizontal line AE, and let it represent the path of a body falling from rest at A; choose any portion AC of this path. Through C draw any inclined plane, CG, along which the motion is continued after fall through AC. Then, I say, that the distance traversed along this plane CG, during the time-interval equal to that of the fall through AC, is more than twice, but less

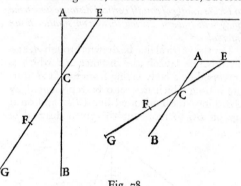

Fig. 78

than three times, this same distance AC. Let us lay off CF equal to AC, and extend the plane GC until it meets the horizontal in E; choose G such that $CE : EF = EF : EG$. If now we assume that the time of fall along AC is represented by the length AC, then CE will represent the time of descent along CE, while CF, or CA, will represent the time of descent along CG. It now remains to be shown that the distance CG is more than twice, and less than three times, the distance CA itself. Since $CE : EF = EF : EG$, it follows that $CE : EF = CF : FG$; but $EC < EF$; therefore CF will be less than FG and GC will be more than twice FC, or AC. Again since $FE < 2EC$ (for EC is greater than CA, or CF), we have GF less than twice FC, and also GC less than three times CF, or CA. Q. E. D.

This proposition may be stated in a more general form; since what has been proven for the case of a vertical and inclined plane holds equally well in the case of motion along a plane of any inclination followed by motion along any plane of less steepness, as can be seen from the adjoining figure. The method of proof is the same.

PROBLEM VIII, PROPOSITION XXII

Given two unequal time-intervals, also the distance through which a body will fall along a vertical line, from rest, during the shorter of these intervals, it is required to pass through the highest point of this vertical line a plane so inclined that the time of de-

scent along it will be equal to the longer of the given intervals.

Let *A* represent the longer and *B* the shorter of the two unequal time-intervals, also let *CD* represent the length of the vertical fall, from

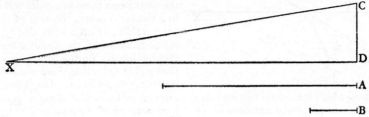

Fig. 79

rest, during the time *B*. It is required to pass through the point *C* a plane of such a slope that it will be traversed in the time *A*.

Draw from the point *C* to the horizontal a line *CX* of such a length that *B : A=CD : CX*. It is clear that *CX* is the plane along which a body will descend in the given time *A*. For it has been shown that the time of descent along an inclined plane bears to the time of fall through its vertical height the same ratio which the length of the plane bears to its vertical height. Therefore, the time along *CX* is to the time along *CD* as the length *CX* is to the length *CD*, that is, as the time-interval *A* is to the time-interval *B*: but *B* is the time required to traverse the vertical distance, *CD*, starting from rest; therefore *A* is the time required for descent along the plane *CX*.

Problem IX, Proposition XXIII

Given the time employed by a body in falling through a certain distance along a vertical line, it is required to pass through the lower terminus of this vertical fall, a plane so inclined that this body will, after its vertical fall, traverse on this plane, during a time-interval equal to that of the vertical fall, a distance equal to any assigned distance, provided this assigned distance is more than twice and less than three times the vertical fall.

Let *AS* be any vertical line, and let *AC* denote both the length of the vertical fall, from rest at *A*, and also the time required for this fall. Let *IR* be a distance more than twice and less than three times, *AC*. It is required to pass a plane through the point *C* so inclined that a body, after fall through *AC*, will, during the time *AC*, traverse a distance equal to *IR*. Lay off *RN* and *NM* each equal to *AC*. Through the point *C*, draw a plane *CE* meeting the horizontal, *AE*, at such a point that *IM : MN=AC :*

CE. Extend the plane at *O*, and lay off *CF*, *FG* and *GO* equal to *RN*, *NM*, and *MI* respectively. Then, I say, the time along the inclined plane *CO*, after fall through *AC*, is equal to the time of fall, from rest at *A*, through *AC*. For since

OG : GF=FC : CE, it follows, *componendo*, that *OF : FG=OF : FC=FE : EC*, and since an antecedent is to its consequent as the sum of the antecedents is to the sum of the consequents,

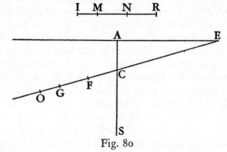

Fig. 80

we have *OE : EF=EF : EC*. Thus *EF* is a mean proportional between *OE* and *EC*. Having agreed to represent the time of fall through *AC* by the length *AC* it follows that *EC* will represent the time along *EC*, and *EF* the time along the entire distance *EO*, while the difference *CF* will represent the time along the difference *CO;* but *CF=CA;* therefore the problem is solved. For the time *CA* is the time of fall, from rest at *A*, through *CA* while *CF* (which is equal to *CA*) is the time required to traverse *CO* after descent along *EC* or after fall through *AC*.   Q. E. F.

It is to be remarked also, that the same solution holds if the antecedent motion takes place, not along a vertical, but along an inclined plane. This case is illustrated in the following figure where the antecedent motion is along the inclined plane *AS* underneath the horizontal *AE*. The proof is identical with the preceding.

Scholium

On careful attention, it will be clear that, the nearer the given line *IR* approaches to three times the length *AC*, the nearer the inclined

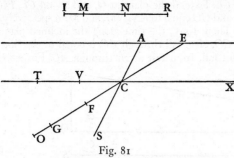

Fig. 81

plane, *CO*, along which the second motion takes place, approaches the perpendicular along which the space traversed, during the time *AC*, will be three times the distance *AC*. For if *IR* be taken nearly equal to three times *AC*, then *IM* will be almost equal to *MN;* and since, by construction, *IM : MN= AC : CE*, it follows that *CE* is but little greater than *CA:* consequently the point *E* will lie near the point *A*, and the lines *CO* and *CS*, forming a very acute angle, will almost coincide. But, on the other hand, if the given line, *IR*, be only the least bit longer than twice *AC*, the line *IM* will be very short; from which it follows that *AC* will be very small in comparison with *CE* which is now so long that it almost coincides with the horizontal line drawn through C. Hence we can infer that, if, after descent along the inclined plane *AC* of the adjoining figure, the motion is continued along a horizontal line, such as *CT*, the distance traversed by a body, during a time equal to the time of fall through *AC*, will be exactly twice the distance *AC*. The argument here employed is the same as the preceding. For it is clear, since *OE : EF= EF : EC*, that *FC* measures the time of descent along *CO*. But, if the horizontal line *TC* which is twice as long as *CA*, be divided into two equal parts at *V* then this line must be extended indefinitely in the direction of *X* before it will intersect the line *AE* produced; and accordingly, the ratio of the infinite length *TX* to the infinite length *VX* is the same as the ratio of the infinite distance *VX* to the infinite distance *CX*.

The same result may be obtained by another method of approach, namely, by returning to the same line of argument which was employed in the proof of the first proposition. Let us consider the triangle *ABC*, which, by lines drawn parallel to its base, represents for us a velocity increasing in proportion to the time; if these lines are infinite in number, just as the points in the line *AC* are infinite or as the number of instants in any interval of time is infinite, they will form the area of the triangle. Let us now suppose that the maximum velocity attained— that represented by the line BC—to be continued, without acceleration and at constant value through another interval of time equal to the first. From these velocities will be built up, in a similar manner, the area of the parallelogram *ADBC*, which is twice that of the triangle *ABC;* accordingly, the distance traversed with these velocities during any given interval of time will be twice that traversed with the velocities represented by the triangle during an equal interval of time. But along a horizontal plane the motion is uniform since here it experiences neither acceleration nor retardation; therefore we conclude that the distance *CD* traversed during a time-interval equal to *AC* is twice the distance *AC*; for the latter is covered by a motion, starting from rest and increasing in speed in proportion to the parallel lines in the triangle, while the former is traversed by a motion represented by the parallel lines of the parallelogram which, being also infinite in number, yield an area twice that of the triangle.

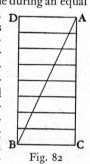

Fig. 82

Furthermore, we may remark that any velocity once imparted to a moving body will be rigidly maintained as long as the external causes of acceleration or retardation are removed, a condition which is found only on horizontal planes; for in the case of planes which slope downwards there is already present a cause of acceleration, while on planes sloping upward there is retardation; from this it follows that motion along a horizontal plane is perpetual; for, if the velocity be uniform, it cannot be diminished or slackened, much less destroyed. Further, although any velocity which a body may have acquired through natural fall is permanently maintained so far as its own nature is concerned, yet it must be remembered that if, after descent along a plane inclined downwards, the body is deflected to a plane inclined upward, there is already existing in this latter plane a cause of retardation; for in any such plane this same body is subject to a natural acceleration downwards. Accordingly, we have here the superposition of two different states, namely, the velocity acquired during the preceding fall which if acting alone would carry the body at a uniform rate to infinity, and the velocity which results from a natural acceleration downwards common to all bodies. It seems altogether reasonable, therefore, if we wish to trace the future history of a body which has descended along some inclined plane and has been deflected along some plane inclined upwards, for us to assume that the maximum speed acquired during descent is permanently maintained during the ascent. In the ascent, however, there supervenes a natural inclination downwards, namely, a motion which, starting from rest, is accelerated at the usual rate. If perhaps this discussion is a little obscure, the following figure will help to make it clearer.

Let us suppose that the descent has been made along the downward sloping plane AB, from which the body is deflected so as to continue its motion along the upward sloping plane BC; and first let these planes be of equal length and placed so as to make equal angles with the horizontal line GH. Now it is well known that a body, starting from rest at A, and descending along AB, acquires a speed which is proportional

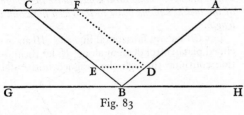

Fig. 83

to the time, which is a maximum at B, and which is maintained by the body so long as all causes of fresh acceleration or retardation are removed; the acceleration to which I refer is that to which the body would be subject if its motion were continued along the plane AB extended, while the retardation is that which the body would encounter if its motion were deflected along the plane BC inclined upwards; but, upon the horizontal plane GH, the body would maintain a uniform velocity equal to that which it had acquired at B after fall from A; moreover, this velocity is such that, during an interval of time equal to the time of descent through AB, the body will traverse a horizontal distance equal to twice AB. Now let us imagine this same body to move with the same uniform speed along the plane BC so that here also during a time-interval equal to that of descent along AB, it will traverse along BC extended a distance twice AB; but let us suppose that, at the very instant the body begins its ascent it is subjected, by its very nature, to the same influences which surrounded it during its descent from A along AB, namely, it descends from rest under the same acceleration as that which was

effective in AB, and it traverses, during an equal interval of time, the same distance along this second plane as it did along AB; it is clear that, by thus superposing upon the body a uniform motion of ascent and an accelerated motion of descent, it will be carried along the plane BC as far as the point C where these two velocities become equal.

If now we assume any two points D and E, equally distant from the vertex B, we may then infer that the descent along BD takes place in the same time as the ascent along BE. Draw DF parallel to BC; we know that, after descent along AD, the body will ascend along DF; or, if, on reaching D, the body is carried along the horizontal DE, it will reach E with the same momentum with which it left D; hence from E the body will ascend as far as C, proving that the velocity at E is the same as that at D.

From this we may logically infer that a body which descends along any inclined plane and continues its motion along a plane inclined upwards will, on account of the momentum acquired, ascend to an equal height above the horizontal; so that if the descent is along AB the body will be carried up the plane BC as far as the horizontal line ACD: and this is true whether the inclinations of the planes are the same or different, as in the case of the planes AB and BD. But by a previous postulate the speeds acquired by fall along variously inclined

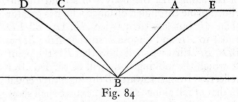

Fig. 84

planes having the same vertical height are the same. If therefore, the planes EB and BD have the same slope, the descent along EB will be able to drive the body along BD as far as D; and since this propulsion comes from the speed acquired on reaching the point B, it follows that this speed at B is the same whether the body has made its descent along AB or EB. Evidently, then the body will be carried up BD whether the descent has been made along AB or along EB. The time of ascent along BD is however greater than that along BC, just as the descent along EB occupies more time than that along AB; moreover it has been demonstrated that the ratio between the lengths of these times is the same as that between the lengths of the planes. We must next discover what ratio exists between the distances traversed in equal times along planes of different slope, but of the same elevation, that is, along planes which are included between the same parallel horizontal lines. This is done as follows:

THEOREM XV, PROPOSITION XXIV

Given two parallel horizontal planes and a vertical line connecting them; given also an inclined plane passing through the lower extremity of this vertical line; then, if a body fall freely along the vertical line and have its motion reflected along the inclined plane, the distance which it will traverse along this plane, during a time equal to that of the vertical fall, is greater than once but less than twice the vertical line.

Let BC and HG be the two horizontal planes, connected by the perpendicular AE; also let EB represent the inclined plane along which

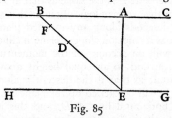

Fig. 85

the motion takes place after the body has fallen along AE and has been reflected from E towards B. Then, I say, that, during a time equal to that of fall along AE, the body will ascend the inclined plane through a distance which is greater than AE but less than twice AE. Lay off ED equal to AE and choose F so that $EB : BD = BD : BF$. First we shall show that F is the point to which the moving body will be carried after reflection from E towards B during a time equal to that of fall along AE; and next we shall show that the distance EF is greater than EA but less than twice that quantity.

Let us agree to represent the time of fall along AE by the length AE, then the time of descent along BE, or what is the same thing, ascent along EB will be represented by the distance EB.

Now, since DB is a mean proportional between EB and BF, and since BE is the time of descent for the entire distance BE, it follows that BD will be the time of descent through BF, while the remainder DE will be the time of descent along the remainder FE. But the time of descent along the fall from rest at B is the same as the time of ascent from E to F after reflection from E with the speed acquired during fall either through AE or BE. Therefore, DE represents the time occupied by the body in

passing from E to F, after fall from A to E and after reflection along EB. But by construction ED is equal to AE. This concludes the first part of our demonstration.

Now since the whole of EB is to the whole of BD as the portion DB is to the portion BF, we have the whole of EB is to the whole of BD as the remainder ED is to the remainder DF; but $EB > BD$ and hence $ED > DF$, and EF is less than twice DE or AE.   Q. E. D.

The same is true when the initial motion occurs, not along a perpendicular, but upon an inclined plane: the proof is also the same provided the upward sloping plane is less steep, i.e., longer, than the downward sloping plane.

THEOREM XVI, PROPOSITION XXV

If descent along any inclined plane is followed by motion along a horizontal plane, the time of descent along the inclined plane bears to the time required to traverse any assigned length of the horizontal plane the same ratio which twice the length of the inclined plane bears to the given horizontal length.

Let CB be any horizontal line and AB an inclined plane; after descent along AB let the motion continue through the assigned horizontal

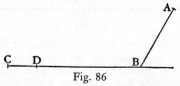

Fig. 86

distance BD. Then, I say, the time of descent along AB bears to the time spent in traversing BD the same ratio which twice AB bears to BD. For, lay off BC equal to twice AB then it follows, from a previous proposition, that the time of descent along AB is equal to the time required to traverse BC; but the time along BC is to the time along DB as the length CB is to the length BD. Hence the time of descent along AB is to the time along BD as twice the distance AB is to the distance BD.   Q. E. D.

PROBLEM X, PROPOSITION XXVI

Given a vertical height joining two horizontal parallel lines; given also a distance greater than once and less than twice this vertical height, it is required to pass through the foot of the given perpendicular an inclined plane such that, after fall through the given vertical height, a body whose motion is deflected along the plane will traverse the assigned distance in a time equal to the time of vertical fall.

Let AB be the vertical distance separating

two parallel horizontal lines *AO* and *BC;* also let *FE* be greater than once and less than twice *BA*. The problem is to pass a plane through *B*, extending to the upper horizontal line, and such that a body, after having fallen from *A* to *B*, will, if its motion be deflected along the inclined plane, traverse a distance equal to *EF* in a time equal to that of fall along *AB*. Lay off *ED* equal to *AB;* then the remainder *DF* will be less than *AB* since the entire length *EF* is less than twice this quantity; also lay off *DI* equal to *DF*, and choose the point *X* such that *EI : ID=DF : FX;* from *B*, draw the plane *BO* equal in length to *EX*. Then, I say, that the plane *BO* is the one along which, after fall through *AB*, a body will traverse the assigned distance *FE* in a time equal to the time of fall through *AB*. Lay off *BR* and *RS* equal to *ED* and *DF* respectively; then since *EI : ID=DF : FX*, we have, *componendo*, *ED : DI=DX : XF=ED : DF=EX : XD=BO : OR=RO : OS*.

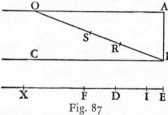
Fig. 87

If we represent the time of fall along *AB* by the length *AB*, then *OB* will represent the time of descent along *OB*, and *RO* will stand for the time along *OS*, while the remainder *BR* will represent the time required for a body starting from rest at *O* to traverse the remaining distance *SB*. But the time of descent along *SB* starting from rest at *O* is equal to the time of ascent from *B* to *S* after fall through *AB*. Hence *BO* is that plane, passing through *B*, along which a body, after fall through *AB*, will traverse the distance *BS*, equal to the assigned distance *EF*, in the time-interval *BR* or *BA*.   Q. E. F.

THEOREM XVII, PROPOSITION XXVII

If a body descends along two inclined planes of different lengths but of the same vertical height, the distance which it will traverse, in the lower part of the longer plane, during a time-interval equal to that of descent over the shorter plane, is equal to the length of the shorter plane plus a portion of it to which the shorter plane bears the same ratio which the longer plane bears to the excess of the longer over the shorter plane.

Let *AC* be the longer plane, *AB*, the shorter, and *AD* the common elevation; on the lower

part of *AC* lay off *CE* equal to *AB*. Choose *F* such that *CA : AE=CA : CA−AB=CE : EF*. Then, I say, that *FC* is that distance which will, after fall from *A* be traversed during a time-

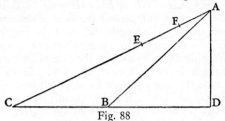
Fig. 88

interval equal to that required for descent along *AB*. For since *CA : AE=CE : EF*, it follows that the remainder *EA:* the remainder *AF= CA : AE*. Therefore *AE* is a mean proportional between *AC* and *AF*. Accordingly, if the length *AB* is employed to measure the time of fall along *AB*, then the distance *AC* will measure the time of descent through *AC;* but the time of descent through *AF* is measured by the length *AE*, and that through *FC* by *EC*. Now *EC=AB;* and hence follows the proposition.

PROBLEM XI, PROPOSITION XXVIII

Let *AG* be any horizontal line touching a circle; let *AB* be the diameter passing through the point of contact; and let *AE* and *EB* represent any two chords. The problem is to determine what ratio the time of fall through *AB*

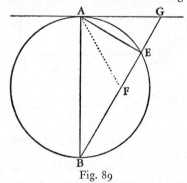
Fig. 89

bears to the time of descent over both *AE* and *EB*. Extend *BE* till it meets the tangent at *G*, and draw *AF* so as to bisect the angle *BAE*. Then, I say, the time through *AB* is to the sum of the times along *AE* and *EB* as the length *AE* is to the sum of the lengths *AE* and *EF*. For since the angle *FAB* is equal to the angle *FAE*, while the angle *EAG* is equal to the angle *ABF* it follows that the entire angle *GAF* is equal to the sum of the angles *FAB* and *ABF*. But the angle GFA is also equal to the sum of these two angles. Hence the length GF is equal to the length $GA;$ and since the rectangle $BG.GE$ is equal to the square of GA, it will also be equal to the square of GF, or $BG : GF = GF : GE$. If now we agree to represent the time of descent along AE by the length AE, then the length GE will represent the time of descent along GE, while GF will stand for the time of descent through the entire distance $GB;$ so also EF will denote the time through EB after fall from G or from A along AE. Consequently the time along AE, or AB, is to the time along AE and EB as the length AE is to $AE + EF$.   Q. E. D.

A shorter method is to lay off GF equal to GA, thus making GF a mean proportional between BG and GE. The rest of the proof is as above.

<h4>THEOREM XVIII, PROPOSITION XXIX</h4>

Given a limited horizontal line, at one end of which is erected a limited vertical line whose length is equal to one-half the given horizontal line; then a body, falling through this given height and having its motion deflected into a horizontal direction, will traverse the given horizontal distance and vertical line in less time than it will any other vertical distance plus the given horizontal distance.

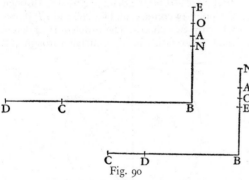

Fig. 90

Let BC be the given distance in a horizontal plane; at the end B erect a perpendicular, on which lay off BA equal to half BC. Then, I say, that the time required for a body, starting from rest at A, to traverse the two distances, AB and BC, is the least of all possible times in which this same distance BC together with a vertical portion, whether greater or less than AB, can be traversed.

Lay off EB greater than AB, as in the first figure, and less than AB, as in the second. It must be shown that the time required to traverse the distance EB plus BC is greater than that required for AB plus BC. Let us agree that

the length AB shall represent the time along AB, then the time occupied in traversing the horizontal portion BC will also be AB, seeing that $BC = 2AB;$ consequently the time required for both AB and BC will be twice AB. Choose the point O such that $EB : BO = BO : BA$, then BO will represent the time of fall through EB. Again lay off the horizontal distance BD equal to twice $BE;$ whence it is clear that BO represents the time along BD after fall through EB. Select a point N such that $DB : BC = EB : BA = OB : BN$. Now since the horizontal motion is uniform and since OB is the time occupied in traversing BD, after fall from E, it follows that NB will be the time along BC after fall through the same height EB. Hence it is clear that OB plus BN represents the time of traversing EB plus BC; and, since twice BA is the time along AB plus BC, it remains to be shown that $OB + BN > 2BA$.

But since $EB : BO = BO : BA$, it follows that $EB : BA = \overline{OB}^2 : \overline{BA}^2$. Moreover since $EB : BA = OB : BN$ it follows that $OB : BN = \overline{OB}^2 : \overline{BA}^2$. But $OB : BN = (OB : BA) (BA : BN)$, and therefore $AB : BN = OB : BA$, that is, BA is a mean proportional between BO and BN. Consequently $OB + BN > 2BA$.   Q. E. D.

<h4>THEOREM XIX, PROPOSITION XXX</h4>

A perpendicular is let fall from any point in a horizontal line; it is required to pass through any other point in this same horizontal line a plane which shall cut the perpendicular and along which a body will descend to the perpendicular in the shortest possible time. Such a plane will cut from the perpendicular a portion equal to the distance of the assumed point in the horizontal from the upper end of the perpendicular.

Let AC be any horizontal line and B any point in it from which is dropped the vertical line BD. Choose any point C in the horizontal line and lay off, on the vertical, the distance BE equal to $BC;$ join C and E. Then, I say, that of all inclined planes that can be passed through C, cutting the perpendicular, CE is that one along which the descent to the perpendicular is accomplished in the shortest time. For, draw the plane CF cutting the vertical above E, and the plane CG cutting the vertical below $E;$ and draw IK, a parallel vertical line, touching at C a circle described with BC as radius. Let EK be drawn parallel to CF, and extended to meet the tangent, after cutting the circle at L. Now it is clear that the time of fall along LE is equal to the time along $CE;$ but the time along KE is

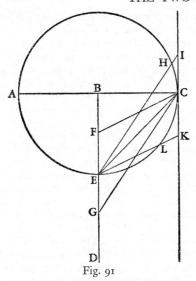

Fig. 91

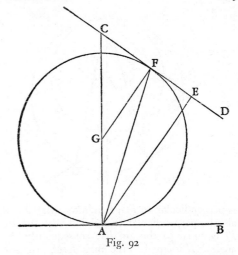

Fig. 92

greater than along *LE;* therefore the time along *KE* is greater than along *CE.* But the time along *KE* is equal to the time along *CF,* since they have the same length and the same slope; and, in like manner, it follows that the planes *CG* and *IE,* having the same length and the same slope, will be traversed in equal times. Also, since *HE < IE,* the time along *HE* will be less than the time along *IE.* Therefore, also the time along *CE* (equal to the time along *HE*), will be shorter than the time along *IE.*

Q. E. D.

Theorem XX, Proposition XXXI

If a straight line is inclined at any angle to the horizontal and if, from any assigned point in the horizontal, a plane of quickest descent is to be drawn to the inclined line, that plane will be the one which bisects the angle contained between two lines drawn from the given point, one perpendicular to the horizontal line, the other perpendicular to the inclined line.

Let *CD* be a line inclined at any angle to the horizontal *AB;* and from any assigned point *A* in the horizontal draw *AC* perpendicular to *AB,* and *AE* perpendicular to *CD;* draw *FA* so as to bisect the angle *CAE.* Then, I say, that of all the planes which can be drawn through the point *A,* cutting the line *CD* at any points whatsoever *AF* is the one of quickest descent. Draw *FG* parallel to *AE;* the alternate angles *GFA* and *FAE* will be equal; also the angle *EAF* is equal to the angle *FAG.* Therefore the sides *GF* and *GA* of the triangle *FGA* are equal. Accordingly, if we describe a circle about *G* as

centre, with *GA* as radius, this circle will pass through the point *F,* and will touch the horizontal at the point *A* and the inclined line at *F;* for *GFC* is a right angle, since *GF* and *AE* are parallel. It is clear therefore that all lines drawn from *A* to the inclined line, with the single exception of *FA,* will extend beyond the circumference of the circle, thus requiring more time to traverse any of them than is needed for *FA.*

Q. E. D.

Lemma

If two circles one lying within the other are in contact, and if any straight line be drawn tangent to the inner circle, cutting the outer circle, and if three lines be drawn from the point at which the circles are in contact to three points on the tangential straight line, namely, the point of tangency on the inner circle and the two points where the straight line extended cuts the outer circle, then these three lines will contain equal angles at the point of contact.

Let the two circles touch each other at the point *A,* the centre of the smaller being at *B,* the centre of the larger at *C.* Draw the straight line *FG* touching the inner circle at *H,* and cutting the outer at the points *F* and *G;* also draw the three lines *AF, AH,* and *AG.* Then, I say, the angles contained by these lines, *FAH* and *GAH,* are equal. Prolong *AH* to the circumference at *I;* from the centres of the circles, draw *BH* and *CI;* join the centres *B* and *C* and extend the line until it reaches the point of contact at *A* and cuts the circles at the points *O* and *N.* But now the lines *BH* and *CI* are parallel, because the angles *ICN* and *HBO* are equal, each being twice the angle *IAN.* And since *BH,* drawn from the centre to the point of contact

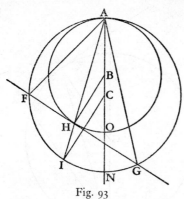

Fig. 93

is perpendicular to *FG*, it follows that *CI* will also be perpendicular to *FG* and that the arc *FI* is equal to the arc *IG*; consequently the angle *FAI* is equal to the angle *IAG*.   Q. E. D.

Theorem XXI, Proposition XXXII

If in a horizontal line any two points are chosen, and if through one of these points a line be drawn inclined towards the other, and if from this other point a straight line is drawn to the inclined line in such a direction that it cuts off from the inclined line a portion equal to the distance between the two chosen points on the horizontal line, then the time of descent along the line so drawn is less than along any other straight line drawn from the same point to the same inclined line. Along other lines which make equal angles on opposite sides of this line, the times of descent are the same.

Let *A* and *B* be any two points on a horizontal line: through *B* draw an inclined straight line *BC*, and from *B* lay off a distance *BD* equal to *BA*; join the points *A* and *D*. Then, I say, the time of descent along *AD* is less than along any other line drawn from *A* to the inclined line *BC*. From the point *A* draw *AE* perpendicular to *BA*; and from the point *D* draw *DE*

perpendicular to *BD*, intersecting *AE* at *E*. Since in the isosceles triangle *ABD*, we have the angles *BAD* and *BDA* equal, their complements *DAE* and *EDA* are equal. Hence if, with *E* as centre and *EA* as radius, we describe a circle it will pass through *D* and will touch the lines *BA* and *BD* at the points *A* and *D*. Now since *A* is the end of the vertical line *AE*, the descent along *AD* will occupy less time than along any other line drawn from the extremity *A* to the line *BC* and extending beyond the circumference of the circle; which concludes the first part of the proposition.

If however, we prolong the perpendicular line *AE*, and choose any point *F* upon it, about which as centre, we describe a circle of radius *FA*, this circle *AGC*, will cut the tangent line in the points *G* and *C*. Draw the lines *AG* and *AC* which will according to the preceding lemma, deviate by equal angles from the median line *AD*. The time of descent along either of these lines is the same, since they start from the highest point *A*, and terminate on the circumference of the circle *AGC*.

Problem XII, Proposition XXXIII

Given a limited vertical line and an inclined plane of equal height, having a common upper terminal; it is required to find a point on the vertical line, extended upwards, from which a body will fall and, when deflected along the inclined plane, will traverse it in the same time-interval which is required for fall, from rest, through the given vertical height.

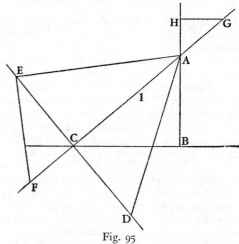

Fig. 95

Let *AB* be the given limited vertical line and *AC* an inclined plane having the same altitude. It is required to find on the vertical *BA*,

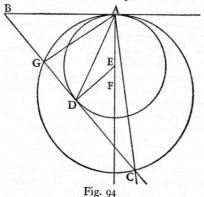

Fig. 94

extended above *A*, a point from which a falling body will traverse the distance *AC* in the same time which is spent in falling, from rest at *A*, through the given vertical line *AB*. Draw the line *DCE* at right angles to *AC*, and lay off *CD* equal to *AB;* also join the points *A* and *D;* then the angle *ADC* will be greater than the angle *CAD*, since the side *CA* is greater than either *AB* or *CD*. Make the angle *DAE* equal to the angle *ADE*, and draw *EF* perpendicular to *AE;* then *EF* will cut the inclined plane, extended both ways, at *F*. Lay off *AI* and *AG* each equal to *CF;* through *G* draw the horizontal line *GH*. Then, I say, *H* is the point sought.

For, if we agree to let the length *AB* represent the time of fall along the vertical *AB*, then *AC* will likewise represent the time of descent from rest at *A*, along *AC;* and since, in the right-angled triangle *AEF*, the line *EC* has been drawn from the right angle at *E* perpendicular to the base *AF*, it follows that *AE* will be a mean proportional between *FA* and *AC*, while *CE* will be a mean proportional between *AC* and *CF*, that is between *CA* and *AI*. Now, since *AC* represents the time of descent from *A* along *AC*, it follows that *AE* will be the time along the entire distance *AF*, and *EC* the time along *AI*. But since in the isosceles triangle *AED* the side *EA* is equal to the side *ED* it follows that *ED* will represent the time of fall along *AF*, while *EC* is the time of fall along *AI*. Therefore *CD*, that is *AB*, will represent the time of fall, from rest at *A*, along *IF;* which is the same as saying that *AB* is the time of fall, from *G* or from *H*, along *AC*.   Q. E. F.

Problem XIII, Proposition XXXIV

Given a limited inclined plane and a vertical line having their highest point in common, it is required to find a point in the vertical line extended such that a body will fall from it and then traverse the inclined plane in the same time which is required to traverse the inclined plane alone, starting from rest at the top of said plane.

Let *AC* and *AB* be an inclined plane and a vertical line respectively, having a common highest point at *A*. It is required to find a point in the vertical line, above *A*, such that a body, falling from it and afterwards having its motion directed along *AB*, will traverse both the assigned part of the vertical line and the plane *AB* in the same time which is required for the plane *AB* alone, starting from rest at *A*. Draw *BC* a horizontal line and lay off *AN* equal to *AC;* choose the point *L* so that *AB* : *BN*=*AL* : *LC*,

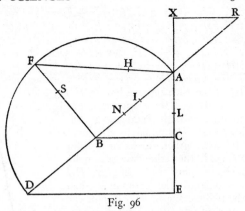

Fig. 96

and lay off *AI* equal to *AL;* choose the point *E* such that *CE*, laid off on the vertical *AC* produced, will be a third proportional to *AC* and *BI*. Then, I say, *CE* is the distance sought; so that, if the vertical line is extended above *A* and if a portion *AX* is laid off equal to *CE*, then a body falling from *X* will traverse both the distances, *XA* and *AB*, in the same time as that required, when starting from *A*, to traverse *AB* alone.

Draw *XR* parallel to *BC* and intersecting *BA* produced in *R;* next draw *ED* parallel to *BC* and meeting *BA* produced in *D;* on *AD* as diameter describe a semicircle; from *B* draw *BF* perpendicular to *AD*, and prolong it till it meets the circumference of the circle; evidently *FB* is a mean proportional between *AB* and *BD*, while *FA* is a mean proportional between *DA* and *AB*. Take *BS* equal to *BI* and *FH* equal to *FB*. Now since *AB* : *BD*=*AC* : *CE* and since *BF* is a mean proportional between *AB* and *BD*, while *BI* is a mean proportional between *AC* and *CE*, it follows that *BA* : *AC*=*FB* : *BS*, and since *BA* : *AC*=*BA* : *BN*=*FB* : *BS* we shall have, *convertendo, BF* : *FS*= *AB* : *BN*=*AL* : *LC*. Consequently the rectangle formed by *FB* and *CL* is equal to the rectangle whose sides are *AL* and *SF;* moreover, this rectangle *AL*.*SF* is the excess of the rectangle *AL*.*FB*, or *AI*.*BF*, over the rectangle *AI*.*BS*, or *AI*.*IB*. But the rectangle *FB*.*LC* is the excess of the rectangle *AC*.*BF* over the rectangle *AL*.*BF;* and moreover the rectangle *AC*.*BF* is equal to the rectangle *AB*.*BI* since *BA* : *AC*=*FB* : *BI;* hence the excess of the rectangle *AB*.*BI* over the rectangle *AI*.*BF*, or *AI*.*FH*, is equal to the excess of the rectangle *AI*.*FH* over the rectangle *AI*.*IB;* therefore twice the rectangle *AI*.*FH* is equal to the sum of the rectangles *AB*.*BI* and *AI*.*IB*, or $2AI.FH=2AI.IB+\overline{BI}^2$. Add $\overline{AI}^2$ to each side, then $2AI.IB+\overline{BI}^2+\overline{AI}^2=\overline{AB}^2=$ $2AI.FH+\overline{AI}^2$. Again add $\overline{BF}^2$ to each side, then $\overline{AB}^2+\overline{BF}^2=\overline{AF}^2=2AI.FH+\overline{AI}^2+\overline{BF}^2=$ $2AI.FH+\overline{AI}^2+\overline{FH}^2$. But $\overline{AF}^2=2AH.HF+$ $\overline{AH}^2+\overline{HF}^2$; and hence $2AI.FH+\overline{AI}^2+$ $\overline{FH}^2=2AH.HF+\overline{AH}^2+\overline{HF}^2$. Subtracting $\overline{HF}^2$ from each side we have $2AI.FH+\overline{AI}^2=$ $2AH.HF+\overline{AH}^2$. Since now FH is a factor common to both rectangles, it follows that AH is equal to AI; for if AH were either greater or smaller than AI, then the two rectangles $AH \cdot HF$ plus the square of HA would be either larger or smaller than the two rectangles $AI.FH$ plus the square of IA, a result which is contrary to what we have just demonstrated.

If now we agree to represent the time of descent along AB by the length AB, then the time through AC will likewise be measured by AC; and IB, which is a mean proportional between AC and CE, will represent the time through CE, or XA, from rest at X. Now, since AF is a mean proportional between DA and AB or between RB and AB, and since BF, which is equal to FH, is a mean proportional between AB and BD, that is between AB and AR, it follows, from a preceding proposition [XIX, corollary], that the difference AH represents the time of descent along AB either from rest at R or after fall from X, while the time of descent along AB, from rest at A, is measured by the length AB. But as has just been shown, the time of fall through XA is measured by IB, while the time of descent along AB, after fall, through RA or through XA, is IA. Therefore the time of descent through XA plus AB is measured by the length AB, which, of course, also measures the time of descent, from rest at A, along AB alone.   Q. E. F.

PROBLEM XIV, PROPOSITION XXXV

Given an inclined plane and a limited vertical line, it is required to find a distance on the inclined plane which a body, starting from rest, will traverse in the same time as that needed to traverse both the vertical and the inclined plane.

Let AB be the vertical line and BC the inclined plane. It is required to lay off on BC a distance which a body, starting from rest, will traverse in a time equal to that which is occupied by fall through the vertical AB and by descent of the plane. Draw the horizontal line

AD, which intersects at E the prolongation of the inclined plane CB; lay off BF equal to BA, and about E as centre, with EF as radius describe the circle FIG. Prolong FE until it intersects the circumference at G. Choose a point H such that $GB : BF = BH : HF$. Draw the line HI tangent to the circle at I. At B draw the line BK perpendicular to FG, cutting the line

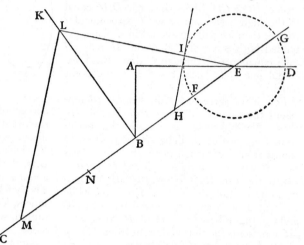

Fig. 97

EIL at L; also draw LM perpendicular to EL and cutting BC at M. Then, I say, BM is the distance which a body, starting from rest at B, will traverse in the same time which is required to descend from rest at A through both distances AB and BM. Lay off EN equal to EL; then since $GB : BF = BH : HF$, we shall have, *permutando*, $GB : BH = BF : HF$, and, *dividendo*, $GH : BH = BH : HF$. Consequently the rectangle $GH.HF$ is equal to the square on BH; but this same rectangle is also equal to the square on HI; therefore BH is equal to HI. Since, in the quadrilateral $ILBH$, the sides HB and HI are equal and since the angles at B and I are right angles, it follows that the sides BL and LI are also equal: but $EI = EF$; therefore the total length LE, or NE, is equal to the sum of LB and EF. If we subtract the common part EF, the remainder FN will be equal to LB: but, by construction, $FB = BA$ and, therefore, $LB = AB + BN$. If again we agree to represent the time of fall through AB by the length AB, then the time of descent along EB will be measured by EB; moreover, since EN is a mean proportional between ME and EB, it will represent the time of descent along the whole distance EM; therefore the difference of these distances, BM, will be traversed, after fall from EB, or

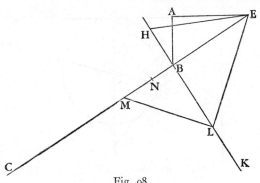

Fig. 98

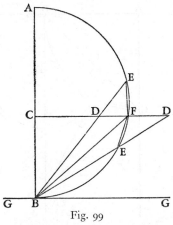

Fig. 99

AB, in a time which is represented by BN. But having already assumed the distance AB as a measure of the time of fall through AB, the time of descent along AB and BM is measured by $AB+BN$. Since EB measures the time of fall, from rest at E, along EB, the time from rest at B along BM will be the mean proportional between BE and BM, namely, BL. The time therefore for the path $AB+BM$, starting from rest at A is $AB+BN$; but the time for BM alone, starting from rest at B, is BL; and since it has already been shown that $BL=AB+BN$, the proposition follows.

Another and shorter proof is the following: Let BC be the inclined plane and BA the vertical; at B draw a perpendicular to EC, extending it both ways; lay off BH equal to the excess of BE over BA; make the angle HEL equal to the angle BHE; prolong EL until it cuts BK in L; at L draw LM perpendicular to EL and extend it till it meets BC in M; then, I say, BM is the portion of BC sought. For, since the angle MLE is a right angle, BL will be a mean proportional between MB and BE, while LE is a mean proportional between ME and BE; lay off EN equal to LE; then $NE=EL=LH$, and $HB=NE$-BL. But also $HB=NE$-$(NB+BA)$; therefore $BN+BA=BL$. If now we assume the length EB as a measure of the time of descent along EB, the time of descent, from rest at B, along BM will be represented by BL; but, if the descent along BM is from rest at E or at A, then the time of descent will be measured by BN; and AB will measure the time along AB. Therefore the time required to traverse AB and BM, namely, the sum of the distances AB and BN, is equal to the time of descent, from rest at B, along BM alone.   Q. E. F.

LEMMA

Let DC be drawn perpendicular to the diameter BA; from the extremity B draw the line BED at random; draw the line FB. Then, I say, FB is a mean proportional between DB and BE. Join the points E and F. Through B, draw the tangent BG which will be parallel to CD. Now, since the angle DBG is equal to the angle FDB, and since the alternate angle of GBD is equal to EFB, it follows that the triangles FDB and FEB are similar and hence $BD : BF = FB : BE$.

LEMMA

Let AC be a line which is longer than DF, and let the ratio of AB to BC be greater than that of DE to EF. Then, I say, AB is greater

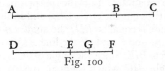

Fig. 100

than DE. For, if AB bears to BC a ratio greater than that of DE to EF, then DE will bear to some length shorter than EF, the same ratio which AB bears to BC. Call this length EG; then since $AB : BC = DE : EG$, it follows, componendo et convertendo, that $CA : AB = GD : DE$. But since CA is greater than GD, it follows that BA is greater than DE.

LEMMA

Let $ACIB$ be the quadrant of a circle; from B draw BE parallel to AC; about any point in the line BE describe a circle $BOES$, touching AB at B and intersecting the circumference of the quadrant at I. Join the points C and B; draw the line CI, prolonging it to S. Then, I say, the line CI is always less than CO. Draw the line AI touching the circle BOE. Then, if the line DI be drawn, it will be equal to DB;

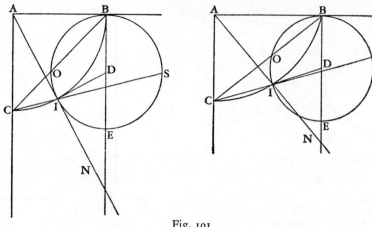

Fig. 101

but, since *DB* touches the quadrant, *DI* will also be tangent to it and will be at right angles to *AI;* thus *AI* touches the circle *BOE* at *I*. And since the angle *AIC* is greater than the angle *ABC*, subtending as it does a larger arc, it follows that the angle *SIN* is also greater than the angle *ABC*. Wherefore the arc *IES* is greater than the arc *BO*, and the line *CS*, being nearer the centre is longer than *CB*. Consequently *CO* is greater than *CI*, since *SC : CB= OC : CI*.

This result would be all the more marked if, as in the second figure, the arc *BIC* were less than a quadrant. For the perpendicular *DB* would then cut the circle *CIB;* and so also would *DI* which is equal to *BD;* the angle *DIA* would be obtuse and therefore the line *AIN* would cut the circle *BIE*. Since the angle *ABC* is less than the angle *AIC*, which is equal to *SIN*, and still less than the angle which the tangent at *I* would make with the line *SI*, it follows that the arc *SEI* is far greater than the arc *BO;* whence etc.   Q. E. D.

THEOREM XXII, PROPOSITION XXXVI

If from the lowest point of a vertical circle, a chord is drawn subtending an arc not greater than a quadrant, and if from the two ends of this chord two other chords be drawn to any point on the arc, the time of descent along the two latter chords will be shorter than along the first, and shorter also, by the same amount, than along the lower of these two latter chords.

Let *CBD* be an arc, not exceeding a quadrant, taken from a vertical circle whose lowest point is *C;* let *CD* be the chord subtending this arc, and let there be two other chords drawn from *C* and *D* to any point *B* on the arc. Then,

I say, the time of descent along the two chords *DB* and *BC* is shorter than along *DC* alone, or along *BC* alone, starting from rest at *B*. Through

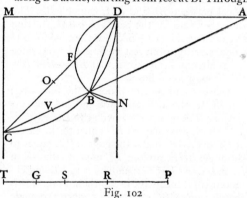

Fig. 102

the point *D*, draw the horizontal line *MDA* cutting *CB* extended at *A:* draw *DN* and *MC* at right angles to *MD*, and *BN* at right angles to *BD;* about the right-angled triangle *DBN* describe the semicircle *DFBN*, cutting *DC* at *F*. Choose the point *O* such that *DO* will be a mean proportional between *CD* and *DF;* in like manner select *V* so that *AV* is a mean proportional between *CA* and *AB*. Let the length *PS* represent the time of descent along the whole distance *DC* or *BC*, both of which require the same time. Lay off *PR* such that *CD : DO=timePS. timePR*. Then *PR* will represent the time in which a body, starting from *D*, will traverse the distance *DF*, while *RS* will measure the time in which the remaining distance, *FC*, will be traversed. But since *PS* is also the time of descent, from rest at *B*, along *BC*, and if we choose *T* such that *BC : CD=PS : PT* then *PT* will measure the time of descent from *A* to *C*, for we have already shown that DC is a mean proportional between AC and CB. Finally choose the point G such that $CA : AV = PT : PG$, then PG will be the time of descent from A to B, while GT will be the residual time of descent along BC following descent from A to B. But, since the diameter, DN, of the circle DFN is a vertical line, the chords DF and DB will be traversed in equal times; wherefore if one can prove that a body will traverse BC, after descent along DB, in a shorter time than it will FC after descent along DF he will have proved the theorem. But a body descending from D along DB will traverse BC in the same time as if it had come from A along AB, seeing that the body acquires the same momentum in descending along DB as along AB. Hence it remains only to show that descent along BC after AB is quicker than along FC after DF. But we have already shown that GT represents the time along BC after AB; also that RS measures the time along FC after DF. Accordingly it must be shown that RS is greater than GT, which may be done as follows: Since $SP : PR = CD : DO$, it follows, *invertendo et convertendo*, that $RS : SP = OC : CD$; also we have $SP : PT = DC : CA$. And since $TP : PG = CA : AV$, it follows, *invertendo*, that $PT : TG = AC : CV$, therefore, *ex æquali*, $RS : GT = OC : CV$. But, as we shall presently show, OC is greater than CV; hence the time RS is greater than the time GT, which was to be shown. Now, since CF is greater than CB and FD smaller than BA, it follows that $CD : DF > CA : AB$. But $CD : DF = CO : OF$, seeing that $CD : DO = DO : DF$; and $CA : AB = \overline{CV}^2 : \overline{VB}^2$. Therefore $CO : OF > CV : VB$, and, according to the preceding lemma, $CO > CV$. Besides this it is clear that the time of descent along DC is to the time along DBC as DOC is to the sum of DO and CV.

Scholium

From the preceding it is possible to infer that the path of quickest descent from one point to another is not the shortest path, namely, a straight line, but the arc of a circle. In the quadrant $BAEC$, having the side BC vertical, divide the arc AC into any number of equal parts, AD, DE, EF, FG, GC, and from C draw straight lines to the points A, D, E, F, G; draw also the straight lines AD, DE, EF, FG, GC. Evidently descent along the path ADC is quicker than along AC alone or along DC from rest at D. But a body, starting from rest at A, will traverse DC more quickly than the path ADC; while, if it starts from rest at A, it will

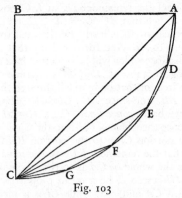

Fig. 103

traverse the path DEC in a shorter time than DC alone. Hence descent along the three chords $ADEC$, will take less time than along the two chords ADC. Similarly, following descent along ADE, the time required to traverse EFC is less than that needed for EC alone. Therefore descent is more rapid along the four chords $ADEFC$ than along the three $ADEC$. And finally a body, after descent along $ADEF$, will traverse the two chords, FGC, more quickly than FC alone. Therefore, along the five chords, $ADEFGC$, descent will be more rapid than along the four, $ADEFC$. Consequently the nearer the inscribed polygon approaches a circle the shorter is the time required for descent from A to C.

What has been proven for the quadrant holds true also for smaller arcs; the reasoning is the same.

Problem XV, Proposition XXXVII

Given a limited vertical line and an inclined plane of equal altitude; it is required to find a distance on the inclined plane which is equal to the vertical line and which is traversed in an interval equal to the time of fall along the vertical line.

Let AB be the vertical line and AC the inclined plane. We must locate, on the inclined plane, a distance equal to the vertical line AB and which will be traversed by a body starting from rest at A in the same time needed for fall along the vertical line. Lay off AD equal to AB,

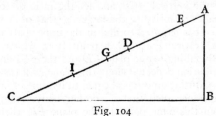

Fig. 104

and bisect the remainder DC at I. Choose the point E such that $AC : CI = CI : AE$ and lay off DG equal to AE. Clearly EG is equal to AD, and also to AB. And further, I say that EG is that distance which will be traversed by a body, starting from rest at A, in the same time which is required for that body to fall through the distance AB. For since $AC : CI = CI : AE = ID : DG$, we have, *convertendo*, $CA : AI = DI : IG$. And since the whole of CA is to the whole of AI as the portion CI is to the portion IG, it follows that the remainder IA is to the remainder AG as the whole of CA is to the whole of AI. Thus AI is seen to be a mean proportional between CA and AG, while CI is a mean proportional between CA and AE. If therefore, the time of fall along AB is represented by the length AB, the time along AC will be represented by AC, while CI, or ID, will measure the time along AE. Since AI is a mean proportional between CA and AG, and since CA is a measure of the time along the entire distance AC, it follows that AI is the time along AG, and the difference IC is the time along the difference GC; but DI was the time along AE. Consequently the lengths DI and IC measure the times along AE and CG respectively. Therefore the remainder DA represents the time along EG, which of course is equal to the time along AB.   Q. E. F.

Corollary

From this it is clear that the distance sought is bounded at each end by portions of the inclined plane which are traversed in equal times.

Problem XVI, Proposition XXXVIII

Given two horizontal planes cut by a vertical line, it is required to find a point on the upper part of the vertical line from which bodies may fall to the horizontal planes and there, having their motion deflected into a horizontal direction, will, during an interval equal to the time of fall, traverse distances which bear to each other any assigned ratio of a smaller quantity to a larger.

Let CD and BE be the horizontal planes cut by the vertical ACB, and let the ratio of the smaller quantity to the larger be that of N to FG. It is required to find in the upper part of the vertical line, AB, a point from which a body falling to the plane CD and there having its motion deflected along this plane, will traverse, during an interval equal to its time of fall a distance such that if another body, falling from this same point to the plane BE, there

have its motion deflected along this plane and continued during an interval equal to its time of fall, will traverse a distance which bears to the former distance the ratio of FG to N. Lay off GH equal to N, and select the point L so that $FH : HG = BC : CL$. Then, I say, L is the point sought. For, if we lay off CM equal to twice CL, and draw the line LM cutting the plane BE at O, then BO will be equal to twice BL. And since $FH : HG = BC : CL$, we have, *componendo et convertendo*, $HG : GF = N : GF = CL : LB = CM : BO$. It is clear that, since CM is double the distance LC, the space CM is that

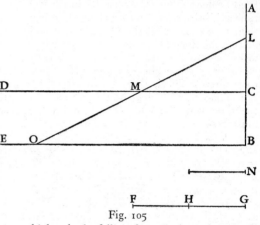

Fig. 105

which a body falling from L through LC will traverse in the plane CD; and, for the same reason, since BO is twice the distance BL, it is clear that BO is the distance which a body, after fall through LB, will traverse during an interval equal to the time of its fall through LB.

                                                        Q. E. F.

SAGR. Indeed, I think we may concede to our Academician, without flattery, his claim that in the principle laid down in this treatise he has established a new science dealing with a very old subject. Observing with what ease and clearness he deduces from a single principle the proofs of so many theorems, I wonder not a little how such a question escaped the attention of Archimedes, Apollonius, Euclid and so many other mathematicians and illustrious philosophers, especially since so many ponderous tomes have been devoted to the subject of motion.

SALV. There is a fragment of Euclid which treats of motion, but in it there is no indication that he ever began to investigate the property of acceleration and the manner in which it varies with slope. So that we may say the door is now opened, for the first time, to a new method fraught with numerous and wonderful results which in future years will command the attention of other minds.

SAGR. I really believe that just as, for instance, the few properties of the circle proven by Euclid in the Third Book of his *Elements* lead to many others more recondite, so the principles which are set forth in this little treatise will, when taken up by speculative minds, lead to many another more remarkable result; and it is to be believed that it will be so on account of the nobility of the subject, which is superior to any other in nature.

During this long and laborious day, I have enjoyed these simple theorems more than their proofs, many of which, for their complete comprehension, would require more than an hour each; this study, if you will be good enough to leave the book in my hands, is one which I mean to take up at my leisure after we have read the remaining portion which deals with the motion of projectiles; and this if agreeable to you we shall take up tomorrow.

SALV. I shall not fail to be with you.

• • •

FOURTH DAY

SALVIATI. Once more, Simplicio is here on time; so let us without delay take up the question of motion. The text of our Author is as follows:

THE MOTION OF PROJECTILES

In the preceding pages we have discussed the properties of uniform motion and of motion naturally accelerated along planes of all inclinations. I now propose to set forth those properties which belong to a body whose motion is compounded of two other motions, namely, one uniform and one naturally accelerated; these properties, well worth knowing, I propose to demonstrate in a rigid manner. This is the kind of motion seen in a moving projectile; its origin I conceive to be as follows:

Imagine any particle projected along a horizontal plane without friction; then we know, from what has been more fully explained in the preceding pages, that this particle will move along this same plane with a motion which is uniform and perpetual, provided the plane has no limits. But if the plane is limited and elevated, then the moving particle, which we imagine to be a heavy one, will on passing over the edge of the plane acquire, in addition to its previous uniform and perpetual motion, a downward propensity due to its own weight; so that the resulting motion which I call projection, is compounded of one which is uniform and horizontal and of another which is vertical and naturally accelerated. We now proceed to demonstrate some of its properties, the first of which is as follows:

THEOREM I, PROPOSITION I

A projectile which is carried by a uniform horizontal motion compounded with a naturally accelerated vertical motion describes a path which is a semi-parabola.

SAGR. Here, Salviati, it will be necessary to stop a little while for my sake and, I believe, also for the benefit of Simplicio; for it so happens that I have not gone very far in my study of Apollonius and am merely aware of the fact that he treats of the parabola and other conic sections, without an understanding of which I hardly think one will be able to follow the proof of other propositions depending upon them. Since even in this first beautiful theorem the author finds it necessary to prove that the path of a projectile is a parabola, and since, as I imagine, we shall have to deal with only this kind of curves, it will be absolutely necessary to have a thorough acquaintance, if not with all the properties which Apollonius has demonstrated for these figures, at least with those which are needed for the present treatment.

SALV. You are quite too modest, pretending ignorance of facts which not long ago you acknowledged as well known—I mean at the time when we were discussing the strength of materials and needed to use a certain theorem of Apollonius which gave you no trouble.

SAGR. I may have chanced to know it or may possibly have assumed it, so long as needed, for that discussion; but now when we have to follow all these demonstrations about such curves we ought not, as they say, to swallow it whole, and thus waste time and energy.

SIMP. Now even though Sagredo is, as I believe, well equipped for all his needs, I do not understand even the elementary terms; for although our philosophers have treated the motion of projectiles, I do not recall their having described the path of a projectile except to state in a general way that it is always a curved line, unless the projection be vertically upwards. But if the little Euclid which I have learned since our previous discussion does not enable me to understand the demonstrations which are to follow, then I shall be obliged to accept the theorems on faith without fully comprehending them.

SALV. On the contrary, I desire that you should understand them from the Author himself, who, when he allowed me to see this work of his, was good enough to prove for me two of the principal properties of the parabola because I did not happen to have at hand the books of Apollonius. These properties, which are the only ones we shall need in the present discussion, he proved in such a way that no prerequisite knowledge was required. These theorems are, indeed, given by Apollonius, but after many preceding ones, to follow which would take a long while. I wish to shorten our task by deriving the first property purely and simply from the mode of generation of the parabola, and proving the second immediately from the first.

Beginning now with the first, imagine a right cone, erected upon the circular base *ibkc* with apex at *l*. The section of this cone made by a

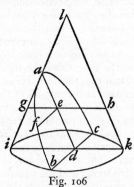

Fig. 106

plane drawn parallel to the side *lk* is the curve which is called a *parabola*. The base of this parabola *bc* cuts at right angles the diameter *ik* of the circle *ibkc*, and the axis *ad* is parallel to the side *lk;* now having taken any point *f* in the curve *bfa* draw the straight line *fe* parallel to *bd;* then, I say, the square of *bd* is to the square of *fe* in the same ratio as the axis *ad* is to the portion *ae*. Through the point *e* pass a plane parallel to the circle *ibkc*, producing in the cone a circular section whose diameter is the line *geh*. Since *bd* is at right angles to *ik* in the circle *ibk*, the square of *bd* is equal to the rectangle formed by *id* and *dk;* so also in the upper circle which passes through the points *gfh* the square of *fe* is equal to the rectangle formed by *ge* and *eh;* hence the square of *bd* is to the square of *fe* as the rectangle *id·dk* is to the rectangle *ge·eh*. And since the line *ed* is parallel to *hk*, the line *eh*, being parallel to *dk*, is equal to it; therefore the rectangle *id·dk* is to the rectangle *ge·eh* as *id* is to *ge*, that is, as *da* is to *ae;* whence also the rectangle *id·dk* is to the rectangle *ge·eh*, that is, the square of *bd* is to the square of *fe*, as the axis *da* is to the portion *ae*.   Q. E. D.

The other proposition necessary for this discussion we demonstrate as follows. Let us draw a parabola whose axis *ca* is prolonged upwards to a point *d;* from any point *b* draw the line *bc* parallel to the base of the parabola; if now the point *d* is chosen so that *da = ca*, then, I say, the straight line drawn through the points *b* and *d* will be

tangent to the parabola at *b*. For imagine, if possible, that this line cuts the parabola above or that its prolongation cuts it below, and through any point *g* in it draw the straight line *fge*. And

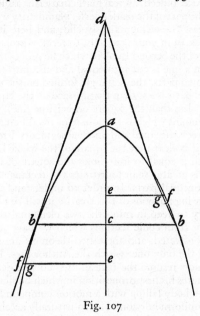

Fig. 107

since the square of *fe* is greater than the square of *ge*, the square of *fe* will bear a greater ratio to the square of *bc* than the square of *ge* to that of *bc;* and since, by the preceding proposition, the square of *fe* is to that of *bc* as the line *ea* is to *ca*, it follows that the line *ea* will bear to the line *ca* a greater ratio than the square of *ge* to that of *bc*, or, than the square of *ed* to that of *cd* (the sides of the triangles *deg* and *dcb* being proportional). But the line *ea* is to *ca*, or *da*, in the same ratio as four times the rectangle *ea·ad* is to four times the square of *ad*, or, what is the same, the square of *cd*, since this is four times the square of *ad;* hence four times the rectangle *ea·ad* bears to the square of *cd* a greater ratio than the square of *ed* to the square of *cd;* but that would make four times the rectangle *ea·ad* greater than the square of *ed;* which is false, the fact being just the opposite, because the two portions *ea* and *ad* of the line *ed* are not equal. Therefore the line *db* touches the parabola without cutting it.   Q. E. D.

SIMP. Your demonstration proceeds too rapidly and, it seems to me, you keep on assuming that all of Euclid's theorems are as familiar and available to me as his first axioms, which is far from true. And now this fact which you spring upon us, that four times the rectangle *ea·ad* is less than the square of *de* because the two portions *ea* and *ad* of the line *de* are not equal brings me little composure of mind, but rather leaves me in suspense.

SALV. Indeed, all real mathematicians assume on the part of the reader perfect familiarity with at least the elements of Euclid; and here it is necessary in your case only to recall a proposition of the Second Book in which he proves that when a line is cut into equal and also into two unequal parts, the rectangle formed on the unequal parts is less than that formed on the equal (*i. e.*, less than the square on half the line), by an amount which is the square of the difference between the equal and unequal segments. From this it is clear that the square of the whole line which is equal to four times the square of the half is greater than four times the rectangle of the unequal parts. In order to understand the following portions of this treatise it will be necessary to keep in mind the two elemental theorems from conic sections which we have just demonstrated; and these two theorems are indeed the only ones which the Author uses. We can now resume the text and see how he demonstrates his first proposition in which he shows that a body falling with a motion compounded of a uniform horizontal and a naturally accelerated one describes a semi-parabola.

Let us imagine an elevated horizontal line or plane *ab* along which a body moves with uniform speed from *a* to *b*. Suppose this plane to

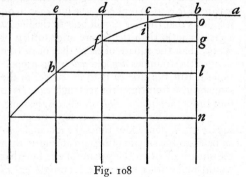

Fig. 108

end abruptly at *b;* then at this point the body will, on account of its weight, acquire also a natural motion downwards along the perpendicular *bn*. Draw the line *be* along the plane *ba* to represent the flow, or measure, of time; divide this line into a number of segments, *bc*, *cd*, *de*, representing equal intervals of time; from the points *b, c, d, e*, let fall lines which are parallel to the perpendicular *bn*. On the first of these lay off any distance *ci*, on the second a distance

four times as long, *df;* on the third, one nine times as long, *eh;* and so on, in proportion to the squares of *cb*, *db*, *eb*, or, we may say, in the squared ratio of these same lines. Accordingly, we see that while the body moves from *b* to *c* with uniform speed, it also falls perpendicularly through the distance *ci*, and at the end of the time-interval *bc* finds itself at the point *i*. In like manner at the end of the time-interval *bd*, which is the double of *bc*, the vertical fall will be four times the first distance *ci;* for it has been shown in a previous discussion that the distance traversed by a freely falling body varies as the square of the time; in like manner the space *eh* traversed during the time *be* will be nine times *ci;* thus it is evident that the distances *eh*, *df*, *ci* will be to one another as the squares of the lines *be*, *bd*, *bc*. Now from the points *i, f, h* draw the straight lines *io, fg, hl* parallel to *be;* these lines *hl, fg, io* are equal to *eb, db* and *cb*, respectively; so also are the lines *bo, bg, bl* respectively equal to *ci, df*, and *eh*. The square of *hl* is to that of *fg* as the line *lb* is to *bg;* and the square of *fg* is to that of *io* as *gb* is to *bo;* therefore the points *i, f, h*, lie on one and the same parabola. In like manner it may be shown that, if we take equal time-intervals of any size whatever, and if we imagine the particle to be carried by a similar compound motion, the positions of this particle, at the ends of these time-intervals, will lie on one and the same parabola.   Q. E. D.

SALV. This conclusion follows from the converse of the first of the two propositions given above. For, having drawn a parabola through the points *b* and *h*, any other two points, *f* and *i*, not falling on the parabola must lie either within or without; consequently the line *fg* is either longer or shorter than the line which terminates on the parabola. Therefore the square of *hl* will not bear to the square of *fg* the same ratio as the line *lb* to *bg*, but a greater or smaller; the fact is, however, that the square of *hl* *does* bear this same ratio to the square of *fg*. Hence the point *f* does lie on the parabola, and so do all the others.

SAGR. One cannot deny that the argument is new, subtle and conclusive, resting as it does upon this hypothesis, namely, that the horizontal motion remains uniform, that the vertical motion continues to be accelerated downwards in proportion to the square of the time, and that such motions and velocities as these combine without altering, disturbing, or hindering each other, so that as the motion proceeds the path of the projectile does not change into a different curve: but this, in my opinion, is impossible.

For the axis of the parabola along which we imagine the natural motion of a falling body to take place stands perpendicular to a horizontal surface and ends at the centre of the earth; and since the parabola deviates more and more from its axis no projectile can ever reach the centre of the earth or, if it does, as seems necessary, then the path of the projectile must transform itself into some other curve very different from the parabola.

SIMP. To these difficulties, I may add others. One of these is that we suppose the horizontal plane, which slopes neither up nor down, to be represented by a straight line as if each point on this line were equally distant from the centre, which is not the case; for as one starts from the middle and goes toward either end, he departs farther and farther from the centre [of the earth] and is therefore constantly going uphill. Whence if follows that the motion cannot remain uniform through any distance whatever, but must continually diminish. Besides, I do not see how it is possible to avoid the resistance of the medium which must destroy the uniformity of the horizontal motion and change the law of acceleration of falling bodies. These various difficulties render it highly improbable that a result derived from such unreliable hypotheses should hold true in practice.

SALV. All these difficulties and objections which you urge are so well founded that it is impossible to remove them; and, as for me, I am ready to admit them all, which indeed I think our Author would also do. I grant that these conclusions proved in the abstract will be different when applied in the concrete and will be fallacious to this extent, that neither will the horizontal motion be uniform nor the natural acceleration be in the ratio assumed, nor the path of the projectile a parabola, etc. But, on the other hand, I ask you not to begrudge our Author that which other eminent men have assumed even if not strictly true. The authority of Archimedes alone will satisfy everybody. In his *Mechanics* and in his first quadrature of the parabola he takes for granted that the beam of a balance or steelyard is a straight line, every point of which is equidistant from the common centre of all heavy bodies, and that the cords by which heavy bodies are suspended are parallel to each other.

Some consider this assumption permissible because, in practice, our instruments and the distances involved are so small in comparison with the enormous distance from the centre of the earth that we may consider a minute of arc on a great circle as a straight line, and may regard the perpendiculars let fall from its two extremities as parallel. For if in actual practice one had to consider such small quantities, it would be necessary first of all to criticise the architects who presume, by use of a plumbline, to erect high towers with parallel sides. I may add that, in all their discussions, Archimedes and the others considered themselves as located at an infinite distance from the centre of the earth, in which case their assumptions were not false, and therefore their conclusions were absolutely correct. When we wish to apply our proven conclusions to distances which, though finite, are very large, it is necessary for us to infer, on the basis of demonstrated truth, what correction is to be made for the fact that our distance from the centre of the earth is not really infinite, but merely very great in comparison with the small dimensions of our apparatus. The largest of these will be the range of our projectiles—and even here we need consider only the artillery—which, however great, will never exceed four of those miles of which as many thousand separate us from the centre of the earth; and since these paths terminate upon the surface of the earth only very slight changes can take place in their parabolic figure which, it is conceded, would be greatly altered if they terminated at the centre of the earth.

As to the perturbation arising from the resistance of the medium this is more considerable and does not, on account of its manifold forms, submit to fixed laws and exact description. Thus if we consider only the resistance which the air offers to the motions studied by us, we shall see that it disturbs them all and disturbs them in an infinite variety of ways corresponding to the infinite variety in the form, weight, and velocity of the projectiles. For as to velocity, the greater this is, the greater will be the resistance offered by the air; a resistance which will be greater as the moving bodies become less dense. So that although the falling body ought to be displaced in proportion to the square of the duration of its motion, yet no matter how heavy the body, if it falls from a very considerable height, the resistance of the air will be such as to prevent any increase in speed and will render the motion uniform; and in proportion as the moving body is less dense this uniformity will be so much the more quickly attained and after a shorter fall. Even horizontal motion which, if no impediment were offered, would be uniform and constant is altered by the resistance of the air and finally ceases; and here again the less dense the body the quicker the process. Of these properties of weight, of velocity, and also of form, infinite in number, it is not possible to give any exact description; hence, in order to handle this matter in a scientific way, it is necessary to cut loose from these difficulties; and having discovered and demonstrated the theorems, in the case of no resistance, to use them and apply them with such limitations as experience will teach. And the advantage of this method will not be small; for the material and shape of the projectile may be chosen, as dense and round as possible, so that it will encounter the least resistance in the medium. Nor will the spaces and velocities in general be so great but that we shall be easily able to correct them with precision.

In the case of those projectiles which we use, made of dense material and round in shape, or of lighter material and cylindrical in shape, such as arrows, thrown from a sling or crossbow, the deviation from an exact parabolic path is quite insensible. Indeed, if you will allow me a little greater liberty, I can show you, by two experiments, that the dimensions of our apparatus are so small that these external and incidental resistances, among which that of the medium is the most considerable, are scarcely observable.

I now proceed to the consideration of motions through the air, since it is with these that we are now especially concerned; the resistance of the air exhibits itself in two ways: first by offering greater impedance to less dense than to very dense bodies, and secondly by offering greater resistance to a body in rapid motion than to the same body in slow motion.

Regarding the first of these, consider the case of two balls having the same dimensions, but one weighing ten or twelve times as much as the other; one, say, of lead, the other of oak, both allowed to fall from an elevation of 150 or 200 cubits.

Experiment shows that they will reach the earth with slight difference in speed, showing us that in both cases the retardation caused by the air is small; for if both balls start at the same moment and at the same elevation, and if the leaden one be slightly retarded and the wooden one greatly retarded, then the former ought to reach the earth a considerable distance in advance of the latter, since it is ten times as heavy. But this does not happen; indeed, the gain in distance of one over the other does not amount to the hundredth part of the entire fall. And in the case of a ball of stone weighing only a third or half as much as one of lead, the difference in their times of reaching the earth will be scarcely noticeable. Now since the speed acquired by a

leaden ball in falling from a height of 200 cubits is so great that if the motion remained uniform the ball would, in an interval of time equal to that of the fall, traverse 400 cubits, and since this speed is so considerable in comparison with those which, by use of bows or other machines except fire arms, we are able to give to our projectiles, it follows that we may, without sensible error, regard as absolutely true those propositions which we are about to prove without considering the resistance of the medium.

Passing now to the second case, where we have to show that the resistance of the air for a rapidly moving body is not very much greater than for one moving slowly, ample proof is given by the following experiment. Attach to two threads of equal length—say four or five yards—two equal leaden balls and suspend them from the ceiling; now pull them aside from the perpendicular, the one through 80 or more degrees, the other through not more than four or five degrees; so that, when set free, the one falls, passes through the perpendicular, and describes large but slowly decreasing arcs of 160, 150, 140 degrees, etc.; the other swinging through small and also slowly diminishing arcs of 10, 8, 6, degrees, etc.

In the first place it must be remarked that one pendulum passes through its arcs of 180°, 160°, etc., in the same time that the other swings through its 10°, 8°, etc., from which it follows that the speed of the first ball is 16 and 18 times greater than that of the second. Accordingly, if the air offers more resistance to the high speed than to the low, the frequency of vibration in the large arcs of 180° or 160°, etc., ought to be less than in the small arcs of 10°, 8°, 4°, etc., and even less than in arcs of 2°, or 1°; but this prediction is not verified by experiment; because if two persons start to count the vibrations, the one the large, the other the small, they will discover that after counting tens and even hundreds they will not differ by a single vibration, not even by a fraction of one.

This observation justifies the two following propositions, namely, that vibrations of very large and very small amplitude all occupy the same time and that the resistance of the air does not affect motions of high speed more than those of low speed, contrary to the opinion hitherto generally entertained.

SAGR. On the contrary, since we cannot deny that the air hinders both of these motions, both becoming slower and finally vanishing, we have to admit that the retardation occurs in the same proportion in each case. But how? How, indeed, could the resistance offered to the one body be greater than that offered to the other except by the impartation of more momentum and speed to the fast body than to the slow? And if this is so the speed with which a body moves is at once the cause and measure of the resistance which it meets. Therefore, all motions, fast or slow, are hindered and diminished in the same proportion; a result, it seems to me, of no small importance.

SALV. We are able, therefore, in this second case to say that the errors, neglecting those which are accidental, in the results which we are about to demonstrate are small in the case of our machines where the velocities employed are mostly very great and the distances negligible in comparison with the semidiameter of the earth or one of its great circles.

SIMP. I would like to hear your reason for putting the projectiles of fire arms, i. e., those using powder, in a different class from the projectiles employed in bows, slings, and crossbows, on the ground of their not being equally subject to change and resistance from the air.

SALV. I am led to this view by the excessive and, so to speak, supernatural violence with which such projectiles are launched; for, indeed, it appears to me that without exaggeration one might say that the speed of a ball fired either from a musket or from a piece of ordnance is supernatural. For if such a ball be allowed to fall from some great elevation its speed will, owing to the resistance of the air, not go on increasing indefinitely; that which happens to bodies of small density in falling through short distances —I mean the reduction of their motion to uniformity—will also happen to a ball of iron or lead after it has fallen a few thousand cubits; this terminal or final speed is the maximum which such a heavy body can naturally acquire in falling through the air. This speed I estimate to be much smaller than that impressed upon the ball by the burning powder.

An appropriate experiment will serve to demonstrate this fact. From a height of one hundred or more cubits fire a gun loaded with a lead bullet, vertically downwards upon a stone pavement; with the same gun shoot against a similar stone from a distance of one or two cubits, and observe which of the two balls is the more flattened. Now if the ball which has come from the greater elevation is found to be the less flattened of the two, this will show that the air has hindered and diminished the speed initially imparted to the bullet by the powder, and that the air will not permit a bullet to acquire so great a

speed, no matter from what height it falls; for if the speed impressed upon the ball by the fire does not exceed that acquired by it in falling freely then its downward blow ought to be greater rather than less.

This experiment I have not performed, but I am of the opinion that a musket-ball or cannon-shot, falling from a height as great as you please, will not deliver so strong a blow as it would if fired into a wall only a few cubits distant, i. e., at such a short range that the splitting or rending of the air will not be sufficient to rob the shot of that excess of supernatural violence given it by the powder.

The enormous momentum of these violent shots may cause some deformation of the trajectory, making the beginning of the parabola flatter and less curved than the end; but, so far as our Author is concerned, this is a matter of small consequence in practical operations, the main one of which is the preparation of a table of ranges for shots of high elevation, giving the distance attained by the ball as a function of the angle of elevation; and since shots of this kind are fired from mortars using small charges and imparting no supernatural momentum they follow their prescribed paths very exactly.

But now let us proceed with the discussion in which the Author invites us to the study and investigation of the motion of a body when that motion is compounded of two others; and first the case in which the two are uniform, the one horizontal, the other vertical.

THEOREM II, PROPOSITION II

When the motion of a body is the resultant of two uniform motions, one horizontal, the other perpendicular, the square of the resultant momentum is equal to the sum of the squares of the two component momenta.

Let us imagine any body urged by two uniform motions and let *ab* represent the vertical displacement, while *bc* represents the displace-

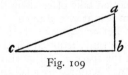

Fig. 109

ment which, in the same interval of time, takes place in a horizontal direction. If then the distances *ab* and *bc* are traversed, during the same time-interval, with uniform motions the corresponding momenta will be to each other as the distances *ab* and *bc* are to each other; but the body which is urged by these two motions describes the diagonal *ac;* its momentum is proportional to *ac.* Also the square of *ac* is equal to the sum of the squares of *ab* and *bc.* Hence the square of the resultant momentum is equal to the sum of the squares of the two momenta *ab* and *bc.*

Q. E. D.

Simp. At this point there is just one slight difficulty which needs to be cleared up; for it seems to me that the conclusion just reached contradicts a previous proposition in which it is claimed that the speed of a body coming from *a* to *b* is equal to that in coming from *a* to *c;* while now you conclude that the speed at *c* is greater than that at *b.*

Salv. Both propositions, Simplicio, are true, yet there is a great difference between them. Here we are speaking of a body urged by a single motion which is the resultant of two uniform motions, while there we were speaking of two bodies each urged with naturally accelerated motions, one along the vertical *ab* the other along the inclined plane *ac.* Besides the time-intervals were there not supposed to be equal, that along the incline *ac* being greater than that along the vertical *ab;* but the motions of which we now speak, those along *ab, bc, ac,* are uniform and simultaneous.

Simp. Pardon me; I am satisfied; pray go on.

Salv. Our Author next undertakes to explain what happens when a body is urged by a motion compounded of one which is horizontal and uniform and of another which is vertical but naturally accelerated; from these two components results the path of a projectile, which is a parabola. The problem is to determine the speed of the projectile at each point. With this purpose in view our Author sets forth as follows the manner, or rather the method, of measuring such speed along the path which is taken by a heavy body starting from rest and falling with a naturally accelerated motion.

Theorem III, Proposition III

Let the motion take place along the line *ab,* starting from rest at *a,* and in this line choose any point *c.* Let *ac* represent the time, or the measure of the time, required for the body to fall through the space *ac;* let *ac* also represent the velocity at *c* acquired by a fall through the distance *ac.* In the line *ab* select any other point *b.* The problem now is to determine the velocity at *b* acquired by a body in falling through the distance *ab* and to express this in terms of the velocity at *c,* the measure of which is the length *ac.* Take *as* a mean proportional between *ac* and *ab.* We shall prove that the velocity at *b* is to

that at *c* as the length *as* is to the length *ac.* Draw the horizontal line *cd,* having twice the length of *ac,* and *be,* having twice the length of *ba.* It then follows, from the preceding theorems, that

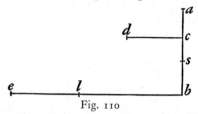

Fig. 110

a body falling through the distance *ac,* and turned so as to move along the horizontal *cd* with a uniform speed equal to that acquired on reaching *c* will traverse the distance *cd* in the same interval of time as that required to fall with accelerated motion from *a* to *c.* Likewise *be* will be traversed in the same time as *ba.* But the time of descent through *ab* is *as;* hence the horizontal distance *be* is also traversed in the time *as.* Take a point *l* such that the time *as* is to the time *ac* as *be* is to *bl;* since the motion along *be* is uniform, the distance *bl,* if traversed with the speed acquired at *b,* will occupy the time *ac;* but in this same time-interval, *ac,* the distance *cd* is traversed with the speed acquired in *c.* Now two speeds are to each other as the distances traversed in equal intervals of time. Hence the speed at *c* is to the speed at *b* as *cd* is to *bl.* But since *dc* is to *be* as their halves, namely, as *ca* is to *ba,* and since *be* is to *bl* as *ba* is to *sa;* it follows that *dc* is to *bl* as *ca* is to *sa.* In other words, the speed at *c* is to that at *b* as *ca* is to *sa,* that is, as the time of fall through *ab.*

The method of measuring the speed of a body along the direction of its fall is thus clear; the speed is assumed to increase directly as the time.

But before we proceed further, since this discussion is to deal with the motion compounded of a uniform horizontal one and one accelerated vertically downwards—the path of a projectile, namely, a parabola—it is necessary that we define some common standard by which we may estimate the velocity, or momentum of both motions; and since from the innumerable uniform velocities one only, and that not selected at random, is to be compounded with a velocity acquired by naturally accelerated motion, I can think of no simpler way of selecting and measuring this than to assume another of the same kind.[1] For the sake of clearness, draw the verti-

---

[1] Galileo here proposes to employ as a standard of velocity the terminal speed of a body falling freely from a given height. Trans.

cal line *ac* to meet the horizontal line *bc*. *Ac* is
the height and *bc* the amplitude of the semi-
parabola *ab*, which is the resultant of the two
motions, one that of a body falling from rest at
a, through the distance *ac*, with naturally ac-

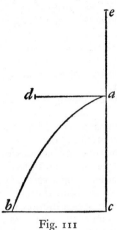

Fig. 111

celerated motion, the other a uniform motion
along the horizontal *ad*. The speed acquired at
c by a fall through the distance *ac* is determined
by the height *ac;* for the speed of a body falling
from the same elevation is always one and the
same; but along the horizontal one may give a
body an infinite number of uniform speeds.
However, in order that I may select one out of
this multitude and separate it from the rest in a
perfectly definite manner, I will extend the
height *ca* upwards to *e* just as far as is necessary
and will call this distance *ae* the "sublimity."
Imagine a body to fall from rest at *e*; it is clear
that we may make its terminal speed at *a* the
same as that with which the same body travels
along the horizontal line *ad*; this speed will be
such that, in the time of descent along *ea*, it will
describe a horizontal distance twice the length
of *ea*. This preliminary remark seems necessary.

The reader is reminded that above I have
called the horizontal line *cb* the "amplitude" of
the semi-parabola *ab*; the axis *ac* of this parabola, I have called its "altitude"; but the line *ea*
the fall along which determines the horizontal
speed I have called the "sublimity." These matters having been explained, I proceed with the
demonstration.

SAGR. Allow me, please, to interrupt in order
that I may point out the beautiful agreement
between this thought of the Author and the
views of Plato concerning the origin of the
various uniform speeds with which the heavenly bodies revolve. The latter chanced upon the
idea that a body could not pass from rest to any
given speed and maintain it uniformly except
by passing through all the degrees of speed intermediate between the given speed and rest.
Plato thought that God, after having created
the heavenly bodies, assigned them the proper
and uniform speeds with which they were forever to revolve; and that He made them start
from rest and move over definite distances under a natural and rectilinear acceleration such
as governs the motion of terrestrial bodies. He
added that once these bodies had gained their
proper and permanent speed, their rectilinear
motion was converted into a circular one, the
only motion capable of maintaining uniformity, a motion in which the body revolves without either receding from or approaching its desired goal. This conception is truly worthy of
Plato; and it is to be all the more highly prized
since its underlying principles remained hidden
until discovered by our Author who removed
from them the mask and poetical dress and set
forth the idea in correct historical perspective.
In view of the fact that astronomical science
furnishes us such complete information concerning the size of the planetary orbits, the distances of these bodies from their centres of
revolution, and their velocities, I cannot help
thinking that our Author (to whom this idea of
Plato was not unknown) had some curiosity to
discover whether or not a definite "sublimity"
might be assigned to each planet, such that, if
it were to start from rest at this particular height
and to fall with naturally accelerated motion
along a straight line, and were later to change
the speed thus acquired into uniform motion,
the size of its orbit and its period of revolution
would be those actually observed.

SALV. I think I remember his having told me
that he once made the computation and found
a satisfactory correspondence with observation. But he did not wish to speak of it, lest in
view of the odium which his many new discoveries had already brought upon him, this
might be adding fuel to the fire. But if any one
desires such information he can obtain it for
himself from the theory set forth in the present
treatment.

We now proceed with the matter in hand,
which is to prove:

PROBLEM I, PROPOSITION IV

*To determine the momentum of a projectile at
each particular point in its given parabolic path.*

Let *bec* be the semi-parabola whose amplitude is *cd* and whose height is *db*, which latter

extended upwards cuts the tangent of the parabola *ca* in *a*. Through the vertex draw the horizontal line *bi* parallel to *cd*. Now if the amplitude *cd* is equal to the entire height *da*, then *bi* will be equal to *ba* and also to *bd;* and if we take *ab* as the measure of the time required for fall through the distance *ab* and also of the momentum acquired at *b* in consequence of its fall from rest at *a*, then if we turn into a horizontal direction the momentum acquired by fall through *ab*, the space traversed in the same interval of time will be represented by *dc* which is twice *bi*. But a body which falls from rest at *b* along the line *bd* will during the same time-interval fall through the height of the parabola *bd*. Hence a body falling from rest at *a*, turned into a horizontal direction with the speed *ab*, will traverse a space equal to *dc*. Now if one superposes upon this motion a fall along *bd*, traversing the height *bd* while the parabola *bc* is described, then the momentum of the body at

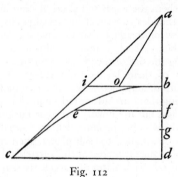

Fig. 112

the terminal point *c* is the resultant of a uniform horizontal momentum, whose value is represented by *ab*, and of another momentum acquired by fall from *b* to the terminal point *d* or *c;* these two momenta are equal. If, therefore, we take *ab* to be the measure of one of these momenta, say, the uniform horizontal one, then *bi*, which is equal to *bd*, will represent the momentum acquired at *d* or *c;* and *ia* will represent the resultant of these two momenta, that is, the total momentum with which the projectile, travelling along the parabola, strikes at *c*.

With this in mind let us take any point on the parabola, say *e*, and determine the momentum with which the projectile passes that point. Draw the horizontal *ef* and take *bg* a mean proportional between *bd* and *bf*. Now since *ab*, or *bd*, is assumed to be the measure of the time and of the momentum acquired by falling from rest at *b* through the distance *bd*, it follows that *bg*

will measure the time and also the momentum acquired at *f* by fall from *b*. If therefore we lay off *bo*, equal to *bg*, the diagonal line joining *a* and *o* will represent the momentum at the point *e;* because the length *ab* has been assumed to represent the momentum at *b* which, after diversion into a horizontal direction, remains constant; and because *bo* measures the momentum at *f* or *e*, acquired by fall, from rest at *b*, through the height *bf*. But the square of *ao* equals the sum of the squares of *ab* and *bo*. Hence the theorem sought.

SAGR. The manner in which you compound these different momenta to obtain their resultant strikes me as so novel that my mind is left in no small confusion. I do not refer to the composition of two uniform motions, even when unequal, and when one takes place along a horizontal, the other along a vertical direction; because in this case I am thoroughly convinced that the resultant is a motion whose square is equal to the sum of the squares of the two components. The confusion arises when one undertakes to compound a uniform horizontal motion with a vertical one which is naturally accelerated. I trust, therefore, we may pursue this discussion more at length.

SIMP. And I need this even more than you since I am not yet as clear in my mind as I ought to be concerning those fundamental propositions upon which the others rest. Even in the case of the two uniform motions, one horizontal, the other perpendicular, I wish to understand better the manner in which you obtain the resultant from the components. Now, Salviati, you understand what we need and what we desire.

SALV. Your request is altogether reasonable and I will see whether my long consideration of these matters will enable me to make them clear to you. But you must excuse me if in the explanation I repeat many things already said by the Author.

Concerning motions and their velocities or momenta whether uniform or naturally accelerated, one cannot speak definitely until he has established a measure for such velocities and also for time. As for time we have the already widely adopted hours, first minutes and second minutes. So for velocities, just as for intervals of time, there is need of a common standard which shall be understood and accepted by everyone, and which shall be the same for all. As has already been stated, the Author considers the velocity of a freely falling body adapted to this purpose, since this velocity increases according to the same law in all parts of the world; thus for instance the speed acquired by a leaden ball of a pound weight starting from rest and falling vertically through the height of, say, a spear's length is the same in all places; it is therefore excellently adapted for representing the momentum acquired in the case of natural fall.

It still remains for us to discover a method of measuring momentum in the case of uniform motion in such a way that all who discuss the subject will form the same conception of its size and velocity. This will prevent one person from imagining it larger, another smaller, than it really is; so that in the composition of a given uniform motion with one which is accelerated different men may not obtain different values for the resultant. In order to determine and represent such a momentum and particular speed our Author has found no better method than to use the momentum acquired by a body in naturally accelerated motion. The speed of a body which has in this manner acquired any momentum whatever will, when converted into uniform motion, retain precisely such a speed as, during a time-interval equal to that of the fall, will carry the body through a distance equal to twice that of the fall. But since this matter is one which is fundamental in our discussion it is well that we make it perfectly clear by means of some particular example.

Let us consider the speed and momentum acquired by a body falling through the height, say, of a spear as a standard which we may use in the measurement of other speeds and momenta as occasion demands; assume for instance that the time of such a fall is four seconds; now in order to measure the speed acquired from a fall through any other height, whether greater or less, one must not conclude that these speeds bear to one another the same ratio as the heights of fall; for instance, it is not true that a fall through four times a given height confers a speed four times as great as that acquired by descent through the given height; because the speed of a naturally accelerated motion does not vary in proportion to the time. As has been shown above, the ratio of the spaces is equal to the square of the ratio of the times.

If, then, as is often done for the sake of brevity, we take the same limited straight line as the measure of the speed, and of the time, and also of the space traversed during that time, it follows that the duration of fall and the speed acquired by the same body in passing over any other distance, is not represented by this second distance, but by a mean proportional between the two distances. This I can better illustrate by

an example. In the vertical line ac, lay off the portion ab to represent the distance traversed by a body falling freely with accelerated motion: the time of fall may be represented by any limited straight line, but for the sake of brevity, we shall represent it by the same length ab; this length may also be employed as a measure of the momentum and speed acquired during the motion; in short, let ab be a measure of the various physical quantities which enter this discussion.

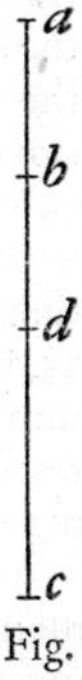

Having agreed arbitrarily upon ab as a measure of these three different quantities, namely, space, time, and momentum, our next task is to find the time required for fall through a given vertical distance ac, also the momentum acquired at the terminal point c, both of which are to be expressed in terms of the time and momentum represented by ab. These two required quantities are obtained by laying off ad, a mean proportional between ab and ac; in other words, the time of fall from a to c is represented by ad on the same scale on which we agreed that the time of fall from a to b should be represented by ab. In like manner, we may say that the momentum acquired at c is related to that acquired at b, in the same manner that the line ad is related to ab, since the velocity varies directly as the time, a conclusion, which although employed as a postulate in Proposition III, is here amplified by the Author.

This point being clear and well-established we pass to the consideration of the momentum in the case of two compound motions, one of which is compounded of a uniform horizontal and a uniform vertical motion, while the other is compounded of a uniform horizontal and a naturally accelerated vertical motion. If both components are uniform, and one at right angles to the other, we have already seen that the square of the resultant is obtained by adding the squares of the components [p. 244], as will be clear from the following illustration.

Fig. 113

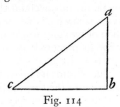

Fig. 114

Let us imagine a body to move along the vertical ab with a uniform momentum of 3, and on reaching *b* to move toward *c* with a momentum of 4, so that during the same time-interval it will traverse 3 cubits along the vertical and 4 along the horizontal. But a particle which moves with the resultant velocity will, in the same time, traverse the diagonal *ac*, whose length is not 7 cubits—the sum of *ab* (3) and *bc* (4)—but 5, which is *in potenza* equal to the sum of 3 and 4, that is, the squares of 3 and 4 when added make 25, which is the square of *ac*, and is equal to the sum of the squares of *ab* and *bc*. Hence *ac* is represented by the side—or we may say the root—of a square whose area is 25, namely 5.

As a fixed and certain rule for obtaining the momentum which results from two uniform momenta, one vertical, the other horizontal, we have therefore the following: take the square of each, add these together, and extract the square root of the sum, which will be the momentum resulting from the two. Thus, in the above example, the body which in virtue of its vertical motion would strike the horizontal plane with a momentum of 3, would, owing to its horizontal motion alone, strike at *c* with a momentum of 4; but if the body strikes with a momentum which is the resultant of these two, its blow will be that of a body moving with a momentum of 5; and such a blow will be the same at all points of the diagonal *ac*, since its components are always the same and never increase or diminish.

Let us now pass to the consideration of a uniform horizontal motion compounded with the vertical motion of a freely falling body starting from rest. It is at once clear that the diagonal which represents the motion compounded of these two is not a straight line, but, as has been demonstrated, a semi-parabola, in which the momentum is always increasing because the speed of the vertical component is always increasing. Wherefore, to determine the momentum at any given point in the parabolic diagonal, it is necessary first to fix upon the uniform horizontal momentum and then, treating the body as one falling freely, to find the vertical momentum at the given point; this latter can be determined only by taking into account the duration of fall, a consideration which does not enter into the composition of two uniform motions where the velocities and momenta are always the same; but here where one of the component motions has an initial value of zero and increases its speed in direct proportion to the time, it follows that the time must determine the speed at the assigned point. It only remains to obtain the momentum resulting from these two components (as in the case of uniform motions) by placing

the square of the resultant equal to the sum of the squares of the two components. But here again it is better to illustrate by means of an example.

On the vertical *ac* lay off any portion *ab* which we shall employ as a measure of the space traversed by a body falling freely along the perpendicular, likewise as a measure of the time and also of the speed or, we may say, of the momenta. It is at once clear that if the momentum of a body at *b*, after having fallen from rest at *a*, be

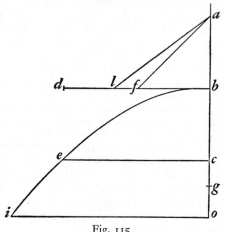

Fig. 115

diverted along the horizontal direction *bd*, with uniform motion, its speed will be such that, during the time-interval *ab*, it will traverse a distance which is represented by the line *bd* and which is twice as great as *ab*. Now choose a point *c*, such that *bc* shall be equal to *ab*, and through *c* draw the line *ce* equal and parallel to *bd*; through the points *b* and *e* draw the parabola *bei*. And since, during the time-interval *ab*, the horizontal distance *bd* or *ce*, double the length *ab*, is traversed with the momentum *ab*, and since during an equal time-interval the vertical distance *bc* is traversed, the body acquiring at *c* a momentum represented by the same horizontal, *bd*, it follows that during the time *ab* the body will pass from *b* to *e* along the parabola *be*, and will reach *e* with a momentum compounded of two momenta each equal to *ab*. And since one of these is horizontal and the other vertical, the square of the resultant momentum is equal to the sum of the squares of these two components, *i. e.*, equal to twice either one of them.

Therefore, if we lay off the distance *bf*, equal to *ba*, and draw the diagonal *af*, it follows that the momentum at *e* will exceed that of a body at *b* after having fallen from *a*, or what is the same thing, will exceed the horizontal momentum along *bd*, in the ratio of *af* to *ab*.

Suppose now we choose for the height of fall a distance *bo* which is not equal to but greater than *ab*, and suppose that *bg* represents a mean proportional between *ba* and *bo;* then, still retaining *ba* as a measure of the distance fallen through, from rest at *a*, to *b*, also as a measure of the time and of the momentum which the falling body acquires at *b*, it follows that *bg* will be the measure of the time and also of the momentum which the body acquires in falling from *b* to *o*. Likewise just as the momentum *ab* during the time *ab* carried the body a distance along the horizontal equal to twice *ab*, so now, during the time-interval *bg*, the body will be carried in a horizontal direction through a distance which is greater in the ratio of *bg* to *ba*. Lay off *lb* equal to *bg* and draw the diagonal *al*, from which we have a quantity compounded of two velocities, one horizontal, the other vertical; these determine the parabola. The horizontal and uniform velocity is that acquired at *b* in falling from *a;* the other is that acquired at *o*, or, we may say, at *i*, by a body falling through the distance *bo*, during a time measured by the line *bg*, which line *bg* also represents the momentum of the body. And in like manner we may, by taking a mean proportional between the two heights, determine the momentum at the extreme end of the parabola where the height is less than the sublimity *ab;* this mean proportional is to be drawn along the horizontal in place of *bf*, and also another diagonal in place of *af*, which diagonal will represent the momentum at the extreme end of the parabola.

To what has hitherto been said concerning the momenta, blows or shocks of projectiles, we must add another very important consideration; to determine the force and energy of the shock it is not sufficient to consider only the speed of the projectiles, but we must also take into account the nature and condition of the target which, in no small degree, determines the efficiency of the blow. First of all, it is well known that the target suffers violence from the speed of the projectile in proportion as it partly or entirely stops the motion; because if the blow falls upon an object which yields to the impulse without resistance such a blow will be of no effect; likewise, when one attacks his enemy with a spear and overtakes him at an instant when he is fleeing with equal speed, there will be no blow but merely a harmless touch. But if the shock falls upon an object which yields only in part then the blow will not have its full effect, but the damage will be in proportion to the excess of the speed of the projectile over that of the receding body; thus, for example, if the shot reaches the target with a speed of 10 while the latter recedes with a speed of 4, the momentum and shock will be represented by 6. Finally the blow will be a maximum, in so far as the projectile is concerned, when the target does not recede at all but if possible completely resists and stops the motion of the projectile. I have said *in so far as the projectile is concerned* because if the target should approach the projectile the shock of collision would be greater in proportion as the sum of the two speeds is greater than that of the projectile alone.

Moreover it is to be observed that the amount of yielding in the target depends not only upon the quality of the material, as regards hardness, whether it be of iron, lead, wool, etc., but also upon its position. If the position is such that the shot strikes it at right angles, the momentum imparted by the blow will be a maximum; but if the motion be oblique, that is to say slanting, the blow will be weaker; and more and more so in proportion to the obliquity; for, no matter how hard the material of the target thus situated, the entire momentum of the shot will not be spent and stopped; the projectile will slide by and will, to some extent, continue its motion along the surface of the opposing body.

All that has been said above concerning the amount of momentum in the projectile at the extremity of the parabola must be understood to refer to a blow received on a line at right angles to this parabola or along the tangent to the parabola at the given point; for, even though the motion has two components, one horizontal, the other vertical, neither will the momentum along the horizontal nor that upon a plane perpendicular to the horizontal be a maximum, since each of these will be received obliquely.

SAGR. Your having mentioned these blows and shocks recalls to my mind a problem, or rather a question, in mechanics of which no author has given a solution or said anything which diminishes my astonishment or even partly relieves my mind.

My difficulty and surprise consist in not being able to see whence and upon what principle is derived the energy and immense force which makes its appearance in a blow; for instance, we see the simple blow of a hammer, weighing not more than 8 or 10 lbs., overcoming resistances which, without a blow, would not yield to the weight of a body producing impetus by pressure alone, even though that body weighed many hundreds of pounds. I would like to discover a method of measuring the force of such a percussion. I can hardly think it infinite, but incline rather to the view that it has its limit and can be counterbalanced and measured by other forces, such as weights, or by levers or screws or other mechanical instruments which are used to multiply forces in a manner which I satisfactorily understand.

SALV. You are not alone in your surprise at this effect or in obscurity as to the cause of this remarkable property. I studied this matter myself for a while in vain; but my confusion merely increased until finally meeting our Academician I received from him great consolation. First he told me that he also had for a long time been groping in the dark; but later he said that, after having spent some thousands of hours in speculating and contemplating thereon, he had arrived at some notions which are far removed from our earlier ideas and which are remarkable for their novelty. And since now I know that you would gladly hear what these novel ideas are I shall not wait for you to ask but promise that, as soon as our discussion of projectiles is completed, I will explain all these fantasies, or if you please, vagaries, as far as I can recall them from the words of our Academician. In the meantime we proceed with the propositions of the author.

PROPOSITION V, PROBLEM

Having given a parabola, find the point, in its axis extended upwards, from which a particle must fall in order to describe this same parabola.

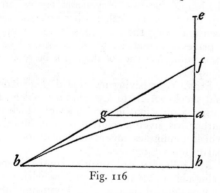

Fig. 116

Let ab be the given parabola, hb its amplitude, and he its axis extended. The problem is to find the point e from which a body must fall

in order that, after the momentum which it acquires at a has been diverted into a horizontal direction, it will describe the parabola ab. Draw the horizontal ag, parallel to bh, and having laid off af equal to ah, draw the straight line bf which will be a tangent to the parabola at b, and will intersect the horizontal ag at g: choose e such that ag will be a mean proportional between af and ae. Now I say that e is the point above sought. That is, if a body falls from rest at this point e, and if the momentum acquired at the point a be diverted into a horizontal direction, and compounded with the momentum acquired at h in falling from rest at a, then the body will describe the parabola ab. For if we understand ea to be the measure of the time of fall from e to a, and also of the momentum acquired at a, then ag (which is a mean proportional between ea and af) will represent the time and momentum of fall from f to a or, what is the same thing, from a to h; and since a body falling from e, during the time ea, will, owing to the momentum acquired at a, traverse at uniform speed a horizontal distance which is twice ea, it follows that, the body will if impelled by the same momentum, during the time-interval ag traverse a distance equal to twice ag which is the half of bh. This is true because, in the case of uniform motion, the spaces traversed vary directly as the times. And likewise if the motion be vertical and start from rest, the body will describe the distance ah in the time ag. Hence the amplitude bh and the altitude ah are traversed by a body in the same time. Therefore the parabola ab will be described by a body falling from the sublimity of e.

Q. E. F.

COROLLARY

Hence it follows that half the base, or amplitude, of the semi-parabola (which is one-quarter of the entire amplitude) is a mean proportional between its altitude and the sublimity from which a falling body will describe this same parabola.

PROPOSITION VI, PROBLEM

Given the sublimity and the altitude of a parabola, to find its amplitude.

Let the line ac, in which lie the given altitude cb and sublimity ab, be perpendicular to the horizontal line cd. The problem is to find the amplitude, along the horizontal cd, of the semi-parabola which is described with the sublimity ba and altitude bc. Lay off cd equal to twice the mean proportional between cb and

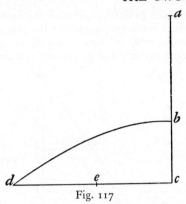

Fig. 117

ba. Then cd will be the amplitude sought, as is evident from the preceding proposition.

THEOREM. PROPOSITION VII

If projectiles describe semi-parabolas of the same amplitude, the momentum required to describe that one whose amplitude is double its altitude is less than that required for any other.

Let bd be a semi-parabola whose amplitude cd is double its altitude cb; on its axis extended upwards lay off ba equal to its altitude bc. Draw the line ad which will be a tangent to the parabola at d and will cut the horizontal line be at the point e, making be equal to bc and also to ba. It is evident that this parabola will be described by a projectile whose uniform horizontal momentum is that which it would acquire at b in falling from rest at a and whose naturally accelerated vertical momentum is that of the body falling to c, from rest at b. From this it follows that the momentum at the terminal point d, compounded of these two, is represented by the diagonal ae, whose square is equal to the sum of the squares of the two components. Now let gd be any other parabola whatever having the same amplitude cd, but whose altitude cg is either greater or less than the altitude bc. Let hd be the tangent cutting the horizontal through g at k. Select a point l such that hg : gk = gk : gl. Then from a preceding proposition [V], it follows that gl will be the height from which a body must fall in order to describe the parabola gd.

Let gm be a mean proportional between ab and gl; then gm will [Prop. IV] represent the time and momentum acquired at g by a fall from l; for ab has been assumed as a measure of both time and momentum. Again let gn be a mean proportional between bc and cg; it will then represent the time and momentum which the body acquires at c in falling from g. If now we join m and n, this line mn will represent the momentum at d of the projectile traversing the parabola dg; which momentum is, I say, greater that that of the projectile travelling along the parabola bd whose measure was given by ae. For since gn has been taken as a mean proportional between bc and gc; and since bc is equal to be and also to kg (each of them being the half of dc) it follows that cg : gn = gn : gk, and as cg or (hg) is to gk so is $\overline{ng}^2$ to $\overline{gk}^2$: but by construction hg : gk = gk : gl. Hence $\overline{ng}^2 : \overline{gk}^2 = gk : gl$. But gk : gl = $\overline{gk}^2 : \overline{gm}^2$, since gm is a mean proportional between kg and gl. Therefore the three squares ng, kg, mg form a continued proportion, $\overline{gn}^2 : \overline{gk}^2 = gk^2 : gm^2$. And the sum of the two extremes which is equal to the square of mn is greater

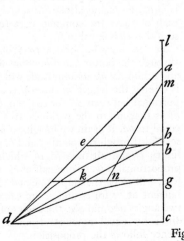

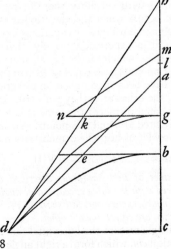

Fig. 118

than twice the square of *gk;* but the square of *ae* is double the square of *gk.* Hence the square of *mn* is greater than the square of *ae* and the length *mn* is greater than the length *ae.*

Q. E. D.

COROLLARY

Conversely, it is evident that less momentum will be required to send a projectile from the terminal point *d* along the parabola *bd* than along any other parabola having an elevation greater or less than that of the parabola *bd*, for which the tangent at *d* makes an angle of 45° with the horizontal. From which it follows that if projectiles are fired from the terminal point *d*, all having the same speed, but each having a different elevation, the maximum range, *i.e.*, amplitude of the semi-parabola or of the entire parabola, will be obtained when the elevation is 45°: the other shots, fired at angles greater or less will have a shorter range.

SAGR. The force of rigid demonstrations such as occur only in mathematics fills me with wonder and delight. From accounts given by gunners, I was already aware of the fact that in the use of cannon and mortars, the maximum range, that is the one in which the shot goes farthest, is obtained when the elevation is 45° or, as they say, at the sixth point of the quadrant; but to understand why this happens far outweighs the mere information obtained by the testimony of others or even by repeated experiment.

SALV. What you say is very true. The knowledge of a single fact acquired through a discovery of its causes prepares the mind to understand and ascertain other facts without need of recourse to experiment, precisely as in the present case, where by argumentation alone the Author proves with certainty that the maximum range occurs when the elevation is 45°. He thus demonstrates what has perhaps never been observed in experience, namely, that of other shots those which exceed or fall short of 45° by equal amounts have equal ranges; so that if the balls have been fired one at an elevation of 7 points, the other at 5, they will strike the level at the same distance: the same is true if the shots are fired at 8 and at 4 points, at 9 and at 3, etc. Now let us hear the demonstration of this.

THEOREM. PROPOSITION VIII

The amplitudes of two parabolas described by projectiles fired with the same speed, but at angles of elevation which exceed and fall short of 45° by equal amounts, are equal to each other.

In the triangle *mcb* let the horizontal side *bc* and the vertical *cm*, which form a right angle at

c, be equal to each other; then the angle *mbc* will be a semi-right angle; let the line *cm* be prolonged to *d*, such a point that the two angles at *b*, namely *mbe* and *mbd*, one above and the

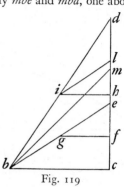

Fig. 119

other below the diagonal *mb*, shall be equal. It is now to be proved that in the case of two parabolas described by two projectiles fired from *b* with the same speed, one at the angle of *ebc*, the other at the angle of *dbc*, their amplitudes will be equal. Now since the external angle *bmc* is equal to the sum of the internal angles *mdb* and *dbm* we may also equate to them the angle *mbc;* but if we replace the angle *dbm* by *mbe*, then this same angle *mbc* is equal to the two *mbe* and *bdc*: and if we subtract from each side of this equation the angle *mbe*, we have the remainder *bdc* equal to the remainder *ebc.* Hence the two triangles *dcb* and *bce* are similar. Bisect the straight lines *dc* and *ec* in the points *h* and *f* : and draw the lines *hi* and *fg* parallel to the horizontal *cb*, and choose *l* such that $dh : hi = ih : hl$. Then the triangle *ihl* will be similar to *ihd*, and also to the triangle *egf;* and since *ih* and *gf* are equal, each being half of *bc*, it follows that *hl* is equal to *fe* and also to *fc;* and if we add to each of these the common part *fh*, it will be seen that *ch* is equal to *fl.*

Let us now imagine a parabola described through the points *h* and *b* whose altitude is *hc* and sublimity *hl*. Its amplitude will be *cb* which is double the length *hi* since *hi* is a mean proportional between *dh* (or *ch*) and *hl*. The line *db* is tangent to the parabola at *b*, since *ch* is equal to *hd*. If again we imagine a parabola described through the points *f* and *b*, with a sublimity *fl* and altitude *fc*, of which the mean proportional is *fg*, or one-half of *cb*, then, as before, will *cb* be the amplitude and the line *eb* a tangent at *b;* for *ef* and *fc* are equal. But the two angles *dbc* and *ebc*, the angles of elevation, differ by equal amounts from a 45° angle. Hence follows the proposition.

THEOREM. PROPOSITION IX

The amplitudes of two parabolas are equal when their altitudes and sublimities are inversely proportional.

Let the altitude *gf* of the parabola *fh* bear to the altitude *cb* of the parabola *bd* the same ratio which the sublimity *ba* bears to the sublimity *fe;* then, I say, the amplitude *hg* is equal to the amplitude *dc.* For since the first of these quantities, *gf*, bears to the second, *cb*, the same ratio which the third, *ba*, bears to the fourth, *fe*, it follows that the area of the rectangle *gf·fe* is equal to that of the rectangle *cb·ba;* therefore

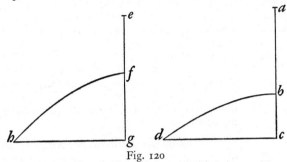

Fig. 120

squares which are equal to these rectangles are equal to each other. But [by Proposition VI] the square of half of *gh* is equal to the rectangle *gf·fe;* and the square of half of *cd* is equal to rectangle *cb·ba.* Therefore these squares and their sides and the doubles of their sides are equal. But these last are the amplitudes *gh* and *cd.* Hence follows the proposition.

LEMMA FOR THE FOLLOWING PROPOSITION

If a straight line be cut at any point whatever and mean proportionals between this line and each of its parts be taken, the sum of the squares of these mean proportionals is equal to the square of the entire line.

Let the line *ab* be cut at *c.* Then, I say, that the square of the mean proportional between

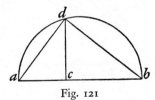

Fig. 121

ab and *ac* plus the square of the mean proportional between *ab* and *cb* is equal to the square of the whole line *ab.* This is evident as soon as

we describe a semicircle upon the entire line *ab*, erect a perpendicular *cd* at *c*, and draw *da* and *db.* For *da* is a mean proportional between *ab* and *ac* while *db* is a mean proportional between *ab* and *bc:* and since the angle *adb*, inscribed in a semicircle, is a right angle the sum of the squares of the lines *da* and *db* is equal to the square of the entire line *ab.* Hence follows the proposition.

THEOREM. PROPOSITION X

The momentum acquired by a particle at the terminal point of any semi-parabola is equal to that which it would acquire in falling through a vertical distance equal to the sum of the sublimity and the altitude of the semi-parabola.

Let *ab* be a semi-parabola having a sublimity *da* and an altitude *ac*, the sum of which is the perpendicular *dc.* Now, I say, the momentum of the particle at *b* is the same as that which it would acquire in falling freely from *d* to *c.* Let us take the length of *dc* itself as a measure of time and momentum, and lay off *cf* equal to the mean proportional between *cd* and *da;* also lay off *ce* a mean proportional between *cd* and *ca.* Now *cf* is the measure of the time and of the momentum acquired by fall, from rest at *d*, through the distance *da;* while *ce* is the time and momentum of fall, from rest at *a*, through the distance *ca;* also the diagonal *ef* will represent a momentum which is the resultant of these two, and is therefore the momentum at the terminal point of the parabola, *b.*

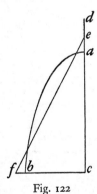

Fig. 122

And since *dc* has been cut at some point *a* and since *cf* and *ce* are mean proportionals between the whole of *cd* and its parts, *da* and *ac*, it follows, from the preceding lemma, that the sum of the squares of these mean proportionals is equal to the square of the whole: but the square of *ef* is also equal to the sum of these same squares; whence it follows that the line *ef* is equal to *dc.*

Accordingly, the momentum acquired at *c* by a particle in falling from *d* is the same as that acquired at *b* by a particle traversing the parabola *ab.*   Q. E. D.

Corollary

Hence it follows that, in the case of all parabolas where the sum of the sublimity and altitude is a constant, the momentum at the terminal point is a constant.

Problem. Proposition XI

Given the amplitude and the speed at the terminal point of a semi-parabola, to find its altitude.

Let the given speed be represented by the vertical line *ab*, and the amplitude by the horizontal line *bc*; it is required to find the sublimity of the semi-parabola whose terminal speed is *ab* and amplitude *bc*. From what precedes [Cor. Prop. V] it is clear that half the amplitude *bc* is a mean proportional between the altitude

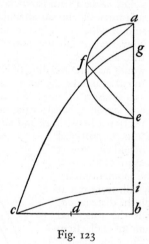

Fig. 123

and sublimity of the parabola of which the terminal speed is equal, in accordance with the preceding proposition, to the speed acquired by a body in falling from rest at *a* through the distance *ab*. Therefore the line *ba* must be cut at a point such that the rectangle formed by its two parts will be equal to the square of half *bc*, namely *bd*. Necessarily, therefore, *bd* must not exceed the half of *ba;* for of all the rectangles formed by parts of a straight line the one of greatest area is obtained when the line is divided into two equal parts. Let *e* be the middle point of the line *ab;* and now if *bd* be equal to *be* the problem is solved; for *be* will be the altitude and *ea* the sublimity of the parabola. (Incidentally, we may observe a consequence already demonstrated, namely: of all parabolas described with any given terminal speed that

for which the elevation is 45° will have the maximum amplitude.)

But suppose that *bd* is less than half of *ba*, which is to be divided in such a way that the rectangle upon its parts may be equal to the square of *bd*. Upon *ea* as diameter describe a semicircle *efa*, in which draw the chord *af*, equal to *bd*: join *fe* and lay off the distance *eg* equal to *fe*. Then the rectangle *bg·ga* plus the square of *eg* will be equal to the square of *ea*, and hence also to the sum of the squares of *af* and *fe*. If now we subtract the equal squares of *fe* and *ge* there remains the rectangle *bg·ga* equal to the square of *af*, that is, of *bd*, a line which is a mean proportional between *bg* and *ga;* from which it is evident that the semi-parabola whose amplitude is *bc* and whose terminal speed is represented by *ba* has an altitude *bg* and a sublimity *ga*.

If however we lay off *bi* equal to *ga*, then *bi* will be the altitude of the semi-parabola *ic*, and *ia* will be its sublimity. From the preceding demonstration we are able to solve the following problem.

Problem. Proposition XII

To compute and tabulate the amplitudes of all semi-parabolas which are described by projectiles fired with the same initial speed.

From the foregoing it follows that, whenever the sum of the altitude and sublimity is a con-

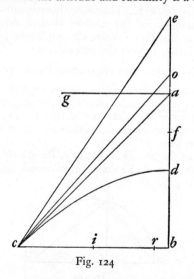

Fig. 124

stant vertical height for any set of parabolas, these parabolas are described by projectiles having the same initial speed; all vertical heights thus obtained are therefore included between two parallel horizontal lines. Let cb represent a horizontal line and ab a vertical line of equal length; draw the diagonal ac; the angle acb will be one of 45°; let d be the middle point of the vertical line ab. Then the semi-parabola dc is the one which is determined by the sublimity ad and the altitude db, while its terminal speed at c is that which would be acquired at b by a particle falling from rest at a. If now ag be drawn parallel to bc, the sum of the altitude and sublimity for any other semi-parabola having the same terminal speed will, in the manner explained, be equal to the distance between the parallel lines ag and bc. Moreover, since it has already been shown that the amplitudes of two semi-parabolas are the same when their angles of elevation differ from 45° by like amounts, it follows that the same computation which is employed for the larger elevation will serve also for the smaller. Let us also assume 10000 as the greatest amplitude for a parabola whose angle of elevation is 45°; this then will be the length of the line ba and the amplitude of the semi-parabola bc. This number, 10000, is selected because in these calculations we employ a table of tangents in which this is the value of the tangent of 45°. And now, coming down to business, draw the straight line ce making an acute angle ecb greater than acb: the problem now is to draw the semi-parabola to which the line ec is a tangent and for which the sum of the sublimity and the altitude is the distance ba. Take the length of the tangent be from the table of tangents, using the angle bce as an argument: let f be the middle point of be; next find a third proportional to bf and bi (the half of bc) which is of necessity greater than fa. Call this fo. We have now discovered that, for the parabola inscribed in the triangle ecb having the tangent ce and the amplitude cb, the altitude is bf and the sublimity fo. But the total length of bo exceeds the distance between the parallels ag and cb, while our problem was to keep it equal to this distance: for both the parabola sought and the parabola dc are described by projectiles fired from c with the same speed. Now since an infinite number of greater and smaller parabolas, similar to each other, may be described within the angle bce we must find another parabola which like cd has for the sum of its altitude and sublimity the height ba, equal to bc.

Therefore lay off cr so that, $ob:ba = bc:cr$; then cr will be the amplitude of a semi-parabola

for which bce is the angle of elevation and for which the sum of the altitude and sublimity is the distance between the parallels ga and cb, as desired. The process is therefore as follows: One draws the tangent of the given angle bce; takes half of this tangent, and adds to it the quantity, fo, which is a third proportional to the half of this tangent and the half of bc; the desired amplitude cr is then found from the following proportion $ob:ba = bc:cr$. For example, let the angle ecb be one of 50°; its tangent is 11918, half of which, namely bf, is 5959; half of bc is 5000; the third proportional of these halves is 4195, which added to bf gives the value 10154 for bo. Further, as ob is to ab, that is, as 10154 is to 10000, so is bc, or 10000 (each being the tangent of 45°) to cr, which is the amplitude sought and which has the value 9848, the maximum amplitude being bc, or 10000. The amplitudes of the entire parabolas are double these, namely, 19696 and 20000. This is also the amplitude of a parabola whose angle of elevation is 40°, since it deviates by an equal amount from one of 45°.

SAGR. In order to thoroughly understand this demonstration I need to be shown how the third proportional of bf and bi is, as the Author indicates, necessarily greater than fa.

SALV. This result can, I think, be obtained as follows. The square of the mean proportional between two lines is equal to the rectangle formed by these two lines. Therefore the square of bi (or of bd which is equal to bi) must be equal to the rectangle formed by fb and the desired third proportional. This third proportional is necessarily greater than fa because the rectangle formed by bf and fa is less than the square of bd by an amount equal to the square of df, as shown in Euclid, II. 1. Besides it is to be observed that the point f, which is the middle point of the tangent eb, falls in general above a and only once at a; in which cases it is self-evident that the third proportional to the half of the tangent and to the sublimity bi lies wholly above a. But the Author has taken a case where it is not evident that the third proportional is always greater than fa, so that when laid off above the point f it extends beyond the parallel ag.

Now let us proceed. It will be worth while, by the use of this table, to compute another giving the altitudes of these semi-parabolas described by projectiles having the same initial speed. The construction is as follows:

Amplitudes of semi-parabolas described with the same initial speed.

Angle of Elevation		Angle of Elevation
45°	10000	
46	9994	44°
47	9976	43
48	9945	42
49	9902	41
50	9848	40
51	9782	39
52	9704	38
53	9612	37
54	9511	36
55	9396	35
56	9272	34
57	9136	33
58	8989	32
59	8829	31
60	8659	30
61	8481	29
62	8290	28
63	8090	27
64	7880	26
65	7660	25
66	7431	24
67	7191	23
68	6944	22
69	6692	21
70	6428	20
71	6157	19
72	5878	18
73	5592	17
74	5300	16
75	5000	15
76	4694	14
77	4383	13
78	4067	12
79	3746	11
80	3420	10
81	3090	9
82	2756	8
83	2419	7
84	2079	6
85	1736	5
86	1391	4
87	1044	3
88	698	2
89	349	1

Altitudes of semi-parabolas described with the same initial speed.

Angle of Elevation		Angle of Elevation	
1°	3	46°	5173
2	13	47	5346
3	28	48	5523
4	50	49	5698
5	76	50	5868
6	108	51	6038
7	150	52	6207
8	194	53	6379
9	245	54	6546
10	302	55	6710
11	365	56	6873
12	432	57	7033
13	506	58	7190
14	585	59	7348
15	670	60	7502
16	760	61	7649
17	855	62	7796
18	955	63	7939
19	1060	64	8078
20	1170	65	8214
21	1285	66	8346
22	1402	67	8474
23	1527	68	8597
24	1685	69	8715
25	1786	70	8830
26	1922	71	8940
27	2061	72	9045
28	2204	73	9144
29	2351	74	9240
30	2499	75	9330
31	2653	76	9415
32	2810	77	9493
33	2967	78	9567
34	3128	79	9636
35	3289	80	9698
36	3456	81	9755
37	3621	82	9806
38	3793	83	9851
39	3962	84	9890
40	4132	85	9924
41	4302	86	9951
42	4477	87	9972
43	4654	88	9987
44	4827	89	9998
45	5000	90	10000

PROBLEM. PROPOSITION XIII

From the amplitudes of semi-parabolas given in the preceding table to find the altitudes of each of the parabolas described with the same initial speed.

Let bc denote the given amplitude; and let ob, the sum of the altitude and sublimity, be the measure of the initial speed which is under-

stood to remain constant. Next we must find and determine the altitude, which we shall accomplish by so dividing ob that the rectangle contained by its parts shall be equal to the square of half the amplitude, bc. Let f denote this point of division and d and i be the middle points of ob and bc respectively. The square of ib is equal to the rectangle bf·fo; but the square of do is equal to the sum of the rectangle bf·fo and the square of fd. If, therefore, from the square of do we subtract the square of bi which is equal to the rectangle bf·fo, there will remain the square of fd. The altitude in question, bf, is now obtained by adding to this length, fd, the line bd. The process is then as follows: From the square of half of bo which is known, subtract the square of bi which is also known; take the square root of the remainder and add to it the known length db; then you have the required altitude, bf.

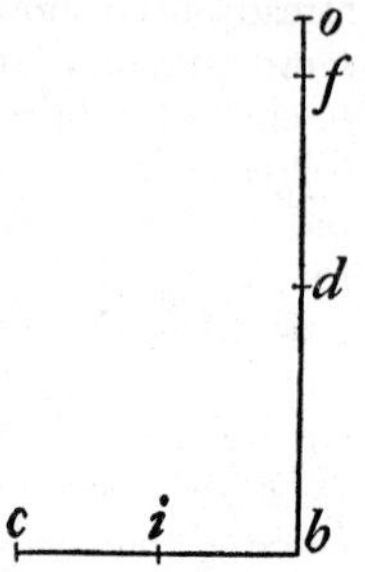

Example. To find the altitude of a semi-parabola described with an angle of elevation of 55°. From the preceding table the amplitude is seen to be 9396, of which the half is 4698, and the square 22071204. When this is subtracted from the square of the half of bo, which is always 25,000,000, the remainder is 2928796, of which the square root is approximately 1710. Adding this to the half of bo, namely 5000, we have 6710 for the altitude of bf.

Fig. 125

It will be worth while to add a third table giving the altitudes and sublimities for parabolas in which the amplitude is a constant.

SAGR. I shall be very glad to see this; for from it I shall learn the difference of speed and force required to fire projectiles over the same range with what we call mortar shots. This difference will, I believe, vary greatly with the elevation so that if, for example, one wished to employ an elevation of 3° or 4°, or 87° or 88° and yet give the ball the same range which it had with an elevation of 45° (where we have shown the initial speed to be a minimum) the excess of force required will, I think, be very great.

SALV. You are quite right, sir; and you will find that in order to perform this operation completely, at all angles of elevation, you will have to make great strides toward an infinite speed. We pass now to the consideration of the table.

Table giving the altitudes and sublimities of parabolas of constant amplitude, namely 10000, computed for each degree of elevation.

Angle of Elevation	Altitude	Sublimity	Angle of Elevation	Altitude	Sublimity
1°	87	286533	46°	5177	4828
2	175	142450	47	5363	4662
3	262	95802	48	5553	4502
4	349	71531	49	5752	4345
5	437	57142	50	5959	4196
6	525	47573	51	6174	4048
7	614	40716	52	6399	3906
8	702	35587	53	6635	3765
9	792	31565	54	6882	3632
10	881	28367	55	7141	3500
11	972	25720	56	7413	3372
12	1063	23518	57	7699	3247
13	1154	21701	58	8002	3123
14	1246	20056	59	8332	3004
15	1339	18663	60	8600	2887
16	1434	17405	61	9020	2771
17	1529	16355	62	9403	2658
18	1624	15389	63	9813	2547
19	1722	14522	64	10251	2438
20	1820	13736	65	10722	2331
21	1919	13024	66	11230	2226
22	2020	12376	67	11779	2122
23	2123	11778	68	12375	2020
24	2226	11230	69	13025	1919
25	2332	10722	70	13237	1819
26	2439	10253	71	14521	1721
27	2547	9814	72	15388	1624
28	2658	9404	73	16354	1528
29	2772	9020	74	17437	1433
30	2887	8659	75	18660	1339
31	3008	8336	76	20054	1246
32	3124	8001	77	21657	1154
33	3247	7699	78	23523	1062
34	3373	7413	79	25723	972
35	3501	7141	80	28356	881
36	3633	6882	81	31569	792
37	3768	6635	82	35577	702
38	3906	6395	83	40222	613
39	4049	6174	84	47572	525
40	4196	5959	85	57150	437
41	4346	5752	86	71503	349
42	4502	5553	87	95405	262
43	4662	5362	88	143181	174
44	4828	5177	89	286499	87
45	5000	5000	90	infinita	

PROPOSITION XIV

To find for each degree of elevation the altitudes and sublimities of parabolas of constant amplitude.

The problem is easily solved. For if we assume a constant amplitude of 10000, then half the tangent at any angle of elevation will be the altitude. Thus, to illustrate, a parabola having an angle of elevation of 30° and an amplitude of 10000, will have an altitude of 2887, which is approximately one-half the tangent. And now the altitude having been found, the sublimity is derived as follows. Since it has been proved that half the amplitude of a semi-parabola is the mean proportional between the altitude and sublimity, and since the altitude has already been found, and since the semi-amplitude is a constant, namely 5000, it follows that if we divide the square of the semi-amplitude by the altitude we shall obtain the sublimity sought. Thus in our example the altitude was found to be 2887: the square of 5000 is 25,000,-000 which divided by 2887 gives the approximate value of the sublimity, namely 8659.

SALV. Here we see, first of all, how very true is the statement made above, that, for different angles of elevation, the greater the deviation from the mean, whether above or below, the greater the initial speed required to carry the projectile over the same range. For since the speed is the resultant of two motions, namely, one horizontal and uniform, the other vertical and naturally accelerated; and since the sum of the altitude and sublimity represents this speed, it is seen from the preceding table that this sum is a minimum for an elevation of 45° where the altitude and sublimity are equal, namely, each 5000; and their sum 10000. But if we choose a greater elevation, say 50°, we shall find the altitude 5959, and the sublimity 4196, giving a sum of 10155; in like manner we shall find that this is precisely the value of the speed at 40° elevation, both angles deviating equally from the mean.

Secondly, it is to be noted that, while equal speeds are required for each of two elevations that are equidistant from the mean, there is this curious alternation, namely, that the altitude and sublimity at the greater elevation correspond inversely to the sublimity and altitude at the lower elevation. Thus in the preceding example, an elevation of 50° gives an altitude of 5959 and a sublimity of 4196; while an elevation of 40° corresponds to an altitude of 4196 and a sublimity of 5959. And this holds true in general; but it is to be remembered that, in order to escape tedious calculations, no account has been taken of fractions which are of little moment in comparison with such large numbers.

SAGR. I note also in regard to the two components of the initial speed that the higher the shot the less is the horizontal and the greater the vertical component; on the other hand, at lower elevations where the shot reaches only a small height the horizontal component of the initial speed must be great. In the case of a projectile fired at an elevation of 90°, I quite understand that all the force in the world would not be sufficient to make it deviate a single finger's breadth from the perpendicular and that it would necessarily fall back into its initial position; but, in the case of zero elevation, when the shot is fired horizontally, I am not so certain that some force, less than infinite, would not carry the projectile some distance; thus not even a cannon can fire a shot in a perfectly horizontal direction, or as we say, point blank, that is, with no elevation at all. Here, I admit, there is some room for doubt. The fact I do not deny outright, because of another phenomenon apparently no less remarkable, but yet one for which I have conclusive evidence. This phenomenon is the impossibility of stretching a rope in such a way that it shall be at once straight and parallel to the horizon; the fact is that the cord always sags and bends and that no force is sufficient to stretch it perfectly straight.

SALV. In this case of the rope then, Sagredo, you cease to wonder at the phenomenon because you have its demonstration; but if we consider it with more care we may possibly discover some correspondence between the case of the gun and that of the string. The curvature of the path of the shot fired horizontally appears to result from two forces, one (that of the weapon) drives it horizontally and the other (its own weight) draws it vertically downward. So in stretching the rope you have the force which pulls it horizontally and its own weight which acts downwards. The circumstances in these two cases are, therefore, very similar. If then you attribute to the weight of the rope a power and energy sufficient to oppose and overcome any stretching force, no matter how great, why deny this power to the bullet?

Besides I must tell you something which will both surprise and please you, namely, that a cord stretched more or less tightly assumes a curve which closely approximates the parabola. This similarity is clearly seen if you draw a parabolic curve on a vertical plane and then invert it so that the apex will lie at the bottom and the base remain horizontal; for, on hanging a chain below the base, one end attached to each extremity of the base, you will observe that, on slackening the chain more or less, it bends and fits itself to the parabola; and the coincidence is more exact in proportion as the parabola is drawn with less curvature or, so to speak, more stretched; so that using parabolas described with elevations less than 45° the chain fits its parabola almost perfectly.

SAGR. Then with a fine chain one would be able to quickly draw many parabolic lines upon a plane surface.

SALV. Certainly, and with no small advantage as I shall show you later.

SIMP. But before going further, I am anxious to be convinced at least of that proposition of which you say that there is a rigid demonstration; I refer to the statement that it is impossible by any force whatever to stretch a cord so that it will lie perfectly straight and horizontal.

SAGR. I will see if I can recall the demonstration; but in order to understand it, Simplicio, it will be necessary for you to take for granted concerning machines what is evident not alone from experiment but also from theoretical considerations, namely, that the velocity of a moving body, even when its force is small, can overcome a very great resistance exerted by a slowly moving body, whenever the velocity of the moving body bears to that of the resisting body a greater ratio than the resistance of the resisting body to the force of the moving body.

SIMP. This I know very well for it has been demonstrated by Aristotle in his *Questions in Mechanics*; it is also clearly seen in the lever and the steelyard where a counterpoise weighing not more than 4 pounds will lift a weight of 400, provided that the distance of the counterpoise from the axis about which the steelyard rotates be more than one hundred times as great as the distance between this axis and the point of support for the large weight. This is true because the counterpoise in its descent traverses a space more than one hundred times as great as that moved over by the large weight in the same time; in other words, the small counterpoise moves with a velocity which is more than one hundred times as great as that of the large weight.

SAGR. You are quite right; you do not hesitate to admit that however small the force of the moving body it will overcome any resistance, however great, provided it gains more in velocity than it loses in force and weight. Now let us return to the case of the cord. In the accompanying figure *ab* represents a line passing through two fixed points *a* and *b;* at the extremities of this line hang, as you see, two large weights *c* and *d*, which stretch it with great force and keep it truly straight, seeing that it is merely a line without weight. Now I wish to remark, that if from the middle point of this line, which we may call e, you suspend any small weight, say h, the line ab will yield toward the point f and on account of its elongation will compel the two heavy weights c and d to rise. This I shall demonstrate as follows: with the points a and b as centres describe the two quadrants, eig and elm; now since the two semidiameters ai and bl are equal to ae and eb, the remainders fi and fl are the excesses of the lines af and fb over ae and eb; they therefore deter-

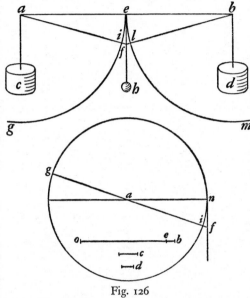

Fig. 126

mine the rise of the weights c and d, assuming of course that the weight h has taken the position f. But the weight h will take the position f, whenever the line ef which represents the descent of h bears to the line fi—that is, to the rise of the weights c and d—a ratio which is greater than the ratio of the weight of the two large bodies to that of the body h. Even when the weights of c and d are very great and that of h very small this will happen; for the excess of the weights c and d over the weight of h can never be so great but that the excess of the tangent ef over the segment fi may be proportionally greater. This may be proved as follows: Draw a circle of diameter gai: draw the line bo such that the ratio of its length to another length $c, c > d$, is the same as the ratio of the weights c and d to the weight h. Since $c > d$, the ratio of bo to d is greater than that of bo to c. Take be a third proportional to ob and d: prolong the diameter

gi to a point f such that $gi:if = oe:eb$; and from the point f draw the tangent fn; then since we already have $oe:eb = gi:if$, we shall obtain, by compounding ratios, $ob:eb = gf:if$. But d is a mean proportional between ob and be; while nf is a mean proportional between gf and fi. Hence nf bears to fi the same ratio as that of cb to d, which is greater than that of the weights c and d to the weight h. Since then the descent, or velocity, of the weight h bears to the rise, or velocity, of the weights c and d a greater ratio than the weight of the bodies c and d bears to the weight of h, it is clear that the weight h will descend and the line ab will cease to be straight and horizontal.

And now this which happens in the case of a weightless cord ab when any small weight h is attached at the point e, happens also when the cord is made of ponderable matter but without any attached weight; because in this case the material of which the cord is composed functions as a suspended weight.

SIMP. I am fully satisfied. So now Salviati can explain, as he promised, the advantage of such a chain and, afterwards, present the speculations of our Academician on the subject of impulsive forces.

SALV. Let the preceding discussions suffice for to-day; the hour is already late and the time remaining will not permit us to clear up the subjects proposed; we may therefore postpone our meeting until another and more opportune occasion.

SAGR. I concur in your opinion, because after various conversations with intimate friends of our Academician I have concluded that this question of impulsive forces is very obscure, and I think that, up to the present, none of those who have treated this subject have been able to clear up its dark corners which lie almost beyond the reach of human imagination; among the various views which I have heard expressed one, strangely fantastic, remains in my memory, namely, that impulsive forces are indeterminate, if not infinite. Let us, therefore, await the convenience of Salviati. Meanwhile, tell me what is this which follows the discussion of projectiles.

SALV. These are some theorems pertaining to the centres of gravity of solids, discovered by our Academician in his youth, and undertaken by him because he considered the treatment of Federigo Comandino to be somewhat incomplete. The propositions which you have before you would, he thought, meet the deficiencies of Comandino's book. The investigation was undertaken at the instance of the Illustrious Marquis Guidobaldo dal Monte, a very distinguished mathematician of his day, as is evidenced by his various publications. To this gentleman our Academician gave a copy of this work, hoping to extend the investigation to other solids not treated by Comandino. But a little later there chanced to fall into his hands the book of the great geometrician, Luca Valerio, where he found the subject treated so completely that he left off his own investigations, although the methods which he employed were quite different from those of Valerio.

Sagr. Please be good enough to leave this volume with me until our next meeting so that I may be able to read and study these propositions in the order in which they are written.

Salv. It is a pleasure to comply with your request and I only hope that the propositions will be of deep interest to you.

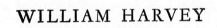

WILLIAM HARVEY

BIOGRAPHICAL NOTE
William Harvey, 1578–1657

Harvey was born at Folkestone on April 1, 1578, the eldest of the seven sons of Thomas Harvey, a prosperous Kentish yeoman. At the age of ten he was sent to the King's School at Canterbury and five years later to Caius-Gonvil College, Cambridge, where he took his A.B. degree in 1597. To prepare himself for a medical career he went to the University of Padua, then the most celebrated school of medicine. Harvey was there while Galileo was achieving his first fame at Padua. He followed the anatomy lectures of the great Fabricius of Aquapendente and in the spring of 1602 took his degree at Padua; later that same year he was made a Doctor of Medicine at Cambridge.

Shortly afterwards, Harvey settled in London, married the daughter of Dr. Lancelot Browne, Queen Elizabeth's physician, and began to practise medicine. In 1604 he became a candidate of the Royal College of Physicians and was duly admitted a fellow three years later. Upon the recommendation of the king and the president of the college, he was appointed in 1609 assistant physician of St. Bartholomew's Hospital and in the following year succeeded to the post of physician. His practice prospered, and, although Aubrey, who knew Harvey, says that his anatomy was better than his therapy, it is known that he performed difficult surgical operations and had many illustrious patients, among them Francis Bacon and King James I, to whom he became physician extraordinary.

Upon his appointment as the Lumleian lecturer at the College of Physicians in 1615, Harvey began his lectures on anatomy in which he made known his work on the motions of the heart and blood. In his lectures he professed "to learn and teach anatomy, not from books, but from dissections, not from the positions of the philosophers but from the fabric of nature"; and during his lifetime he dissected more than eighty kinds of animals. His teaching also showed his wide knowledge of books. He knew all the anatomists from Vesalius to his own time; he had studied Aristotle, whom he quotes more often than any other author, and Galen; he was especially fond of Virgil, had read Plautus, Horace, Caesar, Cicero, Vitruvius, and St. Augustine, and was thoroughly familiar with the Bible.

In 1628, after "nine years and more" of teaching, Harvey published his work on the circulation of the blood, *Exercitatio Anatomica de Motu Cordis et Sanguinis in Animalibus*. The book was dedicated to Charles I, whom Harvey served as physician. It immediately attracted wide attention, although at first, and particularly on the continent, it was mostly of an adverse character. Harvey for the most part left the defense of his work to his supporters, and he lived to see his teaching generally accepted. His friend, Hobbes, declared that Harvey was "the only one I know who has overcome public odium and established a new doctrine during his own lifetime."

After the publication of his work Harvey became more closely associated with Charles I, and until 1646 his fortunes were involved with those of the king. By the king's command he relinquished his functions at the College of Physicians in 1629 to accompany James Stuart, the young duke of Lennox, on his travels to the continent. Four years later he went to Nuremberg and Rome with the Earl of Arundel, who had been sent as an ambassador to the German emperor. As royal physician, he several times attended the king on his journeys. Despite his close connection with king and court, Harvey himself seems to have taken little interest in politics. In 1641 he still attended the king not only with the consent but also at the desire of parliament. But with the outbreak of war between the king and parliament, Harvey became identified with the royal cause. At the battle of Edgehill, Aubrey reports that he was given charge of the Prince of Wales and the Duke of York but was so little concerned with the battle that "he withdrew with them under a hedge and took out of his pocket a book and read." Harvey went to Oxford with the retreating royal forces in 1642 and remained there until the surrender of that city in 1646.

He then returned to London and for the rest of his life lived there with his brothers, who were eminent merchants.

During the fifteen years that Harvey was in close attendance upon the king, he continued to pursue his medical investigations. In studying the process of generation he enjoyed the interest and support of Charles I, who not only placed the royal deer parks at his disposal, but also watched his demonstration of the growth of the chick with the same interest that he had shown for the movements of the heart. Even the Civil War did not completely interrupt his research. He notes that his "enemies abstracted from my museum the fruits of many years of toil" with the result that "many observations, particularly on the generation of insects, have perished, with detriment, I venture to say, to the republic of letters." Despite this loss, he had collected a large number of observations and had embodied the results of his investigations in a treatise. Finally, in 1651 his friend and disciple, George Ent, obtained the manuscripts and with the author's permission made public the work on generation, *Exercitationes de Generatione Animalium.*

This was the last of Harvey's labors. He had now reached his seventy-third year and was honored at home and abroad. His college at Cambridge voted a statue in his honor, and the College of Physicians in 1654 elected him president, an office he declined because of age. He had already served three terms as censor (1613, 1625, 1629), and in that capacity, together with three of his colleagues, had supervised practitioners, taken necessary proceedings against quacks, and inspected apothecaries. The same year that he was offered the presidency he built and equipped a library for the College, to which in 1656 he also made over his property in Essex with provision for a salary to the college librarian and the endowment of an annual oration. This address, according to Harvey's orders, is to exhort the fellows "to search out and study the secrets of nature by way of experiment, and also for the honor of the profession to continue mutual love and affection among themselves."

Although afflicted by the gout, Harvey enjoyed the active use of all his faculties until his eightieth year. On June 3, 1657, he was attacked by paralysis and though deprived of speech was able to send for his nephews and distribute his personal things among them. He died the same evening and was buried with great honor in Hempstead Church, Essex.

CONTENTS

An Anatomical Disquisition on the Motion of the Heart and Blood in Animals

To the Most Illustrious and Indomitable Prince,
CHARLES,
KING OF GREAT BRITAIN, FRANCE, AND IRELAND,
DEFENDER OF THE FAITH

MOST ILLUSTRIOUS PRINCE!

The heart of animals is the foundation of their life, the sovereign of everything within them, the sun of their microcosm, that upon which all growth depends, from which all power proceeds. The King, in like manner, is the foundation of his kingdom, the sun of the world around him, the heart of the republic, the fountain whence all power, all grace doth flow. What I have here written of the motions of the heart I am the more emboldened to present to your Majesty, according to the custom of the present age, because almost all things human are done after human examples, and many things in a King are after the pattern of the heart. The knowledge of his heart, therefore, will not be useless to a Prince, as embracing a kind of Divine example of his functions—and it has still been usual with men to compare small things with great. Here, at all events, best of Princes, placed as you are on the pinnacle of human affairs, you may at once contemplate the prime mover in the body of man, and the emblem of your own sovereign power. Accept therefore, with your wonted clemency, I most humbly beseech you, illustrious Prince, this, my new Treatise on the Heart; you, who are yourself the new light of this age, and indeed its very heart; a Prince abounding in virtue and in grace, and to whom we gladly refer all the blessings which England enjoys, all the pleasure we have in our lives.

Your Majesty's most devoted servant,
WILLIAM HARVEY

[London . . . . 1628.]

TO HIS VERY DEAR FRIEND, DOCTOR ARGENT, THE EXCELLENT AND
ACCOMPLISHED PRESIDENT OF THE ROYAL COLLEGE OF PHYSICIANS,
AND TO OTHER LEARNED PHYSICIANS, HIS MOST ESTEEMED COLLEAGUES

I have already and repeatedly presented you, my learned friends, with my new views of the motion and function of the heart, in my anatomical lectures; but having now for nine years and more confirmed these views by multiplied demonstrations in your presence, illustrated them by arguments, and freed them from the objections of the most learned and skilful anatomists, I at length yield to the requests, I might say entreaties, of many, and here present them for general consideration in this treatise.

Were not the work indeed presented through you, my learned friends, I should scarce hope that it could come out scatheless and complete; for you have in general been the faithful witnesses of almost all the instances from which I have either collected the truth or confuted error; you have seen my dissections, and at my demonstrations of all that I maintain to be objects of sense, you have been accustomed to stand by and bear me out with your testimony. And as this book alone declares the blood to course and revolve by a new route, very different from the ancient and beaten pathway trodden for so many ages, and illustrated by such a host of learned and distinguished men, I was greatly afraid lest I might be charged with presumption did I lay my work before the public at home, or send it beyond seas for impression, unless I had first proposed its subject to you, had confirmed its conclusions by ocular demonstrations in your presence, had replied to your doubts and objections, and secured the assent and support of our distinguished President. For I was most intimately persuaded, that if I could make good my proposition before you and our College, illustrious by its numerous body of learned individuals, I had less to fear from others; I even ventured to hope that I should have the comfort of finding all that you had granted me in your sheer love of truth, conceded by others who were philosophers like yourselves. For true philosophers, who are only eager for truth and knowledge, never regard themselves as already so thoroughly informed, but that they welcome further information from whomsoever and from whencesoever it may come; nor are they so narrow-minded as to imagine any of the arts or sciences transmitted to us by the ancients, in such a state of forwardness or completeness, that nothing is left for the ingenuity and industry of others; very many, on the contrary, maintain that all we know is still infinitely less than all that still remains unknown; nor do philosophers pin their faith to others' precepts in such wise that they lose their liberty, and cease to give credence to the conclusions of their proper senses. Neither do they swear such fealty to their mistress Antiquity, that they openly, and in sight of all, deny and desert their friend Truth. But even as they see that the credulous and vain are disposed at the first blush to accept and to believe everything that is proposed to them, so do they observe that the dull and unintellectual are indisposed to see what lies before their eyes, and even to deny the light of the noonday sun. They teach us in our course of philosophy as sedulously to avoid the fables of the poets and the fancies of the vulgar, as the false conclusions of the sceptics. And then the studious, and good, and true, never suffer their minds to be warped by the passions of hatred and envy, which unfit men duly to weigh the arguments that are advanced in behalf of truth, or to appreciate the proposition that is even fairly demonstrated; neither do they think it unworthy of them to change their opinion if truth and undoubted demonstration require them so to do; nor do they esteem it discreditable to desert error, though sanctioned by the highest antiquity; for they know full well that to err, to be deceived, is human; that many things are discovered by accident, and that many may be learned indifferently from any quarter, by an old man from a youth, by a person of understanding from one of inferior capacity.

My dear colleagues, I had no purpose to swell this treatise into a large volume by quoting the names and writings of anatomists, or to make a parade of the strength of my memory, the extent of my reading, and the amount of my pains; because I profess both to learn and to teach anatomy, not from books but from dissections; not from the positions of philosophers but from the fabric of nature; and then because I do not think it right or proper to strive to take from the ancients any honour that is their due, nor yet to dispute with the moderns, and enter into controversy with those who have excelled in anatomy and been my teachers. I would not charge with wilful falsehood anyone who was sincerely anxious for truth, nor lay it to anyone's door as a crime that he had fallen into error. I avow myself the partisan of truth alone; and I can indeed say that I have used all my endeavours, bestowed all my pains on an attempt to produce something that should be agreeable to the good, profitable to the learned, and useful to letters.

Farewell, most worthy Doctors,

And think kindly of your Anatomist,

WILLIAM HARVEY

INTRODUCTION

As we are about to discuss the motion, action, and use of the heart and arteries, it is imperative on us first to state what has been thought of these things by others in their writings, and what has been held by the vulgar and by tradition, in order that what is true may be confirmed, and what is false set right by dissection, multiplied experience, and accurate observation.

Almost all anatomists, physicians, and philosophers, up to the present time, have supposed, with Galen, that the object of the pulse was the same as that of respiration, and only differed in one particular, this being conceived to depend on the animal, the respiration on the vital faculty; the two, in all other respects, whether with reference to purpose or to motion, comporting themselves alike. Whence it is affirmed, as by Hieronymus Fabricius of Aquapendente, in his book on *Respiration*, which has lately appeared, that as the pulsation of the heart and arteries does not suffice for the ventilation and refrigeration of the blood, therefore were the lungs fashioned to surround the heart. From this it appears that whatever has hitherto been said upon the systole and diastole, on the motion of the heart and arteries, has been said with especial reference to the lungs.

But as the structure and movements of the heart differ from those of the lungs, and the motions of the arteries from those of the chest, so seems it likely that other ends and offices will thence arise, and that the pulsations and uses of the heart, likewise of the arteries, will differ in many respects from the heavings and uses of the chest and lungs. For did the arterial pulse and the respiration serve the same ends; did the arteries in their diastole take air into their cavities, as commonly stated, and in their systole emit fuliginous vapours by the same pores of the flesh and skin; and further, did they, in the time intermediate between the diastole and the systole, contain air, and at all times either air, or spirits, or fuliginous vapours, what should then be said to Galen, who wrote a book on purpose to show that by nature the arteries contained blood, and nothing but blood; neither spirits nor air, consequently, as may be readily gathered from the experiments and reasonings contained in the same book? Now if the arteries are filled in the diastole with air then taken into them (a larger quantity of air penetrating when the pulse is large and full), it must come to pass that if you plunge into a bath of water or of oil when the pulse is strong and full, it ought forthwith to become either smaller or much slower, since the circumambient bath will render it either difficult or impossible for the air to penetrate. In like manner, as all the arteries, those that are deep-seated as well as those that are superficial, are dilated at the same instant, and with the same rapidity, how were it possible that air should penetrate to the deeper parts as freely and quickly through the skin, flesh, and other structures, as through the mere cuticle? And how should the arteries of the fœtus draw air into their cavities through the abdomen of the mother and the body of the womb? And how should seals, whales, dolphins, and other cetaceans, and fishes of every description, living in the depths of the sea, take in and emit air by the diastole and systole of their arteries through the infinite mass of waters? For to say that they absorb the air that is infixed in the water, and emit their fumes into this medium, were to utter something very like a mere figment. And if the arteries in their systole expel fuliginous vapours from their cavities through the pores of the flesh and skin, why not the spirits, which are said to be contained in these vessels, at the same time, since spirits are much more subtile than fuliginous vapours or smoke? And further, if the arteries take in and cast out air in the systole and diastole, like the lungs in the process of respiration, wherefore do they not do the same thing when a wound is made in one of them, as is done in the operation of arteriotomy? When the windpipe is divided, it is sufficiently obvious that the air enters and returns through the wound by two opposite movements; but when an artery is divided, it is equally manifest that blood escapes in one continuous stream, and that no air either enters or issues. If the pulsations of the arteries fan and refrigerate the several parts of the body as the lungs do the heart, how comes it, as is commonly said, that the arteries carry the vital blood into the different parts, abundantly charged with vital spirits, which cherish the heat of these parts, sustain them when asleep, and recruit them when exhausted? And how should it happen that, if you tie the arteries, immediately the parts not only become torpid, and frigid, and look pale, but at length cease even to be nourished? This, according to Galen, is because they are deprived of the heat which flowed through all parts from the heart, as its source; whence it would appear that the arteries rather carry warmth to the parts than serve for any fanning or refrigeration. Besides, how can the diastole draw spirits from the heart to warm the body and its parts, and, from without, means of cooling or tempering them? Still further, although some affirm that the lungs, arteries, and heart have all the same offices, they yet maintain that the heart is the workshop of the spirits, and that the arteries contain and transmit them; denying, however, in opposition to the opinion of Columbus, that the lungs can either make or contain spirits; and then they assert, with Galen, against Erasistratus, that it is blood, not spirits, which is contained in the arteries.

These various opinions are seen to be so incongruous and mutually subversive, that every one of them is not unjustly brought under suspicion. That it is blood and blood alone which is contained in the arteries is made manifest by the experiment of Galen, by arteriotomy, and by wounds; for from a single artery divided, as Galen himself affirms in more than one place, the whole of the blood may be withdrawn in the course of half an hour, or less. The experiment of Galen alluded to is this: "If you include a portion of an artery between two ligatures, and slit it open lengthways, you will find nothing but blood"; and thus he proves that the arteries contain blood only. And we too may be permitted to proceed by a like train of reasoning: if we find the same blood in the arteries that we find in the veins, which we have tied in the same way, as I have myself repeatedly ascertained, both in the dead body and in living animals, we may fairly conclude that the arteries contain the same blood as the veins, and nothing but the same blood. Some, whilst they attempt to lessen the difficulty here, affirming that the blood is spirituous and arterious, virtually concede that the office of the arteries is to carry blood from the heart into the whole of the body, and that they are therefore filled with blood; for spirituous blood is not the less blood on that account. And then no one denies that the blood as such, even the portion of it which flows in the veins, is imbued with spirits. But if that portion which is contained in the arteries be richer in spirits, it is still to be believed that these spirits are inseparable from the blood, like those in the veins; that the blood and spirits constitute one body (like whey and butter in milk, or heat [and water] in hot water), with which the arteries are charged, and for the distribution of which from the heart they are provided, and that this body is nothing else than blood. But if this blood be said to be drawn from the heart into the arteries by the diastole of these vessels, it is then assumed that the arteries by their distension are filled with blood, and not with the ambient air, as heretofore; for if they be said also to become filled with air from the ambient atmosphere, how and when, I ask, can they receive blood from the heart? If it be answered: during the systole; I say, that seems impossible; the arteries would then have to fill whilst they contracted; in other words, to fill, and yet not become distended. But if it be said: during the diastole, they would then, and for two opposite purposes, be receiving both blood and air, and heat and cold; which is improbable. Further, when it is affirmed that the diastole of the heart and arteries is simultaneous, and the systole of the two is also concurrent, there is another in-

congruity. For how can two bodies mutually connected, which are simultaneously distended, attract or draw anything from one another; or, being simultaneously contracted, receive anything from each other? And then, it seems impossible that one body can thus attract another body into itself, so as to become distended, seeing that to be distended is to be passive, unless, in the manner of a sponge, previously compressed by an external force, whilst it is returning to its natural state. But it is difficult to conceive that there can be anything of this kind in the arteries. The arteries dilate, because they are filled like bladders or leathern bottles; they are not filled because they expand like bellows. This I think easy of demonstration; and indeed conceive that I have already proved it. Nevertheless, in that book of Galen headed *Quod sanguis contineatur in arteriis*, he quotes an experiment to prove the contrary: An artery, having been exposed, is opened longitudinally, and a reed or other pervious tube, by which the blood is prevented from being lost, and the wound is closed, is inserted into the vessel through the opening. "So long," he says, "as things are thus arranged, the whole artery will pulsate; but if you now throw a ligature about the vessel and tightly compress its tunics over the tube, you will no longer see the artery beating beyond the ligature." I have never performed this experiment of Galen's, nor do I think that it could very well be performed in the living body, on account of the profuse flow of blood that would take place from the vessel which was operated on; neither would the tube effectually close the wound in the vessel without a ligature; and I cannot doubt but that the blood would be found to flow out between the tube and the vessel. Still Galen appears by this experiment to prove both that the pulsative faculty extends from the heart by the walls of the arteries, and that the arteries, whilst they dilate, are filled by that pulsific force, because they expand like bellows, and do not dilate because they are filled like skins. But the contrary is obvious in arteriotomy and in wounds; for the blood spurting from the arteries escapes with force, now farther, now not so far, alternately, or in jets; and the jet always takes place with the diastole of the artery, never with the systole. By which it clearly appears that the artery is dilated by the impulse of the blood; for of itself it would not throw the blood to such a distance, and whilst it was dilating; it ought rather to draw air into its cavity through the wound, were those things true that are commonly stated concerning the uses of the arteries. Nor let the thickness of the arterial tunics impose upon us, and lead us to conclude that the pulsative property proceeds along them from the heart. For in several animals the arteries do not apparently differ from the veins; and in extreme parts of the body, where the arteries are minutely subdivided, as in the brain, the hand, &c., no one could distinguish the arteries from the veins by the dissimilar characters of their coats; the tunics of both are identical. And then, in an aneurism proceeding from a wounded or eroded artery, the pulsation is precisely the same as in the other arteries, and yet it has no proper arterial tunic. This the learned Riolanus testifies to, along with me, in his Seventh Book.

Nor let any one imagine that the uses of the pulse and the respiration are the same, because under the influence of the same causes, such as running, anger, the warm bath, or any other heating thing, as Galen says, they become more frequent and forcible together. For, not only is experience in opposition to this idea, though Galen endeavours to explain it away, when we see that with excessive repletion the pulse beats more forcibly, whilst the respiration is diminished in amount; but in young persons the pulse is quick, whilst respiration is slow. So is it also in alarm, and amidst care, and under anxiety of mind; sometimes, too, in fevers, the pulse is rapid, but the respiration is slower than usual.

These and other objections of the same kind may be urged against the opinions mentioned. Nor are the views that are entertained of the offices and pulse of the heart, perhaps, less bound up with great and most inextricable difficulties. The heart, it is vulgarly said, is the fountain and workshop of the vital spirits, the centre from whence life is dispensed to the several parts of the body; and yet it is denied that the right ventricle makes spirits; it is rather held to supply nourishment to the lungs; whence it is maintained that fishes are without any right ventricle (and indeed every animal wants a right ventricle which is unfurnished with lungs), and that the right ventricle is present solely for the sake of the lungs.

1. Why, I ask, when we see that the structure of both ventricles is almost identical, there being the same apparatus of fibres, and braces, and valves, and vessels, and auricles, and in both the same infarction of blood, in the subjects of our dissections, of the like black colour, and coagulated—why, I say, should their uses be imagined to be different, when the ac-

tion, motion, and pulse of both are the same? If the three tricuspid valves placed at the entrance into the right ventricle prove obstacles to the reflux of the blood into the vena cava, and if the three semilunar valves which are situated at the commencement of the pulmonary artery be there, that they may prevent the return of the blood into the ventricle; wherefore, when we find similar structures in connexion with the left ventricle, should we deny that they are there for the same end, of preventing here the egress, there the regurgitation of the blood?

2. And again, when we see that these structures, in point of size, form, and situation, are almost in every respect the same in the left as in the right ventricle, wherefore should it be maintained that things are here arranged in connexion with the egress and regress of spirits, there, i.e., in the right, of blood. The same arrangement cannot be held fitted to favour or impede the motion of blood and of spirits indifferently.

3. And when we observe that the passages and vessels are severally in relation to one another in point of size, viz., the pulmonary artery to the pulmonary veins; wherefore should the one be imagined destined to a private or particular purpose, that, to wit, of nourishing the lungs, the other to a public and general function?

4. And, as Realdus Columbus says, how can it be conceived that such a quantity of blood should be required for the nutrition of the lungs; the vessel that leads to them, the vena arteriosa or pulmonary artery being of greater capacity than both the iliac veins?

5. And I ask further; as the lungs are so close at hand, and in continual motion, and the vessel that supplies them is of such dimensions, what is the use or meaning of the pulse of the right ventricle? and why was nature reduced to the necessity of adding another ventricle for the sole purpose of nourishing the lungs?

When it is said that the left ventricle obtains materials for the formation of spirits, air to wit, and blood, from the lungs and right sinuses of the heart, and in like manner sends spirituous blood into the aorta, drawing fuliginous vapours from thence, and sending them by the arteria venosa into the lungs, whence spirits are at the same time obtained for transmission into the aorta, I ask how, and by what means, is the separation effected? and how comes it that spirits and fuliginous vapours can pass hither and thither without admixture or confusion? If the mitral cuspidate valves do not prevent the egress of fuliginous vapours to the lungs, how should they oppose the escape of air? And how should the semilunars hinder the regress of spirits from the aorta upon each supervening diastole of the heart? And, above all, how can they say that the spirituous blood is sent from the arteria venalis (pulmonary veins) by the left ventricle into the lungs without any obstacle to its passage from the mitral valves, when they have previously asserted that the air entered by the same vessel from the lungs into the left ventricle, and have brought forward these same mitral valves as obstacles to its retrogression? Good God! how should the mitral valves prevent regurgitation of air and not of blood?

Further, when they dedicate the vena arteriosa (or pulmonary artery), a vessel of great size, and having the tunics of an artery, to none but a kind of private and single purpose, that, namely, of nourishing the lungs, why should the arteria venalis (or pulmonary vein), which is scarcely of similar size, which has the coats of a vein, and is soft and lax, be presumed to be made for many—three or four, different uses? For they will have it that air passes through this vessel from the lungs into the left ventricle; that fuliginous vapours escape by it from the heart into the lungs; and that a portion of the spirituous or spiritualized blood is distributed by it to the lungs for their refreshment.

If they will have it that fumes and air—fumes flowing from, air proceeding towards the heart—are transmitted by the same conduit, I reply that nature is not wont to institute but one vessel, to contrive but one way for such contrary motions and purposes, nor is anything of the kind seen elsewhere.

If fumes or fuliginous vapours and air permeate this vessel, as they do the pulmonary bronchia, wherefore do we find neither air nor fuliginous vapours when we divide the arteria venosa? Why do we always find this vessel full of sluggish blood, never of air?—whilst in the lungs we find abundance of air remaining.

If anyone will perform Galen's experiment of dividing the trachea of a living dog, forcibly distending the lungs with a pair of bellows, and then tying the trachea securely, he will find, when he has laid open the thorax, abundance of air in the lungs, even to their extreme investing tunic, but none in either the pulmonary veins, or left ventricle of the heart. But did the heart either attract air from the lungs, or did the lungs transmit any air to the heart, in the living

dog, by so much the more ought this to be the case in the experiment just referred to. Who, indeed, doubts that, did he inflate the lungs of a subject in the dissecting-room, he would instantly see the air making its way by this route, were there actually any such passage for it? But this office of the pulmonary veins, namely, the transference of air from the lungs to the heart, is held of such importance, that Hieronymus Fabricius of Aquapendente, maintains the lungs were made for the sake of this vessel, and that it constitutes the principal element in their structure.

But I should like to be informed wherefore, if the pulmonary vein were destined for the conveyance of air, it has the structure of a blood-vessel here. Nature had rather need of annular tubes, such as those of the bronchia, in order that they might always remain open, not have been liable to collapse; and that they might continue entirely free from blood, lest the liquid should interfere with the passage of the air, as it so obviously does when the lungs labour from being either greatly oppressed or loaded in a less degree with phlegm, as they are when the breathing is performed with a sibilous or rattling noise.

Still less is that opinion to be tolerated which (as a two-fold matter, one aëreal, one sanguineous, is required for the composition of vital spirits) supposes the blood to ooze through the septum of the heart from the right to the left ventricle by certain secret pores, and the air to be attracted from the lungs through the great vessel, the pulmonary vein; and which will have it, consequently, that there are numerous pores in the septum cordis adapted for the transmission of the blood. But, in faith, no such pores can be demonstrated, neither, in fact, do any such exist. For the septum of the heart is of a denser and more compact structure than any portion of the body, except the bones and sinews. But even supposing that there were foramina or pores in this situation, how could one of the ventricles extract anything from the other—the left, e.g., obtain blood from the right, when we see that both ventricles contract and dilate simultaneously? Wherefore should we not rather believe that the right took spirits from the left, than that the left obtained blood from the right ventricle, through these foramina? But it is certainly mysterious and incongruous that blood should be supposed to be most commodiously drawn through a set of obscure or invisible pores, and air through perfectly open passages, at one and the same moment. And why, I ask, is recourse had to secret and invisible porosities, to uncertain and obscure channels, to explain the passage of the blood into the left ventricle, when there is so open a way through the pulmonary veins? I own it has always appeared extraordinary to me that they should have chosen to make, or rather to imagine, a way through the thick, hard, and extremely compact substance of the septum cordis, rather than to take that by the open vas venosum or pulmonary vein, or even through the lax, soft and spongy substance of the lungs at large. Besides, if the blood could permeate the substance of the septum, or could be imbibed from the ventricles, what use were there for the coronary artery and vein, branches of which proceed to the septum itself, to supply it with nourishment? And what is especially worthy of notice is this: if in the fœtus, where everything is more lax and soft, Nature saw herself reduced to the necessity of bringing the blood from the right into the left side of the heart by the foramen ovale, from the vena cava through the arteria venosa, how should it be likely that in the adult she should pass it so commodiously, and without an effort, through the septum ventriculorum, which has now become denser by age?

Andreas Laurentius,[1] resting on the authority of Galen[2] and the experience of Hollerius, asserts and proves that the serum and pus in empyema, absorbed from the cavities of the chest into the pulmonary vein, may be expelled and got rid of with the urine and fæces through the left ventricle of the heart and arteries. He quotes the case of a certain person affected with melancholia, and who suffered from repeated fainting fits, who was relieved from the paroxysms on passing a quantity of turbid, fetid, and acrid urine; but he died at last, worn out by the disease; and when the body came to be opened after death, no fluid like that he had micturated was discovered either in the bladder or in the kidneys; but in the left ventricle of the heart and cavity of the thorax plenty of it was met with; and then Laurentius boasts that he had predicted the cause of the symptoms. For my own part, however, I cannot but wonder, since he had divined and predicted that heterogeneous matter could be discharged by the course he indicates, why he could not or would not perceive, and inform us that, in the natural state of things, the blood might be commodiously transferred from the

lungs to the left ventricle of the heart by the very same route.

Since, therefore, from the foregoing considerations and many others to the same effect, it is plain that what has heretofore been said concerning the motion and function of the heart and arteries must appear obscure, or inconsistent or even impossible to him who carefully considers the entire subject; it will be proper to look more narrowly into the matter; to contemplate the motion of the heart and arteries, not only in man, but in all animals that have hearts; and further, by frequent appeals to vivisection, and constant ocular inspection, to investigate and endeavour to find the truth.

CHAPTER 1. *The author's motives for writing*

WHEN I first gave my mind to vivisections, as a means of discovering the motions and uses of the heart, and sought to discover these from actual inspection, and not from the writings of others, I found the task so truly arduous, so full of difficulties, that I was almost tempted to think, with Fracastorius, that the motion of the heart was only to be comprehended by God. For I could neither rightly perceive at first when the systole and when the diastole took place, nor when and where dilatation and contraction occurred, by reason of the rapidity of the motion, which in many animals is accomplished in the twinkling of an eye, coming and going like a flash of lightning; so that the systole presented itself to me now from this point, now from that; the diastole the same; and then everything was reversed, the motions occurring, as it seemed, variously and confusedly together. My mind was therefore greatly unsettled, nor did I know what I should myself conclude, nor what believe from others; I was not surprised that Andreas Laurentius should have said that the motion of the heart was as perplexing as the flux and reflux of Euripus had appeared to Aristotle.

At length, and by using greater and daily diligence, having frequent recourse to vivisections, employing a variety of animals for the purpose, and collating numerous observations, I thought that I had attained to the truth, that I should extricate myself and escape from this labyrinth, and that I had discovered what I so much desired, both the motion and the use of the heart and arteries; since which time I have not hesitated to expose my views upon these subjects, not only in private to my friends, but also in public, in my anatomical lectures, after the manner of the Academy of old.

[1] Book IX, Chap. II, q. 12.
[2] *De locis affectis*, VI, 7.

These views, as usual, pleased some more, others less; some chid and calumniated me, and laid it to me as a crime that I had dared to depart from the precepts and opinion of all anatomists; others desired further explanations of the novelties, which they said were both worthy of consideration, and might perchance be found of signal use. At length, yielding to the requests of my friends, that all might be made participators in my labours, and partly moved by the envy of others, who, receiving my views with uncandid minds and understanding them indifferently, have essayed to traduce me publicly, I have been moved to commit these things to the press, in order that all may be enabled to form an opinion both of me and my labours. This step I take all the more willingly, seeing that Hieronymus Fabricius of Aquapendente, although he has accurately and learnedly delineated almost every one of the several parts of animals in a special work, has left the heart alone untouched. Finally, if any use or benefit to this department of the republic of letters should accrue from my labours, it will, perhaps, be allowed that I have not lived idly, and, as the old man in the comedy says:

For never yet hath any one attained
To such perfection, but that time, and place,
And use, have brought addition to his knowl-
    edge;
Or made correction, or admonished him,
That he was ignorant of much which he
Had thought he knew; or led him to reject
What he had once esteemed of highest price.

So will it, perchance, be found with reference to the heart at this time; or others, at least, starting from hence, the way pointed out to them, advancing under the guidance of a happier genius, may make occasion to proceed more fortunately, and to inquire more accurately.

CHAPTER 2. *Of the motions of the heart, as seen in the dissection of living animals*

In the first place, then, when the chest of a living animal is laid open and the capsule that immediately surrounds the heart is slit up or removed, the organ is seen now to move, now to be at rest; there is a time when it moves, and a time when it is motionless.

These things are more obvious in the colder animals, such as toads, frogs, serpents, small fishes, crabs, shrimps, snails and shell-fish. They also become more distinct in warm-blooded animals, such as the dog and hog, if they be at-

tentively noted when the heart begins to flag, to move more slowly, and, as it were, to die: the movements then become slower and rarer, the pauses longer, by which it is made much more easy to perceive and unravel what the motions really are, and how they are performed. In the pause, as in death, the heart is soft, flaccid, exhausted, lying, as it were, at rest.

In the motion, and interval in which this is accomplished, three principal circumstances are to be noted:

1. That the heart is erected, and rises upwards to a point, so that at this time it strikes against the breast and the pulse is felt externally.

2. That it is everywhere contracted, but more especially towards the sides, so that it looks narrower, relatively longer, more drawn together. The heart of an eel taken out of the body of the animal and placed upon the table or the hand, shows these particulars; but the same things are manifest in the heart of small fishes and of those colder animals where the organ is more conical or elongated.

3. The heart being grasped in the hand, it is felt to become harder during its action. Now this hardness proceeds from tension, precisely as when the forearm is grasped, its tendons are perceived to become tense and resilient when the fingers are moved.

4. It may further be observed in fishes, and the colder blooded animals, such as frogs, serpents, &c., that the heart, when it moves, becomes of a paler colour, when quiescent of a deeper blood-red colour.

From these particulars it appeared evident to me that the motion of the heart consists in a certain universal tension—both contraction in the line of its fibres, and constriction in every sense. It becomes erect, hard, and of diminished size during its action; the motion is plainly of the same nature as that of the muscles when they contract in the line of their sinews and fibres; for the muscles, when in action, acquire vigour and tenseness, and from soft become hard, prominent and thickened: in the same manner the heart.

We are therefore authorized to conclude that the heart, at the moment of its action, is at once constricted on all sides, rendered thicker in its parietes and smaller in its ventricles, and so made apt to project or expel its charge of blood. This, indeed, is made sufficiently manifest by the fourth observation preceding, in which we have seen that the heart, by squeezing out the blood it contains becomes paler, and then when it sinks into repose and the ventricle is filled anew with blood, that the deeper crimson colour returns. But no one need remain in doubt of the fact, for if the ventricle be pierced the blood will be seen to be forcibly projected outwards upon each motion or pulsation when the heart is tense.

These things, therefore, happen together or at the same instant: the tension of the heart, the pulse of its apex, which is felt externally by its striking against the chest, the thickening of its parietes, and the forcible expulsion of the blood it contains by the constriction of its ventricles.

Hence the very opposite of the opinions commonly received appears to be true; inasmuch as it is generally believed that when the heart strikes the breast and the pulse is felt without, the heart is dilated in its ventricles and is filled with blood; but the contrary of this is the fact, and the heart, when it contracts, is emptied. Whence the motion which is generally regarded as the diastole of the heart, is in truth its systole. And in like manner the intrinsic motion of the heart is not the diastole but the systole; neither is it in the diastole that the heart grows firm and tense, but in the systole, for then only, when tense, is it moved and made vigorous.

Neither is it by any means to be allowed that the heart only moves in the line of its straight fibres, although the great Vesalius, giving this notion countenance, quotes a bundle of osiers bound into a pyramidal heap in illustration; meaning, that as the apex is approached to the base, so are the sides made to bulge out in the fashion of arches, the cavities to dilate, the ventricles to acquire the form of a cupping-glass and so to suck in the blood. But the true effect of every one of its fibres is to constringe the heart at the same time that they render it tense; and this rather with the effect of thickening and amplifying the walls and substance of the organ than enlarging its ventricles. And, again, as the fibres run from the apex to the base, and draw the apex towards the base, they do not tend to make the walls of the heart bulge out in circles, but rather the contrary; inasmuch as every fibre that is circularly disposed, tends to become straight when it contracts; and is distended laterally and thickened, as in the case of muscular fibres in general, when they contract, that is, when they are shortened longitudinally, as we see them in the bellies of the muscles of the body at large. To all this let it be added that not only are the ventricles contracted in virtue of the direction and condensa-

tion of their walls, but further, that those fibres, or bands, styled *nerves* by Aristotle, which are so conspicuous in the ventricles of the larger animals, and contain all the straight fibres (the parietes of the heart containing only circular ones), when they contract simultaneously, by an admirable adjustment all the internal surfaces are drawn together, as if with cords, and so is the charge of blood expelled with force.

Neither is it true, as vulgarly believed, that the heart by any dilatation or motion of its own, has the power of drawing the blood into the ventricles; for when it acts and becomes tense, the blood is expelled; when it relaxes and sinks together it receives the blood in the manner and wise which will by and by be explained.

CHAPTER 3. *Of the motions of arteries, as seen in the dissection of living animals*

IN connexion with the motions of the heart these things are further to be observed having reference to the motions and pulses of the arteries:

1. At the moment the heart contracts, and when the breast is struck, when, in short, the organ is in its state of systole, the arteries are dilated, yield a pulse, and are in the state of diastole. In like manner, when the right ventricle contracts and propels its charge of blood, the arterial vein is distended at the same time with the other arteries of the body.

2. When the left ventricle ceases to act, to contract, to pulsate, the pulse in the arteries also ceases; further, when this ventricle contracts languidly, the pulse in the arteries is scarcely perceptible. In like manner, the pulse in the right ventricle failing, the pulse in the vena arteriosa ceases also.

3. Further, when an artery is divided or punctured, the blood is seen to be forcibly propelled from the wound at the moment the left ventricle contracts; and, again, when the pulmonary artery is wounded, the blood will be seen spouting forth with violence at the instant when the right ventricle contracts.

So also in fishes, if the vessel which leads from the heart to the gills be divided, at the moment when the heart becomes tense and contracted, at the same moment does the blood flow with force from the divided vessel.

In the same way, finally, when we see the blood in arteriotomy projected now to a greater, now to a less distance, and that the greater jet corresponds to the diastole of the artery and to the time when the heart contracts and strikes the ribs, and is in its state of systole, we understand that the blood is expelled by the same movement.

From these facts it is manifest, in opposition to commonly received opinions, that the diastole of the arteries corresponds with the time of the heart's systole; and that the arteries are filled and distended by the blood forced into them by the contraction of the ventricles; the arteries, therefore, are distended, because they are filled like sacs or bladders, and are not filled because they expand like bellows. It is in virtue of one and the same cause, therefore, that all the arteries of the body pulsate, viz., the contraction of the left ventricle; in the same way as the pulmonary artery pulsates by the contraction of the right ventricle.

Finally, that the pulses of the arteries are due to the impulses of the blood from the left ventricle may be illustrated by blowing into a glove, when the whole of the fingers will be found to become distended at one and the same time, and in their tension to bear some resemblance to the pulse. For in the ratio of the tension is the pulse of the heart, fuller, stronger, more frequent as that acts more vigorously, still preserving the rhythm and volume, and order of the heart's contractions. Nor is it to be expected that because of the motion of the blood, the time at which the contraction of the heart takes place, and that at which the pulse in an artery (especially a distant one) is felt, shall be otherwise than simultaneous: it is here the same as in blowing up a glove or bladder; for in a plenum (as in a drum, a long piece of timber, &c.) the stroke and the motion occur at both extremities at the same time. Aristotle, too, has said, "the blood of all animals palpitates within their veins, (meaning the arteries) and by the pulse is sent everywhere simultaneously."[1] And further, "thus do all the veins pulsate together and by successive strokes, because they all depend upon the heart; and, as it is always in motion, so are they likewise always moving together, but by successive movements."[2] It is well to observe with Galen, in this place, that the old philosophers called the arteries *veins*.

I happened upon one occasion to have a particular case under my care, which plainly satisfied me of this truth: a certain person was affected with a large pulsating tumour on the right side of the neck, called an aneurism, just at that part where the artery descends into the axilla, produced by an erosion of the artery itself, and daily increasing in size; this tumour was visibly distended as it received the charge of blood brought to it by the artery, with each stroke of the heart: the connexion of parts was obvious when the body of the patient came to be opened after his death. The pulse in the corresponding arm was small, in consequence of the greater portion of the blood being diverted into the tumour and so intercepted.

Whence it appears that wherever the motion of the blood through the arteries is impeded, whether it be by compression or infarction, or interception, there do the remote divisions of the arteries beat less forcibly, seeing that the pulse of the arteries is nothing more than the impulse or shock of the blood in these vessels.

CHAPTER 4. *Of the motion of the heart and its auricles, as seen in the bodies of living animals*

BESIDES the motions already spoken of, we have still to consider those that appertain to the auricles.

Caspar Bauhin and John Riolan,[3] most learned men and skilful anatomists, inform us from their observations that if we carefully watch the movements of the heart in the vivisection of an animal, we shall perceive four motions distinct in time and in place, two of which are proper to the auricles, two to the ventricles. With all deference to such authority, I say that there are four motions distinct in point of place, but not of time; for the two auricles move together, and so also do the two ventricles, in such wise that though the places be four, the times are only two. And this occurs in the following manner:

There are, as it were, two motions going on together; one of the auricles, another of the ventricles; these by no means taking place simultaneously, but the motion of the auricles preceding, that of the heart itself following; the motion appearing to begin from the auricles and to extend to the ventricles. When all things are becoming languid, and the heart is dying, as also in fishes and the colder blooded animals, there is a short pause between these two motions, so that the heart aroused, as it were, appears to respond to the motion, now more quickly, now more tardily; and at length, and when near to death, it ceases to respond by its proper motion, but seems, as it were, to nod the head, and is so obscurely moved that it appears rather to give signs of motion to the pulsating auricle, than actually to move. The heart, therefore, ceases to pulsate sooner than

[1] *History of Animals.* III, 19.
[2] *On Breathing*, 20.
[3] Bauhin, II, 21; Riolan, VIII, 1.

the auricles, so that the auricles have been said to outlive it, the left ventricle ceasing to pulsate first of all; then its auricle, next the right ventricle; and, finally, all the other parts being at rest and dead, as Galen long since observed, the right auricle still continues to beat; life, therefore, appears to linger longest in the right auricle. Whilst the heart is gradually dying, it is sometimes seen to reply, after two or three contractions of the auricles, roused as it were to action, and making a single pulsation, slowly, unwillingly, and with an effort.

But this especially is to be noted, that after the heart has ceased to beat, the auricles, however, still contracting, a finger placed upon the ventricles perceives the several pulsations of the auricles, precisely in the same way and for the same reason, as we have said, that the pulses of the ventricles are felt in the arteries, to wit, the distension produced by the jet of blood. And if at this time, the auricles alone pulsating, the point of the heart be cut off with a pair of scissors, you will perceive the blood flowing out upon each contraction of the auricles. Whence it is manifest how the blood enters the ventricles, not by any attraction or dilatation of the heart, but thrown into them by the pulses of the auricles.

And here I would observe, that whenever I speak of pulsations as occurring in the auricles or ventricles, I mean contractions: first the auricles *contract*, and then and subsequently the heart itself *contracts*. When the auricles contract they are seen to become whiter, especially where they contain but little blood; but they are filled as magazines or reservoirs of the blood, which is tending spontaneously and, by the motion of the veins, under pressure towards the centre; the whiteness indicated is most conspicuous towards the extremities or edges of the auricles at the time of their contractions.

In fishes and frogs, and other animals which have hearts with but a single ventricle, and for an auricle have a kind of bladder much distended with blood, at the base of the organ, you may very plainly perceive this bladder contracting first, and the contraction of the heart or ventricle following afterwards.

But I think it right to describe what I have observed of an opposite character: the heart of an eel, of several fishes, and even of some animals taken out of the body, beats without auricles; nay, if it be cut in pieces the several parts may still be seen contracting and relaxing; so that in these creatures the body of the heart may be seen pulsating, palpitating, after the cessation of all motion in the auricle. But is not this perchance peculiar to animals more tenacious of life, whose radical moisture is more glutinous, or fat and sluggish, and less readily soluble? The same faculty indeed appears in the flesh of eels, generally, which even when skinned and embowelled, and cut into pieces, are still seen to move.

Experimenting with a pigeon upon one occasion, after the heart had wholly ceased to pulsate, and the auricles too had become motionless, I kept my finger wetted with saliva and warm for a short time upon the heart, and observed that under the influence of this fomentation it recovered new strength and life, so that both ventricles and auricles pulsated, contracting and relaxing alternately, recalled as it were from death to life.

Besides this, however, I have occasionally observed, after the heart and even its right auricle had ceased pulsating, when it was *in articulo mortis* in short, that an obscure motion, an undulation or palpitation, remained in the blood itself, which was contained in the right auricle, this being apparent so long as it was inbued with heat and spirit. And indeed a circumstance of the same kind is extremely manifest in the course of the generation of animals, as may be seen in the course of the first seven days of the incubation of the chick: a drop of blood makes its appearance which palpitates, as Aristotle had already observed; from this, when the growth is further advanced and the chick is fashioned, the auricles of the heart are formed, which pulsating henceforth give constant signs of life. When at length, and after the lapse of a few days, the outline of the body begins to be distinguished, then is the ventricular part of the heart also produced; but it continues for a time white and apparently bloodless, like the rest of the animal; neither does it pulsate or give signs of motion. I have seen a similar condition of the heart in the human fœtus about the beginning of the third month, the heart being then whitish and bloodless, although its auricles contained a considerable quantity of purple blood. In the same way in the egg, when the chick was formed and had increased in size, the heart too increased and acquired ventricles, which then began to receive and to transmit blood.

And this leads me to remark that he who inquires very particularly into this matter will not conclude that the heart, as a whole, is the *primum vivens, ultimum moriens*—the first part to live, the last to die, but rather its auricles, or the part which corresponds to the auricles in serpents, fishes, &c., which both lives before the heart and dies after it.

Nay, has not the blood itself or spirit an obscure palpitation inherent in it, which it has even appeared to me to retain after death? And it seems very questionable whether or not we are to say that life begins with the palpitation or beating of the heart. The seminal fluid of all animals—the prolific spirit, as Aristotle observed, leaves their body with a bound and like a living thing; and nature in death, as Aristotle[1] further remarks, retracing her steps, reverts to whence she had set out, returns at the end of her course to the goal whence she had started; and as animal generation proceeds from that which is not animal, entity from non-entity, so, by a retrograde course, entity, by corruption, is resolved into non-entity; whence that in animals, which was last created, fails first; and that which was first, fails last.

I have also observed that almost all animals have truly a heart, not the larger creatures only, and those that have red blood, but the smaller, and bloodless ones also, such as slugs, snails, scallops, shrimps, crabs, crayfish, and many others; nay, even in wasps, hornets and flies, I have, with the aid of a magnifying glass, and at the upper part of what is called the tail, both seen the heart pulsating myself, and shown it to many others.

But in the exsanguine tribes the heart pulsates sluggishly and deliberately, contracting slowly as in animals that are moribund, a fact that may readily be seen in the snail, whose heart will be found at the bottom of that orifice in the right side of the body which is seen to be opened and shut in the course of respiration, and whence saliva is discharged, the incision being made in the upper aspect of the body, near the part which corresponds to the liver.

This, however, is to be observed: that in winter and the colder season, exsanguine animals, such as the snail, show no pulsations; they seem rather to live after the manner of vegetables, or of those other productions which are therefore designated plant-animals.

It is also to be noted that all animals which have a heart, have also auricles, or something analogous to auricles; and further, that wherever the heart has a double ventricle there are always two auricles present, but not otherwise. If you turn to the production of the chick in ovo, however, you will find at first no more than a vesicle or auricle, or pulsating drop of

[1] *On the Motion of Animals*, 8.

blood; it is only by and by, when the development has made some progress, that the heart is fashioned: even so in certain animals not destined to attain to the highest perfection in their organization, such as bees, wasps, snails, shrimps, crayfish, &c., we only find a certain pulsating vesicle, like a sort of red or white palpitating point, as the beginning or principle of their life.

We have a small shrimp in these countries, which is taken in the Thames and in the sea, the whole of whose body is transparent; this creature, placed in a little water, has frequently afforded myself and particular friends an opportunity of observing the motions of the heart with the greatest distinctness, the external parts of the body presenting no obstacle to our view, but the heart being perceived as though it had been seen through a window.

I have also observed the first rudiments of the chick in the course of the fourth or fifth day of the incubation, in the guise of a little cloud, the shell having been removed and the egg immersed in clear tepid water. In the midst of the cloudlet in question there was a bloody point so small that it disappeared during the contraction and escaped the sight, but in the relaxation it reappeared again, red and like the point of a pin; so that betwixt the visible and invisible, betwixt being and not being, as it were, it gave by its pulses a kind of representation of the commencement of life.

CHAPTER 5. *Of the motion, action, and office of the heart*

FROM these and other observations of the like kind, I am persuaded it will be found that the motion of the heart is as follows:

First of all, the auricle contracts, and in the course of its contraction throws the blood (which it contains in ample quantity as the head of the veins, the storehouse and cistern of the blood) into the ventricle, which being filled, the heart raises itself straightway, makes all its fibres tense, contracts the ventricles, and performs a beat, by which beat it immediately sends the blood supplied to it by the auricle into the arteries; the right ventricle sending its charge into the lungs by the vessel which is called vena arteriosa, but which, in structure and function, and all things else, is an artery; the left ventricle sending its charge into the aorta, and through this by the arteries to the body at large.

These two motions, one of the ventricles, another of the auricles, take place consecutively, but in such a manner that there is a kind of harmony or rhythm preserved between them, the two concurring in such wise that but one motion is apparent, especially in the warmer blooded animals, in which the movements in question are rapid. Nor is this for any other reason than it is in a piece of machinery, in which, though one wheel gives motion to another, yet all the wheels seem to move simultaneously; or in that mechanical contrivance which is adapted to firearms, where the trigger being touched, down comes the flint, strikes against the steel, elicits a spark, which falling among the powder, it is ignited, upon which the flame extends, enters the barrel, causes the explosion, propels the ball, and the mark is attained—all of which incidents, by reason of the celerity with which they happen, seem to take place in the twinkling of an eye. So also in deglutition: by the elevation of the root of the tongue, and the compression of the mouth, the food or drink is pushed into the fauces, the larynx is closed by its own muscles, and the epiglottis, whilst the pharynx, raised and opened by its muscles no otherwise than is a sac that is to be filled, is lifted up, and its mouth dilated; upon which, the mouthful being received, it is forced downwards by the transverse muscles, and then carried farther by the longitudinal ones. Yet are all these motions, though executed by different and distinct organs, performed harmoniously, and in such order, that they seem to constitute but a single motion and act, which we call deglutition.

Even so does it come to pass with the motions and action of the heart, which constitute a kind of deglutition, a transfusion of the blood from the veins to the arteries. And if anyone, bearing these things in mind, will carefully watch the motions of the heart in the body of a living animal, he will perceive not only all the particulars I have mentioned, viz., the heart becoming erect, and making one continuous motion with its auricles; but further, a certain obscure undulation and lateral inclination in the direction of the axis of the right ventricle, twisting itself slightly in performing its work. And indeed everyone may see when a horse drinks that the water is drawn in and transmitted to the stomach at each movement of the throat, the motion being accompanied with a sound, and yielding a pulse both to the ear and the touch; in the same way it is with each motion of the heart, when there is the delivery of a quantity of blood from the veins to the arteries, that a pulse takes place, and can be heard within the chest.

The motion of the heart, then, is entirely of this description, and the one action of the heart is the transmission of the blood and its distribution, by means of the arteries, to the very extremities of the body; so that the pulse which we feel in the arteries is nothing more than the impulse of the blood derived from the heart.

Whether or not the heart, besides propelling the blood, giving it motion locally, and distributing it to the body, adds anything else to it—heat, spirit, perfection—must be inquired into by and by, and decided upon other grounds. So much may suffice at this time, when it is shown that by the action of the heart the blood is transfused through the ventricles from the veins to the arteries, and distributed by them to all parts of the body.

So much, indeed, is admitted by all, both from the structure of the heart and the arrangement and action of its valves. But still they are like persons purblind or groping about in the dark; and then they give utterance to diverse, contradictory, and incoherent sentiments, delivering many things upon conjecture, as we have already had occasion to remark.

The grand cause of hesitation and error in this subject appears to me to have been the intimate connexion between the heart and the lungs. When men saw both the vena arteriosa and the arteriæ venosæ losing themselves in the lungs, of course, it became a puzzle to them to know how or by what means the right ventricle should distribute the blood to the body, or the left draw it from the venæ cavæ. This fact is borne witness to by Galen, whose words, when writing against Erasistratus in regard to the origin and use of the veins and the coction of the blood, are the following: "You will reply," he says, "that the effect is so; that the blood is prepared in the liver, and is thence transferred to the heart to receive its proper form and last perfection; a statement which does not appear devoid of reason; for no great and perfect work is ever accomplished at a single effort, or receives its final polish from one instrument. But if this be actually so, then show us another vessel which draws the absolutely perfect blood from the heart, and distributes it as the arteries do the spirits over the whole body."[1] Here then is a reasonable opinion not allowed, because, forsooth, besides not seeing the true means of transit, he could not discover the vessel which should transmit the blood from the heart to the body at large!

[1] *De placitis Hippocratis et Platonis*, VI.

But had anyone been there in behalf of Erasistratus, and of that opinion which we now espouse, and which Galen himself acknowledges in other respects consonant with reason, to have pointed to the aorta as the vessel which distributes the blood from the heart to the rest of the body, I wonder what would have been the answer of that most ingenious and learned man? Had he said that the artery transmits spirits and not blood, he would indeed sufficiently have answered Erasistratus, who imagined that the arteries contained nothing but spirits; but then he would have contradicted himself, and given a foul denial to that for which he had keenly contended in his writings against this very Erasistratus, to wit, that blood in substance is contained in the arteries, and not spirits; a fact which he demonstrated not only by many powerful arguments, but by experiments.

But if the divine Galen will here allow, as in other places he does, "that all the arteries of the body arise from the great artery, and that this takes its origin from the heart; that all these vessels naturally contain and carry blood; that the three semilunar valves situated at the orifice of the aorta prevent the return of the blood into the heart, and that nature never connected them with this, the most noble viscus of the body, unless for some most important end"; if, I say, this father of physic admits all these things—and I quote his own words—I do not see how he can deny that the great artery is the very vessel to carry the blood, when it has attained its highest term of perfection, from the heart for distribution to all parts of the body. Or would he perchance still hesitate, like all who have come after him, even to the present hour, because he did not perceive the route by which the blood was transferred from the veins to the arteries, in consequence, as I have already said, of the intimate connexion between the heart and the lungs? And that this difficulty puzzled anatomists not a little, when in their dissections they found the pulmonary artery and left ventricle full of thick, black, and clotted blood, plainly appears, when they felt themselves compelled to affirm that the blood made its way from the right to the left ventricle by sweating through the septum of the heart. But this fancy I have already refuted. A new pathway for the blood must therefore be prepared and thrown open, and being once exposed, no further difficulty will, I believe, be experienced by anyone in admitting what I have already proposed in regard to the pulse of

the heart and arteries, *viz.*, the passage of the blood from the veins to the arteries, and its distribution to the whole of the body by means of these vessels.

CHAPTER 6. *Of the course by which the blood is carried from the vena cava into the arteries, or from the right into the left ventricle of the heart*

SINCE the intimate connexion of the heart with the lungs, which is apparent in the human subject, has been the probable cause of the errors that have been committed on this point, they plainly do amiss who, pretending to speak of the parts of animals generally, as anatomists for the most part do, confine their researches to the human body alone, and that when it is dead. They obviously act no otherwise than he who, having studied the forms of a single commonwealth, should set about the composition of a general system of polity; or who, having taken cognizance of the nature of a single field, should imagine that he had mastered the science of agriculture; or who, upon the ground of one particular proposition, should proceed to draw general conclusions.

Had anatomists only been as conversant with the dissection of the lower animals as they are with that of the human body, the matters that have hitherto kept them in a perplexity of doubt would, in my opinion, have met them freed from every kind of difficulty.

And, first, in fishes, in which the heart consists of but a single ventricle, they having no lungs, the thing is sufficiently manifest. Here the sac, which is situated at the base of the heart, and is the part analogous to the auricle in man, plainly throws the blood into the heart, and the heart, in its turn, conspicuously transmits it by a pipe or artery, or vessel analogous to an artery; these are facts which are confirmed by simple ocular inspection, as well as by a division of the vessel, when the blood is seen to be projected by each pulsation of the heart.

The same thing is also not difficult of demonstration in those animals that have either no more, or, as it were, no more than a single ventricle to the heart, such as toads, frogs, serpents, and lizards, which, although they have lungs in a certain sense, as they have a voice (and I have many observations by me on the admirable structure of the lungs of these animals, and matters appertaining, which, however, I cannot introduce in this place), still their anatomy plainly shows that the blood is transferred in them from the veins to the arteries in the same manner as in higher animals, viz., by the action of the heart; the way, in fact, is patent, open, manifest; there is no difficulty, no room for hesitating about it; for in them the matter stands precisely as it would in man, were the septum of his heart perforated or removed, or one ventricle made out of two; and this being the case, I imagine that no one will doubt as to the way by which the blood may pass from the veins into the arteries.

But as there are actually more animals which have no lungs than there are which be furnished with them, and in like manner a greater number which have only one ventricle than there are which have two, it is open to us to conclude, judging from the mass or multitude of living creatures, that for the major part, and generally, there is an open way by which the blood is transmitted from the veins through the sinuses or cavities of the heart into the arteries.

I have, however, cogitating with myself, seen further, that the same thing obtained most obviously in the embryos of those animals that have lungs; for in the fœtus the four vessels belonging to the heart, viz., the vena cava, the vena arteriosa or pulmonary artery, the arteria venalis or pulmonary vein, and the arteria magna or aorta, are all connected otherwise than in the adult; a fact sufficiently known to every anatomist. The first contact and union of the vena cava with the arteria venosa or pulmonary veins, which occurs before the cava opens properly into the right ventricle of the heart, or gives off the coronary vein, a little above its escape from the liver, is by a lateral anastomosis; this is an ample foramen, of an oval form, communicating between the cava and the arteria venosa, or pulmonary vein, so that the blood is free to flow in the greatest abundance by that foramen from the vena cava into the arteria venosa or pulmonary vein, and left auricle, and from thence into the left ventricle; and further, in this foramen ovale, from that part which regards the arteria venosa, or pulmonary vein, there is a thin tough membrane, larger than the opening, extended like an operculum or cover; this membrane in the adult blocking up the foramen, and adhering on all sides, finally closes it up, and almost obliterates every trace of it. This membrane, however, is so contrived in the fœtus, that falling loosely upon itself, it permits a ready access to the lungs and heart, yielding a passage to the blood which is streaming from the cava, and hindering the tide at the same time from flowing back into that vein. All things, in short, permit us to believe that in the embryo the blood must constantly pass by this foramen from the vena cava into the arteria venosa, or pulmonary vein, and from thence into the left auricle of the heart; and having once entered there, it can never regurgitate.

Another union is that by the vena arteriosa, or pulmonary artery, and is effected when that vessel divides into two branches after its escape from the right ventricle of the heart. It is as if to the two trunks already mentioned a third were superadded, a kind of arterial canal, carried obliquely from the vena arteriosa, or pulmonary artery, to perforate and terminate in the arteria magna or aorta. In the embryo, consequently, there are, as it were, two aortas, or two roots of the arteria magna, springing from the heart. This canalis arteriosus shrinks gradually after birth, and is at length and finally almost entirely withered, and removed, like the umbilical vessels.

The canalis arteriosus contains no membrane or valve to direct or impede the flow of the blood in this or in that direction: for at the root of the vena arteriosa, or pulmonary artery, of which the canalis arteriosus is the continuation in the fœtus, there are three sigmoid or semilunar valves, which open from within outwards, and oppose no obstacle to the blood flowing in this direction or from the right ventricle into the pulmonary artery and aorta; but they prevent all regurgitation from the aorta or pulmonic vessels back upon the right ventricle; closing with perfect accuracy, they oppose an effectual obstacle to everything of the kind in the embryo. So that there is also reason to believe that when the heart contracts, the blood is regularly propelled by the canal or passage indicated from the right ventricle into the aorta.

What is commonly said in regard to these two great communications, to wit, that they exist for the nutrition of the lungs, is both improbable and inconsistent; seeing that in the adult they are closed up, abolished, and consolidated, although the lungs, by reason of their heat and motion, must then be presumed to require a larger supply of nourishment. The same may be said in regard to the assertion that the heart in the embryo does not pulsate, that it neither acts nor moves, so that nature was forced to make these communications for the nutrition of the lungs. This is plainly false; for simple inspection of the incubated egg, and of embryos just taken out of the uterus, shows that the heart moves precisely in them as in adults, and that nature feels no such necessity. I have my-self repeatedly seen these motions, and Aristotle is likewise witness of their reality. "The pulse," he observes, "inheres in the very constitution of the heart, and appears from the beginning, as is learned both from the dissection of living animals, and the formation of the chick in the egg."[1] But we further observe that the passages in question are not only pervious up to the pe-riod of birth in man, as well as in other animals, as anatomists in general have described them, but for several months subsequently, in some indeed for several years, not to say for the whole course of life; as, for example, in the goose, snipe, and various birds, and many of the smaller animals. And this circumstance it was, perhaps, that imposed upon Botallus, who thought he had discovered a new passage for the blood from the vena cava into the left ventricle of the heart; and I own that when I met with the same arrangement in one of the larger members of the mouse family, in the adult state, I was my-self at first led to something of a like conclusion.

From this it will be understood that in the human embryo, and in the embryos of animals in which the communications are not closed, the same thing happens, namely, that the heart by its motion propels the blood by obvious and open passages from the vena cava into the aorta through the cavities of both the ventricles; the right one receiving the blood from the auricle, and propelling it by the vena arteriosa, or pul-monary artery, and its continuation, named the ductus arteriosus, into the aorta; the left, in like manner, charged by the contraction of its auricle, which has received its supply through the foramen ovale from the vena cava, con-tracting, and projecting the blood through the root of the aorta into the trunk of that vessel.

In embryos, consequently, whilst the lungs are yet in a state of inaction, performing no function, subject to no motion any more than if they had not been present, nature uses the two ventricles of the heart as if they formed but one, for the transmission of the blood. The con-dition of the embryos of those animals which have lungs, whilst these organs are yet in abey-ance and not employed, is the same as that of those animals which have no lungs.

So clearly, therefore, does it appear in the case of the fœtus, viz., that the heart by its ac-tion transfers the blood from the vena cava into the aorta, and that by a route as obvious and open, as if in the adult the two ventricles were made to communicate by the removal of their

[1] De spiritu, 5 [a pseudo-Aristotelian work].

septum. Since, then, we find that in the greater number of animals, in all, indeed, at a certain period of their existence, the channels for the transmission of the blood through the heart are so conspicuous, we have still to inquire where-fore in some creatures—those, namely, that have warm blood, and that have attained to the adult age, man among the number—we should not conclude that the same thing is accom-plished through the substance of the lungs, which in the embryo, and at a time when the function of these organs is in abeyance, nature effects by the direct passages described, and which, indeed, she seems compelled to adopt through want of a passage by the lungs; or wherefore it should be better (for nature always does that which is best) that she should close up the various open routes which she had formerly made use of in the embryo and fœtus, and still uses in all other animals; not only opening up no new apparent channels for the passage of the blood, therefore, but even entirely shutting up those which formerly existed.

And now the discussion is brought to this point, that they who inquire into the ways by which the blood reaches the left ventricle of the heart and pulmonary veins from the vena cava, will pursue the wisest course if they seek by dis-section to discover the causes why in the larger and more perfect animals of mature age, nature has rather chosen to make the blood percolate the parenchyma of the lungs, than as in other instances chosen a direct and obvious course—for I assume that no other path or mode of transit can be entertained. It must be either be-cause the larger and more perfect animals are warmer, and when adult their heat greater—ignited, as I might say, and requiring to be damped or mitigated; therefore it may be that the blood is sent through the lungs, that it may be tempered by the air that is inspired, and prevented from boiling up, and so becoming extinguished, or something else of the sort. But to determine these matters, and explain them satisfactorily, were to enter on a speculation in regard to the office of the lungs and the ends for which they exist; and upon such a subject, as well as upon what pertains to eventilation, to the necessity and use of the air, &c., as also to the variety and diversity of organs that exist in the bodies of animals in connexion with these matters, although I have made a vast number of observations, still, lest I should be held as wandering too wide of my present purpose, which is the use and motion of the heart, and be charged with speaking of things beside the question, and rather complicating and quitting than illustrating it, I shall leave such topics till I can more conveniently set them forth in a treatise apart. And now, returning to my immediate subject, I go on with what yet remains for demonstration, viz., that in the more perfect and warmer adult animals, and man, the blood passes from the right ventricle of the heart by the vena arteriosa, or pulmonary artery, into the lungs, and thence by the arteriæ venosæ, or pulmonary veins, into the left auricle, and thence into the left ventricle of the heart. And, first, I shall show that this may be so, and then I shall prove that it is so in fact.

CHAPTER 7. *The blood percolates the substance of the lungs from the right ventricle of the heart into the pulmonary veins and left ventricle*

THAT this is possible, and that there is nothing to prevent it from being so, appears when we reflect on the way in which water percolating the earth produces springs and rivulets, or when we speculate on the means by which the sweat passes through the skin, or the urine through the parenchyma of the kidneys. It is well known that persons who use the Spa waters, or those of La Madonna, in the territories of Padua, or others of an acidulous or vitriolated nature, or who simply swallow drinks by the gallon, pass all off again within an hour or two by urine. Such a quantity of liquid must take some short time in the concoction: it must pass through the liver (it is allowed by all that the juices of the food we consume pass twice through this organ in the course of the day); it must flow through the veins, through the parenchyma of the kidneys, and through the ureters into the bladder.

To those, therefore, whom I hear denying that the blood, aye the whole mass of the blood may pass through the substance of the lungs, even as the nutritive juices percolate the liver, asserting such a proposition to be impossible, and by no means to be entertained as credible, I reply, with the poet, that they are of that race of men who, when they will, assent full readily, and when they will not, by no manner of means; who, when their assent is wanted, fear, and when it is not, fear not to give it.

The parenchyma of the liver is extremely dense, so is that of the kidney; the lungs, again, are of a much looser texture, and if compared with the kidneys are absolutely spongy. In the liver there is no forcing, no impelling power; in the lungs the blood is forced on by the pulse of the right ventricle, the necessary effect of whose impulse is the distension of the vessels and pores of the lungs. And then the lungs, in respiration, are perpetually rising and falling; motions, the effect of which must needs be to open and shut the pores and vessels, precisely as in the case of a sponge, and of parts having a spongy structure, when they are alternately compressed and again are suffered to expand. The liver, on the contrary, remains at rest, and is never seen to be dilated and constricted. Lastly, if no one denies the possibility of the whole of the ingested juices passing through the liver, in man, oxen, and the larger animals generally, in order to reach the vena cava, and for this reason, that if nourishment is to go on, these juices must needs get into the veins, and there is no other way but the one indicated, why should not the same arguments be held of avail for the passage of the blood in adults through the lungs? Why not, with Columbus, that skilful and learned anatomist, maintain and believe the like, from the capacity and structure of the pulmonary vessels; from the fact of the pulmonary veins and ventricle corresponding with them, being always found to contain blood, which must needs have come from the veins, and by no other passage save through the lungs? Columbus, and we also, from what precedes, from dissections, and other arguments, conceive the thing to be clear. But as there are some who admit nothing unless upon authority, let them learn that the truth I am contending for can be confirmed from Galen's own words, namely, that not only may the blood be transmitted from the pulmonary artery into the pulmonary veins, then into the left ventricle of the heart, and from thence into the arteries of the body, but that this is effected by the ceaseless pulsation of the heart and the motion of the lungs in breathing.

There are, as everyone knows, three sigmoid or semilunar valves situated at the orifice of the pulmonary artery, which effectually prevent the blood sent into the vessel from returning into the cavity of the heart. Now Galen, explaining the uses of these valves, and the necessity for them, employs the following language: "There is everywhere a mutual anastomosis and inosculation of the arteries with the veins, and they severally transmit both blood and spirit, by certain invisible and undoubtedly very narrow passages. Now if the mouth of the vena arteriosa, or pulmonary artery, had stood in like manner continually open, and nature had found no contrivance for closing it when requisite, and opening it again, it would have been impossible that the blood could ever have passed by the invisible and delicate mouths, during the contractions of the thorax, into the arteries; for all things are not alike readily attracted or repelled; but that which is light is more readily drawn in, the instrument being dilated, and forced out again when it is contracted, than that which is heavy; and in like manner is anything drawn more rapidly along an ample conduit, and again driven forth, than it is through a narrow tube. But when the thorax is contracted, the pulmonary veins, which are in the lungs, being driven inwardly, and powerfully compressed on every side, immediately force out some of the spirit they contain, and at the same time assume a certain portion of blood by those subtile mouths; a thing that could never come to pass were the blood at liberty to flow back into the heart through the great orifice of the pulmonary artery. But its return through this great opening being prevented, when it is compressed on every side, a certain portion of it distils into the pulmonary veins by the minute orifices mentioned."[1] And shortly afterwards, in the very next chapter, he says: "The more the thorax contracts, the more it strives to force out the blood, the more exactly do these membranes (viz., the sigmoid valves) close up the mouth of the vessel, and suffer nothing to regurgitate." The same fact he has also alluded to in a preceding part of the tenth chapter: "Were there no valves, a three-fold inconvenience would result, so that the blood would then perform this lengthened course in vain; it would flow inwards during the diastoles of the lungs, and fill all their arteries; but in the systoles, in the manner of the tide, it would ever and anon, like the Euripus, flow backwards and forwards by the same way, with a reciprocating motion, which would nowise suit the blood. This, however, may seem a matter of little moment; but if it meantime appear that the function of respiration suffer, then I think it would be looked upon as no trifle," &c. And again, and shortly afterwards: "And then a third inconvenience, by no means to be thought lightly of, would follow, were the blood moved backwards during the expirations, had not our Maker instituted those supplementary membranes." Whence, in the eleventh chapter, he concludes: "That they have all a common use (to wit, the valves), and that it is to prevent regurgitation or backward motion; each, however, having a proper function, the one set drawing matters from the heart, and prevent-

[1] *De usu partium*, VI. 10.

ing their return, the other drawing matters into the heart, and preventing their escape from it. For nature never intended to distress the heart with needless labour, neither to bring aught into the organ which it had been better to have kept away, nor to take from it again aught which it was requisite should be brought. Since, then, there are four orifices in all, two in either ventricle, one of these induces, the other educes." And again he says: "Further, since there is one vessel, consisting of a simple tunic, implanted in the heart, and another, having a double tunic, extending from it (Galen is here speaking of the right side of the heart, but I extend his observations to the left side also), a kind of reservoir had to be provided, to which both belonging, the blood should be drawn in by the one, and sent out by the other."

This argument Galen adduces for the transit of the blood by the right ventricle from the vena cava into the lungs; but we can use it with still greater propriety, merely changing the terms, for the passage of the blood from the veins through the heart into the arteries. From Galen, however, that great man, that father of physicians, it clearly appears that the blood passes through the lungs from the pulmonary artery into the minute branches of the pulmonary veins, urged to this both by the pulses of the heart and by the motions of the lungs and thorax; that the heart, moreover, is incessantly receiving and expelling the blood by and from its ventricles, as from a magazine or cistern, and for this end is furnished with four sets of valves, two serving for the induction and two for the eduction of the blood, lest, like the Euripus, it should be incommodiously sent hither and thither, or flow back into the cavity which it should have quitted, or quit the part where its presence was required, and so the heart be oppressed with labour in vain, and the office of the lungs be interfered with.[2] Finally, our position that the blood is continually passing from the right to the left ventricle, from the vena cava into the aorta, through the porous structure of the lungs, plainly appears from this, that since the blood is incessantly sent from the right ventricle into the lungs by the pulmonary artery, and in like manner is incessantly drawn from the lungs into the left ventricle, as appears from what precedes and the position of the valves, it cannot do otherwise than pass through continuously. And then, as

[2] See the commentary of the learned Hofmann upon the Sixth Book of Galen, *De usu partium*, a work which I first saw after I had written what precedes.

the blood is incessantly flowing into the right ventricle of the heart, and is continually passed out from the left, as appears in like manner, and as is obvious both to sense and reason, it is impossible that the blood can do otherwise than pass continually from the vena cava into the aorta.

Dissection consequently shows distinctly what takes place in the greater number of animals, and indeed in all, up to the period of their [foetal] maturity; and that the same thing occurs in adults is equally certain, both from Galen's words, and what has already been said on the subject, only that in the former the transit is effected by open and obvious passages, in the latter by the obscure porosities of the lungs and the minute inosculations of vessels. Whence it appears that, although one ventricle of the heart, the left to wit, would suffice for the distribution of the blood over the body, and its eduction from the vena cava, as indeed is done in those creatures that have no lungs, nature, nevertheless, when she ordained that the same blood should also percolate the lungs, saw herself obliged to add another ventricle, the right, the pulse of which should force the blood from the vena cava through the lungs into the cavity of the left ventricle. In this way, therefore, it may be said that the right ventricle is made for the sake of the lungs, and for the transmission of the blood through them, not for their nutrition; seeing it were unreasonable to suppose that the lungs required any so much more copious a supply of nutriment, and that of so much purer and more spirituous a kind, as coming immediately from the ventricle of the heart, than either the brain with its peculiarly pure substance, or the eyes with their lustrous and truly admirable structure, or the flesh of the heart itself, which is more commodiously nourished by the coronary artery.

CHAPTER 8. *Of the quantity of blood passing through the heart from the veins to the arteries; and of the circular motion of the blood*

THUS far I have spoken of the passage of the blood from the veins into the arteries, and of the manner in which it is transmitted and distributed by the action of the heart; points to which some, moved either by the authority of Galen or Columbus, or the reasonings of others, will give in their adhesion. But what remains to be said upon the quantity and source of the blood which thus passes is of so novel and unheard-of character, that I not only fear injury to myself from the envy of a few, but I tremble lest I have

mankind at large for my enemies, so much doth wont and custom, that become as another nature, and doctrine once sown and that hath struck deep root, and respect for antiquity influence all men: still the die is cast, and my trust is in my love of truth, and the candour that inheres in cultivated minds. And sooth to say, when I surveyed my mass of evidence, whether derived from vivisections, and my various reflections on them, or from the ventricles of the heart and the vessels that enter into and issue from them, the symmetry and size of these conduits—for nature doing nothing in vain, would never have given them so large a relative size without a purpose—or from the arrangement and intimate structure of the valves in particular, and of the other parts of the heart in general, with many things besides, I frequently and seriously bethought me, and long revolved in my mind, what might be the quantity of blood which was transmitted, in how short a time its passage might be effected, and the like; and not finding it possible that this could be supplied by the juices of the ingested aliment without the veins on the one hand becoming drained, and the arteries on the other getting ruptured through the excessive charge of blood, unless the blood should somehow find its way from the arteries into the veins, and so return to the right side of the heart; I began to think whether there might not be a MOTION, AS IT WERE, IN A CIRCLE. Now this I afterwards found to be true; and I finally saw that the blood, forced by the action of the left ventricle into the arteries, was distributed to the body at large, and its several parts, in the same manner as it is sent through the lungs, impelled by the right ventricle into the pulmonary artery, and that it then passed through the veins and along the vena cava, and so round to the left ventricle in the manner already indicated. Which motion we may be allowed to call circular, in the same way as Aristotle says that the air and the rain emulate the circular motion of the superior bodies; for the moist earth, warmed by the sun, evaporates; the vapours drawn upwards are condensed, and descending in the form of rain, moisten the earth again; and by this arrangement are generations of living things produced; and in like manner too are tempests and meteors engendered by the circular motion, and by the approach and recession of the sun.

And so, in all likelihood, does it come to pass in the body, through the motion of the blood; the various parts are nourished, cherished, quickened by the warmer, more perfect, vaporous, spirituous, and, as I may say, alimentive blood; which, on the contrary, in contact with these parts becomes cooled, coagulated, and, so to speak, effete; whence it returns to its sovereign the heart, as if to its source, or to the inmost home of the body, there to recover its state of excellence or perfection. Here it resumes its due fluidity and receives an infusion of natural heat—powerful, fervid, a kind of treasury of life, and is impregnated with spirits, and it might be said with balsam; and thence it is again dispersed; and all this depends on the motion and action of the heart.

The heart, consequently, is the beginning of life; the sun of the microcosm, even as the sun in his turn might well be designated the heart of the world; for it is the heart by whose virtue and pulse the blood is moved, perfected, made apt to nourish, and is preserved from corruption and coagulation; it is the household divinity which, discharging its function, nourishes, cherishes, quickens the whole body, and is indeed the foundation of life, the source of all action. But of these things we shall speak more opportunely when we come to speculate upon the final cause of this motion of the heart.

Hence, since the veins are the conduits and vessels that transport the blood, they are of two kinds, the cava and the aorta; and this not by reason of there being two sides of the body, as Aristotle has it, but because of the difference of office; nor yet, as is commonly said, in consequence of any diversity of structure, for in many animals, as I have said, the vein does not differ from the artery in the thickness of its tunics, but solely in virtue of their several) destinies and uses. A vein and an artery, both styled vein by the ancients, and that not undeservedly, as Galen has remarked, because the one, the artery, to wit, is the vessel which carries the blood from the heart to the body at large, the other or vein of the present day bringing it back from the general system to the heart; the former is the conduit from, the latter the channel to, the heart; the latter contains the cruder, effete blood, rendered unfit for nutrition; the former transmits the digested, perfect, peculiarly nutritive fluid.

CHAPTER 9. *That there is a circulation of the blood is confirmed from the first proposition*

BUT lest any one should say that we give them words only, and make mere specious assertions without any foundation, and desire to innovate without sufficient cause, three points present themselves for confirmation, which being stated,

I conceive that the truth I contend for will follow necessarily, and appear as a thing obvious to all. First, the blood is incessantly transmitted by the action of the heart from the vena cava to the arteries in such quantity that it cannot be supplied from the ingesta, and in such wise that the whole mass must very quickly pass through the organ; second, the blood under the influence of the arterial pulse enters and is impelled in a continuous, equable, and incessant stream through every part and member of the body, in much larger quantity than were sufficient for nutrition, or than the whole mass of fluids could supply; third, the veins in like manner return this blood incessantly to the heart from all parts and members of the body. These points proved, I conceive it will be manifest that the blood circulates, revolves, propelled and then returning, from the heart to the extremities, from the extremities to the heart, and thus that it performs a kind of circular motion.

Let us assume, either arbitrarily or from experiment, the quantity of blood which the left ventricle of the heart will contain when distended to be, say two ounces, three ounces, one ounce and a half—in the dead body I have found it to hold upwards of two ounces. Let us assume further, how much less the heart will hold in the contracted than in the dilated state; and how much blood it will project into the aorta upon each contraction—and all the world allows that with the systole something is always projected, a necessary consequence demonstrated in the third chapter, and obvious from the structure of the valves; and let us suppose as approaching the truth that the fourth, or fifth, or sixth, or even but the eighth part of its charge is thrown into the artery at each contraction; this would give either half an ounce, or three drachms, or one drachm of blood as propelled by the heart at each pulse into the aorta; which quantity, by reason of the valves at the root of the vessel, can by no means return into the ventricle. Now in the course of half an hour, the heart will have made more than one thousand beats, in some as many as two, three, and even four thousand. Multiplying the number of drachms propelled by the number of pulses, we shall have either one thousand half ounces, or one thousand times three drachms, or a like proportional quantity of blood, according to the amount which we assume as propelled with each stroke of the heart, sent from this organ into the artery; a larger quantity in every case than is contained in the whole body!

In the same way, in the sheep or dog, say that but a single scruple of blood passes with each stroke of the heart, in one half hour we should have one thousand scruples, or about three pounds and a half of blood injected into the aorta; but the body of neither animal contains above four pounds of blood, a fact which I have myself ascertained in the case of the sheep.

Upon this supposition, therefore, assumed merely as a ground for reasoning, we see the whole mass of blood passing through the heart, from the veins to the arteries, and in like manner through the lungs.

But let it be said that this does not take place in half an hour, but in an hour, or even in a day; any way it is still manifest that more blood passes through the heart in consequence of its action, than can either be supplied by the whole of the ingesta, or than can be contained in the veins at the same moment.

Nor can it be allowed that the heart in contracting sometimes propels and sometimes does not propel, or at most propels but very little, a mere nothing, or an imaginary something: all this, indeed, has already been refuted; and is, besides, contrary both to sense and reason. For if it be a necessary effect of the dilatation of the heart that its ventricles become filled with blood, it is equally so that, contracting, these cavities should expel their contents; and this not in any trifling measure, seeing that neither are the conduits small, nor the contractions few in number, but frequent, and always in some certain proportion, whether it be a third or a sixth, or an eighth, to the total capacity of the ventricles, so that a like proportion of blood must be expelled, and a like proportion received with each stroke of the heart, the capacity of the ventricle contracted always bearing a certain relation to the capacity of the ventricle when dilated. And since in dilating, the ventricles cannot be supposed to get filled with nothing, or with an imaginary something; so in contracting they never expel nothing or aught imaginary, but always a certain something, viz., blood, in proportion to the amount of the contraction. Whence it is to be inferred, that if at one stroke the heart in man, the ox or the sheep, ejects but a single drachm of blood, and there are one thousand strokes in half an hour, in this interval there will have been ten pounds, five ounces expelled: were there with each stroke two drachms expelled, the quantity would of course amount to twenty pounds and ten ounces; were there half an ounce, the quantity would come to forty-one pounds and eight ounces; and were there one ounce it would be as much as eighty-three pounds and four ounces; the whole of which, in the course of one half hour, would have been transfused from the veins to the arteries. The actual quantity of blood expelled at each stroke of the heart, and the circumstances under which it is either greater or less than ordinary, I leave for particular determination afterwards, from numerous observations which I have made on the subject.

Meantime this much I know, and would here proclaim to all that the blood is transfused at one time in larger, at another in smaller quantity; and that the circuit of the blood is accomplished now more rapidly, now more slowly, according to the temperament, age, &c. of the individual, to external and internal circumstances, to naturals and non-naturals—sleep, rest, food, exercise, affections of the mind, and the like. But indeed, supposing even the smallest quantity of blood to be passed through the heart and the lungs with each pulsation, a vastly greater amount would still be thrown into the arteries and whole body than could by any possibility be supplied by the food consumed; in short it could be furnished in no other way than by making a circuit and returning.

This truth, indeed, presents itself obviously before us when we consider what happens in the dissection of living animals; the great artery need not be divided, but a very small branch only (as Galen even proves in regard to man), to have the whole of the blood in the body, as well that of the veins as of the arteries, drained away in the course of no long time— some half hour or less. Butchers are well aware of the fact and can bear witness to it; for, cutting the throat of an ox and so dividing the vessels of the neck, in less than a quarter of an hour they have all the vessels bloodless—the whole mass of blood has escaped. The same thing also occasionally occurs with great rapidity in performing amputations and removing tumours in the human subject.

Nor would this argument lose any of its force, did anyone say that in killing animals in the shambles, and performing amputations, the blood escaped in equal, if not perchance in larger quantity by the veins than by the arteries. The contrary of this statement, indeed, is certainly the truth; the veins, in fact, collapsing, and being without any propelling power, and further, because of the impediment of the valves, as I shall show immediately, pour out but very little blood; whilst the arteries spout it forth with force abundantly, impetuously, and as if it were propelled by a syringe. And then the experiment is easily tried of leaving the vein untouched, and only dividing the artery in the neck of a sheep or dog, when it will be seen with what force, in what abundance, and how quickly, the whole blood in the body, of the veins as well as of the arteries, is emptied. But the arteries receive blood from the veins in no other way than by transmission through the heart, as we have already seen; so that if the aorta be tied at the base of the heart, and the carotid or any other artery be opened, no one will now be surprised to find it empty, and the veins only replete with blood.

And now the cause is manifest, wherefore in our dissections we usually find so large a quantity of blood in the veins, so little in the arteries; wherefore there is much in the right ventricle, little in the left; circumstances which probably led the ancients to believe that the arteries (as their name implies) contained nothing but spirits during the life of an animal. The true cause of the difference is this perhaps: that as there is no passage to the arteries, save through the lungs and heart, when an animal has ceased to breathe and the lungs to move, the blood in the pulmonary artery is prevented from passing into the pulmonary veins, and from thence into the left ventricle of the heart; just as we have already seen the same transit prevented in the embryo, by the want of movement in the lungs and the alternate opening and shutting of their minute orifices and invisible pores. But the heart not ceasing to act at the same precise moment as the lungs, but surviving them and continuing to pulsate for a time, the left ventricle and arteries go on distributing their blood to the body at large and sending it into the veins; receiving none from the lungs, however, they are soon exhausted, and left, as it were, empty. But even this fact confirms our views, in no trifling manner, seeing that it can be ascribed to no other than the cause we have just assumed.

Moreover, it appears from this that the more frequently or forcibly the arteries pulsate, the more speedily will the body be exhausted in an hemorrhagy. Hence, also, it happens, that in fainting fits and in states of alarm, when the heart beats more languidly and with less force, hemorrhages are diminished or arrested.

Still further, it is from this that after death, when the heart has ceased to beat, it is impossible by dividing either the jugular or femoral veins and arteries, by any effort to force out more than one half of the whole mass of the blood. Neither could the butcher, did he neglect to cut the throat of the ox which he has knocked on the head and stunned, until the heart had ceased beating, ever bleed the carcass effectually.

Finally, we are now in a condition to suspect wherefore it is that no one has yet said anything to the purpose upon the anastomosis of the veins and arteries, either as to where or how it is effected, or for what purpose. I now enter upon the investigation of the subject.

CHAPTER 10. *The first position: of the quantity of blood passing from the veins to the arteries; and that there is a circuit of the blood, freed from objections, and further confirmed by experiment*

So far our first position is confirmed, whether the thing be referred to calculation or to experiment and dissection, viz., that the blood is incessantly infused into the arteries in larger quantities than it can be supplied by the food; so that the whole passing over in a short space of time, it is matter of necessity that the blood perform a circuit, that it return to whence it set out.

But if anyone shall here object that a large quantity may pass through and yet no necessity be found for a circulation, that all may come from the meat and drink consumed, and quote as an illustration the abundant supply of milk in the mammæ—for a cow will give three, four, and even seven gallons and more in a day, and a woman two or three pints whilst nursing a child or twins, which must manifestly be derived from the food consumed; it may be answered, that the heart by computation does as much and more in the course of an hour or two.

And if not yet convinced, he shall still insist, that when an artery is divided a preternatural route is, as it were, opened, and that so the blood escapes in torrents, but that the same thing does not happen in the healthy and uninjured body when no outlet is made; and that in arteries filled, or in their natural state, so large a quantity of blood cannot pass in so short a space of time as to make any return necessary; to all this it may be answered, that from the calculation already made, and the reasons assigned, it appears that, by so much as the heart in its dilated state contains in addition to its contents in the state of constriction, so much in a general way must it emit upon each pulsation, and in such quantity must the blood pass, the body being healthy and naturally constituted.

But in serpents, and several fishes, by tying the veins some way below the heart, you will perceive a space between the ligature and the heart speedily to become empty; so that, unless you would deny the evidence of your senses, you must needs admit the return of the blood to the heart. The same thing will also plainly appear when we come to discuss our second position.

Let us here conclude with a single example, confirming all that has been said, and from which everyone may obtain conviction through the testimony of his own eyes.

If a live snake be laid open, the heart will be seen pulsating quietly, distinctly, for more than an hour, moving like a worm, contracting in its longitudinal dimensions (for it is of an oblong shape), and propelling its contents; becoming of a paler colour in the systole, of a deeper tint in the diastole; and almost all things else by which I have already said that the truth I contend for is established, only that here everything takes place more slowly, and is more distinct. This point in particular may be observed more clearly than the noonday sun: the vena cava enters the heart at its lower part, the artery quits it at the superior part; the vein being now seized either with forceps or between the finger and thumb, and the course of the blood for some space below the heart interrupted, you will perceive the part that intervenes between the fingers and the heart almost immediately to become empty, the blood being exhausted by the action of the heart; at the same time the heart will become of a much paler colour, even in its state of dilatation, than it was before; it is also smaller than at first, from wanting blood; and then it begins to beat more slowly, so that it seems at length as if it were about to die. But the impediment to the flow of blood being removed, instantly the colour and the size of the heart are restored.

If, on the contrary, the artery instead of the vein be compressed or tied, you will observe the part between the obstacle and the heart, and the heart itself, to become inordinately distended, to assume a deep purple or even livid colour, and at length to be so much oppressed with blood that you will believe it about to be choked; but the obstacle removed, all things immediately return to their pristine state—the heart to its colour, size, stroke, &c.

Here then we have evidence of two kinds of death: extinction from deficiency, and suffocation from excess. Examples of both have now been set before you, and you have had oppor-

tunity of viewing the truth contended for with your own eyes in the heart.

CHAPTER 11. *The second position is demonstrated*

THAT this may the more clearly appear to everyone, I have here to cite certain experiments, from which it seems obvious that the blood enters a limb by the arteries, and returns from it by the veins; that the arteries are the vessels carrying the blood from the heart, and the veins the returning channels of the blood to the heart; that in the limbs and extreme parts of the body the blood passes either immediately by anastomosis from the arteries into the veins, or mediately by the pores of the flesh, or in both ways, as has already been said in speaking of the passage of the blood through the lungs; whence it appears manifest that in the circuit the blood moves from thence hither, and from hence thither; from the centre to the extremities, to wit; and from the extreme parts back again to the centre. Finally, upon grounds of calculation, with the same elements as before, it will be obvious that the quantity can neither be accounted for by the ingesta, nor yet be held necessary to nutrition.

The same thing will also appear in regard to ligatures, and wherefore they are said to *draw;* though this is neither from the heat, nor the pain, nor the vacuum they occasion, nor indeed from any other cause yet thought of; it will also explain the uses and advantages to be derived from ligatures in medicine, the principle upon which they either suppress or occasion hemorrhage; how they induce sloughing and more extensive mortification in extremities; and how they act in the castration of animals and the removal of warts and fleshy tumours. But it has come to pass, from no one having duly weighed and understood the causes and rationale of these various effects, that though almost all, upon the faith of the old writers, recommend ligatures in the treatment of disease, yet very few comprehend their proper employment, or derive any real assistance from them in effecting cures.

Ligatures are either very tight or of middling tightness. A ligature I designate as tight or perfect when it is drawn so close about an extremity that no vessel can be felt pulsating beyond it. Such a ligature we use in amputations to control the flow of blood; and such also are employed in the castration of animals and the removal of tumours. In the latter instances, all afflux of nutriment and heat being prevented by the ligature, we see the testes and large fleshy tumours dwindle, and die, and finally fall off.

Ligatures of middling tightness I regard as those which compress a limb firmly all around, but short of pain, and in such a way as still suffers a certain degree of pulsation to be felt in the artery beyond them. Such a ligature is in use in bloodletting, an operation in which the fillet applied above the elbow is not drawn so tight but that the arteries at the wrist may still be felt beating under the finger.

Now let any one make an experiment upon the arm of a man, either using such a fillet as is employed in bloodletting, or grasping the limb lightly with his hand, the best subject for it being one who is lean, and who has large veins, and the best time after exercise, when the body is warm, the pulse is full, and the blood carried in larger quantity to the extremities, for all then is more conspicuous; under such circumstances let a ligature be thrown about the extremity, and drawn as tightly as can be borne, it will first be perceived that beyond the ligature, neither in the wrist nor anywhere else, do the arteries pulsate, at the same time that immediately above the ligature the artery begins to rise higher at each diastole, to throb more violently, and to swell in its vicinity with a kind of tide, as if it strove to break through and overcome the obstacle to its current; the artery here, in short, appears as if it were preternaturally full. The hand under such circumstances retains its natural colour and appearance; in the course of time it begins to fall somewhat in temperature, indeed, but nothing is *drawn* into it.

After the bandage has been kept on for some short time in this way, let it be slackened a little, brought to that state or term of middling tightness which is used in bleeding, and it will be seen that the whole hand and arm will instantly become deeply suffused and distended, and the veins show themselves tumid and knotted; after ten or fifteen pulses of the artery, the hand will be perceived excessively distended, injected, gorged with blood, *drawn*, as it is said, by this middling ligature, without pain, or heat, or any horror of a vacuum, or any other cause yet indicated.

If the finger be applied over the artery as it is pulsating by the edge of the fillet, at the moment of slackening it, the blood will be felt to glide through, as it were, underneath the finger; and he, too, upon whose arm the experiment is made, when the ligature is slackened, is distinctly conscious of a sensation of warmth, and of something, *viz.*, a stream of blood suddenly making its way along the course of the vessels and diffusing itself through the hand, which at the same time begins to feel hot, and becomes distended.

As we had noted, in connexion with the tight ligature, that the artery above the bandage was distended and pulsated, not below it, so, in the case of the moderately tight bandage, on the contrary, do we find that the veins below, never above, the fillet, swell, and become dilated, whilst the arteries shrink; and such is the degree of distention of the veins here that it is only very strong pressure that will force the blood beyond the fillet, and cause any of the veins in the upper part of the arm to rise.

From these facts it is easy for every careful observer to learn that the blood enters an extremity by the arteries; for when they are effectually compressed nothing is *drawn* to the member; the hand preserves its colour; nothing flows into it, neither is it distended; but when the pressure is diminished, as it is with the bleeding fillet, it is manifest that the blood is instantly thrown in with force, for then the hand begins to swell; which is as much as to say that when the arteries pulsate the blood is flowing through them, as it is when the moderately tight ligature is applied; but where they do not pulsate, as, when a tight ligature is used, they cease from transmitting anything; they are only distended above the part where the ligature is applied. The veins again being compressed, nothing can flow through them; the certain indication of which is that below the ligature they are much more tumid than above it and than they usually appear when there is no bandage upon the arm.

It therefore plainly appears that the ligature prevents the return of the blood through the veins to the parts above it, and maintains those beneath it in a state of permanent distention. But the arteries, in spite of its pressure, and under the force and impulse of the heart, send on the blood from the internal parts of the body to the parts beyond the bandage. And herein consists the difference between the tight and the medium bandage, that the former not only prevents the passage of the blood in the veins, but in the arteries also; the latter, however, whilst it does not prevent the pulsific force from extending beyond it, and so propelling the blood to the extremities of the body, compresses the veins, and greatly or altogether impedes the return of the blood through them.

Seeing, therefore, that the moderately tight

ligature renders the veins turgid, and the whole hand full of blood, I ask, whence is this? Does the blood accumulate below the ligature coming through the veins, or through the arteries, or passing by certain secret pores? Through the veins it cannot come; still less can it come by any system of invisible pores; it must needs arrive by the arteries, then, in conformity with all that has been already said. That it cannot flow in by the veins appears plainly enough from the fact that the blood cannot be forced towards the heart unless the ligature be removed; when on a sudden all the veins collapse, and disgorge themselves of their contents into the superior parts, the hand at the same time resuming its natural pale colour, the tumefaction and the stagnating blood have disappeared.

Moreover, he whose arm or wrist has thus been bound for some little time with the medium bandage, so that it has not only got swollen and livid but cold, when the fillet is undone is aware of something cold making its way upwards along with the returning blood, and reaching the elbow or the axilla. And I have myself been inclined to think that this cold blood rising upwards to the heart was the cause of the fainting that often occurs after bloodletting: fainting frequently supervenes even in robust subjects, and mostly at the moment of undoing the fillet, as the vulgar say, from the turning of the blood.

Further, when we see the veins below the ligature instantly swell up and become gorged, when from extreme tightness it is somewhat relaxed, the arteries meantime continuing unaffected, this is an obvious indication that the blood passes from the arteries into the veins, and not from the veins into the arteries, and that there is either an anastomosis of the two orders of vessels, or pores in the flesh and solid parts generally that are permeable to the blood. It is further an indication that the veins have frequent communications with one another, because they all become turgid together, whilst under the medium ligature applied above the elbow; and if any single small vein be pricked with a lancet, they all speedily shrink, and disburthening themselves into this they subside almost simultaneously.

These considerations will enable anyone to understand the nature of the attraction that is exerted by ligatures, and perchance of fluxes generally; how, for example, the veins when compressed by a bandage of medium tightness applied above the elbow, the blood cannot escape, whilst it still continues to be driven in, to wit, by the forcing power of the heart, by which the parts are of necessity filled, gorged with blood. And how should it be otherwise? Heat and pain and the *vis vacui* draw, indeed; but in such wise only that parts are filled, not preternaturally distended or gorged, not so suddenly and violently overwhelmed with the charge of blood forced in upon them, that the flesh is lacerated and the vessels ruptured. Nothing of the kind as an effect of heat, or pain, or the vacuum force, is either credible or demonstrable.

Besides, the ligature is competent to occasion the afflux in question without either pain, or heat, or *vis vacui*. Were pain in any way the cause, how should it happen that, with the arm bound above the elbow, the hand and fingers should swell below the bandage, and their veins become distended? The pressure of the bandage certainly prevents the blood from getting there by the veins. And then, wherefore is there neither swelling nor repletion of the veins, nor any sign or symptom of attraction or afflux, above the ligature? But this is the obvious cause of the preternatural attraction and swelling below the bandage, and in the hand and fingers, that the blood is entering abundantly, and with force, but cannot pass out again.

Now is not this the cause of all tumefaction, as indeed Avicenna has it, and of all oppressive redundancy in parts, that the access to them is open, but the egress from them is closed? Whence it comes that they are gorged and tumefied. And may not the same thing happen in local inflammations, where, so long as the swelling is on the increase, and has not reached its extreme term, a full pulse is felt in the part, especially when the disease is of the more acute kind, and the swelling usually takes place most rapidly. But these are matters for after discussion. Or does this, which occurred in my own case, happen from the same cause? Thrown from a carriage upon one occasion, I struck my forehead a blow upon the place where a twig of the artery advances from the temple, and immediately, within the time in which twenty beats could have been made, I felt a tumour the size of an egg developed, without either heat or any great pain: the near vicinity of the artery had caused the blood to be effused into the bruised part with unusual force and quickness.

And now, too, we understand wherefore in phlebotomy we apply our fillet above the part that is punctured, not below it; did the flow come from above, not from below, the bandage in this case would not only be of no service, but would prove a positive hinderance; it would have to be applied below the orifice, in order to have the flow more free, did the blood descend by the veins from superior to inferior parts; but as it is elsewhere forced through the extreme arteries into the extreme veins, and the return in these last is opposed by the ligature, so do they fill and swell, and being thus filled and distended, they are made capable of projecting their charge with force, and to a distance, when any one of them is suddenly punctured; but the flllet being slackened, and the returning channels thus left open, the blood forthwith no longer escapes, save by drops; and, as all the world knows, if in performing phlebotomy the bandage be either slackened too much or the limb be bound too tightly, the blood escapes without force, because in the one case the returning channels are not adequately obstructed; in the other the channels of influx, the arteries, are impeded.

CHAPTER 12. *That there is a circulation of the blood is shown from the second position demonstrated*

IF these things be so, another point which I have already referred to, viz., the continual passage of the blood through the heart will also be confirmed. We have seen that the blood passes from the arteries into the veins, not from the veins into the arteries; we have seen, further, that almost the whole of the blood may be withdrawn from a puncture made in one of the cutaneous veins of the arm if a bandage properly applied be used; we have seen, still further, that the blood flows so freely and rapidly that not only is the whole quantity which was contained in the arm beyond the ligature, and before the puncture was made, discharged, but the whole which is contained in the body, both that of the arteries and that of the veins.

Whence we must admit, first, that the blood is sent along with an impulse, and that is urged with force below the fillet; for it escapes with force, which force it receives from the pulse and power of the heart; for the force and motion of the blood are derived from the heart alone. Second, that the afflux proceeds from the heart, and through the heart by a course from the great veins; for it gets into the parts below the ligature through the arteries, not through the veins; and the arteries nowhere receive blood from the veins, nowhere receive blood save and except from the left ventricle of the heart. Nor could so large a quantity of blood be drawn from one vein (a ligature having been duly applied), nor with such impetuosity, such readiness, such celerity, unless through the medium of the impelling power of the heart.

But if all things be as they are now represented, we shall feeel ourselves at liberty to calculate the quantity of the blood, and to reason on its circular motion. Should anyone, for instance, in performing phlebotomy, suffer the blood to flow in the manner it usually does, with force and freely, for some half hour or so, no question but that the greatest part of the blood being abstracted, faintings and syncopes would ensue, and that not only would the arteries but the great veins also be nearly emptied of their contents. It is only consonant with reason to conclude that in the course of the half hour hinted at, so much as has escaped has also passed from the great veins through the heart into the aorta. And further, if we calculate how many ounces flow through one arm, or how many pass in twenty or thirty pulsations under the medium ligature, we shall have some grounds for estimating how much passes through the other arm in the same space of time, how much through both lower extremities, how much through the neck on either side, and through all the other arteries and veins of the body, all of which have been supplied with fresh blood; and as this blood must have passed through the lungs and ventricles of the heart, and must have come from the great veins, we shall perceive that a circulation is absolutely necessary, seeing that the quantities hinted at cannot be supplied immediately from the ingesta, and are vastly more than can be requisite for the mere nutrition of the parts.

It is still further to be observed that the truths contended for are sometimes confirmed in another way; for having tied up the arm properly, and made the puncture duly, still, if from alarm or any other causes, a state of faintness supervenes, in which the heart always pulsates more languidly, the blood does not flow freely, but distils by drops only. The reason is that with the somewhat greater than usual resistance offered to the transit of the blood by the bandage, coupled with the weaker action of the heart, and its diminished impelling power, the stream cannot make its way under the fillet; and further, owing to the weak and languishing state of the heart, the blood is not transferred in such quantity as wont from the veins to the arteries through the sinuses of that organ. So also, and for the same reasons, are the menstrual fluxes of women, and indeed hemorrhages of every kind, controlled. And now, a contrary state of things occurring, the patient getting rid of his fear and recovering his courage, the pulsific power is increased, the arteries begin again to beat with greater force, and to drive the blood even into the part that is bound; so that the blood now springs from the puncture in the vein, and flows in a continuous stream.

CHAPTER 13. *The third position is confirmed; and the circulation of the blood is demonstrated from it*

THUS far have we spoken of the quantity of blood passing through the heart and the lungs in the centre of the body, and in like manner from the arteries into the veins in the peripheral parts and the body at large. We have yet to explain, however, in what manner the blood finds its way back to the heart from the extremities by the veins, and how and in what way these are the only vessels that convey the blood from the external to the central parts; which done, I conceive that the three fundamental propositions laid down for the circulation of the blood will be so plain, so well established, so obviously true, that they may claim general credence. Now the remaining position will be made sufficiently clear from the valves which are found in the cavities of the veins themselves, from the uses of these, and from experiments cognizable by the senses.

The celebrated Hieronymus Fabricius of Aquapendente, a most skilful anatomist, and venerable old man, or, as the learned Riolan will have it, Jacobus Silvius, first gave representations of the valves in the veins, which consist of raised or loose portions of the inner membranes of these vessels, of extreme delicacy, and a sigmoid or semilunar shape. They are situated at different distances from one another, and diversely in different individuals; they are connate at the sides of the veins; they are directed upwards or towards the trunks of the veins; the two—for there are for the most part two together—regard each other, mutually touch, and are so ready to come into contact by their edges, that if anything attempt to pass from the trunks into the branches of the veins, or from the greater vessels into the less, they completely prevent it; they are further so arranged that the horns of those that succeed are opposite the middle of the convexity of those that precede, and so on alternately.

The discoverer of these valves did not rightly understand their use, nor have succeeding anatomists added anything to our knowledge: for their office is by no means explained when we are told that it is to hinder the blood, by its weight, from all flowing into inferior parts; for the edges of the valves in the jugular veins hang downwards, and are so contrived that they prevent the blood from rising upwards; the valves, in a word, do not invariably look upwards, but always towards the trunks of the veins, invariably towards the seat of the heart. I, and indeed others, have sometimes found valves in the emulgent veins, and in those of the mesentery, the edges of which were directed towards the vena cava and vena portæ. Let it be added that there are no valves in the arteries, and that dogs, oxen, &c., have invariably valves at the divisions of their crural veins, in the veins that meet towards the top of the os sacrum, and in those branches which come from the haunches, in which no such effect of gravity from the erect positon was to be apprehended. Neither are there valves in the jugular veins for the purpose of guarding against apoplexy, as some have said; because in sleep the head is more apt to be influenced by the contents of the carotid arteries. Neither are the valves present, in order that the blood may be retained in the divarications or smaller trunks and minuter branches, and not be suffered to flow entirely into the more open and capacious channels; for they occur where there are no divarications; although it must be owned that they are most frequent at the points where branches join. Neither do they exist for the purpose of rendering the current of blood more slow from the centre of the body; for it seems likely that the blood would be disposed to flow with sufficient slowness of its own accord, as it would have to pass from larger into continually smaller vessels, being separated from the mass and fountain head, and attaining from warmer into colder places.

But the valves are solely made and instituted lest the blood should pass from the greater into the lesser veins, and either rupture them or cause them to become varicose; lest, instead of advancing from the extreme to the central parts of the body, the blood should rather proceed along the veins from the centre to the extremities; but the delicate valves, while they readily open in the right direction, entirely prevent all such contrary motion, being so situated and arranged, that if anything escapes, or is less perfectly obstructed by the cornua of the one above, the fluid passing, as it were, by the chinks between the cornua, it is immediately received on the convexity of the one beneath, which is placed transversely with reference to the former, and so is effectually hindered from getting any farther.

And this I have frequently experienced in my dissections of the veins: if I attempted to pass a probe from the trunk of the veins into one of the smaller branches, whatever care I took I found it impossible to introduce it far any way, by reason of the valves; whilst, on the contrary, it was most easy to push it along in the opposite direction, from without inwards, or from the branches towards the trunks and roots. In many places two valves are so placed and fitted that when raised they come exactly together in the middle of the vein, and are there united by the contact of their margins; and so accurate is the adaptation, that neither by the eye nor by any other means of examination can the slightest chink along the line of contact be perceived. But if the probe be now introduced from the extreme towards the more central parts, the valves, like the floodgates of a river, give way, and are most readily pushed aside. The effect of this arrangement plainly is to prevent all motion of the blood from the heart and vena cava, whether it be upwards towards the head, or downwards towards the feet, or to either side towards the arms, not a drop can pass; all motion of the blood, beginning in the larger and tending towards the smaller veins, is opposed and resisted by them; whilst the motion that proceeds from the lesser to end in the larger branches is favoured, or, at all events, a free and open passage is left for it.

But that this truth may be made the more apparent, let an arm be tied up above the elbow as if for phlebotomy (*AA, fig.* 1). At intervals in the course of the veins, especially in labouring people and those whose veins are large, certain knots or elevations (*B, C, D, E, F*) will be perceived, and this not only at the places where a branch is received (*E, F*), but also where none enters (*C, D*): these knots or risings are all formed by valves, which thus show themselves externally. And now if you press the blood from the space above one of the valves, from *H* to *O*, (*fig.* 2), and keep the point of a finger upon the vein inferiorly, you will see no influx of blood from above; the portion of the vein between the point of the finger and the valve *O* will be obliterated; yet will the vessel continue sufficiently distended above that valve (*O, G*). The blood being thus pressed out, and the vein emptied, if you now apply a finger of the other hand upon the distended part of the vein above the valve *O*, (*fig.* 3), and press downwards, you will find that you cannot force the blood through or beyond the valve; but the greater effort you use, you will only see the portion of vein that is between the finger and the valve become more distended, that portion of the vein which is below

the valve remaining all the while empty (*H, O, fig.* 3).

It would therefore appear that the function of the valves in the veins is the same as that of the three sigmoid valves which we find at the commencement of the aorta and pulmonary artery, viz., to prevent all reflux of the blood that is passing over them.

Further, the arm being bound as before, and the veins looking full and distended, if you press at one part in the course of a vein with the point of a finger (*L, fig.* 4), and then with another finger streak the blood upwards beyond the next valve (*N*), you will perceive that this portion of the vein continues empty (*L, N*), and that the blood cannot retrograde, precisely as we have already seen the case to be in fig. 2; but the finger first applied (*H, fig.* 2, *L, fig.* 4), being removed, immediately the vein is filled from below, and the arm becomes as it appears at *D C*, fig. 1. That the blood in the veins therefore proceeds from inferior or more remote to superior parts, and towards the heart, moving in these vessels in this and not in the contrary direction, appears most obviously. And although in some places the valves, by not acting with such perfect accuracy, or where there is but a single valve, do not seem totally to prevent the passage of the blood from the centre, still the greater number of them plainly do so; and then, where things appear contrived more negligently, this is compensated either by the more frequent occurrence or more perfect action of the succeeding valves or in some other way: the veins, in short, as they are the free and open conduits of the blood returning *to* the heart, so are they effectually prevented from serving as its channels of distribution *from* the heart.

But this other circumstance has to be noted: the arm being bound, and the veins made turgid, and the valves prominent, as before, apply the thumb or finger over a vein in the situation of one of the valves in such a way as to compress it, and prevent any blood from passing upwards from the hand; then, with a finger of the other hand, streak the blood in the vein upwards till it has passed the next valve above (*N, fig.* 4), the vessel now remains empty; but the finger at *L* being removed for an instant, the vein is immediately filled from below; apply the finger again, and having in the same manner streaked the blood upwards, again remove the finger below, and again the vessel becomes distended as before; and this repeat, say a thousand times, in a short space of time. And now compute the quantity of blood which you have thus pressed up beyond

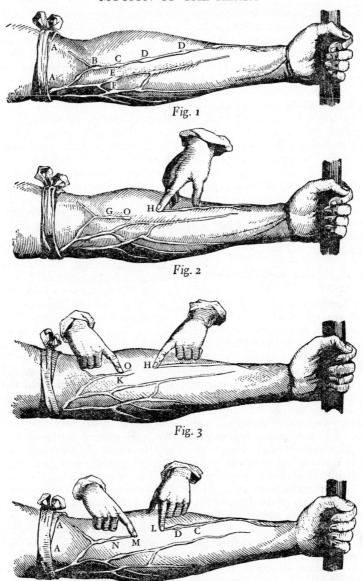

Fig. 1

Fig. 2

Fig. 3

Fig. 4

the valve, and then multiplying the assumed quantity by one thousand, you will find that so much blood has passed through a certain portion of the vessel; and I do now believe that you will find yourself convinced of the circulation of the blood, and of its rapid motion. But if in this experiment you say that a violence is done to nature, I do not doubt but that, if you proceed in the same way, only taking as great a length of vein as possible, and merely remark with what rapidity the blood flows upwards, and fills the vessel from below, you will come to the same conclusion.

CHAPTER 14. *Conclusion of the demonstration of the circulation*

AND now I may be allowed to give in brief my view of the circulation of the blood, and to propose it for general adoption.

Since all things, both argument and ocular demonstration, show that the blood passes through the lungs and heart by the action of the auricles and ventricles, and is sent for distribution to all parts of the body, where it makes its way into the veins and pores of the flesh, and then flows by the veins from the circumference on every side to the centre, from the lesser to the greater veins, and is by them finally discharged into the vena cava and right auricle of the heart, and this in such a quantity or in such a flux and reflux thither by the arteries, hither by the veins, as cannot possibly be supplied by the ingesta, and is much greater than can be required for mere purposes of nutrition; it is absolutely necessary to conclude that the blood in the animal body is impelled in a circle, and is in a state of ceaseless motion; that this is the act or function which the heart performs by means of its pulse; and that it is the sole and only end of the motion and contraction of the heart.

CHAPTER 15. *The circulation of the blood is further confirmed by probable reasons*

IT will not be foreign to the subject if I here show further, from certain familiar reasonings, that the circulation is matter both of convenience and necessity. In the first place, since death is a corruption which takes place through deficiency of heat,[1] and since all living things are warm, all dying things cold, there must be a particular seat and fountain, a kind of home and hearth, where the cherisher of nature, the original of the native fire, is stored and preserved; whence heat and life are dispensed to all parts as from a fountain head; whence sustenance may be derived; and upon which concoction and nutrition, and all vegetative energy may depend. Now, that the heart is this place, that the heart is the principle of life, and that all passes in the manner just mentioned, I trust no one will deny.

The blood, therefore, required to have motion, and indeed such a motion that it should return again to the heart; for sent to the external parts of the body far from its fountain, as Aristotle says, and without motion, it would become congealed. For we see motion generating and keeping up heat and spirits under all circumstances, and rest allowing them to escape and be dissipated. The blood, therefore, become thick or congealed by the cold of the extreme and outward parts, and robbed of its spirits, just as it is in the dead, it was imperative that from its fount and origin, it should again receive heat and spirits, and all else requisite to its preservation—that, by returning, it should be renovated and restored.

We frequently see how the extremities are chilled by the external cold, how the nose and cheeks and hands look blue, and how the blood, stagnating in them as in the pendent or lower parts of a corpse, becomes of a dusky hue; the limbs at the same time getting torpid, so that they can scarcely be moved, and seem almost to have lost their vitality. Now they can by no means be so effectually, and especially so speedily restored to heat and colour and life, as by a new afflux and appulsion of heat from its source. But how can parts attract in which the heat and life are almost extinct? Or how should they whose passages are filled with condensed and frigid blood, admit fresh aliment—renovated blood—unless they had first got rid of their old contents? Unless the heart were truly that fountain where life and heat are restored to the refrigerated fluid, and whence new blood, warm, imbued with spirits, being sent out by the arteries, that which has become cooled and effete is forced on, and all the particles recover their heat which was failing, and their vital stimulus well-nigh exhausted.

Hence it is that if the heart be unaffected, life and health may be restored to almost all the other parts of the body; but the heart being chilled, or smitten with any serious disease, it seems matter of necessity that the whole animal fabric should suffer and fall into decay. When the source is corrupted, there is nothing, as Aristotle says,[2] which can be of service either to it or aught that depends on it. And hence, by the way, it may perchance be wherefore grief, and love, and envy, and anxiety, and all affections of the mind of a similar kind are accompanied with emaciation and decay, or with cacochemy and crudity, which engender all manner of diseases and consume the body of man. For every affection of the mind that is attended with either pain or pleasure, hope or fear, is the cause of an agitation whose influence extends to the heart, and there induces change from the natural constitution, in the temperature, the pulse and the rest, which impairing all nutrition in its source and abating the powers at large, it is no wonder that various forms of incurable disease in the extremities and in the trunk are the consequence, inasmuch as in such circumstances the whole body labours under the effects of vitiated nutrition and a want of native heat.

Moreover, when we see that all animals live

---

[1] Aristotle, *On Youth, Life, and Breathing*, 23, 24; *On the Parts of Animals*, II, 7.

[2] *On the Parts of Animals*, III.

through food concocted in their interior, it is imperative that the digestion and distribution be perfect; and, as a consequence, that there be a place and receptacle where the aliment is perfected and whence it is distributed to the several members. Now this place is the heart, for it is the only organ in the body which contains blood for the general use; all the others receive it merely for their peculiar or private advantage, just as the heart also has a supply for its own especial behoof in its coronary veins and arteries; but it is of the store which the heart contains in its auricles and ventricles that I here speak; and then the heart is the only organ which is so situated and constituted that it can distribute the blood in due proportion to the several parts of the body, the quantity sent to each being according to the dimensions of the artery which supplies it, the heart serving as a magazine or fountain ready to meet its demands.

Further, a certain impulse or force, as well as an impeller or forcer, such as the heart, was required to effect this distribution and motion of the blood; both because the blood is disposed from slight causes, such as cold, alarm, horror, and the like, to collect in its source, to concentrate like parts to a whole, or the drops of water spilt upon a table to the mass of liquid; and then because it is forced from the capillary veins into the smaller ramifications, and from these into the larger trunks by the motion of the extremities and the compression of the muscles generally. The blood is thus more disposed to move from the circumference to the centre than in the opposite direction, were there even no valves to oppose its motion; whence that it may leave its source and enter more confined and colder channels, and flow against the direction to which it spontaneously inclines, the blood requires both force and an impelling power. Now such is the heart and the heart alone, and that in the way and manner already explained.

CHAPTER 16. *The circulation of the blood is further proved from certain consequences*

THERE are still certain phenomena, which, taken as consequences of this truth assumed as proven, are not without their use in exciting belief, as it were, *a posteriori;* and which, although they may seem to be involved in much doubt and obscurity, nevertheless readily admit of having reasons and causes assigned for them. The phenomena alluded to are those that present themselves in connexion with contag-

ions, poisoned wounds, the bites of serpents and rabid animals, lues venerea and the like. We sometimes see the whole system contaminated, though the part first infected remains sound; the lues venerea has occasionally made its attack with pains in the shoulders and head, and other symptoms, the genital organs being all the while unaffected; and then we know that the wound made by a rabid dog having healed, fever and a train of disastrous symptoms nevertheless supervene. Whence it appears that the contagion impressed upon or deposited in a particular part, is by and by carried by the returning current of blood to the heart, and by that organ is sent to contaminate the whole body.

In tertian fever, the morbific cause seeking the heart in the first instance, and hanging about the heart and lungs, renders the patient short-winded, disposed to sighing, indisposed to exertion; because the vital principle is oppressed and the blood forced into the lungs and rendered thick, does not pass through their substance (as I have myself seen in opening the bodies of those who had died in the beginning of the attack) when the pulse is always frequent, small, and occasionally irregular; but the heat increasing, the matter becoming attenuated, the passages forced, and the transit made, the whole body begins to rise in temperature, and the pulse becomes fuller, stronger—the febrile paroxysm is fully formed, whilst the preternatural heat kindled in the heart is thence diffused by the arteries through the whole body along with the morbific matter, which is in this way overcome and dissolved by nature.

When we perceive, further, that medicines applied externally exert their influence on the body just as if they had been taken internally, the truth we are contending for is confirmed. Colocynth and aloes move the belly, cantharides excite the urine, garlic applied to the soles of the feet assists expectoration, cordials strengthen, and an infinite number of examples of the same kind might be cited. It will not, therefore, be found unreasonable perchance, if we say that the veins, by means of their orifices, absorb some of the things that are applied externally and carry this inwards with the blood, not otherwise, it may be, than those of the mesentery imbibe the chyle from the intestines and carry it mixed with the blood to the liver. For the blood entering the mesentery by the cœliac artery, and the superior and inferior mesenterics, proceeds to the intestines, from which, along with the chyle that has been attracted into the veins, it returns by their numerous ramifications into the vena portæ of the liver, and from this into the vena cava, and this in such wise that the blood in these veins has the same colour and consistency as in other veins, in opposition to what many believe to be the fact. Nor indeed can we imagine two contrary motions in any capillary system—the chyle upwards, the blood downwards. This could scarcely take place, and must be held as altogether improbable. But is not the thing rather arranged as it is by the consummate providence of nature? For were the chyle mingled with the blood, the crude with the concoted, in equal proportions, the result would not be concoction, transmutation, and sanguification, but rather, and because they are severally active and passive, a mixture or combination, or medium compound of the two, precisely as happens when wine is mixed with water and syrup. But when a very minute quantity of chyle is mingled with a very large quantity of circulating blood, a quantity of chyle that bears no kind of proportion to the mass of blood, the effect is the same, as Aristotle says, as when a drop of water is added to a cask of wine, or the contrary; the mass does not then present itself as a mixture, but is still sensibly either wine or water. So in the mesenteric veins of an animal we do not find either chyme or chyle and blood, blended together or distinct, but only blood, the same in colour, consistency, and other sensible properties, as it appears in the veins generally. Still as there is a certain though small and inappreciable proportion of chyle or unconcocted matter mingled with this blood, nature has interposed the liver, in whose meandering channels it suffers delay and undergoes additional change, lest arriving prematurely and crude at the heart, it should oppress the vital principle. Hence in the embryo, there is almost no use for the liver, but the umbilical vein passes directly through, a foramen or anastomosis existing from the vena portæ, so that the blood returns from the intestines of the fœtus, not through the liver, but into the umbilical vein mentioned, and flows at once into the heart, mingled with the natural blood which is returning from the placenta; whence also it is that in the development of the fœtus the liver is one of the organs that is last formed; I have observed all the members perfectly marked out in the human fœtus, even the genital organs, whilst there was yet scarcely any trace of the liver. And indeed at the period when all the parts, like the heart itself in the beginning, are

still white, and save in the veins there is no appearance of redness, you shall see nothing in the seat of the liver but a shapeless collection, as it were, of extravasated blood, which you might take for the effects of a contusion or ruptured vein.

But in the incubated egg there are, as it were, two umbilical vessels, one from the albumen passing entire through the liver, and going straight to the heart; another from the yelk, ending in the vena portæ; for it appears that the chick, in the first instance, is entirely formed and nourished by the white; but by the yelk after it has come to perfection and is excluded from the shell; for this part may still be found in the abdomen of the chick many days after its exclusion, and is a substitute for the milk to other animals.

But these matters will be better spoken of in my observations on the formation of the fœtus, where many propositions, the following among the number, will be discussed: wherefore is this part formed or perfected first, that last?—and of the several members: what part is the cause of another? And many points having special reference to the heart, such as: wherefore does it first acquire consistency, and appear to possess life, motion, sense, before any other part of the body is perfected, as Aristotle says in *On the Parts of Animals*, III? And so also of the blood: wherefore does it precede all the rest? And in what way does it possess the vital and animal principle? And show a tendency to motion, and to be impelled hither and thither, the end for which the heart appears to be made? In the same way, in considering the pulse: wherefore one kind of pulse should indicate death, another recovery? And so of all the other kinds of pulse, what may be the cause and indication of each. So also in the consideration of crises and natural critical discharges; of nutrition, and especially the distribution of the nutriment; and of defluxions of every description. Finally, reflecting on every part of medicine, physiology, pathology, semeiotics, therapeutics, when I see how many questions can be answered, how many doubts resolved, how much obscurity illustrated, by the truth we have declared, the light we have made to shine, I see a field of such vast extent in which I might proceed so far, and expatiate so widely, that this my tractate would not only swell out into a volume, which was beyond my purpose, but my whole life, perchance, would not suffice for its completion.

In this place, therefore, and that indeed in a single chapter, I shall only endeavour to refer the various particulars that present themselves in the dissection of the heart and arteries to their several uses and causes; for so I shall meet with many things which receive light from the truth I have been contending for, and which, in their turn, render it more obvious. And indeed I would have it confirmed and illustrated by anatomical arguments above all others.

There is but a single point which indeed would be more correctly placed among our observations on the use of the spleen, but which it will not be altogether impertinent to notice in this place incidentally. From the splenic branch which passes into the pancreas, and from the upper part, arise the posterior coronary, gastric, and gastroepiploic veins, all of which are distributed upon the stomach in numerous branches and twigs, just as the mesenteric vessels are upon the intestines; in like manner, from the inferior part of the same splenic branch, and along the back of the colon and rectum proceed the hemorrhoidal veins. The blood returning by these veins, and bringing the cruder juices along with it, on the one hand from the stomach, where they are thin, watery, and not yet perfectly chylified; on the other thick and more earthy, as derived from the fæces, but all poured into this splenic branch, are duly tempered by the admixture of contraries; and nature mingling together these two kinds of juices, difficult of coction by reason of most opposite defects, and then diluting them with a large quantity of warm blood (for we see that the quantity returned from the spleen must be very large when we contemplate the size of its arteries), they are brought to the porta of the liver in a state of higher preparation; the defects of either extreme are supplied and compensated by this arrangement of the veins.

CHAPTER 17. *The motion and circulation of the blood are confirmed from the particulars apparent in the structure of the heart, and from those things which dissection unfolds*

I do not find the heart as a distinct and separate part in all animals; some, indeed, such as the zoophytes, have no heart; this is because these animals are coldest, of no great bulk, of soft texture or of a certain uniform sameness or simplicity of structure; among the number I may instance grubs and earthworms, and those that are engendered of putrefaction and do not preserve their species. These have no heart, as not requiring any impeller of nourishment into the extreme parts; for they have bodies which are connate and homogeneous, and without limbs;

so that by the contraction and relaxation of the whole body they assume and expel, move and remove the aliment. Oysters, mussels, sponges, and the whole genus of zoophytes or plant-animals have no heart; for the whole body is used as a heart, or the whole animal is a heart. In a great number of animals, almost the whole tribe of insects, we cannot see distinctly by reason of the smallness of the body; still in bees, flies, hornets, and the like, we can perceive with the help of a magnifying glass something pulsating; in pediculi, also, the same thing may be seen, and as the body is transparent, the passage of the food through the intestines, like a black spot or stain, may be perceived by the aid of the same magnifying glass.

In some of the bloodless and colder animals, further, as in snails, whelks, shrimps, and shellfish, there is a part which pulsates—a kind of vesicle or auricle without a heart—slowly indeed, and not to be perceived save in the warmer season of the year. In these creatures this part is so contrived that it shall pulsate, as there is here a necessity for some impulse to distribute the nutritive fluid, by reason of the variety of organic parts, or of the density of the substance; but the pulsations occur infrequently, and sometimes in consequence of the cold not at all, an arrangement the best adapted to them as being of a doubtful nature, so that sometimes they appear to live, sometimes to die; sometimes they show the vitality of an animal, sometimes of a vegetable. This seems also to be the case with the insects which conceal themselves in winter, and lie, as it were, defunct, or merely manifesting a kind of vegetative existence. But whether the same thing happens in the case of certain animals that have red blood, such as frogs, tortoises, serpents, swallows, may be made a question without any kind of impropriety.

In all the larger and warmer, because blooded animals, there was need of an impeller of the nutritive fluid, and that perchance possessing a considerable amount of power. In fishes, serpents, lizards, tortoises, frogs, and others of the same kind there is a heart present, furnished with both an auricle and a ventricle, whence it is perfectly true, as Aristotle has observed,[1] that no blooded animal is without a heart, by the impelling power of which the nutritive fluid is forced, both with greater vigour and rapidity to a greater distance; it is not merely agitated by an auricle as it is in lower forms. And then in regard to animals that are yet

[1] *On the Parts of Animals*, III.

larger, warmer, and more perfect, as they abound in blood, which is ever hotter and more spirituous, and possess bodies of greater size and consistency, they require a larger, stronger, and more fleshy heart, in order that the nutritive fluid may be propelled with yet greater force and celerity. And further, inasmuch as the more perfect animals require a still more perfect nutrition, and a larger supply of native heat, in order that the aliment may be thoroughly concocted and acquire the last degree of perfection, they required both lungs and a second ventricle, which should force the nutritive fluid through them.

Every animal that has lungs has, therefore, two ventricles to its heart, one right, another left; and wherever there is a right, there also is there a left ventricle; but the contrary of this does not hold good: where there is a left there is not always a right ventricle. The left ventricle I call that which is distinct in office, not in place from the other, that one namely which distributes the blood to the body at large, not to the lungs only. Hence the left ventricle seems to form the principal part of the heart; situated in the middle, more strongly marked, and constructed with greater care, the heart seems formed for the sake of the left ventricle, and the right but to minister to it; for the right neither reaches to the apex of the heart, nor is it nearly of such strength, being three times thinner in its walls, and in some sort jointed on to the left (as Aristotle says); though indeed it is of greater capacity, inasmuch as it has not only to supply material to the left ventricle, but likewise to furnish aliment to the lungs.

It is to be observed, however, that all this is otherwise in the embryo, where there is not such a difference between the two ventricles; but as in a double nut, they are nearly equal in all respects, the apex of the right reaching to the apex of the left, so that the heart presents itself as a sort of double-pointed cone. And this is so, because in the fœtus, as already said, whilst the blood is not passing through the lungs from the right to the left cavities of the heart, but flowing by the foramen ovale and ductus arteriosus, directly from the vena cava into the aorta, whence it is distributed to the whole body, both ventricles have in fact the same office to perform, whence their equality of constitution. It is only when the lungs come to be used, and it is requisite that the passages indicated should be blocked up, that the difference in point of strength and other things between the two ventricles begins to be apparent: in the altered circumstances the right has only to throw the blood through the lungs, whilst the left has to impel it through the whole body.

There are further within the heart numerous braces, so to speak, fleshy columns and fibrous bands, which Aristotle, in his third book on *Respiration*, and the *Parts of Animals*, entitles *nerves*. These are variously extended, and are either distinct or contained in grooves in the walls and partition, where they occasion numerous pits or depressions. They constitute a kind of small muscles, which are superadded and supplementary to the heart, assisting it to execute a more powerful and perfect contraction, and so proving subservient to the complete expulsion of the blood. They are in some sort like the elaborate and artful arrangement of ropes in a ship, bracing the heart on every side as it contracts, and so enabling it more effectually and forcibly to expel the charge of blood from its ventricles. This much is plain, at all events, that some animals have them strongly marked, others have them less so; and, in all that have them, they are more numerous and stronger in the left than in the right ventricle; and whilst some have them in the left, there are yet none present in the right ventricle. In the human subject, again, these fleshy columns and braces are more numerous in the left than in the right ventricle, and they are more abundant in the ventricles than in the auricles; occasionally, indeed, in the auricles there appear to be none present whatsoever. In large, more muscular and hardier bodies, as of countrymen, they are numerous; in more slender frames and in females they are fewer.

In those animals in which the ventricles of the heart are smooth within, and entirely without fibres or muscular bands, or anything like foveæ, as in almost all the smaller birds, the partridge and the common fowl, serpents, frogs, tortoises, and also fishes, for the major part, there are no chordæ tendineæ, nor bundles of fibres, neither are there any tricuspid valves in the ventricles.

Some animals have the right ventricle smooth internally, but the left provided with fibrous bands, such as the goose, swan, and larger birds; and the reason here is still the same as elsewhere: as the lungs are spongy, and loose, and soft, no great amount of force is required to force the blood through them; hence the right ventricle is either without the bundles in question, or they are fewer and weaker, not so fleshy or like muscles; those of the left ventricle, however, are both stronger and more numerous, more fleshy and muscular, because the left ventricle requires to be stronger, inasmuch as the blood which it propels has to be driven through the whole body. And this, too, is the reason why the left ventricle occupies the middle of the heart, and has parietes three times thicker and stronger than those of the right. Hence all animals—and among men it is not otherwise—that are endowed with particularly strong frames, and that have large and fleshy limbs at a great distance from the heart, have this central organ of greater thickness, strength, and muscularity. And this is both obvious and necessary. Those, on the contrary, that are of softer and more slender make have the heart more flaccid, softer, and internally either sparely or not at all fibrous. Consider further the use of the several valves, which are all so arranged that the blood once received into the ventricles of the heart shall never regurgitate, once forced into the pulmonary artery and aorta shall not flow back upon the ventricles. When the valves are raised and brought together they form a three-cornered line, such as is left by the bite of a leech; and the more they are forced, the more firmly do they oppose the passage of the blood. The tricuspid valves are placed, like gate-keepers, at the entrance into the ventricles from the venæ cavæ and pulmonary veins, lest the blood when most forcibly impelled should flow back: and it is for this reason that they are not found in all animals; neither do they appear to have been constructed with equal care in all the animals in which they are found; in some they are more accurately fitted, in others more remissly or carelessly contrived, and always with a view to their being closed under a greater or a slighter force of the ventricle. In the left ventricle, therefore, and in order that the occlusion may be the more perfect against the greater impulse, there are only two valves, like a mitre, and produced into an elongated cone, so that they come together and touch to their middle; a circumstance which perhaps led Aristotle to the error of supposing this ventricle to be double, the division taking place transversely. For the same reason, indeed, and that the blood may not regurgitate upon the pulmonary veins, and thus the force of the ventricle in propelling the blood through the system at large come to be neutralized, it is that these mitral valves excel those of the right ventricle in size and strength, and exactness of closing. Hence, too, it is essential that there can be no heart without a ventricle, since this must be the source and storehouse of the blood. The same law does not hold good in reference to the brain. For almost no genus of birds has a ventricle in the brain, as is obvious in the goose and swan, the brains of which nearly equal that of a rabbit in size; now rabbits have ventricles in the brain, whilst the goose has none. In like manner, wherever the heart has a single ventricle, there is an auricle appended, flaccid, membranous, hollow, filled with blood; and where there are two ventricles, there are likewise two auricles. On the other hand, however, some animals have an auricle without any ventricle; or at all events they have a sac analogous to an auricle; or the vein itself, dilated at a particular part, performs pulsations, as is seen in hornets, bees, and other insects, which certain experiments of my own enable me to demonstrate have not only a pulse, but a respiration in that part which is called the tail, whence it is that this part is elongated and contracted now more rarely, now more frequently, as the creature appears to be blown and to require a larger quantity of air. But of these things, more in our *Treatise on Respiration.*

It is in like manner evident that the auricles pulsate, contract, as I have said before, and throw the blood into the ventricles; so that wherever there is a ventricle an auricle is necessary, not merely that it may serve, according to the general belief, as a source and magazine for the blood: for what were the use of its pulsations had it nothing to do save to contain? No; the auricles are prime movers of the blood, especially the right auricle, which is "the first to live, the last to die"; as already said; whence they are subservient to sending the blood into the ventricle, which, contracting incontinently, more readily and forcibly expels the blood already in motion; just as the ball-player can strike the ball more forcibly and farther if he takes it on the rebound than if he simply threw it. Moreover, and contrary to the general opinion, since neither the heart nor anything else can dilate or distend itself so as to draw aught into its cavity during the diastole, unless, like a sponge, it has been first compressed, and as it is returning to its primary condition; but in animals all local motion proceeds from, and has its original in the contraction of some part: it is consequently by the contraction of the auricles that the blood is thrown into the ventricles, as I have already shown, and from thence, by the contraction of the ventricles, it is propelled and distributed. Which truth concerning local motions, and how the immediate moving organ in every motion of an animal primarily endowed with a motive spirit (as Aristotle has it),[1] is contractile; and in what way the word νεῦρον is derived from νεύω, *nuto, contraho;* and how Aristotle was acquainted with the muscles, and did not unadvisedly refer all motion in animals to the nerves, or to the contractile element, and therefore called those little bands in the heart nerves—all this, if I am permitted to proceed in my purpose of making a particular demonstration of the organs of motion in animals from observations in my possession, I trust I shall be able to make sufficiently plain.

But that we may go on with the subject we have in hand, viz., the use of the auricles in filling the ventricles: we should expect that the more dense and compact the heart, the thicker its parietes, the stronger and more muscular must be the auricle to force and fill it, and *vice versa*. Now this is actually so: in some the auricle presents itself as a sanguinolent vesicle, as a thin membrane containing blood, as in fishes, in which the sac that stands in lieu of the auricle, is of such delicacy and ample capacity, that it seems to be suspended or to float above the heart; in those fishes in which the sac is somewhat more fleshy, as in the carp, barbel, tench, and others, it bears a wonderful and strong resemblance to the lungs.

In some men of sturdier frame and stouter make, the right auricle is so strong, and so curiously constructed within of bands and variously interlacing fibres, that it seems to equal the ventricle of the heart in other subjects; and I must say that I am astonished to find such diversity in this particular in different individuals. It is to be observed, however, that in the foetus the auricles are out of all proportion large, which is because they are present before the heart makes its appearance or suffices for its office even when it has appeared, and they, therefore, have, as it were, the duty of the whole heart committed to them, as has already been demonstrated. But what I have observed in the formation of the foetus as before remarked (and Aristotle had already confirmed all in studying the incubated egg) throws the greatest light and likelihood upon the point. Whilst the foetus is yet in the guise of a soft worm, or, as is commonly said, in the milk, there is a mere bloody point or pulsating vesicle, a portion apparently of the umbilical vein, dilated at its commencement or base; by and by, when the outline of the foetus is distinctly indicated, and it begins to have greater bodily consistence, the vesicle in question having become more fleshy

[1] In the book, *De spiritu*, and elsewhere.

and stronger, and changed its position, passes into the auricles, over or upon which the body of the heart begins to sprout, though as yet it apparently performs no duty; but when the foetus is farther advanced, when the bones can be distinguished from the soft parts, and movements take place, then it has also a heart internately which pulsates, and, as I have said, throws blood by either ventricle from the vena cava into the arteries.

Thus nature, ever perfect and divine, doing nothing in vain, has neither given a heart where it was not required, nor produced it before its office had become necessary; but by the same stages in the development of every animal, passing through the constitutions of all, as I may say (ovum, worm, foetus), it acquires perfection in each. These points will be found elsewhere confirmed by numerous observations on the formation of the foetus.

Finally, it was not without good grounds that Hippocrates, in his book, *De corde*, entitles it a muscle; as its action is the same, so is its function, viz., to contract and move something else, in this case, the charge of blood.

Further, as in muscles at large, so can we infer the action and use of the heart from the arrangement of its fibres and its general structure. All anatomists admit with Galen that the body of the heart is made up of various courses of fibres running straight, obliquely, and transversely, with reference to one another; but in a heart which has been boiled the arrangement of the fibres is seen to be different: all the fibres in the parietes and septum are circular, as in the sphincters; those, again, which are in the columnæ extend lengthwise, and are oblique longitudinally; and so it comes to pass that, when all the fibres contract simultaneously, the apex of the cone is pulled towards its base by the columnæ, the walls are drawn circularly together into a globe, the whole heart in short is contracted, and the ventricles narrowed; it is therefore impossible not to perceive that, as the action of the organ is so plainly contraction, its function is to propel the blood into the arteries.

Nor are we the less to agree with Aristotle in regard to the sovereignty of the heart; nor are we to inquire whether it receives sense and motion from the brain? whether blood from the liver? whether it be the origin of the veins and of the blood? and more of the same description. They who affirm these propositions against Aristotle, overlook, or do not rightly understand the principal argument, to the effect that the heart is the first part which exists, and that it contains within itself blood, life, sensation, motion, before either the brain or the liver were in being, or had appeared distinctly, or, at all events, before they could perform any function. The heart, ready furnished with its proper organs of motion, like a kind of internal creature, is of a date anterior to the body: first formed, nature willed that it should afterwards fashion, nourish, preserve, complete the entire animal, as its work and dwelling place: the heart, like the prince in a kingdom, in whose hands lie the chief and highest authority, rules over all; it is the original and foundation from which all power is derived, on which all power depends in the animal body.

And many things having reference to the arteries further illustrate and confirm this truth. Why does not the arteria venosa pulsate, seeing that it is numbered among the arteries? Or wherefore is there a pulse in the vena arteriosa? Because the pulse of the arteries is derived from the impulse of the blood. Why does an artery differ so much from a vein in the thickness and strength of its coats? Because it sustains the shock of the impelling heart and streaming blood. Hence, as perfect nature does nothing in vain, and suffices under all circumstances, we find that the nearer the arteries are to the heart, the more do they differ from the veins in structure; here they are both stronger and more ligamentous, whilst in extreme parts of the body, such as the feet and hands, the brain, the mesentery, and the testicles, the two orders of vessels are so much alike that it is impossible to distinguish between them with the eye. Now this is for the following very sufficient reasons: for the more remote vessels are from the heart, with so much the less force are they impinged upon by the stroke of the heart, which is broken by the great distance at which it is given. Add to this, that the impulse of the heart exerted upon the mass of blood, which must needs fill the trunks and branches of the arteries, is diverted, divided, as it were, and diminished at every subdivision; so that the ultimate capillary divisions of the arteries look like veins, and this not merely in constitution but in function; for they have either no perceptible pulse, or they rarely exhibit one, and never save where the heart beats more violently than wont, or at a part where the minute vessel is more dilated or open than elsewhere. Hence it happens that at times we are aware of a pulse in the teeth, in inflammatory tumours, and in the fingers; at another time we feel nothing of the sort. Hence, too, by this single symptom I have ascertained

for certain that young persons, whose pulses are naturally rapid, were labouring under fever; in like manner, on compressing the fingers in youthful and delicate subjects during a febrile paroxysm, I have readily perceived the pulse there. On the other hand, when the heart pulsates more languidly, it is often impossible to feel the pulse not merely in the fingers, but at the wrist, and even at the temple; this is the case in persons afflicted with lipothymiæ and asphyxia, and hysterical symptoms, as also in persons of very weak constitution and in the moribund.

And here surgeons are to be advised that, when the blood escapes with force in the amputation of limbs, in the removal of tumours, and in wounds, it constantly comes from an artery; not always *per saltum*, however, because the smaller arteries do not pulsate, especially if a tourniquet has been applied.

And then the reason is the same wherefore the pulmonary artery has not only the structure of an artery, but wherefore it does not differ so widely in the thickness of its tunics from the veins as the aorta: the aorta sustains a more powerful shock from the left ventricle than the pulmonary artery does from the right; and the tunics of this last vessel are thinner and softer than those of the aorta in the same proportion as the walls of the right ventricle of the heart are weaker and thinner than those of the left ventricle; and in like manner, in the same degree in which the lungs are softer and laxer in structure than the flesh and other constituents of the body at large, do the tunics of the branches of the pulmonary artery differ from the tunics of the vessels derived from the aorta. And the same proportion in these several particulars is universally preserved. The more muscular and powerful men are, the firmer their flesh, the stronger, thicker, denser, and more fibrous their heart, in the same proportion are the auricles and arteries in all respects thicker, closer, and stronger. And again, and on the other hand, in those animals the ventricles of whose heart are smooth within, without villi or valves, and the walls of which are thinner, as in fishes, serpents, birds, and very many genera of animals, in all of them the arteries differ little or nothing in the thickness of their coats from the veins.

Further, the reason why the lungs have such ample vessels, both arteries and veins (for the capacity of the pulmonary veins exceeds that of both the crural and jugular vessels), and why they contain so large a quantity of blood, as by experience and ocular inspection we know they do, admonished of the fact indeed by Aristotle, and not led into error by the appearances found in animals which have been bled to death, is, because the blood has its fountain, and store-house, and the workshop of its last perfection in the heart and lungs. Why, in the same way we find in the course of our anatomical dissections the arteria venosa and left ventricle so full of blood, of the same black colour and clotted character, too, as that with which the right ventricle and pulmonary artery are filled, inasmuch as the blood is incessantly passing from one side of the heart to the other through the lungs. Wherefore, in fine, the pulmonary artery or vena arteriosa has the constitution of an artery, and the pulmonary veins or arteriæ venosæ have the structure of veins; because, in sooth, in function and constitution, and everything else, the first is an artery, the others are veins, in opposition to what is commonly believed; and why the pulmonary artery has so large an orifice, because it transports much more blood than is requisite for the nutrition of the lungs.

All these appearances, and many others, to be noted in the course of dissection, if rightly weighed, seem clearly to illustrate and fully to confirm the truth contended for throughout these pages, and at the same time to stand in opposition to the vulgar opinion; for it would be very difficult to explain in any other way to what purpose all is constructed and arranged as we have seen it to be.

The First Anatomical Disquisition on the Circulation of the Blood, Addressed to John Riolan

SOME few months ago there appeared a small anatomical and pathological work from the pen of the celebrated Riolanus, for which, as sent to me by the author himself, I return him my grateful thanks.[1] I also congratulate this author on the highly laudable undertaking in which he has engaged. To demonstrate the seats of all diseases is a task that can only be achieved under favour of the highest abilities; for surely he enters on a difficult province who proposes to bring under the cognizance of the eyes those diseases which almost escape the keenest understanding. But such efforts become the prince of anatomists; for there is no science which does not spring from preëxisting knowledge, and no certain and definite idea which has not derived its origin from the senses. Induced therefore by the subject itself, and the example of so distinguished an individual, which makes me think lightly of the labour, I also intend putting to press my *Medical Anatomy, or Anatomy in its Application to Medicine*. Not with the purpose, like Riolanus, of indicating the seats of diseases from the bodies of healthy subjects, and discussing the several diseases that make their appearance there, according to the views which others have entertained of them; but that I may relate from the many dissections I have made of the bodies of persons diseased, worn out by serious and strange affections, how and in what way the internal organs were changed in their situation, size, structure, figure, consistency, and other sensible qualities, from their natural forms and appearances, such as they are usually described by anatomists; and in what various and remarkable ways they were affected. For even as the dissection of healthy and well-constituted bodies contributes essentially to the advancement of philosophy and sound physiology, so does the inspection of diseased and cachectic subjects powerfully assist philosophical pathology. And, indeed, the physiological

consideration of the things which are according to nature is to be first undertaken by medical men; since that which is in conformity with nature is right, and serves as a rule both to itself and to that which is amiss; by the light it sheds, too, aberrations and affections against nature are defined; pathology then stands out more clearly; and from pathology the use and art of healing, as well as occasions for the discovery of many new remedies, are perceived. Nor could anyone readily imagine how extensively internal organs are altered in diseases, especially chronic diseases, and what monstrosities among internal parts these diseases engender. So that I venture to say, that the examination of a single body of one who has died of tabes or some other disease of long standing, or poisonous nature, is of more service to medicine than the dissection of the bodies of ten men who have been hanged.

I would not have it supposed by this that I in any way disapprove of the purpose of Riolanus, that learned and skilful anatomist; on the contrary, I think it deserving of the highest praise, as likely to be extremely useful to medicine, inasmuch as it illustrates the physiological branch of this science; but I have thought that it would scarcely turn out less profitable to the art of healing, did I place before the eyes of my readers not only the places, but the affections of these places, illustrating them as I proceed with observations, and recording the results of my experience derived from my numerous dissections.

But it is imperative on me first to dispose of those observations contained in the work referred to, which bear upon the circulation of the blood as discovered by me, and which seem to require especial notice at my hands. For the judgment of such a man, who is indeed the prince and leader of all the anatomists of the present age, in such a matter, is not to be lightly esteemed, but is rather to be held of greater weight and authority, either for praise

[1] *Encheiridium anatomicum et pathologicum*, 12mo, Parisiis, 1648.

or blame, than the commendations or censure of all the world besides.

Riolanus, then, admits our motion of the blood in animals,[1] and falls in with our conclusions in regard to the circulation; yet not entirely and avowedly; for he says[2] that the blood contained in the vena portæ does not circulate like that in the vena cava; and again he states[3] that there is some blood which circulates, and that the circulatory vessels are the aorta and vena cava; but then he denies that the continuations of these trunks have any circulation, "because the blood is effused into all the parts of the second and third regions, where it remains for purposes of nutrition; nor does it return to any greater-vessels, unless forcibly drawn back when there is a great lack of blood in the main channels, or driven by a fit of passion when it flows to the greater circulatory vessels"; and shortly afterwards: "thus, as the blood of the veins naturally ascends incessantly or returns to the heart, so the blood of the arteries descends or departs from the heart; still, if the smaller veins of the arms and legs be empty, the blood filling the empty channels in succession, may descend in the veins, as I have clearly shown," he says, "against Harvey and Walæus." And as the authority of Galen and daily experience confirm the anastomoses of the arteries and veins, and the necessity of the circulation of the blood, "you perceive," he continues, "how the circulation is effected, without any perturbation or confusion of fluids and the destruction of the ancient system of medicine."

These words explain the motives by which this illustrious anatomist was actuated when he was led partly to admit, partly to deny the circulation of the blood; and why he only ventures on an undecided and inconclusive opinion of the subject; his fear is lest it destroy the ancient medicine. Not yielding implicitly to the truth, which it appears he could not help seeing, but rather guided by caution, he fears speaking plainly out, lest he offend the ancient physic, or perhaps seem to retract the physiological doctrines he supports in his *Anthropology*. The circulation of the blood does not shake, but much rather confirms the ancient medicine; though it runs counter to the physiology of physicians, and their speculations upon natural subjects, and opposes the anatomical doctrine of the use and action of the heart and lungs, and rest of the viscera. That this is so shall

readily be made to appear, both from his own words and avowal, and partly also from what I shall supply; *viz.*, that the whole of the blood, wherever it be in the living body, moves and changes its place, not merely that which is in the larger vessels and their continuations, but that also which is in their minute subdivisions, and which is contained in the pores or interstices of every part; that it flows from and back to the heart ceaselessly and without pause, and could not pause for ever so short a time without detriment, although I admit that occasionally, and in some places, its motion is quicker or slower.[4]

In the first place, then, our learned anatomist only denies that the contents of the branches in continuation of the vena portæ circulate; but he could neither oppose nor deny this, did he not conceal from himself the force of his own arguments; for he says in his Third Book, chapter 8 ...., "If the heart at each pulsation admits a drop of blood which it throws into the aorta, and in the course of an hour makes two thousand beats, it is a necessary consequence that the quantity of blood transmitted must be great." He is further forced to admit as much in reference to the mesentery, when he sees that far more than single drops of blood are sent into the cœliac and mesenteric arteries at each pulsation; so that there must either be some outlet for the fluid, of magnitude commensurate with its quantity, or the branches of the vena portæ must give way. Nor can the explanation that is had recourse to with a view of meeting the difficulty, *viz.*, that the blood of the mesentery ebbs and flows by the same channels, after the manner of Euripus, be received as either probable or possible. Neither can the reflux from the mesentery be effected by those passages and that system of translation, by which he will have it to disgorge itself into the aorta; this were against the force of the existing current, and by a contrary motion; nor can anything like pause or alternation be admitted, where there is very certainly an incessant influx: the blood sent into the mesentery must as inevitably go elsewhere as that which is poured into the heart. And this is obvious; were it otherwise, indeed, everything like a circulation might be overturned upon the same showing and by the same subterfuge; it might just as well be said that the blood contained in the left ventricle of the heart is propelled into the aorta during the systole, and flows back to it during

---

[1] *Enchiridion*, Book III, chap. 8.

[2] *Ibid.*, Book II, chap. 21.

[3] *Ibid.*, Book III, chap. 8.

[4] See Chapter 3, of the *Disquisition on the Motion of the Heart and Blood.*

the diastole, the aorta disgorging itself into the ventricle, precisely as the ventricle has disgorged itself into the aorta. There would thus be circulation neither in the heart nor in the mesentery, but an alternate flux and reflux—a useless labour, as it seems. If, therefore, and for the reason assigned and approved by him, a circulation through the heart be argued for as a thing necessary, the argument has precisely the same force when applied to the mesentery: if there be no circulation in the mesentery, neither is there any in the heart; for both affirmations, this in reference to the heart, that in reference to the mesentery, merely changing the words, stand or fall together, by force of the very same arguments.

He says: "The sigmoid valves prevent regurgitation into the heart; but there are no valves in the mesentery." To this I reply, that the thing is not so; for there is a valve in the splenic vein, and sometimes also in other veins. And besides, valves are not met with universally in veins; there are few or none in the deep-seated veins of the extremities, but many in the subcutaneous branches. For where the blood is flowing naturally from smaller into greater branches, into which it is disposed to enter, the pressure of the circumjacent muscles is enough, and more than enough to prevent all retrograde movement, and it is forced on where the way lies open; in such circumstances, what use were there for valves? But the quantity of blood that is forced into the mesentery by each stroke of the heart, may be estimated in the same way as you estimate the quantity impelled into the hand when you bind a ligature with medium tightness about the wrist: if in so many beats the vessels of the hand become distended, and the whole extremity swells, you will find that much more than a single drop of blood has entered with each pulse, and which cannot return, but must remain to fill the hand and increase its size. But analogy permits us to say that the same thing takes place in reference to the mesentery and its vessels, in an equal degree at least, if not in a greater degree, seeing that the vessels of the mesentery are considerably larger than those of the carpus. And if anyone will but think on the difficulty that is experienced with all the aid supplied by compresses, bandages, and a multiplied apparatus, in restraining the flow of blood from the smallest artery when wounded, with what force it overcomes all obstacles and soaks through the whole apparatus, he will scarcely, I imagine, think it likely that there can be any retrograde

motion against such an impulse and influx of blood, any retrograde force to meet and overcome a direct force of such power. Turning over these things in his mind, I say, no one will ever be brought to believe that the blood from the branches of the vena portæ can possibly make its way by the same channels against an influx by the artery of such impetuosity and force, and so unload the mesentery.

Moreover, if the learned anatomist does not think that the blood is moved and changed by a circular motion, but that the same fluid always stagnates in the channels of the mesentery, he appears to suppose that there are two descriptions of blood, serving different uses and ends; that the blood of the vena portæ, and that of the vena cava are dissimilar in constitution, seeing that the one requires a circulation for its preservation, the other requires nothing of the kind; which neither appears on the face of the thing, nor is its truth demonstrated by him. Our author then refers to "A fourth order of mesenteric vessels, the lacteal vessels, discovered by Asellius";[1] and having mentioned these, he seems to infer that they extract all the nutriment from the intestines, and transfer this to the liver, the workshop of the blood, whence, having been concocted and changed into blood (so he says in his Third Book, chapter 8), the blood is transferred from the liver to the right ventricle of the heart. "Which things premised," he continues, "all the difficulties which were formerly experienced in regard to the distribution of the chyle and blood by the same channel come to an end; for the lacteal veins carry the chyle to the liver, and as these canals are distinct, so may they be severally obstructed."[2] But truly I would here ask: how this milky fluid can be poured into and pass through the liver, and how from thence gain the vena cava and the ventricle of the heart? when our author denies that the blood of the vena portæ passes through the liver, and that so a circulation is established. I pause for a reply. I would fain know how such a thing can be shown to be probable; especially when the blood appears to be both more spirituous or subtile and penetrating than the chyle or milk contained in these lacteal vessels, and is further impelled by the pulsations of the arteries that it may find a passage by other channels.

Our learned author mentions a certain tract of his on the Circulation of the Blood: I wish I could obtain a sight of it; perhaps I might re-

[1] Enchiridion, Book II, chap. 18.
[2] Ibid.

tract. But had the learned writer been so disposed, I do not see but that having admitted the circular motion of the blood,[1] all the difficulties which were formerly felt in connexion with the distribution of the chyle and the blood by the same channels are brought to an equally satisfactory solution; so much so indeed that there would be no necessity for inquiring after or laying down any separate vessels for the chyle. Even as the umbilical veins absorb the nutritive juices from the fluids of the egg and transport them for the nutrition and growth of the chick, in its embryo state, so do the meseraic veins suck up the chyle from the intestines and transfer it to the liver; and why should we not maintain that they perform the same office in the adult? For all the mooted difficulties vanish when we cease to suppose two contrary motions in the same vessels, and admit but one and the same continuous motion in the mesenteric vessels from the intestines to the liver.

I shall elsewhere state my views of the lacteal veins when I treat of the milk found in different parts of new-born animals, especially of the human subject; for it is met with in the mesentery and all its glands, in the thymus, in the axillæ, also in the breasts of infants. This milk the midwifes are in the habit of pressing out, for the health, as they believe, of the infants. But it has pleased the learned Riolanus, not only to take away circulation from the blood contained in the mesentery; he affirms that neither do the vessels in continuation of the vena cava, nor the arteries, nor any of the parts of the second and third regions, admit of circulation, so that he entitles and enumerates as circulating vessels the vena cava and aorta only. For this he appears to me to give a very indifferent reason: "The blood," he says, "effused into all the parts of the second and third regions, remains there for their nutrition; nor does it return to the great vessels, unless forcibly drawn back by an extreme dearth of blood in the great vessels, nor, unless carried by an impulse, does it flow to the circulatory vessels."[2]

That so much of the blood must remain as is appropriated to the nutrition of the tissues, is matter of necessity; for it cannot nourish unless it be assimilated and become coherent, and form substance in lieu of that which is lost; but that the whole of the blood which flows into a part should there remain, in order that so small a portion should undergo transformation, is nowise necessary; for no part uses so much blood for its nutrition as is contained in its arteries, veins, and interstices. Nor because the blood is continually coming and going is it necessary to suppose that it leaves nothing for nutriment behind it. Consequently it is by no means necessary that the whole remain in order that nutrition be effected. But our learned author, in the same book, where he affirms so much, appears almost everywhere else to assert the contrary. In that paragraph especially where he describes the circulation in the brain, he says: "And the brain by means of the circulation sends back blood to the heart, and thus refrigerates the organ." And in the same way are all the more remote parts said to refrigerate the heart; thus in fevers, when the præcordia are scorched and burn with febrile heat, patients baring their limbs and casting off the bedclothes, seek to cool their heart; and the blood generally, tempered and cooled down, as our learned author states it to be with reference to the brain in particular, returns by the veins and refrigerates the heart. Our author, therefore, appears to insinuate a certain necessity for a circulation from every part, as well as from the brain, in opposition to what he had before said in very precise terms. But then he cautiously and ambiguously asserts, that the blood does not return from the parts composing the second and third regions, unless, as he says, it is drawn by force, and through a signal deficiency of blood in the larger vessels, &c., which is most true if these words be rightly understood; for by the larger vessels, in which the deficiency is said to cause the reflux, I think he must be held to mean the veins not the arteries; for the arteries are never emptied, save into the veins or interstices of parts, but are incessantly filled by the strokes of the heart; but in the vena cava and other returning channels, in which the blood glides rapidly on, hastening to the heart, there would speedily be a great deficiency of blood did not every part incessantly restore the blood that is incessantly poured into it. Add to this, that by the impulse of the blood which is forced with each stroke into every part of the second and third regions, that which is contained in the pores or interstices is urged into the smaller veins, from which it passes into larger vessels, its motion assisted besides by the motion and pressure of circumjacent parts; for from every containing thing compressed and constringed, contained matters are forced out.

---

[1] *Enchiridion*, Book iii, chap. 8: "The blood incessantly and naturally ascends or flows back to the heart in the veins, as in the arteries it descends or departs from the heart."

[2] *Ibid.*

And thus it is that by the motions of the muscles and extremities, the blood contained in the minor vessels is forced onwards and delivered into the larger trunks. But that the blood is incessantly driven from the arteries into every part of the body, there gives a pulse and never flows back in these channels, cannot be doubted, if it be admitted that with each pulse of the heart all the arteries are simultaneously distended by the blood sent into them; and as our learned author himself allows that the diastole of the arteries is occasioned by the systole of the heart, and that the blood once out of the heart can never get back into the ventricles by reason of the opposing valves; if I say, our learned author believes that these things are so, it will be as manifestly true with regard to the force and impulse by which the blood contained in the vessels is propelled into every part of every region of the body. For wheresoever the arteries pulsate, so far must the impulse and influx extend, and therefore is the impulse felt in every part of each several region; for there is a pulse everywhere, to the very points of the fingers and under the nails, nor is there any part of the body where the shooting pain that accompanies each pulse of the artery, and the effort made to effect a solution of the continuity is not experienced when it is the seat of a phlegmon or furuncle.

But, further, that the blood contained in the pores of the living tissues returns to the heart, is manifest from what we observe in the hands and feet. For we frequently see the hands and feet, in young persons especially, during severe weather, become so cold that to the touch they feel like ice, and they are so benumbed and stiffened that they seem scarcely to retain a trace of sensibility or to be capable of any motion; still are they all the while surcharged with blood, and look red or livid. Yet can the extremities be warmed in no way, save by circulation; the chilled blood, which has lost its spirit and heat, being driven out, and fresh, warm, and vivified blood flowing in by the arteries in its stead, which fresh blood cherishes and warms the parts, and restores to them sense and motion; nor could the extremities be restored by the warmth of a fire or other external heat, any more than those of a dead body could be so recovered: they are only brought to life again, as it were, by an influx of internal warmth. And this indeed is the principal use and end of the circulation; it is that for which the blood is sent on its ceaseless course, and to exert its influence continually in its circuit, to wit, that all parts

dependent on the primary innate heat may be retained alive, in their state of vital and vegetative being, and apt to perform their functions; whilst, to use the language of physiologists, they are sustained and actuated by the inflowing heat and vital spirits. Thus, by the aid of two extremes, viz., cold and heat, is the temperature of the animal body retained at its mean. For as the air inspired tempers the too great heat of the blood in the lungs and centre of the body, and effects the expulsion of suffocating fumes, so in its turn does the hot blood, thrown by the arteries into all parts of the body, cherish and nourish and keep them in life, defending them from extinction through the power of external cold.

It would, therefore, be in some sort unfair and extraordinary did not every particle composing the body enjoy the advantages of the circulation and transmutation of the blood; the ends for which the circulation was mainly established by nature would no longer be effected. To conclude then: you see how circulation may be accomplished without confusion or admixture of humours, through the whole body, and each of its individual parts, in the smaller as well as in the larger vessels; and all as matter of necessity and for the general advantage; without circulation, indeed, there would be no restoration of chilled and exhausted parts, no continuance of these in life; since it is apparent enough that the whole influence of the preservative heat comes by the arteries, and is the work of the circulation.

It, therefore, appears to me that the learned Riolanus speaks rather expediently than truly, when in his *Enchiridion* he denies a circulation to certain parts; it would seem as though he had wished to please the mass, and oppose none; to have written with such a bias rather than rigidly and in behalf of the simple truth. This is also apparent when he would have the blood to make its way into the left ventricle through the septum of the heart, by certain invisible and unknown passages, rather than through those ample and abundantly pervious channels, the pulmonary vessels, furnished with valves, opposing all reflux or regurgitation. He informs us that he has elsewhere discussed the reasons of the impossibility or inconvenience of this: I much desire to see his disquisition. It would be extraordinary, indeed, were the aorta and pulmonary artery, with the same dimensions, properties, and structure, not to have the same functions. But it would be more wonderful still were the whole tide of the blood to reach

the left ventricle by a set of inscrutable passages of the septum, a tide which, in quantity
must correspond, first to the influx from the
vena cava into the right side of the heart, and
next to the efflux from the left, both of which
require such ample conduits. But our author
has adduced these matters inconsistently, for
he has established the lungs as an emunctory
or passage from the heart;[1] and he says: "The
lung is affected by the blood which passes
through it, the sordes flowing along with the
blood." And, again: "The lungs receive injury
from distempered and ill-conditioned viscera;
these deliver an impure blood to the heart,
which it cannot correct except by multiplied
circulations." In the same place, he further proceeds, whilst speaking against Galen of bloodletting in peripneumonia and the communication of the veins: "Were it true that the blood
naturally passed from the right ventricle of the
heart to the lungs, that it might be carried into
the left ventricle and from thence into the aorta; and were the circulation of the blood admitted, who does not see that in affections of
the lungs the blood would flow to them in
larger quantity and would oppress them, unless it were taken away, first, freely, and then in
repeated smaller quantities in order to relieve
them, which indeed was the advice of Hippocrates, who, in affections of the lungs takes
away blood from every part—the head, nose,
tongue, arms and feet, in order that its quantity may be diminished and a diversion effected
from the lungs; he takes away blood till the
body is almost bloodless. Now admitting the
circulation, the lungs are most readily depleted
by opening a vein; but rejecting it, I do not
see how any revulsion of the blood can be accomplished by this means; for did it flow back
by the pulmonary artery upon the right ventricle, the sigmoid valves would oppose its entrance, and any escape from the right ventricle
into the vena cava is prevented by the tricuspid valves. The blood, therefore, is soon exhausted when a vein is opened in the arm or
foot, if we admit the circulation; and the opinion of Fernelius is at the same time upset by
this admission, viz., that in affections of the
lungs it is better to bleed from the right than
the left arm; because the blood cannot flow
backwards into the vena cava unless the two
barriers situated in the heart be first broken
down."

He adds yet further in the same place: "If
the circulation of the blood be admitted, and it

be acknowledged that this fluid generally passes
through the lungs, not through the middle partition of the heart, a double circulation becomes requisite; one effected through the lungs,
in the course of which the blood quitting the
right ventricle of the heart passes through the
lungs in order that it may arrive at the left ventricle; leaving the heart on the one hand, therefore, the blood speedily returns to it again; another and longer circulation proceeding from
the left ventricle of the heart performs the circuit of the whole body by the arteries, and by
the veins returns to the right side of the heart."[2]

The learned anatomist might here have added
a third and extremely short circulation, viz.,
from the left to the right ventricle of the heart,
with that blood which courses through the coronary arteries and veins, and by their ramifications is distributed to the body, walls, and septum of the heart.

"He who admits one circulation," proceeds
our author, "cannot repudiate the other"; and
he might, as it appears, have added, "the third."
For why should the coronary arteries of the
heart pulsate, if it were not to force on the
blood by their pulsations? and why should
there be coronary veins, the end and office of
all veins being to receive the blood brought
by the arteries, were it not to deliver and discharge the blood sent into the substance of the
heart? In this consideration let it be remembered that a valve is very commonly found at
the orifice of the coronary vein, as our learned
author himself admits,[3] preventing all ingress,
but offering no obstacle to the egress of the
blood. It therefore seems that he cannot do
otherwise than admit this third circulation,
who acknowledges a general circulation through
the body, and that the blood also passes through
the lungs and the brain.[4] Nor, indeed, can he
deny a similar circulation to every other part
of every other region. The blood flowing in
under the influence of the arterial pulse, and
returning by the veins, every particle of the
body has its circulation.

From the words of our learned writer quoted
above, consequently, his opinion may be gathered both of the general circulation, and then
of the circulation through the lungs and the
several parts of the body; for he who admits the
first, manifestly cannot refuse to acknowledge
the others. How indeed could he who has repeatedly asserted a circulation through the

---

[1] *Encheiridion*, Book III, chap. 6.

[2] *Ibid.*
[3] *Ibid.*, chap. 9.
[4] *Ibid.*, Book IV, chap. 2.

general system and the greater vessels, deny a circulation in the branches continuous with these vessels, or in the several parts of the second and third regions? as if all the veins, and those he calls greater circulatory vessels, were not enumerated by every anatomist, and by himself, as being within the second region of the body. Is it possible that there can be a circulation which is universal, and which yet does not extend through every part? Where he denies it, then, he does so hesitatingly, and vacillates between negations, giving us mere words. Where he asserts the circulation, on the contrary, he speaks out heartily, and gives sufficient reasons, as becomes a philosopher; and then, when he relies on this opinion in a particular instance, he delivers himself like an experienced physician and honest man, and, in opposition to Galen and his favorite Fernelius, advises blood-letting as the chief remedy in dangerous diseases of the lungs.

No learned man and Christian, having doubts in such a case, would have recommended his experience to posterity, to the imminent risk, and even loss of human life; neither would he without very sufficient reasons, have repudiated the authority of Galen and Fernelius, which has usually such weight with him. Whatever he has denied in the circulation of the blood, therefore, whether with reference to the mesentery or any other part, and with an eye to the lacteal veins or the ancient system of physic, or any other consideration, must be ascribed to his courtesy and modesty, and is to be excused.

Thus far, I think, it appears plain enough, from the very words and arguments of our author, that there is a circulation everywhere; that the blood, wherever it is, changes its place, and by the veins returns to the heart; so that our learned author seems to be of the same opinion as myself. It would therefore be labour in vain, did I here quote at greater length the various reasons which I have consigned in my work on the *Motion of the Blood*, in confirmation of my opinions, and which are derived from the structure of the vessels, the position of the valves, and other matters of experience and observation; and this the more, as I have not yet seen the treatise on the *Circulation of the Blood* of the learned writer; nor, indeed, have I yet met with a single argument of his, or more than his simple negation, which would lead me to see wherefore he should reject a circulation which he admits as universal, in certain parts, regions, and vessels.

It is true that by way of subterfuge he has recourse to an anastomosis of the vessels on the authority of Galen, and the evidence of daily experience. But so distinguished a personage, an anatomist so expert, so inquisitive, and careful, should first have shown anastomoses between the larger arteries and larger veins, and these, both obvious and ample, having mouths in relation with such a torrent as is constituted by the whole mass of the blood, and larger than the capacity of the continuous branches (from which he takes away all circulation), before he had rejected those that are familiarly known, that are more likely and more open; he ought to have clearly shown us where these anastomoses are, and how they are fashioned, whether they be adapted only to permit the access of the blood into the veins, and not to allow of its regurgitation, in the same way as we see the ureters connected with the urinary bladder, or in what other manner things are contrived. But —and here I speak over boldly perhaps— neither our learned author himself, nor Galen, nor any experience, has ever succeeded in making such anastomoses as he imagines, sensible to the eye.

I have myself pursued this subject of the anastomosis with all the diligence I could command, and have given not a little both of time and labour to the inquiry; but I have never succeeded in tracing any connexion between arteries and veins by a direct anastomosis of their orifices. I would gladly learn of those who give so much to Galen, how they dare swear to what he says. Neither in the liver, spleen, lungs, kidneys, nor any other viscus, is such a thing as an anastomosis to be seen; and by boiling, I have rendered the whole parenchyma of these organs so friable that it could be shaken like dust from the fibres, or picked away with a needle, until I could trace the fibres of every subdivision, and see every capillary filament distinctly. I can therefore boldly affirm, that there is neither any anastomosis of the vena portæ with the cava, of the arteries with the veins, or of the capillary ramifications of the biliary ducts, which can be traced through the entire liver, with the veins. This alone may be observed in the recent liver: all the branches of the vena cava ramifying through the convexity of the liver, have their tunics pierced with an infinity of minute holes, as is a sieve, and are fashioned to receive the blood in its descent. The branches of the porta are not so constituted, but simply spread out in subdivisions; and the distribution of these two vessels is such that, whilst the one runs upon the convexity, the other proceeds along the concavity of the liver to its outer margin, and all the while without anastomosing.

In three places only do I find anything that can be held equivalent to an anastomosis. From the carotids, as they are creeping over the base of the brain, numerous interlaced fibres arise, which afterwards form the choroid plexus, and passing through the lateral ventricles, finally unite and terminate in the third sinus, which performs the office of a vein. In the spermatic vessels, commonly called vasa præparantia, certain minute arteries proceeding from the great artery adhere to the venæ præparantes, which they accompany, and are at length taken in and included within their coats, in such a way that they seem to have a common ending, so that where they terminate on the upper portion of the testis, on that cone-shaped process called the corpus varicosum et pampiniforme, it is altogether uncertain whether we are to regard their terminations as veins, or as arteries, or as both. In the same way are the ultimate ramifications of the arteries which run to the umbilical vein, lost in the tunics of this vessel.

What doubt can there be, if by such channels the great arteries, distended by the stream of blood sent into them, are relieved of so great and obvious a torrent, but that nature would not have denied distinct and visible passages, vortices, and estuaries, had she intended to divert the whole current of the blood, and had wished in this way to deprive the lesser branches and the solid parts of all the benefit of the influx of that fluid?

Finally, I shall quote this single experiment, which appears to me sufficient to clear up all doubts about the anastomoses, and their uses, if any exist, and to set at rest the question of a passage of the blood from the veins to the arteries, by any special channels, or by regurgitation.

Having laid open the thorax of an animal, and tied the vena cava near the heart, so that nothing shall pass from that vessel into its cavities, and immediately afterwards, having divided the carotid arteries on both sides, the jugular veins being left untouched; if the arteries be now perceived to become empty but not the veins, I think it will be manifest that the blood does nowhere pass from the veins into the arteries except through the ventricles of the heart. Were it not so, as observed by Galen, we should see the veins as well as the arteries emptied in a very short time, by the efflux from their corresponding arteries.

For what further remains, oh Riolanus! I congratulate both myself and you: myself, for the opinion with which you have graced my circulation; and you, for your learned, polished, and terse production, than which nothing more elegant can be imagined. For the favour you have done me in sending me this work, I feel most grateful, and I would gladly, as in duty bound, proclaim my sense of its merits, but I confess myself unequal to the task; for I know that the *Enchiridion* bearing the name of Riolanus inscribed upon it, has thereby more of honour conferred upon it than it can derive from any praise of mine, which nevertheless I would yield without reserve. The famous book will live for ever; and when marble shall have mouldered, will proclaim to posterity the glory that belongs to your name. You have most happily conjoined anatomy with pathology, and have greatly enriched the subject with a new and most useful osteology. Proceed in your worthy career, most illustrious Riolanus, and love him who wishes that you may enjoy both happiness and length of days, and that all your admirable works may conduce to your eternal fame.   WILLIAM HARVEY

A Second Disquisition to John Riolan

It is now many years, most learned Riolanus, since, with the aid of the press, I published a portion of my work. But scarce a day, scarce an hour, has passed since the birth-day of the *Circulation of the Blood*, that I have not heard something for good or for evil said of this my discovery. Some abuse it as a feeble infant, and yet unworthy to have seen the light; others, again, think the bantling deserves to be cherished and cared for; these oppose it with much ado, those patronize it with abundant commendation; one party holds that I have completely demonstrated the circulation of the blood by experiment, observation, and ocular inspection, against all force and array of argument; another thinks it scarcely yet sufficiently illustrated—not yet cleared of all objections. There are some, too, who say that I have shown a vainglorious love of vivisections, and who scoff at and deride the introduction of frogs and serpents, flies, and others of the lower animals upon the scene, as a piece of puerile levity, not even refraining from opprobrious epithets.

To return evil speaking with evil speaking, however, I hold to be unworthy in a philosopher and searcher after truth; I believe that I shall do better and more advisedly if I meet so many indications of ill breeding with the light of faithful and conclusive observation. It cannot be helped that dogs bark and vomit their foul stomachs, or that cynics should be numbered among philosophers; but care can be taken that they do not bite or inoculate their mad humours, or with their dogs' teeth gnaw the bones and foundations of truth.

Detractors, mummers, and writers defiled with abuse, as I resolved with myself never to read them, satisfied that nothing solid or excellent, nothing but foul terms, was to be expected from them, so have I held them still less worthy of an answer. Let them consume on their own ill nature; they will scarcely find many well-disposed readers, I imagine, nor does God give that which is most excellent and chiefly to be desired—wisdom, to the wicked; let them go on railing, I say, until they are weary, if not ashamed.

If for the sake of studying the meaner animals you should even enter the bakehouse with Heraclitus, as related in Aristotle, I bid you approach; for neither are the immortal gods absent here, and the great and Almighty Father is sometimes most visible in His lesser, and to the eye least considerable works.

In my book *On the Motion of the Heart and Blood in Animals*, I have only adduced those facts from among many other observations, by which either errors were best refuted, or truth was most strongly supported; I have left many proofs, won by dissection and appreciable to sense, as redundant and unnecessary; some of these, however, I now supply in brief terms, for the sake of the studious, and those who have expressed their desire to have them.

The authority of Galen is of such weight with all, that I have seen several hesitate greatly with that experiment before them, in which the artery is tied upon a tube placed within its cavity; and by which it is proposed to prove that the arterial pulse is produced by a power communicated from the heart through the coats of the arteries, and not from the shock of the blood contained within them; and thence, that the arteries dilate as bellows, are not filled as sacs. This experiment is spoken of by Vesalius, the celebrated anatomist; but neither Vesalius nor Galen says that he had tried the experiment, which, however, I did. Vesalius only prescribes, and Galen advises it, to those anxious to discover the truth, and for their better assurance, not thinking of the difficulties that attend its performance, nor of its futility when done; for indeed, although executed with the greatest skill, it supplies nothing in support of the opinion which maintains that the coats of the vessel are the cause of the pulse; it much rather proclaims that this is owing to the impulse of the blood. For the moment you have thrown your ligature around the artery upon the reed or tube, immediately, by the force of the blood thrown in from above, it is dilated beyond the circle of the tube, by which the flow is impeded, and the shock is broken; so that the artery which is tied only pulsates obscurely, being now cut off from the full force of the blood that flows through it, the shock being reverberated, as it were, from that part of the vessel which is above the ligature; but if the artery below the ligature be now divided, the contrary of what has been maintained will be apparent, from the spurting of the blood impelled through the tube; just as happens in the cases of aneurism, referred to in my book *On the Motion of the Blood*, which arise from an erosion of the coats of the vessel, and when the blood is contained in a membranous sac, formed not by the coats of the vessel dilated, but preternaturally produced from the surrounding tissues and flesh. The arteries beyond an aneurism of this kind will be felt beating very feebly, whilst in those above it and in the swelling itself the pulse will be perceived of great strength and fulness. And here we cannot imagine that the pulsation and dilatation take place by the coats of the arteries, or any power communicated to the walls of the sac; they are plainly due to the shock of the blood.

But that the error of Vesalius, and the inexperience of those who assert their belief that the part below the tube does not pulsate when the ligature is tied, may be made the more apparent, I can state, after having made the trial, that the inferior part will continue to pulsate if the experiment be properly performed; and whilst they say that when you have undone the ligature the inferior arteries begin again to pulsate, I maintain that the part below beats less forcibly when the ligature is untied than it did when the thread was still tight. But the effusion of blood from the wound confuses everything, and renders the whole experiment unsatisfactory and nugatory, so that nothing certain can be shown, by reason, as I have said, of the hemorrhage. But if, as I know by experience, you lay bare an artery, and control the divided portion by the pressure of your fingers, you may try many things at pleasure by which the truth will be made to appear. In the first place, you will feel the blood coming down in the artery at each pulsation, and visibly dilating the vessel. You may also at will suffer the blood to escape, by relaxing the pressure, and leaving a small outlet; and you will see that it jets out with each stroke, with each contraction of the heart, and with each dilatation of the artery, as I have said in speaking of arteriotomy, and the experiment of perforating the heart. And if you suffer the efflux to go on uninterruptedly, either from the simple divided artery or

from a tube inserted into it, you will be able to perceive by the sight, and if you apply your hand, by the touch likewise, every character of the stroke of the heart in the jet; the rhythm, order, intermission, force, &c., of its pulsations, all becoming sensible there, no otherwise than would the jets from a syringe, pushed in succession and with different degrees of force, received upon the palm of the hand, be obvious to sight and touch. I have occasionally observed the jet from a divided carotid artery to be so forcible, that, when received on the hand, the blood rebounded to the distance of four or five feet.

But that the question under discussion, *viz.*, that the pulsific power does not proceed from the heart by the coats of the vessels, may be set in yet a clearer light, I beg here to refer to a portion of the descending aorta, about a span in length, with its division into the two crural trunks, which I removed from the body of a nobleman, and which is converted into a bony tube; by this hollow tube, nevertheless, did the arterial blood reach the lower extremities of this nobleman during his life, and cause the arteries in these to beat; and yet the main trunk was precisely in the same condition as is the artery in the experiment of Galen, when it is tied upon a hollow tube; where it was converted into bone it could neither dilate nor contract like bellows, nor transmit the pulsific power from the heart to the inferior vessels; it could not convey a force which it was incapable of receiving through the solid matter of the bone. In spite of all, however, I well remember to have frequently noted the pulse in the legs and feet of this patient whilst he lived, for I was myself his most attentive physician, and he my very particular friend. The arteries in the inferior extremities of this nobleman must therefor and of necessity have been dilated by the impulse of the blood like flaccid sacs, and not have expanded in the manner of bellows through the action of their tunics. It is obvious that, whether an artery be tied over a hollow tube, or its tunics be converted into a bony and unyielding canal, the interruption to the pulsific power in the inferior part of the vessel must be the same.

I have known another instance in which a portion of the aorta near the heart was found converted into bone, in the body of a nobleman, a man of great muscular strength. The experiment of Galen, therefore, or, at all events, a state analogous to it, not effected on purpose but encountered by accident, makes it sufficiently to appear that compression or ligature of the coats of an artery does not interfere with the pulsative properties of its derivative branches; and indeed, if the experiment which Galen recommends were properly performed by anyone, its results would be found in opposition to the views which Vesalius believed they would support.

But we do not therefore deny everything like motion to the tunics of the arteries; on the contrary, we allow them the same motions which we concede to the heart, viz., a diastole, and a systole or return from the distended to the natural state; this much we believe to be effected by a power inherent in the coats themselves. But it is to be observed that they are not both dilated and contracted by the same, but by different causes and means; as may be observed of the motions of all parts, and of the ventricle of the heart itself, which is distended by the auricle, contracted by its own inherent power; so, the arteries are dilated by the stroke of the heart, but they contract or collapse of themselves.[1]

You may also perform another experiment at the same time: if you fill one of two basins of the same size with blood issuing *per saltum* from an artery, the other with venous blood from a vein of the same animal, you will have an opportunity of perceiving by the eye, both immediately and by and by, when the blood in either vessel has become cold, what differences there are between them. You will find that it is not as they believe who fancy that there is one kind of blood in the arteries and another in the veins, that in the arteries being of a more florid colour, more frothy, and imbued with an abundance of I know not what spirits, effervescing and swelling, and occupying a greater space, like milk or honey set upon the fire. For were the blood which is thrown from the left ventricle of the heart into the arteries, fermented into any such frothy and flatulent fluid, so that a drop or two distended the whole cavity of the aorta; unquestionably, upon the subsidence of this fermentation, the blood would return to its original quantity of a few drops (and this, indeed, is the reason that some assign for the usually empty state of the arteries in the dead body); and so should it be with the arterial blood in the cup, for so it is with boiling milk and honey when they come to cool. But if in either basin you find blood nearly of the same colour, not of very different consistency in the

coagulated state, forcing out serum in the same manner, and filling the cups to the same height when cold that it did when hot, this will be enough for any one to rest his faith upon, and afford argument enough, I think, for rejecting the dreams that have been promulgated on the subject. Sense and reason alike assure us that the blood contained in the left ventricle is not of a different nature from that in the right. And then, when we see that the mouth of the pulmonary artery is of the same size as the aorta, and in other respects equal to that vessel, it were imperative on us to affirm that the pulmonary artery was distended by a single drop of spumous blood, as well as the aorta, and so that the right as well as the left side of the heart was filled with a brisk or fermenting blood.

The particulars which especially dispose men's minds to admit diversity in the arterial and venous blood are three in number: one, because in arteriotomy the blood that flows is of a more florid hue than that which escapes from a vein; a second, because in the dissection of dead bodies the left ventricle of the heart, and the arteries in general, are mostly found empty; a third, because the arterial blood is believed to be more spirituous, and being replete with spirit is made to occupy a much larger space. The causes and reasons, however, wherefore all these things are so, present themselves to us when we ask after them.

1st. With reference to the colour it is to be observed that wherever the blood issues by a very small orifice, it is in some measure strained, and the thinner and lighter part, which usually swims on the top and is the most penetrating, is emitted. Thus, in phlebotomy, when the blood escapes forcibly and to a distance, in a full stream, and from a large orifice, it is thicker, has more body, and a darker colour; but, if it flows from a small orifice, and only drop by drop, as it usually does when the bleeding fillet is untied, it is of a brighter hue; for then it is strained as it were, and the thinner and more penetrating portion only escapes; in the same way, in the bleeding from the nose, in that which takes place from a leech-bite, or from scarifications, or in any other way by diapedesis or transudation, the blood is always seen to have a brighter cast, because the thickness and firmness of the coats of the arteries render the outlet or outlets smaller, and less disposed to yield a ready passage to the outpouring blood; it happens also that when fat persons are let blood, the orifice of the vein is apt to be com-

[1] See Chapter 3, of the *Disquisition on the Motion of the Heart and Blood.*

pressed by the subcutaneous fat, by which the blood is made to appear thinner, more florid, and in some sort arterious. On the other hand, the blood that flows into a basin from a large artery freely divided, will look venous. The blood in the lungs is of a much more florid colour than it is in the arteries, and we know how it is strained through the pulmonary tissue.

2d. The emptiness of the arteries in the dead body, which probably mislead Erasistratus in supposing that they only contained aereal spirits, is caused by this, that when respiration ceases the lungs collapse, and then the passages through them are closed; the heart, however, continues for a time to contract upon the blood, whence we find the left auricle more contracted, and the corresponding ventricle, as well as the arteries at large, appearing empty, simply because there is no supply of blood flowing round to fill them. In cases, however, in which the heart has ceased to pulsate and the lungs to afford a passage to the blood simultaneously, as in those have died from drowning or syncope, or who die suddenly, you will find the arteries, as well as the veins, full of blood.

3d. With reference to the third point, or that of the spirits, it may be said that, as it is still a question what they are, how extant in the body, of what consistency, whether separate and distinct from the blood and solids, or mingled with these—upon each and all of these points there are so many and such conflicting opinions, that it is not wonderful that the spirits, whose nature is thus left so wholly ambiguous, should serve as the common subterfuge of ignorance. Persons of limited information, when they are at a loss to assign a cause for anything, very commonly reply that it is done by the spirits; and so they bring the spirits into play upon all occasions; even as indifferent poets are always thrusting the gods upon the stage as a means of unravelling the plot, and bringing about the catastrophe.

Fernelius, and many others, suppose that there are aereal spirits and invisible substances. Fernelius proves that there are animal spirits, by saying that the cells in the brain are apparently unoccupied, and as nature abhors a vacuum, he concludes that in the living body they are filled with spirits, just as Erasistratus had held that, because the arteries were empty of blood, therefore they must be filled with spirits. But medical schools admit three kinds of spirits: the natural spirits flowing through the veins, the vital spirits through the arteries, and the animal spirits through the nerves; whence

physicians say, out of Galen, that sometimes the parts of the brain are oppressed by sympathy, because the faculty with the essence, *i. e.*, the spirit, is overwhelmed; and sometimes this happens independently of the essence. Further, besides the three orders of influxive spirits adverted to, a like number of implanted or stationary spirits seem to be acknowledged; but we have found none of all these spirits by dissection, neither in the veins, nerves, arteries, nor other parts of living animals. Some speak of corporeal, others of incorporeal spirits; and they who advocate the corporeal spirits will have the blood, or the thinner portion of the blood, to be the bond of union with the soul, the spirit being contained in the blood as the flame is in the smoke of a lamp or candle, and held admixed by the incessant motion of the fluid; others, again, distinguish between the spirits and the blood. They who advocate incorporeal spirits have no ground of experience to stand upon; their spirits indeed are synonymous with powers or faculties, such as a concoctive spirit, a chylopoietic spirit, a procreative spirit, &c.—they admit as many spirits, in short, as there are faculties or organs.

But then the schoolmen speak of a spirit of fortitude, prudence, patience, and the other virtues, and also of a most holy spirit of wisdom, and of every divine gift; and they besides suppose that there are good and evil spirits that roam about or possess the body, that assist or cast obstacles in the way. They hold some diseases to be owing to a Cacodæmon or evil spirit, as there are others that are due to a cacochemy or defective assimilation.

Although there is nothing more uncertain and questionable, then, than the doctrine of spirits that is proposed to us, nevertheless physicians seem for the major part to conclude, with Hippocrates, that our body is composed or made up of three elements, *viz.*, containing parts, contained parts, and causes of action, spirits being understood by the latter term. But if spirits are to be taken as synonymous with causes of activity, whatever has power in the living body and a faculty of action must be included under the denomination. It would appear, therefore, that all spirits were neither aereal substances, nor powers, nor habits; and that all were not incorporeal.

But keeping in view the points that especially interest us, others, as leading to tediousness, being left unnoticed, it seems that the spirits which flow by the veins or the arteries are not distinct from the blood, any more than the flame of a lamp is distinct from the inflammable vapour that is on fire; in short, that the blood and these spirits signify one and the same thing, though different—like generous wine and its spirit; for as wine, when it has lost all its spirit, is no longer wine, but a vapid liquor or vinegar; so blood without spirit is not blood, but something else—clot or cruor; even as a hand of stone, or of a dead body, is no hand in the most complete sense, neither is blood void of the vital principle proper blood; it is immediately to be held as corrupt when deprived of its spirit. The spirit, therefore, which inheres in the arteries, and especially in the blood which fills them, is to be regarded either as its act or agent, in the same way as the spirit of wine in wine, and the spirit of aqua vitæ in brandy, or as a flame kindled in alcohol, which lives and feeds on, or is nourished by itself. The blood, consequently, though richly imbued with spirits, does not swell, nor ferment, nor rise to a head through them, so as to require and occupy a larger space—a fact that may be ascertained beyond the possibility of question by the two cups of equal size; it is to be regarded as wine, possessed of a large amount of spirits, or, in the Hippocratic sense, of signal powers of acting and effecting.

It is, therefore, the same blood in the arteries that is found in the veins, although it may be admitted to be more spirituous, possessed of higher vital force in the former than in the latter; but it is not changed into anything more vaporous, or more aereal, as if there were no spirits but such as are aereal, and no cause of action or activity that is not of the nature of flatus or wind. But neither the animal, natural, nor vital spirits which inhere in the solids, such as the ligaments and nerves (especially if they be of so many different species), and are contained within the viewless interstices of the tissues, are to be regarded as so many different aereal forms, or kinds of vapour.

And here I would gladly be informed by those who admit corporeal spirits, but of a gaseous or vaporous consistency, in the bodies of animals, whether or not they have the power of passing hither and thither, like distinct bodies independently of the blood? Or whether the spirits follow the blood in its motions, either as integral parts of the fluid or as indissolubly connected with it, so that they can neither quit the tissues nor pass hither nor thither without the influx and reflux, and motion of the blood? For if the spirits exhaling from the blood, like the vapour of water attenuated by heat, exist in a state of constant flow and succession as the pabulum of the tissues, it necessarily follows that they are not distinct from this pabulum, but are incessantly disappearing; whereby it seems that they can neither have influx nor reflux, nor passage, nor yet remain at rest without the influx, the reflux, the passage of the blood, which is the fluid that serves as their vehicle or pabulum.

And next I desire to know of those who tell us that the spirits are formed in the heart, being compounded of the vapours or exhalations of the blood (excited either by the heat of the heart or the concussion) and the inspired air, whether such spirits are not to be accounted much colder than the blood, seeing that both the elements of their composition, namely, air and vapour, are much colder? For the vapour of boiling water is much more bearable than the water itself; the flame of a candle is less burning than the red-hot snuff, and burning charcoal than incandescent iron or brass. Whence it would appear that spirits of this nature rather receive their heat from the blood, than that the blood is warmed by these spirits; such spirits are rather to be regarded as fumes and excrementitious effluvia proceeding from the body in the manner of odours, than in any way as natural artificers of the tissues; a conclusion which we are the more disposed to admit, when we see that they so speedily lose any virtue they may possess, and which they had derived from the blood as their source—they are at best of a very frail and evanescent nature. Whence also it becomes probable that the expiration of the lungs is a means by which these vapours being cast off, the blood is fanned and purified; whilst inspiration is a means by which the blood in its passage between the two ventricles of the heart is tempered by the cold of the ambient atmosphere, lest, getting heated, and blown up with a kind of fermentation, like milk or honey set over the fire, it should so distend the lungs that the animal got suffocated; somewhat in the same way, perchance, as one labouring under a severe asthma, which Galen himself seems to refer to its proper cause when he says it is owing to an obstruction of the smaller arteries, viz., the vasa venosa et arteriosa. And I have found by experience that patients affected with asthma might be brought out of states of very imminent danger by having cupping-glasses applied, and a plentiful and sudden affusion of cold water. Thus much—and perhaps it is more than was necessary—have I said on the subject of spirits in this place, for I felt it proper to define them, and to say something of their nature in a physiological disquisition.

I shall only further add that they who descant on the calidum innatum or innate heat, as an instrument of nature available for every purpose, and who speak of the necessity of heat as the cherisher and retainer in life of the several parts of the body, who at the same time admit that this heat cannot exist unless connected with something, and because they find no substance of anything like commensurate mobility, or which might keep pace with the rapid influx and reflux of this heat (in affections of the mind especially), take refuge in spirits as most subtile substances, possessed of the most penetrating qualities, and highest mobility—these persons see nothing less than the wonderful and almost divine character of the natural operations as proceeding from the instrumentality of this common agent, viz., the calidum innatum; they further regard these spirits as of a sublime, lucid, ethereal, celestial, or divine nature, and the bond of the soul; even as the vulgar and unlettered, when they do not comprehend the causes of various effects, refer them to the immediate interposition of the Deity. Whence they declare that the heat perpetually flowing into the several parts is in virtue of the influx of spirits through the channels of the arteries; as if the blood could neither move so swiftly, nor penetrate so intimately, nor cherish so effectually. And such faith do they put in this opinion, such lengths are they carried by their belief, that they deny the contents of the arteries to be blood! And then they proceed with trivial reasonings to maintain that the arterial blood is of a peculiar kind, or that the arteries are filled with such aereal spirits, and not with blood; all the while, in opposition to everything which Galen has advanced against Erasistratus, both on grounds of experiment and of reason. But that arterial blood differs in nothing essential from venous blood has been already sufficiently demonstrated; and our senses likewise assure us that the blood and spirits do not flow in the arteries separately and disjoined, but as one body.

We have occasion to observe so often as our hands, feet, or ears have become stiff and cold, that as they recover again by the warmth that flows into them, they acquire their natural colour and heat simultaneously; that the veins which had become small and shrunk, swell visibly and enlarge, so that when they regain their heat suddenly they become painful; from which it appears that that which by its influx brings heat is the same which causes repletion and colour; now this can be and is nothing but blood.

When an artery and a vein are divided, anyone may clearly see that the part of the vein towards the heart pours out no blood, whilst that beyond the wound gives a torrent; the divided artery, on the contrary (as in my experiment on the carotids), pours out a flood of pure blood from the orifice next the heart, and in jets as if it were forced from a syringe, whilst from the farther orifice of the divided artery little or no blood escapes. This experiment therefore plainly proves in what direction the current sets in either order of vessels—towards the heart in the veins, from the heart in the arteries; it also shows with what velocity the current moves, not gradually and by drops, but even with violence. And lest anyone, by way of subterfuge, should take shelter in the notion of invisible spirits, let the orifice of the divided vessel be plunged under water or oil, when, if there be any air contained in it, the fact will be proclaimed by a succession of visible bubbles. Hornets, wasps, and other insects of the same description plunged in oil, and so suffocated, emit bubbles of air from their tail whilst they are dying; whence it is not improbable that they thus respire when alive; for all animals submerged and drowned, when they finally sink to the bottom and die, emit bubbles of air from the mouth and lungs. It is also demonstrated by the same experiment, that the valves of the veins act with such accuracy, that air blown into them does not penetrate; much less then can blood make its way through them: it is certain, I say, that neither sensibly nor insensibly, nor gradually and drop by drop, can any blood pass from the heart by the veins.

And that no one may seek shelter in asserting that these things are so when nature is disturbed and opposed, but not when she is left to herself and at liberty to act; that the same things do not come to pass in morbid and unusual states as in the healthy and natural condition; they are to be met by saying that, if it were so, if it happened that so much blood was lost from the farther orifice of a divided vein because nature was disturbed, still that the incision does not close the nearer orifice, from which nothing either escapes or can be expressed, whether nature be disturbed or not. Others argue in the same way, maintaining that, although the blood immediately spurts out in such profusion with every beat, when an artery is divided near the heart, it does not therefore follow that the blood is propelled by the pulse when the heart and artery are entire. It is most probable, however, that every stroke impels something; and that there would be no pulse of the container, without an impulse being communicated to the thing contained, seems certain. Yet some, that they may seize upon a further means of defence, and escape the necessity of admitting the circulation, do not fear to affirm that the arteries in the living body and in the natural state are already so full of blood that they are incapable of receiving another drop; and so also of the ventricles of the heart. But it is indubitable that, whatever the degree of distension and the extent of contraction of the heart and arteries, they are still in a condition to receive an additional quantity of blood forced into them, and that this is far more than is usually reckoned in grains or drops, seems also certain. For if the ventricles become so excessively distended that they will admit no more blood, the heart ceases to beat (and we have occasional opportunities of observing the fact in our vivisections) and, continuing tense and resisting, death by asphyxia ensues.

In the work, *On the Motion of the Heart and Blood*, I have already sufficiently discussed the question as to whether the blood in its motion was attracted, or impelled, or moved by its own inherent nature. I have there also spoken at length of the action and office, of the dilatation and contraction of the heart, and have shown what these truly are, and how the heart contracts during the diastole of the arteries; so that I must hold those who take points for dispute from among them as either not understanding the subject, or as unwilling to look at things for themselves, and to investigate them with their own senses.[1]

For my part, I believe that no other kind of attraction can be demonstrated in the living body save that of the nutriment, which gradually and incessantly passes on to supply the waste that takes place in the tissues; in the same way as the oil rises in the wick of a lamp to be consumed by the flame. Whence I conclude that the primary and common organ of all sensible attraction and impulsion is of the nature of sinew (*nervus*), or fibre, or muscle, and this to the end that it may be contractile, that contracting it may be shortened, and so either stretch out, draw towards, or propel. But these topics will be better discussed elsewhere, when we speak of the organs of motion in the animal body.

[1] See chapter 14.

To those who repudiate the circulation because they neither see the efficient nor final cause of it, and who exclaim, *cui bono?* I have yet to reply, having hitherto taken no note of the ground of objection which they take up. And first I own I am of opinion that our first duty is to inquire whether the thing be or not, before asking wherefore it is? for from the facts and circumstances which meet us in the circulation admitted, established, the ends and objects of its institution are especially to be sought. Meantime I would only ask, how many things we admit in physiology, pathology, and therapeutics, the causes of which are unknown to us? That there are many, no one doubts—the causes of putrid fevers, of revulsions, of the purgation of excrementitious matters, among the number.

Whoever, therefore, sets himself in opposition to the circulation, because, if it be acknowledged, he cannot account for a variety of medical problems, nor in the treatment of diseases and the administration of medicines, give satisfactory reasons for the phenomena that appear; or who will not see that the precepts he has received from his teachers are false; or who thinks it unseemly to give up accredited opinions; or who regards it as in some sort criminal to call in question doctrines that have descended through a long succession of ages, and carry the authority of the ancients—to all of these I reply: that the facts cognizable by the senses wait upon no opinions, and that the works of nature bow to no antiquity; for indeed there is nothing either more ancient or of higher authority than nature.

To those who object to the circulation as throwing obstacles in the way of their explanations of the phenomena that occur in medical cases (and there are persons who will not be content to take up with a new system, unless it explains everything, as in astronomy), and who oppose it with their own erroneous assumptions, such as that, if it be true, phlebotomy cannot cause revulsion, seeing that the blood will still continue to be forced into the affected part; that the passage of excrementitious matters and foul humours through the heart, that most noble and principal viscus, is to be apprehended; that an efflux and excretion, occasionally of foul and corrupt blood, takes place from the same body, from different parts, even from the same part and at the same time, which, were the blood agitated by a continuous current, would be shaken and effectually mixed in passing through the heart, and many points of the like kind admitted in our medical schools, which are seen to be repugnant to the doctrine of the circulation—to them I shall not answer further here, than that the circulation is not always the same in every place, and at every time, but is contingent upon many circumstances: the more rapid or slower motion of the blood, the strength or weakness of the heart as the propelling organ, the quantity and quality or constitution of the blood, the rigidity or laxity of the tissues, and the like. A thicker blood, of course, moves more slowly through narrower channels; it is more effectually strained in its passage through the substance of the liver than through that of the lungs. It has not the same velocity through flesh and the softer parenchymatous structures and through sinewy parts of greater compactness and consistency: for the thinner and purer and more spirituous part permeates more quickly, the thicker more earthy and indifferently concocted portion moves more slowly, or is refused admission. The nutritive portion, or ultimate aliment of the tissues, the dew or cambium, is of a more penetrating nature, inasmuch as it has to be added everywhere, and to everything that grows and is nourished in its length and thickness, even to the horns, nails, hair and feathers; and then the excrementitious matters have to be secreted in some places, where they accumulate, and either prove a burthen or are concocted. But I do not imagine that the excrementitious fluids or bad humours when once separated, nor the milk, the phlegm, and the spermatic fluid, nor the ultimate nutritive part, the dew or cambium, necessarily circulate with the blood: that which nourishes every part adheres and becomes agglutinated to it. Upon each of these topics and various others besides, to be discussed and demonstrated in their several places, viz., in the physiology and other parts of the art of medicine, as well as of the consequences, advantages or disadvantages of the circulation of the blood, I do not mean to touch here; it were fruitless indeed to do so until the circulation has been established and conceded as a fact. And here the example of astronomy is by no means to be followed, in which from mere appearances or phenomena that which is in fact, and the reason wherefore it is so, are investigated. But as he who inquires into the cause of an eclipse must be placed beyond the moon if he would ascertain it by sense, and not by reason, still, in reference to things sensible, things that come under the cognizance of the senses, no more certain demonstration or means of gaining faith can be adduced than examination by the senses, than ocular inspection.

There is one remarkable experiment which I would have every one try who is anxious for truth, and by which it is clearly shown that the arterial pulse is owing to the impulse of the blood. Let a portion of the dried intestine of a dog or wolf, or any other animal, such as we see hung up in the druggists' shops, be taken and filled with water, and then secured at both ends like a sausage: by tapping with the finger at one extremity, you will immediately feel a pulse and vibration in any other part to which you apply the fingers, as you do when you feel the pulse at the wrist. In this way, indeed, and also by means of a distended vein, you may accurately either in the dead or living body, imitate and show every variety of the pulse, whether as to force, frequency, volume, rhythm, &c. Just as in a long bladder full of fluid, or in an oblong drum, every stroke upon one end is immediately felt at the other; so also in a dropsy of the belly and in abscesses under the skin, we are accustomed to distinguish between collections of fluid and of air, between anasarca and tympanites in particular. If a slap or push given on one side is clearly felt by a hand placed on the other side, we judge the case to be tympanites, not, as falsely asserted, because we hear a sound like that of a drum, and this produced by flatus, which never happens; but because, as in a drum, even the slightest tap passes through and produces a certain vibration on the opposite side; for it indicates that there is a serous and ichorous substance present, of such a consistency as urine, and not any sluggish or viscid matter as in anasarca, which when struck retains the impress of the blow or pressure, and does not transmit the impulse.

Having brought forward this experiment I may observe that a most formidable objection to the circulation of the blood rises out of it, which, however, has neither been observed nor adduced by anyone who has written against me. When we see by the experiment just described, that the systole and diastole of the pulse can be accurately imitated without any escape of fluid, it is obvious that the same thing may take place in the arteries from the stroke of the heart, without the necessity for a circulation, but like Euripus, with a mere motion of the blood alternately backwards and forwards. But we have already satisfactorily replied to this difficulty; and now we venture to say that the thing could not be so in the arteries of a living animal; to be assured of this it is enough to see that the right auricle is incessantly injecting the right ventricle of the heart with blood, the return of which is effectually prevented by the tricuspid valves; the left auricle in like manner filling the left ventricle, the return of the blood there being opposed by the mitral valves; and then the ventricles in their turn are propelling the blood into either great artery, the reflux in each being prevented by the sigmoid valves in its orifice. Either, consequently, the blood must move on incessantly through the lungs, and in like manner within the arteries of the body, or stagnating and pent up, it must rupture the containing vessels, or choke the heart by over distension, as I have shown it to do in the vivisection of a snake, described in my book *On the Motion of the Blood*. To resolve this doubt I shall relate two experiments among many others, the first of which, indeed, I have already adduced, and which show with singular clearness that the blood flows incessantly and with great force and in ample abundance in the veins towards the heart. The internal jugular vein of a live fallow deer having been exposed (many of the nobility and his Most Serene Majesty the King, my master, being present), was divided; but a few drops of blood were observed to escape from the lower orifice rising up from under the clavicle; whilst from the superior orifice of the vein and coming down from the head, a round torrent of blood gushed forth. You may observe the same fact any day in practising phlebotomy: if with a finger you compress the vein a little below the orifice, the flow of blood is immediately arrested; but the pressure being removed, forthwith the flow returns as before.

From any long vein of the forearm get rid of the blood as much as possible by holding the hand aloft and pressing the blood towards the trunk, you will perceive the vein collapsed and leaving, as it were, in a furrow of the skin; but now compress the vein with the point of a finger, and you will immediately perceive all that part of it which is towards the hand, to enlarge and to become distended with the blood that is coming from the hand. How comes it when the breath is held and the lungs thereby compressed, a large quantity of air having been taken in, that the vessels of the chest are at the same time obstructed, the blood driven into the face, and the eyes rendered red and suffused? Why is it, as Aristotle asks in his *Problems*, that all the actions are more energetically performed when the breath is held than when it is given? In like manner, when the frontal and lingual veins are incised, the blood is made to flow more freely by compressing the neck and holding the breath. I have several times opened the breast and pericardium of a man within two hours after his execution by hanging, and before the colour had totally left the face, and in presence of many witnesses, have demonstrated the right auricle of the heart and the lungs distended with blood; the auricle in particular of the size of a large man's fist, and so full of blood that it looked as if it would burst. This great distension, however, had disappeared next day, the body having stiffened and become cold, and the blood having made its escape through various channels. These and other similar facts, therefore, make it sufficiently certain that the blood flows through the whole of the veins of the body towards the base of the heart, and that unless there was a further passage afforded it, it would be pent up in these channels, or would oppress and overwhelm the heart; as on the other hand, did it not flow outwards by the arteries, but was found regurgitating, it would soon be seen how much it would oppress.

I add another observation. A noble knight, Sir Robert Darcy, an ancestor of that celebrated physician and most learned man, my very dear friend Dr. Argent, when he had reached to about the middle period of life, made frequent complaint of a certain distressing pain in the chest, especially in the night season; so that dreading at one time syncope, at another suffocation in his attacks he led an unquiet and anxious life. He tried many remedies in vain, having had the advice of almost every medical man. The disease going on from bad to worse, he by and by became cachectic and dropsical, and finally, grievously distressed, he died in one of his paroxysms. In the body of this gentleman, at the inspection of which there were present Dr. Argent, then president of the College of Physicians, and Dr. Gorge, a distinguished theologian and preacher, who was pastor of the parish, we found the wall of the left ventricle of the heart ruptured, having a rent in it of size sufficient to admit any of my fingers, although the wall itself appeared sufficiently thick and strong; this laceration had apparently been caused by an impediment to the passage of the blood from the left ventricle into the arteries.

I was acquainted with another strong man, who having received an injury and affront from one more powerful than himself, and upon whom he could not have his revenge, was so overcome with hatred and spite and passion, which he yet communicated to no one, that at last he fell into a strange distemper, suffering from extreme oppression and pain of the heart and breast, and the prescriptions of none of the very best physicians proving of any avail, he fell in the course of a few years into a scorbutic and cachectic state, became tabid and died. This patient only received some little relief when the whole of his chest was pummelled or kneaded by a strong man, as a baker kneads dough. His friends thought him poisoned by some maleficent influence, or possessed with an evil spirit. His jugular arteries, enlarged to the size of the thumb, looked like the aorta itself, or they were as large as the descending aorta; they had pulsated violently, and appeared like two long aneurisms. These symptoms had led to trying the effects of arteriotomy in the temples, but with no relief. In the dead body I found the heart and aorta so much gorged and distended with blood, that the cavities of the ventricles equalled those of a bullock's heart in size. Such is the force of the blood pent up, and such are the effects of its impulse.

We may, therefore, conclude, that although there may be impulse without any exit, as illustrated in the experiment lately spoken of, still that this could not take place in the vessels of living creatures without most serious dangers and impediments. From this, however, it is manifest that the blood in its course does not everywhere pass with the same celerity, neither with the same force in all places and at all times, but that it varies greatly according to age, sex, temperament, habit of body, and other contingent circumstances, external as well as internal, natural or non-natural. For it does not course through intricate and obstructed passages with the same readiness that it does through straight, unimpeded, and pervious channels. Neither does it run through close, hard, and crowded parts with the same velocity as through spongy, soft, and permeable tissues. Neither does it flow and penetrate with such swiftness when the impulse is slow and weak, as when this is forcible and frequent, in which case the blood is driven onwards with vigour and in large quantity. Nor is the same blood, when it has become more consistent or earthy, so penetrative as when it is more serous and attenuated or liquid. And then it seems only reasonable to think that the blood in its circuit passes more slowly through the kidneys than through the substance of the heart; more swiftly through the liver than through the kidneys; through the spleen more quickly than through the lungs, and through the lungs more speedily than through any of the other viscera or the muscles, in proportion always to the denseness or sponginess of the tissue of each.

We may be permitted to take the same view of the influence of age, sex, temperament, and habit of body, whether this be hard or soft; of that of the ambient cold which condenses bodies, and makes the veins in the extremities to shrink and almost to disappear, and deprives the surface both of colour and heat; and also of that of meat and drink which render the blood more watery, by supplying fresh nutritive matter. From the veins, therefore, the blood flows more freely in phlebotomy when the body is warm than when it is cold. We also observe the signal influence of the affections of the mind when a timid person is bled and happens to faint: immediately the flow of blood is arrested, a deadly pallor overspreads the surface, the limbs stiffen, the ears sing, the eyes are dazzled or blinded, and, as it were, convulsed. But here I come upon a field where I might roam freely and give myself up to speculation. And, indeed, such a flood of light and truth breaks in upon me here; occasion offers of explaining so many problems, of resolving so many doubts, of discovering the causes of so many slighter and more serious diseases, and of suggesting remedies for their cure, that the subject seems almost to demand a separate treatise. And it will be my business in my *Medical Observations*, to lay before my reader matter upon all these topics which shall be worthy of the gravest consideration.

And what indeed is more deserving of attention than the fact that in almost every affection, appetite, hope, or fear, our body suffers, the countenance changes, and the blood appears to course hither and thither. In anger the eyes are fiery and the pupils contracted; in modesty the cheeks are suffused with blushes; in fear, and under a sense of infamy and of shame, the face is pale, but the ears burn as if for the evil they heard or were to hear; in lust how quickly is the member distended with blood and erected! But, above all, and this is of the highest interest to the medical practitioner, how speedily is pain relieved or removed by the detraction of blood, the application of cupping-glasses, or the compression of the artery which leads to a part! It sometimes vanishes as if by magic. But these are topics that I must refer to my *Medical Observations*, where they will be found exposed at length and explained.

Some weak and inexperienced persons vainly seek by dialectics and far-fetched arguments, either to upset or establish things that are only to be founded on anatomical demonstration, and believed on the evidence of the senses. He who truly desires to be informed of the question in hand, and whether the facts alleged be sensible, visible, or not, must be held bound either to look for himself, or to take on trust the conclusions to which they have come who have looked; and indeed there is no higher method of attaining to assurance and certainty. Who would pretend to persuade those who had never tasted wine that it was a drink much pleasanter to the palate than water? By what reasoning should we give the blind from birth to know that the sun was luminous, and far surpassed the stars in brightness? And so it is with the circulation of the blood, which the world has now had before it for so many years, illustrated by proofs cognizable by the senses, and confirmed by various experiments. No one has yet been found to dispute the sensible facts, the motion, efflux and afflux of the blood, by like observations based on the evidence of sense, or to oppose the experiments adduced, by other experiments of the same character; nay, no one has yet attempted an opposition on the ground of ocular testimony.

There have not been wanting many who, inexperienced and ignorant of anatomy, and making no appeal to the senses in their opposition, have, on the contrary, met it with empty assertions, and mere suppositions, with assertions derived from the lessons of teachers and captious cavillings; many, too, have vainly sought refuge in words, and these not always very nicely chosen, but reproachful and contumelious; which, however, have no further effect than to expose their utterer's vanity and weakness, and ill breeding and lack of the arguments that are to be sought in the conclusions of the senses, and false sophistical reasonings that seem utterly opposed to sense. Even as the waves of the Sicilian sea, excited by the blast, dash against the rocks around Charybdis, and then hiss and foam, and are tossed hither and thither; so do they who reason against the evidence of their senses.

Were nothing to be acknowledged by the senses without evidence derived from reason, or occasionally even contrary to the previously received conclusions of reason, there would now be no problem left for discussion. Had we not our most perfect assurances by the senses, and were not their perceptions confirmed by reasoning, in the same way as geometricians proceed with their figures, we should admit no science of any kind; for it is the business of geometry, from things sensible, to make rational demonstration of things that are not sensible; to render credible or certain things abstruse and beyond sense from things more manifest and better known. Aristotle counsels us better when, in treating of the generation of bees, he says: "Faith is to be given to reason, if the matters demonstrated agree with those that are perceived by the senses; when the things have been thoroughly scrutinized, then are the senses to be trusted rather than the reason."[1] Whence it is our duty to approve or disapprove, to receive or reject everything only after the most careful examination; but to examine, to test whether anything have been well or ill advanced, to ascertain whether some falsehood does not lurk under a proposition, it is imperative on us to bring it to the proof of sense, and to admit or reject it on the decision of sense. Whence Plato in his *Critias*, says that the explanation of those things is not difficult of which we can have experience; whilst they are not of apt scientific apprehension who have no experience.

How difficult is it to teach those who have no experience, the things of which they have not any knowledge by their senses! And how useless and intractable, and unimpregnable to true science are such auditors! They show the judgment of the blind in regard to colours, of the deaf in reference to concords. Who ever pretended to teach the ebb and flow of the tide, or from a diagram to demonstrate the measurements of the angles and the proportions of the sides of a triangle to a blind man, or to one who had never seen the sea nor a diagram? He who is not conversant with anatomy, inasmuch as he forms no conception of the subject from the evidence of his own eyes, is virtually blind to all that concerns anatomy, and unfit to appreciate what is founded thereon; he knows nothing of that which occupies the attention of the anatomist, nor of the principles inherent in the nature of the things which guide him in his reasonings; facts and inferences as well as their sources are alike unknown to such a one. But no kind of science can possibly flow, save from some preëxisting knowledge of more obvious things; and this is one main reason why our science in regard to the nature of celestial bodies, is so uncertain and conjectural. I would ask of those who profess a knowledge of the causes of all things, why the two eyes keep constantly moving together, up or down, to this side or to

[1] *On the Generation of Animals*, III. 10.

that, and not independently, one looking this way, another that; why the two auricles of the heart contract simultaneously, and the like? Are fevers, pestilence, and the wonderful properties of various medicines to be denied because their causes are unknown? Who can tell us why the fœtus *in utero*, breathing no air up to the tenth month of its existence, is yet not suffocated? Born in the course of the seventh or eighth month, and having once breathed, it is nevertheless speedily suffocated if its respiration be interrupted. Why can the fœtus still contained within the uterus, or enveloped in the membranes, live without respiration; whilst once exposed to the air, unless it breathes it inevitably dies?[1]

Observing that many hesitate to acknowledge the circulation, and others oppose it, because, as I conceive, they have not rightly understood me, I shall here recapitulate briefly what I have said in my work *On the Motion of the Heart and Blood*. The blood contained in the veins, in its magazine, and where it is collected in largest quantity, *viz.*, in the vena cava, close to the base of the heart and right auricle, gradually increasing in temperature by its internal heat, and becoming attenuated, swells and rises like bodies in a state of fermentation, whereby the auricle being dilated, and then contracting, in virtue of its pulsative power, forthwith delivers its charge into the right ventricle; which being filled, and the systole ensuing, the charge, hindered from returning into the auricle by the tricuspid valves, is forced into the pulmonary artery, which stands open to receive it, and is immediately distended with it. Once in the pulmonary artery, the blood cannot return, by reason of the sigmoid valves; and then the lungs, alternately expanded and contracted during inspiration and expiration, afford it passage by the proper vessels into the pulmonary veins; from the pulmonary veins, the left auricle, acting equally and synchronously with the right auricle, delivers the blood into the left ventricle; which acting harmoniously with the right ventricle, and all regress being prevented by the mitral valves, the blood is projected into the aorta, and consequently impelled into all the arteries of the body. The arteries, filled by this sudden push, as they cannot discharge themselves so speedily, are distended; they receive a shock, or undergo their diastole. But as this process goes on incessantly, I infer that the arteries both of the lungs and of the body at

[1] See Chapter 6, of the *Disquisition on the Motion of the Heart and Blood*.

large, under the influence of such a multitude of strokes of the heart and injections of blood, would finally become so over-gorged and distended that either any further injection must cease, or the vessels would burst, or the whole blood in the body would accumulate within them, were there not an exit provided for it.

The same reasoning is applicable to the ventricles of the heart: distended by the ceaseless action of the auricles, did they not disburthen themselves by the channels of the arteries, they would by and by become over-gorged, and be fixed and made incapable of all motion. Now this, my conclusion, is true and necessary, if my premises be true; but that these are either true or false, our senses must inform us, not our reason—ocular inspection, not any process of the mind.

I maintain, further, that the blood in the veins always and everywhere flows from less to greater branches, and from every part towards the heart; whence I gather that the whole charge which the arteries receive, and which is incessantly thrown into them, is delivered to the veins, and flows back by them to the source whence it came. In this way, indeed, is the circulation of the blood established: by an efflux and reflux from and to the heart; the fluid being forcibly projected into the arterial system, and then absorbed and imbibed from every part by the veins, it returns through these in a continuous stream. That all this is so, sense assures us; and necessary inference from the perceptions of sense takes away all occasion for doubt. Lastly, this is what I have striven, by my observations and experiments, to illustrate and make known; I have not endeavoured from causes and probable principles to demonstrate my propositions, but, as of higher authority, to establish them by appeals to sense and experiment, after the manner of anatomists.

And here I would refer to the amount of force, even of violence, which sight and touch make us aware of in the heart and greater arteries; and to the systole and diastole constituting the pulse in the large warm-blooded animals, which I do not say is equal in all the vessels containing blood, nor in all animals that have blood; but which is of such a nature and amount in all, that a flow and rapid passage of the blood through the smaller arteries, the interstices of the tissues, and the branches of the veins, must of necessity take place; and, therefore, there is a circulation.

For neither do the most minute arteries, nor the veins, pulsate; but the larger arteries and those near the heart pulsate, because they do not transmit the blood so quickly as they receive it.[1] Having exposed an artery, and divided it so that the blood shall flow out as fast and freely as it is received, you will scarcely perceive any pulse in that vessel; and for the simple reason that, an open passage being afforded, the blood escapes, merely passing through the vessel, not distending it. In fishes, serpents, and the colder animals, the heart beats so slowly and feebly that a pulse can scarcely be perceived in the arteries; the blood in them is transmitted gradually. Whence in them, as also in the smaller branches of the arteries in man, there is no distinction between the coats of the arteries and veins, because the arteries have to sustain no shock from the impulse of the blood.

An artery denuded and divided in the way I have indicated, sustains no shock, and therefore does not pulsate; whence it clearly appears that the arteries have no inherent pulsative power, and that neither do they derive any from the heart; but that they undergo their diastole solely from the impulse of the blood; for in the full stream, flowing to a distance, you may see the systole and diastole, all the motions of the heart—their order, force, rhythm, &c.,[2] as it were in a mirror, and even perceive them by the touch. Precisely as in the water that is forced aloft, through a leaden pipe, by working the piston of a forcing-pump, each stroke of which, though the jet be many feet distant, is nevertheless distinctly perceptible—the beginning, increasing strength, and end of the impulse, as well as its amount, and the regularity or irregularity with which it is given, being indicated, the same precisely is the case from the orifice of a divided artery; whence, as in the instance of the forcing engine quoted, you will perceive that the efflux is uninterrupted, although the jet is alternately greater and less. In the arteries, therefore, besides the concussion or impulse of the blood, the pulse or beat of the artery, which is not equally exhibited in all, there is a perpetual flow and motion of the blood, which returns in an unbroken stream to the point from whence it commenced—the right auricle of the heart.

All these points you may satisfy yourself upon, by exposing one of the longer arteries, and having taken it between your finger and thumb, dividing it on the side remote from the heart. By the greater or less pressure of your fingers, you can have the vessel pulsating less or more, or losing the pulse entirely, and recovering it at will. And as these things proceed thus when the chest is uninjured, so also do they go on for a short time when the thorax is laid open, and the lungs having collapsed, all the respiratory motions have ceased; here, nevertheless, for a little while you may perceive the left auricle contracting and emptying itself, and becoming whiter; but by and by growing weaker and weaker, it begins to intermit, as does the left ventricle also, and then it ceases to beat altogether, and becomes quiescent. Along with this, and in the same measure, does the stream of blood from the divided artery grow less and less, the pulse of the vessel weaker and weaker, until at last, the supply of blood and the impulse of the left ventricle failing, nothing escapes from it. You may perform the same experiment, tying the pulmonary veins, and so taking away the pulse of the left auricle, or relaxing the ligature, and restoring it at pleasure. In this experiment, too, you will observe what happens in moribund animals, *viz.*, that the left ventricle first ceases from pulsation and motion, then the left auricle, next the right ventricle, finally the right auricle; so that where the vital force and pulse first begin, there do they also last fail.

All of these particulars having been recognized by the senses, it is manifest that the blood passes through the lungs, not through the septum, and only through them when they are moved in the act of respiration, not when they are collapsed and quiescent; whence we see the probable reason wherefore nature has instituted the foramen ovale in the fœtus, instead of sending the blood by the way of the pulmonary artery into the left auricle and ventricle, which foramen she closes when the newborn creature begins to breathe freely. We can also now understand why, when the vessels of the lungs become congested and oppressed, and in those who are affected with serious diseases, it should be so dangerous and fatal a symptom when the respiratory organs become implicated.

We perceive, further, why the blood is so florid in the lungs, which is, because it is thinner, as having there to undergo filtration.

Still further; from the summary which precedes, and by way of satisfying those who are importunate in regard to the causes of the circulation, and incline to regard the power of the heart as competent to everything—as that it is not only the seat and source of the pulse which

[1] See Chapter 3, of the *Disquisition on the Motion of the Heart and Blood.*
[2] *Ibid.*

propels the blood, but also, as Aristotle thinks, of the power which attracts and produces it; moreover, that the spirits are engendered by the heart, and the influxive vital heat, in virtue of the innate heat of the heart, as the immediate instrument of the soul, or common bond and prime organ in the performance of every act of vitality; in a word, that the motion, perfection, heat, and every property besides of the blood and spirits are derived from the heart, as their fountain or original (a doctrine as old as Aristotle, who maintained all these qualities to inhere in the blood, as heat inheres in boiling water or pottage), and that the heart is the primary cause of pulsation and life; to those persons, did I speak openly, I should say that I do not agree with the common opinion; there are numerous particulars to be noted in the production of the parts of the body which incline me this way, but which it does not seem expedient to enter upon here. Before long, perhaps, I shall have occasion to lay before the world things that are more wonderful than these, and that are calculated to throw still greater light upon natural philosophy.

Meantime I shall only say, and, without pretending to demonstrate it, propound—with the good leave of our learned men, and with all respect for antiquity—that the heart, with the veins and arteries and the blood they contain, is to be regarded as the beginning and author, the fountain and original of all things in the body, the primary cause of life; and this in the same acceptation as the brain with its nerves, organs of sense and spinal marrow inclusive, is spoken of as the one and general organ of sensation. But if by the word "heart" the mere body of the heart, made up of its auricles and ventricles, be understood, then I do not believe that the heart is the fashioner of the blood; neither do I imagine that the blood has powers, properties, motion, or heat, as the gift of the heart; lastly, neither do I admit that the cause of the systole and contraction is the same as that of the diastole or dilatation, whether in the arteries, auricles, or ventricles; for I hold that that part of the pulse which is designated the diastole depends on another cause different from the systole, and that it must always and everywhere precede any systole; I hold that the innate heat is the first cause of dilatation, and that the primary dilatation is in the blood itself, after the manner of bodies in a state of fermentation, gradually attenuated and swelling, and that in the blood is this finally extinguished; I assent to Aristotle's example of gruel or milk

upon the fire, to this extent, that the rising and falling of the blood does not depend upon vapours or exhalations, or spirits, or anything rising in a vaporous or aereal shape, nor upon any external agency, but upon an internal principle under the control of nature.

Nor is the heart, as some imagine, anything like a chauffer or fire, or heated kettle, and so the source of the heat of the blood; the blood, instead of receiving, rather gives heat to the heart, as it does to all the other parts of the body; for the blood is the hottest element in the body; and it is on this account that the heart is furnished with coronary arteries and veins; it is for the same reason that other parts have vessels, viz., to secure the access of warmth for their due conservation and stimulation; so that the warmer any part is, the greater is its supply of blood, or otherwise; where the blood is in largest quantity, there also is the heat highest. For this reason is the heart, remarkable through its cavities, to be viewed as the elaboratory, fountain, and perennial focus of heat, and as comparable to a hot kettle, not because of its proper substance, but because of its contained blood; for the same reason, because they have numerous veins or vessels containing blood, are the liver, spleen, lungs, &c. reputed hot parts. And in this way do I view the native or innate heat as the common instrument of every function, the prime cause of the pulse among the rest. This, however, I do not mean to state absolutely, but only propose it by way of thesis. Whatever may be objected to it by good and learned men, without abusive or contemptuous language, I shall be ready to listen to—I shall even be most grateful to any one who will take up and discuss the subject.

These then, are, as it were, the very elements and indications of the passage and circulation of the blood, viz., from the right auricle into the right ventricle; from the right ventricle by the way of the lungs into the left auricle; thence into the left ventricle and aorta; whence by the arteries at large through the pores or interstices of the tissues into the veins, and by the veins back again with great rapidity to the base of the heart.

There is an experiment on the veins by which any one that chooses may convince himself of this truth: let the arm be bound with a moderately tight bandage, and then, by opening and shutting the hand, make all the veins to swell as much as possible, and the integuments below the fillet to become red; and now let the arm and hand be plunged into very cold water, or snow, until the blood pent up in the veins shall have become cooled down; then let the fillet be undone suddenly, and you will perceive, by the cold blood returning to the heart, with what celerity the current flows, and what an effect it produces when it has reached the heart; so that you will no longer be surprised that some should faint when the fillet is undone after venesection.[1] This experiment shows that the veins swell below the ligature not with attenuated blood, or with blood raised by spirits or vapours, for the immersion in the cold water would repress their ebullition, but with blood only, and such as could never make its way back into the arteries, either by open-mouthed communications or by devious passages; it shows, moreover, how and in what way those who are travelling over snowy mountains are sometimes stricken suddenly with death, and other things of the same kind.

Lest it should seem difficult for the blood to make its way through the pores of the various structures of the body, I shall add one illustration: the same thing happens in the bodies of those that are hanged or strangled, as in the arm that is bound with a fillet: all the parts beyond the noose—the face, lips, tongue, eyes, and every part of the head appear gorged with blood, swollen and of a deep red or livid colour; but if the noose be relaxed, in whatever position you have the body, before many hours have passed you will perceive the whole of the blood to have quitted the head and face, and gravitated through the pores of the skin, flesh, and other structures, from the superior parts towards those that are inferior and dependent, until they become tumid and of a dark colour. But if this happens in the dead body, with the blood dead and coagulated, the frame stiffened with the chill of death, the passages all compressed or blocked up, it is easy to perceive how much more apt it will be to occur in the living subject, when the blood is alive and replete with spirits, when the pores are all open, the fluid ready to penetrate, and the passage in every way made easy.

When the ingenious and acute Descartes (whose honourable mention of my name demands my acknowledgments) and others, having taken out the heart of a fish, and put it on a plate before them, see it continuing to pulsate (in contracting), and when it raises or erects itself and becomes firm to the touch, they think it enlarges, expands, and that its ventricles

[1] See Chapter 11, of the *Disquisition on the Motion of the Heart and Blood.*

thence become more capacious. But, in my opinion, they do not observe correctly; for, at the time the heart gathers itself up, and becomes erect, it is certain that it is rather lessened in every one of its dimensions; that it is in its systole, in short, not in its diastole. Neither, on the contrary, when it collapses and sinks down, is it then properly in its state of diastole and distension, by which the ventricles become more capacious. But as we do not say that the heart is in the state of diastole in the dead body, as having sunk relaxed after the systole, but is then collapsed, and without all motion—in short, is in a state of rest, and not distended. It is only truly distended, and in the proper state of diastole, when it is filled by the charge of blood projected into it by the contraction of the auricles; a fact which sufficiently appears in the course of vivisections. Descartes, therefore, does not perceive how much the relaxation and subsidence of the heart and arteries differ from their distension or diastole; and that the cause of the distension, relaxation, and constriction is not one and the same; as contrary effects so must they rather acknowledge contrary causes; as different movements they must have different motors; just as all anatomists know that the flexion and extension of an extremity are accomplished by opposite antagonist muscles, and contrary or diverse motions are necessarily performed by contrary and diverse organs instituted by nature for the purpose. Neither do I find the efficient cause of the pulse aptly explained by this philosopher, when with Aristotle he assumes the cause of the systole to be the same as that of the diastole, *viz.*, an effervescence of the blood due to a kind of ebullition. For the pulse is a succession of sudden strokes and quick percussions; but we know of no kind of fermentation or ebullition in which the matter rises and falls in the twinkling of an eye; the heaving is always gradual where the subsidence is notable. Besides, in the body of a living animal laid open, we can with our eyes perceive the ventricles of the heart both charged and distended by the contraction of the auricles, and more or less increased in size according to the charge; and, further, we can see that the distension of the heart is rather a violent motion, the effect of an impulsion, and not performed by any kind of attraction.

Some are of opinion that, as no kind of impulse of the nutritive juices is required in vegetables, but that these are attracted by the parts which require them, and flow in to take the place of what has been lost; so neither is there any necessity for an impulse in animals, the vegetative faculty in both working alike. But there is a difference between plants and animals. In animals, a constant supply of warmth is required to cherish the members, to maintain them in life by the vivifying heat, and to restore parts injured from without. It is not merely nutrition that has to be provided for.

So much for the circulation; any impediment, or perversion or excessive excitement of which, is followed by a host of dangerous diseases and remarkable symptoms: in connexion with the veins—varices, abscesses, pains, hemorrhoids, hemorrhages; in connexion with the arteries—enlargements, phlegmons, severe and lancinating pains, aneurisms, sarcoses, fluxions, sudden attacks of suffocation, asthmas, stupors, apoplexies, and innumerable other affections. But this is not the place to enter on the consideration of these; neither may I say under what circumstances and how speedily some of these diseases, that are even reputed incurable, are remedied and dispelled, as if by enchantment. I shall have much to put forth in my *Medical Observations and Pathology*, which, so

far as I know, has as yet been observed by no one.

That I may afford you still more ample satisfaction, most learned Riolanus, as you do not think there is a circulation in the vessels of the mesentery, I shall conclude by proposing the following experiment: throw a ligature around the porta close to the liver, in a living animal, which is easily done. You will forthwith perceive the veins below the ligature swelling in the same way as those of the arm when the bleeding fillet is bound above the elbow; a circumstance which will proclaim the course of the blood there. And as you still seem to think that the blood can regurgitate from the veins into the arteries by open anastomoses, let the vena cava be tied in a living animal near the divarication of the crural veins, and immediately afterwards let an artery be opened to give issue to the blood: you will soon observe the whole of the blood discharged from all the veins, that of the ascending cava among the number, with the single exception of the crural veins, which will continue full; and this certainly could not happen were there any retrograde passage for the blood from the veins to the arteries by open anastomoses.

Anatomical Exercises on the Generation of Animals

TO THE LEARNED AND ILLUSTRIOUS THE PRESIDENT AND FELLOWS
OF THE COLLEGE OF PHYSICIANS OF LONDON

HARASSED with anxious, and in the end not much availing cares, about Christmas last, I sought to rid my spirit of the cloud that oppressed it, by a visit to that great man, the chief honour and ornament of our College, Dr. William Harvey, then dwelling not far from the city. I found him, Democritus-like, busy with the study of natural things, his countenance cheerful, his mind serene, embracing all within its sphere. I forthwith saluted him, and asked if all were well with him? "How can it," said he, "whilst the Commonwealth is full of distractions, and I myself am still in the open sea? And truly," he continued, "did I not find solace in my studies, and a balm for my spirit in the memory of my observations of former years, I should feel little desire for longer life. But so it has been, that this life of obscurity, this vacation from public business, which causes tedium and disgust to so many, has proved a sovereign remedy to me."

I answering said, "I can readily account for this: whilst most men are learned through others' wits, and under cover of a different diction and a new arrangement, vaunt themselves on things that belong to the ancients, thou ever interrogatest nature herself concerning her mysteries. And this line of study as it is less likely to lead into error, so is it also more fertile in enjoyment, inasmuch as each particular point examined often leads to others which had not before been surmised. You yourself, I well remember, informed me once that you had never dissected any animal—and many and many a one have you examined—but that you discovered something unexpected, something of which you were formerly uninformed."

"It is true," said he: "the examination of the bodies of animals has always been my delight; and I have thought that we might thence not only obtain an insight into the lighter mysteries of nature, but there perceive a kind of image or reflex of the omnipotent Creator himself.

And though much has already been made out by the learned men of former times, I have still thought that much more remained behind, hidden by the dusky night of nature, uninterrogated; so that I have oftentimes wondered and even laughed at those who have fancied that everything had been so consummately and absolutely investigated by an Aristotle or a Galen, or some other mighty name, that nothing could by possibility be added to their knowledge. Nature, however, is the best and most faithful interpreter of her own secrets; and what she presents either more briefly or obscurely in one department, that she explains more fully and clearly in another. No one indeed has ever rightly ascertained the use or function of a part who has not examined its structure, situation, connexions by means of vessels, and other accidents, in various animals, and carefully weighed and considered all he has seen. The ancients, our authorities in science, even as their knowledge of geography was limited by the boundaries of Greece, so neither did their knowledge of animals, vegetables, and other natural objects extend beyond the confines of their country. But to us the whole earth lies open, and the zeal of our travellers has made us familiar not only with other countries and the manners and customs of their inhabitants, but also with the animals, vegetables, and minerals that are met with in each. And truly there is no nation so barbarous which has not discovered something for the general good, whether led to it by accident or compelled by necessity, which had been overlooked by more civilized communities. But shall we imagine that nothing can accrue to the wide domains of science from such advantages, or that all knowledge was exhausted by the first ages of the world? If we do, the blame very certainly attaches to our indolence, nowise to nature.

"To this there is another evil added: many

329

persons, wholly without experience, from the presumed verisimilitude of a previous opinion, are often led by and by to speak of it boldly, as a matter that is certainly known; whence it comes, that not only are they themselves deceived, but that they likewise lead other incautious persons into error."

Discoursing in this manner, and touching upon many topics besides with wonderful fluency and facility, as is his custom, I interposed by observing, "How free you yourself are from the fault you indicate all know who are acquainted with you; and this is the reason wherefore the learned world, who are aware of your unwearied industry in the study of philosophy, are eagerly looking for your further experiments."

"And would you be the man," said Harvey, smiling, "who should recommend me to quit the peaceful haven, where I now pass my life, and launch again upon the faithless sea? You know full well what a storm my former lucubrations raised. Much better is it oftentimes to grow wise at home and in private, than by publishing what you have amassed with infinite labour, to stir up tempests that may rob you of peace and quiet for the rest of your days."

"True," said I; "it is the usual reward of virtue to have received ill for having merited well. But the winds which raised those storms, like the northwestern blast, which drowns itself in its own rain, have only drawn mischief on themselves."

Upon this he showed me his *Exercises on the Generation of Animals*, a work composed with vast labour and singular care; and having it in my hands, I exclaimed, "Now have I what I so much desired! and unless you consent to make this work public, I must say that you will be wanting both to your own fame and to the public usefulness. Nor let any fear of further trouble in the matter induce you to withhold it longer: I gladly charge myself with the whole business of correcting the press."

Making many difficulties at first, urging, among other things, that his work must be held imperfect, as not containing his investigations on the generation of insects, I nevertheless prevailed at length, and he said to me, "I intrust these papers to your care with full authority either speedily to commit them to the press, or to suppress them till some future time." Having returned him many thanks, I bade him adieu, and took my leave, feeling like another Jason laden with the Golden Fleece. On returning home I forthwith proceeded to examine my prize in all its parts, and could not but wonder

with myself that such a treasure should have lain so long concealed; and that whilst others produce their trifles and emptinesses with much ado, their messes twice, aye, an hundred times, heated up, our Harvey should set so little store by his admirable observations. And indeed, so often as he has sent forth any of his discoveries to the world, he has not comported himself like those who, when they publish, would have us believe that an oak had spoken, and that they had merited the rarest honours—a draught of hen's milk at the least. Our Harvey rather seems as though discovery were natural to him, a thing of ease and of course, a matter of ordinary business; though he may nevertheless have expended infinite labour and study on his works. And we have evidence of his singular candour in this, that he never hostilely attacks any previous writer, but ever courteously sets down and comments upon the opinions of each; and indeed he is wont to say that it is argument of an indifferent cause when it is contended for with violence and distemper; and that truth scarce wants an advocate.

It would have been easy for our illustrious colleague to have woven the whole of this web from materials of his own; but to escape the charge of envy, he has rather chosen to take Aristotle and Fabricius of Aquapendente as his guides, and to appear as contributing but his portion to the general fabric. Of him, whose virtue, candour, and genius are so well known to you all, I shall say no more, lest I should seem to praise to his face one whose singular worth has exalted him beyond the reach of all praise. Of myself I shall only say that I have done no more than perform the midwife's office in this business, ushering into the light this product of our colleague's genius as you see it, consummate and complete, but long delayed, and fearing perchance some envious blast: in other words, I have overlooked the press; and as our author writes a hand which no one without practice can easily read (a thing that is common among our men of letters), I have taken some pains to prevent the printer committing any very grave blunders through this—a point which I observe not to have been sufficiently attended to in the small work of his which lately appeared.

Here then, my learned friends, you have the cause of my addressing you at this time, *viz.*, that you may know that our Harvey presents an offering to the benefit of the republic of letters, to your honour, to his own eternal fame.

Farewell, and prosper.

GEORGE ENT

INTRODUCTION

It will not, I trust, be unwelcome to you, candid reader, if I yield to the wishes, I might even say the entreaties, of many, and in these *Exercises on Animal Generation*, lay before the student and lover of truth what I have observed on this subject from anatomical dissections, which turns out to be very different from anything that is delivered by authors, whether philosophers or physicians.

Physicians, following Galen, teach that from the semen of the male and female mingled in coition the offspring is produced, and resembles one or other, according to the *predominance* of this one or of that; and, further, that in virtue of the same predominance, it is either male or female. Sometimes they declare the semen masculinum as the *efficient cause*, and the semen femininum as supplying the *matter;* and sometimes, again, they advocate precisely the opposite doctrine. Aristotle, one of Nature's most diligent inquirers, however, affirms the *principles* of generation to be the male and the female, she contributing the matter, he the form; and that immediately after the sexual act the vital principle and the first particle of the future fœtus, *viz.*, the heart, in animals that have red blood, are formed from the menstrual blood in the uterus.

But that these are erroneous and hasty conclusions is easily made to appear: like phantoms of darkness they suddenly vanish before the light of anatomical inquiry. Nor is any long refutation necessary where the truth can be seen with one's proper eyes; where the inquirer by simple inspection finds everything in conformity with reason; and where at the same time he is made to understand how unsafe, how base a thing it is to receive instruction from others' comments without examination of the objects themselves, the rather as the book of Nature lies so open and is so easy of consultation.

What I shall deliver in these my *Exercises on Animal Generation* I am anxious to make publicly known, not merely that posterity may there perceive the sure and obvious truth, but further, and especially, that by exhibiting the method of investigation which I have followed, I may propose to the studious a new and, unless I mistake, a safer way to the attainment of knowledge.

For although it is a new and difficult road in studying nature, rather to question things themselves than, by turning over books, to discover the opinions of philosophers regarding them, still it must be acknowledged that it is the more open path to the secrets of natural philosophy, and that which is less likely to lead into error.

Nor is there any just cause wherefore the labour should deter anyone, if he will but think that he himself only lives through the ceaseless working of his heart. Neither, indeed, would the way I propose be felt as so barren and lonely, but for the custom, or vice rather, of the age we live in, when men, inclined to idleness, prefer going wrong with the many, to becoming wise with the few through dint of toil and outlay of money. The ancient philosophers, whose industry even we admire, went a different way to work, and by their unwearied labour and variety of experiments, searching into the nature of things, have left us no doubtful light to guide us in our studies. In this way it is that almost everything we yet possess of note or credit in philosophy, has been transmitted to us through the industry of ancient Greece. But when we acquiesce in the discoveries of the ancients, and believe (which we are apt to do through indolence) that nothing further remains to be known, we suffer the edge of our ingenuity to be taken off, and the lamp which they delivered to us to be extinguished. No one of a surety will allow that all truth was engrossed by the ancients, unless he be utterly ignorant (to pass by other arts for the present) of the many remarkable discoveries that have lately been made in anatomy, these having been principally achieved by individuals who, either intent upon some particular matter, fell upon the novelty by accident, or (and this is the more excellent way) who, following the traces of nature with their own eyes, pursued her through devious but most assured ways till they reached her in the citadel of truth. And truly in such pursuits it is sweet not merely to toil, but even to grow weary, when the pains of discovering are amply compensated by the pleasures of discovery. Eager for novelty, we are wont to travel far into unknown countries that, with our own eyes, we may witness what we have heard reported as having been seen by others, where, however, we for the most part find

——minuit præsentia famam:

that the presence lessens the repute. It were disgraceful, therefore, with this most spacious and admirable realm of nature before us, and where the reward ever exceeds the promise, did we take the reports of others upon trust, and go on coining crude problems out of these, and on them hanging knotty and captious and petty disputations. Nature is herself to be addressed; the paths she shows us are to be boldly trodden; for thus, and whilst we consult our proper senses, from inferior advancing to superior levels, shall we penetrate at length into the heart of her mystery.

Of the Manner and Order of acquiring Knowledge

Although there is but one road to science, that, to wit, in which we proceed from things more known to things less known, from matters more manifest to matters more obscure; and universals are principally known to us, science springing by reasonings from universals to particulars; still the comprehension of universals by the understanding is based upon the perception of individual things by the senses. Both of Aristotle's propositions, therefore, are true: first, the one in his *Physics*,[1] where he says, "The way is naturally prepared, from those things that are more obvious and clear to us, to those things that are more obvious and clear by nature. For, indeed, the same things are not both known to us and extant simply: whence it is indispensable to proceed in this way, viz., from those things that are of a more obscure nature, but to us are more apparent, to those that are of a nature more obvious and distinct. Now those things are, in the first instance, more perspicuous and manifest to us that are most confused in fact; whence it is necessary to proceed from universals to particulars; for the whole, according to the dictates of sense, is the more obvious; and the universal is a certain whole." And again, that other in his *Analytics*,[2] where he thus expresses himself: "Singulars are to us more known, and are the first that exist according to the information of sense; for, indeed, there is nothing in the understanding which was not first in the sense. And although that reasoning is naturally prior and more known which proceeds by syllogism, still is that more perspicuous to us which is based on induction. And, therefore, do we more readily define singulars than universals, for there is more of equivocation in universals: whence it is advisable from singulars to pass to universals."

All this agrees with what we have previously said, although at first blush it may seem contradictory; inasmuch as universals are first imbibed from particulars by the senses, and in so far are only known to us as an universal is a certain whole and indistinct thing, and a whole is known to us according to sense. For though in all knowledge we begin from sense, because, as the philosopher quoted has it, sensible particulars are better known to sense, still the sensation itself is an universal thing. For, if you observe rightly, although in the external sense the object perceived is singular, as, for example, the colour which we call yellow in the eye, still when this impression comes to be made an abstraction, and to be judged of and understood by the internal sensorium, it is an universal. Whence it happens that several persons abstract several species, and conceive different notions, from viewing the same object at the same time. This is conspicuous among poets and painters, who, although they contemplate one and the same object in the same place at the same moment, and with all other circumstances agreeing, nevertheless regard and describe it variously, and as each has conceived or formed an idea of it in his imagination. In the same way, the painter having a certain portrait to delineate, if he draw the outline a thousand times, he will still give a different face, and each not only differing from the other, but from the original countenance; with such slight variety, however, that looking at them singly, you shall conceive you have still the same portrait set before you, although, when set side by side, you perceive how different they are. Now the reason is this: that in vision, or the act of seeing itself, each particular is clear and distinct; but the moment the object is removed, as it is by merely shutting the eyes, when it becomes an abstraction in the fancy, or is only retained in the memory, it appears obscure and indistinct; neither is it any longer apprehended as a particular, but as a something that is common and universal. Seneca explains this subtlety, according to Plato's views, in very elegant terms: "An idea," he says, "is an eternal copy of the things that have place in nature. I add an explanation of this definition, that the matter may be made plainer to you. I desire to take your portrait; I have you as the prototype of the picture, from which my mind takes a certain impression which it transfers to the canvass. The countenance, therefore, which teaches and directs me, and from which the imitation is sought, is the idea."[3] A little farther on he proceeds: "I have but just made use of the image which a painter forms in his mind, by way of illustration. Now, if he would paint a likeness of Virgil, he forms an intuitive image of his subject: the idea is the

[1] Book 1, 1.
[2] *Posterior Analytics*, 1, 2.
[3] Letter 58.

face of Virgil, the type of his future work; and this which the artist conveys and transfers to his work is the resemblance or portrait. What difference is there? you ask: the one is the pattern or prototype, the other the form taken from the pattern and fixed in the work; the artist imitates the one, he creates the other. A statue has a certain expression of face; this is the *eidos,* the species or representation; the prototype himself has a certain expression, which the statuary conceiving, transfers to his statue: this is the idea. Do you desire yet another illustration of the distinction? The *eidos* is in the work; the idea without the work, and not only without the work, but it even existed before the work was begun." For the things that have formerly been noted, and that by use or wont have become firmly fixed in the mind of the artist, do, in fact, constitute art and the artistic faculty; art, indeed, is the reason of the work in the mind of the artist. On the same terms, therefore, as art is attained to, is all knowledge and science acquired; for as art is a habit with reference to things to be done, so is science a habit in respect of things to be known: as that proceeds from the imitation of types or forms, so this proceeds from the knowledge of natural things. Each has its origin in sense and experience, and it is impossible that there can rightly be either art or science without visible instance or example. In both, that which we perceive in sensible objects differs from the image itself which we retain in our imagination or memory. That is the type, idea, *forma informans;* this is the imitation, the *eidos,* the abstract species. That is a thing natural, a real entity; this a representation or similitude, and a thing of the reason. That is occupied with the individual thing, and itself is single and particular; this is a certain universal and common thing. That in the artist and man of science is a sensible thing, clearer, more perfect; this a matter of reason and more obscure: for things perceived by sense are more assured and manifest than matters inferred by reason, inasmuch as the latter proceed from and are illustrated by the former. Finally, sensible things are of themselves and antecedent; things of intellect, however, are consequent, and arise from the former, and, indeed, we can in no way attain to them without the help of the others. And hence it is, that without the due admonition of the senses, without frequent observation and reiterated experiment, our mind goes astray after phantoms and appearances. Diligent observation is, therefore, requisite in every science, and the senses are frequently to be appealed to. We are, I say, to strive after personal experience, not to rely on the experience of others; without which, indeed, no one can properly become a student of any branch of natural science, nor show himself a competent judge of what I am about to say on the subject of generation; for without experience and skill in anatomy, he would not better understand me than could one born blind appreciate the nature and difference of colours, or one deaf from birth judge of sounds. I would, therefore, have you, gentle reader, to take nothing on trust from me concerning the generation of animals; I appeal to your own eyes as my witnesses and judge. For as all true science rests upon those principles which have their origin in the operation of the senses, particular care is to be taken that by repeated dissection the grounds of our present subject be fully established. If we do otherwise, we shall but come to empty and unstable opinions; solid and true science will escape us altogether: just as commonly happens to those who form their notions of distant countries and cities, or who pretend to get a knowledge of the parts of the human body, from drawings and engravings, which but too frequently present things under false and erroneous points of view. And so it is, that in the present age we have an abundance of writers and pretenders to knowledge, but very few who are really learned and philosophers.

Thus much have I thought good, gentle reader, to present to you, by way of preface, that understanding the nature of the assistance to which I have trusted, and the counsel by which I have been led in publishing these my observations and experiments; and that you yourself in passing over the same ground, may not merely be in a condition to judge between Aristotle and Galen, but, quitting subtleties and fanciful conjectures, embracing nature with your own eyes, that you may discover many things unknown to others, and of great importance.

Of the same matters, according to Aristotle

There is no such thing as innate knowledge, according to Aristotle; neither opinion, nor art, nor understanding, nor speech, nor reason itself, inhere in us by nature and from our birth; but all of these, as well as the qualities and habitudes, which are believed to be spontaneous, and to lie under the control of our will, are to be regarded as among the number of those things that reach us from without according to nature: such as the virtues and the vices, for which men are either praised and rewarded or reproved and punished. All our knowledge, therefore, of every kind has to be acquired. But this is not the place to inquire into the first principles of knowledge.

I believe, however, that it will not be useless if I premise a few words as to whence and how our knowledge reaches us, both with a view to rendering what I shall say on the subject of generation more readily intelligible, and of removing any doubts that may arise out of this opinion of the Stagirite,[1] who asserts that all doctrine and discipline based on reason are derived from antecedent knowledge; whence it seems to follow that there is either no first knowledge, or that this must be innate, a conclusion which is in contradiction with what has already been stated.

The doubt, however, is by and by resolved by Aristotle[2] himself, when he treats of the mode in which knowledge is acquired: for after he has taught that all certain knowledge is obtained through syllogism and demonstration, and made it manifest that every demonstrative syllogism proceeds from true and necessary first principles; he goes on to inquire how principles become known, and what the faculty is that knows; at the same time, too, he discusses the question: whether habits, if not innate, are engendered; and whether, being innate, they lie concealed? "We have not," he says, "these habits; for it happens that they are concealed from those who acquire the most admirable kinds of knowledge through demonstration. If, however, we receive them, not having had them previously, how should we become informed, how learn from non-antecedent knowledge? It is obvious, therefore, that they are neither possessed, nor can they be engendered in the ignorant and those who are endowed with no habit. Whence it is essential that some faculty be possessed, not, however, any which were more excellent, more exquisite than they. Now it seems a thing common to all animals that they have a congenital power of judging, which we call sense. Since sense is innate, then, the things perceived by sense remain in some animals; in others they do not remain. Those in whom they do not remain, however, have either no knowledge at all, or at least none beyond the simple perception of the things which do not remain; others, again, when they perceive, retain a certain something in their soul. Now, as there are many animals of this description, there is already a distinction between one animal and another; and to this extent, that in some there is reason from the memory of things; and in others there is none. Memory, therefore, as is said, follows from sense; but from repeated recollection of the same thing springs experience (for repeated acts of memory constitute a single experience). From experience, however, or from the whole and universal stored quietly in the mind (one, to wit, in place of a multitude —because in the whole crowd of particulars there is one and the same universal), is derived the principle of art and of science: of art, if it belong to production (*i. e.*, action); of science, if it belong to that which is (*i. e.*, the knowledge of entity). Consequently, there are neither any definite habits that are innate, nor any habits that are formed from other and more known habits, but from sense."

From which words of Aristotle it plainly appears by what order or method any art or science is acquired, *viz.*, the thing perceived by sense remains; from the permanence of the thing perceived results memory; from multiplied memory, experience; from experience, universal reason, definitions, and maxims or common axioms, the most certain principles of knowledge; for example, the same thing under like conditions cannot be and not be; every affirmation or negation is either true or false; and so on.

Wherefore, as we have said above, there is no perfect knowledge which can be entitled ours, that is innate; none but what has been obtained from experience, or derived in some way from our senses; all knowledge, at all events, is examined by these, approved by them, and finally presents itself to us firmly grounded upon some preëxisting knowledge which we possessed: because without memory there is no experience, which is nothing else than reiterated memory; in like manner memory cannot exist without endurance of the things perceived, and the thing perceived cannot remain where it has never been.

The supreme dictator in philosophy again and elsewhere expresses himself very elegantly in the same direction: "All men desire by nature to know; the evidence of this is the pleasure they take in using their senses, among which the sight is that which is particularly preferred, because this especially serves us to acquire knowledge, and informs us of the greatest number of differences. Nature, therefore, endowed animals with sense; some of them,

[1] *Posterior Analytics*, I. I.
[2] *Ibid*, II. 19.

however, have no memory from the operations of their senses; others, again, have memory; and this is the reason wherefore some are more intelligent, and some more capable of receiving instruction than others, those, namely, that want recollection. Some show discretion independently of tuition: inasmuch as there are many that do not hear, such as bees and others of the same kind. But all animals which along with memory have the faculty of hearing are susceptible of education. Other creatures, again, live possessed of fancy and memory, but they have little store of experience; the human kind, however, have both art and reasoning. Now experience comes to man through memory; for many memories of the same thing have the force of a single experience: so that experience appears to be almost identical with certain kinds of art and science; and, indeed, men acquire both art and science by experience: for experience, as Polus[1] rightly remarks, begets art, inexperience is waited on by accident."[2]

By this he plainly tells us that no one can truly be entitled discreet or well-informed, who does not of his own experience, *i. e.*, from repeated memory, frequent perception by sense, and diligent observation, know that a thing is so in fact. Without these, indeed, we only imagine or believe, and such knowledge is rather to be accounted as belonging to others than to us. The method of investigating truth commonly pursued at this time, therefore, is to be held as erroneous and almost foolish, in which so many inquire what others have said, and omit to ask whether the things themselves be actually so or not; and single universal conclusions being deduced from several premises, and analogies being thence shaped out, we have frequently mere verisimilitudes handed down to us instead of positive truths. Whence it comes that pretenders to knowledge and sophists, trimming up the discoveries of others, changing the arrangement only, or the language, and adding a few things of no importance, audaciously send them forth as their own, and so render philosophy, which ought to be certain and perspicuous, obscure and intricate. For he who reads the words of an author and fails, through his own senses, to obtain images of the things that are conveyed in these words, derives not true ideas, but false fancies and empty visions; whence he conjures up shadows and chimeras, and his whole theory or contemplation, which, however, he regards as knowledge, is nothing

more than a waking dream, or such a delirium as the sick fancy engenders.

I, therefore, whisper in your ear, friendly reader, and recommend you to weigh carefully in the balance of exact experience all that I shall deliver in these *Exercises on the Generation of Animals;* I would not that you gave credit to aught they contain save in so far as you find it confirmed and borne out by the unquestionable testimony of your own senses.

The same course is even advised by Aristotle, who, after having gone over a great many particulars about bees, says at length: "That the generation of bees takes place in this way appears both from reason and from those things that are seen to occur in their kind. Still all the incidents have not yet been sufficiently examined. And when the investigation shall be complete, then will sense be rather to be trusted than reason; reason, however, will also deserve credit, if the things demonstrated accord with the things that are perceived by sense."[3]

Of the Method to be pursued in studying Generation

Since in animal generation (and, indeed, in all other subjects upon which information is desired) inquiry must be begun from the causes, especially the material and efficient ones, it appears advisable to me to look back from the perfect animal, and to inquire by what process it has arisen and grown to maturity, to retrace our steps, as it were, from the goal to the starting place; so that when at last we can retreat no farther, we shall feel assured that we have attained to the principles; at the same time we shall perceive from what primary matter, and from what efficient principle, and in what way from these the plastic force proceeds; as also what processes nature brings into play in the work. For primary and more remote matter, by abstraction and negation (being stripped of its garments, as it were), becomes more conspicuous; and whatever is first formed or exists primarily in generation is the material cause of everything that succeeds. For example, before a man attains to maturity, he was a boy, an infant, an embryo. And then it is indispensable to inquire further as to what he was in his mother's womb before he was an embryo or fœtus; whether made up of three bubbles, or a shapeless mass, or a conception or coagulum proceeding from the mingled seminal fluids of his parents, or what else, as we have it delivered to us by writers. In like manner, before a fowl had

[1] Plato in *Gorgias.*
[2] *Metaphysics,* I. I.
[3] *On the Generation of Animals,* III. 10.

attained to maturity or perfection—because capable of engendering its like—it was a chicken; previous to which it was an embryo or fœtus in the egg; and before this, Hieronymus Fabricius of Aquapendente, has observed rudiments of the head, eyes, and spine. But when he asserts that the bones are formed before the muscles, heart, liver, lungs, and precordial parts, and contends that all the internal organs must exist before the external ones, he follows probabilities according to previous notions rather than inspection; and quitting the evidences of sense that rest on anatomy, he seeks refuge in reasonings upon mechanical principles; a procedure that is anything but becoming in a great anatomist, whose duty it was faithfully to narrate the changes he observed taking place day by day in the egg, up to the period when the fœtus is perfected; and this the rather as he expressly proposed to himself to write the history of the formation of the chick in the egg, and to exhibit in figures what happens in the course of each successive day. It would have been in harmony with such a design, I say, had we been informed, on the testimony of the senses, of what parts are formed first, together, or subsequently in the egg; and not had mere opinions or musty conjectures, and the instances of houses and ships, adduced in illustration of the order and mode of formation of the parts.

We, therefore, in conformity with the method proposed, shall show in the first place in the egg, and then in the conceptions of other animals, what parts are first, and what are subsequently formed by the great God of Nature with inimitable providence and intelligence, and most admirable order. Next we shall inquire into the primary matter out of which, and the efficient cause by which generation is accomplished, and also the order and economy of generation, as observed by us; that from thence, from its own work, we may have some certain information of the several faculties of the formative and vegetative soul, and of the nature of the soul itself, judging from its members or organs, and their functions.

This, indeed, cannot be done in all animals: first, because a sufficient number of several of these cannot be commanded; and again, because, from the small size of many, they escape our powers of vision. It must suffice, therefore, that this is done in some kinds which are more familiarly known to us, and that we refer all the rest to these as types or standards.

We have, therefore, selected those that may tend to render our experiments more undeniable, *viz.*, the larger and more perfect animals, and that are easily within reach. For in the larger animals all things are more conspicuous; in the more perfect, they are also more distinct; and in those that we can command, and that live with us, everything is more readily examined: we have it in our power so often as we please to repeat our observations, and so to free them from all uncertainty and doubt. Now, among oviparous animals of this description, we have the common fowl, the goose, duck, pigeon; and then we have frogs, and serpents, and fishes; crustacea, testacea, and mollusca; among insects, bees, wasps, butterflies, and silkworms; among viviparous creatures, we have sheep, goats, dogs, cats, deer, and oxen; lastly, we have the most perfect of all animals, man.

Having studied and made ourselves familiar with these, we may turn to the consideration of the more abstruse nature of the vegetative soul, and feel ourselves in a condition to understand the method, order, and causes of generation in animals generally; for all animals resemble one or other of those above mentioned, and agree with them either generally or specifically, and are procreated in the same manner, or the mode of their generation at least is referrible by analogy to that of one or other of them. For Nature, perfect and divine, is ever in the same things harmonious with herself, and as her works either agree or differ (*viz.*, in genus, species, or some other proportion), so is her agency in these (*viz.*, generation or development) either the same or diverse. He who enters on this new and untrodden path, and out of the vast realm of Nature endeavours to find the truth by means of anatomical dissections and experiments, is met by such a multitude of facts, and these of so unusual an aspect, that he may find it more difficult to explain and describe to others the things he has seen, than he reckoned it labour to make his observations; so many things are encountered that require naming; such is the abundance of matter and the dearth of words. But if he would have recourse to metaphors, and by means of old and familiar terms would make known his ideas concerning the things he has newly discovered, the reader would have little chance of understanding him better than if they were riddles that were propounded; and of the thing itself, which he had never seen, he could have no conception. But then, to have recourse to new and unusual terms were less to bring a torch to lighten, than to darken things still more with a cloud: it were to attempt an explanation of a matter unknown by one still more unknown, and to impose a greater toil on the reader to understand the meaning of words than to comprehend the things themselves. And so it happens that Aristotle is believed by the inexperienced to be obscure in many places; and on this account, perhaps, Fabricius of Aquapendente rather intended to exhibit the chick in ovo in his figures than to explain its formation in words.

Wherefore, courteous reader, be not displeased with me, if, in illustrating the history of the egg, and in my account of the generation of the chick, I follow a new plan, and occasionally have recourse to unusual language. Think me not eager for vainglorious fame rather than anxious to lay before you observations that are true, and that are derived immediately from the nature of things. That you may not do me this injustice, I would have you know that I tread in the footsteps of those who have already thrown a light upon this subject, and that, wherever I can, I make use of their words. And foremost of all among the ancients I follow Aristotle; among the moderns, Fabricius of Aquapendente; the former as my leader, the latter as my informant of the way. For even as they who discover new lands, and first set foot on foreign shores, are wont to give them new names which mostly descend to posterity, so also do the discoverers of things and the earliest writers with perfect propriety give names to their discoveries. And now I seem to hear Galen admonishing us, that we should but agree about the things, and not dispute greatly about the words.

On Animal Generation

EXERCISE 1. *Wherefore we begin with the history of the hen's egg*

HIERONYMUS FABRICIUS of Aquapendente (whom, as I have said, I have chosen my informant of the way I am to follow), in the beginning of his book on the *Formation of the Ovum and Chick*, has these words: "My purpose is to treat of the formation of the fœtus in every animal, setting out from that which proceeds from the egg: for this ought to take precedence of all discussion of the subject, both because from this it is not difficult to make out Aristotle's views of the matter, and because his treatise on the *Formation of the Fœtus* from the egg, is by far the fullest, and the subject is by much the most extensive and difficult."

We, however, commence with the history of the hen's egg as well for the reasons above assigned, as because we can thence obtain certain data which, as more familiar to us, will serve to throw light on the generation of other animals; for as eggs cost little, and are always to be had, we have an opportunity from them of observing the first clear and unquestionable commencements of generation, how nature proceeds in the process, and with what admirable foresight she governs every part of the work.

Fabricius proceeds: "Now that the contemplation of the formation of the chick from the egg is of very ample scope, appears from this that the greater number of animals are produced from ova. Passing by almost all insects and the whole of the less perfect animals, which are obviously produced from eggs, the greater number of the more perfect are also engendered from eggs." And then he goes on to particularize: "All feathered creatures; fishes likewise, with the single exception of the whale tribes; crustacea, testacea, and all mollusca; among land animals, reptiles, millepeds, and all creeping things; and among quadrupeds, the entire tribe of lizards."

We, however, maintain (and shall take care to show that it is so) that all animals whatsoever, even the viviparous, and man himself not excepted, are produced from ova; that the first conception, from which the fœtus proceeds in

all, is an ovum of one description or another, as well as the seeds of all kinds of plants. Empedocles, therefore, spoke not improperly of the *oviparum genus arboreum*, "the egg-bearing race of trees."[1] The history of the egg is, therefore, of the widest scope, inasmuch as it illustrates generation of every description.

We shall, therefore, begin by showing where, whence, and how eggs are produced; and then inquire by what means and order and successive steps the fœtus or chick is formed and perfected in and from the egg.

Fabricius has these additional words: "The fœtus of animals is engendered in one case from an ovum, in another from the seminal fluid, in a third from putrefaction; whence some creatures are oviparous, others viviparous, and yet others, born of putrefaction or by the spontaneous act of nature, automatically."

Such a division as this, however, does not satisfy me, inasmuch as all animals whatsoever may be said in a certain sense to spring from ova, and in another certain sense from seminal fluid; and they are entitled oviparous, viviparous, or vermiparous, rather in respect of their mode of bringing forth than of their first formation. Even the creatures that arise spontaneously are called automatic, not because they spring from putrefaction, but because they have their origin from accident, the spontaneous act of nature, and are equivocally engendered, as it is said, proceeding from parents unlike themselves. And, then, certain other animals bring forth an egg or a worm as their conception and semen, from which, after it has been exposed abroad, a fœtus is produced; whence such animals are called oviparous or vermiparous. Viviparous animals are so entitled because they retain and cherish their conception in their interior, until from thence the fœtus comes forth into the light completely formed and alive.

EXERCISE 2. *Of the seat of generation*

"Nature," says Fabricius, "was first solicitous about the place, which she determined should be either within or without the animal: within

[1] Aristotle, *On the Generation of Animals*, i. 20.

she ordained the uterus; without, the ovum: in the uterus the blood and seminal fluid engendering; in the ovum, however, the fluids or elements of which it consists supplying pabulum for the production of the foetus."

Now, whatever is procreated of the semen properly so called originates and is perfected either in the same place or in different places. All viviparous creatures derive their origin and have their completion in the uterus itself; but oviparous animals, as they have their beginning within their parents, and there become ova, so is it beyond their parents that they are perfected into the foetal state. Among oviparous animals, however, there are some that retain their ova till such time as they are mature and perfect; such as all the feathered tribes, reptiles and serpents. Others, again, extrude their semina in a state still immature and imperfect, and it is without the body of the parent that increase, maturity, and perfection, are attained. Under this head we range frogs, many kinds of fishes, crustaceous, molluscous, and testaceous animals, the ova of which, when first extruded, are but beginnings, sketches, yelks which afterwards surround themselves with whites, and attracting, concocting, and attaching nutriment to themselves, are changed into perfect seeds or eggs. Such also are the semina of insects (called worms by Aristotle), which, imperfect on their extrusion and in the beginning, seek food for themselves, upon which they are nourished, and grow from a grub into a chrysalis: from an imperfect into a perfect egg or seed. Birds, however, and the rest of the oviparous tribes, lay perfect eggs; whence without the uterus the foetus is engendered. And it was on this account that Fabricius admitted two seats of generation: one internal, the uterus; another external, the ovum. But he would have had more reason, in my opinion, had he called the nest, or place where the eggs are laid, the external seat, that, to wit, in which the extruded seed or egg is cherished, matured, and perfected into a foetus; for it is from the differences of this seat that the generation of oviparous animals is principally distinguished: And it is, indeed, a thing most worthy of admiration to see these creatures selecting and preparing their nests with so much foresight, and fashioning, and furnishing, and concealing them with such inimitable art and ingenuity; so that it seems imperative on us to admit in them a certain spark of the divine flame (as the poet said of bees); and, indeed, we can more readily admire than imitate their untaught art and sapience.

EXERCISE 3. *Of the upper part of the hen's uterus, or the ovary*

The uterus of the fowl is divided by Fabricius into the superior and inferior portions, and the superior portion he calls the ovary.

The ovary is situated immediately beneath the liver, close to the spine, over the descending aorta. In this situation, in the larger animals with red blood, the coeliac artery enters the mesentery, at the origin, namely, of the emulgent veins, or a little lower; in the situation moreover in which in the other red-blooded and viviparous animals the vasa præparantia, tending to the testes, take their origin: in the same place at which the testes of the cock-bird are situated, there is the ovary of the hen discovered. For some animals carry their testicles externally; others have them within the body, in the loins, in the space midway from the origins of the vasa præparantia. But the cock has his testicles at the very origin of these vessels, as if his spermatic fluid needed no preparation.

Aristotle[1] says that the ovum begins at the diaphragm; "I, however," says Fabricius, "in my treatise on *Respiration* have denied that the feathered kinds have any diaphragm. The difficulty is resolved by admitting that birds are not entirely destitute of a kind of diaphragm, inasmuch as they have a delicate membrane in the place of this septum, which Aristotle calls a cincture and septum. Still they have no diaphragm that is muscular, and that might aid respiration, like other animals. But, indeed, Aristotle did not know the muscles."

Thus is the prince of philosophers accused and excused in the same breath, his challenger being himself not free from error; because it is certain that Aristotle knew both the muscles, as I have elsewhere shown, and the membranes, which in birds are not only situated transversely in the direction of the cincture of the body, but extended in the line of the longitudinal direction of the belly, supplying the place of the diaphragm and being subservient to respiration, as I have shown in the clearest manner in my disquisitions on the *Respiration of Animals*. And, passing over other particulars at this time, I shall only direct attention to the fact that birds breathe with great freedom, and in singing also modulate their voice in the most admirable manner, their lungs all the while being so closely connected with their sides and ribs, that they can neither be dilated and rise, nor

[1] *History of Animals*, VI. 2.

suffer contraction in any considerable degree.

The bronchia or ends of the trachea in birds, moreover, are perforate, and open into the abdomen (and this is an observation which I do not remember to have met with elsewhere), so that the air inspired is received into and stored up within the cells or cavities formed by the membranes mentioned above. In the same manner as fishes and serpents draw air into ample bladders situated in the abdomen, and there store it up, by which they are thought to swim more lightly; and as frogs and toads, when in the height of summer they respire more vigorously assume more than the usual quantity of air into their vesicular lungs (whence they acquire so large a size), which they afterwards freely expire, croaking all the while; so in the feathered tribes are the lungs rather the route and passage for respiration than its adequate instrument.

Now, had Fabricius seen this, he would never have denied that these membranes (with the assistance of the abdominal muscles at all events) could subserve respiration and perform the office of the diaphragm, which, indeed, of itself, and without the assistance of the abdominal muscles, were incompetent to act as an instrument of respiration. And, then, the diaphragm has another duty to perform in those creatures in whom it is muscular or fleshy, viz., to depress the stomach filled with food, and the intestines distended with flatus, so that the heart and lungs shall not be invaded, and life itself oppressed in its citadel. But as there was no danger of anything of this kind in birds, they have a membranous septum, perfectly well adapted to the purposes of respiration, so that they have very properly been said to have a diaphragm. And were birds even entirely without anything in the shape of a diaphragm, still would Aristotle not be liable to criticism for speaking of the ova commencing at the septum transversum, because by this title he merely indicates the place where the diaphragm is usually met with in other animals. In the same way we ourselves say that the ovary is situated at the origin of the spermatic vasa præparantia, although the hen has, in fact, no such vessels.

The perforations of the lungs discovered by me (and to which I merely direct attention in this place) are neither obscure nor doubtful, but, in birds especially, sufficiently conspicuous, so that in the ostrich I found many conduits which readily admitted the points of my fingers. In the turkey, fowl, and, indeed, almost all birds, you will find that a probe passed downwards by the trachea makes its way out of the lungs, and is discovered lying naked and exposed in one or another of the abdominal cells. Air blown into the lungs of these creatures with a pair of bellows passes on with a certain force even into the most inferior of these cells.

We may even be permitted to ask, whether in man, whilst he lives, there is not a passage from openings of the same kind into the cavity of the thorax? For how else should the pus poured out in empyema and the blood extravasated in pleurisy make its escape? In penetrating wounds of the chest, the lungs themselves being uninjured, air often escapes by the wound; or liquids thrown into the cavity of the thorax, are discharged with the expectoration. But our views of this subject will be found fully expressed elsewhere, viz., in our disquisitions On the Causes, Uses, and Organs of Respiration.

I return to the ovary and the upper portion of the fowl's uterus, in which the rudiments of the eggs are produced. These, according to Aristotle,[1] in the first instance are small, and of a white colour; growing larger, they subsequently become of a paler and then of a deeper yellow.

The superior uterus of Fabricius, however, has no existence until after the hen has conceived, and contains the rudiments of ova within it; when it may be designated as a cluster of papulæ. And he therefore observes very properly, "The superior uterus is nothing more than an almost infinite congeries of yelks, which appear collected as it were into a single cluster, of a rounded form, and of every size, from that of a grain of mustard to that almost of a walnut or medlar. This multitude of vitelli is aggregated and conjoined very much in the manner of a bunch of grapes, for which reason I shall constantly speak of it as the vitellarium or raceme of yelks; a comparison which Aristotle himself made in speaking of the soft or scaleless fishes, when he says[2] their ovary or roe is extruded agglutinated into a kind of raceme or bunch of grapes. And in the same way as in a bunch of grapes the several berries are seen to be of different sizes, some large, some small, some of very diminutive proportions, each hanging by its several peduncle, so do we find precisely the same thing in the vitellarium of the fowl."

In fishes, frogs, crustacea, and testacea, however, matters are otherwise arranged. The ovary

[1] History of Animals, vi. 2.
[2] On the Generation of Animals, iii. 8.

or vitellary here contains ova of one uniform size only, which being extruded increase, attain maturity, and give birth to fœtuses simultaneously. But in the ovary of the common fowl, and almost all the rest of the oviparous tribes, the yelks are found in various stages of their growth, from dimensions that are scarcely visible up to the full size. Nevertheless the eggs of the fowl and other birds (not otherwise than in those cases where the eggs are all engendered and laid at the same moment) ripen their fœtuses under the influence of incubation in the same nest, and produce them perfect, nearly at the same time. In the family of the pigeons, however (which lay and incubate no more than two eggs in the same nest), I have observed that all the ova crowded together in the ovary, with the exception of a single pair, were of the same dimensions; this pair was very much larger than any of the others, and already prepared to descend into the second or lower uterus. In these creatures, therefore, the number of young is great, not because of the multitude produced at a time, but of the frequency with which births take place, *viz.*, every month. In the same way, among cartilaginous fishes, such as the skates, dog-fishes, &c., two eggs only come to maturity together, one of which descends from the right, the other from the left corner of the uterus into the inferior portion, where they are cherished, and where they finally produce living fœtuses, precisely as happens among viviparous animals; in the ovary, nevertheless, there is almost infinite store of ova of various sizes—in the ray I have counted upwards of a hundred.

The ova of the other oviparous tribes are either perfected externally, as in the case of fishes, or they are concocted or matured, as in the instance of testacea, crustacea, and spiders. Testaceous animals lay their eggs amidst froth; the crustaceous tribes, such as the shrimp, crab, and lobster, bear them about with them, attached to certain appendages; and the spiders carry them about and cherish them, laid up in a kind of purse or basket, made of their web. The beetle rolls its eggs in dung, using its hind legs in the operation, and buries them. Now, in all these creatures the quantity of eggs is almost incredibly great: in fishes they form two oblong bladders or follicles, as may be seen in the carp, herring, and smelt, in all of which, as there is no uterus, but merely an ovary present, so is this sometimes crowded with ova to such a degree that it comes to surpass the body in bulk.

Of such ovaries of the mullet and carp, salted and pressed, and dried in the smoke, was prepared that article of food in such request among the Greeks and old Italians (called *botorcha* by the latter, ὠὰ τάριχα, *i.e.*, salted eggs, by the former) and very similar, we may presume, to the masses which we find in the insides of our smoked herrings, and to the compact granular red-coloured roe of our lobsters. The article prepared from the salted roe of the sturgeon, which is called caviare, and resembles black soap, is still the delight of epicures.

In those fishes that are highly prolific such a quantity of eggs is engendered that the whole abdomen can scarcely contain them, even when they are first produced, still less when they have grown to any size. In fishes, therefore, there is no part save the ovary dedicated to purposes of reproduction. The ova of these animals continue to grow without the body, and do not require the protection of an uterus for their evolution. And the ovary here appears to bear an analogy to the testicles or vesiculæ seminales, not only because it is found in the same place as the testes in the male (the testes in the cock being situated, as we have said, close to the origin of the cœliac artery, near the waist, in the very same place as the ovary in the hen), but because among fishes, in both sexes, as the time of spawning approaches, two follicles, alike in situation, size, and shape, are discovered, extending the whole length of the abdomen; which increase and become distended at the same period: in the male with a homogeneous milky spermatic matter (whence the term milk or milt of fishes); in the female with innumerable granules, which, from their diminutive size and close texture, in the beginning of the season, escape the powers of vision, and present themselves as constituting an uniform body, bearing the strongest resemblance to the milt of the male regularly coagulated. By and by they are seen in the guise of minute grains of sand, adhering together within their follicles.

In the smaller birds that lay but once a year, and a few eggs only, you will scarcely discover any ovary. Still, in the place where the testicles are situated in the male, there in the female, and not less obviously than the testicles of the male, you will perceive three or four vesicles (the number being in proportion to that of the eggs of which they are the rudiments), by way of ovary.

In the cornua of the uterus of snakes (which resemble the vasa deferentia in male animals), the first rudiments of the ova present themselves as globules strung upon a thread, in the same way as women's bracelets, or like a rosary composed of amber beads.

Those ova that are found in the ovary of the fowl consequently are not to be regarded as perfect eggs, but only as their rudiments; and they are so arranged on the cluster, they succeed each other in such an order and of such dimensions, that they are always ready for each day's laying. But none of the eggs in the ovary are surrounded with albumen; there the yelk exists alone, and each, as it enlarges, extricates itself from the general congeries of smaller ones, in order that it may the more readily find space to grow. Fabricius, therefore, is right when he says, "The yelks which are on the surface of the cluster are larger than those of the middle, which are surrounded as it were by the larger ones. The very smallest of all the ova are situated towards the centre."[1] That is to say, those that grow acquire larger dimensions and become detached from the rest, and as this proceeds, the several yelks, besides their tunica propria, are invested with another from the ovary, which embraces them externally, and connects them with the base whence they spring. This coat is, therefore, entitled the *peduncle* by Fabricius, and its office is that of a foot-stalk, viz., to supply nourishment to the ovum, in the same way as fruit is nourished through the stalk by which it is connected with the tree. "For this peduncle is a hollow membranous bond of union, extending from the foundation of the cluster to the yelk, coming into contact with which, it is dilated and expanded in the same way as the optic nerve in the eye, and covers the vitellus with an external tunic. This perchance was what Aristotle called the στόλον ὀμφαλοώδην, or umbilical appendix, and described as forming a kind of tube. This peduncle includes numerous vessels, which are distributed on all sides around the yelk."

So much is accurately related by Fabricius; but he errs when he says, "This tunic does not surround the entire vitellus, but only extends upon it a little beyond the middle, very much in the manner of an acorn within its cup; whence it comes that the outer portion of the yelk, which is not invested by the membrane in question, presents itself free from vessels, and to appearance naked." The membrane, nevertheless, surrounds the yelk completely; but on the outer aspect it is not very easily distinguished from the tunica propria, both of them being of extreme delicacy. Posteriorly, however, and

[1] *Op. cit.*, p. 3.

where the yelk is turned towards the basis of the cluster, the tunic in question does not adhere to the vitellus, neither does it send any vessels to this part, but merely embraces it in the manner of a sac.

Each vitellus receives a distinct tunic from the ovarian basis; whence this is not to be regarded as the common uterus, since nothing is discovered here except the cluster or heap of ova, of many different sizes, proceeding from the same foundation.

Now, this foundation or basis is a body *sui generis*, arising on the spine of the feathered kinds, connected by means of large arteries and veins, and of a loose, porous, and spongy texture, in order that multitudes of ova may be produced from it, and that it may supply tunics to all; which tunics, when the yelks have grown to their full size, are distended by them, and then the tunics surround the vitelli, in the manner of sacks with narrower necks and more capacious bellies, very much like the flasks that are formed by the breath of the glass-blower.

Fabricius then proceeds: "The yelks, as they proceed from small beginnings, from the size of millet or mustard seeds, and are at first not only extremely small, but colourless, as Aristotle says, so do they increase by degrees, and, according to Aristotle, become first of a paler and then of a deeper yellow, until they have attained to the dimensions familiar to all." I, however, have observed ova vastly smaller than millet seeds, ova which, like papulæ or sudamina, or the finest grains of sand (such as we have indicated as found in the roe of fishes), almost escaped the powers of sight; their places, indeed, were only proclaimed by a kind of roughness of the membranes.

EXERCISE 4. *Of the infundibulum*

The next succeeding portion of the uterus of the common fowl is called the *infundibulum* by Fabricius. It forms a kind of funnel or tube, extending downwards from the ovary (which it everywhere embraces), and becoming gradually wider, terminates in the superior produced portion of the uterus. This infundibulum yields a passage to the yelks when they have broken from their foot-stalks in their descent from the ovary into the second uterus (so it is styled by Fabricius). It resembles the tunica vaginalis in the scrotum, and is a most delicate membrane, very easily dilatable, fitted to receive the yelks that are daily cast loose, and to transmit them to the uterus mentioned.

Would you have an example of these structures? Figure to yourself a small plant, whose tuberous roots should represent the congeries of yelks; its stalk the infundibulum. Now, as the stalk of this plant dies in the winter and disappears, in like manner, when the fowl ceases to lay eggs, the whole ovary, with the infundibulum, withers, shrinks, and is annulled; the basis and indication of the roots being still left.

This infundibulum seems only to discharge the office of a conduit, or tube of passage: the yelk is never observed sticking in it; but as the testes at times creep upwards through the tunicæ vaginales into the groins, and in some animals—the hare and the mole—even become concealed within the abdomen, and nevertheless again descend and show themselves externally, so are the vitelli transmitted through the infundibulum from the ovary into the uterus. Its office is served, and even its form is imitated, by the funnel which we make use of when we pour fluids from one vessel into another having a narrower mouth.

EXERCISE 5. *Of the external portion of the uterus of the common fowl*

Fabricius pursues his account of the uterus after having described the ovary, and in such an inverse order, that he premises a description of the superior portion or appendage of the uterus before he approaches the uterus itself. He assigns to it three turns or spirals, with somewhat too much of precision or determinateness, and settles the respective situations of these spirals, which are nevertheless of uncertain seat. Here, too, he very unnecessarily repeats his definition of the infundibulum. I would, therefore, in this place, beg to be allowed to give my own account of the uterus of the fowl, according to the anatomical method, which I consider the more convenient, and proceeding from external to internal parts, in opposition to the method of Fabricius.

In the fowl stripped of its feathers, the fundament will be observed not contracted circularly, as in other animals, but forming a depressed orifice, slit transversely, and consisting of two lips lying over against each other, the superior of the two covering and concealing the inferior, which is puckered together. The superior labium, or velabrum, as it is called, arises from the root of the rump, and as the upper eyelid covers the eye, so does this cover the three orifices of the pudenda, *viz.*, the anus, the uterus, and the ureters, which lie concealed under the velabrum as under a kind of prepuce; very much as in the pudenda of the woman we have the orifice of the vulva and the meatus urinarius concealed between the labia and the nymphæ. So that without the use of the knife, or a somewhat forcible retraction of the velabrum in the fowl, neither the orifice by which the fæces pass from the intestines, nor that by which the urine issues from the ureters, nor yet that by which the egg escapes from the uterus, can be perceived. And as the two excrementitious discharges (the urine and the fæces) are expelled together as from a common cloaca, the velabrum being raised at the time, and the respective outlets exposed; so, during intercourse, the hen on the approach of the cock uncovers the vulva, and prepares for his reception, a circumstance observed by Fabricius in the turkey hen when she is eager for the male. I have myself observed a female ostrich, when her attendant gently scratched her back, which seemed to excite the sexual appetite, to lie down on the ground, lift up the velabrum, and exhibit and protrude the vulva, seeing which the male, straightway inflamed with a like œstrum, mounted, one foot being kept firm on the ground, the other set upon the back of the prostrate female; the immense penis (you might imagine it a neat's tongue!) vibrated backwards and forwards, and the process of intercourse was accompanied with much ado in murmuring and noise—the heads of the creatures being at the same time frequently thrust out and retracted—and other indications of enjoyment. Nor is it peculiar to birds, but common to animals at large, that, wagging the tail and protruding the genital parts, they prepare for the access of the male. And, indeed, the tail in the majority of animals has almost the same office as the velabrum in the common fowl; unless it were raised or drawn aside, it would interfere with the discharge of the fæces and the access of the male.

In the female red-deer, fallow-deer, roe, and others of the more temperate animals, there is a corresponding protection to their private parts, a membranous velabrum covering the vulva and meatus urinarius, which must be raised before the penis of the male can be introduced.

In animals that have a tail, moreover, parturition could not take place unless this part were lifted up; and even the human female is assisted in her labour by having the coccyx anointed and drawn outwards with the finger.

A surgeon, a trustworthy man, and with whom I am upon intimate terms, on his return from the East Indies informed me, in perfect sincerity, that some inland and mountainous parts of the island of Borneo are still inhabited by a race of caudate human beings (a circumstance of which we also read in Pausanias), one of whom, a virgin, who had only been captured with great difficulty, for they live in the woods, he himself had seen, with a tail, thick, fleshy, and a span in length, reflected between the buttocks, and covering the anus and pudenda: so regularly has nature willed to cover these parts.

To return. The structure of the velabrum in the fowl is like that of the upper eyelid; that is to say, it is a fleshy and muscular fold of the skin, having fibres extending from the circumference on every side towards the centre; its inner surface, like that of the eyelid and prepuce, being soft. Along its margin also there is a semicircular tarsus, after the manner of that of the eyelid; and in addition, between the skin and fleshy membrane, an interposed cartilage, extending from the root of the rump, the sickle-shaped tarsus being connected with it at right angles (very much as we observe a small tail comprehended between the wing on either side, in bats). By this structure the velabrum is enabled more readily to open and close the foramina pudendi that have been mentioned.

The velabrum being now raised and removed, certain foramina are brought into view, some of which are very distinct, others more obscure. The more obvious are the anus and vulva, or the outlet of the fæcal matters and the inlet to the uterus. The more obscure are, first, that by which the urine is excreted from the kidneys, and, second, the small orifice discovered by Fabricius, "into which," he says, "the cock immits the spermatic fluid," a foramen, however, which neither Antony Ulm, a careful dissector, has indicated in Aldrovandus, nor any one else except Fabricius, so far as I know, has ever observed.

All these foramina are so close to one another that they seem almost to meet in a single cavity, which, as being common to the fæces and urine, may be called the cloaca. In this cavity, the urine, as it descends from the kidneys, is mingled with the feculent matters of the bowels, and the two are discharged together. Through this, too, the egg, as it is laid, forces itself a passage.

Now, the arrangements in this cavity are such, that both excrements descending into a common sac, the urine is made use of as a natural clyster for their evacuation. The cloaca is therefore thicker and more rugous than the intestine; and at the moment of laying and of coition, it is everted (the velabrum which covers it being raised as I have already said), the lower portion of the bowel being as it were prolapsed. At this moment all the foramina that terminate in the cloaca are conspicuous; on the return or reduction of the prolapsed portion, however, they are concealed, being all collected together as it were into the common purse or pouch.

The more conspicuous foramina, those, *viz.*, of the anus and uterus, are situated, with reference to one another, differently in birds from what they are in other animals. In these the pudendum, or female genital part, is situated anteriorly between the rectum and bladder; in birds, however, the excrementitious outlet is placed anteriorly, so that the inlet to the uterus is situated between this and the rump.

The foramen, into which Fabricius believes the cock to inject his fluid, is discovered between the orifice of the vulva and the rump. I, however, deny any such use to this foramen; for in young chickens it is scarcely to be seen, and in adults it is present indifferently both in males and females. It is obvious, therefore, that it is both an extremely small and obscure orifice, and can have no such important function to perform: it will scarcely admit a fine needle or a bristle, and it ends in a blind cavity; neither have I ever been able to discover any spermatic fluid within it, although Fabricius asserts that this fluid is stored up there even for a whole year, and that all the eggs contained in the ovary may be thence fecundated, as it is afterwards stated.

All birds, serpents, oviparous quadrupeds, and likewise fishes, as may readily be seen in the carp, have kidneys and ureters through which the urine distils, a fact which was unknown to Aristotle and philosophers up to this time. In birds and serpents, which have spongy or largely vesicular lungs, the quantity of urine secreted is small, because they drink little, and that by sipping; there was, therefore, no occasion for an urinary bladder in these creatures: the renal secretion, as already stated, is accumulated in a common cavity or cloaca, along with the drier intestinal excrement. Nevertheless, I do find an urinary bladder in the carp and some other fishes.

In the common fowl the ureters descend from the kidneys, which are situated in long and ample cavities on either side of the back, to terminate in the common cavity or cloaca. Their terminations, however, are so obscure and so hidden by the margin of the cavity, that to discover them from without and pass a fine probe into them would be found impossible. Nor is this at all surprising, because in all, even the largest animals, the insertion of the ureters near the neck of the bladder is so tortuous and obscure, that although the urine distils freely from them into the bladder, and calculi even make their way out of them, still neither fluids nor air can be made to enter them by the use of any amount of force. On the other hand, in birds as well as other animals, a probe or a bristle passed downwards from the kidney towards the bladder by the ureters, readily makes its way into the cloaca or bladder.

These facts are particularly distinct in the ostrich, in which, besides the external orifice of the common cavity which the velabrum covers, I find another within the anus, having a round and constricted orifice, shutting in some sort in the manner of a sphincter.

Passing by these particulars, however, let us turn to others that bear more immediately upon our subject. The uterine outlet or vulva, then, or the passage from the common cavity to the uterus of the fowl, is a certain protuberance, soft, lax, wrinkled, and orbicular, resembling the orifice of the prepuce when closed, or appearing as if formed by a prolapse of the internal membrane of the uterus. Now this outlet is situated, as I have said, between the anus and rump, and slightly to the left of the middle line of the body, which Ulysses Aldrovandi imagines to be for the purpose of "facilitating intercourse, and the entrance of the genital organ of the cock." I have myself observed, however, repeatedly, that the hen turned the common orifice to the right or left indifferently, according to the side from which the cock approached her. Neither do I find any penis in the cock—neither, indeed, could Fabricius—although in the goose and duck it is very conspicuous. But in its stead I discover an orifice in the cock, not otherwise than in the hen, although it is smaller and more contracted in her than in him; and in the swan, goose, and duck the same thing also appears, the penis of the male goose and duck protruding through this orifice during intercourse.

In a black drake I noticed the penis of such a length that after intercourse it trailed on the ground, and a fowl following, pecked at it greedily, thinking it an earth-worm, as I imagine, so that it was retracted more quickly than usual.

In the male ostrich I have found within this pudendal orifice a very large glans, and the red body of the penis, as we discover them within the prepuce of the horse, resembling a deer's or a small neat's tongue in form and magnitude; and I have frequently observed this organ, rigid and somewhat hooked during the coitus, and when entered into the vulva of the female, held for some considerable time there without any movement: it was precisely as if the two creatures had been fastened together with a nail. Meantime, by the gesticulations of their heads and necks, and by their noises, they seemed to notify their nuptials, and to express the great degree of pleasure they experienced.

I have read in a treatise of Dr. Du Val, a learned physician of Rouen, that a certain hermaphrodite was referred to the surgeons and accoucheurs, that they might determine whether it were a man or a woman. They, from an examination of the genital organs, adjudged the party to be of the feminine gender, and a dress in accordance with this decision was ordered. By and by, however, the individual was accused of soliciting women, and of discharging the man's office; and then it was found, that from a prepuce, as from the private parts of a woman, a penis protruded, and served to perform the male's business. I have myself occasionally seen the penis of a certain man so greatly shrunk in size, that, unless when excited, nothing was visible in the wrinkled prepuce above the scrotum but the extremity of the glans.

In the horse and some other animals, the principal and ample length of the member is protruded from its concealment. In the mole, too, which is a small animal, there is a remarkable retraction of the penis between the skin and muscles of the belly; and the vulva in the female of this creature is also longer and deeper than usual.

The cock, which is without a penis, performs copulation, as I imagine, in the same manner as the smaller birds, among which the process is rapidly executed, and by mere contact. The orifices of the male and female cloaca, which at the moment are protuberant externally, which, especially in the male, become tense and injected, like the glans penis, encounter, and coition is effected by a succession of salutes, not by any longer intromission of parts, for I do not think that the organs of the cock enter those of the hen at all.

In the copulation of horses, dogs, cats, and the like, the female presents her organ rigid and injected to the penis of the male. And this also takes place in birds which, if they be tame and suffer themselves to be handled, when inflamed with desire present their parts, which will then be found resisting and hard to the finger.

Birds are sometimes so lustful, that if you but stroke their backs gently with your hand, they will immediately lie down and expose and protrude their uterine orifice; and if this part be touched with the finger, they will not fail to proclaim their satisfaction. And that the females may thereby be made to lay eggs, as testified to by Aristotle,[1] I have myself found in the case of the blackbird, thrush, and others. I learned the fact, indeed, in former years by accident, and to my detriment; for my wife had a beautiful parrot, a great pet, learned and talkative enough, and so tame that it was allowed to roam at liberty about the house: when its mistress was absent it sought her everywhere; on her return it caressed her, and loudly proclaimed its joy; when called to, it would answer; would fly to its mistress, and then seizing her clothes with beak and feet alternately, it climbed to her shoulder, whence creeping down the arm, it reached her hand, its usual seat. When ordered to speak or to sing, it would obey, although it were the night season and quite dark. Full of play and lasciviousness, it would frequently sit in its mistress's lap, where it loved to have her scratch its head and stroke its back, upon which, fluttering with its wings and making a gentle noise, it testified the pleasure it experienced. I believed all this to proceed from his usual familiarity and love of being noticed; for I always regarded the creature as a male, by reason of his proficiency in talking and singing. For among birds, the females rarely sing or challenge one another by their note; the males alone solace their mates by their tuneful warblings, and call them to the rites of love. And it is on this account that Aristotle says, "If partridges be placed over against the males, and the wind blow towards them from where the males sit, they are impregnated and conceive. They even for the most part conceive from the note of the male bird, if they be in season and full of desire. The flight of the male over them will also have the same effect, the male bird casting down a fertilizing influence

[1] *History of Animals,* VI. 2.

upon the female."[2] Now this happens especially in the spring season, whence the poet sings:

> Earth teems in Spring, and craves the genial
>   seed.
> The almighty father, Æther, then descends,
> In fertilizing showers, into the lap
> Of his rejoicing spouse, and mingling there
> In wide embrace sustains the progeny
> Innumerous that springs. The pathless woods
> Then ring with the wild bird's song, and
>   flocks and herds
> Disport and spend the livelong day in love.[3]

Not long after the caressings mentioned, the parrot, which had lived in health for many years, fell sick, and by and by being seized with repeated attacks of convulsions, seated in the lap of its mistress, it expired, grievously regretted. Having opened the body in search of the cause of death, I discovered an egg, nearly perfect, in the uterus, but in consequence of the want of a male, in a state of putrefaction; and this, indeed, frequently happens among birds confined in cages, which show desire for the company of the male.

These and other instances induce me to believe that the common fowl and the pheasant do not only solace their females with their crowing, but, further, give them the faculty of producing eggs by its means; for when the cock crows in the night some of the hens perched near him bestir themselves, clapping their wings and shaking their heads; shuddering and gesticulating as they are wont to do after intercourse.

A certain bird, as large again as a swan, and which the Dutch call a cassowary, was imported no long time ago from the island of Java, in the East Indies, into Holland. Ulysses Aldrovandus[4] gives a figure of this bird, and informs us that it is called an emeu by the Indians. It is not a two-toed bird, like the ostrich, but has three toes on each foot, one of which is furnished with a spur of such length, strength, and hardness, that the creature can easily kick through a board two fingers' breadth in thickness. The cassowary defends itself by kicking forwards. In the body, legs, and thighs it resembles the ostrich; it has not a broad bill like the ostrich however, but one that is rounded and black. On its head, by way of crest, it has an orbicular protuberant horn. It has no tongue, and devours everything that is presented to it

[2] *History of Animals,* v. 5; VI. 2.
[3] Virgil, *Georgics,* II.
[4] *Ornithol.,* Book XX, p. 541.

—stones, coals, even though alight, pieces of glass—all without distinction. Its feathers sprout in pairs from each particular quill, and are of a black colour, short and slender, approaching to hair or down in their characters. Its wings are very short and imperfect. The whole aspect of the creature is truculent, and it has numbers of red and blue wattles longitudinally disposed along the neck.

This bird remained for more than seven years in Holland, and was then sent, among other presents, by the illustrious Maurice Prince of Orange, to his Serene Majesty our King James, in whose gardens it continued to live for a period of upwards of five years. By and by, however, when a pair of ostriches, male and female, were brought to the same place, and the cassowary heard and saw these in a neighbouring inclosure, at their amours, unexpectedly it began to lay eggs, excited, as I imagine, through sympathy with the acts of an allied genus; I say unexpectedly, for all who saw the cassowary, judging from the weapons and ornaments, had regarded it as a male rather than a female. Of these eggs, one was laid entire, and this I opened, and found it perfect: the yelk surrounded by the white, the chalazæ attached on either side, and a small cavity in the blunt end; there was also a cicatricula or macula alba present; the shell was thick, hard, and strong; and having taken off the top, I had it formed into a cup, in the same way as ostriches' eggs are commonly fashioned. This egg was somewhat less than that of an ostrich, and, as I have said, perfect in all respects. Undoubtedly, however, it was a sort of accidental egg, and, by reason of the absence of the male, unfruitful. I predicated the death of the cassowary as likely to happen soon when she began laying, moved to do so by what Aristotle says: "Birds become diseased and die unless they produce fruitful eggs."[1] And my prediction came true not long afterwards. On opening the body of the cassowary, I discovered an imperfect and putrid egg in the upper part of the uterus, as the cause of its untimely death, just as I had found the same thing in the parrot, and other instances besides.

Many birds, consequently, the more salacious they are, the more fruitful are they; and occasionally, when abundantly fed, or from some other cause, they will even lay eggs without the access of the male. It rarely happens, however, that the eggs so produced are either perfected or laid; the birds are commonly soon

seized with serious disorders, and at length die. The common fowl, nevertheless, not only conceives eggs, but lays them, quite perfect in appearance too; but they are always wind eggs, and incapable of producing a chick. In like manner many insects, among the number silkworms and butterflies, conceive eggs and lay them, without the access of the male, but they are still adventitious and barren. Fishes also do the same.

It is of the same significance in these animals when they conceive eggs, as it is in young women when their uterus grows hot, their menses flow, and their bosoms swell—in a word, when they become marriageable; and who, if they continue too long unwedded, are seized with serious symptoms—hysterics, furor uterinus, &c. or fall into a chachectic state, and distemperatures of various kinds. All animals, indeed, grow savage when in heat, and unless they are suffered to enjoy one another, become changed in disposition. In like manner women occasionally become insane through ungratified desire, and to such a height does the malady reach in some, that they are believed to be poisoned, or moon-struck, or possessed by a devil. And this would certainly occur more frequently than it does, without the influence of good nurture, respect for character, and the modesty that is innate in the sex, which all tend to tranquillize the inordinate passions of the mind.

EXERCISE 6. *Of the uterus of the fowl*

The passage from the external uterine orifice to the internal parts and uterus itself, where the egg is perfected, is by that part which in other animals is called the vagina or vulva. In the fowl, however, this passage is so intricate, and its internal membrane is so loose and wrinkled, that although there is a ready passage from within outwards, and a large egg makes its way through all without much difficulty, still it scarcely seems likely that the penis of the male could penetrate or the spermatic fluid make its way through it; for I have found it impossible to introduce either a probe or a bristle; neither could Fabricius pass anything of the sort, and he says that he could not even inflate the uterus with air. Whence he was led I fancy to give an account of the uterus, proceeding from more internal to more external parts. Considering this structure of the uterus also, he denies that the spermatic fluid of the male can reach the cavity of the uterus, or go to constitute any part of the egg.[2] To this

[1] *On the Generation of Animals*, III.

[2] *Op. cit.*, p. 31.

statement I most willingly subscribe; for, indeed, there is nothing in the fruitful egg which is not also in the barren one; there is nothing in the way of addition or change which indicates that the seminal fluid of the male has either made its way into the uterus, or come into contact with the egg. Moreover, although without the access of the cock all eggs laid are winded and barren, still through his influence, and long after intercourse, fruitful eggs are deposited, the rudiments or matter of which did not exist at the time of the communication.

With a view to explaining how the spermatic fluid of the cock renders eggs fecund, Fabricius says: "Since the semen does not appear in the egg, and yet is thrown into the uterus by the cock, it may be asked why this is done if the fluid does not enter the egg? Further: if not present in the egg, how is that egg made fruitful by the spermatic fluid of the cock which it yet does not contain? My opinion is that the semen of the cock thrown into the commencement of the uterus, produces an influence on the whole of the uterus, and at the same time renders fruitful the whole of the yelks, and finally of the perfect eggs which fall into it; and this the semen effects by its peculiar property or irradiative spirituous substance, in the same manner as we see other animals rendered fruitful by the testicles and semen. For if anyone will but bring to mind the incredible change that is produced by castration, when the heat, strength, and fecundity are lost, he will readily admit that what we have proposed may happen in reference to the single uterus of a fowl. But that it is in all respects true, and that the faculty of impregnating the whole of the ova, and also the uterus itself, proceeds from the semen of the cock, appears from the custom of those housewives who keep hens at home but no cock, that they commit their hens for a day or two to a neighbour's cock, and in this short space of time the whole of the eggs that will be laid for a certain season are rendered prolific. And this fact is confirmed by Aristotle,[1] who will have it that, among birds, one intercourse suffices to render almost all the eggs fruitful. For the fecundating influence of the seminal fluid, as it cannot exhale, so is it long retained in the uterus, to which it imparts the whole of its virtue; nature herself stores it up, placing it in a cavity appended to the uterus, near the fundament, furnished with an entrance only, so that, being there laid up, its virtue is the better preserved

and communicated to the entire uterus."[2]

I, however, suspected the truth of the above views, all the more when I saw that the words of the philosopher referred to were not accurately quoted. Aristotle does not say that "Birds which have once copulated almost all continue to lay prolific eggs," but simply "almost all continue to lay eggs"; the word "prolific" is an addition by Fabricius. But it is one thing to have birds conceiving eggs after intercourse, and another to say that these eggs are fruitful through this intercourse. And this is the more obvious from Aristotle's previous words, where he says, "Nor in the family of birds can those eggs even that are produced by intercourse acquire their full size unless the intercourse between the sexes be continued. And the reason is that as the menstrual excretion in women is attracted by the intercourse of their husbands (for the uterus, being warmed, draws the moisture, and the passages are opened), so in birds it comes to pass that, as the menstruous discharge takes place very gradually, because of its being in small quantity, it cannot make its way externally, but is contained superiorly as high as the waist, and only distils down into the uterus itself. For the egg is increased by this, just as the fœtus of oviparous animals is nourished by that which reaches it through the umbilicus. For when once birds have copulated, almost all continue to lay eggs, but of small size and imperfect"; and therefore unprolific, for the perfection of an egg is its being fertile. If, therefore, without continued intercourse, not even those eggs that were conceived in consequence of intercourse grow to their proper size, or, as Fabricius interprets it, are "perfected," much less are those eggs prolific which fowls continue to lay independently of intercourse with the male bird.

But lest any one should think that these words, "for the uterus warmed, draws, and the passages are opened," signify that the uterus can attract the semen masculinum into its cavity, let him be aware that the philosopher does not say that the uterus attracts the semen from without into its cavity, but that in females, from the veins and passages, opened by the heat of intercourse, the menstruous blood is attracted from its own body; so in birds the blood is attracted to the uterus, warmed by repeated intercourse, whereby the eggs grow, as the fœtus of oviparous animals grows through the umbilicus.

---

[1] *On the Generation of Animals*, III, 1.

[2] *Op. cit.*, p. 37.

But what Fabricius adds upon that cavity or bursa, in which he thinks the semen of the cock may be stored up for a whole year, has been already refuted by us, where we have stated that it contains no seminal fluid, and that it exists in the cock as well as in the hen. Wherefore, though I readily believed (if by fecundity we are to understand a greater number of larger eggs) that the hens of poor people, indifferently fed in all probability, will lay both fewer and smaller eggs unless they have the company of a cock; agreeably to what the philosopher quoted avers, viz.: "that hens which have once been trodden continue to lay larger, better, and a greater number of eggs through the whole of the year" (a result on which the abundance and the good quality of the food has unquestionably a great influence); still that hens should continue for a whole year to lay prolific eggs after a few addresses of the cock, appeared to me by no means probable: for, had a small number of contacts sufficed for the purposes of generation during so long a period, nature, which does nothing in vain, would have constituted the males among birds less salacious than they are; nor should we see the cock soliciting his hens so many times a day, even against their inclination.

We know that the hen, as soon as she quits the nest where she has just laid an egg, cackles loudly, and seems to entice the cock, who on his part crowing lustily, singles her out and straightway treads her, which surely nature had never permitted unless for purposes of procreation.

A male pheasant kept in an aviary was so inflamed with lust, that unless he had the company of several hen-birds, six at the least, he literally maltreated them, though his repeated addresses rather interfered with their breeding than promoted it. I have seen a single hen-pheasant shut up with a cock-bird (which she could in no way escape) so worn out, and her back so entirely stript of feathers through his reiterated assaults, that at length she died exhausted. In the body of this bird, however, I did not discover even the rudiments of eggs.

I have also observed a male duck, having none of his own kind with him, but associating with hens, inflamed with such desire that he would follow a pullet even for several hours, would seize her with his bill, and mounting at length upon the creature, worn out with fatigue, would compel her to submit to his pleasure.

The common cock, victorious in a battle, not only satisfies his desires upon the sultanas of the vanquished, but upon the body of his rival himself.

The females of some animals are likewise so libidinous that they excite their males by pecking or biting them gently about the head; they seem as if they whispered into their ears the sweets of love; and then they mount upon their backs and invite them by other arts to fruition: among the number may be mentioned pigeons and sparrows.

It did not therefore appear likely that a few treads, in the beginning of the year, should suffice to render fertile the whole of the eggs that are to be laid in its course.

Upon one occasion, however, in the spring season, by way of helping out Fabricius, and that I might have some certain data as to the time during which the fecundating influence of intercourse would continue, and the necessity of renewed communication, I had a couple of hens separated from the cock for four days, each of which laid three eggs, all of which were prolific. Another hen was secluded, and the egg she laid on the tenth day afterwards was fruitful. The egg which another laid on the twentieth day of her seclusion also produced a chick. It would therefore seem that intercourse, once or twice repeated, suffices to impregnate the whole bunch of yelks, the whole of the eggs that will be laid during a certain season.

I shall here relate another observation which I made at this time. When I returned two of the hens, which I had secluded for a time, to the cock, one of which was big with egg, the other having but just laid, the cock immediately ran to the latter and trod her greedily three or four times; the former he went round and round, tripping himself with his wing and seeming to salute her, and wish her joy of her return; but he soon returned to the other and trod her again and again, even compelling her to submit; the one big with egg, however, he always speedily forsook, and never solicited her to his pleasure. I wondered with myself by what signs he knew that intercourse would advantage one of these hens and prove unavailing to the other. But indeed it is not easy at any time to understand how male animals, even from a distance, know which females are in season and desirous of their company; whether it be by sight, or hearing, or smell, it is difficult to say. Some on merely hearing the voice of the female, or smelling at the place where she has made water, or even the ground over which she has passed, are straightway seized with desire and set off in pursuit to gratify it. But I shall have more to say on this subject in my treatise on the *Loves, Lusts, and Sexual Acts of Animals*. I return to the matter we have in hand.

EXERCISE 7. *Of the abdomen of the common fowl and of other birds*

From the external orifice proceeding through the vulva we come to the uterus of the fowl, in which the egg is perfected, surrounded with the white and covered with its shell. But before speaking of the situation and connexions of this part it seems necessary to premise a few words on the particular anatomy of the abdomen of birds. For I have observed that the stomach, intestines, and other viscera of the feathered kinds were otherwise placed in the abdomen, and differently constituted, than they are in quadrupeds.

Almost all birds are provided with a double stomach; one of which is the crop, the other the stomach, properly so called. In the former the food is stored and undergoes preparation, in the latter it is dissolved and converted into chyme. The familiar names of the two stomachs of birds are the crop or craw, and the gizzard. In the crop the entire grain, &c. that is swallowed is moistened, macerated, and softened, and then it is sent on to the stomach that it may there be crushed and comminuted. For this end almost all the feathered tribes swallow sand, pebbles, and other hard substances, which they preserve in their stomachs, nothing of the sort being found in the crop. Now the stomach in birds consists of two extremely thick and powerful muscles (in the smaller birds they appear both fleshy and tendinous), so placed that, like a pair of millstones connected by means of hinges, they may grind and bruise the food; the place of teeth, which birds want, being supplied by the stones which they swallow. In this way is the food reduced and turned into chyme; and then by compression (just as we are wont, after having bruised an herb or a fruit, to squeeze out the juice or pulp) the softer or more liquid part is forced out, comes to the top, and is transferred to the commencement of the intestinal canal; which in birds takes its rise from the upper part of the stomach near the entrance of the œsophagus. That this is the case in many genera of birds is obvious; for the stones and other hard and rough substances which they have swallowed, if long retained, become so smooth and polished that they are unfit to comminute the food, when they are discharged. Hence birds, when they select stones, try them with their tongue, and, unless they find them rough, reject them. In the stomach of both the ostrich and cassowary I found pieces of iron and silver, and stones much worn down and almost reduced to nothing; and this is the reason why the vulgar believe that these creatures digest iron and are nourished by it.

If you apply the body of a hawk or an eagle, or other bird of prey, whilst fasting, to your ear, you will hear a distinct noise, occasioned by the rubbing, one against another, of the stones contained in the stomach. For hawks do not swallow pebbles with a view to cool their stomachs, as falconers commonly but erroneously believe, but that the stones may serve for the comminution of their food; precisely as other birds, which have muscular stomachs, swallow pebbles, sand, or something else of the same nature, to crush and grind the seeds upon which they live.

The stomach of birds, then, is situated within the cavity of the abdomen, below the heart, lungs and liver: the crop, however, is without the body in some sort, being situated at the lower part of the neck, over the os jugale or merry-thought. In this bag, as I have said, the food is only macerated and softened; and several birds regurgitate and give it to their young, in some measure as quadrupeds feed their progeny with milk from their breasts; this occurs in the whole family of the pigeons, and also among rooks. Bees, too, when they have returned to their hives, disgorge the honey which they have collected from the flowers and concocted in their stomachs, and store it in their waxen cells; and so also do hornets and wasps feed their young. The bitch has likewise been seen to vomit the food which she had eaten some time before, in a half-digested state, and give it to her whelps: it is not, therefore, to be greatly wondered at, if we see the poor women, who beg from door to door, when their milk fails, feeding their infants with food which they have chewed and reduced to a pulp in their own mouths.

The intestines commence in birds, as has been said, from the upper part of the stomach, and are folded up and down in the line of the longitudinal direction of the body, not transversely as in man. Immediately below the heart, about the waist, and where the diaphragm is situated in quadrupeds, for birds have no diaphragm, we find the liver, of ample size, divided into two lobes situated one on either side (for birds have no spleen) and filling the hypochondria. The stomach lies below the liver, and downwards from the stomach comes the mass of intestines, with numerous delicate membranes, full of air, interposed; the trachea opening in birds, as already stated, by several gaping orifices into membranous abdominal cells. The kidneys, which are of large size in birds, are of an oblong shape, look as if they were made up of fleshy vesicles, without cavities, and lie along the spine on either side, with the descending aorta and vena cava abdominalis adjacent; they further extend into and seem to lie buried within ample cavities of the ossa ilia. The ureters proceed from the anterior aspects of the kidneys, and run longitudinally towards the cloaca and podex, in which they terminate, and into which they pour the liquid excretion of the kidneys. This, however, is not in any great quantity in birds, because they drink little, and some of them, the eagle for example, not at all. Nor is the urine discharged separately and by itself, as in other animals; but, as we have said, it distils from the ureters into the common cloaca, which is also the recipient of the fæces, and the discharge of which it facilitates. The urine is also different in birds from what it is in other animals; for, as the urine in the generality of animals consists of two portions, one more serous and liquid, another thicker, which, in healthy subjects constitutes the hypostasis or sediment, and subsides when the urine becomes cold; so is it in birds, but the sedimentary portion is the more abundant, and is distinguished from the liquid by its white or silvery colour: nor is this sediment met with only in the cloaca (where it abounds, indeed, and surrounds the fæces), but in the whole course of the ureters, which are distinguished from the coverings of the kidneys by their white colour. Nor is it only in birds that this abundant thicker renal secretion is seen; it is conspicuous in serpents and other ovipara, particularly in those whose eggs are covered with a harder or firmer membrane. And here, too, is the thicker in larger proportion than the thinner and more serous portion; its consistency being midway between thick urine and stercoraceous excrement: so that, in its passage through the ureters, it resembles coagulated or inspissated milk; once discharged it soon concretes into a friable mass.

EXERCISE 8. *Of the situation and structure of the remaining parts of the fowl's uterus*

Between the stomach and the liver, over the spine, and where, in man and other animals the pancreas is situated; between the trunk of the porta and the descending cava; at the origin of the renal and spermatic arteries, and where the cæliac artery plunges into the mesentery, there, in the fowl and other birds, do the ovary and the cluster of yelks present themselves; having in their front the trunk of the porta, the gullet, and the orifice of the stomach: behind them, the vena cava and the aorta descending along the spine; above the liver, and beneath the stomach, lie adjacent. The infundibulum, therefore, which is a most delicate membrane, descends from the ovary longitudinally with the spine, between it and the gizzard. And from the infundibulum (between the gizzard, the intestines, the kidneys, and the loins), the processus uteri or superior portion of this organ descends with a great many turnings and cells (like the colon and rectum in man), into the uterus itself. Now the uterus, which is continuous with this process, is situated below the gizzard, between the loins, the kidneys, and the rectum, in the lower part of the abdomen, close to the cloaca; so that the egg surrounded with its white, which the uterus contains, is situated so low that, with the fingers, it is easy to ascertain whether it be soft or hard, and near the laying.

The uterus in the common fowl varies both in point of size and of structure. In the fowl that is with egg, or that has lately laid, it is very different from what it is in the pullet, the uterus of which is fleshy and round, like an empty purse, and its cavity so insignificant that it would scarcely contain a bean; smooth externally, it is wrinkled and occupied by a few longitudinal plicæ internally: at first sight you might very well mistake it either for a large urinary bladder or for a second smaller stomach. In the gravid state, however, and in the fowl arrived at maturity (a fact which is indicated by the redder colour of the comb), the uterus is of much larger dimensions and far more fleshy; its plicæ are also larger and thicker, it in general approaches the size which we should judge necessary to receive an egg; it extends far upwards in the direction of the spinal column, and consists of numerous divisions or cells, formed by replications of the extended uterus, similar to those of the colon in quadrupeds and man. The inferior portion of the uterus, as the largest and thickest, and most fleshy of all, is strengthened by many plicæ of large size. Its configuration internally is oval, as if it were the mould of the egg. The ascending or produced portion of the uterus I designate the processus uteri: this part Fabricius calls the *uterus secundus*, and says that it consists of three spiral turns or flexures; Ulyssus Aldrovandus, again, names it the *stomachum uteri*. I must admit that in this part there are usually three turns to be observed; they are not, however, by any means so regular but that, as in the case of the cells of the colon, nature sometimes departs from her usual procedure here.

The uterus as it ascends higher, so does it become ever the thinner and more delicate, containing fewer and smaller plicæ, until at length going off into a mere membrane, and that of the most flimsy description, it constitutes the infundibulum; which, reaching as high as the waist or cincture of the body, embraces the entire ovary.

On this account, therefore, Fabricius describes the uterus as consisting of three portions; viz., the commencement, the middle, and the end. "The commencement," says he, "degenerating into a thin and most delicate membrane, forms an ample orifice, and bears a resemblance to an open-mouthed tube or funnel. The next portion (which I call the processus uteri), consisting of three transverse spiral turns, serves for the supply of the albumen, and extends downwards to the most inferior and capacious portion—the termination of the uterus—in which the chalazæ, the two membranes, and the shell are formed."[1]

The whole substance of the uterus, particularly the parts about the plicæ, both in its body and in its process, are covered with numerous ramifications of blood-vessels, the majority of which are arterial rather than venous branches.

The folds which appear oblique and transverse in the interior of the uterus are fleshy substances; they have a fine white or milky colour, and a sluggish fluid oozes from them, so that the whole of the interior of the uterus, as well the body as the process, is moistened with an abundance of thin albumen, whereby the vitellus as it descends is increased, and the albumen that is deposited around it is gradually perfected.

The uterus of the fowl is rarely found otherwise than containing an egg, either sticking in the spiral process or arrived in the body of the organ. If you inflate this process when it is empty it then presents itself as an oblique and contorted tube, and rises like a turbinated shell or cone into a point. The general arrangement of the spirals and folds composing the uterus, is

[1] *Op. cit.*, p. 17.

such as we have already observed it in the vulva: there is a ready enough passage for the descending egg, but scarce any return even for air blown in towards the superior parts.

The processus uteri with its spirals, very small in the young pullet, is so much diminished in the hen which has ceased laying, that it shrinks into the most delicate description of membrane, and then entirely disappears, so that no trace of it remains, any more than of the ovary or infundibulum: nothing but a certain glandular-looking and spongy mass appears in the place these bodies occupied, which in a boiled fowl tastes sweet, and bears some affinity to the pancreas and thymus of young mammiferous animals, which, in the vernacular tongue, are called the sweetbread.

The uterus and the processus uteri are connected with the back by means of a membranous attachment, which Fabricius designates by the name of "mesometrium; because the second uterus, together with this vascular and membranous body, may very fairly be compared with the intestines and the mesentery." For, as the intestine is bound down by the mesentery, so is this portion of the uterus attached to the spinal column by an oblong membranous process; lest by being too loose, and getting twisted, the passage of the yelks should be interfered with, instead of having a free and open transit afforded them as at present. The mesometrium also transmits numerous blood-vessels, surcharged with blood, to each of the folds of the uterus. In its origin, substance, structure, use, and office, this part is therefore analogous to the mesentery. Moreover, from the fundus of the uterus lengthwise, and extending even to the infundibulum, there is a ligament bearing some resemblance to a tape-worm, similar to that which we notice in the upper part of the colon. It is as if a certain portion or stripe of the external tunic had been condensed and shortened in such a manner that the rest of the process is thrown into folds and cells: were you to draw a thread through a piece of intestine taken out of the body, and to tie this thread firmly on one side, you would cause the other side of the bowel to pucker up into wrinkles and cells.

This then, in brief, is the structure of the uterus in the fowl that is laying eggs: fleshy, large, extensible both longitudinally and transversely, tortuous or winding in spirals and convolutions from the cloaca upwards, in the line of the vertebral column, and continued into the infundibulum.

EXERCISE 9. *Of the extrusion of the egg, or parturition of the fowl, in general*

The yelk, although only a minute speck in the ovary, gaining by degrees in depth of colour and increasing in size, gradually acquires the dimensions and characters that distinguish it at last. Cast loose from the cluster, it descends by the infundibulum, and, transmitted through the spirals and cells of the processus uteri, it becomes surrounded with albumen; and this, without in any place adhering to the uterus (as was rightly observed by Fabricius in opposition to Aristotle), or growing by means of any system of umbilical vessels; but as the eggs of fishes and frogs, when extruded and laid in the water provide and surround themselves with albumen, or as beans, vetches, and other seeds and grains swell when moistened, and thence supply nourishment to the germs that spring from them, so, from the folds of the uterus that have been described, as from an udder, or uterine placenta, an albuminous fluid exudes, which the vitellus, in virtue of its inherent vegetative heat and faculty, attracts and digests into the surrounding white. There is, indeed, an abundance of fluid having the taste of albumen, contained in the cavity of the uterus and entangled between the folds that cover its interior. In this way does the yelk, descending by degrees, become surrounded with albumen, until at last, having in the extreme part of the uterus acquired a covering of firmer membranes and a harder shell, it is perfected and rendered fit for extrusion.

EXERCISE 10. *Of the increase and nutrition of the egg*

Let us hear Fabricius on these topics. He says: "As the action of the stomach is to prepare the chyle, and that of the testes to secrete the seminal fluid (because in the stomach chyle is discovered, and in the testes semen), so we declare the act of the uterus in birds to be the production of eggs, because eggs are found there. But this, as it appears, is not the only action of uteri; to it must be added the increase of the egg, which succeeds immediately upon its production, and which proceeds until it is perfected and attains its due size. For a fowl does not naturally lay an egg until it is perfect and has attained to its proper dimensions. The office of the uterus is, therefore, the growth as well as the generation of the egg; but growth implies and includes the idea of nutrition; and, as all generation is the act of two principles, one

the agent, another the matter, the agent in the production of eggs is nothing else than the organs or instruments indicated, *viz.*, the compound uterus; and the matter nothing but the blood."

We, studious of brevity, and shunning all controversy, as in duty bound, as we readily admit that the office and use of the uterus is the procreation of the egg, so do we maintain the "adequate efficient," as it has been called, the immediate agent to inhere in the egg itself; and we assert, further, that the egg is both engendered and made to increase, not by the uterus, but by a certain natural principle peculiar to itself; and that this principle flows from the whole fowl into the rudiments of the vitellus, and whilst it was yet but a speck, and under the influence either of the calidum innatum or of nature, causes it to be nourished and to grow; just as there is a certain faculty in every particle of the body which secures its nutrition and growth.

As regards the manner in which the yelk is surrounded by the albumen, Aristotle appears to have believed[1] that in the sharp end of the egg (where he placed the commencement of the egg), whilst it was yet surrounded by soft membranes, there existed an umbilical canal, by which it was nourished; a view which Fabricius[2] challenges, denying that there is any such canal, or that the vitellus has any kind of connexion with the uterus. He further lessens the doubt in regard to the albumen of the extruded egg, observing, that "the egg increases in a twofold manner, inasmuch as the uterus consists of two portions, one superior, another inferior; and the egg itself consists of two matters—the yelk and the white. The yelk increases with a true growth, to wit, by means of the blood, which is sent to it through the veins whilst it is yet connected with the vitellarium. The albumen, however, increases and grows otherwise than the yelk; *viz.*, not by means of the veins, nor by proper nutrition like the yelk, but, by juxtaposition, adhering to the vitellus as it is passing through the second uterus."

But my opinion is that the egg increases everywhere in the same manner as the yelk does in the cluster; *viz.*, by an inherent concocting principle; with this single difference, that in the ovary the nourishment is brought to it by means of vessels, whilst in the uterus it finds that which it imbibes already prepared for it. Juxtaposition of parts is equally necessary in

[1] *On the Generation of Animals*, III. 2.
[2] *Op cit.*, p. 11.

every kind of nutrition and growth, and so also are concoction and distribution of the applied nutriment. Nor is one of these to be less accounted true nutrition than the other, inasmuch as in both there is accession of new aliment, apposition, agglutination, and transmutation of particles. Nor can vetches or beans, when they attract moisture from the earth through their skins, imbibing it like sponges, be said with less propriety to be nourished than if they had obtained the needful moisture through the mouths of veins; and trees, when they absorb the dew and the rain through their bark, are as truly nourished as when they pump them in by their roots. With reference to the mode in which nutrition is effected, we have set down much in another place. It is another difficulty that occupies us at this time, *viz.*, whether the yelk, whilst it is acquiring the white, does not make a certain separation and distinction in it; whether, in the course of the increase, a more earthy portion does not subside into the yelk or middle of the egg as towards the centre, which Aristotle believed, and another lighter portion surrounds this. For between the yelk which is still in the cluster, and the yelk which is found in the middle of a perfect egg, there is this principal difference, that although the former be of a yellow colour, still, in point of consistence, it rather resembles the white; and by boiling, it is, like the latter, thickened, compacted, inspissated, and becomes divisible into layers; whilst the yelk of the perfect egg is rendered friable by boiling, and is rather of an earthy consistency, not thick and gelatinous like albumen.

EXERCISE 11. *Of the covering or shell of the egg*

It will now be proper, having spoken of the production of eggs, to treat of their parts and diversities. "An egg," says Fabricius, "consists of a yelk, the albumen, two chalazæ, three membranes, *viz.*, one proper to the vitellus, two common to the entire egg, and a shell. To these two others are to be added, which, however, cannot be correctly reckoned among the parts of an egg; one of these is a small cavity in the blunt end of the egg, under the shell; the other is a very small white spot, a kind of round cicatricula connected with the surface of the yelk. The history of each of these parts and accidents must now be given more particularly, and we shall begin from without and proceed inwards.

"The external covering of the egg, called by Pliny the cortex and putamen, by Quintus Serenus the testa ovi, is a hard but thin, friable and porous covering, of different colours in different cases—white, light green, speckled, &c. All eggs are not furnished with a shell on their extrusion: the eggs of serpents have none; and some fowls occasionally, though rarely, lay eggs that are without shells. The shell, though everywhere hard, is not of uniform hardness; it is hardest towards the upper end." From this Fabricius[1] opines that we are to doubt as to the matter of which, and the season at which the shells of eggs are produced. Aristotle[2] and Pliny[3] affirm that the shell is not formed within the body of the fowl, but when the egg is laid; and that as it issues it sets by coming in contact with the air, the internal heat driving off moisture. And this, says Aristotle,[4] is so arranged to spare the animal pain, and to render the process of parturition more easy. An egg softened in vinegar is said to be easily pushed into a vessel with a narrow mouth."

Fabricius was long indisposed to this opinion, "because he had found an egg within the body of the fowl covered with a hard shell; and housewives are in the daily practice of trying the bellies of their hens with their fingers in order that they may know by the hardness whether the creatures are likely to lay that day or not." But by and by, when "he had been assured by women worthy of confidence, that the shells of eggs became hardened in their passage into the air, which dissipates a certain moisture diffused over the egg on its exit, fixing it in the shell not yet completely hardened"; and having afterwards "confirmed this by his own experience," he altered his opinion, and came to the conclusion, "that the egg surrounded with a shell, and having a consistency betwixt hard and soft, hardened notably at the moment of its extrusion, in consequence, according to Aristotle's views, of the concretion and dissipation of the thinner part of a certain viscid and tenacious humour, bedewed with which the egg is extruded; sticking to the recent shell this humour is dried up and hardened, the cold of the ambient air contributing somewhat to the effect. Of all this," he says, "you will readily be satisfied if you have a fowl in the house, and dexterously catch the egg in your hand as it is dropping."

I was myself long fettered by this statement of Aristotle, indeed until certain experience

---

[1] *Loc. cit.*, p. 13.
[2] *History of Animals*, vi. 2; *On the Generation of Animals*, i. 8.
[3] *Hist. nat.*, x. 52.
[4] *On the Generation of Animals*, iii. 2.

had assured me of its erroneousness; for I found the egg still contained in the uterus, almost always covered with a hard shell; and I once saw an egg taken from the body of a living fowl, and still warm, without a shell but covered with a tenacious moisture; this egg, however, did not acquire any hardness through the concretion or evaporation of the moisture in question, as Fabricius would have us believe, neither was it in any way changed by the cold of the surrounding air; but it retained the same degree of softness which it had had in the uterus.

I have also seen an egg just laid by a fowl, surrounded by a complete shell, and this shell covered externally with a soft and membranous skin, which however did not become hard. I have further seen another hen's egg covered with a shell everywhere except at the extremity of the sharp end, where a certain small and soft projection remained, very likely such as was taken by Aristotle for the remains of an umbilicus.

Fabricius, therefore, appears to me to have wandered from the truth; nor was I ever so dexterous as to catch an egg in its exit, and discover it in the state between soft and hard. And this I confidently assert, that the shell is formed internally, or in the uterus, and not otherwise than all the other parts of the egg, *viz.*, by the peculiar plastic power. A statement which I make all the more confidently because I have seen a very small egg covered with a shell, contained within another larger egg, perfect in all respects, and completely surrounded with a shell. An egg of this kind Fabricius calls an ovum centeninum; and our housewives ascribe it to the cock. This egg I showed to his Serene Majesty King Charles, my most gracious master, in the presence of many persons. And the same year, in cutting up a large lemon, I found another perfect but very small lemon included within it, having a yellow rind like the other; and I hear that the same thing has frequently been seen in Italy.

It is a common mistake with those who pursue philosophical studies in these times, to seek for the cause of diversity of parts in diversity of the matter whence they arise. Thus medical men assert that the several parts of the body are both engendered and nourished by diverse matters, either the blood or the seminal fluid; *viz.*, the softer parts, such as the flesh, by the thinner matter, the harder and more earthy parts, such as the bones, &c. by the firmer and thicker matter. But we have elsewhere refuted this too prevalent error. Nor do they err less who, with Democritus, compose all things of atoms; or with Empedocles, of elements. As if *generation* were nothing more than a separation, or aggregation, or disposition of things. It is not indeed to be denied that when one thing is to be produced from another, all these are necessary, but generation itself is different from them all. I find Aristotle to be of this opinion; and it is my intention, by and by, to teach that out of the same albumen (which all allow to be uniform, not composed of diverse parts), all the parts of the chick, bones, nails, feathers, flesh, &c. are produced and nourished. Moreover, they who philosophize in this way, assign a material cause, and deduce the causes of natural things either from the elements concurring spontaneously or accidentally, or from atoms variously arranged; they do not attain to that which is first in the operations of nature and in the generation and nutrition of animals; viz., they do not recognize that efficient cause and divinity of nature which works at all times with consummate art, and providence, and wisdom, and ever for a certain purpose, and to some good end; they derogate from the honour of the Divine Architect, who has not contrived the shell for the defence of the egg with less of skill and of foresight than he has composed all the other parts of the egg of the same matter, and produced it under the influence of the same formative faculty.

Although what has already been said be the fact, namely, that the egg, even whilst contained in the uterus, is provided with a hard shell, still the authority of Aristotle has always such weight with me that I never think of differing from him inconsiderately; and I therefore believe, and my observations bear me out in so much, that the shell does gain somewhat in solidity from the ambient air upon its extrusion; that the sluggish and slippery fluid with which it is moistened when laid, immediately becomes hardened on its exposure to the air. For the shell, whilst the egg is in the uterus, is much thinner and more transparent, and smoother on the surface; when laid, however, the shell is thicker, less translucid, and the surface is rough—it appears as if it were powdered over with a fine white dust which had but just adhered to it.

Let us, as we are upon this subject, expatiate a little:

In the desert islands off the east coast of Scotland, such flights of almost every kind of seafowl congregate, that were I to state what I have heard from parties very worthy of credit, I fear I should be held guilty of telling greater stories than they who have committed themselves in regard to the Scottish geese produced, as they say, from the fruits of certain trees that had fallen into the sea. These geese the narrators themselves had never seen so produced; but I will here relate that which I have myself witnessed.

There is a small island which the Scots call the Bass Island (and speaking of this one will suffice for all), situated in the open ocean, not far from the shore, of the most abrupt and precipitous character, so that it rather resembles one huge rock or stone than an island, and indeed it is not more than a mile in circumference. The surface of this island in the months of May and June is almost completely covered with nests, eggs, and young birds, so that you can scarce find free footing anywhere; and then such is the density of the flight of the old birds above, that like a cloud they darken the sun and the sky; and such the screaming and din that you can scarce hear the voice of one who addresses you. If you turn your eyes below, and from your lofty stance and precipice regard the sea, there you perceive on all sides around an infinite variety of different kinds of sea-fowl swimming about in pursuit of their prey: the face of the ocean is very like that of a pool in the spring season, when it appears swarming with frogs; or to those sunny hills and cliffy mountains looked at from below, that are covered with numerous flocks of sheep and goats. If you sail round the island and look up, you see on every ledge and shelf, and recess, innumerable flocks of birds of almost every size and order; more numerous than the stars that appear in the unclouded moonless sky; and if you regard the flights that incessantly come and go you may imagine that it is a mighty swarm of bees you have before you. I should scarcely be credited did I name the revenue which was annually derived from the feathers, the eggs, and the old nests, which, as useful for firing, are all made objects of traffic by the proprietor; the sum he mentioned to me exceeds credibility. There was this particular feature which, as it refers to our subject, I shall mention, and also as it bears me out in my report of the multitudes of sea-fowl: the whole island appears of a brilliant white colour to those who approach it—all the cliffs look as if they consisted of the whitest chalk; the true colour of the rock, however, is dusky and black. It is a friable white crust that is spread over all, which gives the island its whiteness and splendour, a crust, having the same consistency, colour, and nature as an egg-shell, which plasters everything with a hard, though friable and testaceous kind of covering. The lower part of the rock, laved by the ebbing and flowing tide, preserves its native colour, and clearly shows that the whiteness of the superior parts is due to the liquid excrements of the birds, which are voided along with the alvine fæces; which liquid excrements, white, hard, and brittle like the shell of the egg, cover the rock, and, under the influence of the cold of the air, incrust it. Now this is precisely the way in which Aristotle and Pliny will have it that the shell of the egg is formed. None of the birds are permanent occupants of the island, but visitors for purposes of procreation only, staying there for a few weeks, in lodgings, as it were, and until their young ones can take wing along with them. The white crust is so hard and solid, and adheres so intimately to the rock, that it might readily be mistaken for the natural soil of the place.

The liquid, white, and shining excrement is conveyed from the kidneys of birds by the ureters, into the common receptacle or cloaca; where it covers over the alvine fæces, and with them is discharged. It constitutes, in fact, the thicker portion of the urine of these creatures, and corresponds with that which, in our urine, we call the hypostase or sediment. We have already said something above on this topic, and have entered into it still more fully elsewhere. We always find an abundance of this white excrement in mews; where hawks besmear walls beside their perches, they cover them with a kind of gypseous crust, or make them look as if they were painted with white lead.

In the cloaca of a dead ostrich I found as much of this gypseous cement as would have filled the hand. And in like manner the same substance abounds in tortoises and other oviparous animals; discharged from the body it soon concretes either into a friable crust, or into a powder which greatly resembles pulverized egg-shells, in consequence of the evaporation of its thinner part.

Among the many different kinds of birds which seek the Bass Island for the sake of laying and incubating their eggs, and which have such variety of nests, one bird was pointed out to me which lays but one egg, and this it places upon the point of a rock, with nothing like a nest or bed beneath it, yet so firmly that the mother can go and return without injury to it; but if anyone move it from its place, by no art can it be fixed or balanced again; left at liberty, it straightway rolls off and falls into the sea. The place, as I have said, is crusted over with a white cement, and the egg, when laid, is bedewed with a thick and viscid moisture, which setting speedily, the egg is soldered as it were, or agglutinated to the subjacent rock.

An instance of like rapid concretion may be seen any day at a statuary's, when he uses his cement of burnt alabaster or gypsum tempered with water; by means of which the likeness of one dead, or the cast of anything else may be speedily taken, and used as a mould.

There is also in like manner a certain earthy or solid something in almost all liquids, as, for example, tartar in wine, mud or sand in water, salt in lixivium, which, when the greater portion of the water has been dissipated, concretes and subsides; and so do I conceive the white sediment of birds to descend along with the urine from the kidneys into the cloaca, and there to cover over and incrust the egg, much as the pavement of a mews is plastered over by falcons, and every cliff of the aforementioned island by the birds that frequent it; much also as chamber utensils, and places where many persons make water, become covered with a yellow incrustation; that substance, in fact, concreting externally, of which calculi in the kidneys, bladder, and other parts are formed. I did formerly believe then, as I have said, persuaded especially by the authority of Aristotle and Pliny, that the shell of the hen's egg was formed of this white sediment, which abounds in all the oviparous animals whose eggs are laid with a hard shell, the matter concreting through contact with the air when the egg was laid. And so many additional observations have since strengthened this conclusion that I can scarcely keep from believing that some part at least of the shell is thus produced.

Nevertheless, I would say with Fabricius: "Let all reasoning be silent when experience gainsays its conclusions." The too familiar vice of the present age is to obtrude as manifest truths, mere fancies, born of conjecture and superficial reasoning, altogether unsupported by the testimony of sense.

For I have very certainly discovered that the egg still contained in the uterus, in these countries at least, is covered with its shell; although Aristotle and Pliny assert the contrary, and Fabricius thinks that "it is not to be too obstinately gainsaid." In warmer places, perhaps, and where the fowls are stronger, the eggs may be extruded soft, and for the most part without shells. With us this very rarely happens. When I was at Venice in former years, Aromatarius, a learned physician, showed me a small leaf which had grown between the two valves of a peascod, whilst with us there is nothing more apparent in these pods than a small point where the germ is about to be produced. So much do a milder climate, a brighter sky, and a softer air, conduce to increase and rapidity of growth.

EXERCISE 12. *Of the remaining parts of the egg*

We have already spoken partially of the place where, the time when, and the manner how the remaining parts of the egg are engendered, and we shall have something more to add when we come to speak of their several uses.

"The albumen," says Fabricius, "is the *ovi albus liquor* of Pliny, the *ovi candidum* of Celsus, the *ovi albor* of Palladius, the *ovi album et albumentum* of Apicius, the λευκὸν of the Greeks, the ὠοῦ λεύκωμα of Aristotle, the ὄρνιθος γάλα, or bird's milk, of Anaxagoras. This is the cold, sluggish, white fluid of the egg, of different thickness at different places (thinner at the blunt and sharp ends, thicker in other situations) and also in variable quantity (for it is more abundant at the blunt end, less so at the sharp end, and still less so in the other parts of the egg), covering and surrounding the yelk on every side."[1]

In the hen's egg, however, I have observed that there are not only differences in the albumen, but two albumens, each surrounded with its proper membrane. One of these is thinner, more liquid, and almost of the same consistence as that humour which, remaining among the folds of the uterus, we have called the matter and nourishment of the albumen; the other is thicker, more viscid, and rather whiter in its colour, and in old and stale eggs, and those that have been sat upon for some days, it is of a yellowish cast. As this second albumen everywhere surrounds the yelk, so is it, in like manner, itself surrounded by the more external fluid. That these two albumens are distinct appears from this, that if after having removed the shell you pierce the two outermost membranes, you will perceive the external albuminous liquid to make its escape, and the membranes to become collapsed and to sink down in the dish; the internal and thicker albumen, however, all the while retains its place and globular figure, inasmuch as it is bounded by its proper membrane, although this is of such tenuity that it entirely escapes detection by the

[1] *Loc. cit.*, p. 22.

eye; but if you then prick it, the second albumen will forthwith begin to flow out, and the mass will lose its globular shape; just as the water contained in a bladder escapes when it is punctured; in like manner the proper investing membrane of the vitellus being punctured, the yellow fluid of which it consists escapes, and the original globular form is destroyed.

"The vitellus," says Fabricius, "is so called from the word *vita*, because the chick lives upon it; from its colour it is also spoken of as the yellow of the egg, having been called by the Greeks generally, χρυσὸν, by Hippocrates χλωρὸν, and by Aristotle ὠχρὸν and λεκυθὸν; the ancients, such as Suidas in Menander, called it νεοτὸν, *i. e.*, the chick, because they believed the chick to be engendered from this part. It is the smoothest portion of the egg, and is contained within a most delicate membrane, immediately escaping if this be torn, and losing all figure; it is sustained in the middle of the egg; and in one egg is of a yellow colour, in another of a tint between white and yellow; it is quite round, of variable size, according to the size of the bird that lays the egg, and, according to Aristotle, of a deeper yellow in water birds, of a paler hue in land birds."[1] The same author[2] also maintains that "the yellow and the white of an egg are of opposite natures, not only in colour but in qualities; for the yellow is inspissated by cold, which the white is not, but is rather rendered more liquid; and the white, on the contrary, is thickened by heat, which the yellow is not, unless it be burned or overdone, and it is more hardened and dried by boiling than by roasting." As in the macrocosm the earth is placed in the centre, and is surrounded by the water and the air, so is the yelk, the more earthy part of the egg, surrounded by two albuminous layers, one thicker, another thinner. And, indeed, Aristotle says that "if we put a number of yelks and whites together, and mix them in a pan, and then boil them with a slow and gentle fire, the whole of the yelks will set into a globular mass in the middle, and appear surrounded by the whites."[3] But many physicians have been of opinion that the white was the colder portion of the egg. Of these matters, however, more by and by.

The chalazæ, the treads or treadles (*gralladura* in Italian) are two in number in each egg, one in the blunt, another in the sharp end.

The larger portion of them is contained in the white; but they are most intimately connected with the yelk, and with its membrane. They are two long-shaped bodies, firmer than the albumen and whiter; knotty, not without a certain transparency like hail, whence their name; each chalaza, in fact, is made up of several hailstones, as it seems, connected by means of albumen. One of them is larger than the other, and this extends from the yelk towards the blunt end of the egg; the other and smaller chalaza stretches from the yelk towards the sharp end of the egg. The larger is made up of two or three knots or seeming hailstones, at a trifling distance from one another, and of successively smaller size.

The chalazæ are found in the eggs of all birds, and in wind and unprolific as well as in perfect or prolific eggs, duly disposed in both their extremities. Whence the supposition among housewives that the chalazæ are the tread or spermatic fluid of the cock, and that the chick is generated from them is discovered to be a vulgar error. But Fabricius himself, although he denies that they consist of the semen of the cock, still gives various reasons for maintaining that "they are the immediate matter which the cock fecundates, and from which the chick is produced"; a notion which he seeks to prop by this feeble statement: "because in a boiled egg, the chalazæ are so contracted on themselves that they present the figure of a chick already formed and hatched." But it is not likely that several rudiments of a single fœtus should be wanted in one egg, neither has anyone ever discovered the rudiments of the future chick save in the blunt end of the egg. Moreover the chalazæ present no sensible difference in eggs that are fecundated by the intercourse of the two sexes, from those of eggs that are barren. Our distinguished author is, therefore, mistaken in regard to the use of the chalazæ in the egg, as shall further be made to appear by and by.

In the eggs of even the smallest birds there is a slender filament, the rudiments of the chalazæ, to be discovered; and in those of the ostrich and cassowary I have found, in either end of the egg very thick chalazæ, of great length, and very white colour, made up of several globules gradually diminishing in size.

A small cavity is observed in the inside of an egg under the shell, at the blunt end; sometimes exactly in the middle, at other times more to one side, almost exactly corresponding to the chalaza that lies below it. The figure of

[1] *Op. cit.*, p. 23.
[2] *History of Animals*, vi. 2.
[3] *Ibid.; On the Generation of Animals*, iii. 1.

this cavity is generally circular, though in the goose and duck it is not exactly so. It is seen as a dark spot if you hold an egg opposite a candle in a dark place, and apply your hand edgeways over the blunt end. In the egg just laid it is of small size—about the size of the pupil of the human eye; but it grows larger daily as the egg is older, and the air is warmer; it is much increased after the first day of incubation; as if by the exhalation of some of the more external and liquid albumen the remainder contracted, and left a larger cavity; for the cavity in question is produced between the shell and the membrane which surrounds the whole of the fluids of the egg. It is met with in all eggs; I have discovered it, even in those that are still contained in the uterus, as soon as they had become invested with the shell. They who are curious in such matters say that if this cavity be in the point or end of the egg it will produce a male, if towards the side, a female. This much is certain: if the cavity be small it indicates that the egg is fresh-laid; if large, that it is stale. But we shall have occasion anon to say more on this head.

There is a white and very small circle apparent in the investing membrane of the vitellus, which looks like an inbranded cicatrice, which Fabricius therefore calls *cicatricula;* but he makes little of this spot, and looks on it rather as an accident or blemish than as any essential part of the egg. The cicatricula in question is extremely small; not larger than a tiny lentil, or the pupil of a small bird's eye; white, flat, and circular. This part is also found in every egg, and even from its commencement in the vitellarium. Fabricius, therefore, is mistaken when he thinks that this spot is nothing more than the trace or cicatrice of the severed peduncle, by which the egg was in the first instance connected with the ovary. For the peduncle, as he himself admits, is hollow, and as it approaches the vitellus expands, so as to surround or embrace, and inclose the yelk in a kind of pouch: it is not connected with the yelk in the same way as the stalks of apples and other fruits are infixed, and so as to leave any cicatrice when the yelk is cast loose. And if you sometimes find two cicatriculæ in a large yelk, as Fabricius states, this might, perhaps, lead to the production of a monster and double fœtus, (as shall be afterwards shown), but would be no indication of the pre-existence of a double peduncle. He is, however, immensely mistaken when he imagines that the cicatricula serves no purpose; for it is, in fact, the most important part of the whole egg, and that for whose sake all the

others exist; it is that, in a word, from which the chick takes its rise. Parisanus, too, is in error, when he contends that this is the semen of the cock.

EXERCISE 13. *Of the diversities of eggs*

"The word *ovum*, or egg, is taken in a twofold sense, proper and improper. An ovum, properly so designated, I call that body to which the definition given by Aristotle[1] applies: An egg, says he, is that from part of which an animal is engendered, and the remainder of which is food for the animal so produced. But I hold that body to be improperly styled an egg which is defined by Aristotle[2] in the same place, to be that from the whole of which an animal is engendered; such as the eggs of ants, flies, spiders, some butterflies, and others of the tribe of extremely small eggs; which Aristotle almost always fears to commit himself by calling eggs, but which he rather styles *vermiculi.*" What precedes is from Fabricius;[3] but we, whose purpose it is to treat especially of the generation of the hen's egg, have no intention to speak of the differences of all kinds of eggs; we shall limit ourselves to the diversities among hen's eggs.

The more recently laid are whiter than the staler, because by age, and especially by incubation, they become darker; the cavity in the blunt end of a stale egg is also larger than in a recent egg; eggs just laid are also somewhat rough to the feel from a quantity of white powder which covers the shell, but which is soon rubbed off, when the egg becomes smoother as well as darker. New-laid eggs, unbroken, if placed near a fire will sweat, and are much more palatable than those that have been kept for some time—they are, indeed, accounted a delicacy by some. Eggs, after two or three days' incubation, are still better flavoured than stale eggs; revived by the gentle warmth of the hen, they seem to return to the quality and entireness of the egg just laid. Further, I have boiled an egg to hardness, after the fourteenth day of incubation, when the chick had already begun to get its feathers, when it occupied the middle of the egg, and nearly the whole of the yelk remained, in order that I might better distinguish the position of the chick: I found it lying, as it were, within a mould of the albumen, and the yelk possessed the same agreeable flavour and sweetness as that of the new-laid egg, boiled to

[1] *History of Animals*, I. 5.
[2] *Ibid.*, 2.
[3] *Op. cit.*, p. 19.

the same degree of hardness. The yelk taken from the ovarium of a live fowl, and eaten immediately, tastes much sweeter raw than boiled.

Eggs also differ from one another in shape; some are longer and more pointed, others rounder and blunter. According to Aristotle,[1] the long-shaped and pointed eggs produce females; the blunt, on the contrary, yield males. Pliny,[2] however, maintains the opposite. "The rounder eggs," he says, "produce females, the others males"; and with him Columella[3] agrees: "He who desires to have the greater number of his brood cocks, let him select the longest and sharpest eggs for incubation; and on the contrary, when he would have the greater number females, let him choose the roundest eggs." The ground of Aristotle's opinion was this: because the rounder eggs are the hotter, and it is the property of heat to concentrate and determine, and that heat can do most which is most powerful. From the stronger and more perfect principle, therefore, proceeds the stronger and more perfect animal. Such is the male compared with the female, especially in the case of the common fowl. On the contrary, again, the smaller eggs are reckoned among the imperfect ones, and the smallest of all are regarded as entirely unproductive. It was on this account too that Aristotle, to secure the highest quality of eggs, recommends that the hens be frequently trodden. Barren and adventitious eggs, he asserts, are smaller and less savoury, because they are humid and imperfect. The differences indicated are to be understood as referring to the eggs of the same fowl; for when a certain hen goes on laying eggs of a certain character, they will all produce either males or females. If you understand this point otherwise, the guess as to males or females, from the indications given, would be extremely uncertain. Because different hens lay eggs that differ much in respect of size and figure: some habitually lay more oblong, others, rounder eggs, that do not differ greatly one from another; and although I sometimes found diversities in the eggs of the same fowl, these were still so trifling in amount that they would have escaped any other than the practised eye. For as all the eggs of the same fowl acquire nearly the same figure, in the same womb or mould in which the shell is deposited (much as the excrements are moulded into scybala in the cells of the colon), it necessarily falls out that they greatly resemble one

another; so that I myself, without much experience, could readily tell which hen in a small flock had laid a given egg, and they who have given much attention to the point, of course succeed much better. But that which we note every day among huntsmen is far more remarkable; for the more careful keepers who have large herds of stags or fallow deer under their charge, will very certainly tell to which herd the horns which they find in the woods or thickets belonged. A stupid and uneducated shepherd, having the charge of a numerous flock of sheep, has been known to become so familiar with the physiognomy of each, that if any one had strayed from the flock, though he could not count them, he could still say which one it was, give the particulars as to where it had been bought, or whence it had come. The master of this man, for the sake of trying him, once selected a particular lamb from among forty others in the same pen, and desired him to carry it to the ewe which was its dam, which he did forthwith. We have known huntsmen who, having only once seen a particular stag, or his horns, or even his print in the mud (as a lion is known by his claws), have afterwards been able to distinguish him by the same marks from every other; some, too, from the foot-prints of deer, seen for the first time, will draw inferences as to the size, and grease, and power of the stag which has left them; saying whether he were full of strength, or weary from having been hunted; and further, whether the prints are those of a buck or a doe. I shall say thus much more: there are some who, in hunting, when there are some forty hounds upon the trace of the game, and all are giving tongue together, will nevertheless, and from a distance, tell which dog is at the head of the pack, which at the tail, which chases on the hot scent, which is running off at fault; whether the game is still running, or is at bay; whether the stag have run far, or have but just been raised from his lair. And all this amid the din of dogs, and men, and horns, and surrounded by an unknown and gloomy wood. We should not, therefore, be greatly surprised when we see those who have experience telling by what hen each particular egg in a number has been laid. I wish there were some equally ready way from the child of knowing the true father.

The principal difference between eggs, however, is their fecundity or barrenness—the distinction of fruitful eggs from hypenemic, adventitious, or wind eggs. Those eggs are called hypenemic (as if the progeny of the wind) that

[1] *History of Animals*, VI. 2.
[2] *Hist. nat.*, Book x, chap. 52; Book IX.
[3] *De re rust.*, 5; Scaliger, *in loc.*

are produced without the concourse of the male, and are unfit for setting; although Varro[1] declares that the mares, in Lusitania, conceive by the wind. For zephyrus was held a fertilizing wind, whence its name, as if it were ζωηφερὸς, or life-bringing. So that Virgil says:

And Zephyrus, with warming breath resolves
The bosom of the ground, and melting rains
Are poured o'er all, and every field brings
*   forth.*

Hence the ancients, when with this wind blowing in the spring season, they saw their hens begin laying, without the concurrence of the cock, conceived that zephyrus, or the west wind, was the author of their fecundity. There are also what are called addle, and dog-day eggs, produced by interrupted incubation, and so called because eggs often rot in the dog-days, being deserted by the hens in consequence of the excessive heat; and also because at this season of the year thunder is frequent; and Aristotle[2] asserts that eggs die if it thunders whilst the hen is sitting.

Those eggs are regarded as prolific, which, no unfavorable circumstances intervening, under the influence of a gentle heat, produce chicks. And this they will do, not merely through the incubation of the mother, but of any other bird, if it be but of sufficient size to cherish and cover them, or by a gentle temperature obtained in any way whatever. "Eggs are hatched with the same celerity," says Aristotle, "spontaneously in the ground, as by incubation. Wherefore in Egypt, it is the custom to bury them in dung, covered with earth. And there was a tale in Syracuse, of a drunken fellow, who was accustomed to continue his potations until a number of eggs, placed under a mat bestrewed with earth, were hatched."[3] The empress Livia, is also said to have carried an egg in her bosom until a chick was produced from it. And in Egypt, and other countries, at the present time, chickens are reared from eggs placed in ovens. "The egg, therefore," as Fabricius truly says, "is not only the uterus, and place where the generation of the chick proceeds, but it is that upon which its whole formation depends; and this the egg accomplishes as agent, as matter, as instrument, as place, and as all else that concurs."[4]

For it is certain that the chick is formed by a principle inherent in the egg, and that nothing accrues to a perfect egg from incubation, beyond the warmth and protection; in the same way as to the chick when disclosed, the hen gives nothing more than her warmth and her care, by which she defends it from the cold and from injury, and directs it to its proper food. The grand desideratum, therefore, once the chickens are hatched, is that the hen lead them about, seek for and supply them with proper food, and cherish them under her wings. And this you will not easily supply by any kind of artifice.

Capons, and hybrids between the common fowl and the pheasant, produced in our aviaries, will incubate and hatch a set of eggs; but they never know how to take care of the brood—to lead them about properly, and to provide with adequate care for their nurture.

And here I would pause for a moment (for I mean to treat of the matter more fully by and by) to express my admiration of the perseverance and patience with which the females of almost every species of bird sit upon the nest for so many days and nights incessantly, macerating their bodies, and almost destroying themselves from want of food; what dangers they will face in defence of their eggs, and when compelled to quit them for ever so short a time, through necessity, with what eagerness and haste they return to them again, and brood over them! Ducks and geese, when they quit the nest for a few minutes, cover and conceal it with straw. With what true magnanimity do these ill-furnished mothers defend their eggs! which, after all, perhaps, are mere wind or addle eggs, or not their own, or artificial eggs of chalk or ivory—it is still the same, they defend all with equal courage. It is truly a remarkable love which birds display for inert and lifeless eggs; and their solicitude is repaid by no kind of advantage or enjoyment. Who does not wonder at the affection, or passion rather, of the clucking hen, which can only be extinguished by a drenching with cold water. In this state of her feeling she neglects everything, her wings droop, her feathers are unpruned and ruffled, she wanders about restless and dissatisfied, disturbing other hens on their nests, seeking eggs everywhere, which she commences forthwith to incubate; nor will she be at peace until her desire has been gratified, until she has a brood to lead about with her, upon which she may expend her fervour, which she may cherish, feed, and defend. How pleasantly are we moved to laughter when we see the poor hen following to the

[1] *De re rust.*, II. I.
[2] *History of Animals*, VI. 2; Pliny, *Hist. nat.*, x. 54.
[3] *Ibid.*
[4] *Op. cit.*, p. 19.

water the supposititious brood of ducklings she has hatched, wandering restlessly round the pool, attempting to wade after them to her own imminent peril, and by her noises and various artifices striving to entice them back to the shore!

According to Aristotle,[1] barren eggs do not produce chicks because their fluids do not thicken under incubation, nor is the yelk or the white altered from its original constitution. But we shall revert to this subject in our general survey of generation.

Our housewives, that they may distinguish the eggs that are addled from those that will produce chicks, take them from the fourteenth to the sixteenth day of the incubation, and drop them softly into tepid water, when the spoilt ones sink, whilst the fruitful ones swim. If the included chick be well forward, and moves about with alacrity, the egg not only rolls over but even dances in the water. And if you apply the egg to your ear for several days before the hatching, you may hear the chick within kicking, scratching, and even chirping. When the hen that is sitting hears these noises, she turns the eggs and lays them otherwise than they were, until the chicks, getting into a comfortable position, become quiet; even as watchful mothers are wont to treat their infants when they are restless and cry in their cradles.

Hens lay eggs in variable numbers: "Some hens," says the philosopher, "except the two winter months, lay through the whole year; some of the better breeds will lay as many as sixty eggs before they show a disposition to sit; though these eggs are not so prolific as those of the commoner kinds. The Adrianic hens are small, and lay every day, but they are ill-tempered, and often kill their young ones; they are particoloured in their plumage. Some domestic fowls will even lay twice a day; and some, by reason of their great fecundity, die young."[2]

In England some of the hens lay every day; but the more prolific commonly lay two days continuously and then miss a day: the first day the egg is laid in the morning, next day in the afternoon, and the third day there is a pause. Some hens have a habit of breaking their eggs and deserting their nests; whether this be from disease or vice is not known.

Certain differences may also be observed in the incubation: some fowls only sit once, others twice, or thrice, or repeatedly. Florentius says that in Alexandria, in Egypt, there are fowls called *monosires*, from which the fighting cocks

are descended, which go on sitting for two or three periods, each successive brood being removed as it is hatched, and brought up apart. In this way the same hen will hatch forty, sixty, and even a greater number of chickens, at a single sitting.

Some eggs too, are larger, others smaller; a few extremely small; these, in Italy, are commonly called *centenina;* and our country folks still believe that such eggs are laid by the cock, and that were they set they would produce basilisks. "The vulgar," says Fabricius, "think that this small egg is the last that will be laid, and that it comes as the hundredth in number, whence the name; that it has no yelk, though all the other parts are present—the chalazæ, the albumen, the membranes, and the shell. And it seems probable that it is produced when all the other yelks have been fashioned into eggs, and no more remain in the vitellary; on the other hand, however, a modicum of albumen remains, and out of this, it may be inferred, is the small egg in question produced."[3] To me, nevertheless, this does not appear likely; because it is certain that the whole ovary being removed, the uterus secundus also diminishes in size in the same proportion, and shrinks into a mere membrane, which contains neither any fluid nor any albumen. Fabricius proceeds: "The *ova centenina* are met with of two kinds: one of them being without a yelk, and this is the true centenine egg, because it is the last which the hen will lay at that particular season—she will now cease from laying for a time. The other is also a small egg, but it has a yelk, and will not prove the last which the hen will then lay, but is intermediate between those of the usual size that have preceded, and others that will follow. It is of small size because there has been a failure of the vegetative function, as happens to the peach, and other fruit, of which we see many of adequate size, but a few that are very diminutive." This may be in consequence of the inclemency of the weather, or the want of sun, or from defective nutriment in point either of quantity or quality. I should not readily allow, however, that the eggs last laid are always small.

Monstrous eggs are not wanting; "for the augurs," says Aristotle, "held it portentous when eggs were laid that were all yellow; or when, on a fowl being laid open, eggs were found under the septum transversum, where the rudimentary eggs of the female usually appear, of the magnitude of perfect eggs."[4]

[1] *History of Animals*, VI. 2.
[2] *Ibid.*, VI. I

[3] *Op. cit.*, p. 10.
[4] Aldrovandus, *Ornithologica*, XIV, p. 260.

To this head may be referred those eggs that produce twins, that have two yelks. Such an egg I lately found in the uterus of a fowl, perfect in all respects, and covered with a shell; the yelks, cicatriculæ, and thicker albuminous portions being all double, and the chalazæ present in two pairs: a single thinner albumen, however, surrounded all these, and this in its turn was included within the usual double common membrane, and single shell. For, indeed, although Aristotle says that fowls always lay some eggs of this kind, I shall hardly be induced to believe that this does not occur against the ordinary course of nature. And although twin chicks are produced from such eggs as I have ascertained in opposition to the opinion of Fabricius, who says that they produce chicks having four legs, or four wings and two heads, which, however, are not capable of living, but for the most part speedily die, either by reason of want of room or of air in the shell, or because the one proves a hinderance to the other and blights it; nor can it happen that both should be equally prepared for exclusion—that one should not prove an abortion.

Briefly and summarily the differences among eggs are principally of three kinds: some are prolific, some unprolific; some will produce males and some females; some are the produce of the two sexes of the same species, others of allied species and will produce hybrids, such as we see between the common hen and the pheasant, the progeny being referrible either to the first or to the last male that had connexion with the hen. Because, according to Aristotle, "the egg, which receives its constitution by intercourse, passes from its own into another genus, if the hen be trodden when she carries either an adventitious egg or one that was conceived under the influence of another male, and this renewed intercourse take place before the yellow is changed into the white. So that hypenemic or wind eggs are made fruitful, and fruitful eggs receive the form of the male which has connexion last. But if the change has taken place into the white, it cannot happen either that the wind egg is turned into a fertile one, or that the egg which is contained in the uterus in virtue of a previous intercourse, shall be altered into the genus of the male which has the second communication."[1] For the seminal fluid of the cock, as Scaliger wittily remarks, is like a testament, the last will or disposition in which is that which stands in force.

To these particulars it might perhaps be add-

[1] *History of Animals*, VI. 21.

ed, that some eggs are more strong and lusty than others, more full of life, if the expression may be used; though as there is a vital principle in the egg, so must there inhere the corresponding virtue that flows from it. For, as in other kinds of animals, some of the females are so replete with desire, so full of Venus, that they conceive from any and every intercourse, even once submitted to, and from a weakly male, and produce several young from the same embrace; others, on the contrary, are so torpid and sluggish, that unless they are assailed by a vigorous male, under the influence of strong desire, and that not once, but repeatedly, and for a certain time, they continue barren. This is also the case with eggs, some of which, though they may have been conceived in consequence of intercourse, still remain unprolific unless perfected by repeated and continued connexions. Whence it happens that some eggs are more speedily changed by incubation than others, exhibiting traces of the fœtus from the third day; others again, either become spoiled, or suffer transformation into the fœtus more slowly, exhibiting no indications of the future chick even up to the seventh day, as shall be made to appear by and by, in speaking of the generation of the chick from the egg.

Thus far have we discoursed of the uterus of the fowl, and its function; of the production of the hen's egg, and of its differences and peculiarities, from immediate observation; and from the instances quoted, conclusions may be drawn with reference to other oviparous animals.

We have now to pursue the history of the generation and formation of the fœtus from the egg. For indeed, as I have said above, the entire contemplation of the family of birds is comprehended in these two propositions: how is an egg engendered of a male and female; and by what process do males and females proceed from eggs?—the circle by which, under favour of nature, their kinds are continued to eternity.

EXERCISE 14. *Of the production of the chick from the egg of the hen*

Of the growth and generation of the hen's egg enough has already been said; and we have now to lay before the reader our observations on the procreation of the chick from the egg—a duty which is equally difficult, and profitable, and pleasant. For in general the first processes of nature lie hid, as it were, in the depths of night, and by reason of their subtlety escape the keenest reason no less than the most piercing eye.

Nor in truth is it a much less arduous business to investigate the intimate mysteries and obscure beginnings of generation than to seek to discover the frame of the world at large, and the manner of its creation. The eternity of things is connected with the reciprocal interchange of generation and decay; and as the sun, now in the east and then in the west, completes the measure of time by his ceaseless revolutions, so are the fleeting things of mortal existence made eternal through incessant change, and kinds and species are perpetuated though individuals die.

The writers who have treated of this subject have almost all taken different paths; but having their minds preoccupied, they have hitherto gone to work to frame conclusions in consonance with the particular views they had adopted.

Aristotle,[1] among the ancients, and Hieronymus Fabricius of Aquapendente, among the moderns, have written with so much accuracy on the generation and formation of the chick from the egg that little seems left for others to do. Ulyssus Aldrovandus,[2] nevertheless, described the formation of the chick *in ovo;* but he appears rather to have gone by the guidance of Aristotle than to have relied on his own experience. For Volcherus Coiter, living at this time in Bologna, and encouraged, as he tells us, by Aldrovandus, his master, opened incubated eggs every day, and illustrated many points besides those noted by Aldrovandus;[3] these discoveries, however, could scarcely have remained unknown to Aldrovandus. Æmilius Parisanus, a Venetian physician, having discarded the opinions of others, has also given a new account of the formation of the chick from the egg.

But since our observations lead us to conclude that many things of great consequence are very different from what they have hitherto been held to be, I shall myself give an account of what goes on in the egg from day to day, and what parts are there transmuted, directing my attention to the first days especially, when all is most obscure and confused, and difficult of observation, and in reference to which writers have more particularly drawn the sword against one another in defence of their several discordant observations, which, in sooth, they accommodate rather to their preconceived opinions respecting the material and

[1] *History of Animals*, VI. 2, 3.
[2] *Ornithol.*, XIV.
[3] *Nobil. exercit.*, VI.

efficient cause of animal generation than to simple truth.

What Aristotle says on the subject of the reproduction of the chick *in ovo* is perfectly correct. Nevertheless, as if he had not himself seen the things he describes, but received them at second hand from another expert observer, he does not give the periods rightly; and then he is grievously mistaken in respect of the place in which the first rudiments of the egg are fashioned, stating this to be the sharp end, for which he is fairly challenged by Fabricius. Neither does he appear to have observed the commencement of the chick in the egg; nor could he have found the things which he says are necessary to all generation in the place which he assigns them. He will, for instance, have it that the white is the constituent matter (since nothing naturally can by possibility be produced from nothing). And he did not sufficiently understand how the efficient cause (the seminal fluid of the cock) acted without contact; nor how the egg could, of its own accord, without any inherent generative matter of the male, produce a chick.

Aldrovandus, adopting an error akin to that of Aristotle, says besides, that the yelk rises during the first days of the incubation into the sharp end of the egg, a proposition which no eyes but those of the blind would assent to; he thinks also that the chalazæ are the semen of the cock, and that the chick arises from them, though it is nourished both by the yelk and the white. In this he is obviously in opposition to Aristotle, who held that the chalazæ contributed nothing to the reproductive powers of the egg.

Volcherus Coiter is, on the whole, much more correct; and his statements are far more consonant with what the eye perceives. But his tale of the three globules is a fable. Neither did he rightly perceive the true commencement of the chick *in ovo*.

Hieronymus Fabricius contends that the chalazæ are not the sperma of the cock; but then he will have it that "from these, fecundated by the seminal fluid of the cock, as from the appropriate matter, the chick is incorporated." Fabricius observed the point of origin of the chick, the spot or cicatricula, namely, which presents itself upon the tunica propria of the yelk; but he regarded it as a cicatrice or scar left on the place where the peduncle had been attached; he viewed it as a blemish in the egg, not as any important part.

Parisanus completely refutes Fabricius'

ideas of the chalazæ; but he himself obviously raves when he speaks of certain circles, and principal parts of the fœtus, *viz.*, the liver and heart. He appears to have observed the commencement of the fœtus *in ovo;* but what it was he obviously did not know, when he says, "that the white point in the middle of the circles is the semen of the cock, from which the chick is produced."

Thus it comes to pass that everyone, in adducing reasons for the formation of the chick *in ovo*, in accordance with preconceived opinions, has wandered from the truth. Some will have it that the semen or the blood is the matter whence the chick is engendered; others, that the semen is the agent or efficient cause of its formation. Yet to him who dispassionately views the question is it quite certain that there is no prepared matter present, nor any menstruous blood to be coagulated at the time of intercourse by the semen masculinum, as Aristotle will have it; neither does the chick originate in the egg from the seed of the male, nor from that of the female, nor from the two commingled.

EXERCISE 15. *The first examination of the egg; or of the effect of the first day's incubation upon the egg*

That we may be the more clearly informed of the effect which the first day's incubation produces upon the egg, we must set out by ascertaining what changes take place in an egg spontaneously, changes that distinguish a stale egg from one that is new-laid, when what is due to the incubation *per se* will first be clearly apprehended.

The space or cavity in the blunt end is present, as we have said, in every egg; but the staler the egg the larger does this hollow continually grow; and this is more especially the case when eggs are kept in a warm place, or when the weather is hot; the effect being due to the exhalation of a certain portion of the thinner albumen, as has been stated in the history of the egg. This cavity, as it increases, extends rather in the line of the length than of the breadth of the egg, and comes finally to be no longer orbicular.

The shell, already less transparent, becomes dingy.

The albumen grows thicker and more viscid, and acquires a straw or yellow colour.

The tunica propria of the vitellus becomes more lax, and appears wrinkled, for it seems that some even of this fluid is dissipated in the course of time.

The chalazæ are found in either end of every egg, in the same situation, and having the same consistence—whether the egg be recent or stale, fruitful or barren, it does not signify; by their means a firm connexion is established between the yelk and the white, and the two fluids preserve their relative positions. The chalazæ, indeed, are two mutually opposed supports or poles, and hinges of this microcosm; and are constructed as if made up of numerous coats of the albumen, twisted together at either end into a knotted rope, by which they are attached to the vitellus. And hence it happens that the yelk is separated from the white with difficulty, unless the chalazæ are either first divided with a knife or torn with the fingers; this done, the white immediately falls away from the yelk. It is by means of these hinges that the vitellus is both retained in the centre of the egg and preserved of its proper consistence. And they are so connected that the principal part, the cicatricula, to wit, always regards the same region of the egg, or its upper part, and is preserved equidistant from either end. For this spot or cicatricula is observed to be of the same consistence, dimensions, and colour, and in the same situation in the stale as in the new-laid egg. But as soon as the egg, under the influence of the gentle warmth of the incubating hen, or of warmth derived from another source, begins to pullulate, this spot forthwith dilates, and expands like the pupil of the eye, and from thence, as the grand centre of the egg, the latent plastic force breaks forth and germinates. This first commencement of the chick, however, so far as I am aware, has not yet been observed by any one.

On the second day of the incubation, after the egg has been exposed to warmth for twenty-four hours, under the hen, as the cavity in the blunt end has enlarged greatly and descended, so has the internal constitution of the egg also begun to be changed. The yelk, which had hitherto lain in the middle of the albumen, rises towards the blunt end, and its middle, where the cicatricula is situated, is lifted up and applied to the membrane that bounds the empty space, so that the yelk now appears to be connected with the cavity by means of the cicatricula; and in the same measure as the yelk rises does the thicker portion of the albumen sink into the sharp or lower end of the egg. Whence it appears, as Fabricius rightly remarks, that Aristotle[1] was either in error, or that there is a mistake in the codex, when it is said, "In this time" (*viz.*, between three and

[1] *History of Animals*, vi. 3.

four days, and as many nights), "the yelk is brought to the summit, where the commencement of the egg is, and the egg is exposed in this part," *i. e.*, under the enlarged empty space. Now Aristotle[1] calls the principium ovi, or commencement of the egg, its smaller end, which is last extruded. But it is certain that the yelk ascends towards the blunt end of the egg, and that the cavity there enlarges. And Aldrovandus is undoubtedly in error when he speaks as if he had experience of the fact, and says that the yelk rises to the sharp end. I will confess, nevertheless, that on the second or third day I have occasionally observed the cicatricula expanded and the beginning of the chick already laid, the yelk not having yet risen; this, however, happens rarely, and I am inclined to ascribe it to some weakness in the egg.

On the second day of the incubation, or first day of inspection, the cicatricula in question is found to have enlarged to the dimensions of a pea or lentil, and is divided into circles, such as might be drawn with a pair of compasses, having an extremely minute point for their centre. It is very probable that Aldrovandus observed this spot, for he says: "In the midst of the yellow a certain whitish something makes its appearance, which was not noticed by Aristotle"; and also by Coiter, when he expresses himself thus: "On the second day there is in the middle of the yelk a part whiter than the rest"; Parisanus, too, may have seen it; he observes: "In the course of the second day I observe a white body of the size and form of a middling lentil; and this is the semen of the cock covered over with a white and most delicate tunic, which underlies the two common membranes of the entire egg, but overlies the tunica propria of the yelk." I believe, however, that no one has yet said that this cicatricula occurs in every egg, or has acknowledged it to be the origin of the chick.

Meantime the chalazæ or treadles will be seen to decline from either end of the egg towards its sides, this being occasioned by that alteration which we have noticed in the relative situations of the two fluids. The treadle from the blunt end descends somewhat; the one from the sharp end rises in the same proportion: as in a globe whose axis is set obliquely, one pole is as much depressed below the horizon as the other is raised above it.

The vitellus, too, particularly in the situation of the cicatricula, begins to grow a little more diffluent than it was, and raises its tunica

[1] *Ibid.*, III. 2.

propria (which we have found in stale eggs before incubation to be somewhat lax and wrinkled) into a tumour; and it now appears to have recovered the same colour, consistency, and sweetness of taste that it had in the egg just laid.

Such is the process in the course of the first day that leads to the production of a new being, such the earliest trace of the future chick. Aldrovandus adds: "the albumen suffers no change," which is correct; but when he asserts that "the semen of the cock can be seen in it," he as manifestly errs. Resting on a most insufficient reason, he thought that the chalazæ were the semen of the cock, "because," forsooth, "the eggs that are without chalazæ are unfruitful." This I can very well believe; for these were then no proper eggs; for all eggs, wind eggs as well as those that are prolific, have chalazæ. But he, misled perhaps by the country women, who in Italian call the chalazæ *galladura*, fell into the vulgar error. Nor is Hieronymus Fabricius guilty of a less grave mistake when he exhibits the formation of the chick in a series of engravings, and contends that it is produced from the chalazæ; overlooking the fact that the chalazæ are present the whole of the time, and unchanged, though they have shifted their places; and that the commencement of the chick is to be sought for at a distance from them.

EXERCISE 16. *Second inspection of the egg*

The second day gone by, the circles of the cicatricula that have been mentioned, have become larger and more conspicuous, and may now be of the size of the nail of the ring-finger, sometimes even of that of the middle finger. By these rings the whole cicatricula is indistinctly divided into two, occasionally into three regions, which are frequently of different colours, and bear a strong resemblance to the cornea of the eye, both as respects dimensions, a certain degree of prominence, and the presence of a transparent and limpid fluid included within it. The centre of the cicatricula here stands for the pupil; but it is occupied with a certain white speck, and appears like the pupil of some small bird's eye obscured by a suffusion or cataract, as it is called. On this account we have called the entire object the *oculum ovi*, the eye of the egg.

Within the circles of the cicatricula, I say, there is contained a quantity of perfectly bright and transparent fluid, even purer than any crystalline humour; which, if it be viewed transversely and against the light, the whole spot will rather appear to be situated in the albumen than sunk into the membrane of the yelk, as before: it presents itself as a portion of the albumen dissolved and clarified, and included within a most delicate tunica propria. Hence I entitle this fluid the *oculum seu colliquamentum album;* it is as if a portion of the albumen, liquefied by the heat, shone apart (which it does, unless disturbed by being shaken) and formed a more spirituous and better digested fluid, separated from the rest of the albumen by a tunica propria, and situated between the two masses of liquid, the yelk and the albumen. It differs from the rest of the albumen by its clearness and transparency, as the water of a pellucid spring differs from that of a stagnant pool. The tunic which surrounds this fluid is so fragile and delicate that, unless the egg be handled with great care, it is apt to give way, when the pure spring is rendered turbid by a mixture of fluids.

I was long in doubt what I should conclude as to this clear diffluent fluid, whether I should regard it as the innate heat, or radical moisture; as a matter prepared for the future fœtus, or a perfectly-concocted nourishment, such as dew is held to be among the secondary humours. For it is certain, as shall be afterwards shown, that the earliest rudiments of the fœtus are cast in its middle, that from this the chick derives its first nutriment, and even when of larger size continues to live amidst it.

This solution, therefore, increases rapidly in quantity, particularly in its internal region, which, as it expands, forces out and obliterates the external regions. This change is effected in the course of a single day, as is shown in the second figure of Fabricius. It is very much as it is with the eyes of those animals which have a very ample pupil, and see better by night than by day, such as owls, cats, and others, whose pupils expand very much in the dusk and dark, and, on the contrary, contract excessively in a brilliant light: one of these animals being taken quickly from a light into a shady place, the pupil is seen to enlarge in such wise that the coloured ring, called the iris, is very much diminished in size, and indeed almost entirely disappears.

Parisanus, falling upon these regions, is grossly mistaken when he speaks of "a honey-coloured, a white, a gray, and another white circle"; and says that "the fœtus is formed from the white middle point" (which, indeed, appears in these regions), and that "this is the semen of the cock." That he may exalt himself on

a more notable subtlety he continues: "Before any redness is apparent in the body of the fœtus, two minute vesicles present themselves in it; in the beginning, however, neither of them is tinged with red"; one of these he would have us receive as the heart, the other as the liver. But in truth there is neither any vesicle present sooner than the redness of the blood is disclosed; nor does the embryo ever suddenly become red in the course of the first days of its existence; nor yet does any of these vesicles present us with a trace of the liver. Both of them belong, in fact, to the heart, prefiguring its ventricles and auricles, and palpitating, as we shall afterwards show, they respond reciprocally by their systoles and diastoles.

Aristotle appears to have known this dissolved fluid, when he says: "A membrane, too, marked with sanguineous fibres, surrounds the white fluid at this time (the third day), arising from those orifices of the veins."[1] Now the philosopher can neither be supposed by the words "white fluid," to refer to the albumen at large, because at this period the membrane of the white is not yet covered with veins; it is only the membrane of the dissolved fluid which appears with a few branches of veins distributed over it here and there. And because he says: "this membrane, too," as if he understood another than those which he had spoken of as investing the albumen and the yelk before incubation, and designated this one as first arising after the third day, and from the orifices of the veins.

Coiter seems also to have known of this dissolved fluid; he says: "A certain portion of the albumen acquiring a white colour, another becoming thicker." The fluid in question is surrounded with its proper membrane, and is distinct and separate from the rest of the albumen before there is any appearance of blood. We shall have occasion, by and by, to speak of the singular importance of this fluid to the fœtuses of every animal. Whilst they float in it they are safe from succussion and contusion, and other external injury of every kind; and they, moreover, are nourished by it. I once showed to their Serene Majesties the King and Queen, an embryo, the size of a French-bean, which had been taken from the uterus of a doe; all its membranes were entire, and from its genital organs we could readily tell that it was a male. It was, in truth, a most agreeable natural spectacle; the embryo perfect and elegant, floating in this pure, transparent, and crystalline fluid, in-

[1] *History of Animals,* VI. 3.

vested with its pellucid tunica propria, as if in a glass vessel of the greatest purity, of the size of a pigeon's egg.

EXERCISE 17. *The third inspection of the egg*

Having seen the second process or preparation of the egg, towards the production of the embryo which presents itself in the course of the third day, we proceed to the third stage, which falls to be considered after the lapse of three days and as many nights. Aristotle says: "Traces of generation commence in the egg of the hen after three days and three nights";[1] for example, on Monday morning, if in the morning of the preceding Friday the egg has been put under the hen. This stage forms the subject of the third figure in Fabricius.

If the inspection of the egg be made on the fourth day, the metamorphosis is still greater, and the change likewise more wonderful and manifest with every hour in the course of the day. It is in this interval that the transition is made in the egg from the life of the plant to the life of the animal. For now the margin of the diffluent fluid looks red, and is purpurescent with a sanguineous line, and nearly in its centre there appears a leaping point, of the colour of blood, so small that at one moment, when it contracts, it almost entirely escapes the eye, and again, when it dilates, it shows like the smallest spark of fire. Such at the outset is animal life, which the plastic force of nature puts in motion from the most insignificant beginnings!

The above particulars you may perceive towards the close of the third day, with very great attention, and under favour of a bright light (as of the sun), or with the assistance of a magnifying glass. Without these aids you would strain your eyes in vain, so slender is the purple line, so slight is the motion of the palpitating point. But at the beginning of the fourth day you may readily, and at its close most readily, perceive the "palpitating bloody point, which already moves," says Aristotle, "like an animal, in the transparent liquid (which I call *colliquamentum*); and from this point two vascular branches proceed, full of blood, in a winding course" into the purpurescent circle and the investing membrane of the resolved liquid; distributing in their progress numerous fibrous offshoots, which all proceed from one original, like the branches and twigs of a tree from the same stem. Within the entering angle of this root, and in the middle of the resolved liquid,

[1] *Ibid.*

is placed the red palpitating point, which keeps order and rhythm in its pulsations, composed of systoles and diastoles. In the diastole, when it has imbibed a larger quantity of blood, it becomes enlarged, and starts into view; in the systole, however, subsiding instantaneously as if convulsed by the stroke, and expelling the blood, it vanishes from view.

Fabricius depicts this palpitating point in his third figure; and mistakes it—a thing which is extraordinary—for the body of the embryo; as if he had never seen it leaping or pulsating, or had not understood, or had entirely forgotten the passage in Aristotle. A still greater subject of amazement, however, is his total want of solicitude about his chalazæ all this while, although he had declared the rudiments of the embryo to be derived from them.

Ulyssus Aldrovandus, writing from Bologna nearly at the same time, says: "There appears in the albumen, as it were, a minute palpitating point, which The Philosopher declares to be the heart. And I have unquestionably seen a venous trunk arising from this, from which two other branches proceeded; these are the blood-vessels, which he says extend to either investing membrane of the yelk and white. And I am myself entirely of his opinion, and believe these to be veins, and pulsatile, and to contain a purer kind of blood, adapted to the production of the principal parts of the body, the liver, to wit, the lungs, and others of the same description."[2] Both of the vessels in question, however, are not veins, neither do they both pulsate; but one of them is an artery, another a vein, as we shall see by and by, when we shall further show that these passages constitute the umbilical vessels of the embryo.

Volcher Coiter has these words: "The sanguineous point or globule, which was formerly found in the yelk, is now observed more in the albumen, and pulsates distinctly." He says, erroneously, "formerly found in the yelk"; for the point discovered in the vitellus is white, and does not pulsate; nor does the sanguineous point or globe appear to pulsate at the end of the second day of incubation. But the point which we have indicated in the middle of the circle, and as constituting its centre in connexion with the vitellus, disappears before that point which is characterized by Aristotle as palpitating, can be discerned; or, as I conceive, having turned red, begins to pulsate. For both points are situated in the centre of the resolved fluid, and near the root of the veins which

[2] *Ornithologia*, XIV, p. 217.

thence arise; but they are never seen simultaneously: in the place of the white point there appears a red and palpitating point.

That portion of Coiter's sentence, however, where he says: "the punctus saliens is now seen in the albumen rather than in the yelk," is perfectly accurate. And, indeed, moved by these words, I have inquired whether the white point in question is turned into the blood-red point, inasmuch as both are nearly of the same size, and both make their appearance in the same situation. And I have, indeed, occasionally found an extremely delicate bright purple circle ending near the ruddy horizon surrounding the resolved liquid, in the centre of which there was the white point, but not the red and pulsating point apparent; for I have never observed these two points at one and the same time. It were certainly of great moment to determine: whether or not the blood was extant before the pulse? and whether the pulsating point arose from the veins, or the veins from the pulsating point?

So far as my observations enable me to conclude, the blood has seemed to go before the pulse. This conclusion is supported by the following instance: on Wednesday evening I set three hen's eggs, and on Saturday evening, somewhat before the same hour, I found these eggs cold, as if forsaken by the hen: having opened one of them, notwithstanding, I found the rudiments of an embryo, viz., a red and sanguinolent line in the circumference; and in the centre, instead of a pulsating point, a white and bloodless point. By this indication I saw that the hen had left her nest no long time before; wherefore, catching her, and shutting her up in a box, I kept her upon the two remaining eggs, and several others, through the ensuing night. Next morning, very early, both of the eggs with which the experiment was begun, had revived, and in the centre there was the pulsating point, much smaller than the white point, from which, like a spark darting from a cloud, it made its appearance in the diastole; it seemed to me, therefore, that the red point emanated from the white point; that the punctum saliens was in some way engendered in that white point; that the punctum saliens, the blood being already extant, was either originally there produced, or there began to move. I have, indeed, repeatedly seen the punctum saliens when all but dead, and no longer giving any signs of motion, recover its pulsatile movements under the influence of renewed warmth. In the order of generation, then, I conceive that the punctum and the blood first exist, and that pulsation only occurs subsequently.

This at all events is certain, that nothing whatever of the future fœtus is apparent on this day, save and except certain sanguineous lines, the punctum saliens, and those veins that all present themselves as emanating from a single trunk (as this itself proceeds from the punctum saliens), and are distributed in numerous branches over the whole of the colliquament or dissolved fluid. These vessels afterwards constitute the umbilical vessels, by means of which, distributed far and wide, the fœtus as it grows obtains its nourishment from the albumen and vitellus. You have a striking example of similar vessels and their branchings in the leaves of trees, the whole of the veins of which arise from the peduncle or foot-stalk, and from a single trunk are distributed to the rest of the leaf.

The entire including membrane of the colliquament traversed by blood-vessels, corresponds in form and dimensions with the two wings of a moth; and this, in fact, is the membrane which Aristotle describes as "possessing sanguineous fibres, and at the same time containing a limpid fluid, proceeding from those mouths of the veins."[1]

Towards the end of the fourth day, and the beginning of the fifth, the blood-red point, increased into a small and most delicate vesicle, is perceived to contain blood in its interior, which it propels by its contractions, and receives anew during its diastoles.

Up to this point I have not been able to perceive any difference in the vessels: the arteries are not distinguished from the veins, either by their coats or their pulsations. I am therefore of opinion that all the vessels may be spoken of indifferently under the name of veins, or, adopting Aristotle's[2] term, of venous canals.

"The punctum saliens," says Aristotle, "is already possessed of spontaneous motion, like an animal." Because an animal is distinguished from that which is none, by the possession of sense and motion. When this point begins to move for the first time, consequently, we say well that it has assumed an animal nature; the egg, originally imbued with a vegetative soul, now becomes endowed in addition with a motive and sensitive force; from the vegetable it passes into the animal; and at the same time the living principle, which fashions the chick from the egg, and afterwards gives it the measure of intelligence it manifests, enters into the embryo. For, from the actions or manifestations,

[1] *Loc. supra cit.*   [2] *Ibid.*

The Philosopher[1] concludes demonstratively, that the faculties or powers of acting are inherent, and through these the cause and principle of life, the soul, to wit, and the actions, inasmuch as manifestation is action.

I am myself further satisfied from numerous experiments, that not only is motion inherent in the punctum saliens, which indeed no one denies, but sensation also. For on any the slightest touch, you may see the point variously commoved, and, as it were, irritated; just as sensitive bodies generally give indications of their proper sensations by their motions; and, the injury being repeated, the punctum becomes excited and disturbed in the rhythm and order of its pulsations. Thus do we conclude that in the sensitive-plant, and in zoophytes, there is inherent sensibility, because when touched they contract, as if they felt uncomfortable.

I have seen, I repeat, very frequently, and those who have been with me have seen this punctum, when touched with a needle, a probe, or a finger, and even when exposed to a higher temperature, or a severer cold, or subjected to any other molesting circumstance or thing, give various indications of sensibility, in the variety, force, and frequency of its pulsations. It is not to be questioned, therefore, that this punctum lives, moves, and feels like an animal.

An egg, moreover, too long exposed to the colder air, the punctum saliens beats more slowly and languidly; by the finger, or some other warmth being applied, it forthwith recovers its powers. And further, after the punctum has gradually languished, and, replete with blood, has even ceased from all kind of motion, or other indication of life, still, on applying my warm finger, in no longer a time than is measured by twenty beats of my pulse, lo! the little heart is revivified, erects itself anew, and, returning from Hades as it were, is restored to its former pulsations. The same thing happens through heat applied in any other way—that of the fire, or of hot water—as has been proved by myself and others again and again; so that it seemed as if it lay in our power to deliver the poor heart over to death, or to recall it to life at our will and pleasure.

What has now been stated, for the most part comes to pass on the fourth day from the commencement of the incubation—I say, for the most part, because it is not invariably so, inasmuch as there is great diversity in the maturity of eggs, and some are more speedily perfected than others. As in trees laden with fruit, some,

more forward and precocious, falls from the branches, and some, more crude and immature, still hangs firmly on the bough; so are some eggs less forward on the fifth day than others in the course of the third. This, that I might give it forth as a thing attested and certain, I have repeatedly ascertained in numerous eggs, incubated for the same length of time, and opened on the same day. Nor can I ascribe it to any difference of sex, or inclemency of weather, or neglect of incubation, or to any other cause but an inherent weakness of the egg itself, or some deficiency of the native heat.

Hypenemic or unfruitful eggs, begin to change at this time, as the critical day when they must show their disposition. As fertile eggs are changed by the inherent plastic force into colliquament (which afterwards passes into blood), so do wind-eggs now begin to change and to putrefy. I have, nevertheless, occasionally observed the spot or cicatricula to expand considerably even in hypenemic eggs, but never to rise into a cumulus, nor to become circumscribed by regularly disposed concentric circles. Sometimes I have even observed the vitellus to get somewhat clearer, and to become liquefied; but this was unequally; there were flocks, as if formed by sudden coagulation, swimming dispersed through it like clouds. And although such eggs could not yet be called putrid, nor were they offensive, still were they disposed to putrefaction; and, if continued under the hen, they soon arrived at this state, the rottenness commencing at the very spot where in fruitful eggs the reproductive germ appears.

The more perfect or forward eggs then, about the end of the fourth day, contain a double or bipartite pulsating vesicle, each portion reciprocating the other's motion, in such order and manner that whilst one is contracting, the other is distended with blood and ruddy in colour; but this last contracting anon forces out its charge of blood, and, an instant being interposed, the former rises again and repeats its pulse. And it is easy to perceive that the action of these vesicles is contraction, by which the blood is moved and propelled into the vessels.

"On the fourth day," says Aldrovandus,[2] "two puncta are perceived, both of which are in motion; these, undoubtedly, are the heart and the liver, viscera which Aristotle allowed to eggs incubated for three days."

The Philosopher,[3] however, nowhere says anything of the kind; neither, for the most

[1] On the Soul.

[2] Op. cit., p. 217.

[3] On the Generation of Animals, III. 4.

part, are the viscera mentioned conspicuous before the tenth day. And I am indeed surprised that Aldrovandus should have taken one of these pulsating points for the liver, as if this viscus were ever moved in any such manner! It seems much better to believe that with the growth of the embryo one of the pulsating points is changed into the auricles, the other into the ventricles of the heart. For in the adult, the ventricles are filled in the same manner by the auricles, and by their contraction they are straightway emptied again, as we have shown in our treatise *On the Motion of the Heart and Blood*.

In more forward eggs, towards the end of the fourth day, I have occasionally found I know not what cause of obscurity intervening and preventing me from seeing these pulsating vesicles with the same distinctness as before; it was as if there had been a haze interposed between them and the eye. In a clearer light, nevertheless, and with the use of magnifying glasses, the observations of one day being further collated with those of the next succeeding day, it was discovered that the indistinctness was caused by the rudiments of the body—a nebula concocted from part of the colliquament, or an effluvium concreting around the commencements of the veins.

Aldrovandus appears to have observed this: "On the fifth day," says he, "the punctum, which we have stated to be the heart, is no longer seen to move externally, but to be covered over and concealed; still its two meatus venosi are perceived more distinctly than before, one of them being, further, larger than the other." But our learned author was mistaken here; for this familiar divinity, the heart, enters into his mansion and shuts himself up in its inmost recesses a long time afterwards, and when the house is almost completely built. Aldrovandus also errs when he says, "by the vis insita of the veins, the remaining portion of the albumen acquires a straw colour," for this colour is observed in the thicker albumen of every spoilt egg, and it goes on increasing in depth from day to day as the egg grows staler, and this without any influence of the veins, the thinner portion only being dissipated.

But the embryo enlarging, as we say below, and the ramifications of the meatus venosi extending far and wide to the albumen and vitellus, portions of both of these fluids become liquefied, not indeed in the way Aldrovandus will have it, from some vis insita in the vessels, but from the heat of the blood which they contain. For into whatsoever part of either fluid the vessels in question extend, straightway liquefaction appears in their vicinity; and it is on this account that the yelk about this epoch appears double: its superior portion, which is in juxtaposition with the blunt end of the egg, has already become more diffluent than the rest, and appears like melted yellow wax in contrast with the other colder firmer portion; like bodies in general in a state of fusion, it also occupies a larger space. Now this superior portion, liquefied by the genial heat, is separated from the other liquids of the egg, but particularly the albumen, by a tunica propria of extreme tenuity. It therefore happens that if this most delicate, fragile, and invisible membrane be torn, immediately there ensues an admixture and confusion of the albumen and vitellus, by which everything is obscured. And such an accident is a frequent cause of failure in the reproductive power (for the different fluids in question are possessed of opposite natures), according to Aristotle,[1] in the place already so frequently referred to: "Eggs are spoiled and become addled in warm weather especially, and with good reason; for as wine grows sour in hot weather, the lees becoming diffused through it (which is the cause of its spoiling), so do eggs perish when the yelk spoils, for the lees and the yelk are the more earthy portion in each. Wherefore wine is destroyed by an admixture with its dregs, and an egg by the diffusion of its yelk."[2] And here, too, we may not improperly refer to that passage where he says: "When it thunders, the eggs that are under incubation are spoiled"[3]; for it must be a likely matter that a membrane so delicate should give way amidst a conflict of the elements. And perhaps it is because thunder is frequent about the dog-days that eggs which are rotten have been called *cynosura;* so that Columella rightly informs us that "the summer solstice, in the opinion of many, is not a good season for breeding chickens."

This at all events is certain, that eggs are very readily shaken and injured when the fowls are disturbed during incubation, at which time the fluids are liquefied and expanded, and their containing membranes are distended and extremely tender.

EXERCISE 18. *The fourth inspection of the egg*

"In the course of the fifth day of incubation," says Aristotle,[4] "the body of the chick is first distinguished, of very small dimensions

[1] *On the Generation of Animals*, III. 2.
[2] *History of Animals*, VI. 2.
[3] *Ibid.*, VIII. 5.   [4] *Ibid.*, VI. 3.

indeed, and white; but the head conspicuous and the eyes extremely prominent, a state in which they afterwards continue long; for they only grow smaller and shrink at a later period. In the lower portion of the body there is no rudimentary member corresponding with what is seen in the upper part. But of the channels which proceed from the heart, one now tends to the investing membrane, the other to the yelk; together they supply the office of an umbilical cord. The chick, therefore, derives its origin from the albumen, but it is afterwards nourished by the yelk, through the umbilicus."

These words of Aristotle appear to subdivide the entire generation of the chick into three stages or periods, *viz.*: from the first day of the incubation to the fifth; from thence on to the tenth or fourteenth: and from this or that to the twentieth. It seems as if he had only given an account in his history of the circumstances he observed at these three epochs; and it is then indeed that the greatest changes take place in the egg; as if these three critical seasons, or these three degrees in the process which leads from the perfect egg to the evolution of the chicken, were especially to be distinguished. On the fourth day the first particle of the embryo appears, *viz.*: the punctum saliens and the blood; and then the new being is incorporated. On the seventh day the chick is distinguished by its extremities, and begins to move. On the tenth it is feathered. About the twentieth it breathes, chirps, and endeavours to escape. The life of the egg, up to the fourth day, seems identical with that of plants, and can only be accounted as of a vegetative nature. From this onwards to the tenth day, however, like an animal, it is possessed by a sensitive and motive principle, with which it continues to increase, and is afterwards gradually perfected, becoming covered with feathers, furnished with a beak, nails, and all else that is necessary to its escape from the shell; emancipated from which, it enters at length on its own independent existence.

Of the incidents that happen after the fourth day, Aristotle enumerates three particularly, *viz.*: the construction of the body; the distribution of the veins, which have already the office and nature of the umbilicus; and the matter whence the embryo first arises, and is constituted and nourished.

In reference to the structure of the body, he speaks of its size and colour, of the parts which are most conspicuous in it (the head and eyes), and of the distinction of its extremities.

The body is indeed extremely minute, and of the form of the common maggot that gives birth to the fly; it is of a white colour, too, like the maggot of the flesh-fly which we see cherished and nourished in putrid meat. He happily adds, "it is most remarkable for its head and eyes." For what first appears is homogeneous and indistinct, a kind of concretion or coagulation of the colliquament, like the jelly prepared from hartshorn; it is a mere transparent cloud, and scarcely recognizable, save as it appears, divided, seemingly, into two parts, one of which is globular and much larger than the other; this is the rudiment of the head, which first becomes visible on the fifth day, very soon after which the eyes are distinguishable, being from the first of large size and prominent, and marked off from the rest of the head and body by a certain circumfusion of black matter. Either of the eyes is larger than the whole of the rest of the head, in the same way as the head surpasses the remainder of the body in dimensions. The whiteness of the body, and prominence of the eyes (which, as well as the brain, are filled internally with perfectly pellucid water, but externally are of a dark colour) continue for some time—up to the tenth day, and even longer; for, as we have seen, Aristotle says that "the eyes decrease at a late period, and contract to the proper proportion." But for my own part, I do not think that the eyes of birds ever contract in the same ratio which we observe between the head and eyes of a viviparous animal. For if you strip off the integuments from the head and eyes of a fowl or another bird, you will perceive one of the eyes to equal the entire brain in dimensions; in the woodcock and others, one of the eyes indeed is as large as the whole head, if you make abstraction of the bill. But this is common to all birds that the orbit or cavity which surrounds the eye is larger than the brain, a fact that is apparent in the cranium of every bird. Their eyes, however, are made to look smaller, because every part, except the pupil, is covered with skin and feathers; neither are they possessed of such a globular form as would cause them to project; they are of a flatter configuration, as in fishes.

"In the lower part of the body," says the Philosopher, "we perceive the rudiments of no member corresponding with the superior members." And the thing is so in fact; for as the body at first appears to consist of little but head and eyes, so inferiorly there is neither any extremity—wings, legs, sternum, rump—nor any viscus apparent; the body indeed is still without any kind of proper form; in so far as I am able to perceive, it consists of a small mass adjacent to the vein, like the bent keel of a boat, like a maggot or an ant, without a vestige of ribs, wings, or feet, to which a globular and much more conspicuous mass is appended, the rudiment of the head, to wit, divided, as it seems, into three vesicles when regarded from either side, but in fact consisting of four cells, two of which, of great size and a black colour, are the rudiments of the eyes; of the remaining two one being the brain, the other the cerebellum. All of these are full of perfectly limpid water. In the middle of the blackness of the eye, the pupil is perceived shining like a transparent central spark or crystal. I imagine that three of these vesicles being particularly conspicuous, has been the cause of indifferent observers falling into error. For as they had learned from the schoolmen that there was a triple dominion in the animal body, and they believed that these principal parts, the brain, the heart, and the liver, performed the highest functions in the economy, they easily persuaded themselves that these three vesicles were the rudiments and commencements of these parts. Coiter, however, as becomes an experienced anatomist, affirms more truly that whilst he had observed the beak and eyes from the seventh day of incubation, he could yet discover nothing of the viscera.

But let us hear the Philosopher further: "Of the conduits which lead from the heart, one tends to the investing membrane, another to the yelk, in order to perform the office of umbilicus." The embryo having now taken shape, these veins do indeed perform the function of the umbilical cord, the ramifications of one of them proceeding to be distributed to the outer tunic which invests the albumen, those of the other running for distribution to the vitellary membrane and its included fluid. Whence it clearly appears that both of these fluids are alike intended for the nourishment of the embryo. And although Aristotle says that "the chick has its commencement in the albumen, and is nourished through the umbilicus by the yelk," he still does not say that the chick is formed from the albumen. The embryo, in fact, is formed from that clear liquid which we have spoken of under the name of the colliquament, and the whole of what we have called the eye of the egg is contained or included within the albumen. Neither does our author say that the whole and sole nutriment of the

embryo reaches it through the umbilicus. My own observations lead me to interpret his words in this way: although the embryo of the fowl begins to be formed in the albumen, nevertheless it is not nourished solely by that, but also by the yelk, to which one of the two umbilical conduits pertains, and from whence it derives nourishment in a more especial manner; for the albumen, according to Aristotle's opinion, is the more concoct and purer liquid, the yelk the more earthy and solid one, and, therefore, more apt to sustain the chick when it has once attained to greater consistency and strength; and further because, as shall be explained below, the yelk supplies the place of milk, and is the last part that is consumed, a residuary portion, even after the chick is born, and when it is following its mother, being still contained in its abdomen.

What has now been stated takes place from the fourth to the tenth day. I have yet to speak of the order and manner in which each of the particulars indicated transpires.

In the inspection made on the fifth day, we observed around the short vein which proceeds from the angle where the two alternately pulsating points are situated, something whiter and thicker, like a cloud, although still transparent, through which the vein just mentioned is seen obscurely, and, as it were, through a haze. The same thing I have occasionally seen in the more forward eggs in the course of the fourth day. Now this is the rudiment of the body, and from hour to hour it goes on increasing in compactness and solidity; both surrounding the afore-named vein, and being appended to it in the guise of a kind of globule. This globular rudiment far exceeds the coronal portion, as I shall call it, of the vermicular body; it is triangular in figure, being obscurely divided into three parts, like so many swelling buds of a tree. One of these is orbicular and larger than either of the other two; and it is darkened by most delicate filaments proceeding from the circumference to the centre; this appears to be the commencement of the ciliary body, and therefore proclaims that this is the part which is to undergo transformation into the eye. In its middle the minute pupil, shining like a bright point, as already stated, is conspicuous; and it was from this indication especially that I ventured to conjecture that the whole of the globular mass was the rudiment of the future head, and this black circle one of the eyes, having the other over against it; for the two are so situated that they can by no means be seen at once and together, one always lying over and concealing the other.

The first rudiment of the future body, which we have stated to sprout around the vein, acquires an oblong and somewhat bent figure, like the keel of a boat. It is of a mucaginous consistence, like the white mould that grows upon damp things excluded from the air. The vein to which this mucor attaches, as I have said, is the vena cava, descending along the spinal column, as my subsequent observations have satisfied me. And if you carefully note the order of contraction in the pulsating vesicles, you may see the one which contracts last impelling its blood into the root of this vein and distending it.

Thus there are two manifest contractions and two similar dilatations in the two vesicles which are seen moving and pulsating alternately; and the contraction of the one which precedes causes the distension or dilatation of the other; for the blood escapes from the cavity of the former vesicle, when it contracts, into that of the latter, which it fills, distends, and causes to pulsate; but this second vesicle, contracting in its turn, throws the blood, which it had received from the former vesicle, into the root of the vein aforesaid, and at the same time distends it. I go on speaking of this vessel as a vein, though from its pulsation I hold it to be the aorta, because the veins are not yet distinguished from the arteries by any difference in the thickness of their respective coats.

After having contemplated these points with great care, and in many eggs, I remained for some time in suspense as to the opinion I should adopt; whether I should conclude that the concrete appended globular mass proceeded from the colliquament in which it swam, becoming a compacted and coagulated matter in the way that clouds are formed from invisible vapour condensed in the upper regions of the air; or believe that it took its rise from a certain effluvium exhaled from the sanguineous conduit mentioned, originating by diapedesis or transudation, and by deriving nourishment from thence, was enabled to increase. For the beginnings of even the greatest things are often extremely small, and, by reason of this minuteness, sufficiently obscure.

This much I think I have sufficiently determined at all events, viz., that the puncta salientia and meatus venosi, and the vena cava itself, are the parts that first exist; and that the globular mass mentioned afterwards grows to them. I am further certain that the blood is thrown from the punctum saliens into the vein, and

that from this does the corpuscle in question grow, and by this is it nourished. The fungus or mucor first originates from an effluvium of the vein on which it appears, and it is thence nourished and made to increase; in the same way as mouldiness grows in moist places, in the dark corners of houses which long escape cleansing; or, like camphor upon cedar wood tables, and moss upon rocks and the bark of trees; lastly, as a kind of delicate down grows upon certain grubs.

Upon the same occasion I also debated with myself whether or not I should conclude, that with the coagulation of the colliquament accomplished, the rudiments of the head and body existed simultaneously with the punctum saliens and the blood, but in a pellucid state, and so delicate that they almost escaped the eye, until becoming inspissated into a fungus or mucor, they acquired a more opaque white colour, and then came into view; the blood meantime from its greater spissitude and purple colour being readily perceptible in the diaphanous colliquament. But now when I look at the thing more narrowly, I am of opinion that the blood exists before any particle of the body appears; that it is the first-born of all the parts of the embryo; that from it both the matter out of which the fœtus is embodied, and the nutriment by which it grows are derived; that it is in fine, if such thing there be, the primary generative particle. But wherefore I am led to adopt this idea shall afterwards be shown more at length when I come to treat of the primary genital part, of the innate heat, and the radical moisture; and, at the same time, conclude as to what we are to think of the vital principle (anima), from a great number of observations compared with one another.

About this period almost every hour makes a difference; every thing grows larger, more definite and distinct; the rate of change in the egg is rapid, and one change succeeds immediately upon the back of another. The cavity in the egg is now much larger, and the whole of its upper portion is empty; it is as if a fifth part of the egg had been removed.

The ramifications of the veins extend more widely, and are more numerous, not only in the colliquament as before, but they spread on one hand into the albumen, and on the other into the yelk, so that both of these fluids are everywhere covered over with blood-vessels. The upper portion of the yelk has now become much dissolved, so that it very obviously differs from the lower portion; there are now, as it were, two yelks, or two kinds of yelk; whilst the superior, like melted wax, is expanded and looks pellucid, the inferior has become more dense, and with the thicker portion of the albumen has subsided to the sharp end of the egg. The tunica propria of the upper portion of the yelk is so thin that it gives way on the slightest succussion, when there ensues admixture of the fluids, and, as we have said, interruption to the further progress of the process of generation.

And now it is that the rudiments of the embryo first become conspicuous, as may be seen in the fifth and sixth figure of Fabricius; the egg being put into fair water it will be easy to perceive what parts of the body are formed, what are still wanting. The embryo now presents itself in the form of a small worm or maggot, such as we encounter on the leaves of trees, in spots of their bark, in fruit, flowers, and elsewhere; but especially in the apples of the oak, in the centre of which, surrounded with a case, a limpid fluid is contained, which, gradually inspissated and congealed, acquires a most delicate outline, and finally assumes the form of a maggot; for some time, however, it remains motionless; but by and by, endowed with motion and sensation it becomes an animal, and subsequently it breaks forth and takes its flight as a fly.

Aristotle ascribes a similar mode of production to those creatures that are spontaneously engendered. "Some are engendered of the dew," he says, "which falls upon the leaves." And by and by he adds, "butterflies are engendered from caterpillars, but these, in their turn, spring from green leaves, particularly that species of raphanus which is called cabbage. They are smaller than millet seeds at first, and then they grow into little worms; next, in the course of three days into caterpillars; after which they cease from motion, change their shape, and pass into chrysalides, when they are inclosed in a hard shell; although, if touched, they will still move. The shell after a long time cracks and gives way, and the winged animal, which we call a butterfly, emerges."[1]

But our doctrine—and we shall prove it by and by—is, that all animal generation is effected in the same way; that all animals, even the most perfect, are produced from worms; a fact which Aristotle himself seems to have noted when he says: "In all, nevertheless, even those that lay perfect eggs, the first conception grows whilst it is yet invisible; and this, too, is the nature of the worm."[2] For there is this difference between the generation of worms and of other animals, that the former acquire dimensions before they have any definite form or are distinguished into parts, in conformity with what the philosopher says in the following sentence: "An animal is fashioned from an entire worm, not from any one particular part, as in the case of an egg, but the whole increases and becomes an articulated animal,"[3] i. e., in its growth it separates into parts.

It is indeed matter worthy of admiration that the rudiments of all animals, particularly those possessed of red blood, such as the dog, horse, deer, ox, common fowl, snake, and even man himself, should so signally resemble a maggot in figure and consistence, that with the eye you can perceive no difference between them.

Towards the end of the fifth day or the beginning of the sixth, the head is divided into three vesicles: the first of these, which is also the largest, is rounded and black; this is the eye, in the centre of which the pupil can be distinguished like a crystalline point. Under this there lies a smaller vesicle, concealed in part, which represents the brain; and over this lies the third vesicle, like an added crest or rounded summit crowning the whole, from which the cerebellum is at length produced. In the whole of these there is nothing to be discovered but a little perfectly limpid water.

And now the rudiment of the body, which we have called the carina, distinctly proclaims itself to be the spinal column, to which sides soon begin to be added, and the wings and the lower extremities present themselves, projecting slightly from the body of the maggot. The venous conduits are, further, now clearly referrible to the umbilical vessels.

EXERCISE 19. *The fifth inspection of the egg*

On the sixth day the three cells of the head present themselves more distinctly, and the coats of the eyes are now apparent; the legs and the wings also bud forth, much in the way in which, towards the end of June, we see tadpoles getting their extremities, when they quit the water, and losing their tails assume the form of frogs.

In the chick, the rump has still no other form than is conspicuous in animals at large, even in serpents; it is a round and slender tail. The substance of the heart now grows upon the pulsating vesicle; and shortly afterwards the rudiments of the liver and lungs are distinguished; the bill, too, makes its appearance at the same

---

[1] *History of Animals*, v. 19.
[2] *On the Generation of Animals*, III. 9.
[3] *History of Animals*, v. 19.

time. Everything is of a pure white colour, especially the bill. About the same epoch all the viscera and the intestines are conspicuous. But the heart takes precedence of all the parts; and the lungs are visible before the liver or brain. The eyes, however, are seen first of all, by reason of their large size and black colour.

And now, too, the embryo has a power of motion, and raises its head and slightly twists itself, although there is still nothing of the brain to be seen, but only a little limpid fluid inclosed in a vesicle. It is at length a perfect maggot, only differing from a caterpillar in this, that when worms are set free from their cells they creep about hither and thither and seek their food, whilst the worm in the egg is stationary, and, surrounded with its proper food, is furnished with aliment through the umbilicus.

The viscera and intestines being now formed, and the fœtus able to execute motions, the anterior portion of the body, without either thorax or abdomen, is perceived to be completely open; so that the heart itself, the liver and the intestines, are seen to hang pendulous externally.

Towards the end of this day and the beginning of the seventh, the toes are distinguished, and the embryo already presents the outlines of the chick, and opens its beak, and kicks with its feet; in short, all the parts are sketched out, but the eyes, above all, are conspicuous. The viscera, on the contrary, are so indistinct, that Coiter affirms, that whilst he plainly saw the eyes and beak he could discover no viscus, even obscurely and confusedly shadowed forth.

The changes that take place from the beginning of the sixth to the end of the seventh day, occur for the major part in some eggs more quickly, in others a little more tardily. The coats of the eyes are now visible, but they only include a colourless and limpid fluid in their interior. The eyes themselves project somewhat beyond their orbits, and each of them does not less exceed the brain in size, than the head with which they are connected exceeds the whole of the rest of the body.

The vesicle, which like a ridge or crest expands beyond the confines of the brain, occupies the place of the cerebellum; and, like the other vesicles, is filled with a transparent fluid.

The brain is perceived to be obscurely bipartite, and refracts the light less than the cerebellum, though it is of a whiter colour. And as the heart is seen lying without the confines of the thorax, so likewise does the cerebellum protrude beyond the limits of the head.

If the head be removed, the vessels ascending to the brain may be observed as bloody points, with the use of a magnifying glass. And now, too, the rudiments of the spine begin to be first perceived distinct from the rest of the pulp, of a milky colour, but firmer consistence. So in the same way, and like flimsy threads of a spider's web, the ribs and other bones make their appearance in the guise of milky lines, amidst the pulp of the body; and the same thing appears more clearly in the formation of the larger oviparous animals. The heart, lungs, liver, and by way of intestines certain most delicate filaments, all present themselves of a white colour. The parenchyma of the liver is developed upon delicate fibrous stamens over the umbilical vein at the part where it enters, almost in the same manner as we have said that the rudiments of the body grow to the vein descending from the heart, or the vesicula pulsans. For in the same way as grapes grow upon the stalk of the bunch, buds upon twigs, and the ear upon the straw, does the liver adhere to the umbilical vein, and arise from it, even as fungi do from trees and excessive granulations from ulcers, or as sarcoses or morbid growths spring around the minute branches of conterminous arteries by which they are nourished, and occasionally attain to an excessive size.

Looking back upon this office of the arteries, or the circulation of the blood, I have occasionally and against all expectation completely cured enormous sarcoceles, by the simple means of dividing or tying the little artery that supplied them, and so preventing all access of nourishment or spirit to the part affected; by which it came to pass that the tumour, on the verge of mortification, was afterwards easily extirpated with the knife, or the searing iron. One man in particular (and this case I can confirm by the testimony of many respectable persons) had an enormous hernia carnosa, or sarcocosis of the scrotum, larger than a human head, and hanging as low as the knee; from its upper part a fleshy mass, of the thickness of the wrist, or such a rope as is used on ship-board, extended into the abdomen; and the evil had attained to such a height, that no one durst attempt the cure, either with the knife or any other means. Nevertheless, by the procedure above indicated, I succeeded in completely removing this huge excrescence which distended the scrotum, and involved the testicle in its middle; this latter organ, with its vas præparans and vas deferens, and other parts which descend in the tunica vaginalis, being left all the while safe and uninjured. But this cure, as well as various others, accomplished in opposition to vulgar opinion and by unusual procedures, I shall relate at greater length in my *Medical Observations*, if God grant me longer life.

I mention such cases with a view of more clearly showing that the liver grows upon the vessels, and is only developed some time after the appearance of the blood; that its parenchyma is derived from the arteries whence the matter is effused, and that for a while it remains white and bloodless, like various other parts of the body. Now in the same manner and order precisely as the chick is developed from the egg, is the generation of man and other animals accomplished.

Whence it appears that the doctrine which makes the liver the author and fashioner of the blood, is altogether groundless, although both formerly and at the present time this view obtained universal assent; this was the reason wherefore the liver was reckoned as among the principal and first-formed organs of the body. This viscus indeed was so highly dignified that it was thought to be produced in the very beginning, and simultaneously with the heart, from the seminal fluid of the mother; and the medical fable of the three vesicles or three kids, as they were called, was eagerly defended. Among the number of modern abettors of such views, Parisanus has of late with confidence enough, but little skill, been singing to the old measure. These good people do not consider that the vesicles are in motion in the egg, that the heart is palpitating and the blood present and perfectly concocted, before any sign or vestige of the liver appears. The blood is much rather to be accounted the efficient cause of the liver, than this the author of the blood: for the liver is engendered after the blood, and from it, being adnate to the vessels that contain it.

But neither can I agree with the Aristotelians, who maintain that the heart is the author of the blood; for its parenchyma or proper substance arises some little time after the blood, and is superadded to the pulsating vesicles. I am, however, in much doubt as to whether the pulsating vesicle or point, or the blood itself be the older; whether it be the fluid contained, or the containing sacs. It is obvious, nevertheless, that that which contains is formed for the sake of that which is contained, and is, therefore, made later. And this much, upon the faithful testimony of our eyes, is certain, that the first particle and prime basis of the body are the veins, to which all the other parts are post-humous and superadded. But upon this point we shall say more by and by.

Meantime we may be permitted to smile at that factitious division of the parts into spermatic and sanguineous; as if any part were produced immediately from the seminal fluid, and all did not spring from the same source!

I return to our subject. The colliquament now extends over more than half the egg. The heart, hanging outwards, is at some short distance from the body. And if you look attentively you may perceive some of the umbilical vessels pulsating.

EXERCISE 20. *The sixth inspection*

Everything is still more distinct upon the seventh day, and the rudiments of several of the particular parts are now conspicuous, *viz.*, the wings, legs, genital organs, divisions for the toes, thighs, ilia, &c. The embryo now moves and kicks, and the form of the perfect chick is recognizable; from this time forward, indeed, nothing is superadded; the very delicate parts only increase in size. The more the parts grow the more is the albumen consumed, and the external membranes united come to be of the nature of the secundines, and ever more and more closely represent the umbilical cord. Wherefore I conceive that, from the seventh, we may at once pass on to the tenth day, nothing of any moment occurring in this interval which is not particularly noted by other writers, especially by Aristotle.

It happens, nevertheless, that when a number of eggs are examined together, some are found more precocious and forward, having everything more distinct; others, again, are more sluggish, and these have the parts less apparent. The season of the year, the place where the incubation is carried on, the sedulousness with which it is performed, and other accidents, have undoubtedly great influence on this diversity of result. I remember on one occasion, on the seventh day to have seen the cavity in the blunt end enlarged in a sluggish egg, the colliquament covered with veins, the vermicular embryo in its middle, the rudiments of the eyes, and all the rest as it is met with in the generality of eggs on the fifth day; but the pulsatory vesicles were not yet apparent, nor was the trunk or root of the veins from which we have said that they originate, yet to be discovered. I, therefore, regarded this egg as of a feeble nature and left behind, as possessed of an inadequate reproductive faculty, and near to its death; all the more when I observed its colliquament less pellucid and refractive than usual, and the vessels not of such a bright red colour as wont. When the vital spirit is about to escape, that part which is first influenced in generation and earliest attracts attention is also the first that fails and disappears.

EXERCISE 21. *The inspection after the tenth day*

All that presents itself on the tenth day is so accurately described by Aristotle that scarcely anything remains for us to add. Now his opinion, according to my interpretation of it, is this, *viz.*, that "on the tenth day the entire chick is conspicuous,"[1] being pellucid and white in every part except the eyes and the venous ramifications. "The head at this time is larger than the whole of the rest of the body; and eyes larger than the head are connected with it," (adhering, and being in some sort appended to the head), "but having as yet no pupils" (perfectly formed pupils must here be understood, for it is not difficult to make out the distinct tunics of the eye at this epoch); "the eyes, if removed at this time, will be found as large as beans and black, and if they be incised, a clear humour flows out, cold, and refracting the light powerfully, but nothing else," *i. e.*, in the whole head there is nothing but the limpid water which has been mentioned. Such is the state of matters from the seventh to the tenth day, as we have said above. "At the same time," he continues, "the viscera also appear, and all that appertains to the abdomen and intestines," *viz.*, the substance of the heart, the lungs, liver, &c., all of a white colour, mucilaginous, pulpy, without any kind of consistency. "The veins, too, that issue from the heart are already in connexion with the umbilicus, from which one vein extends to the membrane that includes the vitellus, which has now become more liquid and diffluent than it was originally; another to the membrane which surrounds everything" (*i. e.*, the tunica colliquamenti) "and embraces the fœtus, the vitellus and the interjacent fluid. For the embryo increasing somewhat, one portion of the vitellus is superior, another inferior; but the albumen in the middle is liquid, and still extends under the inferior portion of the vitellus, as it did previously." Thus far Aristotle.

And now the arteries are seen distinctly accompanying the veins, both those that proceed to the albumen and those that are distributed to the vitellus. The vitellus also at this time liquefies still more and becomes more diffluent,

[1] *History of Animals*, VI. 3.

not entirely, indeed, but, as already said, that portion of it which is uppermost; neither do the branches of the veins proceed to every part of the vitellus alike, but only to that part which we have spoken of as resembling melted wax. The veins that are distributed to the albumen have, in like manner, arteries accompanying them. The larger portion of the albumen now dissolves into a clear fluid, the colliquament, which surrounds the embryo that swims in its middle, and comes between the two portions of the vitellus, *viz.*, the superior and the inferior; underneath all (in the sharp end of the egg), the thicker and more viscid portion of the albumen is contained. The superior portion of the yelk already appears more liquid and diffluent than the inferior; and wherever the branches of the veins extend, there the matter seems suddenly to swell and become more diffluent.

"On the tenth day," continues our author, "the albumen subsides, having now become a small tenacious, viscid, and yellowish mass"— so much of it, that is to say, as has not passed into the state of colliquament.

For already the larger portion of the white has become dissolved, and has even passed into the body of the embryo, *viz.*, the whole of the thinner albumen, and the greater portion of the thicker. The yelk, on the contrary, rather looks larger than it did in the beginning. Whence it clearly appears that the yelk has not as yet served for the nutrition of the embryo, but is reserved to perform this office by and by. In so far as we can conjecture from the course and distribution of the veins, the embryo from the commencement is nourished by the colliquament; upon this blood-vessels are first distributed, and then they spread over the membrane of the thinner albumen, next over the thicker albumen, and finally over the vitellus. The thicker albumen serves for nutriment after the thinner; the vitellus is drawn upon last of all.

The delicate embryo, consequently, whilst it is yet in the vermicular state, is nourished with the thinnest and best concocted aliment, the colliquament and thinner albumen; but when it is older it has food supplied to it more in harmony with its age and strength.

Aristotle describes the relative situation of the several parts in the following words: "In the anterior and posterior part, the membrane of the egg lies under the shell—I do not mean the membrane of the shell itself, but one under this, in which there is contained a clear fluid"—

the colliquament; "then the chick and the membrane including it, which keeps it distinct from the fluid around it." But here I suspect that there is an error in the text; for as the author himself indicates the thing, it ought rather to stand thus: "then the chick, enveloped in a membrane, continues or swims in the clear fluid"; which membrane is not exterior to the one that immediately lines the shell, but another lying under this; which, when the first or external albumen is consumed, and the remainder of the thicker albumen is depressed into the sharp end of the egg, of two membranes forms a single tunic that now begins to present itself like the secundine called the chorion. And Aristotle says well, "there is a clear fluid contained in it," by which words he does not mean the albumen, but the colliquament derived from the albumen, and in which the embryo swims; for the albumen that remains subsides into the small end of the egg.

EXERCISE 22. *The inspection after the fourteenth day*

From the seventh to the fourteenth day everything has grown and become more conspicuous. The heart and all the other viscera have now become concealed within the abdomen of the embryo, and the parts that formerly were seen naked and projecting externally, can now only be perceived when the thorax and abdomen are laid open. The chick too now begins to be covered with feathers, the roots of which are first perceived as black points. The pupils of the eyes are distinguished; the eyelids appear, as does also the membrana nictitans in the greater canthus of the eye, a membrane which is proper to birds, and which they use for cleansing the eyeball. The convolutions of the brain further make their appearance; the cerebellum is included within the skull; and the tail acquires the characteristic shape of the bird's rump.

After the fourteenth day the viscera, which up to this time have been white, gradually begin to assume a flesh or reddish colour. The heart, having now entered the penetralia of the thorax and been covered with the sternum, inhabits the dwelling place which itself had formed. The cerebrum and cerebellum acquire solidity under the dome of the skull; the stomach and intestines, however, are not yet included within the abdomen, but, connected with the parts within, hang pendulous externally.

Of the two vessels that proceed from the ab-domen to the umbilicus, near the anus, one is an artery, as its pulse proclaims, and arises from the arteria magna or aorta, the other is a vein, and extends from the vitellus by the side of the intestines to the vena portæ, situated in the concave part of the liver. The other trunk of the umbilical vessels, collecting its branches from the albumen, passes the convexity of the liver, and enters the vena cava near the base of the heart.

As all these things go on becoming clearer from day to day, so the greater portion of the albumen is also gradually consumed; this, however, is nowise the case with the vitellus, which remains almost entire up to this time, and indeed is seen of the same size as it was the first day.

In the course of the following days five umbilical vessels are conspicuous; one of these is the great vein, arising from the cava above the liver, and distributing its branches to the albumen; two other veins proceed from the porta, both having the same origin, and run to the two portions of the vitellus, which we have but just described; and these are accompanied by two arteries arising one on either side from the lumbars.

The chick now occupies a larger space in the egg than all the rest of the matter included in it, and begins to be covered with feathers; the larger the embryo grows, the smaller is the quantity of albumen that is present. It is also worthy of observation, that the membrane of the colliquament which we have said unites with the external investing membrane, and constitutes the secundine or chorion, now includes the whole of the vitellus in one, and becoming contracted, draws the vitellus along with the intestines towards the chick, conjoins them with its body, and incloses them, as it were, in a thick sac. Everything that was previously extremely delicate and transparent, becomes more opaque and fleshy as the sac contracts, which at length, like a hernial tumour of the scrotum, includes and supports both the intestines and the yelk; contracting every day in a greater and greater degree, it comes finally, to constitute the abdomen of the chick. You will find the yelk, about the eighteenth day, lying among the intestines, the belly at large being lax; yet are the parts not so firmly fixed but that the intestines (as in the case of a scrotal hernia), along with the vitellus, can be pushed up into the belly, or forced out of it as it were into a pouch. I have occasionally seen the vitellus prolapsed in this way from the abdominal cavity of a pigeon, which had been prematurely excluded from the shell in the summer season.

The chick at this epoch looks big-bellied and as if it were affected with a hernia, as I have said. And now the colliquament, which was at first in large quantity, gradually grows turbid, suffers change, and is consumed, so that the chick comes to lie bent over the vitellus. At the same period, before the liver assumes its sanguineous colour, and performs the business of what is called the second concoction, the bile, which is commonly believed to be separated as an excretion by the power of the liver, is seen of a green colour between the lobes of that organ. In the cavity of the stomach there is a limpid fluid contained, obviously of the same appearance and taste as the colliquament in which the fœtus swims; this passing on by the intestines, gradually changes its colour, and is converted into chyle; and finally in the lower portion of the bowels an excrementitious matter is encountered, of the same character as that which is met with in the lower intestines of chicks already excluded from the egg. When the chick is further advanced you may even see this fluid concocted and coagulated; just as in those animals that feed on milk, a coagulum is formed, which afterwards separates into serum and firmer curd.

When the albumen is almost all removed, and only a very small quantity of the colliquament is left, for several days before the exclusion, the chick no longer swims, but, as I have said, bends over the vitellus; and rolled up into a round ball, with the head for the most part placed between the right thigh and wing, it is seen with its beak, nails, feathers, and all other parts complete. Sometimes it sleeps, and sometimes it wakes, and moving about it breathes and chirps. If you apply the egg to your ear, you will hear the chick within making a noise, kicking, and unquestionably chirping; according to Aristotle, he now also uses his eyes. If you cautiously drop the egg into warm water, it will swim, and the chick within, aroused by the warmth, will leap, and, as I have already said, cause the egg to tumble about. And it is by this means that our country folks distinguish prolific from unproductive eggs which sink when put into water.

When the albumen is entirely gone, just before the exclusion, the umbilical vessel, which we have described as distributed to the albumen, is obliterated; or as Aristotle says, "that umbilicus which proceeds to the external secun-

dines is detached from the animal and dies; but the one which leads to the vitellus becomes connected with the small intestine of the chick."[1]

The excrement that is first formed in the intestines is white and turbid, like softened eggshell; and some of the same matter may be found contained in the secundines. The philosopher admits this when he says: "At the same time, too, the chick discharges a large quantity of excrement into the outer membrane; and there are white excrements within the abdomen, as well as those that have been evacuated."

Time running on, very shortly before the exclusion, light green fæces are formed, similar to those which the chick discharges when excluded from the egg. In the crop, too, we can discover a portion of the colliquament which has been swallowed; and in the stomach some curd or coagulum.

Up to this time the liver has not yet acquired its purple or blood-red colour, but has a tint verging from white into yellow, such as the liver of fishes presents. The lungs, however, are of a florid red.

The yelk is now contained in the abdomen among the intestines: and this is the case not merely whilst the chick is in the egg, but even after its exclusion, and when it is running about following its mother in search of food. So that what Aristotle frequently asserts appears to be absolutely true, viz., that the yelk is destined for the food of the chick; and the chick does certainly use it for food, included in his interior as it is, during the few first days after his exclusion, and until such time as his bill gains the hardness requisite to break and prepare his food, and his stomach the strength necessary to digest it. And, indeed, the yelk of the egg is very analogous to milk. Aristotle gives us his support in this opinion in the place already so frequently referred to: "The chick now lies over much of the yellow, which at last diminishes, and, in process of time, disappears entirely, being all taken into the body of the bird, where it is stored, so that on the tenth day after the exclusion of the chick, if the belly be laid open, you will still find a little of the yelk upon the intestines."[2] I have myself found certain remains of the yelk even upon the thirteenth day; and if the argument derivable from the duct of the umbilical veins which we have described as terminating in the porta of the liver by one or another trunk be of any avail, the chick is already nourished almost in the

[1] *History of Animals*, vi. 3.
[2] *Ibid.*

same manner as it is subsequently, the sustenance being attracted from the yelk by the umbilical vessels, in the same way as chyle is by and by transmitted by the mesenteric veins from the intestines. For the vessels terminate in either case in the porta of the liver, to which the nourishment attracted in the same way is in like manner transmitted. It is not necessary, therefore, to have recourse to any lacteal vessels of the mesentery, which, in the feathered tribes, are nowhere to be distinguished.

Let me be permitted here to add what I have frequently found: with a view to discovering more distinctly the relative situations of the embryo and the fluids, I have boiled an egg hard, from the fourteenth day of the incubation up to the day when the exclusion would have taken place, the major part of the albumen being already consumed, and the vitellus divided. Breaking the shell, and regarding the position of the chick, I found both the remains of the albumen and the two portions of the vitellus (which we have said are divided by the colliquation induced by the gentle heat) possessing the consistency, colour, taste, and other qualities which distinguish the yelks of unincubated eggs similarly boiled. I have, therefore, frequently asked myself how it came to pass that unprolific eggs set under a hen are made to putrefy and become offensive by the same extraneous heat which produces no such effect upon prolific eggs, both of the fluids of which remain sweet and unchanged, although they have an embryo in the midst of them (and this even containing some small quantity of excrementitious matter within it), so that did any one eat the yelk of such an egg in the dark, he would not distinguish it from that of a fresh egg which had never been sat upon.

EXERCISE 23. *Of the exclusion of the chick, or the birth from the egg*

The egg is, as we have said, a kind of exposed uterus, and place in which the embryo is fashioned: for it performs the office of the uterus and enfolds the chick until the due time of its exclusion arrives, when the creature is born perfect. Oviparous animals consequently are not distinguished from viviparous by the circumstance of the one bringing forth their young alive, and the other not doing so; for the chick not only lives and moves within the egg, but even breathes and chirps whilst there; and, when it escapes from the shell, enjoys a more perfect existence than the fœtus of animals in general. Oviparous and viviparous animals rather differ in their modes of bringing forth; the uterus or place in which the embryo is formed being within the animal in viviparous tribes, where it is cherished and brought to maturity, whilst in oviparous tribes the uterus, or egg, is exposed or without the animal, which, nevertheless, by sitting on it does not cherish it less truly than if it were still contained within the body.

For though the mother occasionally quits her eggs on various errands, it is only for a short season; she still has such affection for them that she speedily returns, covers them over, cherishes them beneath her breast and carefully defends them; and this on to the twenty-first or twenty-second day, when the chicks, in search of freer air, break the shell and emerge into the light.

Now we must not overlook a mistake of Fabricius, and almost every one else in regard to this exclusion or birth of the chick. Let us hear Fabricius.

"The chick wants air sooner than food, for it has still some store of nourishment within it; in which case the chick, by his chirping, gives a sign to his mother of the necessity of breaking the shell, which he himself cannot accomplish by reason of the hardness of the shell and the softness of his beak, to say nothing of the distance of the shell from the beak, and of the position of the head under the wing. The chick, nevertheless, is already so strong, and the cavity in the egg is so ample, and the air contained within it so abundant, that the breathing becomes free and the creature can emit the sounds that are proper to it; these can be readily heard by a bystander, and were recognized both by Pliny and Aristotle,[1] and perchance have something of the nature of a petition in their tone. For the hen hearing the chirping of the chick within, and knowing thereby the necessity of now breaking the shell in order that the chick may enjoy the air which has become needful to it, or if you will, you may say, that desiring to see her dear offspring, she breaks the shell with her beak, which is not hard to do, for the part over the hollow, long deprived of moisture, and exposed to the heat of incubation, has become dry and brittle. The chirping of the chick is consequently the first and principal indication of the creature desiring to make its escape, and of its requiring air. This the hen perceives so nicely, that if she hears the chirping to be low and internal, she straightway turns the egg over with her feet, that she may break the shell

[1] Pliny, x. 53; Aristotle, *History of Animals*, vi. 3.

at the place whence the voice proceeds without detriment to the chick."[1] Hippocrates adds, "Another indication or reason of the chick's desiring to escape from the shell, is that when it wants food it moves vigorously, in search of a larger supply, by which the membrane around it is torn, and the mother breaking the shell at the place where she hears the chick moving most lustily, permits it to escape."[2]

All this is stated pleasantly and well by Fabricius; but there is nothing of solid reason in the tale. For I have found by experience that it is the chick himself and not the hen that breaks open the shell, and this fact is every way in conformity with reason. For how else should the eggs that are hatched in dunghills and ovens, as in Egypt and other countries, be broken in due season, where there is no mother present to attend to the voice of the supplicating chick, and to bring assistance to the petitioner? And how again are the eggs of sea and land tortoises, of fishes, silkworms, serpents, and even ostriches to be chipped? The embryos in these have either no voice with which they can notify their desire for deliverance, or the eggs are buried in the sand or slime where no chirping or noise could be heard. The chick therefore is born spontaneously, and makes its escape from the eggshell through its own efforts. That this is the case appears from unquestionable arguments: when the shell is first chipped, the opening is much smaller than accords with the beak of the mother; but it corresponds exactly to the size of the bill of the chick, and you may always see the shell chipped at the same distance from the extremity of the egg, and the broken pieces, especially those that yield to the first blows, projecting regularly outwards in the form of a circlet. But as anyone on looking at a broken pane of glass can readily determine whether the force came from without or from within, by the direction of the fragments that still adhere, so in the chipped egg it is easy to perceive, by the projection of the pieces around the entire circlet, that the breaking force comes from within. And I myself and many others with me besides, hearing the chick scraping against the shell with its feet, have actually seen it perforate this part with its beak, and extend the fracture in a circle like a coronet. I have further seen the chick raise up the top of the shell upon its head and remove it.

We have gone at length into some of these matters, as thinking that they were not without all speculative interest, as we shall show by and by. The arguments of Fabricius are easily answered. For I admit that the chick *in ovo* produces sounds, and these perchance may even have something of the implorative in their nature; but it does not therefore follow that the shell is broken by the mother. Neither is the bill of the chick so soft, nor yet so far from the shell, that it cannot pierce through its prison walls, particularly when we see that the shell, for the reasons assigned, is extremely brittle. Neither does the chick always keep its head under its wing, so as to be thereby prevented from breaking the shell, but only when it sleeps or has died. For the creature wakes at intervals and scrapes and kicks, and struggles, pressing against the shell, tearing the investing membranes, and chirps (and that this is done whilst petitioning for assistance I willingly concede), all of which things may readily be heard by any one who will use his ears. And the hen listening attentively when she hears the chirping deep within the egg does not break the shell, but she turns the egg with her feet and gives the chick within another and a more commodious position. But there is no occasion to suppose that the chick by his chirping informs his mother of the propriety of breaking the shell, or seeks deliverance from it. For very frequently for two days before the exclusion you may hear the chick chirping within the shell. Neither is the mother, when she turns the egg, looking for the proper place to break it; but as the child when uncomfortably laid in his cradle is restless and whimpers and cries, and his fond mother turns him this way and that, and rocks him till he is composed again, so does the hen when she hears the chick restless and chirping within the egg, and feels it, when hatched, moving uneasily about in the nest, immediately raise herself and observe that she is not pressing on it with her weight, or keeping it too warm, or the like, and then with her bill and her feet she moves and turns the egg until the chick within is again at its ease and quiet.

EXERCISE 24. *Of twin-bearing eggs*

Twin-bearing eggs are such as produce twin chickens, and according to Aristotle, "are possessed of two yelks, which, in some are separated by a layer of thin albumen, that they may less encroach on one another; in others, however, there is nothing of the sort, and then the two yelks are in contact."[3]

I have frequently seen twin eggs, each of the

[1] *Op. cit.*, p. 59.
[2] In the book *De nat. pueri.*
[3] *History of Animals*, VI. 3.

yelks in which was surrounded by an albumen, with common and proper membranes surrounding them. I have also met with eggs having two yelks connate, as it were, both of which were embraced by a single and common albumen.

"Some fowls" says Aristotle,[1] "always produce twins, in which the particulars relating to the yelk that have been stated are clearly perceived. A certain fowl laid within two of twenty eggs, all of which, except those that were unprolific, produced twins. Of the twins, however, one was always larger, the other smaller, and the smaller chick was frequently deformed in addition."

With us twin eggs are occasionally produced, and twin chicks too, although very rarely, are engendered. I have never myself, however, seen both of these chicks live and thrive; one of them either died within the egg or at the time of the exclusion. And this the words of Aristotle prepare us to expect, when he says "one of the two is larger, the other smaller"; this is as much as to say that one of them is stronger and of greater age, the other weaker and less prepared for quitting the shell: my own opinion, therefore, is that the two yelks are of different origins and maturity. It is therefore scarcely possible but that the stronger and more advanced chick, if the egg be broken and it emerge into the light, will cause the blight and abortion of the other. But if the stronger bird do not chip the shell, he himself is threatened with a present danger, *viz.*, want of air. At the exclusion from the shell, consequently, certain death hangs over one or other, if not over both.

Fabricius, either not observing the above words of Aristotle, or neglecting them, says: "If an egg have now and then two yelks, it engenders a chick having four legs or wings, and two heads—a monster, in short; never two chicks distinct from one another, and that can be spoken of as a pair; there is but one trunk, to which are appended two heads," &c.

Whence we may infer that he himself had never seen nor heard from credible persons that such eggs produce two pullets, and therefore that he agrees with me in regarding such eggs as rare, and in holding that they never produce two chicks both alike capable of living.

I am surprised, nevertheless, that, with the authority of Aristotle before him, he should have said that "two chicks, distinct and separate, are *never* produced from such eggs," but always a monster; the rather as he thinks that

[1] *Ibid.*

the embryo is engendered from the chalazæ as from the appropriate matter, and he could not but see that there are four chalazæ in every twin-egg.

I should rather imagine that when two vitelli are included by the same albumen in a twin-egg, and are so intimately associated that their cicatriculæ, when they are resolved together, constitute a single eye or colliquament, may engender a monstrous embryo with four feet, two heads, &c., because I see nothing to hinder this; and such a production do I conceive to have been engendered by the egg of which Fabricius speaks.

But where two yelks have existed separately, parted by their several membranes, and furnished with chalazæ, albumens, and all else requisite to the generation of the chick, I hold that we must conclude, with Aristotle, that such an egg, as it has all the parts of two eggs except the shell, so does it also possess the faculty or faculties of as many; and unless it be a wind or barren egg, that it will for the most part produce two embryos, and but rarely a single monstrous individual.

EXERCISE 25. *Certain deductions from the preceding history of the egg*

Such is the history of the hen's egg; in which we have spoken of its production, and of its action or faculty to engender a chick, at too great length, it may appear to those who do not see the end and object of such painstaking, of such careful observation. Wherefore I think it advisable here to state what fruits may follow our industry, and in the words of the learned Lord Verulam, to "enter upon our second vintage." Certain theorems, therefore, will have to be gathered from the history given; some of which will be quite certain, some questionable and requiring further sifting, and some paradoxical and opposed to popular persuasion. Some of these, moreover, will have reference to the male, some to the female, several to the egg, and finally, a few to the formation of the chick. When these have been carefully discussed *seriatim*, we shall be in a condition to judge with greater certainty and facility of the generation of all other animals.

EXERCISE 26. *Of the nature of the egg*

Of the theorems that refer to the egg, some teach us what it is, some show its mode of formation, and others tell of the parts which compose it.

It is certain, in the first place, that one egg

produces one chick only. Although the egg be in a certain sense an external uterus, still it most rarely engenders several embryos, but by far the most frequently produces no more than a single pullet. And when an egg produces two chicks, which it does sometimes, still is this egg to be reputed not single but double, and as possessed of the nature and parts of two eggs.

For an egg is to be viewed as a conception proceeding from the male and the female, equally endued with the virtue of either, and constituting an unity from which a single animal is engendered.

Nor is it the beginning only, but the fruit and conclusion likewise. It is the beginning as regards the being to be engendered; the fruit in respect of the two parents: at once the end proposed in their engendering, and the origin of the chick that is to be. "But the seed and the fruit," according to Aristotle,[1] "differ from one another in the relations of prior and posterior; for the fruit is that which comes of another, the seed is that from which this other comes: were it otherwise, both would be the same."

The egg also seems to be a certain mean; not merely in so far as it is beginning and end, but as it is the common work of the two sexes and is compounded by both; containing within itself the matter and the plastic power, it has the virtue of both, by which it produces a fœtus that resembles the one as well as the other. It is further a mean between the animate and the inanimate world; for neither is it wholly endowed with life, nor is it entirely without vitality. It is still further the mid-passage or transition stage between parents and offspring, between those who are, or were, and those who are about to be; it is the hinge and pivot upon which the whole generation of the bird revolves. The egg is the terminus from which all fowls, male and female, have sprung, and to which all their lives tend— it is the result which nature has proposed to herself in their being. And thus it comes that individuals in procreating their like for the sake of their species, endure for ever. The egg, I say, is a period or portion of this eternity; for it were hard to say whether an egg exists for the sake of the chick that it engenders, or the pullet exists for the sake of the egg which it is to engender. Which of these was the prior, whether with reference to time or nature—the egg or the pullet? This question, when we come to speak of the generation of animals in general, we shall discuss at length.

[1] On the Generation of Animals, i. 13.

The egg, moreover—and this is especially to be noted—corresponds in its proportions with the seeds of plants, and has all the same conditions as these, so that it is to be regarded, not without reason, as the seed or sperma of the common fowl, in the same way as the seeds of plants are justly entitled their eggs, not only as being the *matter* or that from which, but the *efficient* or that by which the pullet is engendered. In which, finally, no part of the future offspring exists *de facto*, but in which all parts inhere *in potentia*.

The seed, properly so called, differs, however, from the *geniture*, which by Aristotle is defined to be "that which, proceeding from the generator, is the cause, that which first obtains the principle of generation; in those, to wit, whom nature destined to copulate. But the seed is that which proceeds from these two in their connexion: and such is the seed of all vegetables, and of some animals, in which the sexes are not distinct; like that which is first produced by male and female commingled, a kind of promiscuous conception, or animal; for this already possesses what is required of both."

The egg, consequently, is a natural body endowed with animal virtues, *viz.*, principles of motion and rest, of transmutation and conservation; it is, moreover, a body which, under favorable circumstances, has the capacity to pass into an animal form; heavy bodies indeed do not sink more naturally, nor light ones float, when they are unimpeded, than do seeds and eggs in virtue of their inherent capacity become changed into vegetables and animals. So that the seed and the egg are alike the fruit and final result of the things of which they are the beginning and efficient cause.

For a single pullet there is a single egg; and so Aristotle says: "from one seed one body is engendered; for example, from a single grain of wheat one plant; from a single egg one animal; for a twin egg is, in fact, two eggs."[2]

And Fabricius with truth observes: "The egg is not only an exposed uterus, and place of generation, but that also on which the whole reproduction of the pullet depends, and which the egg achieves as agent, as matter, as instrument, as seat, and all else, if more there be, that is needful to generation."[3] He shows it to be an organ because it consists of several parts, and this, from the statement of Galen, who will have the very essence of an organ to be that "it

[2] Ibid., i. 20.
[3] Loc. cit., p. 47.

consist of several parts, all of which conspire to one and the same action though diverse in faculty and use; for some are principal instruments in the action; some are indispensable to it—without them it could not take place; some secure its better performance; and some, in fine, are extant for the safety and preservation of everything else." He also shows it to be an *agent*, when from Aristotle and Galen he lays down the two actions of the egg, *viz.*: "the generation of the chick, and the growth and nutrition of the pullet." At the conclusion he expresses himself clearly in these words: "In the works of nature we see conjunct and one, the artificer, the instrument, and the matter; the liver, for instance, is both the agent and the instrument for the production of the blood; and so every part of the body; Aristotle,[1] therefore, said well that the moving powers were not easily distinguished from the instruments. In artificial things, indeed, the artificer and the instrument are distinct, as much so as the workman and his hammer, the painter and his pencil. And the reason adduced by Galen[2] is this: that in things made by art the artificer is without the work; in natural things, again, the artificer is within it, conjunct with the instruments, and pervading the whole organization."

To this I add these perspicuous words of Aristotle. "Of extant things some are consistent with nature, others with other causes. Animals and their parts, and plants, and simple bodies, as earth, fire, air, and water, consist with nature, and are allowed universally to do so; but these bodies differ entirely from those that do not consist with nature. For whatsoever consists with nature is seen to have within itself a principle of motion and of rest, now according to place, now according to increment and decrement, and again according to change. A couch or litter, a garment, and other things of the same description, however designated, inasmuch as they are made by art, have no inherent faculty of change; but inasmuch as they are made of earth, or stone, or of mixtures of these, they have such a faculty. As if nature were a certain principle and cause wherefore that should move and be at rest in which she inheres originally, independently, and not by accident. I say, particularly, *not by accident*, because it might happen that one being a physician should himself be the cause of his own good health; but he is not familiar with medi-

cine in the same respect as he has worked his own cure; it happens simply that the man who here recovers his health is a physician. It, therefore, occasionally happens that these two things are distinct and separate. But it is not otherwise with everything besides that is of art: none of these has in itself a principle of performance or action, though some of them have such a principle in other things and beyond themselves, such as a house, and aught else that is made with hands; and some have even such a principle inherent, but not *per se* and independently: everything, for example, may by accident become a cause to itself. Nature is, therefore, as stated; and those things have nature within them which possess this principle. Now all such are substances; for nature is always some subject, and inheres in the subject."[3]

These things I have spoken of at length, and even quoted the words of the writers appealed to, that it might thence appear first, that all I attribute to the egg is actually there, *viz.*: matter, organ, efficient cause, place, and everything else requisite to the generation of the chick; and next more especially, that the truth in regard to the following very difficult questions might be made clearly to appear, *viz.*: Which and what principle is it whence motion and generation proceed? By what virtue does the semen act, according to Aristotle? What is it that renders the semen itself fruitful? (for the philosopher will have it that nature in all natural bodies is the innate principle of motion and of rest, and not any second accident). Whether is that which in the egg is cause, artificer, and principle of generation and of all the vital and vegetative operations—conservation, nutrition, growth—innate or superadded? And whether does it inhere primarily, of itself, and as a kind of nature, or intervene by accident, as the physician in curing diseases? Whether is that which transforms the egg into a pullet inherent or acquired, or is it already conceived in the ovary, and does it nourish, augment, and perfect the egg there?

What is it besides that preserves the egg sweet after it is laid? What is it that renders an egg fruitful—is it to be called soul, or a portion of the soul, or something belonging to the soul, or something having a soul, or is it intelligence, or, finally, is it Divinity seeing that it acts to a definite end, and orders all with inimitable providence and art, and yet in an incomprehensible manner, always obtaining what is best both for simple being and for well-being,

---

[1] *On the Generation of Animals*, II. 4.
[2] *De form. foet.*

[3] *Physics*, II. I.

for protection also and for ornament? And all this not only in the fruitful egg which it fecundates, but in the hypenemic egg which it nourishes, causes to increase, and preserves. Nay, it is not merely the vitellus in the vitellarium or egg-bed, but the smallest speck whence the yelk is produced, of no greater size than a millet or a mustard-seed, that it nourishes and makes to grow, and finally envelopes with albumen, and furnishes with chalazæ, and surrounds with membranes and a shell. For it is probable that even the barren egg, whilst it is included within the fowl and is connected with her, is nourished and preserved by its internal and inherent principle, and made to increase (not otherwise than the eggs of fishes and frogs, exposed externally, increase and are perfected), and to be transformed from a small speck into a yelk, and transferred from the ovary to the uterus (though it have no connexion with the uterus), there to be endued with albumen, and at length to be completed with its chalazæ, membranes, and shell.

But what that may be in the hypenemic egg as well as in the fruitful one, which in a similar manner and from the same causes or principles produces the same effects; whether it be the same soul, or the same part of the soul, or something else inherent in both, must be worthy of inquiry: it seems probable, however, that the same things should proceed from similar causes.

Although the egg whilst it is being produced is contained within the fowl, and is connected with the ovary of the mother by a pedicle, and is nourished by blood-vessels, it is not therefore to be spoken of as a part of the mother; nor is it to be held as living and vegetating through her vital principle, but by a virtue peculiar to itself and an internal principle; just as fungi, and mosses, and the mistletoe, which although they adhere to vegetables and are nourished by the same sap as their leaves and germs, still form no part of these vegetables, nor are they ever so esteemed. Aristotle, with a view to meeting these difficulties, concedes a vegetative soul to the egg, even to the hypenemic one. He says: "Females, too, and all things that live are endowed with the vegetative virtue of the soul, as has been often said; and therefore this egg is perfect as the conception of a plant, but imperfect as that of an animal."[1] And he inculcates the same doctrine elsewhere, when he asks: "In what manner or sense are hypenemic eggs said to live? For they cannot do so in the same sense as fruitful eggs, otherwise a living thing might

be engendered by their agency. Nor do they comport themselves like wood or stone; because these perish by a kind of corruption, as having formerly had life in a certain manner. It is positive, therefore, that hypenemic eggs have a certain kind of soul potentially; but what? of necessity that ultimate soul, which is the appanage of vegetables; for this equally inheres in all things, in animals as well as vegetables."[2]

But it is not the same soul that is found in hypenemic as in fruitful eggs; otherwise would a pullet be indifferently produced from both; but how and in what respects the soul attached to each is different from the other, Aristotle does not sufficiently explain, when he inquires: "Wherefore are all the parts of an egg present in the hypenemic egg, and it still incapable of producing a chick? because," he replies, "it is requisite that it have a sensitive soul."[3] As if in fruitful eggs, besides the vegetative soul, there were a sensitive soul present. Unless you understand the vegetative soul as inhering *actually* in the fruitful egg, which contains the sensitive soul within it *potentially;* whence the animal, and the sensible parts of the animal are subsequently produced. But neither do writers satisfactorily untie this knot, nor set the mind of the inquirer free from the difficulties that entangle him. For he sees that the egg is a true animal seed, according to this sentence of the Stagyrite: "In those things endowed with life, in which the male and female sexes are not distinct, the seed is already present as a conception. I entitle *conception* the first mixture from the male and female (the analogue of the vegetable seed therefore). Wherefore from one seed there is engendered one body, as from one egg one animal."[4]

It appears, consequently, that for one egg there is one soul or vital principle. But whether is this that of the mother, or that of the father, or a mixture of the two? And here the greatest difficulties are occasioned by those eggs that are produced by the concurrence of animals of different species, as, for example, of the common fowl and pheasant. In such an egg, I ask, is it the vital principle of the father or that of the mother, which inheres? or is it a mixture of the two? But how can vital principles be mingled, if the vital principle (as form) be act and substance, which it is, according to Aristotle? For no one will deny, whatever it be ultimately

[1] *On the Generation of Animals*, III. 7.

[2] *Ibid.*, II. 4.
[3] *Ibid.*, II. 4.
[4] *Ibid.*, I. 20.

which in the fruitful egg is the beginning and cause of the effects we witness, that it is a substance susceptible of divers powers, forces, or faculties, and even conditions—virtues, vices, health, and sickness. For some eggs are esteemed to be longer, others shorter lived; some engender chickens endowed with the qualities and health of body that distinguished their parents, others produce young that are predisposed to disease. Nor is it to be said that this is from any fault of the mother, seeing that the diseases of the father or male parent are transferred to the progeny, although he contributes nothing to the matter of the egg; the procreative or plastic force which renders the egg fruitful alone proceeding from the male; none of its parts being contributed by him. For the semen which is emitted by the male during intercourse does by no means enter the uterus of the female, in which the egg is perfected; nor can it, indeed (as I first announced, and Fabricius agrees with me), by any manner or way get into the inner recesses of that organ, much less ascend as high as the ovary, near the waist or middle of the body, so that besides its peculiar virtue it might impart a portion of matter to the numerous ova whose rudiments are there contained. For we know, and are assured by unquestionable experience, that several ova are fecundated by one and the same connexion— not those only that are met with in the uterus and ovary, but those likewise that are in some sort not yet begun, as we shall state by and by, and indeed, as we have already had occasion to assert in our history.

If, therefore, an egg be rendered fruitful by its proper vital principle, or be endowed with its own inherent fecundating force, whence or whereby either a common fowl, or a hybrid betwixt the fowl and the pheasant is produced, and that either male or female, like the father or the mother, healthy or diseased; we must infallibly conclude that the egg, even when contained in the ovary, does not live by the vital principle of the mother, but is, like the youth who comes of age, made independent even from its first appearance; as the acorn taken from the oak, and the seeds of plants in general, are no longer to be considered parts of the tree or herb that has supported them, but things made in their own right, and which already enjoy life in virtue of a proper and inherent vegetative power.

But if we now admit that there is a living principle in a fertile egg, it may become matter of discussion whether it is the same living principle which already inheres in the egg that will inhere in the future chick, or whether it is a different one that actuates each? For it is matter of necessity that we admit the inherence of a certain principle which constitutes and causes the egg to grow, and which further engenders and makes the chick to increase. We have to inquire, therefore, whether the animating principle of the egg and of the chick be one and the same, or several and different? And then, were several vital principles recognized, some appertaining to the egg, others to the chick, we should next have to inquire: whence and at what epoch the animating principle of the chick entered it? and what is it in the egg which causes the cicatricula to dilate before the advent of the living principle; which draws the eye of the vitellus upwards, as stated, and produces the colliquament, changes the constitution of the fluids of the egg, and preordains everything for the construction of the future chick before there is even a vestige of it to be seen? Or whence shall we say the aliment fit for the embryo is derived, and by which it is nourished and made to grow, before it is yet in being? For these acts are seen to be the work of the vegetative soul of the embryo, and have reference to the coming pullet, ensuring its nutrition and growth. And again, when the embryo is begun, or the chick is half formed, what is it which constitutes that embryo or that chick one and continuous and connects with the liquids of the egg? What nourishes and makes the chick to grow, and preserves the fluids that are fit for its nutrition from putrefaction, and prepares, and liquefies, and concocts them?

If the vital principle be the act of the organic body possessing life *in potentia*, it seems incredible that this principle can inhere in the chick before something in the shape of an organized body is extant. Nor is it more credible that the vital principle of the egg and chick can be identical, if the vital principle be conservative of that only to which it belongs; but the egg and the chick are different things, and manifest dissimilar and even opposite vital acts, in so much so that one appears to be produced by the destruction of the other. Or should we perchance maintain that the same principle and cause of life inheres in both, in the pullet half fashioned, to wit, and the egg half consumed, as if it were one and a simple act of the same body; or as if from parts producing one natural body, one soul or vital principle also arose, which was all in all, as is commonly said, and all in each particular part? Just as with leaves and fruit conspicuous on the stem of a tree, wherever a division is made we still say that the principle or first cause of the slip and of the whole tree is the same; the leaves and the fruit are, as it were, the form and end, the trunk of the tree the beginning. So too in a line, wherever a division is made, this will become the end or boundary of the part behind it, the commencement of the part before it. And the same thing is seen to obtain in respect of quality and motion, that is to say, in every kind of transmutation and generation.

So much at this time upon these topics, which will by and by engage us at greater length, when we come to speak of the nature of the living principle of the embryos of animals in general; of its being; of its accession in respect of the how and the when; and how it is all in all, and all in each particular part, the same and yet different. Points which we shall determine from numerous observations.

EXERCISE 27. *The egg is not the product of the uterus, but of the vital principle*

"As we have said," says Fabricius,[1] "that the action of the stomach was to convert the food into chyle, and the action of the testicles to produce semen, because in the stomach we find chyle, in the testes semen, so do we definitely assert that the egg is the product of the uterus of birds, because it is found in this part. The organ and seat of the generation of eggs is, therefore, intimately known and obvious to us. And further, inasmuch as there are two uteri in birds, one superior and the other inferior, and these are considerably different from one another, and consequently perform different offices, it is in like manner clear what particular action is to be ascribed to each. The superior is devoted to the production of the yelk, the inferior to that of the albumen and remaining parts, or of the perfect egg, as lies obvious to sense; for in the superior uterus we never find aught beyond a multitude of yelks, nor in the inferior uterus, other than entire and perfect eggs. But these are not all the functions of the uteri as it appears, but the following are further to be noted and enumerated, *viz.*: the increase of the egg, which succeeds immediately upon its production, and proceeds until it is perfected and acquires its proper dimensions. For the fowl does not naturally lay an egg until it has become complete and has acquired its due dimensions. The actions of the uteri are consequently the increase as well as the engenderment of the egg; but increase supposes and includes nutrition, as is obvious. And since all generation is the effect of the concurrence of two, *viz.*, the agent and the matter, the agent in the generation of an egg is nothing else than the instruments or organs aforesaid, to wit, the double uterus; and the matter is nothing but the blood."

Now whilst I admit the action of the uterus to be in a manner the generation of the egg, I by no means allow that the egg is nourished and increased by this organ. And this, both for the reasons already alleged by us when we treated of the vital principle of the egg, which is that which nourishes it, and also because it appears little likely (according to Aristotle,[2] it is impossible) that all the internal parts of the egg, in all their dimensions, should be fashioned and made to increase by an external agent, such as the uterus is with reference to the egg; for how, I beseech you, can that which is extrinsic arrange the natural matter in things that are internal, and supply fresh matter according to the several dimensions in the place of that which has been lost? How can anything be affected or moved by that which does not touch it? Wherefore, without question, the same things happen in the engenderment of eggs which take place in the beginning of all living things whatsoever, *viz.*: they are primarily constituted by external and pre-existing beings; but so soon as they are endowed with life, they suffice for their own nourishment and increase, and this in virtue of peculiar inherent forces, innate, implanted from the beginning.

What has already been said of the vital principle appears clearly to proclaim that the egg is neither the work of the uterus, nor governed by that organ; for it is manifest that the vegetative principle inheres even in the hypenemic egg, inasmuch as we have seen that this egg is nourished and is preserved, increases and vegetates, all of which acts are indications of the presence of the principle mentioned. But neither from the mother nor the uterus can this principle proceed, seeing that the egg has no connexion or union with them, but is free and unconnected, like a son emancipated from pupillage, rolling round within the cavity of the uterus and perfecting itself, even as the seeds of plants are perfected in the bosom of the earth, *viz.*, by an internal vegetative principle, which can be nothing else than the vegetative soul.

And it will appear all the more certain that it is possessed of a soul or vital principle, if we consider by what compact, what moving power,

---

[1] *Op. cit.*, p. 8.

[2] *On the Generation of Animals*, II. I.

the round and ample yelk, detached from the cluster of the ovary, descends through the infundibulum—a most slender tube composed of a singularly delicate membrane, and possessed of no motory fibres—and opening a path for itself, approaches the uterus through such a number of straits, arrived in which it continues to be nourished, and grows and is surrounded with albumen. Now as there is no motory organ discoverable either in the ovary which expels the vitellus, or in the infundibulum which transmits, or in the uterus which attracts it, and as the egg is not connected with the uterus, nor yet with the ovary by means of vessels, nor hangs from either by an umbilical cord, as Fabricius truly states, and demonstrates most satisfactorily, what remains for us contemplating such great and important processes but that we exclaim with the poet:

'Tis innate soul sustains; and mind infused
Through every part, that actuates the mass.[1]

And although the rudiments of eggs, which we have said are mere specks, and have compared to millet seeds in size, are connected with the ovary by means of veins and arteries, in the same manner as seeds are attached to plants, and consequently seem to be part and parcel of the fowl, and to live and be nourished after the manner of her other parts, it is nevertheless manifest, that seeds once separated from the plants which have produced them, are no longer regarded as parts of these, but like children come of age and freed from leading-strings, they are maintained and governed by their own inherent capacities.

But of this matter we shall speak more fully, when we come to treat of the soul or living principle of the embryo in general, and of the excellence and divine nature of the vegetative soul from a survey of its operations, all of which are carried on with such foresight, art, and divine intelligence; which, indeed, surpass our powers of understanding not less than Deity surpasses man, and are allowed, by common consent, to be so wonderful that their ineffable lustre is in no way to be penetrated by the dull edge of our apprehension.

What shall we say of the animalcules which are engendered in our bodies, and which no one doubts are ruled and made to vegetate by a peculiar vital principle (anima)? of this kind are lumbrici, ascarides, lice, nits, syrones, acari, &c.; or what of the worms which are produced from plants and their fruits, as from gall-nuts,

the dog-rose, and various others? "For in almost all dry things growing moist, or moist things becoming dry, an animal may be engendered."[2] It certainly cannot be that the living principles of the animals which arise in gall-nuts existed in the oak, although these animals live attached to the oak, and derive their sustenance from its juices. In like manner it is credible that the rudiments of eggs exist in the ovarian cluster by their proper vital principle, not by that of the mother, although they are connected with her body by means of arteries and veins, and are nourished by the same food as herself. Because, as we have stated in our history, all the vitellary specks do not increase together, like the grapes of a bunch, or the corns of an ear of wheat, as if they were pervaded by one common actuating force or concocting and forming cause; they come on one after another, as if they grew by their own peculiar energy, each that is most in advance severing itself from the rest, changing its colour and consistence, and from a white speck becoming a yelk, in regular and determinate sequence. And what is more particularly astonishing is that which we witness among pigeons and certain other birds, where two yelks only come to maturity upon the ovarian cluster together, one of which, for the major part, produces a male, the other a female, an abundance of other vitellary specks remaining stationary in the ovary, until the term comes round for two more to increase and make ready for a new birth. It is as if each successive pair received fertility from the repeated addresses of the male; as if the two became possessed of the vital principle together; which, once infused, they forthwith increase spontaneously, and govern themselves, living of their own not through their mother's right. And, in sooth, what else can you conceive working, disposing, selecting, and perfecting, as respects this pair of vitellary papulæ and none others, but a peculiar vital principle? And although they attract nourishment from the mother, they still do so no otherwise than as plants draw food from the ground, or as the embryo obtains it from the albumen and vitellus.

Lastly, since the papula existing in the ovary receives fecundity from the access of the male, and this of such a kind that it passes into the form and likeness of the concurring male, whether he were a common cock or a pheasant, and there is as great diversity in the papulæ as there are males of different kinds; what shall we hold as inherent in the papulæ themselves,

[1] Virgil, Æneid, vi.

[2] Aristotle, History of Animals, v. 32.

by whose virtue they are distinguished from one another and from the mother? Undoubtedly it must be the vital principle by which they are distinguished both from each other and from the mother.

It is in a similar manner that fungi and parasitic plants live upon trees. And besides, we in our own bodies frequently suffer from cancers, sarcoses, melicerides, and other tumours of the same description, which are nourished and grow as it seems by their own inherent vegetative principle, the true or natural parts of the body meantime shrinking and perishing. And this apparently because these tumours attract all the nourishment to themselves, and defraud the other parts of the body of their nutritious juices or proper genius. Whence the familiar names of phagedæna and lupus; and Hippocrates, by the words το θεῖον, perhaps understood those diseases which arise from poison or contagion; as if in these there was a certain vitality and divine principle inherent, by which they increase and through contagion generate similar diseases even in other bodies. Aristotle, therefore, says: "all things are full of soul";[1] and elsewhere he seems to think that "even the winds have a kind of life, and a birth and a death."[2] But there is no doubt that the vitellus, when it is once cast loose and freed from all connexion with the fowl, during its passage through the infundibulum and its stay in the cavity of the uterus, attracts a sluggish moisture to itself, which it absorbs, and by which it is nourished; there too it surrounds itself with albumen, furnishes itself with membranes and a shell, and finally perfects itself. All of which things, rightly weighed, we must needs conclude that it is possessed by a proper vital principle (anima).

EXERCISE 28. *The egg is not produced without the hen*

Leaving points that are doubtful, and disquisitions bearing upon the general question, we now approach more definite and obvious matters.

And first, it is manifest that a fruitful egg cannot be produced without the concurrence of a cock and hen: without the hen no egg can be formed; without the cock it cannot become fruitful. But this view is opposed to the opinion of those who derive the origin of animals from the slime of the ground. And truly when we see that the numerous parts concurring in the act

of generation—the testes and vasa deferentia in the male, the ovarium and uterus and bloodvessels supplying them in the female—are all contrived with such signal art and forethought, and everything requisite to reproduction in a determinate direction—situation, form, temperature—arranged so admirably, it seems certain, as Nature does nothing in vain, nor works in any round-about way when a shorter path lies open to her, that an egg can be produced in no other manner than that in which we now see it engendered, *viz.*, by the concurring act of the cock and hen. Neither, in like manner, in the present constitution of things, can a cock or hen ever be produced otherwise than from an egg. Thus the cock and the hen exist for the sake of the egg, and the egg, in the same way, is their antecedent cause; it were therefore reasonable to ask, with Plutarch, which of these was the prior, the egg or the fowl? Now the fowl is prior by nature, but the egg is prior in time; for that which is the more excellent is naturally first; but that from which a certain thing is produced must be reputed first in respect of time. Or we may say: this egg is older than that fowl (the fowl having been produced from it); and, on the contrary, this fowl existed before that egg (which she has laid). And this is the round that makes the race of the common fowl eternal; now pullet, now egg, the series is continued in perpetuity; from frail and perishing individuals an immortal species is engendered. By these, and means like to these, do we see many inferior or terrestrial things brought to emulate the perpetuity of superior or celestial things.

And whether we say, or do not say, that the vital principle (*anima*) inheres in the egg, it still plainly appears, from the circuit indicated, that there must be some principle influencing this revolution from the fowl to the egg and from the egg back to the fowl, which gives them perpetuity. Now this, according to Aristotle's views,[3] is analogous to the element of the stars; and is that which makes parents engender, and gives fertility to their ova; and the same principle, Proteus-like, is present under a different form, in the parents as in the eggs. For, as the same intelligence or spirit which incessantly actuates the mighty mass of the universe, and compels the same sun from the rising to the setting, in his passage over the various regions of the earth, so also is there a vis enthea, a divine principle inherent in our common poultry, showing itself now as the plastic, now as the

---

[1] *On the Generation of Animals*, III. 2.
[2] *Ibid.*, IV. 10.

[3] *Ibid.*, II. 3.

nutritive, and now as the augmentative force, though it is always and at all times present as the conservative and vegetative force, and now assumes the form of the fowl, now that of the egg; but the same virtue continues to inhere in either to eternity. And although some animals arise spontaneously, or as is commonly said from putrefaction, and some are produced from the female alone, for Pliny says: "in some genera, as in certain fishes, there are no males, every one taken being found full of roe";[1] still whatever is produced from a perfect egg is so in virtue of the indispensable concurrence of male and female. Aristotle consequently says: "the grand principles of generation must be held to be the male and the female";[2] the first two principles of the egg are therefore the male and the female; and the common point or conception of these is the egg, which combines the virtues of both parents. We cannot, in fact, conceive an egg without the concurrence of a male and female fowl, any more than we can conceive fruit to be produced without a tree. We therefore see individuals, males as well as females, existing for the sake of preparing eggs, that the species may be perennial, though their authors pass away. And it is indeed obvious that the parents are no longer youthful, or beautiful, or lusty, and fitted to enjoy life, than whilst they possess the power of producing and fecundating eggs, and, by the medium of these, of engendering their like. But when they have accomplished this grand purpose of nature, they have already attained to the height, the ακμὴ of their being —the final end of their existence has been accomplished; after this, effete and useless, they begin to wither, and, as if cast off and forsaken of nature and the Deity, they grow old, and, a-weary of their lives, they hasten to their end. How different the males when they make themselves up for intercourse, and swelling with desire are excited by the venereal impulse! It is surprising to see with what passion they are inflamed; and then how trimly they are feathered, how vainglorious they show themselves, how proud of their strength, and how pugnacious they prove! But, the grand business of life accomplished, how suddenly, with failing strength and pristine fervour quenched, do they take in their swelling sails, and, from late pugnacity, grow timid and desponding! Even during the season of jocund masking in Venus' domains, male animals in general are depressed by intercourse, and become submissive and pusillani-

mous, as if reminded that in imparting life to others, they were contributing to their own destruction. The cock alone, replete with spirit and fecundity, still shows himself alert and gay; clapping his wings, and crowing triumphantly, he sings the nuptial song at each of his new espousals! yet even he, after some length of time in Venus' service, begins to fail; like the veteran soldier, he by and by craves discharge from active duty. And the hen, too, like the tree that is past bearing, becomes effete, and is finally exhausted.

EXERCISE 29. *Of the manner, according to Aristotle, in which a perfect and fruitful egg is produced by the male and female fowl*

Shortly before we said that a fruitful egg is not engendered spontaneously, that it is not produced save by a hen, and by her only through the concurrence of the cock. This agrees with the matter of the following sentence of Aristotle: "The principles of generation have particular reference to male and female; the male as supplying the original of motion and reproduction; the female as furnishing the matter."[3]

In our view, however, an egg is a true generative seed, analogous to the seed of a plant; the original conception arising between the two parents, and being the mixed fruit or product of both. For as the egg is not formed without the hen, so is it not made fruitful without the concurrence of the cock.

We have, therefore, to inquire how the egg is produced by the hen and is fertilized by the cock; for we have seen that hypenemic eggs, and these animated too, are engendered by the hen, but that they are not prolific without the intercourse of the cock. The male and the female consequently, both set their mark upon a fruitful egg; but not, I believe, in the way in which Aristotle imagines, viz.: that the male concurs in the motion and commencement of generation only, the female supplying nothing but the matter, because the contrary of this is obvious in hypenemic eggs. And although it be true as he says: "That male and female differ in respect of reason, because the faculty of each is different, and in respect of sense, because certain parts differ likewise. The difference according to reason boasts this distinction, that the male has the power of engendering in another; the female has only the power of engendering in herself; whereby it comes that that which is engendered is pro-

[1] *Hist. natur.*, IX. 16.
[2] *On the Generation of Animals*, I. 2.
[3] *Ibid.*, I. 2.

duced, this being contained in that which engenders. But as males and females are distinguished by certain faculties and functions, and as an instrument is indispensable to every office, and the parts of the body are adapted as instruments of the functions, it was necessary that certain parts should be set aside for purposes of procreation and coition, and these differing from one another, whereby the male differs from the female."

It does not, however, follow from thence, that what he appears inclined to infer is correct, where he says: "The male is the efficient agent, and by the motion of his generative virtue (*genitura*), creates what is intended from the matter contained in the female; for the female always supplies the matter, the male the power of creation, and this it is which constitutes one male, another female. The body and the bulk, therefore, are necessarily supplied by the female; nothing of the kind is required from the male; for it is not even requisite that the instrument, nor the efficient agent itself, be present in the thing that is produced. The body, then, proceeds from the female, the vital principle (*anima*) from the male; for the essence of every body is its vital principle (*anima*)." But an egg, and that animated, is engendered by the pullet without the concurrence of the male; whence it appears that the hen too, or the female, may be the efficient agent, and that all creative force or vital power (*anima*) is not derived exclusively from the male. This view indeed appears to be supported by the instance quoted by Aristotle himself, for he says: "Those animals not of the same species, which copulate (which those animals do that correspond in their seasons of heat and times of uterogestation, and do not differ greatly in their size), produce their first young like themselves, but partaking of the species of both parents; of this description is the progeny of the fox and dog, of the partridge and common fowl, &c.; but in the course of time from diversity results diversity, and the progeny of these different parents at length acquires the form of the female; in the same way as foreign seed is changed at last in conformity with the nature of the soil, which supplies matter and body to the seed."[1]

From this it appears, that in the generation of the partridge with the common fowl it is not the male alone that is efficient, but the female also; inasmuch as it is not the male form only, but one common or subordinate that appears in

[1] *Op. cit.*, II. 4.

the hybrid, as like the female as it is like the male in vital endowment (*anima*), and bodily form. But the vital endowment (*anima*) is that which is the true form and species of an animal.

Further, the female seems even to have a superior claim to be considered the efficient cause: "In the course of time," says the philosopher, "the progeny of different species assumes the form of the female" as if the semen or influence of the male were the less powerful; as if the species impressed by him disappeared with the lapse of time, and were expelled by a more powerful efficient cause. And the instance from the soil confirms this still further: "for foreign seeds are changed at length according to the nature of the soil." Whence it seems probable that the female is actually of more moment in generation than the male; for, "in the world at large it is admitted that the earth is to nature as the female or mother, whilst climate, the sun, and other things of the same description, are spoken of by the names of generator and father."[2] The earth, too, spontaneously engenders many things without seed; and among animals, certain females, but females only, procreate of themselves and without the concurrence of the male: hens, for example, lay hypenemic eggs; but males, without the intervention of females, engender nothing.

By the same arguments, indeed, by which the male is maintained to be the principle and prime *efficient* in generation, it would seem that the female might be confirmed in the prerogative of ἐνεργεία or *efficiency*. For is not that to be accounted efficient in which the reason of the embryo and the form of the work appear; whose obvious resemblance is perceived in the embryo, and which, as first existing, calls forth the other? Since, therefore, the form, cause, and similitude inhere in the female not less—and it might even be said that they inhere more—than in the male, and as she also exists previously as prime mover, let us conclude for certain that the female is equally efficient in the work of generation as the male.

And although Aristotle says well and truly, "that the conception or egg receives no part of its body from the male, but only its form, species, and vital endowment (*anima*), and from the female its body solely, and its dimensions,"[3] it is not yet made sufficiently to appear that the female, besides the matter, does not in some measure contribute form, species, and vital endowment (*anima*). This indeed is obvious in

[2] *Op. cit.*, I. 2.
[3] *Op. cit.*, II. 4.

the hen which engenders eggs without the concurrence of a male; in the same way as trees and herbs, in which there is no distinction of sexes, produce their seeds. For Aristotle himself admits[1] that even the hypenemic egg is endowed with a vital principle (*anima*). The female must therefore be esteemed the efficient cause of the egg.

Admitting that the hypenemic egg is possessed of a certain vital principle, still it is not prolific; so that it must further be confessed that the hen of herself is not the efficient cause of a perfect egg, but that she is made so in virtue of an authority, if I may use the word, or power required of the cock. For the egg, unless prolific, can with no kind of propriety be accounted perfect; it only obtains perfection from the male, or rather from the female, as it were, upon precept from the male; as if the hen received the art and reason, the form and laws of the future embryo from his address. And so in like manner the female fowl, like to a fruitful tree, is made fertile by coition; by this is she empowered not only to lay eggs, but these perfect and prolific eggs. For although the hen have as yet no rudiments of eggs prepared in her ovary, nevertheless, made fertile by the intercourse of the male, she by and by not only produces them there, but lays them, teeming with life, and apt to produce embryos. And here that practice of the poor folks finds its application: "Having hens at home, but no cock, they commit their females to a neighbour's male for a day or two; and from this short sojourn the fecundity of the whole of the eggs that will be laid during the current season is secured."[2] Not only are those eggs which are still nothing more than yelk and have no albumen, or which exist only as most minute specks in the ovary, but eggs not yet extant, that will be conceived long afterwards, rendered fertile by the same property.

EXERCISE 30. *Of the uses of this disquisition on fecundity*

This disquisition on the inherent qualities of the egg and the cause of its fecundity, is alike in point of difficulty and subtlety, but of the highest importance. For it was imperative on us to inquire what there was in the conception, what in the semen masculinum, and what in the female fowl, which renders these fertile; and what there is in the fruitful cock which makes him differ from a bird that is barren. Is

[1] *Op. cit.*, II. 4.
[2] Fabricius, *op. cit.*, p. 37.

the cause identical with that which we have called the vital principle (*anima*) in the embryo, or is it a certain portion of the vegetative principle? Because, in order to apprehend the entire cause of generation, it is of much moment that the first cause be understood; for science is based upon causes, especially first causes, known. Nor is this inquiry less important in enabling us to understand the nature of the vital principle (*anima*). These questions, indeed, rightly apprehended, not only are Aristotle's opinions of the causes of generation refuted or corrected, but all that has been written against him is easily understood.

We ask, therefore, whether it is the same thing or something different, which in the rudimentary ovum, yelk, egg, cock and hen, or her uterus, confers fruitfulness? In like manner in what respect does this something agree or differ in each? Still further, is it a substance whence the fecundating virtue flows?— it appears susceptible of powers, faculties, and accidents. Likewise, is it corporeal also? for that which engenders mixture appears to be mixed —the progeny has a common resemblance to the mother and father, and exhibits a doubtful nature when animals of dissimilar species, such as the pheasant and common fowl, engender; that, too, appears to be corporeal which suffers from without, and to such an extent that not only are weakly embryos procreated, but even deformed and diseased ones, obnoxious to the vices as well as to the virtues of their progenitors.

With respect to these several particulars, we may further be permitted to doubt whether that which confers fecundity is engendered or accrues from without. Whether, to wit, it is transfused from the egg to the embryo and chick, from the hen to the egg, from the cock to the hen. For there appears to be something that is transferred or transfused, something, namely, which from the cock is transfused into the hen, and from her is given to the uterus, to the ovary, to the egg; something which, passing from the seed to the plant, is rendered again by the plant to the seed, and imparts fecundity. Because there is this common to all things which are perpetuated by generation, that they derive their origin from seed. But the semen, the conception, and the egg, are all of the same essential kind, and that which confers fertility on these is one and the same, or of like nature; and this indeed is divine, the analogue of heaven, possessed of art, intelligence, foresight. This is plainly to be seen from its admirable operations, artifices, and wisdom, where nothing is vain, or inconsiderate, or accidental, but all conduces to some good end.

Of the general principles and science of this subject we shall treat more at length in the proper place; we have now said as much incidentally as seems necessary, the occasion having presented itself along with our consideration of the hen's egg, namely, how many things inhere which induce fertility, and how this is induced, and whether it is an affection, a habit, a power, or a faculty; whether it is to be regarded as a form and substance, as a something contained generally, or only in some particular part—since it is quite certain that a hypenemic egg is a perfect egg in so far as each sensible particular is concerned, and yet is barren; the uterus in like manner, and the hen and the cock are all perfect; yet are they severally sterile, as being without that which confers fecundity. All of these matters we shall advert to after we have shown what and how two principles, male and female, concur in the production of the egg and the process of generation, and in what way both may be regarded as efficient causes and parents of the egg.

EXERCISE 31. *The egg is not produced by the cock and hen in the way Aristotle would have it.*

It is certain, as we have said, that a fruitful egg is not produced without the concurrence of the cock and hen; but this is not done in the way that Aristotle thought, *viz.*, by the cock as prime and sole "agent," the hen only furnishing the "matter." Neither do I agree with him when he says: "When the semen masculinum enters the female uterus, it coagulates the purest portion of the catamenia"; and shortly afterwards: "but when the catamenia of the female has set in the uterus, it forms, with the semen masculinum, a coagulum like that of milk; for curd is milk containing vital heat, which attracts like particles around it, and combines and coagulates them; and the semen of the male (*genitura*) bears the same affinity to the nature of the catamenia. For milk and the menstrual discharge are of the same nature. When coagulation has taken place, then an earthy humour is excreted and is drawn around, and the earthy portion drying up, the membranes are produced both as matter of necessity, and also for a certain purpose. And these things take place in the same manner in all creatures, both oviparous and viviparous."[1]

But the business in the generation of an egg

[1] *On the Generation of Animals,* II. 4.

is very different from this; for neither does the semen, or rather the "geniture," proceeding from the male in the act of intercourse, enter the uterus in any way, nor has the hen, after she conceives, any particle of excrementitious matter, even of the purest kind, or any blood in her uterus which might be fashioned or perfected by the discharge of the male. Neither are the parts of the egg, the membranes, to wit, and the fluids, produced by any kind of coagulation; neither is there anything like curdled milk to be discovered in the uterus, as must be obvious from the foregoing exercises. It follows, therefore, and from thence, that neither does the conception, whence the animal springs, as the herb arises from a fruitful seed, comport itself in the manner Aristotle imagined, since this takes place in viviparous animals in the same way as the egg is formed in oviparous animals, as he himself avows, and as shall be demonstrated by and by in our observations. Because it is certain that eggs of every description—prolific and barren—are engendered and formed by the hen singly, but that fecundity accrues from the male alone; the cock, I say, contributes neither form nor matter to the egg, but that only by which it becomes fertile and fit to engender a chick. And this faculty the cock confers by his semen (*genitura*), emitted in the act of intercourse, not only on the egg that is already begun, or is already formed, but on the uterus and ovary, and even on the body of the fowl herself, in such wise that eggs which have yet to be produced, eggs, none of the matter of which yet exists either in the ovary or in any other part of the body, are thence produced possessed of fecundity.

EXERCISE 32. *Nor in the manner imagined by physicians*

Conception, according to the opinion of medical men, takes place in the following way: during intercourse the male and female dissolve in one voluptuous sensation, and eject their seminal fluids (*genituræ*) into the cavity of the uterus, where that which each contributes is mingled with that which the other supplies, the mixture having from both equally the faculty of action and the force of matter; and according to the predominance of this or of that geniture does the progeny turn out male or female. It is further imagined that immediately after the intercourse, the active and passive principles cooperating, something of the conception is formed in the uterus. For contrary to the Aristotelians, they maintain that the male is no more the efficient cause of generation than the female, but some mixture of the two; and that neither the menstrual blood nor its purest part is the prime matter of the conception, but the spermatic fluid; whence the first particles or their rudiments are spoken of as spermatic, these at an after period being nourished and made to increase through the blood.

But it is obvious that neither is the egg engendered by the cock and hen in this way; for the hen in the act of intercourse emits no semen from which an egg might be formed; nor can aught like a seminal fluid of the hen be demonstrated at any time; and indeed the animal is destitute of the organs essential to its preparation, the testes and vasa spermatica. And though the hen have an effective force in common with the cock (as must be manifest from what precedes), and it is a mixture of some sort that renders an egg fruitful, still this does not happen according to the predominance of the genitures, or the manner of their mixture, for it is certain, and Fabricius admits it, that the semen of the cock does not reach the cavity of the uterus; neither is there any trace of the egg to be discovered in the uterus immediately after intercourse, and as its consequence, although Aristotle himself repeatedly avers that there is, asserting that "something of the conception forthwith ensues." But I shall by and by demonstrate that neither does any such imaginary mixture of seminal fluids take place in any animal, nor that immediately upon intercourse, even of a fruitful kind, is there anything in the shape of semen or blood, or of the rudiments of an embryo present or demonstrable in the cavity of the uterus. Nothing is found in the egg or embryo which leads us to suppose that the semen masculinum is either there contained or mingled. The vulgar notion of the chalazæ being the tread of the cock is a sheer mistake; and I am surprised, since there are two of them, one in either end of the egg, that no one has yet been found to maintain that this was the cock's seed, that the hen's. But this popular error is at once answered by the fact that the chalazæ are present with the same characters in every egg, whether it be fertile or barren.

EXERCISE 33. *The male and the female are alike efficient in the business of generation*

The medical writers with propriety maintain, in opposition to the Aristotelians, that both sexes have the power of acting as efficient causes in the business of generation; inasmuch as the being engendered is a mixture of the two which engender: both form and likeness of body, and species are mixed, as we see in the hybrid between the partridge and common fowl. And it does indeed seem consonant with reason to hold that they are the efficient causes of conception whose mixture appears in the thing produced.

Aristotle entertaining this opinion says: "In some animals it is manifest that such as the generator is, such is the engendered; not, however, the same and identical, not one numerically, but one specifically, as in natural things. A man engenders a man, if there be nothing preternatural in the way, as a horse engenders a mule, and other similar instances. For the mule is common to the horse and the ass; it is not spoken of as an allied kind; yet may horse and ass both be there conjoined in a hybrid state."[1] He says further in the same place: "It is enough that the generator generate, and prove the cause that the species be found in the matter: for such and such an entire species is still found associated with such and such flesh and bones—here it is Gallias, there it is Socrates."

Wherefore if such an entire form, as a mule, be a mixture of two, *viz.*, a horse and an ass, the horse does not suffice to produce this form of a mule in the "matter"; but, as the entire form is mixed, so another efficient cause is contributed by the ass and added to that supplied by the horse. That, therefore, which produces a mule compounded of two, must itself be an "adequate efficient," and mixed, if only "univocal." For example, this woman and that man engender this Socrates; not in so far as they are both human beings, and of one and the same species, but in so far as this man and that woman in these bones and muscles constitute human forms, of both of which, if Socrates be a certain mixture, a compound of both, that by which he is made must needs be a mixed univocal compound of the two; *i. e.*, a mixed efficient of a mixed effect. And, therefore, it is that the male and female by themselves, and separately, are not genetic, but become so united *in coitu*, and made one animal, as it were; whence, from the two as one, is produced and educed that which is the true efficient proximate cause of conception.

The medical writers also, in directing their attention to the particulars of human generation alone, come to conclusions on generation at large; and the spermatic fluid proceeding from the parents *in coitu* has in all probability been

[1] *Metaphysics*, VII. 8.

taken by them for true seed, analogous to the seeds of plants. It is not without reason, therefore, that they imagine the mixed efficient cause of the future offspring to be constituted by a mixture of the seminal matters of each parent. And then they go on to assert that the mixture proceeding immediately from intercourse is deposited in the uterus and forms the rudiments of the conception. That things are very different, however, is made manifest by our preceding history of the egg, which is a true conception.

EXERCISE 34. *Of the matter of the egg, in opposition to the Aristotelians and the medical writers*

The position taken up by the medical writers against the Aristotelians, *viz.*, that the blood is not the first element in a conception, is clearly shown from the generation of the egg to be well chosen: neither during intercourse, nor before nor after it, is there a drop of blood contained in the uterus of the fowl; neither are the rudiments of eggs red, but white. Many animals also conceive in whose uteri, if they be suddenly laid open after intercourse, no blood can be demonstrated.

But when they contend that the maternal blood is the food of the foetus *in utero*, especially of its more sanguineous parts, as they style them, and that the foetus from the outset is as it were a portion of the mother, being nourished and growing through her blood, and vegetating through her spirit; so that neither does the heart pulsate, nor the liver compose blood, nor any part of the foetus perform any kind of independent office, but everything is carried on through the mother's means, they in their turn are as certainly mistaken, and argue from erroneous observations. For the embryo in the egg boasts of its own blood, formed from the fluids contained within the egg; and its heart is seen to pulsate from the very beginning: it borrows nothing in the shape either of blood or spirits from the hen, for the purpose of forming its so-called sanguineous parts and its feathers; as most clearly appears to anyone who looks on with an unbiassed mind. From observations afterwards to be communicated, I believe indeed that it will be held as sufficiently proven that even the foetus of viviparous animals still contained in the uterus is not nourished by the blood of the mother and does not vegetate through her spirit; but boasts of its own peculiar vital principle and powers, and its own blood, like the chick *in ovo*.

With reference to the matter which the embryo obtains from its male and female parent, however, and the way and manner of generation as commonly discoursed of in the schools, *viz.*, that conception is produced or becomes prolific from mixture of the genitures and their mutual action and passion, as also of the seminal fluid of the female, and the parts which are spoken of as sanguineous and spermatic, numerous and striking observations afterwards to be related have compelled me to adopt opinions at variance with all such views. At this time I shall only say that I am greatly surprised how physicians, particularly those among them who are conversant with anatomy, should pretend to support their opinions by means of two arguments especially, which rightly understood, seem rather to prove the opposite; *viz.*, from the shock and resolution of the forces and the effusion of fluid which women at the moment of the sexual orgasm frequently experience, they argue that all women pour out a seminal fluid, and that this is necessary to generation.

But passing over the fact that the females of all the lower animals, and all women, do not experience any such emission of fluid, and that conception is nowise impossible in cases where it does not take place, for I have known several, who without anything of the kind were sufficiently prolific, and even some who after experiencing such an emission and having had great enjoyment, nevertheless appeared to have lost somewhat of their wonted fecundity; and then an infinite number of instances might be quoted of women who, although they have great satisfaction in intercourse, still emit nothing, and yet conceive; passing over these facts, I say, I cannot but express surprise at those especially, who, conceiving such an emission on the part of the female necessary to conception, have not adverted to the fact that the fluid emitted is discharged, cast out, and is particularly abundant about the clitoris and orifice of the vulva; that it is seldom poured out within the vulva, never within the uterus, and so as to be mingled with the semen of the male; moreover, it is of a mere serous or ichorous consistency, like urine, by no means thick and apparently unctuous, like the spermatic matter of the male. But how shall we suppose that to be of use internally which is discharged externally? Or shall we say that this humour, as if bidding the uterus farewell, is taken to the verge of the vulva, that it may be then recalled with greater favour by the uterus?

The other argument is drawn from the genital organs of women, the testes, to wit, and vasa spermatica, præparantia et deferentia, which are held to serve for the preparation of the spermatic fluid. I, for my part, greatly wonder how anyone can believe that from parts so imperfect and obscure a fluid like the semen, so elaborate, concoct and vivifying, can ever be produced, endowed with force and spirit and generative influence adequate to overcome that of the male; for this is implied in the discussion concerning the predominance of the male or the female, as to which of them is to become the agent and efficient cause, which the matter and pathic principle. How should such a fluid get the better of another concocted under the influence of a heat so fostering, of vessels so elaborate, and endowed with such vital energy?—how should such a fluid as the male semen be made to play the part of mere matter?—But of these things more hereafter.

Meantime, it is certain that the egg of the hen is not engendered from any such discharge of fluid during sexual intercourse, although after connexion, and brimful of satisfaction, she shakes herself for joy, and, as if already possessed of the richest treasure, as if gifted by supreme Jove, the preserver, with the blessing of fecundity, she sets to work to prune and ornament herself. The pigeon, particularly that kind which comes to us from Africa, expresses the satisfaction she feels from intercourse in a remarkable manner; she leaps, spreads her tail, and sweeps the ground with its extremity, she pecks and prunes her feathers—all her actions are as if she felt raised to the summit of felicity by the gift of fruitfulness.

We have said that the primary matter of the egg does not consist of blood as Aristotle would have it, neither does it proceed from any mixture of the male and female seminal fluids. Whence it truly originates we have already stated in part in our history; and we shall by and by have occasion to speak of the subject more at length when we come to treat generally of the matter from which every conception is originally produced.

EXERCISE 35. *In how far is the fowl efficient in the generation of the egg, according to Aristotle? And wherefore is the concurrence of the male required?*

It has been already stated that the cock and hen are the two principles in the generation of the egg, although of the manner in which they are so I am of a different opinion from Aristotle and medical authorities. From the production of the egg we have clearly shown that the female as well as the male was efficient, and that she had within her a principle whence motion and the faculty of forming flowed; although in the sexual act the male neither confers the matter, nor does the female eject any semen whence the egg is constituted. It is consequently manifest, in some animals at least, that nature has not, on account of the distinction into male and female, established it as a law that the one, as agent, should confer form, the other, as passive, supply matter, as Aristotle apprehended; nor yet that during intercourse each should contribute a seminal fluid, by the mixture of which a conception or ovum should be produced, as physicians commonly suppose.

Now since everything that has been delivered by the ancients on generation is comprehended in these two opinions, it appears to have escaped every one up to this time, first, why the hen by herself does not generate, like vegetables, but requires a male to be associated with her in the work; and then how the conception or ovum is procreated by the male and the female together, or what either of them contributes to the process, and for what end intercourse was established.

Aristotle, in opposition to the entire tenor of his hypothesis, *viz.*, that the male is to be regarded as the agent, the female as supplying the matter only, when he sees that eggs are actually produced by hens without the concurrence of the male, is compelled to admit that the female is likewise efficient; he was further not ignorant of the fact that an egg even when extruded could preserve itself, nourish itself, increase in size and produce an embryo, as happens with the eggs of fishes; and he has besides accorded a vital principle to an egg, even to a hypenemic one. But he endeavours to explain to what extent a female is efficient, and how a hypenemic egg is endowed with a vital principle, in the passage where he says: "Hypenemic eggs admit of generation to a certain point; for that they can ever go the length of producing an animal is impossible, this being the work of the senses. But females and all things that live, as already repeatedly stated, possess the vegetative soul. Wherefore the hypenemic egg as a vegetable is perfect, but as an animal it is imperfect."[1] By this he seems to insinuate that the hypenemic egg is possessed of a vegetative soul, inasmuch as this is inherent in all things that live, and an egg is alive. In like manner he ascribes to the hen the power of creating and of

[1] *On the Generation of Animals*, III. 7.

conferring the vegetative soul; because all females acquire this virtue, so that a hypenemic
egg in so far as it lives as a vegetable is perfect,
in so far as it is an animal, however, it is imperfect. As if a male were not required that a conception or ovum should be produced, and produced perfect; but that from this ovum an animal should be engendered. Not, I say, that an
egg be produced as perfect in all respects as is
the conception of a vegetable; but that it should
be imbued with the animal principle. The egg,
consequently, is formed by the hen, but it is
made prolific by the cock.

Aristotle adds in the same place: "There is a
distinction of sexes through the whole class of
birds. And, therefore, it happens that the hen
perfects her egg, not yet influenced by the intercourse of the male, in so far as it is a plant;
but as it is not a plant, there she does not perfect it: nor does anything come of it which engenders. For neither has it arisen simply, like
the seed of a plant, nor like an animal conception, by intercourse." He is here speaking of the
wind egg; by and by he adds: "But those eggs
that are conceived through intercourse are already characterized in a portion of the albumen: such eggs become fruitful through the
male which first copulated, for they are then
supplied with both principles."

By this he seems to confess that the female is
also effective in the work of generation, or is
possessed of the faculty of engendering; because in every female there inheres a vegetative
soul, whose faculty it is to engender. And,
therefore, when he is speaking of the differences
between the male and female, he still acknowledges both as generative; for he says: "We call
that animal male which engenders in another,
female that which engenders in itself." From
his own showing, therefore, both engender;
and as there is a vegetative soul inherent in
both, so is there also its faculty of generation.
But how they differ has already been shown in
the history of the egg: the hen generates of herself without the concurrence of the cock, as a
plant out of itself produces fruit; but it is a
wind egg that is thus produced: it is not made
fruitful without the concurrence of the cock
either preceding or succeeding. The female generates, then, but it is only up to a certain mark,
and the concurrence of the male is requisite
that this faculty of engendering be made complete, that she may not only lay an egg, but
such an egg as will, under favorable circumstances, produce a pullet. The male appears to
be ordained by nature to supply this deficiency

in the generative powers of the female, as will
be clearly shown by and by, and that that
which the female of herself cannot accomplish, viz., the production of a fruitful egg,
may be supplied and made good by the act of
the male, who imparts this virtue to the fowl
or the egg.

EXERCISE 36. *The perfect hen's egg is of two
colours*

Every egg, then, is not perfect; but some are
to be held imperfect because they have not yet
attained their true dimensions, which they
only receive when extruded; others are imperfect
because they are yet unprolific, and only acquire a fertilizing faculty from without, such
are the eggs of fishes. Other eggs again are held
imperfect by Aristotle, because they are of one
colour only, inasmuch as perfect eggs consist of
yelk and albumen, and are of two colours, as if
better concocted, more distinct in their parts,
endowed with higher heat. The eggs that are
called centenine or hundredth eggs, and which
Fabricius[1] will have it are engendered of certain
remainders of albumen, are of one colour only,
and by reason of their deficiency of heat and
their weakness, are regarded as imperfect. Of
all eggs, there are none more perfect than those
of the hen, which are produced complete in all
their fluids and appendages, of proper size and
fruitful.

Aristotle assigns the following reason wherefore some eggs are of two colours, others of one
hue only: "In the hotter animals those things
from which the principles of their origin are
derived are distinct and separate from those
which furnish their nutrition; now the one of
these is white, the other is yellow."[2] As if the
chick derived its origin from the albumen and
was nourished by the vitellus alone. In the same
place he proceeds thus: "That part which is
hot contributes properly to the form in the
constitution of the extremities; but the part
that is more earthy, and is farther removed,
supplies material for the trunk. Whence in eggs
of two colours the animal derives its origin from
the white, for the commencement of animal
existence is in the white; but the nourishment
is obtained from the yellow." He consequently
thinks that this is the reason why these fluids
are distinct, and why eggs are produced of two
colours.

Now these ideas are partly true, partly false.
It is not true, for instance, that the embryo of

[1] *Op. cit.*, p. 10.
[2] *On the Generation of Animals*, III. 1.

the common fowl is first formed from the albumen and then nourished by the vitellus; for, from the history of the formation of the chick *in ovo*, from the course of the umbilical vessels and the distribution of their branches, which undoubtedly serve for obtaining nourishment, it obviously appears that the constituent matter, and the nutriment are supplied to the chick from its first formation by the yelk, as well as the white; the fluid which we have called the colliquament seems further to be supplied, not less by the vitellus than the albumen; a certain portion of both the fluids seems, in fact, to be resolved. And then the spot, by the expansion of which the colliquament is formed in the first instance, and which we have called the eye, appears to be impressed upon the membrane of the vitellus.

The distinction into yellow and white, however, seems to be a thing necessary: these matters, as they are undoubtedly of different natures, appear also to serve different offices; they are, therefore, completely separate in the perfect egg, one of them being more, the other less, immediately akin to proper alimentary matter; by the one the fœtus is nourished from the very beginning, by the other it is nourished at a later period. For it is certain, as Fabricius asserts, and as we afterwards maintain, that both of them are truly nutritious, the albumen as well as the vitellus, the albumen being the first that is consumed. I, therefore, agree with Aristotle against the physicians, that the albumen is the purer portion of the egg, the better concocted, the more highly elaborated; and, therefore, whilst the egg is getting perfected in the uterus, is the albumen as the hotter portion poured around in the circumference, the yelk or more earthy portion subsiding to the centre. For the albumen appears to contain the larger quantity of animal heat, and so to be nutriment of a more immediate kind. For like reasons it is probable that the albumen is purer and better concocted externally than it is internally.

When medical writers affirm that the yelk is the hotter and more nutritious portion of the egg, this I imagine is meant as it affords food to us, not as it is found to supply the wants of the chick *in ovo*. This, indeed, is obvious from the history of the formation of the chick, by which the thin albumen is absorbed and used up sooner than the thick, as if it formed the more appropriate aliment, and were more readily transmuted into the substance of the embryo, of the chick that is to be. The yelk, therefore,

appears to be a more distant or ultimate aliment than the albumen, the whole of which has been used up before any notable portion of the vitellus is consumed. The yelk, indeed, is still found inclosed within the abdomen of the chick after its exclusion from the shell, as if it were destined to serve the new being in lieu of milk for its sustenance.

Eggs, consisting of white and yellow, are, therefore, more perfect, as more distinct in constitution, and elaborated by a higher temperature. For in the egg there must be included not only the matter of the chick but also its first nutriment; and what is provided for a perfect animal, must, itself, be perfect and highly elaborated; as that is, in fact, which consists of different parts, some of which, as already stated, are prior and purer, and so more easy of digestion; others posterior, and therefore more difficult of transmutation into the substance of the chick. Now the yelk and albumen differ from one another by such kinds of distinction. Perfect eggs are, consequently, of two colours: they consist of albumen and yelk, as if these constituted fluids of easier or more difficult digestion, adapted to the different ages and vigour of the chick.

EXERCISE 37. *Of the manner in which the egg is increased by the albumen*

From the history it appears that the rudiments of the eggs in the ovary are of very small size, mere specks, smaller than millet seeds, white and replete with watery fluid: these specks, however, by and by, become yelks, and then surround themselves with albumen.

Aristotle seems to think that the albumen is generated in the way of secretion from the vitellus. It may be well to add his words: "The sex," he says, "is not the cause of the double colour, as if the white were derived from the male, the yellow from the female; both are furnished by the female. But one of them is hot, the other is cold. Now these two portions are distinct in animals fraught with much heat; in those that are not so fraught the eggs are not thus distinct. And this is the reason why the conceptions of these are of one colour. But the semen of the male alone sets the conception; therefore is the conception of the bird small and white in the first instance; but in the course of time, and when there is a larger infusion of blood, it becomes entirely yellow; and, last of all, when the heat declines, the white portion, as a humour of equal temperature surrounds it on every side. For the white portion of the egg is, by its nature, moist, and includes animal heat in itself; and it is for this reason that it is seen in the circumference, the yellow and earthy portion remaining in the interior."[1]

Fabricius, however, thinks that "the albumen only adheres to the vitellus by juxtaposition. For while the yelk is rolled through the second uterus and gradually descends, it also gradually assumes to itself the albumen which is there produced, and made ready, that it may be applied to the yelk; until the yelk having passed the middle spirals and reached the last of them, already surrounded with the albumen, it now surrounds itself with the membranes and shell." Fabricius will, therefore, have it that the egg increases in a two-fold manner: "partly by means of the veins, as concerns the vitellus, and partly by an appositive increase, as regards the albumen."[2] And, among other reasons, this was perchance one for the above opinion: that when an egg is boiled hard the albumen is readily split into layers lying one over another. But this also occurs to the yelk still connected with the ovary, when boiled hard.

Wherefore, taught by experience, I rather incline to the opinion of Aristotle; for the albumen is not merely perceived as added in the way Fabricius will have it, but fashioned also, distinguished by chalazæ and membranes, and divided into two different portions; and all this in virtue of the inherence of the same vegetative vital principle by which the egg is more conspicuously divided into two distinct substances—a yelk and a white. For the same faculty that presides over the formation of the egg in general presides over the constitution of each of its parts in particular. Neither is it altogether true that the yelk is first formed and the albumen added to it afterwards; for what is seen in the ovary is not the vitellus of the egg, but rather a compound containing the two liquids mingled together. It has the colour of the vitellus, indeed, but in point of consistence it is more like the albumen; and when boiled hard it is not friable like the proper yelk, but, like the white, is concreted, jelly-like, and seen to be composed of thin lamellæ; and it has a kind of white papula, or spot, in the middle.

Aristotle seems to derive this separation from the dissimilar nature of the yelk and white; for he says,[3] as we have already stated, that if a number of eggs be thrown into a pan and boiled, in such wise that the heat shall not be quicker than the separation of the eggs (*citatior quam ovorum distinctio*), the same thing will take place in the mass of eggs which occurs in the individual egg: the whole of the yelks will set in the middle, the whites round about them.

This I have myself frequently found to be true on making the trial, and it is open to anyone to repeat the experiment; let him only beat yelks and whites together, put the mixture into a dutch oven, or between two plates over the fire, and having added some butter, cause it to set slowly into a cake, he will find the albumen covering over the yelks situated at the bottom.

EXERCISE 38. *Of what the cock and hen severally contribute to the production of the egg*

Both cock and hen are to be reputed parents of the chick; for both are necessary principles of an egg, and we have proved both to be alike its efficient: the hen fashions the egg, the cock makes it fertile. Both, consequently, are instruments of the plastic virtue by which this species of animal is perpetuated.

But as in some species there appears to be no occasion for males, females sufficing of themselves to continue the kind; so do we discover no males among these, but females only, containing the fertile rudiments of eggs in their interior; in other species, again, none but males are discovered which procreate and preserve their kinds by emitting something into the mud, or earth, or water. In such instances nature appears to have been content with a single sex, which she has used as an instrument adequate to procreation.

Another class of animals has a generative fluid fortuitously, as it were, and without any distinction of sex; the origin of such animals is spontaneous. But "as some things are made by art, and some depend on accident, health for example,"[4] so also some semen of animals is not produced by the act of an individual agent, as in the case of a man engendered by a man; but in some sort univocally, as in those instances where the rudiments and matter, produced by accident, are susceptible of taking on the same motions as seminal matter, as in "animals which do not proceed from coitus, but arise spontaneously, and have such an origin as insects which engender worms."[5] For as mechanics perform some operations with their unaided hands, and others not without the assistance of particular tools; and as the more excellent and varied and curious works of art require

[1] *On the Generation of Animals*, III. 1.
[2] *Op. cit.*, p. 12.
[3] Fabricius, *op. cit.*, p. 12.

[4] Aristotle, *On the Parts of Animals*, I. I.
[5] *On the Generation of Animals*, III. 9.

a greater variety in the form and size of the tools to bring them to perfection, inasmuch as a greater number of motions and a larger amount of subordinate means are required to bring more worthy labours to a successful issue —art imitating nature here as everywhere else, so also does nature make use of a larger number and variety of forces and instruments as necessary to the procreation of the more perfect animals. For the sun, or Heaven, or whatever name is used to designate that which is understood as the common generator or parent of all animated things, engenders some of themselves, by accident, without an instrument, as it were, and equivocally; and others through the concurrence of a single individual, as in those instances where an animal is produced from another animal of the same genus which supplies both matter and form to the being engendered; so in like manner in the generation of the most perfect animals where principles are distinguished, and the seminal elements of animated beings are divided, a new creation is not effected save by the concurrence of male and female, or by two necessary instruments. Our hen's egg is of this kind; to its production in the perfect state the cock and the hen are necessary. The hen engenders in herself, and therefore does she supply place and matter, nutriment and warmth; but the cock confers fecundity; for the male, as Aristotle says,[1] always perfects generation, secures the presence of a sensitive vital principle, and from such an egg an animal is engendered.

To the cock, therefore, as well as to the hen, are given the organs requisite to the function with which he is intrusted; in the hen all the genital parts are adapted to receive and contain, as in the cock they are calculated to give and immit, or prepare that which transfers fecundity to the female, he engendering, as it were, in another, not in himself.

When we anatomize the organs appropriated to generation, therefore, we readily distinguish what each sex contributes in the process; for a knowledge of the instruments here leads us by a direct path to a knowledge of their functions.

EXERCISE 39. *Of the cock and the particulars most remarkable in his constitution*

The cock, as stated, is the prime efficient of the perfect or fruitful hen's egg, and the chief cause of generation: without the male no chick would ever be produced from an egg, and in many ovipara not even would any egg be produced.

[1] *Ibid.,* II. 5.

It is, therefore, imperative on us that we look narrowly into his offices and uses, and inquire particularly what he contributes to the egg and chick, both in the act of intercourse and at other times.

It is certain that the cock in coition emits his "geniture," commonly called semen, from his sexual parts, although he has no penis, as I maintain; because his testes and long and ample vasa deferentia are full of this fluid. But whether it issues in jets, with a kind of spirituous briskness and repeatedly as in the hotter viviparous animals, or not, I have not been able to ascertain. But as I do not find any vesiculæ containing semen, from which, made brisk and raised into a froth by the spirits, it might be emitted; nor any penis through whose narrower orifice it might be forcibly ejaculated, and so strike upon the interior of the hen; and particularly when I see the act of intercourse so rapidly performed between them; I am disposed to believe that the parts of the hen are merely moistened with a very small quantity of seminal fluid, only as much as will adhere to the orifice of the pudenda, and that the prolific fluid is not emitted by any sudden ejaculation; so that whilst among animals repeated ejaculations take place during the same connexion, among birds, which are not delayed with any complexity of venereal apparatus, the same object is effected by repeated connexions. Animals that are long in connexion, copulate rarely; and this is the case with the swan and ostrich among birds. The cock, therefore, as he cannot stay long in his connexions, supplies by dint of repeated treadings the reiterated ejaculations of the single intercourse in other animals; and as he has neither penis nor glans, still the extremities of the vasa deferentia, inflated with spirits when he treads, become turgid in the manner of a glans penis, and the orifice of the uterus of the hen, compressed by them, her cloaca being exposed for the occasion, is anointed with genital fluid, which consequently does not require a penis for its intromission.

We have said, however, that such was the virtue of the semen of the cock, that not only did it render the uterus, the egg *in utero*, and the vitelline germ in the ovary, but the whole hen prolific, so that even the germs of vitelli, yet to be produced, were impregnated.

Fabricius has well observed that the quantity of spermatic fluid contained in the testes and vasa deferentia of the cock was large; not that the hen requires much to fecundate each of her eggs, but that the cock may have a supply for the large number of hens he serves and for his repeated addresses to them.

The shortness and straight course of the spermatic vessels in the cock also assist the rapid emission of the spermatic fluid: anything that must pass through lengthened and tortuous conduits, of course, escapes more slowly and requires a greater exercise of the impelling power or spirit to force it away.

Among male animals there is none that is more active or more haughty and erect, or that has stronger powers of digestion than the cock, which turns the larger portion of his food into semen; hence it is that he requires so many wives—ten or even a dozen. For there are some animals, single males of which suffice for several females, as we see among deer, cattle, &c.; and there are others, of which the females are so prurient that they are scarcely satisfied with several males, such as the bitch and the wolf; whence prostitutes were called *lupæ* or wolves, as making their persons common; and stews were entitled *lupanaria*. Whilst some animals, of a more chaste disposition, live, as it were, in the conjugal estate, so that the male is married to a single female only, and both take part in providing for the wants of the family; for since nature requires that the male supply the deficiencies of the female in the work of generation, and as she alone in many cases does not suffice to cherish and feed and protect the young, the male is added to the wife that he may take part in the burthen of bringing up the offspring. Partridges lead a wedded life, because the females alone cannot incubate such a number of eggs as they lay (so that they are said, by some, to make two nests), nor to bring up such a family as by and by appears without assistance. The male pigeon also assists in building the nest, takes his turn in incubating the eggs, and is active in feeding the young. In the same way many other instances of conjugal life among the lower animals might be quoted, and indeed we shall have occasion to refer to several in what yet remains to be said.

Those males, among animals, which serve several females, such as the cock, have an abundant secretion of seminal fluid, and are provided with long and ample vasa deferentia. And at whatever time or season the clustered rudimentary papulæ in the ovary come to maturity and require fecundation, that they may go on to be turned into perfect eggs, the males will then be found to have an abundance of seminal fluid, and the testicles to enlarge and become conspicuous in the very situation to which they transfer their fecundating influence, *viz.*, the præcordia. This is remarkable in fishes, birds, and the whole race of oviparous animals; the males of which teem with fecundating seminal fluid at the same precise seasons as the females become full of eggs.

Whatever parts of the hen, therefore, are destined by nature for purposes of generation, *viz.*, the ovary, the infundibulum, the processus uteri, the uterus itself, and the pudenda; as also the situation of these parts, their structure, dimensions, temperature, and all that follows this; all these, I say, are either subordinate to the production and growth of the egg, or to intercourse and the reception of fecundity from the male; or, for the sake of parturition, to which they conduce either as principal and convenient means, or as means necessary, and without which what is done could not be accomplished; for nothing in nature's works is fashioned either carelessly or in vain. In the same way all the parts in the cock are fashioned subordinate to the preparation or concoction of the spermatic fluid, and its transference to the hen.

Now those males that are so vigorously constituted as to serve several females are larger and handsomer, and in the matter of spirit and arms excel their females in a far greater degree than the males of those that live attached to a single female. Neither the male partridge, nor the crow, nor the pigeon, is distinguished from the female bird in the same decided way as the cock from his hens, the stag from his does, &c.

The cock, therefore, as he is gayer in his plumage, better armed, more courageous and pugnacious, so is he replete with semen, and so apt for repeated intercourse, that unless he have a number of wives he distresses them by his frequent assaults; he not only invites but compels them to his pleasure, and leaping upon them at inconvenient and improper seasons (even when they are engaged in the business of incubation) and wearing off the feathers from their backs, he truly does them an injury. I have occasionally seen hens so torn and worn by the ferocious addresses of the cock, that with their backs stript of feathers and laid bare in places, even to the bone, they languished miserably for a time and then died. The same thing also occurs among pheasants, turkeys, and other species.

EXERCISE 40. *Of the hen*

There are two instruments and two first causes of generation, the male and the female— for to the hen seems to belong the formation of the egg, as to the cock the fertilizing principle. In the act of intercourse, then, of these two, that which renders the egg fruitful is either transmitted from the male to the female, or by means of coition is generated in the hen. The nature of this principle, however, is no less difficult to ascertain than are the particulars of its communication, whether, for instance, we suppose such communication to take place with the whole system of the hen, or simply with her womb, or with the egg already formed, or further, with all the eggs now commencing and hereafter about to commence their existence in the ovary. For it is probable, from what I have formerly mentioned, and also from the experiment of Fabricius,[1] that but a few acts of intercourse, and the consorting of the hen with the cock for some days, are sufficient to fecundate her, or at least her womb, during the whole year. And so far I can myself affirm, from my own observation, to wit, that the twentieth egg laid by a hen, after separation from the cock, has proved prolific. So that, in like manner as it is well known that, from the seed of male fishes shed into the water, a large mass of ova is impregnated, and that in dogs, pigs, and other animals, a small number of acts of intercourse suffice for the procreation of many young ones (some even think it well established, that if a bitch have connexion more than three or four times, her fruitfulness is impaired, and that more females than males are then engendered), so may the cock, by a few treadings, render prolific not only the egg in the womb, but also the whole ovarium, and, as has been often said, the hen herself. Nay, what is more remarkable, and indeed wonderful, it is said that in Persia,[2] on cutting open the female mouse, the young ones still contained in the belly are already pregnant; in other words, they are mothers before they are born! as if the male rendered not only the female fruitful, but also impregnated the young which she had conceived; in the same way as our cock fertilizes not merely the hen, but also the eggs which are about to be produced by her.

But this is confidently denied by those physicians who assert that conception is produced from a mixture of the seed of each sex. And hence Fabricius,[3] although he affirms that the seed of the cock ejected in coition never does, nor can, enter the cavity of the womb, where the egg is formed, or takes its increase, and

though he plainly sees that the eggs when first commencing in the ovarium are, no less than those which exist in the womb, fecundated by the same act of coition, and that of these no part could arise from the semen of the cock, yet has he supposed that this semen, as if it must needs be present and permanent, is contained during the entire year in the *bursa* of the fruitful hen, and reserved in a *foramen cæcum*. This opinion we have already rejected, as well because that cavity is found in the male and female equally, as because neither there, nor anywhere else in the hen, have we been able to discover this stagnant semen of the cock; as soon as it has performed its office, and impressed a prolific power on the female, it either escapes out of the body, or is dissolved, or is turned into vapour and vanishes. And although Galen,[4] and all physicians with him, oppose by various reasonings this dissolving of the semen, yet, if they carefully trace the anatomical arrangement of the genital parts, and at the same time weigh other proofs of the strongest kind, they must confess that the semen of the male, as it is derived from the testicles through the vasa deferentia, and as it is contained in the vesiculæ seminales, is not prolific unless it be rendered spiritual and effervesce into a frothy nature by the incitement of intercourse or desire. For it is not, as Aristotle[5] bears witness, its bodily form, or fire, or any such faculty, that renders the semen prolific, but the spirit which is contained in it, and the nature which inheres in it, bearing a proportion to the element of the stars. Wherefore, though we should allow with Fabricius that the semen is retained in the *bursa*, yet, when that prolific effervescence or spirit had been spent, it would forthwith be useless and sterile. Hence, too, physicians may learn that the semen of the male is the architect of the progeny, not because the first conception is embodied out of it, but because it is spiritual and effervescent, as if swelling with a fertilizing spirit, and a preternatural influence. For otherwise the story of Averrhöes, of the woman who conceived in a bath, might bear an appearance of truth. But of these things more in their proper place.

In the same manner then as the egg is formed from the hen, so is it probable, that from the *females* of other animals, as will hereafter be shown, the first conceptions take both material and form; and that, too, some little time after

[1] *Op. cit.*, p. 31.
[2] Aristotle, *History of Animals*, VI. 37.
[3] *Op. cit.*, pp. 38, 39.

[4] cf. Aristotle, *On the Generation of Animals*, II, 3.
[5] *Ibid.*

the semen of the male has been introduced, and has disappeared again. For the cock does not confer any fecundity on the hen, or her eggs, by the simple emission of his semen, but only in so far as that fluid has a prolific quality, and is imbued with a plastic power; that is to say, is spiritual, operative, and analogous to the essence of the stars. The male, therefore, is no more to be considered the first principle, from which conceptions and the embryo arise, because he is capable of secreting and emitting semen, than is the female, which creates an egg without his assistance. But it is on this consideration rather that he is entitled to his prerogative, that he introduces his semen, imbued as it is with the spirit and the virtue of a divine agent, such as, in a moment of time, performs its functions, and conveys fertility. For, as we see things suddenly set on fire and blasted by a spark struck from a flint, or the lightning flashing from a cloud, so equally does the seed of the male instantly affect the female which it has touched with a kind of contagion, and transfer to her its prolific quality, by which it renders fruitful in a moment, not only the eggs, but the uterus also, and the hen herself. For an inflammable material is not set on fire by the contact of flame more quickly than is the hen made pregnant by intercourse with the cock. But what it is that is transferred from him to her, we shall afterwards find occasion to speak of, when we treat this matter specially and at greater length.

In the meantime, we must remark, that, if it be derived from the soul (for whatever is fruitful is probably endowed also with a soul; and we have said before, that the egg, in Aristotle's opinion, as well as the seeds of plants, has a vegetative soul), that soul, or at all events the vegetative one, must be communicated as a graft, and transferred from the male to the female, from the female to the egg, from the egg to the fœtus; or else be generated in each of these successively by the contagion of coition.

The subject, nevertheless, seems full of ambiguity; and so Aristotle, although he allows that the semen of the male has such great virtue that a single emission of it suffices for fecundating very many eggs at the same time, yet, lest this admission should seem to gainsay the efficacy of frequent repetitions of intercourse, he further says, "In birds, not even those eggs which arise through intercourse can greatly increase in size, unless the intercourse be continued; and the reason of this is that, as in women, the menstrual excretion is drawn downwards by sexual intercourse (for the uterus, becoming warm, attracts moisture, and its pores are opened), so also does it happen with birds, in which the menstrual excrement, because it accumulates gradually, and is retained above the cincture, and cannot escape, from being in small quantity, only passes off when it has reached the uterus itself. For by this is the egg increased, as is the fœtus of the viviparous animal by that which flows through the umbilicus. For almost all birds, after but a single act of intercourse, continue to produce eggs, but they are small."[1]

Now, so far perhaps would the opinion of Aristotle be correct, that more and larger eggs are procured by frequently-repeated intercourse; because, as he says, there may be "a flow of more fruitful material to the womb, when warmed by the heat of coition"; not, however, that frequent coition must necessarily take place in order to render the eggs that are laid prolific. For experience, as we have said, teaches the contrary, and the reason which he alleges does not seem convincing; since the rudiments of eggs are not formed in the uterus from menstrual blood, which is found in no part of the hen, but in the ovary, where no blood pre-exists, and originate as well without, as along with the intercourse of the cock.

The hen, as well as all other females, supplies matter, nutrition, and place to the conception. The matter, whence the rudiments of all eggs are produced in the ovary and take their increase, seems to be the very same from which all the other parts of the hen, namely, the fleshy, nervous, and bony structures, as well as the head and the rest of the members, are nourished and grow. Nourishment is in fact conveyed to each single papula and yelk contained in the ovary by means of vessels, in the same way precisely as to all the other parts of the hen. But the place where the egg is provided with membranes, and perfected by the addition of the chalazæ and shell, is the uterus.

But that the hen neither emits any semen during intercourse, nor sheds any blood into the cavity of the uterus, and that the egg is not formed in the mode in which Aristotle supposed a conception to arise, nor, as physicians imagine, from a mixture of the seminal fluids; as also that the semen of the cock does not penetrate into, nor is attracted towards, the cavity of the uterus of the hen, is all made manifestly clear by this one observation, namely, that after intercourse there is nothing more

[1] *On the Generation of Animals*, III. I.

to be found in the uterus, than there was before the act. And when this shall have been
afterwards clearly established and demonstrated to be true of all kinds of animals which
conceive in a uterus, it will at the same time be
equally evident that what has hitherto been
handed down to us from all antiquity on the
generation of animals is erroneous; that the
fœtus is not constituted of the semen either of
the male or female, nor of a mixture of the two,
nor of the menstrual blood, but that in all animals, as well in the prolific conception as after
it, the same series of phenomena occur as in the
generation of the chick from the egg, and as in
the production of plants from the seeds of their
several kinds. For, besides that, it appears the
male is not required as being in himself agent,
workman, and efficient cause; nor the female,
as if she supplied the matter; but that each,
male as well as female, may be said to be in
some sort the operative and parent; and the
fœtus, as a mixture of both, is created a mixed
resemblance and kind. Nor is that true which
Aristotle often affirms, and physicians take for
granted, namely, that immediately after intercourse, something either of the fœtus or the
conception may be found in the uterus (for instance, the heart, the "three bullæ," or some
other principal part), at any rate *something*—
a coagulum, some mixture of the spermatic substances, or other things of the like kind. On the
contrary, it is not till long after intercourse
that the eggs and conception first commence
their existence, among the greater number of
animals, and these the most perfect ones; I
mean in the cases where the females have been
fruitful and have become pregnant. And that
the female is prolific, before any conception is
contained in the uterus, there are many indications, as will be hereafter set forth in the history of viviparous animals: the breasts enlarge,
the uterus begins to swell, and by other symptoms a change of the whole system is discerned.

But the hen, though she have for the most
part the rudiments of eggs in her before intercourse, which are afterwards by this act rendered fruitful, and there be, therefore, something in her immediately after coition, yet even
when she, as in the case of other animals, has as
yet no eggs ready prepared in the ovary, or has
at the time of the intercourse got rid of all she
had, yet does she by and by, even after some
lapse of time, as if in possession of both principles
or the powers of both sexes, generate eggs by
herself after the manner of plants; and these (I
speak from experience) not barren, but prolific.

Nay, what is more, if you remove all the eggs
from beneath a hen that has been fecundated
and is now sitting (after having already laid all
her eggs, and no more remain in the ovary),
she will begin to lay again; and the eggs thus
laid will be prolific, and have both principles
inherent in them.

EXERCISE 41. *Of the sense in which the hen may
be called the "prime efficient": and of her parturition*

It has already been said that the hen is the
efficient cause of generation, or an instrument
of Nature in this work, not indeed immediately, or of herself; but when rendered prolific
by commission from, and in virtue of the male.
But as the male is considered by Aristotle to be
the first principle of generation on his own
merits, because the first impulse toward generation proceeds from him, so may the hen in
some measure be put down as the first cause of
generation; inasmuch as the male is undoubtedly inflamed to venery by the presence of the
female. "The female fish," says Pliny,[1] "will
follow the male at the season of intercourse,
and strike his belly with her nose; at the spawning time the male will do the like to the female." I have myself at times seen male fishes
in shoals following a female that was on the
point of spawning, in the same way as dogs pursue a bitch, that they might sprinkle the ova
just laid with their milk or seed. But this is
particularly to be remarked in the more wan-
ton and lascivious females, who stir up the dormant fires of Cupid, and inspire a silent love;
hence it is that the common cock, so soon as he
sees one of his own hens that has been absent
for ever so short time, or any other stranger-
hen, forthwith feels the sting of desire, and
treads her. Moreover, victorious in a battle, although wounded and tired from the fight, he
straightway sets about treading the wives of his
vanquished foe one after another. And that he
may further feed the flame of love thus kindled
in his breast, by various gesticulations, incite-
ments, and caresses, often crowing the while,
calling his hens to him, approaching and walking round them, and tripping himself with his
wings, he entices his females to intercourse as
by a kind of fascination. Such are the arts of the
male; but sometimes a certain sullenness of the
female, and an apparent disinclination on her
part, contribute not a little to arouse the ar-
dour of the male and stimulate his languishing
desire, so that he fills her more quickly and
more copiously with prolific spirit. But of al-

[1] *Hist. nat.*, IX. 50.

lurements of this kind, and in what degree they promote conception, we shall speak more hereafter. For, if you carefully weigh the works of nature, you will find that nothing in them was made in vain, but that all things were ordered with a purpose and for the sake of some good end.

Almost all females, though they have pleasure in the act of intercourse and impregnation, suffer pain in parturition. But the reverse is the case with the hen, who loudly complains during intercourse and struggles against it; but in parturition, although the egg be very large in comparison with the body and the orifice of the uterus, and it does nothing to further its exit (as is customary with the young of viviparous animals), yet she brings forth easily and without pain, and immediately afterwards commences her exultations; and with her loud cackling calls the cock as it seems to share in her triumph.

But, although many rudiments of eggs are found in the hen's ovary, of various sizes and in different stages, so that some are larger and nearer to maturity than others, yet all of them appear to be fecundated, or to receive the prolific faculty from the tread of the cock at the same time and in the same degree. And though a considerable time elapse (namely, thirty or more days) before the common hen or hen-partridge lay all the eggs which she has conceived, yet in a stated time after the mother has begun to sit upon them (say twenty or two-and-twenty days) all the young are hatched nearly at the same time; nor are they less perfect than if they had commenced their origin simultaneously, from the period of one and the same conception, as the whelps of bitches do.

And while we are here, and while I think how small are the prolific germs of eggs, mere papulæ and exudations less than millet-seeds, and contemplate the full proportions of the cock that springs from thence, his fine spirit, and his handsome plumage, I cannot but express my admiration that such strength should be reposed in the nature of things in such insignificant elements, and that it has pleased the omnipotent Creator out of the smallest beginnings to exhibit some of his greatest works. From a minute and scarce perceptible papula springs the hen, or the cock, a proud and magnificent creature. From a small seed springs a mighty tree; from the minute gemmule or apex of the acorn, how wide does the gnarled oak at length extend his arms, how loftily does he lift his

branches to the sky, how deeply do his roots strike down into the ground! "It is in truth a great miracle of nature," says Pliny,[1] "that from so small an origin is produced a material that resists the axe, and that supplies beams, masts, and battering-rams. Such is the strength, such the power of nature!" But in the seeds of all plants there is a gemmule or bud of such a kind, so small that if the top only, a very point, be lost, all hope of propagation is immediately destroyed; in so small a particle does all the plastic power of the future tree seem lodged! The provident ant by gnawing off this little particle stores safely in her subterraneous hoard the grain and other seeds she gathers, and ingeniously guards against their growing: "The cypress," adds Pliny, in the same place, "bears a seed that is greatly sought after by the ant; which makes us still further wonder that the birth of mighty trees should be consumed in the food of so small an animal." But on these points we shall say more when we show that many animals, especially insects, arise and are propagated from elements and seeds so small as to be invisible (like atoms flying in the air), scattered and dispersed here and there by the winds; and yet these animals are supposed to have arisen spontaneously, or from decomposition, because their ova are nowhere to be found. These considerations, however, may furnish arguments to that school of philosophy which teaches that all things are produced from nothing; and indeed there is hardly any ascertainable proportion between the rudiment and the full growth of any animal.

Nor should we so much wonder what it is in the cock that preserves and governs so perfect and beautiful an animal, and is the first cause of that entity which we call the soul; but much more, what it is in the egg, aye, in the germ of the egg, of so great virtue as to produce such an animal, and raise him to the very summit of excellence. Nor are we only to admire the greatness of the artificer that aids in the production of so noble a work, but chiefly the "contagion" of intercourse, an act which is so momentary! What is it, for instance, that passes from the male into the female, from the female into the egg, from the egg into the chick? What is this transitory thing, which is neither to be found remaining, nor touching, nor contained, as far as the senses inform us, and yet works with the highest intelligence and foresight, beyond all art; and which, even after it has vanished, renders the egg prolific, not be-

[1] *Ibid.*, XVII. 10.

cause it now touches, but because it formerly did so, and that not merely in the case of the perfect and completed egg, but of the imperfect and commencing one when it was yet but a speck; aye, and makes the hen herself fruitful before she has yet produced any germs of eggs, and this too so suddenly, as if it were said by the Almighty, "Let there be progeny," and straight it is so?

Let physicians, therefore, cease to wonder at what always excites their astonishment, namely, the manner in which epidemic, contagious, and pestilential diseases scatter their seeds, and are propagated to a distance through the air, or by some *fomes* producing diseases like themselves, in bodies of a different nature, and in a hidden fashion silently multiplying themselves by a kind of generation, until they become so fatal, and with the permission of the Deity spread destruction far and wide among man and beast; since they will find far greater wonders than these taking place daily in the generation of animals. For agents in greater number and of more efficiency are required in the construction and preservation of an animal, than for its destruction; since the things that are difficult and slow of growth, decay with ease and rapidity. Seneca observes, with his usual elegance, "How long a time is needed for conception to be carried out to parturition! with what labour and tenderness is an infant reared! to what diligent and continued nutrition must the body be subject, to arrive at adolescence! but by what a nothing is it destroyed! It takes an age to establish cities, an hour to destroy them. By great watching are all things established and made to flourish, quickly and of a sudden do they fall in pieces. That which becomes by long growth a forest, quickly, in the smallest interval of time, and by a spark, is reduced to ashes."[1] Nor is even a spark necessary, since by the solar rays transmitted through a small piece of glass and concentrated to a focus, fire may be immediately produced, and the largest things be set in flames. So easy is everything to nature's majesty, who uses her strength sparingly, and dispenses it with caution and foresight for the commencement of her works by imperceptible additions, but hastens to decay with suddenness and in full career. In the generation of things is seen the most excellent, the eternal and almighty God, the divinity of nature, worthy to be looked up to with reverence; but all mortal things run to destruction of their own accord in a thousand ways.

[1] *Nat. quæst.*, III. 27.

EXERCISE 42. *Of the manner in which the generation of the chick takes place from the egg*

Hitherto we have considered the egg as the fruit and end; it still remains for us to treat of it as the seed and beginning. "We must now inquire," says Fabricius[2], "how the generation of the chick results from the egg, setting out from that principle of Aristotle and Galen, which is, even conceded by all, to wit, that all things which are made in this life, are manifestly made by these three: workers, instruments, and matter."

But since in natural phenomena, the work is not extrinsic, but is included in the matter, or the instruments, he concludes that we must take cognizance only of the agent and the matter.

As we are here about to show in what manner the chick arises from the egg, however, I think it may be of advantage for me to preface this by showing the number of modes in which one thing may be said to be made from another.

For so it will appear, more clearly and distinctly, after which of these generation takes place in the egg, and what are the right conclusions in regard to its matter, its instruments, and efficient cause.

Aristotle has laid down that there are four modes in which óne thing is made from another: "first, when we say that from day night is made, or from a boy a man, since one is after the other; secondly, when we say that a statue is made from brass, or a bed from wood, or anything else from a certain material, so that the whole consists of something, which is inherent and made into a form; thirdly, as when from a musical man is made an unmusical one, or from a healthy, a sick one, or contraries in any way: fourthly, as Epicharmus exaggerates it, as of calumnies, cursing; of cursing, fighting. But all these are to be referred to that from whence the movement took its rise; for the calumny is a certain portion of the whole quarrel. Since then these are the methods in which one thing is made from another, it is clear that the seed is in one of two of these. For that which is born arises out of it, either as from matter, or as from the prime mover. For it is not, 'as this is after that,' in the same way as after the Panathenœa navigation; nor as 'one contrary from another'; for in such case, a thing would be born out of its contrary, because it is in a state of decay, and there must be something else as subject-matter."[3]

[2] *Op. cit.*, p. 28.
[3] *On the Generation of Animals*, I. 18.

By these words, Aristotle rightly infers that the semen proceeding from the male is the efficient or instrumental cause of the embryo; since it is no part of what is born, either in the first or third manner (namely, as one thing is after another, or as it is out of its contrary); nor does it arise from the subject-matter.

But then, as he adds, in the same place, "that which comes out of the male in coition, is not with truth and propriety called semen, but rather geniture; and it is different from the seed properly so called. For that is called the geniture which, proceeding from the generant, is the cause which first promotes the beginning of generation. I mean in those creatures which nature designed to have connexion; but the seed is that which derives its origin from the intercourse of the two (*i.e.*, of the male and female); such is the seed of all plants; and of some animals in which the sex is not distinct; it is the produce, as it were, of the male and female mixed together originally, like a kind of promiscuous conception"; and such as we have formerly in our history declared the egg to be, which is called both fruit and seed. For the seed and the fruit are distinct from each other, and in the relation of antecedent and consequent; the fruit is that which is out of something else, the seed is that out of which something else comes; otherwise, both were the same.

It remains then, to inquire, in how many of the aforesaid ways the fœtus may arise, not indeed from the geniture of the male, but out of the true seed, or out of the egg or conception, which is in reality the seed of animals.

EXERCISE 43. *In how many ways the chick may be said to be formed from the egg*

It is admitted, then, that the fœtus is formed from a prolific egg, as out of the proper matter, and as it were by the requisite agency, and that the same egg stands for both causes of the chick. For inasmuch as it derives its origin from the hen, and is considered as a fruit, it is the matter: but, in so far as it contains in its whole structure the prolific and plastic faculty infused by the male, it is called the efficient cause of the chick.

Moreover, not only as Fabricius supposed, are these, namely, the agent and the instrument, inseparably joined in one and the same egg, but it is also necessary that the aliment by which the chick is nourished be present in the same place. Indeed, in the prolific egg, these four are found together, to wit, the agent, the instrument, the matter, and the aliment, as we have shown in our history.

Wherefore, we say, that the chick is formed from the prolific egg in all the aforesaid ways, namely, as from matter, by an efficient, and by an instrument; and moreover, as a man grows out of a boy, as the whole is made up of its parts, and as a thing grows from its nutriment; a contrary thing springs from a contrary.

For after incubation is begun, as soon as by the internal motive principle a certain clear liquid which we have called the eye of the egg is produced, we say that that liquid is made, as it were, out of a contrary; in the same way as we suppose the chyle through concoction to be formed out of its contraries (namely, crude articles of food), and in the same way as we are said to be nourished by contraries; so, from the albumen is formed and augmented that to which we have given the names of the eye and the colliquament; and in the same manner, from that clear fluid do the blood and pulsating vesicle, the first particles of the chick, receive their being, nutrition, and growth. The nutriment, I say, is by the powers of an inherent and innate heat, assimilated by means of concoction, as it were, out of a contrary. For the crude and unconcocted are contrary to the concocted and assimilated, as the unmusical man is to the musical, and the sick to the sound man.

And when the blood is engendered from the clear colliquament, or a clear fluid is produced from the white or the yelk, there is generation as regards the former, corruption as regards the latter; a transmutation, namely, is made from the extremes of contraries, the subject-matter all the while remaining the same. To explain: by the breaking up of the first form of the white, the colliquament is produced; and from the consumption of this colliquament, follows the form of the blood, in the same way precisely as food is converted into the substance of the thing fed.

It is thus, then, that the chick is said to be made out of the egg, as it were by a contrary; for in the nutrition and growth of the chick in the egg, white and yelk are equally broken up and consumed, and finally the whole substance of the egg. It is clear, therefore, that the chick is formed from the egg, as it were, by a contrary, namely the aliment, and as if by an abstraction, and from a non-entity. For the first particle of the chick, *viz.*, the blood or punctum saliens, is constituted out of something which is not blood, and altogether its contrary, the same subject-matter always remaining.

The chick too is made from the egg, as a man is made from a boy. For in the same way, as out of plants seeds arise, and out of seeds, buds, sprouts, stems, flowers, and fruits; so also out of the egg, the seed of the hen is produced, the dilatation of the cicatricula and the colliquament, the blood and the heart, as the first particle of the fœtus or fruit; and all this, in the same way as the day from the night, the summer from the spring, a man from a boy—one follows or comes after the other. So that, in the same way as fruits arise after flowers on the same stem, so likewise is the colliquament formed after the egg, the blood after this, as from the primogeneous humour, the chick after the blood, and out of it, as the whole out of a part; in the same way, as by Epicharmus' exaggeration, out of calumnies comes cursing, and out of cursing, fighting. For the blood first begins its existence with the punctum saliens, and at the same time, seems to be as well a part of the chick, and a kind of efficient or instrument of its generation, inseparable, as Fabricius thinks, from the agent. But how the egg may be called the efficient and instrument of generation, has partly been explained already, and will be illustrated more copiously by what we shall presently say.

So much has been fully established in our history, that the punctum pulsans and the blood, in the course of their growth, attach round themselves the rest of the body, and all the other members of the chick, just as the yelk in the uterus, after being evolved from the ovary, surrounds itself with the white; and this not without concoction and nutrition. Now the common instrument of all vegetative operations, is, in the opinion of all men, an internal heat or calidum innatum, or a spirit diffused through the whole, and in that spirit a soul or faculty of a soul. The egg, therefore, beyond all doubt, has its own operative soul, which is all in the whole, and all in each individual part, and contains within itself a spirit or animal heat, the immediate instrument of that soul. To one who should ask, then, how the chick is made from the egg, we answer: after all the ways recited by Aristotle, and devised by others, in which it is possible for one thing to be made from another.

EXERCISE 44. *Fabricius is mistaken with regard to the matter of the generation of the chick in ovo*

As I proposed to myself at the outset, I continue to follow Fabricius as pointing out the way; and we shall, therefore, consider the three

things which he says are to be particularly regarded in the generation of the chick, *viz.*: the agent, the matter, and the nourishment of the embryo. These must needs be all contained in the egg; he proposes various doubts or questions, and quotes the opinions of the most weighty authorities in regard to them, these opinions being frequently discordant. The first difficulty is in reference to the matter and nourishment of the chick. Hippocrates,[1] Anaxagoras, Alcmaeon, Menander, and the ancient philosophers all thought that the chick was engendered from the vitellus, and was nourished by the albumen. Aristotle,[2] however, and after him, Pliny,[3] maintained, on the contrary, that the chick was incorporated from the albumen, and nourished by the vitellus. But Fabricius himself, will have it that neither the white nor yelk forms the matter of the chick; he strives to combat both of the preceding opinions, and teaches that the white and the yellow alike do no more than nourish the chick. One of his arguments, amongst a great number of others which I think are less to be acquiesced in, appears to me to have some force. The branches of the umbilical vessels, he says, through which the embryo undoubtedly imbibes its nourishment, are distributed to the albumen and the vitellus alike, and both of these fluids diminish as the chick grows. And it is on this ground, that Fabricius in confirmation of his opinion, says: "Of the bodies constituting the egg, and adapted to forward the generation of the chick, there are only three, the albumen, the vitellus, and the chalazæ; now the albumen and vitellus are the nourishment of the chick; so that the chalazæ alone remain as matter from which it can be produced."[4]

Nevertheless, that the excellent Fabricius is in error here, we have demonstrated above in our history. For after the chick is already almost perfected, and its head and its eyes are distinctly visible, the chalazæ can readily be found entire, far from the embryo, and pushed from the apices towards the sides: the office of these bodies, as Fabricius himself admits, is that of ligaments, and to preserve the vitellus in its proper position within the albumen. Nor is that true, which Fabricius adds in confirmation of his opinion, namely, that the chalazæ are situated in the direction of the blunt part of the

[1] *De nat. pueri.*
[2] *History of Animals*, vi. 3; *On the Generation of Animals*, iii. 1, 2.
[3] *Hist. nat.* x. 53.
[4] *Op. cit.*, p. 34.

egg. For after even a single day's incubation, the relative positions of the fluids of the egg are changed, the yelk being drawn upwards, and the chalazæ on either hand removed, as we have already had occasion to say.

He is also mistaken when he speaks of the chalazæ, as proper parts of the egg. The egg consists in fact but of white and yelk; the chalazæ as well as the membranes, are mere appendages of the albumen and vitellus. The chalazæ, in particular, are the extremities of certain membranes, twisted and knotted; they are produced in the same way as a rope is formed by the contortion of its component filaments, and exist for the purpose of more certainly securing the several elements of the egg in their respective places.

Fabricius, therefore, reasons ill when he says, that "the chalazæ are found in the part of the egg where the embryo is produced, wherefore it is engendered from them"; for even on his own showing, this could never take place, he admitting that the chalazæ are extant in either extremity of the egg, whilst the chick never makes its appearance save at the blunt end; in which, moreover, at the first commencement of generation, no chalaza can be seen. Further, if you examine the matter in a fresh egg, you will find the superior chalaza not immediately under the blunt end or its cavity, but declined somewhat to the side; not to that side, however, where the cavity is extending, but rather to the opposite side. Still further, from what has preceded, it is obvious that the relative positions of the fluids of the egg are altered immediately that incubation is begun: the eye increased by the colliquament is drawn up towards the cavity in the blunt end of the egg, whence the white and the chalaza are on either hand withdrawn to the side. For the macula or cicatricula which before incubation was situated midway between the two ends, now increased into the eye of the egg, adjoins the cavity in the blunt end, and whilst one of the chalazæ is depressed from the blunt end, the other is raised from the sharp end, in the same way as the poles of a globe are situated when the axis is set obliquely; the greater portion of the albumen, particularly that which is thicker, subsides at the same time, into the sharp end.

Neither is it correct to say that the chalazæ bear a resemblance in length and configuration to the chick on its first formation, and that the number of their nodules corresponds with the number of the principal parts of the embryo; a statement which gives Fabricius an opportunity of adducing an argument connected with the *matter* of the chick, based on the similarity of its consistency to that of the chalazæ. But the red mass (which Fabricius regarded as the liver) is neither situated in nor near the chalaza, but in the middle of the clear colliquament; and it is not any rudiment of the liver but of the heart alone. Neither does his view square with the example he quotes of the tadpole, "of which," he says, "there is nothing to be seen but the head and the tail, that is to say, the head and spine, without a trace of upper or lower extremities." And he adds, "he who has seen a chalaza, and this kind of conception, in so far as the body is concerned, will believe that in the former, he has already seen the latter." I, however, have frequently dissected the tadpole, and have found the belly of large size, and containing intestines and liver and heart pulsating; I have also distinguished the head and the eyes. The part which Fabricius takes for the head, is the rounded mass of the tadpole, whence the creature is called *gyrinus*, from its circular form. It has a tail with which it swims, but is without legs. About the epoch of the summer solstice, it loses the tail, when the extremities begin to sprout. Nothing however occurs in the nature of a division of the embryo pullet into the head and spine, which should induce us to regard it as produced from the chalazæ, and in the same manner as the tadpole.

The position and fame of Fabricius, however, a man exceedingly well skilled in anatomy, do not allow me to push this refutation further. Nor indeed, is there any necessity so to do, seeing that the thing is so clearly exhibited in our history.

Our author concludes, by stating that his opinion is of great antiquity, and was in vogue even in the times of Aristotle.

For my own part, nevertheless, I regard the view of Ulysses Aldrovandus as the older, he maintaining that the chalazæ are the spermatic fluid of the cock, from which and through which alike the chick is engendered.

Neither notion, however, is founded on fact, but is the popular error of all times: the chalazæ, treads, or treadles, as our English name implies, are still regarded by the country folks as the semen of the cock.

"The treadles (*grandines*)," says Aldrovandus: "are the spermatic fluid of the cock, because no fertile egg is without them." But neither is any unprolific egg without these parts, a fact which Aldrovandus was either ignorant of or concealed. Fabricius admits this fact; but though he has denied that the semen of the male penetrates to the uterus or is ever found in the egg, he, nevertheless, contends that the chalazæ alone of all the parts of the egg are impregnated with the prolific power of the egg, and are the repositories of the fecundating influence; and this, with the fact staring him in the face all the while that there is no perceptible difference between the chalazæ of a prolific and an unprolific egg. And when he admits that the mere rudiments of eggs in the ovary, as well as the vitelli that are surrounded with albumen, become fecundated through the intercourse of the cock, I conceive that this must have been the cause of the error committed by so distinguished an individual. It was the current opinion, as I have said oftener than once, both among philosophers and physicians, that the matter of the embryo in animal generation, was the geniture, either of the male, or of the female, or resulted from a mixture of the two, and that from this, deposited in the uterus, like a seed in the ground, which produces a plant, the animal was engendered. Aristotle, himself, is not very far from the same view, when he maintains the menstrual blood of the female to be the seed, which the semen of the male coagulates, and so composes the conception.

The error which we have announced, having been admitted by all in former times, as a matter of certainty, it is not to be wondered at that various erroneous opinions, based on each man's conjecture, should have emanated from it. They, however, are wholly mistaken, who fancy that anything in the shape of a "prepared or fit matter" must necessarily remain in the uterus after intercourse, from which the fœtus is produced, or the first conception is formed, or that anything is immediately fashioned in the uterine cavity that corresponds to the seed of a plant deposited in the bosom of the ground. For it is quite certain that, in the uterus of the fowl, and the same thing is true of the uterus of every other female animal, there is nothing discoverable after intercourse more than there was before it.

It appears, consequently, that Fabricius erred when he said: "In the same way as a viviparous animal is incorporated from a small quantity of seminal matter, whilst the matter which is taken up as food and nourishment is very large; so a small chalaza suffices for the generation of a chick, and the rest of the matter contained in the egg goes to it in the shape of nutriment."[1] From which it is obvious, that

he sought for some such "prepared matter" in the egg, whence the chick should be incorporated; mainly, as it seems, that he might not be found in contradiction with Aristotle's definition of an egg, viz.: as "that from part of which an animal is engendered; and the remainder of which is food for the thing engendered."[2] This of Fabricius, therefore, has the look of a valid argument, namely, "Since there are only three parts in the egg—the albumen, the vitellus, and the chalazæ; and the two former alone supply aliment; it necessarily follows that the chalazæ alone are the matter from which the chick is constituted."

Thus, our learned anatomist, blinded by a popular error, seeking in the egg for some particular matter fitted to engender the chick distinct from the rest of the contents of the egg, has gone astray. And so it happens to all, who, forsaking the light, which the frequent dissection of bodies, and familiar converse with nature supplies, expect that they are to understand from conjecture, and arguments founded on probabilities, or the authority of writers, the things or the facts which they ought themselves to behold with their own eyes, to perceive with their proper senses. It is not wonderful, therefore, when we see that we have so many errors accredited by general consent, handed down to us from remote antiquity, that men otherwise of great ingenuity, should be egregiously deceived, which they may very well be, when they are satisfied with taking their knowledge from books, and keeping their memory stored with the notions of learned men. They who philosophize in this way, by tradition, if I may so say, know no better than the books they keep by them.

In the egg then, as we have said, there is no distinct part or prepared matter present, from which the fœtus is formed; but in the same way as the apex or gemmule protrudes in a seed; so in the egg, there is a macula or cicatricula, which, endowed with plastic power, grows into the eye of the egg and the colliquament, from which and in which the primordial or rudimentary parts of the chick, the blood, to wit, and the punctum saliens are engendered, nourished, and augmented, until the perfect chick is developed. Neither is Aristotle's definition of an egg correct, as a body from part of which an embryo is formed, and by part of which it is nourished, unless the philosopher is to be understood in the following manner: the egg is a body, from part of which the chick arises, not as from a special

<hr>

[1] Op. sup. cit., p. 35.

[2] History of Animals, III. 8.

matter, but as a man grows out of a boy; or an egg is a perfect conception from which the chick is said to be partly constituted, partly nourished; or to conclude, an egg is a body, the fluids of which serve both for the matter and the nourishment of the parts of the fœtus. In this sense, indeed, Aristotle teaches us that the matter of the human fœtus is the menstrual blood; "which (when poured into the uterus by the veins) nature employs to a new purpose; *viz.*, that of generation, and that a future being may arise, such as the one from which it springs; for potentially it is already such as is the body whose secretion it is, namely the mother."[1]

EXERCISE 45. *What is the material of the chick, and how it is formed in the egg*

Since, then, we are of opinion that for the acquisition of truth we cannot rely on the theories of others, whether these rest on mere assertions, or even may have been confirmed by plausible arguments, except there be added thereto a diligent course of observation; we propose to show, by clearly-arranged remarks derived from the book of nature, what is the material of the fœtus, and in what manner it thence takes its origin. We have seen that one thing is made out of another (*tanquam ex materia*) in two ways, and this as well in works of art, as in those of nature, and more particularly in the generation of animals.

One of these ways, *viz.*, when the object is made out of something pre-existing, is exemplified by the formation of a bed out of wood, or a statue from stone; in which case, the whole material of the future piece of work has already been in existence, before it is finished into form, or any part of the work is yet begun; the second method is, when the material is both made and brought into form at the same time. Just then as the works of art are accomplished in two manners, one, in which the workman cuts the material already prepared, divides it, and rejects what is superfluous, till he leaves it in the desired shape (as is the custom of the statuary); the other, as when the potter educes a form out of clay by the addition of parts, or increasing its mass, and giving it a figure, at the same time that he provides the material, which he prepares, adapts, and applies to his work (and in this point of view, the form may be said rather to have been *made* than *educed*); so exactly is it with regard to the generation of animals.

[1] *On the Generation of Animals*, II. 4.

Some, out of a material previously concocted, and that has already attained its bulk, receive their forms and transfigurations; and all their parts are fashioned simultaneously, each with its distinctive characteristic, by the process called metamorphosis, and in this way a perfect animal is at once born; on the other hand, there are some in which one part is made before another, and then from the same material, afterwards receive at once nutrition, bulk, and form: that is to say, they have some parts made before, some after others, and these are at the same time increased in size and altered in form. The structure of these animals commences from some one part as its nucleus and origin, by the instrumentality of which the rest of the limbs are joined on, and this we say takes place by the method of epigenesis, namely, by degrees, part after part; and this is, in preference to the other mode, generation properly so called.

In the former of the ways mentioned, the generation of insects is effected where by metamorphosis a worm is born from an egg; or out of a putrescent material, the drying of a moist substance or the moistening of a dry one, rudiments are created, from which, as from a caterpillar grown to its full size, or from an aurelia, springs a butterfly or fly already of a proper size, which never attains to any larger growth after it is first born; this is called metamorphosis. But the more perfect animals with red blood are made by epigenesis, or the superaddition of parts. In the former, chance or hazard seems the principal promoter of generation, and there, the form is due to the potency of a pre-existing material; and the first cause of generation is "matter," rather than "an external efficient"; whence it happens too that these animals are less perfect, less preservative of their own races, and less abiding than the red-blooded terrestrial or aquatic animals, which owe their immortality to one constant source, viz., the perpetuation of the same species; of this circumstance we assign the first cause to nature and the vegetative faculty.

Some animals, then, are born of their own accord, concocted out of matter spontaneously, or by chance, as Aristotle seems to assert, when he speaks of animals whose matter is capable of receiving an impulse from itself, *viz.*, the same impulse given by hazard, as is attributable to the seed, in the generation of other animals. And the same thing happens in art, as in the generation of animals. Some things, which are the result of art, are so likewise of chance, as good health; others always owe their existence to art; for instance, a house. Bees, wasps, butterflies, and whatever is generated from caterpillars by metamorphosis, are said to have sprung from chance, and, therefore, to be not preservative of their own race; the contrary is the case with the lion and the cock; they owe their existence, as it were, to nature or an operative faculty of a divine quality, and require for their propagation an identity of species, rather than any supply of fitting material.

In the generation by metamorphosis forms are created as if by the impression of a seal, or as if they were adjusted in a mould; in truth, the whole material is transformed. But an animal which is created by epigenesis attracts, prepares, elaborates, and makes use of the material, all at the same time; the processes of formation and growth are simultaneous. In the former the plastic force cuts up, and distributes, and reduces into limbs the same homogeneous material; and makes out of a homogeneous material organs which are dissimilar. But in the latter, while it creates in succession parts which are differently and variously distributed, it requires and makes a material which is also various in its nature, and variously distributed, and such as is now adapted to the formation of one part, now of another; on which account we believe the perfect hen's-egg to be constituted of various parts.

Now it appears clear from my history that the generation of the chick from the egg is the result of epigenesis, rather than of metamorphosis, and that all its parts are not fashioned simultaneously, but emerge in their due succession and order; it appears, too, that its form proceeds simultaneously with its growth, and its growth with its form; also that the generation of some parts supervenes on others previously existing, from which they become distinct; lastly, that is origin, growth, and consummation are brought about by the method of nutrition; and that at length the fœtus is thus produced. For the formative faculty of the chick rather acquires and prepares its own material for itself than only finds it when prepared, and the chick seems to be formed and to receive its growth from no other than itself. And, as all things receive their growth from the same power by which they are created, so likewise should we believe that by the same power by which the chick is preserved, and caused to grow from the commencement (whether that may have been the soul or a faculty of the soul), by that power, I say, is it also created. For the same efficient and conservative faculty is found

in the egg as in the chick; and of the same material of which it constitutes the first particle of the chick, out of the very same does it nourish, increase, and superadd all the other parts. Lastly, in generation by metamorphosis the whole is distributed and separated *into* parts; but in that by epigenesis the whole is put together *out* of parts in a certain order, and constituted *from* them.

Wherefore Fabricius was in error when he looked for the material of the chick (as a distinct part of the egg, from which its body was formed), as if the chick were created by metamorphosis, or a transformation of the material in mass; and as if all, or at least the principal parts of the body sprang from the same material, and, to use his own words, were incorporated simultaneously. [He is, therefore, of course, opposed to the notion] of the chick being formed by epigenesis, in which a certain order is observed according to the dignity and the use of parts, where at first a small foundation is, as it were, laid, which, in the course of growth, has at one and the same time distinct structures formed and its figure established, and acquires an additional birth of parts afterwards, each in its own order; in the same way, for instance, as the bud bursting from the top of the acorn, in the course of its growth, has its parts separately taking the form of root, wood, pith, bark, boughs, branches, leaves, flowers, and fruit, until at length out comes a perfect tree; just so is it with the creation of the chick in the egg: the little cicatrix, or small spot, the foundation of the future structure, grows into the eye and is at the same time separated into the colliquament; in the centre of which the punctum sanguineum pulsans commences its being, together with the ramification of the veins; to these is presently added the nebula, and the first concretion of the future body; this also, in proportion as its bulk increases, is gradually divided and distinguished into parts, which however do not all emerge at the same time, but one after the other, and each in its proper order. To conclude, then: in the generation of those animals which are created by epigenesis, and are formed in parts (as the chick in the egg), we need not seek one material for the incorporation of the fœtus, another for its commencing nutrition and growth; for it receives such nutrition and growth from the same material out of which it is made; and, vice versa, the chick in the egg is constituted out of the materials of its nutrition and growth. And an animal which is capable of nutrition is of the same potency as one which is augmentative, as we shall afterwards show; and they differ only, as Aristotle says, in their distinctness of being; in all other respects they are alike. For, in so far as anything is convertible into a substance, it is nutritious, and under certain conditions it is augmentative: in virtue of its repairing a loss of substance, it is called nutriment, in virtue of its being added, where there is no such loss of substance, it is called increment. Now the material of the chick, in the processes of generation, nutrition, and augmentation is equally to be considered as aliment and increment. We say simply that anything is generated, when no part of it has pre-existed; we speak of its being nourished and growing when it has already existed. The part of the fœtus which is first formed is said to be begotten or born; all substitutions or additions are called adnascent, or aggenerate. In all there is the same transmutation or generation from the same to the same; as concerns a part, this is performed by the process of nutrition and augmentation, but as regards the whole, by simple generation; in other respects the same processes occur equally. For from the same source from which the material first takes its existence, from that source also does it gain nutriment and increase. Moreover, from what we shall presently say, it will be made clear that all the parts of the body are nourished by a common nutritious juice; for, as all plants arise from one and the same common nutriment (whether it be dew or a moisture from the earth), altered and concocted in a diversity of manners, by which they are also nourished and grow; so likewise to identical fluids of the egg, namely, the albumen and the yelk, do the whole chick and each of its parts owe their birth and growth.

We will explain, also, what are the animals whose generation takes place by metamorphosis, and of what kind is the pre-existent material of insects which take their origin from a worm or a caterpillar; a material from which, by transmutation alone, all their parts are simultaneously constituted and embodied, and a perfect animal is born; likewise, to what animals any constant order in the successive generation of their parts attaches, as is the case with such as are at first born in an imperfect condition, and afterwards grow to maturity and perfection; and this happens to all those that are born from an egg. As in these the processes of growth and formation are carried on at the same time, and a separation and distinction of parts takes place in a regularly observed order, so in their case is there no immediate pre-existing material present, for the incorporation of the fœtus (such as the mixture of the semina of the male and female is generally thought to be, or the menstrual blood, or some very small portion of the egg), but as soon as ever the material is created and prepared, so soon are growth and form commenced; the nutriment is immediately accompanied by the presence of that which it has to feed. And this kind of generation is the result of epigenesis as the man proceeds from the boy; the edifice of the body, to wit, is raised on the punctum saliens as a foundation; as a ship is made from a keel, and as a potter makes a vessel, as the carpenter forms a footstool out of a piece of wood, or a statuary his statue from a block of marble. For out of the same material from which the first part of the chick or its smallest particle springs, from the very same is the whole chick born; whence the first little drop of blood, thence also proceeds its whole mass by means of generation in the egg; nor is there any difference between the elements which constitute and form the limbs or organs of the body, and those out of which all their similar parts, to wit, the skin, the flesh, veins, membranes, nerves, cartilages, and bones, derive their origin. For the part which was at first soft and fleshy, afterwards, in the course of its growth, and without any change in the matter of nutrition, becomes a nerve, a ligament, a tendon; what was a simple membrane becomes an investing tunic; what had been cartilage is afterwards found to be a spinous process of bone, all variously diversified out of the same similar material. For a similar organic body (which the vulgar believe to consist of the elements) is not created out of elements at first existing separately, and then put together, united, and altered; nor is it put together out of constituent parts; but, from a transmutation of it when in a mixed state, another compound is created: to take an instance, from the colliquament the blood is formed, from the blood the structure of the body arises, which appears to be homogeneous in the beginning, and resembles the spermatic jelly; but from this the parts are at first delineated by an obscure division, and afterwards become separate and distinct organs.

Those parts, I say, are not made similar by any successive union of dissimilar and heterogeneous elements, but spring out of a similar material through the process of generation, have their different elements assigned to them by the same process, and are made dissimilar.

Just as if the whole chick was created by a command to this effect, of the Divine Architect: "Let there be a similar colourless mass, and let it be divided into parts and made to increase, and in the meantime, while it is growing, let there be a separation and delineation of parts; and let this part be harder, and denser, and more glistening, that be softer and more coloured," and it was so. Now it is in this very manner that the structure of the chick in the egg goes on day by day; all its parts are formed, nourished, and augmented out of the same material. First, from the spine arise the sides, and the bones are distinguishable from the flesh by minute lines of extreme whiteness; in the head three bullæ are perceived, full of crystalline fluid, which correspond to the brain, the cerebellum, and one eye, easily observable by a black speck; the substance which at first appears a milky coagulum, afterwards gradually becomes cartilaginous, has spinous processes attached to it, and ends in being completely osseous; what was at first of a mucous nature and colourless, is converted at length into red flesh and parenchyma; what was at one time limpid and perfectly pure water, presently assumes the form of brain, cerebellum, and eyes. For there is a greater and more divine mystery in the generation of animals than the simple collecting together, alteration, and composition of a whole out of parts would seem to imply; inasmuch as here the whole has a separate constitution and existence before its parts, the mixture before the elements. But of this more at another time, when we come to specify the causes of these things.

EXERCISE 46. *Of the efficient cause of the generation of the chick and fœtus*

We have thus far spoken of the matter from which the chick *in ovo* is generated. We have still with Fabricius to say a few words on the efficient cause of the chick. As this subject is surrounded with difficulties, however; as writers nowhere else dispute more virulently or more wordily, and Aristotle himself in explaining the matter is singularly intricate and perplexed, and as various questions that can by no means be lightly treated do in fact present themselves for consideration, I conceive that I shall be undertaking a task worthy of the toil if, as I have done in the disquisition on the "matter," I set out here by stating in how many ways anything can be said to be "efficient" or "effective." We shall thus obtain a clearer idea of what it is which we are to inquire after under the name of "efficient," and further, what estimate we are to form of the ideas of writers upon this subject; it will at the same time appear from our observations what is truly and properly to be called "an efficient."

Aristotle defines an efficient cause to be that "whence is derived the first principle of change or quiescence; as a counsel, a father; and simply as doing that which is done; the transmute of the thing transmuted."[1] In the generation of animals, accordingly, many and various kinds of causes inducing motion are brought forward; sometimes an accident or quality is assigned; and so animal heat and the formative faculty are called efficient causes. Sometimes it is an external substance, previously existing, in which inheres the plastic force or formative faculty that is designated in the same way; as the cock or his seminal fluid, by the influence of which the chick is procreated from the egg. Occasionally it is some internal substance, self-existent, such as spirit, or innate heat. And again, it is some other substance, such as form, or nature, or soul, or some portion of the vegetative soul, that is regarded as the efficient, such a principle as we have already declared to inhere in the egg.

Besides, since one thing whence motion proceeds is nearer and another more remote, it sometimes happens that the media between the prime efficient and the thing last effected, and instruments are regarded as efficient causes; subordinate conclusions, likewise, or the principles of subsequents, are reckoned among the number of efficient causes; in this way some parts are themselves spoken of as genital parts, such as the heart, whence Aristotle affirms that all the rest of the body is produced; a statement which we have found borne out by our history. The heart, I repeat, or at all events its rudimentary parts, namely, the vesicle and pulsating point, construct the rest of the body as their future dwelling-place; when erected it enters and conceals itself within its habitation, which it vivifies and governs, and applying the ribs and sternum as a defence, it walls itself about. And there it abides, the household divinity, first seat of the soul, prime receptacle of the innate heat, perennial centre of animal action; source and origin of all the faculties; only solace in adversity!

Moreover, since the "efficient" is so styled with reference to the effect, as some parts produced by epigenesis are posterior in order to other parts, and are different from antecedent

[1] *Metaphysics*, v. 2; *Physics*, II. 3.

parts—as effects differ, so does it seem probable that efficients also vary: from things that produce different operations, different motions likewise proceed. Thus physicians in their physiologies assign certain organs as the agents of chylification, others of sanguification, others of generation, &c.; and anatomists speak of the ossific, carnific, and neurific faculties, which they conceive produce bones, flesh, and nerves.

But in the generation of the chick, of several actions differing not a little from one another, it is certain that the efficient causes must also differ; those that present themselves to us as accidental efficients of generation must nevertheless be necessary, seeing, that unless they are associated or intervene, nothing is effected; those, to wit, are rightly held "efficients" which, whilst they remove external hinderances, either cherish the conception, or stimulate and turn mere potentiality into positive action. Under this head we should arrange incubation, the proper temperature of the air and the place, the spring season, the approach of the sun in the circle of the zodiac; in like manner the preparing causes which lead the vitellus to rise, make the macula to dilate, and the fluids in the egg to liquefy, are all properly held "efficients."

Further, to the number of efficient causes are to be reckoned the generative and architectonic faculties, styled *parts* by Fabricius, viz., the immutative, the concoctive, the formative, the augmentative, as also the effective causes of certain accidentals, viz., that which constitutes the pullet male or female, like the father or the mother, taking after the form of the first or last male having connexion with the mother; that too whence the offspring is an animal; whether perfect or defective; robust and healthy, or diseased; longer or shorter lived; keeping up the characters of the race or degenerating from them; a monster, an hybrid, &c.

Lastly, when we were discussing the efficient causes of the fœtus, we were not inattentive to its admirable structure, to the functions and uses of all its parts and members; neither did we overlook the foresight, the art, the intelligence, the divine inspiration with which all things were ordained and skilfully continued for the ends of life. It is not enough that we inquire what is the "efficient," the architect, the adviser, but that we likewise venerate and adore the omnipotent Creator and preserver of a work, which has been well entitled a microcosm. We also ask whence this divine something comes, when it arrives, and where it resides in the egg; this something which is analogous to the essence of the stars, and is near akin to art and intelligence, and the vicar of the Almighty Creator?

From what precedes it will be apparent how difficult it were to enumerate all the efficient causes of the chick; it is indispensable, indeed, in the complete investigation of this subject to refer to a general disquisition; we could not from the single generation of the chick *in ovo*, and without clearer light derived from investigations extended to other animals, venture on conclusions that should be applicable to the whole animal creation. And this all the more, since Aristotle himself has enumerated such a variety of efficient principles of animals; for he at one time adduces the "male"[1] as the principal efficient cause, as that, to wit, in which the reason of the engendered chick resides, according to the axiom: "all things are made by the same 'univocal' ";[2] at another time he takes "the male semen";[3] or, "the nature of the male emitting semen";[4] sometimes it is "that which inheres in the semen, which causes seeds to be prolific, spirit, to wit, and nature in that spirit corresponding in its qualities to the essence of the stars";[5] elsewhere he says it is "heat";[6] "moderate heat";[7] "a certain and proportionate degree of heat";[8] "the heat in the blood";[9] "the heat of the ambient air"; "the winds";[10] "the sun"; "the heavens"; "Jupiter"; "the soul"; and, somewhere, nature is spoken of by him as "the principle of motion and rest."

Aristotle concludes the discussion on the efficient cause by declaring it "extremely doubtful" whether it be "anything extrinsic; or something inherent in the geniture or semen; and whether it be any part of the soul, or the soul itself, or something having a soul?"[11]

To escape from such a labyrinth of "efficient causes," it were necessary to be furnished with Ariadne's thread, composed from observations on almost every animal that lives; on this account the subject is deferred till we come to our more general disquisition. Meantime we shall recount the particulars which either manifestly appear in the special history of the chick from

[1] *Metaphysics*, I. 2; IV. I.
[2] *Ibid.*, VII. 10.
[3] *On the Parts of Animals*, I. I.
[4] *On the Generation of Animals*, I. 20.
[5] *Ibid.*, II. 3.
[6] *Ibid.*, V. 3.
[7] *Ibid.*, IV. 2.
[8] *Ibid.*, IV. 4.
[9] *On the Parts of Animals*, II. 2.
[10] *On the Generation of Animals*, IV. 2; *History of Animals*, VI. 19.
[11] *On the Generation of Animals*, II. I.

the egg, or which differ from the ideas usually entertained, or that seem to demand further inquiry.

EXERCISE 47. *Of the manner in which the efficient cause of the chick acts, according to Aristotle*

It is universally allowed, that the male is the primary efficient cause in generation, on the ground that in him the species or form resides; and it is further affirmed, that the emission of his "geniture" during coition, is the cause both of the existence and the fertility of the egg. But none of the philosophers nor physicians, ancient or modern, have sufficiently explained in what manner the seed of the cock produced a chick from the egg; nor have they solved the question proposed by Aristotle. Nor, indeed, is Aristotle himself much more explanatory, when he says "that the male contributes not in respect of quantity, but of quality, and is the origin of action; but that it is the female which brings the material." And a little after, "It is not every male that emits seed, and in those which do so, this is no part of the fœtus; just as in the case of a carpenter, nothing is translated from him to the substance of the wood which he uses, nor does any part of the artist's skill reside in the work when completed; but a form and appearance are given by his operation to the matter; and the soul, which originates the idea of forms, and the skill to imitate them, moves the hands, or other limb, whatever it may be, by a motion of a certain quality; or from diversity proceeds difference; or from similarity proceeds resemblance. But the hands and instruments move the material. So the nature of a male, which emits semen, uses that semen as an instrument, and an act having motion; as in works of art the instruments are moved, for in them, in some sort, the motion of the art exists."

By these words he seems to imply that generation is owing to the motion of a certain quality. Just as in art, though the first cause (the *ratio operis*) be in the mind of the artist, yet afterwards, the work is effected by the movement of the hands or other instruments; and although the first cause be removed (as in automatons), yet is it in some sort said to move what it now does not touch, but once has touched, so long as motion continues in the instrument.

Also in the next book, he says: "When the semen of the male has arrived as far as the uterus of the female, it arranges and coagulates the purest part of the excrement (meaning the menstrual blood existing in the uterus); and,

by a motion of this kind, changes the material, which has been prepared in the uterus, till it forms part of the chick; and this, hereafter, although the semen after the performance of this motion disappears, exists as part of the fœtus, and becomes animate (as the heart) and regulates its own powers and growth, as a son emancipated from his father, and having his own establishment. And so it is necessary that there be some commencing principle, from which afterwards the order of the limbs may be delineated, and a proper disposition made of those things that concern the absolution of the animal; a principle, which may be the source of growth and motion to all the other parts; the origin of all, both similar and dissimilar parts, and the source of their ultimate aliment. For that which is already an animal grows, but the ultimate aliment of an animal is the blood, or something corresponding to the blood, whose vessels and receptacles are the veins; wherefore, the heart is the origin of the veins. But veins, like roots, spread to the uterus, and through these the fœtus derives its nourishment. The heart too, being the beginning of all nature and the containing end, ought to be made first; as if it were a genital part by its own nature, which, as the original of all the other parts, and of the whole animal, and of sense, must needs be the first; and by its heat (since all the parts are in the material *potentially*), when once the beginning of the motion has taken place, all that follows is excited, just as in spontaneous miracles; and the parts are commenced, not by change of place, but by alteration in softness, hardness, temperature, and the other differences observed in similar parts, these being now actually made, which had before existed only potentially."

This is, in nearly so many words, the opinion of Aristotle, which supposes that the fœtus is formed from the seed by motion, although it is not at present in communication with the fœtus, but simply has been so at a former time: his reasonings are, indeed, ingenious, and carefully put together, and from what we see in the order of the generation of parts, not improbable. For the heart, with the channel of the veins, is first noticed as an animate principle, in which motion and sense reside; or, as it were, an emancipated son, and a genital part, whence the order of the members is delineated, whence all things pertaining to the completion of the animal are disposed, and which has all the attributes bestowed upon it by Aristotle.

But it seems impossible that the heart should be formed in the egg by the seed of the male, when that seed neither exists in the egg, nor touches it, nor ever has touched it; because the seed does not enter the uterus where the egg is (as is allowed by Fabricius), nor is in any way attracted by it; nay, even the maternal blood is not in the egg, nor any other prepared matter, out of which the seed of the male may form this genital part, the author of all the others. For it is not immediately after coition, while the seed still remains within the body, and is in communication, that any part of the chick exists in the egg, but after many days, when incubation has taken place. Moreover, in fishes, when the geniture of the male does nothing but touch the eggs externally, and does not enter into them, it is not likely that it performs any more ample functions when the agency is external, than does the seed of the cock in the already formed eggs of the hen. Besides, since immediately after coition no trace of the egg as yet exists, but it is afterwards generated by the hen herself (I am speaking of the prolific egg); when now the seed of the cock is departed and vanished, there is no probability that the fœtus is formed in that egg by the aforesaid seed, through means of one or any number of successive motions.

Nor indeed does the difference between prolific and unprolific or wind eggs consist herein, that the former contained the seed of the male, as Aldrovandus supposed; nor has it been noticed that anything has been formed and coagulated in the egg by the seed of the male, nor has any sensible transmutation been discovered (for indeed, there is no sensible difference between the fertile and the wind egg); and yet a prolific egg, conceived long after coition, has in itself the faculties of both sexes; *viz.*, the capability of being both formed itself, and of forming a chick; as if, according to the idea of Aristotle, it had derived its origin from the coition of the two, and their mutual endeavours towards the same end; and compelled by the force of this argument, as mentioned above, when speaking of the generation of the ovum, he has endowed the egg with a vital principle (*anima*). If such really exist, then, without doubt it would be the origin and efficient of all the natural phenomena which take place in the egg. For if we consider the structure of the chick, displaying, as it does, so much art, so divine an intelligence and foresight; when we see the eyes adapted for vision, the bill for taking food, the feet for walking, the wings for flying, and similarly the rest of its parts, each to its own end, we must conclude, whatever the power be which creates such an animal out of an egg, that it is either the soul, or part of the soul, or something having a soul, or something existing previous to, and more excellent than the soul, operating with intelligence and foresight.

From the generation of the chick, it is also manifest that, whatever may have been its principle of life or first vegetative cause, this cause itself first existed in the heart. Now, if this be the soul of the chicken, it is equally clear that that soul must have existed in the punctum saliens and the blood; since we there discover motion and sense; for the heart moves and leaps like an animal. But if a soul exists in the punctum saliens, forming, nourishing, and augmenting the rest of the body, in the manner which we have pointed out in our history, then it, without doubt, flows from the heart, as from a fountain-head, into the whole body. Likewise, if the existence of the vital principle (*anima*) in the egg, or, as Aristotle supposes, if the vegetative part of the soul be the cause of its fertility, it must follow that the punctum saliens, or animate genital part, proceeds from the vital principle (*anima*) of the egg (for nothing is its own author), and that the said vital principle (*anima*) passes from the egg into the punctum saliens, presently into the heart, and thence into the chick.

Moreover, if the egg have a prolific virtue, and a vegetative soul, by which the chick is constructed, and if it owe them, as is allowed on all hands, to the semen of the cock; it is clear that this semen is also endowed with an active principle (*anima*). For such is Aristotle's opinion, when he expresses himself as follows: "As to whether the semen has a vital principle (*anima*) or not, the same reasoning must be adduced which we have employed in the consideration of other parts. For no active principle (*anima*) can exist, except in that thing whose vital principle it is; nor can there be any part which is not partaker of the vital principle, except it be equivocally, as the eye of a dead man. We must, therefore, allow, both that the semen has an active principle (*anima*) and is potential."

Now from these premises, it follows that the male is the primary efficient in which the *ratio* and *forma* reside, which produces a seed or rather a prolific geniture, and imparts it, imbued as it is with an *anima vegetativa* (with which also the rest of its parts are endowed) to the female. The introduction of this geniture begets such a movement in the material of the hen, that the production of an animate egg is the result, and from thence too the first particle of the chick is animated, and afterwards the whole chick. And so, according to Aristotle, either the same soul passes, by means of some metempsychosis, from the cock into his geniture, from the geniture into the material of the female, thence into the egg, and from the egg into the chick; or else, it is raised up in each of the subsequent things by its respective antecedent; namely, in the seed of the male by the male himself, in the egg by the seed, last in the chick by the egg, as light is derived from light.

The efficient, therefore, which we look for in the egg, to explain the birth of the chick, is the vital principle (*anima*); and therefore, the vital principle of the egg; for, according to Aristotle, a soul does not exist except in that thing whose soul it is.

But it is manifest that the seed of the male is not the efficient of the chick; neither as an instrument capable of forming the chick by its motion, as Aristotle would have it, nor as an animate substance transferring its vitality (*anima*) to the chick. For in the egg there is no semen, neither does any touch it, nor has ever done so ("and it is impossible that that which does not touch should move, or that anything should be affected by that which does not move it"); and therefore the vitality of the semen ought not to be said to exist in it; and although the vital principle may be the efficient in the egg, yet it would not appear to result more from the cock or his semen, than from the hen.

Nor, indeed, is it transferred by any metempsychosis or translation from the cock and his semen into the egg, and thence into the chick. For how can this translation be carried on into the eggs that are yet to exist, and to be conceived after intercourse? unless either some animate semen be in the mean time working in some part of the hen; or the vital principle only have been translated without the seed, in order to be infused into any egg which might thereafter be produced; but neither of these alternatives is true. For in no part of the hen is the semen to be found; nor is it possible that the hen after coition should be possessed of a double vital principle, to wit, her own, and that of the future eggs and chicks; since "the living principle or soul is said to be nowhere but in that thing whose soul it is," much less can one or more vital principles lie hidden in the hen, to be afterwards subservient to the future eggs and chicks in their order, as they are produced.

We have adduced these passages out of Aristotle in order to set forth his opinion of the manner in which the seed of the cock produces the chick from the egg; and thereby throw at least some light on this difficult question. But whereas the said passages do not explain the mode in which this is accomplished, nor even solve the doubts proposed by himself, it appears that we are still sticking in the same mud, and caught in the same perplexities (concerning the efficient cause of the fœtus in the generation of animals); indeed, so far from Aristotle's arguments rendering this question more clear, they appear on the contrary to involve it in more and greater doubts.

Wherefore it is no wonder that the most excellent philosopher was in perplexity on this head, and that he has admitted so great a variety of efficient causes, and at one time has been compelled to resort to automatons, coagulation, art, instruments, and motions, for illustrations; at another time to an "*anima*" in the egg, and in the seed of the male. Moreover, when he seems positively and definitively to determine what it is in each seed, whether of plants or animals, which render the same fertile, he repudiates heat and fire as improper agents; nor does he admit any faculty of a similar quality; nor can he find anything in the seed which should be fit for that office; but he is driven to acknowledge something incorporeal, and coming from foreign sources, which he supposes (like art, or the mind) to form the fœtus with intelligence and foresight, and to institute and ordain all its parts for its welfare. He takes refuge, I say, in a thing which is obscure and not recognizable by us; namely, in a spirit contained in the seed, and in a frothy body, and in the nature in that spirit, corresponding in proportion to the elements of the stars. But what that is, he has nowhere informed us.

EXERCISE 48. *The opinion of Fabricius on the efficient cause of the chick is refuted*

As I have chosen Aristotle, the most eminent among the ancient philosophers, and Fabricius of Aquapendente, one of the foremost anatomists of modern times, as my especial guides and sources of information on the subject of animal generation, when I find that I can make nothing of Aristotle upon a particular topic, I straightway turn to Fabricius; and now I desire to know what he thought of the efficient cause of generation.

I find that he endeavours to satisfy three doubts or difficulties involved in this subject: First, What is the "efficient" of the chick? This he answers, by saying, the semen of the male. Secondly, How does this appear in the egg, and in what way does the semen of the cock fecundate the egg? Thirdly and lastly, In what order are the parts of the chick engendered?

As to the first query, it appears from our observations, that the cock and his seminal fluid are verily the "efficient," but not the "adequate" cause of generation; that the hen comes in here as something. In this place, therefore, we are principally to inquire how the semen of the cock fecundates the egg otherwise unprolific, and secures the engenderment of a chick from it?

But let us hear Fabricius: "Those things differ," he observes, "that are produced from eggs, from those that originate from semen, in this, that oviparous animals have the matter from which the embryo is incorporated distinct and separate from the agent; whilst viviparous animals have the efficient cause and the matter associate and concorporate. For the 'agent' in the oviparous animal is the semen of the male, in the fowl the semen of the cock, which neither is nor can be in the egg; the 'matter,' again, is the chalazæ from which the fœtus is incorporated. These two differ widely from one another; for the chalazæ are added after the vitellus is formed, whilst it is passing through the second uterus, and are an accession to the internal egg; the semen galli, on the contrary, is stored near the fundament, is separated from the chalazæ by a great interval, and nevertheless by its irradiating faculty, fecundates both the whole egg and the uterus. Now in the viviparous animal, the semen is both 'matter' and 'agent,' the two consisting and being conjoined in the same body."[1]

Our author appears to have introduced this distinction between oviparous and viviparous animals, that he might spare, or at all events, that he might not directly shock or upset the notions of medical writers on the generation of man, they teaching that the seminal fluids of either sex, projected together in intercourse, are mingled; that as one or other preponderates, this becomes the "efficient," that stands in lieu of the "matter"; and that the two together, tending to the same end, amalgamate into the "conception" of the viviparous animal.

But when he finds that neither in the egg nor uterus of the fowl is there any semen or blood, and avows his belief that nothing is emitted by the male in intercourse, that can by possibility reach the uterus of the female, nor in the egg discovers a trace of aught supplied by the male, he is compelled to doubt how the semen, which

[1] Op. cit., p. 38.

is nowhere to be detected, which is neither mixed with the "geniture" of the female, nor yet is added to it, nor touches it, can fecundate the egg, or constitute the chick. And this all the more urgently, when he has stated that a few connexions in the beginning of the season suffice to secure the fecundity of all the eggs that will be laid in its course. For how should it seem otherwise than impossible that from the semen galli communicated in the spring, but now long vanished, lost or consumed, the eggs that continue to be laid through the summer and autumn, should still be rendered fruitful and fit to produce pullets?

It is that he may meet such a difficulty half way, that he coins the difference which has been noticed. By way of bolstering up his views, he further adduces three additional considerations: First, since the semen galli is neither extant in the egg, nor was ever present in the uterus, nor is added as "material cause" as in viviparous animals, he has chosen to make it resident for a whole year in the body of the hen. And then that he may have a fit receptacle or storehouse for the fecundating fluid, he finds a blind sac near the inlet to the uterus, in which he says the cock deposits his semen, wherein, as in a treasury, it is stored, and from which all the eggs are fecundated. Lastly, although the semen in that bursa comes into contact neither with the uterus, nor the egg, nor the ovary, whereby it might fecundate the egg, or secure the generation of a chick, he says, nevertheless, that from thence, a certain spiritual substance or irradiation penetrates to the egg, fecundates its chalazæ, and from these produces a chick. By this affirmation, however, he appears to support the opinion of Aristotle, namely, that the female supplies the "matter" in generation, the male the "efficient force"; and to oppose the postulate of medical writers about the mixture of seminal fluids, for the sake of which, nevertheless, as I have said, he seems to have laid down his distinction between oviparous and viviparous animals. To give an air of greater likelihood to this notion of his, he goes on to enumerate the changes which the semen, not yet emitted, but laid up in the testes and vesiculæ seminales of animals, occasions.

But besides the fact that all this does not bear upon the question, for the principal element under discussion is, not how the semen galli renders the egg prolific, but rather, how does the semen galli fashion and construct the chick from the egg? Almost everything he adduces in support of his view appears either false or open to suspicion, as is obvious, from the facts stated in our history; for neither is the blind cavity situated at the root of the uropygium or coccyx of the fowl, which he entitles "bursa," destined as a receptacle for the semen of the cock, nor can any semen be discovered there, as we have said; but the cavity is encountered in the male as well as in the female fowl.

Our authority nowhere explains what he understands by a "spiritual substance," and an "irradiation"; nor what he means by "a substance through whose virtue the egg is vivified": he does not say whether it is any "corporeal" or "formal" substance, which by "irradiation" proceeds from the semen laid up in the bursa, and (what is especially required) constructs a pullet from the egg.

In my opinion, Fabricius does no more here than say: "It produces the chick because it irradiates the egg; and forms because it vivifies"; he attempts to explain or illustrate the exceedingly obscure subject of the formation of a living being by means still more obscure. For the same doubt remains untouched, how, to wit, the semen of the cock without contact, an "external efficient" at best, separate in point of place, and existing in the bursa, can form the internal parts of the fœtus in ovo, the heart, liver, lungs, intestines, &c., out of the chalazæ by "irradiation." Unless, indeed, our author will have it that all takes place at the dictum as it were of a creator seated on his throne, and speaking the words: Let such things be! namely, bones for support, muscles for motion, special organs for sense, members for action, viscera for concoction and the like, and all ordered for an end and purpose with foresight, and understanding and art. But Fabricius nowhere demonstrates that the semen has any such virtue, nowhere explains the manner in which without so much as contact the semen can effect such things; particularly when we see that the egg incubated by a bird of another kind than that which laid it, or cherished in any other way, or in dung, or in an oven, far from the bursa of the parent hen, is still quickened and made to produce an embryo.

The same difficulty still remains, I say: how or in what way is the semen of the cock the "efficient" of the chick? It is in no wise removed by invoking the irradiation of a spiritual substance. For did we even admit that the semen was stored in the bursa, and that it incorporated the embryo from the chalazæ by metamorphosis and irradiation, we should not be the less deeply immersed in the difficulty of accounting for the formation of all the internal parts of the chick. But these notions have already been sufficiently refuted by us.

Wherefore, in investigating the efficient cause of the chick, we must look for it as inhering in the egg, not as concealed in the bursa; and it must be such, that although the egg have long been laid, be miles removed from the hen that produced it, and be set under another hen than its parent, even under a bird of a different kind, such as a turkey or guinea-fowl, or merely among hot sand or dung, or in an oven constructed for the purpose, as is done in Egypt, it will still cause the egg to produce a creature of the same species as its parents, like them, both male and female, and if the parents were of different kinds, of a hybrid species, and having a mixed resemblance.

The knot therefore remains untied, neither Aristotle nor Fabricius having succeeded even in loosening it, namely: how the semen of the male or of the cock forms a pullet from an egg, or is to be termed the "efficient" of the chick, especially when it is neither present in, nor in contact with, nor added to the egg. And although almost all assert that the male and his semen are the efficient cause of the chick, still it must be admitted, that no one has yet sufficiently explained how it is so, particularly in our common hen's egg.

EXERCISE 49. *The inquiry into the efficient cause of the chick is one of great difficulty*

The discussion of the efficient cause of the chick is, as we have said, sufficiently difficult, and all the more in consequence of the various titles by which it has been designated. Aristotle, indeed, recites several efficient causes of animals, and numerous controversies have arisen on the subject among writers (these having been particularly hot between medical authors and Aristotelians) who have come into the arena with various explanations, both of the nature of the efficient cause and of the mode of its operation.

And indeed the Omnipotent Creator is nowhere more conspicuous in his works, nowhere is his divinity more loudly proclaimed, than in the structure of animals. And though all know and admit that the offspring derives its origin from male and female, that an egg is engendered by a cock and a hen, and that a pullet proceeds from an egg, still we are not informed either by the medical schools or the sagacious Aristotle, as to the manner in which the cock or his semen fashions the chick from the egg. For from what we have had occasion to say of the generation of oviparous and other animals, it is sufficiently obvious that neither is the opinion of the medical authorities admissible, who derive generation from the admixture of the seminal fluids of the two sexes, nor that of Aristotle, who holds the semen masculinum for the efficient, and the menstrual blood for the material cause of procreation. For neither in the act of intercourse nor shortly after it, is aught transferred to the cavity of the uterus, from which as matter any part of the fœtus is immediately constituted. Neither does the "geniture" proceeding from the male in the act of union (whether it be animated or an inanimate instrument) enter the uterus; neither is it attracted into this organ; neither is it stored up within the fowl; but it is either dissipated or escapes. Neither is there anything contained in the uterus immediately after intercourse, which, proceeding from the male, or from the female, or from both, can be regarded as the matter or rudiment of the future fœtus. Neither is the semen galli stored and retained in the bursa Fabricii of the hen or elsewhere, that from thence, as by the irradiation of some spiritual substance, or by contact, the egg may be fashioned or the chick constituted from the egg. Neither has the hen any other semen save papulæ, yelks, and eggs. These observations of ours, therefore, render the subject of generation one of greater difficulty than ever, inasmuch as all the presumptions upon which the two old opinions repose are totally overthrown. The fact is especial, as we shall afterwards demonstrate, that all animals are alike engendered from eggs; and in the act of intercourse, whether of man or the lower quadrupeds, there is no seminal fluid, proceeding from the male or the female, thrown into the uterus or attracted by this organ; there is nothing to be discovered within its cavity, either before intercourse, during the act, or immediately after it, which can be regarded as the matter of the future fœtus, or as its efficient cause, or as its commencement.

Daniel Sennert, a man of learning and a close observer of nature, having first passed the reasonings of a host of others under review, approaches the subject himself; and concludes that the vital principle inheres in the semen and is almost identical with that which resides in the future offspring. So that Sennert does not hesitate to aver that the rational soul of man is present in his seminal fluid, and by a parity of reasoning that the egg possesses the animating principle of the pullet; that the vital principle is transported to the uterus of the female with the semen of the male, and that from the seminal fluids of either conjoined, not mixed (for mixture, he says, is applied to things of different species), and endowed with soul or the vital principle a perfect animal emerges. And therefore, he says, the semen of either parent is required, whether to the constitution of the ovum or of the embryo. And having said so much, he seems to think that he has overcome all difficulties, and has delivered a certain and perspicuous truth.

But in order that we should concede a soul or vital principle (*anima*) to the egg, and that combined from the souls of the parents, these being occasionally of different species, the horse and the ass, the common fowl and the pheasant, for example, this vital principle not being a mixture but only an union; and allow the pullet to be produced in the manner of the seeds of plants, by the same efficient principle by which the perfect animal is afterwards preserved through the rest of its life, so that it would be absurd to say that the fœtus grew by one vital principle without the uterus or ovum, and by another within the uterus or ovum—did we grant all this, I say (although it is invalid and undeserving faith), our history of generation from the egg, nevertheless, upsets the foundations of the doctrine, and shows it to be entirely false; namely, that the egg is produced from the semen of the cock and hen, or that any seminal fluid from either one or other is carried to the uterus, or that the embryo or any particle of it is fashioned from any seminal fluid transported to the uterus, or that the semen galli, as efficient cause and plastic agent, is anywhere stored up or reserved within the body of the hen to serve when attracted into the uterus, as the matter and nourishment whence the fœtus which it has produced should continue to grow. The conditions are wanting which he himself admits, after Aristotle, to be necessary, viz., that the embryo be constituted by that which is actual and pre-exists, and the chick by that which is present and exists in the place where the chick is first formed and increases; further, that it be produced by that which is accomplished immediately and conjunctly, and is the same by which the chick is preserved and grows through the whole of its life. For the semen galli (and whether it is viewed as animate or inanimate is of no moment) is nowise present and conjunct either in the egg or in the uterus;

neither in the matter from which the chick is fashioned, nor yet in the chick itself already begun, and as contributing either to its formation or perfection.

He dreams, too, when he seeks illustrations of his opinions on an animated semen from such instances as the seeds of plants and acorns; because he does not perceive the difference alleged by Aristotle[1] between the "geniture" admitted in intercourse and the first conception engendered by both parents; neither does he observe on the egg produced originally in the cluster of the vitellarium, and without any geniture, whether proceeding from the male or the female, translated to the uterus. Neither does he understand that the uterus is, even after intercourse, completely empty of matter of every kind, whether transmitted by the parents, or produced by the intercourse, or transmuted in any way whatever. Neither had he read, or at all events he does not refer to the experiment of Fabricius, namely, that a hen is rendered so prolific by a few treads of the cock, that she will continue to lay fruitful eggs for the rest of the year, although in the interval she receives no new accessions of semen for the fecundation of each egg as it is laid, neither does she retain any of the seminal fluid which she received so long ago.

So much is certain, and disputed by no one, that animals, all those at least that proceed from the intercourse of male and female, are the offspring of this intercourse, and that they are procreated as it seems by a kind of contagion, much in the same way as medical men observe contagious diseases, such as leprosy, lues venera, plague, phthisis, to creep through the ranks of mortal men, and by mere extrinsic contact to excite diseases similar to themselves in other bodies; nay, contact is not necessary; a mere halitus or miasm suffices, and that at a distance and by an inanimate medium, and with nothing sensibly altered: that is to say, where the contagion first touches, there it generates an "univocal" like itself, neither touching nor existing in fact, neither being present nor conjunct, but solely because it formerly touched. Such virtue and efficacy is found in contagions. And the same thing perchance occurs in the generation of animals. For the eggs of fishes, which come spontaneously to their full size extrinsically, and without any addition of male seminal fluid, and are therefore indubitably possessed of vitality without it, merely sprinkled and touched with the milt of the male, produce young fishes.

[1] *On the Generation of Animals*, ii, 1.

The semen of the male, I say, is not intromitted in such wise as to perform the part of "agent" in each particular egg, or to fashion the body, or to introduce vitality (*anima*); the ova are only fecundated by a kind of contagion. Whence Aristotle calls the milt of the male fish, or the genital fluid diffused in water, at one time "the genital and fœtific fluid," at another, "the vital virus." For he says: "The male fish sprinkles the ova with his genital semen, and from the ova that are touched by this vital virus young fishes are engendered."[2]

Let it then be admitted as matter of certainty that the embryo is produced by contagion. But a great difficulty immediately arises, when we ask: how, in what way is this contagion the author of so great a work? By what condition do parents through it engender offspring like themselves, or how does the semen masculinum produce an "univocal" like the male whence it flowed? When it disappears after the contact, and is naught in act ulteriorly, either by virtue of contact or presence, but is corrupt and has become a nonentity, how, I ask, does a nonentity act? How does a thing which is not in contact fashion another thing like itself? How does a thing which is dead itself impart life to something else, and that only because at a former period it was in contact?

For the reasoning of Aristotle appears to be false, or at all events defective, where he contends "That generation cannot take place without an active and a passive principle; and that those things can neither act nor prove passive which do not touch; but that those things come into mutual contact which, whilst they are of different sizes, and are in different places, have their extremes together."[3]

But when it clearly appears that contagion from noncontingents, and things not having their extremities together, produce ill effects on animals, wherefore should not the same law avail in respect of their life and generation? There is an "efficient" in the egg which, by its plastic virtue (for the male has only touched though he no longer touches, nor are there any extremes together), produces and fashions the fœtus in its kind and likeness. And through so many media or instruments is this power, the agent of fecundity, transmitted or required that neither by any movement of instruments as in works of art, nor by the instance of the automaton quoted by Aristotle, nor of our clocks, nor of the kingdom in which the mandate of

[2] *History of Animals*, vi, 13.
[3] *On Generation and Corruption*, i, 6.

the sovereign is everywhere of avail, nor yet by the introduction of a vital principle or soul into the semen or "geniture," can the aforementioned doctrine be defended.

And hence have arisen all the controversies and problems concerning the attraction of the magnet and of amber; on sympathy and antipathy; on poisons and the contagion of pestilential diseases; on alexipharmics and medicines which prove curative or injurious through some hidden or rather unknown property, all of which seem to come into play independently of contact. And above all on what it is in generation which, in virtue of a momentary contact—nay, not even of contact, save through several media—forms the parts of the chick from the egg by epigenesis in a certain order, and produces an "univocal" and like itself, and that entirely because it was in contact at a former period. How, I ask again, does that which is not present, and which only enjoyed extrinsic contact, come to constitute and order all the members of the chick in the egg exposed without the body of the parent, and often at a long interval after it is laid? how does it confer life or soul, and a species compounded of those of the concurring generants? Inasmuch as nothing, it seems, can reproduce itself in another's likeness.

EXERCISE 50. *Of the efficient cause of animals, and its conditions*

That we may proceed in our subject, therefore, and penetrate so far into the knowledge of the efficient cause of animal generation as seems needful in this place, we must begin by observing what instruments or media are devoted to it. And here we come at once to the distinction into male and female; seminal fluid and ovum, and its primordium. For some males, as well as some females, are barren, or but little prolific; and the seed of the male is at one time more, at another time less prolific; because the semen masculinum stored up in the vesiculæ seminales is esteemed unfruitful, unless it is raised into froth by the spirits and ejected with force. And even then perchance it is not endowed with equal fecundating force at all times. Neither are all the germs of yelks in the ovary, nor all the eggs in the uterus made fertile at the same instant.

Now I call that fruitful which, unless impeded by some extrinsic cause, attains by its inherent force to its destined end, and brings about the consequence for the sake of which it is ordained. Thus the cock is called fruitful which has his hens more frequently and surely pregnant, the eggs they lay being at the same time perfect and proper for incubation.

The hen in like manner is esteemed fruitful which has the faculty of producing eggs, or of receiving and long retaining the virtue of prolific conception from the cock. The cluster of germs and the ovary itself are regarded as prolific when the germs are numerous and of good size.

The egg in the same way is fruitful which differs from a subventaneous or hypenemic egg, and which, cherished by incubation, or in any other way, does not fail to produce a chick.

Such an efficient cause consequently is required for the chick, as shall impart the virtue of fecundity to it, and secure it the power of acting as an efficient cause in its turn. Because that, or its analogue at least, by means of which they become prolific, is present in all animals. And the inquiry is the same in each case, when we ask what it is in the egg which renders it prolific, and distinguishes it from a wind egg; what in the vitellary germ and ovary; what in the female; what, finally, in the semen and the cock himself? What, moreover, it is in the blood and punctum saliens, or first formed particle of the chick, whence all the other parts arise with their appropriate structures and arrangements; what in the embryo or chick itself whereby it becomes more or less robust and agile, attains to maturity with greater or less rapidity, and lives with various degrees of health, for a longer or shorter period?

Nor is the inquiry very different which goes to ascertain what sex the male and the female, or the cock and the hen, confer upon the prolific egg; and what proceeds from each that contributes to the perfection or resemblance of the chick, viz., whether the egg, the conception, the matter, and the nutriment proceed from the mother, and the plastic virtue from the father; or rather a certain contagion immitted during intercourse, or produced and received from him, which in the body of the hen, or in the eggs, either permanently excites the matter of the eggs, or attracts nourishment from the female, and concocts and distributes it first for the growth of the eggs, and then for the production of the chicks; finally, whether from the male proceeds all that has reference to form and life and fecundity, from the female, again, all that is of matter, constitution, place, and nourishment? For among animals where the sexes are distinct, matters are so arranged, that since the female alone is inadequate to engender an embryo and to nourish and protect the young, a male is associated with her by nature, as the superior and more worthy progenitor, as the consort of her labour, and the means of supplying her deficiencies; in the case of the hen, of correcting by his contagion the inferiority of the hypenemic eggs which she produces, and so rendering them prolific. For as the pullet, engendered of an egg, is indebted to that egg for his body, vitality, and principal or generative part, so and in like manner does the egg receive all that is in it from the female, the female in her turn being dependent on the male for her fecundity which is conferred in coition.

And here we have an opportunity of inquiring, whether the male be the first and principal cause of the generation of the offspring; or whether the male along with the female are the mediate and instrumental causes of nature itself, or of the first and supreme generator? And such an inquiry is both becoming and necessary, for perfect science of every kind depends on a knowledge of causes. To the full understanding of generation, therefore, it is incumbent on us to mount from the final to the first and supreme efficient cause, and to hold each and every cause in especial regard.

We shall have occasion to define that which is the first and supreme efficient cause of the chick *in ovo* by and by, when we treat of that which constitutes the efficient cause among animals in general. Here, meantime, we shall see what its nature may be.

The first condition, then, of the primary efficient cause of generation, properly so called, is, as we have said, that it be the prime and principal fertilizer, whence all mediate causes receive the fecundity imparted. For example, the chick is derived from the punctum saliens in the egg, not only as regards the body, but also, and this especially, as respects the life (*anima*): the punctum saliens, or heart, is derived from the egg, the egg from the hen, and the hen has her fecundity from the cock.

Another condition of the prime efficient is discovered from the work achieved, *viz.*, the chick, because that is the prime efficient in which the reason of the effect is principally displayed. But since every generative efficient engenders another like itself, and the offspring is of a mixed nature, the prime efficient must also be a certain mixed something.

Now, I maintain that the offspring is of a mixed nature, inasmuch as a mixture of both parents appears plainly in it, in the form and lineaments, and each particular part of its body, in its colour, mother-marks, disposition to dis-eases, and other accidents. In mental constitution, also, and its manifestations, such as manners, docility, voice, and gait, a similar temperament is discoverable. For as we say of a certain mixture, that it is composed of elements, because their qualities or virtues, such as heat, cold, dryness, and moisture, are there discovered associated in a certain similar compound body, so, in like manner, the work of the father and mother is to be discerned both in the body and mental character of the offspring, and in all else that follows or accompanies temperament. In the mule, for instance, the body and disposition, the temper and voice, of both parents (of the horse and the ass, e. g.) are mingled; and so, also, in the hybrid between the pheasant and the fowl, in that between the wolf and the dog, &c., corresponding traits are conspicuous.

When, therefore, the chick shows his resemblance to both parents, and is a mixed effect, the primary genital cause (which it resembles) must needs be mixed. Wherefore that which fashions the chick in the egg is of a mixed nature, a certain something mixed or compounded, and the work of both parents. And if any kind of contagion, engendered under the influence of sexual intercourse, in which the male and female mingle and form but one body, either originates or remains in the body of the female, that, too, must be of a mixed nature or power, whence, subsequently, a fertile egg will be produced, endowed with plastic powers, the consequence of a mixed nature, or of a mixed efficient instrument, from which a chick, also of a mixed nature, will be produced.

I have used the word *contagion* above, because Aristotle's view is contradicted by all experience, *viz.*, that a certain part of the embryo is immediately made by intercourse. Neither is it true, as some of the moderns assert, that the vital principle (*anima*) of the future chick is present in the egg; for that cannot be the vital principle of the chick which inheres in no part of its body. Neither can the living principle be said either to be left or to be originated by intercourse; otherwise in every pregnant woman there would be two vital principles (*animæ*) present. Wherefore, until it shall have been determined what the efficient cause of the egg is, what it is of mixed nature that must remain immediately upon intercourse, we may be permitted to speak of it under the title of a *contagion*.

But where this contagion lies hid in the female after intercourse, and how it is communicated and given to the egg, demands quite a special inquiry, and we shall have occasion to treat of the matter when we come to discuss the conception of females in general. It will suffice, meantime, if we say that the same law applies to the prime efficient—in which inheres the reason of the future offspring—as to the offspring; as this is of a mixed nature, the nature of its cause must also be mixed; and it must either proceed equally from both parents, or from something else which is employed by both concurrently as instruments, animated, co-operating, mixed, and in the sexual act coalescing unto one. And this is the third condition of the prime efficient, that it either imparts motion to all the intermediate instruments in succession, or uses them in some other way, but comes not itself into play. Whence the origin of the doubt that has arisen, whether, in the generation of the chick, the cock were the true prime efficient, or whether there were not another prior, superior to him? For, indeed, all things seem to derive their origin from a celestial influence, and to follow the movements of the sun and moon. But we shall be able to speak more positively of this matter after we have shown what we understand by the "instrument," or "instrumental efficient cause," and how it is subdivided.

Instrumental efficients, then, are of different kinds: some, according to Aristotle, are factive, others active; some have no capacity any way unless conjoined with another prior efficient, as the hand, foot, genital organs, &c. with the rest of the body; others have an influence even when separate and distinct, as the seminal fluid and the ovum. Some instruments, again, have neither motion nor action beyond those that are imparted to them by the prime efficient; and others have peculiar inherent principles of action, to which Nature indeed allows no motion in the business of generation, though she still uses their faculties, and prescribes them laws or limits in their operations, not otherwise than the cook makes use of fire in cooking, and the physician of herbs and drugs in curing diseases.

Sennert, that he may uphold the opinion he had espoused of the vital principle (anima) being present in the semen, and the formative faculty of the chick being extant in the egg, asserts that not only is the egg, but the semen of the cock, endowed with the living principle of the future chick. Moreover, he distinctly denies that there is any separate instrumental efficient; and says, that that only ought to be entitled "instrument" which is conjoined with the prime efficient; and that only "instrumental efficient," which has no motion or action save that which is imparted to it by the prime efficient, or which is continuously and successively received, and in virtue of which it acts. And on this ground he rejects the example of projectiles, which have received force from the projecting agent, and, separated from it, act nevertheless; as if swords and spears were properly to be called warlike weapons, but arrows and bullets to be refused this title. He also rejects the argument derived from the republic, denying thereby that magistrates, counsellors, or ministers, are instruments of government; although Aristotle regards a counsel as an efficient, and in express terms calls a minister an instrument.[1] Sennert likewise denies the example of automata; and says and gainsays much besides, with a view to confirming himself in his position, that the semen and the egg are possessed of a living principle (anima), and are not mediate or instrumental, but principal agents. Sennert, nevertheless, as it were compelled by the force of truth, lays down such conditions for a principal agent, as fully and effectually contradict all that he had said before. He tells us, for instance, that "whatever produces a work or an effect more noble than itself, or an effect unlike itself, is not a principal efficient, but an instrumental cause"; granting which, who would not infer that the semen and the egg were instruments? seeing that the pullet is an effect more noble than the egg, and every way unlike either this or the spermatic fluid. Wherefore, when the learned Sennert denies the semen and the egg to be instruments or organs, because they are distinct from the prime agents, he takes his position upon a false basis; because, as the prime generator procreates offspring by various means or media, the medium being here conjunct, as the hand of the workman is with his body, there separate and distinct, as is the arrow let loose from the bow, it is still to be regarded as an instrument.

From the conditions now enumerated of an instrumental cause, it seems to follow that the prime efficient in the generation of the chick is the cock, or, at all events, the cock and hen, because the resulting pullet resembles these; nor can it be held more noble than they, which are its prime efficients or parents. I shall, therefore, add another condition of the prime efficient, whence it may, perhaps, appear that the male is not the prime, but only the instrumental, cause of the chick; viz., that the prime efficient in the formation of the chick makes use of

[1] *Politics*, I. 4.

artifice, and foresight, and wisdom, and good-ness, and intelligence, which far surpass the powers of our rational soul to comprehend, in-asmuch as all things are disposed and perfected in harmony with the purpose of the future work, and that there be action to a determinate end; so that every, even the smallest, part of the chick is fashioned for the sake of a special use and end, and with respect not merely to the rearing of the fabric, but also to its well-being, and elegance and preservation. But the male or his semen is not such either in the act of kind or after it, that art, intelligence, and foresight can be ascribed to him or it.

The proper inference from these premises appears to be that the male, as well as his semi-nal fluid is the efficient instrument; and the fe-male not less than the egg she lays the same. Wherefore, we have to seek refuge in a prior, superior, and more excellent cause, to which, with all propriety, are ascribed foresight, in-telligence, goodness, and skill, and which is by so much more excellent than its effect or work, as the architect is more worthy than the pile he rears, as the king is more exalted than his min-ister, as the workman is better than his hands or tools.

The male and female, therefore, will come to be regarded as merely the efficient instruments, subservient in all respects to the Supreme Cre-ator, or Father of all things. In this sense, con-sequently, it is well said that the sun and moon engender man; because, with the advent and secession of the sun, come spring and autumn, seasons which mostly correspond with the gen-eration and decay of animated beings. So that the great leader in philosophy says: "The first motion is not the cause of generation and de-struction; it is the motion of the ecliptic that is so, this being both continuous and having two movements; for, if future generation and corruption are to be eternal, it is necessary that something likewise move eternally, that inter-changes do not fail, that of the two actions one only do not occur. The cause of the perpetuity is, therefore, the law of the universe; and the obliquity is the cause of the approach and acces-sion, and of his being now nearer, now more re-mote: when he quits us, and removes to a dis-tance, it is then that decay and corruption inter-vene; and, in like manner, when he approaches, it is then that he engenders; and if, as he fre-quently approaches, he engenders; so, because he frequently recedes, does he cause corruption; for the causes of contraries are contrary."[1]

[1] *On Generation and Corruption,* II. 10.

All things, therefore, grow and flourish in spring (on the approach of the sun, that is to say, he being the common parent and producer, or at all events the immediate and universal in-strument of the Creator in the work of repro-duction); and this is true not of plants only but of animals also; nor less of those that come spontaneously, than of those that are propa-gated by the consentient act of male and fe-male. It is as if, with the advent of this glorious luminary, Venus the bountiful descended from heaven, waited on by Cupid and a cohort of graces, and prompted all living things by the bland incitement of love to secure the perpetu-ity of their kinds. Or (and it is thus that we have it in the mythology) it is as if the genital organs of Saturn, cast into the sea at this season, raised a foam, whence sprung Aphrodite. For, in the generation of animals, as the poet says, *"superat tener omnibus humor,"*—a gentle mois-ture all pervades—and the genitals froth and are replete with semen.

The cock and the hen are especially fertile in the spring; as if the sun, or heaven, or nature, or the soul of the world, or the omnipotent God—for all these names signify the same thing—were a cause in generation superior and more divine than they; and thus it is that the sun and man, *i.e.,* the sun through man as the in-strument, engenders man. In the same way the preserver of all things, and the male among birds, give birth to the egg, from whence the chick, the perfect bird, is made eternal in its kind by the approach and recession of the god of day, who, by the Divine will and pleasure, or by fate, serves for the generation of all that lives.

Let us conclude, therefore, that the male, although a prior and more excellent efficient than the female, is still no more than an instru-mental efficient, and that he, not less than the female, must refer his fecundity or faculty of engendering as received from the approaching sun; and, consequently, that the skill and fore-sight, which are apparent in his work, are not to be held as proceeding from him but from God; inasmuch as the male in the act of kind neither uses counsel nor understanding; neither does man engender the rational part of his soul, but only the vegetative faculty; which is not regarded as any principal or more divine faculty of the soul, but one only of a lower order.

Since, then, there is not less of skill and pre-science manifested in the structure of the chick than in the creation of man and the universe at large, it is imperative even in the generation of man to admit an efficient cause, superior to, and more excellent than man himself: otherwise the vegetative faculty, or that part of the soul or living principle which fashions and preserves a man, would have to be accounted far more excellent and divine, and held to bear a closer resemblance to God than the rational portion of the soul, whose excellence, nevertheless, we extol over all the faculties of all animals, and esteem as that which has right and empire in them, and to which all created things are made subservient. Or we should else have to own that in the works of nature there was neither prudence, nor art, nor understanding; but that these appeared to us, who are wont to judge of the divine things of nature after our own poor arts and faculties, or to contrast them with examples due to ourselves; as if the active principles of nature produced their effects in the same way as we are used to produce our artificial works, by counsel, to wit, or discipline acquired through the mind or understanding.

But nature, the principle of motion and rest in all things in which it inheres, and the vegetative soul, the prime efficient cause of all generation, move by no acquired faculty which might be designated by the title of skill or foresight, as in our undertakings; but operate in conformity with determinate laws like fate or special commandments—in the same way and manner as light things rise and heavy things descend. The vegetative faculty of parents, to wit, engenders in the same way, and the semen finally arrives at the form of the fœtus, as the spider weaves her web, as birds build nests, incubate their eggs, and cherish their young, or as bees and ants construct dwellings, and lay up stores for their future wants; all of which is done naturally and from a connate genius or disposition; by no means from forecast, instruction, or reason. That which in us is the principle or cause of artificial operations, and is called art, intellect, or foresight, in the natural operations of the lower animals is nature, which is αὐτοδίδακτος, self-taught, instilled by no one; what in them is innate or connate, is with us acquired. On this account it is, that they who refer all to art and artifice are to be held indifferent judges of nature or natural things; and, indeed, it is wiser to act in the opposite way, and selecting standards in nature to judge of things made by art according to them. For all the arts are but imitations of nature in one way or another; as our reason or understanding is a derivative from the Divine intelligence, manifested in his works; and when perfected by

habit, like another adventitious and acquired soul, gaining some semblance of the Supreme and Divine agent, it produces somewhat similar effects.

Wherefore, according to my opinion, he takes the right and pious view of the matter, who derives all generation from the same eternal and omnipotent Deity, on whose nod the universe itself depends. Nor do I think that we are greatly to dispute about the name by which this first agent is to be called or worshipped; whether it be God, Nature, or the Soul of the universe—whatever the name employed—all still intend by it that which is the beginning and the end of all things; which exists from eternity and is almighty; which is author or creator, and, by means of changing generations, the preserver and perpetuator of the fleeting things of mortal life; which is omnipresent, not less in the single and several operations of natural things, than in the infinite universe; which, by his deity or providence, his art and mind divine, engenders all things, whether they arise spontaneously without any adequate efficient, or are the work of male and female associated together, or of a single sex, or of other intermediate instruments, here more numerous, there fewer, whether they be univocal, or are equivocally or accidentally produced: all natural bodies are both the work and the instruments of that Supreme Good, some of them being mere natural bodies, such as heat, spirit, air, the temperature of the air, matters in putrefaction, &c., or they are at once natural and animated bodies; for he also makes use of the motions, or forces, or vital principles of animals in some certain way, to the perfection of the universe and the procreation of the several kinds of animated beings.

From what has now been said, we are apprized to a certain extent of the share which the male has in the business of generation. The cock confers that upon the egg, which, from unprolific, makes it prolific, this being identical with that which the fruit of vegetables receives from the fervour of the summer sun, which secures to them maturity, and to their seeds fertility; and not different from that which fertilizes things spontaneously engendered, and brings caterpillars from worms, aurelias from caterpillars, from aurelias moths, butterflies, bees, &c.

In this way is the sun, by his approach, both the beginning of motion and transmutation in the coming fruit, and the end, also, inasmuch as he is the author of the fertility of its included seed: and, as early spring is the prime efficient of leaves and flowers and fruits, so is summer, in its strength, the cause of final perfection in the ripeness and fecundity of the seed. With a view to strengthen this position, I shall add this one from among a large number of observations. Some persons in these countries cultivate orange trees with singular care and economy, and the fruit of these trees, which, in the course of the first year, will grow to the size of the point of the thumb, comes to maturity the following summer. This fruit is perfect in all respects, save and except that it is without pips or seeds.

Pondering upon this with myself, I thought that I had here an example of the barren egg, which is produced by the hen without the concurrence of the cock, and which comprises everything that is visible in a fruitful egg, but is still destitute of germinant seed; as if it were the same thing that was imparted by the cock, in virtue of which a wind egg becomes a fruitful egg, which in warmer countries is dispensed by the sun, and causes the fruit of the orange tree to be produced replete with prolific seed. It is as if the summer in England sufficed for the production of the fruit only, as the hen for the production of the egg, but like the female fowl was impotent as a pro-genetrix; whilst in other countries enjoying the sun's light in larger proportion, the summer acquired the characters of the male, and perfected the work of generation.

Thus far have we treated this subject by the way, that, from the instance of the egg, we might learn what conditions were required in the prime efficient in the generation of animals; for it is certain that in the egg there is an agent, as there is also in every conception and germ, which is not merely infused by the mother, but is first communicated *in coitu* by the father, by means of his spermatic fluid; and which is itself primarily endowed with such virtue by heaven and the sun, or the Supreme Creator. It is equally manifest that this agent, existing in every egg and seed, is so imbued with the qualities of the parents, that it builds up the offspring in their likeness, not in its own; and this mingled also as proceeding from both united in copulation. Now, as all this proceeds with the most consummate foresight and intelligence, the presence of the Deity therein is clearly proclaimed.

But we shall have to speak at greater length upon this subject when we strive to show what it is that remains with the female immediately after intercourse, and where it is stored; at the same time that we explain—since there is nothing visible in the cavity of the uterus after intercourse—what that prolific contagion or prime conception is; whether it is corporeal and laid up within the female, or is incorporeal; whether the conception of the uterus be of the same nature or not with the conceptions of the brain, and fecundity be acquired in the same way as knowledge—a conclusion, in favour of which there is no lack of arguments; or, as motion and the animal operations, which we call appetites, derive their origin from the conceptions of the brain, may not the natural motions and the operations of the vegetative principle, and particularly generation, depend on the conception of the uterus? And then we have to inquire how this prolific contagion is of a mixed nature, and is imparted by the male to the female, and by her is transferred to the ovum? Finally, how the contagious principle of all diseases and preternatural affections spreads insensibly, and is propagated?

EXERCISE 51. *Of the order of generation; and, first, of the primary genital particle*

It will be our business, by and by, when we come to treat of the matter in especial, to show what happens to the female from a fruitful embrace; what it is that remains with her after this, and which we have still spoken of under the name of contagion, by which, as by a kind of infection, she conceives, and an embryo subsequently begins to grow of its own accord. Meantime, we shall discourse of those things that manifestly appear in connexion with the organs of generation which seem most worthy of particular comment.

And first, since it appears certain that the chick is produced by epigenesis, or addition of the parts that successively arise, we shall inquire what part is formed first, before any of the rest appear, and what may be observed of this and its particular mode of generation.

What Aristotle[1] says of the generation of the more perfect animals, is confirmed and made manifest by all that passes in the egg, *viz.*: that all the parts are not formed at once and together, but in succession, one after another; and that there first exists a particular genital particle, in virtue of which, as from a beginning, all the other parts proceed. As in the seeds of plants, in beans and acorns, to quote particular instances, we see the gemmula, or apex, protruding, the commencement of the entire prospective herb or tree. "And this particle is like a child emancipated, placed independently, a principle existing of itself, from whence the

[1] *On the Generation of Animals*, II, I.

series of members is subsequently thrown out, and to which belongs all that is to conduce to the perfection of the future animal."[1] Since, therefore, "No part engenders itself, but, after it is engendered, concurs in its own growth, it is indispensable that the part first arise which contains within itself the principle of increase; for whether it be a plant or an animal, still has it within itself the power of vegetation or nutrition";[2] and at the same time distinguishes and fashions each particular part in its several order; and hence, in this same primogenate particle, there is a primary vital principle inherent, which is the author and original of sense and motion, and every manifestation of life.

That, therefore, is the principal particle whence vital spirit and native heat accrue to all other parts, in which the calidum innatum sive implantatum of physicians first shows itself, and the household deity or perennial fire is maintained; whence life proceeds to the body in general, and to each of its parts in particular; whence nourishment, growth, aid, and solace flow; lastly, where life first begins in the being that is born, and last fails in that which dies.

All this is certainly true as regards the first engendered part, and appears manifestly in the formation of the chick from the egg. I am, therefore, of opinion that we are to reject the views of certain physicians, indifferent philosophers, who will have it that three principal and primogenate parts arise together, viz.: the brain, the heart, and the liver; neither can I agree with Aristotle himself, who maintains that the heart is the first engendered and animated part; for I think that the privilege of priority belongs to the blood alone; the blood being that which is first seen of the newly engendered being, not only in the chick in ovo, but in the embryo of every animal whatsoever, as shall plainly be made to appear at a later stage of our inquiry.

There appears at first, I say, a red-coloured pulsating point or vesicle, with lines or canals extending from it, containing blood in their interior, and, in so far as we are enabled to perceive from the most careful examination, the blood is produced before the punctum saliens is formed, and is, further, endowed with vital heat before it is put in motion by a pulse; so that as pulsation commences in it and from it, so, in the last struggle of mortal agony, does motion also end there. I have indeed ascertained by numerous experiments instituted

[1] Ibid.
[2] Ibid., 4.

upon the egg, as well as upon other subjects, that the blood is the element of the body in which, so long as the vital heat has not entirely departed, the power of returning to life is continued.

And since the pulsating vesicle and the sanguineous tubes extending thence are visible before anything else, I hold it as consonant with reason to believe that the blood is prior to its receptacles, the thing contained, to wit, to its container, inasmuch as this is made subservient to that. The vascular ramifications and the veins, therefore, after these the pulsating vesicle, and, finally, the heart, as being every one of them organs destined to receive and contain the blood, are, in all likelihood, constructed for the express purpose of impelling and distributing it, and the blood is, consequently, the principal portion of the body.

This conclusion is favoured by numerous observations; particularly by the fact that some animals, and these red-blooded, too, live for long periods without any pulse; some even lie concealed through the whole winter, and yet escape alive, though their heart had ceased from motion of every kind, and their lungs no longer played; they had lain in fact like those who lie half dead in a state of asphyxia from syncope, leipothymia, or the hysterical passion.

Emboldened by what I have observed both in studying the egg, and whilst engaged in the dissection of living animals, I maintain, against Aristotle, that the blood is the prime part that is engendered, and the heart the mere organ destined for its circulation. The function of the heart is the propulsion of the blood, as clearly appears in all animals furnished with red blood; and the office of the pulsating vesicle in the generation of the chick ab ovo, as well as in the embryos of mammiferous animals, is not different, a fact which I have repeatedly demonstrated to others, showing the vesicula pulsans as a feeble glancing spark, contracting in its action, now forcing out the blood which was contained in it, and again relaxing and receiving a fresh supply.

The supremacy of the blood further appears from this: that the pulse is derived from it; for, as there are two parts in a pulsation, viz.: distension or relaxation, and contraction, or diastole and systole, and, as distension is the prior of these two motions, it is manifest that this motion proceeds from the blood; the contraction, again, from the vesicula pulsans of the embryo in ovo, from the heart in the pullet, in virtue of its own fibres, as an instrument destined for this particular end. Certain it is, that the vesicle in question, as also the auricle of the heart at a later period, whence the pulsation begins, is excited to the motion of contraction by the distending blood. The diastole, I say, takes place from the blood swelling, as it were, in consequence of containing an inherent spirit, so that the opinion of Aristotle in regard to the pulsation of the heart—namely, that it takes place by a kind of ebullition—is not without some mixture of truth; for what we witness every day in milk heated over the fire, and in beer that is brisk with fermentation, comes into play in the pulse of the heart; in which the blood, swelling with a sort of fermentation, is alternately distended and repressed; the same thing that takes place in the liquids mentioned through an external agent, namely adventitious heat, is effected in the blood by an intimate heat, or an innate spirit; and this, too, is regulated in conformity with nature by the vital principle (*anima*), and is continued to the benefit of animated beings.

The pulse, then, is produced by a double agent: first, the blood undergoes distension or dilatation, and secondly, the vesicular membrane of the embryo in the egg, the auricles and ventricles in the extruded chick, effect the constriction. By these alternating motions associated, is the blood impelled through the whole body, and the life of animals is thereby continued.

Nor is the blood to be styled the primogenial and principal portion of the body, because the pulse has its commencement in and through it; but also because animal heat originates in it, and the vital spirit is associated with it, and it constitutes the vital principle itself (*ipsa anima*); for wheresoever the immediate and principal instrument of the vegetative faculty is first discovered, there also does it seem likely will the living principle be found to reside, and thence take its rise; seeing that the life is inseparable from spirit and innate heat.

For "however distinct are the artist and the instrument in things made by art," as Fabricius[1] well reminds us, "in the works of nature they are still conjoined and one. Thus the stomach is the author and the organ of chylopoesis." In like manner are the vital principle and its instrument immediately conjoined; and so, in whatever part of the body heat and motion have their origin, in this also must life take its rise, in this be last extinguished; and no one, I presume, will doubt that there are the lares

[1] *Op. sup. cit.*, p. 28.

and penates of life enshrined, that there the vital principle (*anima*) itself has its seat.

The life, therefore, resides in the blood (as we are also informed in our sacred writings),[2] because in it life and the soul first show themselves, and last become extinct. For I have frequently found, from the dissection of living animals, as I have said, that the heart of an animal that was dying, that was dead, and had ceased to breathe, still continued to pulsate for a time, and retained its vitality. The ventricles failing and coming to a stand, the motion still goes on in the auricles, and finally in the right auricle alone; and even when all motion has ceased, there the blood may still be seen affected with a kind of undulation and obscure palpitation or tremor, the last evidence of life. Everyone, indeed, may perceive that the blood—this author of pulsation and life—longest retains its heat; for when this is gone, and it is no longer blood, but gore, so is there, then, no hope of a return to life. But, truly, as has been stated, both in the chick *in ovo* and in the moribund animal, if you but apply some gentle stimulus either to the punctum saliens or to the right auricle of the heart after the failure of all pulsation, forthwith you will see motion, pulsation, and life restored to the blood—provided always, be it understood, that the innate heat and vital spirit have not been wholly lost.

From this it clearly appears that the blood is the generative part, the fountain of life, the first to live, the last to die, and the primary seat of the soul; the element in which, as in a fountain head, the heat first and most abounds and flourishes; from whose influxive heat all the other parts of the body are cherished, and obtain their life; for the heat, the companion of the blood, flows through and cherishes and preserves the whole body, as I formerly demonstrated in my work on the motion of the blood.

And since blood is found in every particle of the body, so that you can nowhere prick with a needle, nor make the slightest scratch, but blood will instantly appear, it seems as if, without this fluid, the parts could neither have heat nor life. So that the blood, being in ever so trifling a degree concentrated and fixed—Hippocrates called the state ἀπόληψις τῶν φλεβῶν, stasis of the veins—as in lipothymia, alarm, exposure to severe cold, and on the accession of a febrile paroxysm, the whole body is observed to become cold and torpid, and, overspread with pallor and livor, to languish. But the blood, recalled by stimulants, by exercise, by certain

[2] Leviticus, 17. 11, 14.

emotions of the mind, such as joy or anger, suddenly all is hot, and flushed, and vigorous, and beautiful again.

Therefore it is that the red and sanguine parts, such as the flesh, are alone spoken of as hot, and the white and bloodless parts, on the contrary, such as the tendons and ligaments, are designated as cold. And as red-blooded animals excel exsanguine creatures, so also, in our estimate of the parts, are those which are more liberally furnished with native heat and blood, held more excellent than all the others. The liver, spleen, kidneys, lungs, and heart itself—parts which are especially entitled *viscera*—if you will but squeeze out all the blood they contain, become pale and fall within the category of cold parts. The heart itself, I say, receives influxive heat and life along with the blood that reaches it, through the coronary arteries; and only so long as the blood has access to it. Neither can the liver perform its office without the influence of the blood and heat it receives through the cœliac artery; for there is no influx of heat without an afflux of blood by the arteries, and this is the reason wherefore, when parts are first produced, and before they have taken upon them the performance of their respective duties, they all look bloodless and pale, in consequence of which they were formerly regarded as spermatic by physicians and anatomists, and in generation it was usual to say that several days were passed in the milk. The liver, lungs, and substance of the heart itself, when they first appear, are extremely white; and, indeed, the cone of the heart and the walls of the ventricles are still seen to be white, when the auricles, replete with crimson blood, are red, and the coronary vein is purple with its stream. In like manner, the parenchyma of the liver is white, when its veins and their branches are red with blood; nor does it perform any duty until it is penetrated with blood.

The blood, in a word, so flows around and penetrates the whole body, and imparts heat and life conjoined to all its parts, that the vital principle, having its first and chief seat there, may truly be held as resident in the blood; in this way, in common parlance, it comes to be all in all, and all in each particular part.

But so little is it true, as Aristotle and the medical writers assert, that the liver and the heart are the authors and compounders of the blood, that the contrary even appears most obviously from the formation of the chick *in ovo*, viz., that the blood is much rather the fashioner of the heart and liver; a fact which

physicians themselves appear unintentionally to confirm, when they speak of the parenchyma of the liver as a kind of effusion of blood, as if it were nothing more than so much blood coagulated there. But the blood must exist before it can either be shed or coagulated; and experience palpably demonstrates that the thing is so, seeing that the blood is already present before there is a vestige either of the body or of any viscus; and that in circumstances where none of the mother's blood can by possibility reach the embryo, an event which is vulgarly held to occur among viviparous animals.

The liver of fishes is always perceived of a white colour, though their veins are of a deep purple or black; and our fowls, the fatter they become, the smaller and paler grows the liver. Cachectic maidens, and those who labour under chlorosis, are not only pale and blanched in their bodies generally, but in their livers as well, a manifest indication of a want of blood in their system. The liver, therefore, receives both its heat and colour from the blood; the blood is in no wise derived from the liver.

From what has now been said, then, it appears that the blood is the first engendered part, whence the living principle in the first instance gleams forth, and from which the first animated particle of the embryo is formed; that it is the source and origin of all other parts, both similar and dissimilar, which thence obtain their vital heat and become subservient to it in its duties. But the heart is contrived for the sole purpose of ministering between the veins and the arteries—of receiving blood from the veins, and, by its ceaseless contractions, of propelling it to all parts of the body through the arteries.

This fact is made particularly striking, when we find that neither is there a heart found in every animal, neither does it necessarily and in every instance pulsate at all times where it is encountered; the blood, however, or a fluid which stands in lieu of it, is never wanting.

EXERCISE 52. *Of the blood as prime element in the body*

It is unquestionable, then, and obvious to sense, that the blood is the first formed, and therefore the genital part of the embryo, and that it has all the attributes which have been ascribed to it in the preceding exercise. It is both the author and preserver of the body; it is the principal element moreover, and that in which the vital principle (*anima*) has its dwelling-place. Because, as already said, before there is any particle of the body obvious to sight, the blood is already extant, has already increased in quantity, "and palpitates within the veins," as Aristotle[1] expresses it, "being moved hither and thither, and being the only humour that is distributed to every part of the animal body. The blood, moreover, is that alone which lives and is possessed of heat whilst life continues."

And further, from its various motions in acceleration or retardation, in turbulence and strength, or debility, it is manifest that the blood perceives things that tend to injure by irritating, or to benefit by cherishing it. We therefore conclude that the blood lives of itself, and supplies its own nourishment; and that it depends in nowise upon any other part of the body, which is either prior to itself or of greater excellence and worth. On the contrary, the whole body, as posthumous to it, as added and appended, as it were, to it, depends on the blood, though this is not the place to prove the fact; I shall only say, with Aristotle, that "The nature of the blood is the undoubted cause wherefore many things happen among animals, both as regards their tempers and their capacities."[2] To the blood, therefore, we may refer as the cause not only of life in general—inasmuch as there is no other inherent or influxive heat that may be the immediate instrument of the living principle except the blood—but also of longer or shorter life, of sleep and watching, of genius or aptitude, strength, &c. "For through its tenuity and purity," says Aristotle in the same place, "animals are made wiser and have more noble senses; and in like manner they are more timid and courageous, or passionate and furious, as their blood is more dilute, or replete with dense fibres."

Nor is the blood the author of life only, but, according to its diversities, the cause of health and disease likewise: so that poisons, which come from without, such as poisoned wounds, unless they infect the blood, occasion no mischief. Life and death, therefore, flow for us from the same spring. "If the blood becomes too diffluent," says Aristotle,[3] "we fall sick; for it sometimes resolves itself into such a sanguinolent serum, that the body is covered with a bloody sweat; and if there be too great a loss of blood, life is gone." And, indeed, not only do the parts of the body at all times become torpid when blood is lost, but if the loss be excessive, the animal necessarily dies. I do not think

it requisite to quote any particular experiment in confirmation of these views: the whole subject would require to be treated specially.

The admirable circulation of the blood originally discovered by me, I have lived to see admitted by almost all; nor has aught as yet been urged against it by anyone which has seemed greatly to require an answer. Wherefore, I imagine that I shall perform a task not less new and useful than agreeable to philosophers and medical men, if I here briefly discourse of the causes and uses of the circulation, and expose other obscure matters respecting the blood; if I show, for instance, how much it concerns our welfare that by a wholesome and regulated diet we keep our blood pure and sweet. When I have accomplished this it will no longer, I trust, seem so improbable and absurd to anyone as it did to Aristotle[4] in former times, that the blood should be viewed as the familiar divinity, as the soul itself of the body, which was the opinion of Critias and others, who maintained that the prime faculty of the living principle (anima) was to feel, and that this faculty inhered in the body in virtue of the nature of the blood. Thales, Diogenes, Heraclitus, Alcmæon, and others, held the blood to be the soul, because, by its nature, it had a faculty of motion.

Now that both sense and motion are in the blood is obvious from many indications, although Aristotle[5] denies the fact. And, indeed, when we see him, yielding to the force of truth, brought to admit that there is a vital principle even in the hypenemic egg; and in the spermatic fluid and blood a "certain divine something corresponding with the element of the stars," and that it is vicarious of the Almighty Creator; and if the moderns be correct in their views when they say that the seminal fluid of animals emitted in coitu is alive, wherefore should we not, with like reason, affirm that there is a vital principle in the blood, and that when this is first ingested and nourished and moved, the vital spark is first struck and enkindled? Unquestionably the blood is that in which the vegetative and sensitive operations first proclaim themselves; that in which heat, the primary and immediate instrument of life, is innate; that which is the common bond between soul and body, and the vehicle by which life is conveyed into every particle of the organized being.

[1] History of Animals, III. 19.
[2] On the Parts of Animals, II. 4.
[3] History of Animals, III. 19.

[4] On the Soul, I. 2.
[5] History of Animals, I. 19; On the Parts of Animals, II. 3.

Besides, if it be a matter of such difficulty to understand the spermatic fluid as we have found it, to fathom how through it the formation of the body is made to begin and proceed with such foresight, art, and divine intelligence, wherefore should we not, with equal propriety, admit an exalted nature in the blood, and think at least as highly of it as we have been led to do of the semen?—the rather, as this fluid is itself produced from the blood, as appears from the history of the egg; and the whole organized body not only derives its origin, as from a genital part, but even appears to owe its preservation to the blood.

We have, indeed, already said so much incidentally above, intending to speak on the subject more particularly at another time. Nor do I think that we are here to dispute whether it is strictly correct to speak of the blood as a *part;* some deny the propriety of such language, moved especially by the consideration that it is not sensible, and that it flows into all parts of the body to supply them with nourishment. For myself, however, I have discovered not a few things connected with the manner of generation which differ essentially from those motions which philosophers and medical writers generally either admit or reject. At this time I say no more on this point; but though I admit the blood to be without sensation, it does not follow that it should not form a portion, and even a very principal portion, of a body which is endowed with sensibility. For neither does the brain nor the spinal marrow, nor the crystalline or the vitreous humour of the eye, feel anything, though, by the common consent of all, philosophers and physicians alike, these are parts of the body. Aristotle placed the blood among the *partes similares;* Hippocrates, as the animal body according to him is made up of containing, contained, and impelling parts, of course, reckoned the blood among the number of parts contained.

But we shall have more to say on this topic when we treat of that wherein a part consists, and how many kinds of parts there are. Meantime, I cannot be silent on the remarkable fact that the heart itself, this most distinguished member in the body, appears to be insensible.

A young nobleman, eldest son of the Viscount Montgomery, when a child, had a severe fall, attended with fracture of the ribs of the left side. The consequence of this was a suppurating abscess, which went on discharging abundantly for a long time, from an immense gap in his side; this I had from himself and other credible persons who were witnesses. Between the eighteenth and nineteenth years of his age, this young nobleman, having travelled through France and Italy, came to London, having at this time a very large open cavity in his side, through which the lungs, as it was believed, could both be seen and touched. When this circumstance was told as something miraculous to his Serene Majesty King Charles, he straightway sent me to wait on the young man, that I might ascertain the true state of the case. And what did I find? A young man, well grown, of good complexion, and apparently possessed of an excellent constitution, so that I thought the whole story must be a fable. Having saluted him according to custom, however, and informed him of the king's expressed desire that I should wait upon him, he immediately showed me everything, and laid open his left side for my inspection, by removing a plate which he wore there by way of defence against accidental blows and other external injuries. I found a large open space in the chest, into which I could readily introduce three of my fingers and my thumb; which done, I straightway perceived a certain protuberant fleshy part, affected with an alternating extrusive and intrusive movement; this part I touched gently. Amazed with the novelty of such a state, I examined everything again and again, and when I had satisfied myself, I saw that it was a case of old and extensive ulcer, beyond the reach of art, but brought by a miracle to a kind of cure, the interior being invested with a membrane, and the edges protected with a tough skin. But the fleshy part (which I at first sight took for a mass of granulations, and others had always regarded as a portion of the lung, from its pulsating motions and the rhythm they observed with the pulse)—when the fingers of one of my hands were applied to it, those of the other to the artery at the wrist—as well as from their discordance with the respiratory movements, I saw was no portion of the lung that I was handling, but the apex of the heart! covered over with a layer of fungous flesh by way of external defence, as commonly happens in old foul ulcers. The servant of this young man was in the habit daily of cleansing the cavity from its accumulated sordes by means of injections of tepid water; after which the plate was applied, and, with this in its place, the young man felt adequate to any exercise or expedition, and, in short, he led a pleasant life in perfect safety.

Instead of a verbal answer, therefore, I carried the young man himself to the king, that his majesty might with his own eyes behold this wonderful case: that, in a man alive and well, he might, without detriment to the individual, observe the movement of the heart, and, with his proper hand even touch the ventricles as they contracted. And his most excellent majesty, as well as myself, acknowledged that the heart was without the sense of touch; for the youth never knew when we touched his heart, except by the sight or the sensation he had through the external integument.

We also particularly observed the movements of the heart, *viz.*: that in the diastole it was retracted and withdrawn; whilst in the systole it emerged and protruded; and the systole of the heart took place at the moment the diastole or pulse in the wrist was perceived; to conclude, the heart struck the walls of the chest, and became prominent at the time it bounded upwards and underwent contraction on itself.

Neither is this the place for taking up that other controversy; to wit, whether the blood alone serves for the nutrition of the body? Aristotle in several places contends that the blood is the ultimate aliment of the body, and in this view he is supported by the whole body of physicians. But many things of difficult interpretation, and that hang but indifferently together, follow from this opinion of theirs. For when the medical writers speak of the blood in their physiological disquisitions, and teach that the above is its sole use and end, *viz.*: to supply nourishment to the body, they proceed to compose it of four humours, or juices, adducing arguments for such a view from the combinations of the four primary qualities; and then they assert that the mass of the blood is made up of the two kinds of bile, the yellow and the black, of pituita, and the blood properly so called. And thus they arrive at their four humours, of which the pituita is held to be cold and moist; the black bile cold and dry; the yellow bile hot and dry; and the blood hot and moist. Further, of each of these several kinds, they maintain that some are nutritious, and compose the whole of the body; others, again, they say are excrementitious. Still further, they suppose that the blood proper is composed of the nutritious or heterogeneous portions; but the constitution of the mass is such that the pituita is a cruder matter, which the more powerful native heat can convert into perfect blood. They deny, however, that the bile can by any means be thus transformed into blood; although the blood, they say, is readily changed

into bile, an event which they conceive takes place in melancholic diseases, through an excess of the concocting heat.

Now, if all this were true, and there be no retrogressive movement, *viz.*, from black bile to bile, from bile to blood, they would be brought to the dilemma of having to admit that all the juices were present for the production of black bile, and that this was a principal and most highly concocted nutriment. It would further be imperative on them to recognize a kind of twofold blood, *viz.*, one consisting of the entire mass of fluid contained in the veins, and composed of the four humours aforesaid; and another consisting of the purer, more fluid and spirituous portion, the fluid, which in the stricter sense they call blood, which some of them contend is contained in the arteries apart from the rest, and which they then depute upon sundry special offices. On their own showing, therefore, the pure blood is no aliment for the body, but a certain mixed fluid, or rather black bile, to which the rest of the humours tend.

Aristotle,[1] too, although he thought that the blood existed as a means of nourishing the body, still believed that it was composed, as it were, of several portions, *viz.*, of a thicker and black portion which subsides to the bottom of the basin when the blood coagulates, and this portion he held to be of an inferior nature; "for the blood," he says, "if it be entire, is of a red colour and sweet taste; but if vitiated either by nature or disease, it is blacker."[2] He also will have it fibrous in part or partly composed of fibres, which being removed, he continues,[3] the blood neither sets nor becomes any thicker. He further admitted a sanies in the blood: "Sanies is unconcocted blood, or blood not yet completely concocted, or which is as yet dilute like serum." And this part, he says, is of a colder nature. The fibrous he believed to be the earthy portion of the blood.

According to the view of the Stagirite, therefore, the blood of different animals differs in several ways; in one it is more serous and thinner, a kind of ichor or sanies, as in insects, and the colder and less perfect animals; in another it is thicker, more fibrous, and earthy, as in the wild boar, bull, ass, &c. In some where the constitution is distempered, the blood is of a blacker hue; in others it is bright, pure, and florid, as in birds, and the human subject especially.

[1] *On the Parts of Animals*, II. 3.
[2] *History of Animals*, III. 19.
[3] *Ibid.*

Whence, it appears, that in the opinion of the physicians, as well as of Aristotle, the blood consists of several parts, in some sort of the same description, according to the views of each. Medical men, indeed, only pay attention to human blood, taken in phlebotomy and contained in cups and coagulated. But Aristotle took a view of the blood of animals generally, or of the fluid which is analogous to it. And I, omitting all points of controversy, and passing by any discussion of the inconveniences that wait upon the opinions of writers in general, shall here touch lightly upon the points that all are agreed in, that can be apprehended by the senses, and that pertain more especially to our subject; intending, however, to treat of everything at length elsewhere.

Although the blood be, as I have said, a portion of the body—the primogenial and principal part, indeed—still, if it be considered in its mass, and as it presents itself in the veins, there is nothing to hinder us from believing that it contains and concocts nourishment within itself, which it applies to all the other parts of the body. With the matter so considered, we can understand how it should both nourish and be nourished, and how it should be both the matter and the efficient cause of the body, and have the natural constitution which Aristotle held necessary in a primogenial part, *viz.*, that it should be partly of similar, partly of dissimilar constitution; for he says, "As it was requisite for the sake of sensation that there should be similar members in animal bodies, and as the faculty of perceiving, the faculty of moving, and the faculty of nourishing, are all contained in the same member (*viz.*, the primogenate particle), it follows necessarily that this member, which originally contains inherent principles of the above kind, be extant both simply, that it may be capable of sensation of every description, and dissimilarly, that it may move and act. Wherefore, in the tribes that have blood, the heart is held to be such a member; in the bloodless tribes, however, it is proportional to their state."

Now, if Aristotle understands by the heart that which first appears in the embryo of the chick *in ovo*, the blood, to wit, with its containing parts—the pulsating vesicles and veins, as one and the same organ, I conceive that he has expressed himself most accurately; for the blood, as it is seen in the egg and the vesicles, is partly similar and partly dissimilar. But if he understands the matter otherwise, what is seen in the egg sufficiently refutes him, inasmuch as

the substance of the heart, considered independently of the blood—the ventricular cone —is engendered long afterwards, and continues white without any infusion of blood, until the heart has been fashioned into that form of organ by which the blood is distributed through the whole body. Nor indeed does the heart even then present itself with the structure of a similar and simple part, such as might become a primogenial part, but is seen to be fibrous, fleshy, or muscular, and indeed is obviously what Hippocrates styled it, a muscle or instrument of motion. But the blood, as it is first perceived, and as it pulsates, included within its vesicle, has as manifestly the constitution which Aristotle held necessary in a principal part. For the blood, whilst it is naturally in the body, has everywhere apparently the same constitution; when extravasated, however, and deprived of its native heat, immediately, like any dissimilar compound it separates into several parts.

Were the blood destined by nature, however, for the nourishment of the body only, it would have a more *similar* constitution, like the chyle or the albumen of the egg; or at all events it would be truly one and a single body composed of the parts or juices indicated, like the other humours, such as bile of either kind, and pituita or phlegm, which retain the same form and character without the body, which they showed within their appropriate receptacles; they undergo no such sudden change as the blood.

Wherefore, the qualities which Aristotle ascribed to a principal part are found associated in the blood; which as a natural body, existing heterogeneously or *dissimilarly*, is composed of these juices or parts; but as it lives and is a very principal animal part, consisting of these juices mingled together, it is an animated *similar* part, composed of a body and a vital principle. When this living principle of the blood escapes, however, in consequence of the extinction of the native heat, the primary substance is forthwith corrupted and resolved into the parts of which it was formerly composed; first into cruor, afterwards with red and white parts, those of the red parts that are uppermost being more florid, those that are lowest being black. Of these parts, moreover, some are fibrous and tough (and these are the uniting medium of the rest), others ichorous and serous, in which the mass of coagulum is wont to swim. Into such a serum does the blood almost wholly resolve itself at last. But these parts have no existence severally in living blood; it is in that only which has become corrupted and is resolved by death that they are encountered.

Besides the constituents of the blood now indicated, there is yet another which is seen in the blood of the hotter and stronger animals, such as horses, oxen, and men also of ardent constitution. This is seen in blood drawn from the body as it coagulates, in the upper part of the red mass, and bears a perfect resemblance to hartshorn-jelly, or mucilage, or thick white of egg. The vulgar believe this matter to be the pituita; Aristotle designated it the crude and unconcocted portion of the blood.

I have observed that this part of the blood differs both from the others and from the more serous portion in which the coagulated clot is wont to swim in the basin, and also from the urine which percolates through the kidneys from the blood. Neither is it to be regarded as any more crude or colder portion of the blood, but rather, as I conceive, as a more spiritual part; a conclusion to which I am moved by two motives: first, because it swims above the bright and florid portion—commonly thought to be the arterial blood—as if it were hotter and more highly charged with spirits, and takes possession of the highest place in the disintegration of the blood.

Secondly, in venesection, blood of this kind, which is mostly met with among men of warm temperament, strong and muscular, escapes in a longer stream and with greater force, as if pushed from a syringe, in the same way as we say that the spermatic fluid which is ejected vigorously and to a distance is both more fruitful and full of spirits.

That this mucaginous matter differs greatly from the ichorous or watery part of the blood, which, as if colder than the rest, subsides to the bottom of the basin, appears on two distinct grounds: for the watery and sanious portion is too crude and unconcocted ever to pass into purer and more perfect blood; and the thicker and more fibrous mucus swimming above the clot of the blood itself appears more concoct and better elaborated than this; and so in the resolution or separation of the blood it comes that the mucus occupies the upper place, the sanies the lower; the clot and red parts, however—both those of a brighter and those of a darker colour—occupy the middle space.

For it is certain that not only this part, but the whole blood, and indeed the flesh itself—as may be seen in criminals hung in chains—may be reduced to an ichorous sanies; that is to say, become resolved into the matters of which they were composed, like salt into the lixivium from which it had been obtained. In like manner, the blood taken away in any cachexy abounds in serum, and this to such an extent that occasionally scarce any clot is seen—the whole mass of blood forms one sanies. This is observed in leucophlegmatia, and is natural in bloodless animals.

Further, if you take away some blood shortly after a meal, before the second digestion has been completed and the serum has had time to descend by the kidneys, or at the commencement of an attack of intermittent fever, you will find it sanious, inconcoct, and abounding in serum. On the contrary, if you open a vein after fasting, or a copious discharge of urine or sweat, you will find the blood thick, as if without serum, and almost wholly condensed into clot.

And in the same way as in coagulating blood you find a little of the afore-mentioned supernatant mucus, so if you expose the sanies in question, separated from the clot, to a gentle heat over the fire, you will find it to be speedily changed into the mucus; an obvious indication that the water or sanies which separates from the blood in the basin, is perchance a certain element in the urine, but not the urine itself, although in colour and consistence it seems so in fact. The urine is not coagulated or condensed into a fibrous mucus, but rather into a lixivium; the watery or sanious portion of the urine, however, when lightly boiled, does occasionally run into a mucus that swims through the fluid; in the same way, as the mucus in question rendered recrudescent by corruption, liquefies and returns to the state of sanies.

So far at this time have I thought fit to produce these my own observations on this constituent of the blood, intending to speak more fully of it as well as of the other constituents cognizable by the senses, and admitted by Aristotle and the medical writers.

That I may not seem to wander too widely from my purpose, I would here have it understood that with Aristotle I receive the blood as a part of the living animal body, and not as it is commonly regarded in the light of mere gore. The Stagirite says: "The blood is warm, in the sense in which we should understand warm water, did we designate that fluid by a simple name, not viewing it as heated. For heat belongs to its nature; just as whiteness is in the nature of a white man. But when the blood becomes hot through any affection or passion, it is not then hot of itself. The same thing must be said in regard to the qualities of dryness and moistness. Wherefore, in the nature of such things they are partly hot and partly moist; but separated, they congeal and become cold; and such is the blood."[1]

The blood, consequently, as it is a living element of the body, is of a doubtful nature, and falls to be considered under two points of view. Materially and *per se* it is called nourishment; but formally and in so far as it is endowed with heat and spirits, the immediate instruments of the vital principle, and even with vitality (*anima*), it is to be regarded as the familiar divinity and preserver of the body, as the generative first engendered and very principal part. And as the prolific egg contains within it the matter, instrument, and framer of the future pullet, and all physicians admit a mixture of the seminal fluids of the two sexes in the uterus during or immediately after intercourse as constituting the mixed cause, both material and efficient, of the fœtus; so might one with more propriety maintain that the blood was both the matter and preserver of the body, though not the sole aliment; because it is observed that in animals which die of hunger, and in men who perish of marasmus, a considerable quantity of blood is still found after death in the veins. And further, in youthful subjects still growing, and in aged individuals declining and falling away, the relative quantity of blood continues the same, and is in the ratio of the flesh that is present, as if the blood were a part of the body, but not destined solely for its nourishment; for if it were so, no one would die of hunger so long as he had any blood left in his veins, just as the lamp is not extinguished whilst there is a drop of inflammable oil left in the cruse.

Now when I maintain that the living principle resides primarily and principally in the blood, I would not have it inferred from thence that I hold all bloodletting in discredit, as dangerous and injurious; or that I believe with the vulgar that in the same measure as blood is lost, is life abridged, because the sacred writings tell us that the life is in the blood; for daily experience satisfies us that bloodletting has a most salutary effect in many diseases, and is indeed the foremost among all the general remedial means: vitiated states and plethora of the blood, are causes of a whole host of diseases; and the timely evacuation of a certain quantity of the fluid frequently delivers patients from very dangerous diseases, and even from imminent death. In the same measure as blood is de-

[1] *On the Parts of Animals*, II. 3.

tracted, therefore, under certain circumstances, it may be said that life and health are added.

This indeed nature teaches, and physicians at all events propose to themselves to imitate nature; for copious critical discharges of blood from the nostrils, from hemorrhoids, and in the shape of the menstrual flux, often deliver us from very serious diseases. Young persons, therefore, who live fully and lead indolent lives, unless between their eighteenth and twentieth years they have a spontaneous hemorrhage from the nose or lower parts of the body, or have a vein opened, by which they are relieved of the load of blood that oppresses them, are apt to be seized with fever or smallpox, or they suffer from headache and other morbid symptoms of various degrees of severity and danger. Veterinary surgeons are in the habit of beginning the treatment of almost all the diseases of cattle with bloodletting.

EXERCISE 53. *Of the inferences deducible from the course of the umbilical vessels in the egg*

We find the blood formed in the egg and embryo before any other part; and almost at the same moment appear its receptacles, the veins and the vesicula pulsans. Wherefore, if we regard the punctum saliens as the heart, and this along with the blood and the veins as constituting one and the same organ, conspicuous in the very commencement of the embryo, although we should admit that the proper substance of the heart was deposited subsequently, still we should be ready to admit with Aristotle that the heart (an organ made up of ventricles, auricles, vessels, and blood) was in truth the principal and primogenate part of the body, its own prime and essential element having been the blood, both in the order of nature and of genetic production.

The parts that in generation succeed the blood are the veins, for the blood is necessarily inclosed and contained in vessels; so that, as Aristotle observes, we find two meatus venales even from the very first, which canals, as we have shown in our history, afterwards constitute the umbilical vessels. It seems necessary, therefore, to say something here of the situation and course of these vessels.

In the first place, then, it is to be observed that all the arteries and veins have their origin from the heart and are, as it were, appendices or parts added to the central organ. If, therefore, you carefully examine the embryo of the human subject, or one of the lower animals, and having divided the vena cava between the right auricle and the diaphragm, look into it upwards or towards the heart, you will perceive three foramina, the largest and most posterior of which tending to the spine is the vena cava; the anterior and lesser proceeds to the root and trunk of the umbilical vessels; the third and least of all enters the liver and is the origin and trunk of all the ramifications distributed to the convexity of that organ. Whence it clearly appears that the veins do by no means all proceed from the liver as their origin and commencement, but from the heart—unless indeed any one would be hardy enough to contend that a vessel proceeded from its branches, not the branches from the trunk of the vessel.

Moreover, as the vessels in question are distributed equally to the albumen and vitellus of the egg, not otherwise than as the roots of trees are connected with the ground, it is obvious that both of these substances must serve for the nutriment of the embryo, and that they are taken up and carried to it by these vessels. But this view is opposed to that of Aristotle, who everywhere maintains that the chick is formed from the albumen, and receives nourishment through the umbilicus alone. The albumen indeed is first consumed, and the yelk serves subsequently for food, supplying the place of the milk, which viviparous animals receive after their birth from their mothers. The food which Nature provides for the young of viviparous tribes in the dug of the mother, she supplies in the yelk of the egg to the young of oviparous animals. Whence it happens, that when the albumen is almost wholly consumed, the vitellus still remains nearly entire in the egg, the chick being already perfect and complete; more than this, the yelk is still found in the abdomen of the chick long after its exclusion. Aristotle discovered some on the eighteenth day after the hatching; and I have myself seen a small quantity connected with the intestine at the end of six weeks from that epoch.

Nevertheless, from the yelk (which certainly does not decrease in the same ratio as the albumen whilst the chick is forming) that is taken into the abdomen of the chick, and from the distribution of vessels through its substance, the whole of these collecting into a single trunk which enters the porta of the liver, and doubtless carrying that portion of yelk they have absorbed for more perfect elaboration in that viscus—these and other arguments of the like kind force me to say that I cannot do otherwise than admit with Aristotle that the yelk supplies food to the chick, and is analogous to milk.

The whole of the yelk, indeed, does not remain after the fœtus of the fowl is fully formed; for a certain portion of it has been liquefied on the very first appearance of the embryo, and receives branches of vessels no less than the albumen, by which, already prepared, it is carried as nourishment for the chick; still it is certain that the greater portion of the yelk remains after the disappearance of the albumen; that it is laid up in the abdomen of the chick when excluded, and, attracted or absorbed by the branches of the vena portæ, that it is finally carried to the liver.

It is manifest, therefore, that the chick when hatched, is nourished by the yelk in the first period of its independent existence. And as within the egg the embryo was nourished partly by the albumen, partly by the vitellus, but principally by the albumen, which is both present in larger quantity, and is more speedily consumed, so when the chick is hatched, and when all the nourishment that is taken must pass through the liver to undergo ulterior preparation, is it nourished partly by the vitellus and partly by chyle absorbed from the intestines, but principally by chyle, which the host of subdivisions of the mesenteric vessels seize upon, whilst there is but a single vessel from the porta distributed to the vitellus, and by and by but little of it remains. Nature, therefore, acts as does the nurse, who gradually habituates her infant to the food which is to take the place of her failing supply of milk. The pullet is thus gradually brought from food of more easy to food of more difficult digestion, from yelk to chyle.

Wherefore, there is every reason for what we perceive in connexion with the course of the veins in the egg. When the embryo first begins to be formed, they are distributed to the colliquament only, where the blood finds suitable nutriment and matter for the formation of the body; but by and by they extend into the thinner albumen, whence the chick, whilst it is yet in the state of gelatine or mucor, and resembles a maggot in form, derives its increase; the branches next extend into the thicker albumen, and then into the vitellus, that they may also contribute to the support of the fœtus, which, having at length arrived at maturity and been extruded, still preserves a portion of the yelk (or milk) within its abdomen, whereby it is maintained in part, in part by food selected and prepared for it by the mother, until it is able to look out for and to digest its own aliment. Thus does nature most wisely provide food through the whole round of generation, suited to the various strength of the digestive faculty in the future being. In the first period of the fœtal chick's existence a more delicate food is prepared for it; more advanced, firmer and firmer food is supplied; and this is the reason, I apprehend, wherefore, the perfect egg consists not only of two portions of different colours, but is even provided with two kinds of albumen.

Now all this that we discover from actual experience of the matter accords with the opinion of Aristotle, where he says: "The part which is hot is best adapted to give form to the limbs; that which is more earthy rather conduces to the constitution of the body and is more remote. Wherefore in eggs of two colours, the animal begins to be engendered from the white (for the beginning of animal life is in the hot), and derives its nourishment from the yellow. In the warmer animals, consequently, these parts are kept distinct from one another, *viz.*, that from which the beginning is derived, and that whence the nourishment is obtained, and the one is white, the other yellow."[1]

From what has now been said it appears that the chick—and we shall show that it is not otherwise in all other animals—arises and is constituted, as it were, by a principle or soul inherent in the egg, and that in the same way the proper aliment is sought for and is supplied within the egg; whereby it comes that the chick is not dependent on its mother in the same way as plants are dependent on the ground; and it is not more correct to say that the chick is nourished by the blood of its mother, or that its heart beats, and that it lives through the spirits of its parent, than it would be to assert that it moved and felt through the organs, or grew and attained to adult age through the vital principle of its parent. It is manifest, on the contrary, and is allowed by all that the fœtal chick is nourished through its umbilical vessels; and that the vascular ramifications dispersed over the albumen and yelk imbibe nourishment from them and convey it to the fœtus. It is also admitted that the chick, when excluded from the shell, is supplied with nourishment, partly from yelk, partly from chyle, and that in either case the aliment passes by the same route, *viz.*, by the vena portæ into the liver, the branches of this vessel effecting the transit.

[1] *On the Generation of Animals*, III. I.

It is therefore obvious, as I now say by the way, that the chyle by which all animals are nourished is brought by the mesenteric veins from the intestines; nor is there occasion to look for any new passage—by the lacteal vessels, to wit—or any route in adult animals other than that which we discover in the egg and chick. But we shall recur more fully in another place to the inconveniences of such an opinion as that referred to.

Lastly, from the structure of the umbilical vessels of the chick *in ovo*, some of which as stated in the history are veins, others arteries, it is legitimate to conclude that there is here a circular motion of the blood, such as we have already demonstrated in the animal body, in our book *On the Motion of the Blood*, and this for the sake of the nutrition and growth of the embryo, and because the umbilical veins are distributed to either fluid of the egg, that they may thence bring nutriment to the chick, and the arteries accompany the veins, that by their affluxive heat the alimentary matter may be duly concocted, liquefied, and made fit to answer the ends of nutrition.

And hence it happens that wherever veins—and here I would have it understood that both arteries and veins are intended—make their way into the albumen or vitellus, there these fluids look liquefied and different from the rest. For as soon as the branches of the veins shoot forth, the upper portion of the albumen in which they are implanted, passing into colliquament, becomes transparent, whilst the lower portion, continuing thick and compact, is pushed into the inferior angle of the egg. In like manner a separation of the vitellus, as it seems into two portions, makes its appearance, the one being superior, and the other inferior, and these do not differ less from one another in character than melted differs from solid wax; now this division corresponds to the two parts which severally receive or do not receive bloodvessels.

Hence are we further made more certain as to the commencement of animal generation and the prime inherent principle of the egg. For it is assuredly known that the cicatricula or spot on the yelk is the chief point in the egg, that to which all the rest are subordinate, and to which, if to any one thing more than another, is to be referred the cause, whatever it be, of fecundity in the egg:—certain it is that the generation of the embryo is begun within its precincts. Wherefore, as we have said, the first effect of incubation is to cause dilatation of the cicatricula, and the formation of the colliquament, in which the blood first flushes and veins are distributed, and where the effects of the native heat and the influence of the plastic power first show themselves. And then, the more widely the ramifications of these veins extend, in the same proportion do indications of the presence of the vital power and vegetative force appear. For every effect is a clear evidence of its efficient cause.

In a word I say—from the cicatricula (in which the first trace of the native heat appears) proceeds the entire process of generation; from the heart the whole chick, and from the umbilical vessels the whole of the membranes called *secundines* that surround it. We therefore conclude that the parts of the embryo are severally subordinate, and that life is first derived from the heart.

EXERCISE 54. *Of the order of the parts in generation from an egg, according to Fabricius*

Having already determined what part is to be esteemed the first, the blood, to wit, with its receptacles, the heart, veins, and arteries, the next thing we have to do is to speak of the rest of the parts of the body and of the order and manner of their generation.

Fabricius, in whose footsteps we have resolved to tread, in speaking of the generation of the chick *in ovo*, passes in review the actions which take place in the egg, and by the effect of which the parts are produced, discussing them *seriatim*, as if a clearer view were thence to be obtained of the order or sequence of generation. "There are three primary actions," he says,[1] "which present themselves in the egg of the bird: 1st, the generation of the embryo; 2d, its growth; 3d, its nourishment. The first, or generation, is the proper action of the egg; the second and third, *viz.*, growth and nutrition, go on for the major part without the egg, though they are begun and also perfectly performed within it. Now these actions, as they flow from three faculties, the generative, the nutritive, and auctive, so do three operations follow them. From generation all the parts of the chick result; from increase and nutrition, the growth and maintenance of its body. From studying the formation of the chick, we perceive that, under the influence of the generative faculty, the parts of the creature which formerly had no existence are produced: the matter of the egg is changed into the organized body of a chicken. But whilst any part or substance undergoes transmutation into another, it must needs be that its proper essence undergoes change, otherwise would it still remain as it was and unaltered; it must at the same time receive figure, position, and dimensions apt and convenient to its new nature; and indeed it is into these two states or circumstances that procreation of matter resolves itself, *viz.*, transformation and conformation. The transformative and the formative faculties would, therefore, be the cause of these functions; and whilst one of them has produced every individual part of the chick, such as we see it, from the chalaza of the egg, the other has given it figure, articulations, and position, fitting it for its destined uses. The first, the transformative or alterative faculty, is entirely natural, and acts without all consciousness; and taking the hot, the cold, the moist, and the dry, it alters all through the substance of the chalaza, and in altering this substance changes it into the component parts of the chick, that is to say, into flesh, bones, cartilages, ligaments, veins, arteries, nerves, and all the other similar and simple parts of the animal, and these, through the proper and innate heat and spirit of the semen of the cock, out of the substance of the egg, that is to say, its chalaza; by altering and commuting, it engenders, creates, produces the proper substance of the chick, imparting at the same time to every substance its appropriate quality. The other, which is called the formative faculty, and which out of similar forms dissimilar parts—namely, giving them elegance through figure, due dimensions, proper position, and congruous number—is much more noble than the former, is possessed of consummate sapience, and acts not naturally, but with election, and consciousness, and intelligence. For the formative faculty appears to have exact cognizance and foresight both of the future action and use of every part and organ. So much of the primary action of the egg, which is the generation of the chick, and to accomplish which both the semen of the cock as agent and fecundator, and the chalaza as matter are required. In the second place comes accretion or growth, which is accomplished by nutrition, whose faculties consist in attraction, retention, concoction, expulsion, and, finally, apposition, agglutination, and assimilation of food."

But for my part I neither regard such a distribution of actions as correct, or useful, or convenient in this place. It is incorrect, because those actions which he would make distinct in

[1] *Op. supra cit.*, p. 41.

kind and in time—for instance, that parts are first produced similar by the alterative or transformative faculty, to be afterwards fashioned and organized by the formative faculty, and finally made to grow by the auctive faculty—are never apparent in the generation of the chick; for the several parts are produced and distinguished and increased simultaneously. For although in the generation of those animals which are formed by metamorphosis, where from matter previously existing, and already adequate in quantity and duly prepared, all the parts are made distinct and conformed by transformation, as when a butterfly is formed from a caterpillar, a silkworm from a grub, still in generation by epigenesis the thing is very different, nor do the same processes go on as in ordinary nutrition, which is effected by the various actions of different parts working together to a common end, the food being here first assumed and retained, then digested, next distributed, and finally agglutinated. Nor is the *similar constitution* the result of the transformative faculty, void of all foresight, as Fabricius imagined; but the organic comes from the formative faculty which proceeds with both consciousness and foresight. For generation and growth do not proceed without nutrition, nor nutrition or increase without generation; "to nourish" being, in other terms, to substitute for a certain quantity of matter lost as much matter of the same quality, flesh or nerve, in lieu of the matter, flesh or nerve, that has become effete. But what is this but to make or engender flesh or nerve? In like manner, growth cannot go on without generation, for all natural bodies are increased by the accession of new particles similar to those of which they formerly consisted, and this, taking place according to all their dimensions, they are distinguished as regards their parts, and are organized at the same time that they grow.

But to engender the chick is in truth nothing else than to fashion or make its several members and organs, which, although they are produced in a certain order, and some are postgenate to others—the less important to the more principal organs—still, whilst the organs themselves are all distinguished, they are not engendered in such wise and order that the *similar* parts are first formed, and the *organic* parts afterwards compounded from them; or so that certain composing parts existed before other compounded parts which must be fashioned from them. For although the head of the chick and the rest of the body exist in the shape of a mucus or soft jelly, whence each of the parts is afterwards formed in sequence, and all are of *similar* constitution in the first instance, still are they simultaneously produced and augmented in virtue of the same processes directed by the same agent; and in the same proportion as the matter resembling jelly increases, in like measure are the parts distinguished; for they are engendered, transmuted, and formed simultaneously; similar and dissimilar parts exist together, and from a small similar organ a larger one is produced. The thing, in short, is not otherwise than it is among vegetables, where from the straw proceeds the ear, the awns, and the grain—distinctly, severally, and yet together; or as trees put forth buds, from which are produced leaves, flowers, fruit, and finally seed.

All this we learn from an attentive study of the parts and processes of the incubated egg, inasmuch as from things done, actions or operations are apprehended; from operations, faculties or forces, and from these we then infer the artificer, generator, or cause. In the generation of the pullet, consequently, the actions or faculties of the engendering cause enumerated by Fabricius, namely, the metamorphic and formative, do not differ in kind, or even in the relation of sequence, as that one is first and the other second, but, as Aristotle is wont to say, are one and the same in reason; not as happens with reference to the actions of the nutritive faculty—attraction, concoction, distribution and apposition, to wit—which all come into play in several places at several times. Were this not so, the engendering cause itself would be forced to make use of various instruments in order to accomplish its various operations.

Fabricius, therefore, asserts erroneously that the transmutative force works with the properties of the elements—hot, cold, moist, and dry—as its instruments; whilst the formative faculty acts independently of these and by a more divine power, performing its task with consciousness, as it seems, with foresight and election. But if he had looked more closely at the matter he would have seen that the formative as well as the metamorphic force made use of the hot and the cold, the moist and the dry, as instruments; nor would he have been less struck with indications of the Supreme Artificer's interference in the processes of nutrition and transformation than in that of formation itself. For nature ordained each and all of these faculties to some definite end, and everywhere labours with forethought and intelligence.

Whatever it is in the seeds of plants which renders them fertile and exercises a plastic force in their interior; whatever it is which in the egg performs the duty of a most skilful artificer, producing and fashioning the parts of the pullet, warming, cooling, moistening, drying, concocting, condensing, hardening, softening and liquefying at once, impressing distinctive characters on each of them by means of configuration, situation, constitution, temperament, number and order—still is this something at work, disposing and ordering all with no less of foresight, intelligence, and choice in the business of transmuting, than in the processes of nutrition, growth, and formation.

The concoctive and metamorphic, the nutritive and augmentive faculties, which Fabricius would have it act through the qualities of hot, cold, moist, and dry, without all consciousness, I maintain, on the contrary, work no less to a definite end, and with not less of artifice than the formative faculty, which Fabricius declares has knowledge and foresight of the future action and use of every particular part and organ. In the same way as the arts of the physician, cook, and baker, in which heat and cold, moisture and dryness, and similar natural properties are employed, require the use of reason no less than the mechanical arts in which either the hands or various instruments are employed, as in the business of the blacksmith, statuary, potter, &c.; in the same way, as in the greater world, we are told that "All things are full of Jove,"—*Jovis omnia plena*—so in the slender body of the pullet, and in every one of its actions, does the finger of God or nature no less obviously appear.

Wherefore, if from manifestations it be legitimate to judge of faculties, we might say that the vegetative acts appear rather to be performed with art, election, and foresight, than the acts of the rational soul and mind; and this even in the most perfect man, whose highest excellence in science and art, if we may take the God for our guide, is that he KNOW HIMSELF.

A superior and more divine agent than man, therefore, appears to engender and preserve mankind, a higher power than the male bird to produce a young one from the egg. We acknowledge God, the supreme and omnipotent creator, to be present in the production of all animals, and to point, as it were, with a finger to his existence in his works, the parents being in every case but as instruments in his hands. In the generation of the pullet from the egg all things are indeed contrived and ordered with singular providence, divine wisdom, and most admirable and incomprehensible skill. And to none can these attributes be referred save to the Almighty, first cause of all things, by whatever name this has been designated,—the *Divine Mind* by Aristotle; the *Soul of the Universe* by Plato; the *Natura Naturans* by others; *Saturn* and *Jove* by the ancient Greeks and Romans; by ourselves, and as is seeming in these days, the *Creator* and *Father* of all that is in heaven and earth, on whom animals depend for their being, and at whose will and pleasure all things are and were engendered.

Moreover, as I have said, I neither hold this arrangement of the faculties of the vital principle, which Fabricius has placed at the head of his account of the organs of generation, as correct in itself, nor as useful or calculated to assist us in the matter we have in hand. For we do not attain to a knowledge of effects from a discussion of actions or faculties; the contrary is rather the case: from actions we ascend to a knowledge of faculties, inasmuch as manifestations are more cognizable to us than the powers whence they proceed, and the parts which we investigate already formed are more readily appreciated than the actions whence they proceed.

Neither is it well from the generation of a single chick from an egg, to venture upon general conclusions, which can in fact only be correctly arrived at after extensive observations on the mode of generation among animals at large. But of this matter I shall have more to say immediately.

Meantime, however, that we may come to the parts subservient to generation, as Fabricius says, "let us consider and perpend in what order the organs subserving generation are produced—which are formed first, which last. In this investigation two bases are to be laid, one having reference to the corporeal, the other to the incorporeal; that is to say, to nature and the vital principle. The corporeal base," he continues, "I call that which depends on and proceeds from the nature of the body, and of which illustrations are readily supplied from things made by art; as for example, that every building requires a foundation upon which it may be established and reared; from whence walls are raised, by which both floors and ceilings are supported; then are all the supplementary parts added and ornaments appended: and so, in fact, does Nature strive in the construction of the animal body; for first she forms the bones as a foundation, in order that all the parts of the body may grow upon and be appended to and established around them. These are the parts, in other words, that are first formed and solidified; for as the bones derive their origin from a very soft and membranous substance, and by and by become extremely hard, much time is required to complete the formation of a bone, and it is therefore that they are first produced. Hence Galen did not compare the formation of the animal body to every kind of artificial structure, but particularly to a ship; for he says, as the commencement and foundation of a ship is the keel, from which the ribs, circularly curved, proceed on either side at moderate distances from each other, like the sticks of a hurdle, in order that the whole fabric of the vessel may afterwards be reared upon the keel as a suitable basis; so in the formation of the animal body does Nature, by means of the outstretched spine and the ribs drawn around it, secure a keel and suitable foundation for the entire superstructure, which she then raises and perfects."[1]

But experience teaches us that all this is very different in fact, and that the bones are rather among the last parts to be formed. The bones of the extremities and skull, and the teeth, do not arise any sooner than the brain, the muscles, and the other fleshy parts: in new-born fœtuses, perfect in other respects, the place of the bones is supplied by mere membranes or cartilages, which are only subsequently and in the lapse of time converted into bones; a circumstance which sufficiently appears in the crania of new-born infants, and in the state of their ribs and articulations.

And although it be true that the first rudiments of the body are seen in the guise of a recurved keel, still this is a soft mucous and jelly-like substance, which has no affinity in nature, structure, or office to bone; and although certain globules depend from thence, the destined rudiments of the head, still these contain no solid matter, but are mere vesicles full of limpid water, which are afterwards formed into the brain, cerebellum, and eyes, which are all subsequently surrounded by the skull, at a period, however, when the beak and nails have already acquired consistency and hardness.

This view of Fabricius is therefore both imperfect and incorrect; inasmuch as he does not think of what Nature performs in fact in the work of generation, so much as of what in his opinion she ought to do, betrayed into this by

his comparison with the edifice reared by art. As if nature had imitated art, and not rather art nature!—mindful of which he himself says afterwards: "It were better to say that art learned of Nature, and was an imitator of her doings; for, as Galen everywhere reminds us, Nature is both older and displays greater wisdom in her works than art."[2]

And then when we admit that the bones are the foundation of the whole body, without which it could neither support itself nor perform any movement, it is still sufficient if they arise simultaneously with the parts that are attached to them. And indeed the things that are to be supported not yet existing, the supports would be established in vain. Nature, however, does nothing in vain; nor does she form parts before there is a use for them. But animals receive their organs as soon as the offices of these are required. The first basis of Fabricius, therefore, is distinctly overthrown by his own observations on the egg, and the comparison drawn by Galen.

He appears to have come nearer the truth where he says: "The other basis of the parts to be formed first or last is obtained from nature, that is, from the vital principle by which the animal body is ruled and directed. If there be two grades of this principle, the vegetative and animal, the vegetative must be held prior in point of nature and time, inasmuch as it is common to plants and animals; and assuredly the organs officiating in the vegetative office will be engendered and formed before those that belong to the sensitive and motive principle, especially to the chief organs which are in immediate relationship with the governing principle. Now these organs are two in especial— the liver and the heart: the liver as seat of concupiscence, of the vegetative or nutritive faculty; the heart, as the organ whose heat maintains and perfects the vegetative and every other faculty, and in this way has most intimate connexions and relations with the vegetative force. Whence, if after the third day you see the heart palpitating in the point where the chick is engendered, as Aristotle bears witness to the fact that you can, you will not be surprised but rather be disposed to admit that the heart belongs to the vegetative degree and exists for its sake. It is also consonant with reason that the liver should be engendered simultaneously with the heart, but should lie perdue or hidden, as it does not pulsate. And Aristotle himself admits that the heart and liver exist in

---

[1] *Op. supra cit.*, p. 43.

[2] *Op. cit.*, p. 44.

the animal body for similar reasons; so that where there is a heart there also is a liver discovered. If the heart and liver be the parts first produced, then, it is also fair to suppose that the other organs subserving these two should be engendered in the same manner—the lungs which exist for the sake of the heart; and, for the sake of the liver, almost all the viscera which present themselves in the abdomen."[1]

Still is all this very different from the sequence we witness in the egg. Nor is it true that the liver is engendered simultaneously with the heart; nor does the salve avail with which he would cover that infirmity where he says that the liver is concealed because it does not palpitate; for the eyes and vena cava and carina are all conspicuous enough from the commencement, although none of them palpitate. How come the liver and lungs, if they be then extant, to be visible without any palpitation? And then Fabricius himself has indicated a minute point situated in the centre of his figure of the chick of the fourth day, without stating, however, that it had any pulsation; and this he did not perceive to be the heart, but rather believed it to be the rudiment of the body. It is certain, therefore, that Fabricius spoke only from conjecture and preconceived opinion of the origin of the liver; even in the same way as others have done, Aldrovandus and Parisanus among the number, who, lighting upon two points, and perceiving that they did not pulsate simultaneously, straightway held that one was the heart, the other the liver. As if the liver ever pulsated, and these two points were aught but the two pulsating vesicles replying to each other by alternate contractions, in the way and manner we have indicated in our history!

Fabricius, therefore, is either deceived or deceives, when he says, "In the first stage of the production of the chick, the liver, heart, veins, arteries, lungs, and all the organs contained in the cavity of the abdomen, are engendered together; and in like manner are the carina, in other words, the head with the eyes and entire vertebral column and thorax engendered." For the heart, veins, and arteries are perfectly distinguished some time before the carina; the carina, again, is seen before the eyes; the eyes, beak, and sides before the organs contained in the cavity of the abdomen; the stomach and intestines before the liver or lungs; and there are still other particulars connected with the order of production of the parts in

[1] *Op. cit. ut. sup.*

generation, of which we shall speak by and by.

He is also mistaken when he would have the vegetative portion of the vital principle prior in nature and time to the sensitive and motive element. For that which is prior in nature is mostly posterior in the order of generation. In point of time, indeed, the vegetative principle is prior; because without it the sensitive principle cannot exist: an act—if the act of an organic body—cannot take place without organs; and the sensitive and motive organs are the work of the vegetative principle; the sensitive soul before the existence of action, is like a triangle within a quadrangle. But nature intended that that which was primary and most noble should also be primary; wherefore the vegetative force is by nature posterior in point of order, as subordinate and ministrative to the sensitive and motive faculties.

EXERCISE 55. *Of the order of the parts according to Aristotle*

The following appear to be Aristotle's views of the order of generation: "When conception takes place, the germ comports itself like a seed sown in the ground. For seeds likewise contain a first principle, which, existing in the beginning *in potentia*, by and by when it manifests itself, sends forth a stem and a root, by which aliment is taken up; for increase is indispensable. And so in a conception, in which all the parts of the body inhere *in potentia*, and the first principle exists in a state of special activity."[2]

This principle in the egg—the body analogous to the seed of a vegetable—we have called with Fabricius the spot or cicatricula, and have spoken of it as a very primary part of the egg, as that in which all the other parts inhere *in potentia*, and from whence each in its order afterwards arises. In this spot, in fact, is contained that—whatever it may be—by which the egg is made productive; and here is the first action of the formative faculty, the first effect of the vegetative heat revealed.

This spot, as we have said, dilates from the very commencement of the incubation, and expands in circles, in the centre of which a minute white speck is displayed, like the shining point in the pupil of the eye; and here anon is discovered the punctum saliens rubrum, with the ramifications of the sanguiferous vessels, and this as soon as the fluid, which we have called the colliquament, has been produced.

"Wherefore," adds Aristotle,[3] "the heart is

[2] *On the Generation of Animals*, II. 4.
[3] *Ibid.*

the first part perceived in fact; and this is in conformity not only with sense, but also with reason. For as that which is engendered is already disjunct and severed from both parents, and ought to rule and regulate itself like a son who comes of age and has his separate establishment, it must therefore possess a principle, an intrinsic principle, by which the order of the members may be subsequently determined, and whatever is necessary to the constitution of a perfect animal arranged. For if this principle were at any time extrinsic, and entered into the body at a subsequent period, you would not only be in doubt as to the time at which it entered, but as every part is distinct, you would also see it as necessary that that should first exist from which the other parts derive both increase and motion." The same writer elsewhere[1] asserts: "This principle is a portion of the whole, and not anything added, or included apart. For," he proceeds,"the generation of the animal completed, does this principle perish, or does it continue? But nothing can be shown existing intrinsically which is not a part of the whole organized being, whether it be plant or animal; wherefore it would be absurd to maintain that the principle in question perished after the formation either of any one or of any number of parts; for what should form those that were not yet produced? Wherefore," he continues further, "they say not well who with Democritus assert that the external parts of animals are those first seen, and then the internal parts, as if they were rearing an animal of wood and stone, for such a thing would include no principle within itself. But all animals have and hold a principle in their interior. Wherefore the heart is seen as the first distinct part in animals that have blood; for it is the origin of all the parts, whether similar or dissimilar; and the creature that begins to feel the necessity of nourishment, must already be possessed by the principle of an animal and a full-grown fœtus."

From the above, it clearly appears that Aristotle recognizes a certain order and commencement in animal generation, namely, the heart, which he regards as the first produced and first vivified part of the animal, and, like a son set free from the tutelage of his parents, as self-sufficing and independent, whence not only does the order of the parts proceed, but as that by which the animal itself is maintained and preserved, receiving from it at once life and sustenance, and everything needful to the per-

fection of its being. For as Seneca says: "In the semen is comprised the entire cause of the future man; and the unborn babe has written within it the law of a beard and a hoary head. For the whole body and the load of future years are already traced in delicate and obscure outlines in its constitution."[2]

We have already determined whether the heart were this primigenial part or not; in other words, whether Aristotle's words refer to that part which, in the dissection of animals, is seen sooner than all the rest, the punctum saliens, to wit, with its vessels full of blood; and we have cordially assented to an answer in the affirmative. For I believe that the blood, together with its immediate instruments, the umbilical vessels, by which, as by roots, nutriment is attracted, and the pulsating vesicles, by which this nutriment is distributed, to maintain life and growth in every other part, are formed first and foremost of all. For as Aristotle[3] has said, it is the same matter by which a thing grows, and by which it is primarily constituted.

Many, however, err in supposing that different parts of the body require different kinds of matter for their nourishment. As if nutrition were nothing more than the selection and attraction of fit aliment; and in the several parts of the body to be nourished, no concoction, assimilation, apposition, and transmutation were required. This as we learn, was the opinion of Anaxagoras of old:

Who held the principles of things to be
Homœomeric:—bone to be produced
Of small and slender bones; the viscera
Of small and slender viscera; the blood
Of numerous associate drops of blood.[4]

But Aristotle, with the greatest propriety, observes: "Distinction of parts is not effected, as some think, by like being carried by its nature to like; for, besides innumerable difficulties belonging to this opinion in itself, it happens that each similar part is severally created; for example, the bones by themselves, the nerves, the flesh, &c."[5] But the nourishment of all parts is common and homogeneous, such as we see the albumen to be in the egg, not heterogeneous and composed of different parts. Wherefore all we have said of the matter from which parts are made, is to be stated of that by which they in-

[1] *Ibid*, II. I.

[2] *Nat. Quæst.* III. 29.
[3] *On the Generation of Animals*, II. 4.
[4] Lucretius, *On the Nature of Things*, I. 834–838.
[5] *Loc. sup. cit.*

crease: all derive nourishment from that in which they exist *in potentia*, though not in act. Precisely as from the same rain plants of every kind increase and grow; because the moisture which was a like power in reference to all, becomes actually like to each when it is changed into their substances severally: then does it acquire bitterness in rue, sharpness in mustard, sweetness in liquorice, and so on.

He explains, moreover, what parts are engendered before others, and assigns a reason which does not differ from the second basis of Fabricius. "The cause by which, and the cause of this cause, are different; one is first in generation, the other in essence"; by which we are to understand that the end is prior in nature and essence to that which happens for the sake of the end; but that which happens for the sake of the end must be prior in generation. And on this ground Fabricius rightly infers that all those parts which minister to the vegetative principle are engendered before those that serve the sensitive principle, inasmuch as the former is subordinate to the latter.

He subsequently adds the differences of those parts which are made for some special purpose: some parts, for example, are instituted for a purpose by nature, because this purpose ensues; and others because they are instruments which the purpose employs. The former he designates *genitalia*, the latter *instrumenta*. For the end or purpose, he says, in some cases, is posterior, in others prior to that which is its cause. For both the generator and the instruments it uses must exist anteriorly to that which is engendered by or from them. The parts serving the vegetative principle, therefore, are prior to the parts which are the ministers of sense and motion. But the parts dedicated to motion and sensation are posterior to the motive and sensitive faculties, because they are the instruments which the motive and sensitive faculties employ. For it is a law of nature that no parts or instruments be produced before there be some use for them, and the faculty be extant which employs them. Thus there is neither any eye nor any motive organ engendered until the brain is produced, and the faculties pre-exist which are to see and to govern motion.

In like manner, as the pulsating vesicles serve as instruments for the motion of the blood, and the heart in its entire structure does the same (as I have shown in the work *On the Motion of the Blood*), urging the blood in a ceaseless round through every part of the body, we see that the blood must exist before the heart, both in the order of generation and of nature and essence. For the blood uses the heart as an instrument, and moreover, when engendered it continues to nourish the organ by means of the coronary arteries, distributing heat, spirits, and life to it through their ramifications.

We shall have further occasion to show from an entire series of anatomical observations, how this rule of Aristotle in respect of the true priority of the parts is borne out. Meantime we shall see how he himself succeeds in duly inferring the causes of priority in conformity with his rule.

"After the prime part—viz., the heart—is engendered," he says, "the internal parts are produced before the external ones, the superior before the inferior; for the lower parts exist for the sake of the superior, and that they may serve as instruments, after the manner of the seeds of vegetables, which produce roots sooner than branches."

Nature, however, follows no such order in generation; nor is the instance quoted invariably applicable; for in beans, peas, and other leguminous seeds, in acorns, also, and in grain, it is easy to see that the stem shoots upwards and the root downwards from the same germ; and onions and other bulbous plants send off stalks before they strike root.

He then subjoins another cause of this order, viz.: "That as Nature does nothing in vain or superfluously, it follows that she makes nothing either sooner or later than the use she has for it requires." That is to say, those parts are first engendered whose use or function is first required; and some are begun at an earlier period because a longer time is requisite to bring them to perfection; and that so they may be in the same state of forwardness at birth as those that are more rapidly produced. Just as the cook, having to dress certain articles for supper, which by reason of their hardness are done with difficulty, or require gentle boiling for a great length of time, these he puts on the first, and only turns subsequently to those that are prepared more quickly and with less expenditure of heat; and further, as he makes ready the articles that are to come on in the first course first of all, and those that are to be presented in the second course afterwards; so also does Nature in the generation of animals only proceed at a later period to the construction of the soft and moist and fleshy parts, as requiring but a short time for their concoction and formation, whilst the hard parts, such as the bones, as requiring ample evaporation and abundant drying, and their matter long remaining inconcoct, she proceeds to fashion almost from the very beginning. "And the same thing obtains in the brain," he adds, "which, large in quantity and exceedingly moist at first, is by and by better concocted and condensed, so that the brain as well as the eye diminishes in size. The head is, therefore, very large at first, in comparison with the rest of the body, which it far surpasses because of the brain and the eyes, and the large quantity of moisture contained in them. These parts, nevertheless, are among the last to be perfected, for the brain acquires consistence with difficulty, and it is long before it is freed from cold and moisture in any animal, and especially in man. The sinciput, too, is consolidated the last, the bones here being quite soft when the infant sees the light."

He gives another reason, *viz.*, because the parts are formed of different kinds of matter: "Every more excellent part, the sharer in the highest principle is, further, engendered from the most highly concocted, the purest and first nutriment; the other needful parts, produced for the sake of the former, from the worse and excrementitious remainder. For Nature, like the sage head of a family, is wont to throw away nothing that may be turned to any useful purpose. But he still regulates his household so that the best food shall be given to his children, the more indifferent to his menials, the worst to the animals. As then, man's growth being complete and mind having been superadded (in other words, and, as I interpret the passage, adult man having acquired sense and prudence), things are ordered in this way, so does Nature at the period of production even compose the flesh and the other more sensitive parts of the purest matter. Of the excrementitious remainder she makes the bones, sinews, hair, nails, and other parts of the same constitution. And this is the reason why this is done last of all, when Nature has an abundant supply of recrementitious material." Our author then goes on to speak of "a twofold order of aliment": "one for nutrition, another for growth"; "the nutritive is the one which supplies existence to the whole and to the parts; the augmentative, that which causes increase to the bulk."

This is in accordance with what we find in the egg, where the albumen supplies a kind of purer aliment adapted to the nutrition of the embryo in its earlier stages, and the yelk affords the material for the growth of the chick and pullet. The thinner albumen, moreover, as we have seen, is used in fashioning the first and more noble parts; the thicker albumen and the yelk, again, are employed in nourishing and making these to grow, and further in forming the less important parts of the body. "For," he says, "the sinews, too, are produced in the same way as the bones, and from the same material, *viz.*: the seminal and nutritive excrementitious matter. But the nails, hair, horns, beak, and spurs of birds, and all other things of the same description, are engendered of the adventitious and nutritive aliment, which is obtained both from the mother and from without." And then he gives a reason why man, whilst other animals are endowed by nature with defensive and offensive arms, is born naked and defenceless, which is this: that whilst in the lower animals these parts are formed of remainders or excrements, man is compounded of a purer material, "which contains too small a quantity of inconcoct and earthy matter."

Thus far have we followed Aristotle on the subject of "The Order in Generation," the whole of which seems to be referrible to one principle, *viz.*: the perfection of Nature, who in her works does nothing in vain and has no shortcomings, but still does that in the best manner which was best to be done. Hence in generation no part would either precede or follow, did she prefer producing them altogether, *viz.*: in circumstances where she acts freely and by election; for sometimes she works under compulsion, as it were, and beside her purpose, as when through deficiency or superabundance of material, or through some defect in her instruments, or is hindered of her ends by external injuries. And thus it occasionally happens that the final parts are formed before the instrumental parts—understanding by final parts, those that use others as instruments.

And as some of the parts are genital, nature making use of them in the generation of other parts, as the means of removing obstacles the presence of which would interfere with the due progress of the work of reproduction, and others exist for other special ends; it therefore happens that for the disposition of material, and other requisites, some parts are variously engendered before others, some of them being begun earlier but completed at a later period, some being both begun and perfected at an earlier period, and others being begun together but perfected at different times subsequently. And then the same order is not observed in the generation of all animals, but this is variously altered; and in some there is nothing like succession, but all the parts are begun and perfected simultaneously, by metamorphosis, to wit, as has been already stated. Hence it follows, in fine, that the primogenate part must be of such a nature as to contain both the beginning and the end, and be that for whose sake all the rest is made, namely, the living principle, or soul, and that which is the potential and genital cause of this, the heart, or in our view the blood, which we regard as the prime seat of the soul, as the source and perennial centre of life, as the generative heat, and indeed as the inherent heat; in a word, the heart is the first efficient of the whole of the instrumental parts that are produced for the ends of the soul, and used by it as instruments. The heart, according to Aristotle, I say, is that for which all the parts of animals are made, and it is at the same time that which is at once the origin and fashioner of them all.

EXERCISE 56. *Of the order of the parts in generation as it appears from observation*

That we may now propose our own views of the order of the parts in generation as we have gathered it from our observations, it appears that the whole business of generation in all animals may be divided into two periods, or connected with two structures: the ovum, i. e., the conception and seed, or that, whatever it be, which in spontaneous productions corresponds to the seed, whether with Fernelius it be called "the native celestial heat in the primogenial moisture," or with Aristotle, "the vital heat included in moisture." For the conception in viviparous animals, as we have said, is analogous to the seed and fruit of plants; in the same way as it is to the egg of oviparous creatures; to worms in spontaneously engendered animals, or to certain vesicles fruitful by the vital warmth of their included moisture. In each and all of these the same things inhere which might with propriety lead to their being called seeds; they are all bodies, to wit, from which and by which, as previously existing matter, artificer and organ, the whole of an animal body is primarily engendered and produced.

The other structure is the embryo produced from the seed or conception. For both the matter and the moving and efficient cause, and the instruments needful to the operation, must necessarily precede operation of any and every kind.

We have already examined the structure of the egg. Now the embryo to which it gives birth, in so far as this can be made out by observation and dissection, particularly among the more perfect animals with blood, appears to be perfected by four principal degrees or processes, which we reduce to as many orders, in harmony with the various epochs in generation; and we shall demonstrate that what transpires in the egg also takes place in every conception or seed.

The first process is that of the primogenial and genital part, *viz.*, the blood with its receptacles, in other words, the heart and its vessels.

And this part is first engendered for two principal reasons: 1st, because it is the principal part which uses all the rest as instruments, and for whose sake the other parts are formed; and, 2d, because it is the prime genital part, the origin and author of the rest. The part, in a word, in which inhere both the principle whence motion is derived, and the end of that motion, is obviously father and sovereign.

In the generation of this first part, which in the egg is accomplished in the course of the fourth day, although I have not been able to observe any order or sequence, inasmuch as the whole of its elements—the blood, the vessels, and the pulsating vesicles—appear simultaneously, I have nevertheless imagined, as I have said, that the blood exists before the pulse, because, according to nature's laws, it must be antecedent to its receptacles. For the substance and structure of the heart, namely, the conical mass with its auricles and ventricles, as they are produced long subsequently along with the other viscera, so must they be referred to the same class of parts as these, namely, the third.

In the production of the circulating system the veins are sooner seen than the arteries; such at least is our conclusion.

The second process, which begins after the fourth day, is indicated by a certain concrescence, which I designate *vermiculum*—worm or maggot; for it has the life and obscure motions of a maggot; and as it concretes into a mucous matter, it divides into two parts, the larger and superior of which is seen to be conglobed, and divided, as it were, into thin vesicles—the brain, the cerebellum, and the two eyes; the less, again, constituting the carina, arises over the vena cava and extends in the line of its direction.

In the genesis of the head, the eyes are first perceived; by and by a white point makes its appearance in the situation of the beak, and the slime drying around it, it becomes invested with a membrane.

The outline of the rest of the body follows about the same period. First, from the carina something like the sides of a ship are seen to arise; the parts having an uniform consistence in the beginning, but the ribs being afterwards prefigured by means of extremely fine white lines. The instruments of locomotion next arise —the legs and wings; and the carina and the extremities adnate to it are then distinguished into muscles, bones, and articulations.

These two rudiments of the head and trunk appear simultaneously, but as they grow and advance to perfection subsequently, the trunk increases and acquires its shape much more speedily than the head; so that this, which in the first instance exceeded the whole trunk in size, is now relatively much smaller. And the same thing occurs in regard to the human embryo.

The same disparity also takes place between the trunk and the extremities. In the human embryo, from the time when it is not longer than the nail of the little finger, till it is of the size of a frog or mouse, the arms are so short that the extremities of the fingers could not extend across the breast, and the legs are so short that were they reflected on the abdomen they would not reach the umbilicus.

The proportion of the body to the extremities in children after their birth continues excessive until they begin to stand and run. Infants, therefore, resemble dwarfs in the beginning, and they creep about like quadrupeds, attempting progressive motion with the assistance of all their extremities; but they cannot stand erect until the length of the leg and thigh together exceeds the length of the rest of the body. And so it happens, that when they first attempt to walk, they move with the body prone, like the quadruped, and can scarcely rise so erect as the common dunghill fowl.

And so it happens that among adult men the long-legged—they who have longer legs, and especially longer thighs—are better walkers, runners, and leapers than square-built, compact men.

In this second process many actions of the formative faculty are observed following each other in regular order (in the same way as we see one wheel moving another *in automata*, and other pieces of mechanism), and all arising from the same mucaginous and similar matter. Not indeed in the manner that some natural philosophers would have it when they say "that like is carried to its like." We are rather to maintain that parts are moved, not changing their places, but remaining and undergoing change in hardness, softness, colour, &c., whence the diversi-

ties between *similar* parts; those things appearing *in act* which were before *in power*.[1] The extremities, spine, and rest of the body, namely, are formed, grow, and acquire outline and complexion together; the extremities, comprising bones, muscles, tendons, and cartilages, all of which on their first appearance were similar and homogeneous, become distinguished in their progress, and, connected together, compose organs, by whose mutual continuity the whole body is constituted. In like manner, the membrane growing around the head, the brain is composed, and the lustrous eyes receive their polish out of a perfectly limpid fluid.

That is to say, Nature sustains and augments the several parts by the same nourishment with which she fashioned them at first, and not, as many opine, with any diversity of aliment and particles similar to each particular structure. As she is increasing the mucaginous mass or maggot, like a potter she first divides her material, and then indicates the head and trunk and extremities; like a painter, she first sketches the parts in outline, and then fills them in with colours; or like the shipbuilder, who first lays down his keel by way of foundation, and upon this raises the ribs and roof or deck: even as he builds his vessel does Nature fashion the trunk of the body and add the extremities. And in this work she orders all the variety of similar parts—the bones, cartilages, membranes, muscles, tendons, nerves, &c.—from the same primary jelly or mucus. For thick filaments are produced in the first instance, and these by and by are brought to resemble cords; then they are rendered cartilaginous and spinous; and, lastly, they are hardened and concocted into bones. In the same way the thicker membrane which invests the brain is first cartilaginous and then bony, whilst the thinner membrane merely consolidates into the pericranium and integument. In similar order flesh and nerve from soft mucus are confirmed into muscle, tendon, and ligament; the brain and cerebellum are condensed out of a perfectly limpid water into a firm coagulum; for the brain of infants, before the bones of the head have closed, is soft and diffluent, and has no greater consistence than the curd of milk.

The third process is that of the viscera, the formation of which in the chick takes place after the trunk is cast in outline, or about the sixth or seventh day—the liver, lungs, kidneys, cone and ventricles of the heart, and intestines, all become visible nearly at the same moment;

[1] *On the Generation of Animals*, II. 4.

they appear to arise from the veins, and to be connected with them in the same way as fungi grow upon the bark of trees. They are, as I have already said, gelatinous, white, and bloodless, until they take on their proper functions. The stomach and intestines are first discovered as white and tortuous filaments extending lengthwise through the abdomen; along with these the mouth appears, from which a continuous canal extends to the anus, and connects the superior with the inferior parts. The organs of generation likewise appear about the same time.

Up to this period all the viscera, the intestines, and the heart itself inclusive, are excluded from the cavities of the body and hang pendulous without, attached as it were to the veins. The trunk of the body presents itself, in fact, like a boat undecked or a house without a roof, the anterior walls of the thorax and abdomen not being yet extant to close these cavities.

But as soon as the sternum is fashioned the heart enters into the chest as into a dwelling which it had built and arranged for itself; and there, like the tutelary genius, it enters on the government of the surrounding mansion, which it inhabits with its ministering servants the lungs. The liver and stomach are by and by included within the hypochondria, and the intestines are finally surrounded by the abdominal parietes. And this is the reason wherefore without dissection the heart can no longer be seen pulsating in the hen's egg after the tenth day of incubation.

About this epoch the point of the beak and the nails appear of a fine white colour; a quantity of chylous matter presents itself in the stomach; a little excrement is also observed in the intestine, and the liver being now begun, some greenish bile is perceived; facts from which it clearly appears that there is another digestion and preparation of nutriment going on besides that which takes place by the branches of the umbilical veins; and it is reasonable matter of doubt how the bile, the excrementitious matter of the second digestion, can be separated by the instrumentality of the liver from the other humours, when we see it produced at the same time as this organ.

In the order now indicated are the internal organs generated universally; in all the animals which I have dissected, particularly the more perfect ones, and man himself, I have found them produced in the same manner: in these, in the course of the second, third, and fourth month, the heart, liver, lungs, kidneys, spleen, and intestines present themselves inchoate and increasing, and all alike of the same white colour which belongs to the body at large. Wherefore these early days are not improperly spoken of as the days when the embryo is *in the milk;* for with the exception of the veins, particularly those of the umbilicus, everything is as it were spermatic in appearance.

I am of opinion that the umbilical arteries arise after the veins of the same name, because the arteries are scarcely to be discovered in the course of the first month, and take their rise from the branches that descend to either lower extremity. I do not believe, therefore, that they exist until that part of the body whence they proceed is formed. The umbilical veins, on the contrary, are conspicuous long before any part of the body is begun.

What I have now said I have derived from numerous dissections of human embryos of almost every size; for I have had them for inspection from the time they were like tadpoles, till they were seven or eight fingers' breadth in length, and from thence onwards to the full time. I have examined them more particularly, however, through the second, third, and fourth months, in the course of which the greatest number of changes take place, and the order of development is seen with greatest clearness.

In the human embryo, then, of the age of two months, what we have spoken of as taking place in the "second process," is observed to occur. For I rather think that during the first month there is scarcely anything of the conception in the uterus—at all events, I have never been able to discover anything. But the first month past, I have repeatedly seen conceptions thrown off, and similar to the one which Hippocrates mentions as having been voided by the female pipe-player, of the size of a pheasant's or pigeon's egg. Such conceptions resemble an egg without its shell; they are, namely, of an oval figure; the thicker membrane or chorion with which they are surrounded, however, is seen to be covered with a white mucor externally, particularly towards the larger end; internally it is smooth and shining, and is filled with limpid and sluggish water—it contains nothing else.

In the course of the second month I have frequently seen an ovum of this description, or somewhat larger, thrown off with the symptoms of abortion, *viz.,* ichorous lochia; the ovum being sometimes entire, at other times burst, and covered with bloody coagula. Within it was smooth and slippery; it was covered with adhering blood without. Its form was that which

I have just described. In some of these aborted ova, I have discovered embryos, in others I could find none. The embryo, when present, was of the length of the little finger-nail, and in shape like a little frog, save that the head was exceedingly large and the extremities very short, like a tadpole in the month of June, when it gets its extremities, loses its tail, and assumes the form of a frog. The whole substance was white, and so soft and mucilaginous, that unless immersed in clear water, it was impossible to handle it. The face was the same as that of the embryo of one of the lower animals—the dog or cat, for instance, without lips, the mouth gaping, and extending from ear to ear.

Many women, whose conceptions, like the wind eggs of fowls, are barren and without an embryo, miscarry in the third month.

I have occasionally examined aborted ova of this age, of the size of a goose's egg, which contained embryos distinct in all their parts, but misshapen. The head, eyes, and extremities were distinct, but the muscles were indistinct; there were no bones, but certain white lines in their situations, and as it seemed, soft cartilages. The substance of the heart was extremely white, and consisted of two ventricles of like size and thickness of walls, forming a cone with a double apex, which might be compared to a small twin-kernel nut. The liver was very small and of the general white colour. Through the whole of this time, i.e., during the first three months, there is scarcely any appearance of a placenta or uterine cake.

In every conception of this description I have seen, I have always found a surrounding membrane containing a large quantity of watery fluid, between which and the body of the embryo, suspended by its middle by means of a long and twisted umbilical cord, there is such disproportion, that it is impossible to regard this liquid as either sweat or urine; it seems far more probable that like the colliquament in the hen's egg, it is a fluid destined by nature for the nourishment of the foetus. Nor was there any indication to be discovered of these conceptions or ova having been connected with the uterus; there was only on the external surface of their larger extremity a greater appearance of thickening and wrinkling, as if the rudiments of the future placenta had existed there.

These conceptions, therefore, appear to me in the light of ova, which are merely cherished within the uterus, and, like the egg in the uterus of the fowl, grow by their own inherent powers.

In the fourth month, however, it is wonderful to find what rapid strides the foetus has made: from the length of the thumb it has now grown to be a span long. All the members, too, are distinct and are tinged with blood; the bones and muscles can be distinguished; there are vestiges of the nails, and the foetus now begins to move lustily. The head, however, is excessively large; the face without lips, cheeks, and nose; the gape of the mouth is enormous, and the tongue lies in its middle; the eyes are small, without lids to cover them; the middle integument of the regions of the forehead and sinciput is not yet cartilaginous, far less bony; but the occiput is somewhat firm and in some sort cartilaginous, indicating that the skull already begins to acquire solidity.

The organs of generation have now made their appearance, but the testes are contained within the abdomen, in the situation of the female uterus, the scrotum still remaining empty. The female organs are yet imperfect, and the uterus with its tubes resembles the two-horned uterus of the lamb.

The placenta, of larger size, and now attached to the uterus, comprises nearly one half of the entire conception, and presented itself to my eye as a fleshy or fungous excrescence of the womb, so firmly was its gibbous portion connected all around with the uterine walls, which had now grown to greater thickness. The branches of the umbilical vessels struck into the placenta like the roots of a tree into the ground, and by their means was the conception now, for the first time, connected with the uterus.

The brain presented itself as a large and soft coagulum, full of ample vessels. The ventricles of the heart were of equal capacity, and their walls of the same thickness. In the thorax, and covered by the ribs, three cavities, nearly of the same dimensions, were perceived; of these the lowest was occupied by the lungs, which are full of blood, and of the same colour as the liver and kidneys; the middle cavity was filled by the heart and pericardium; the superior cavity, again, was possessed by the gland called the thymus, which is now of very ample size.

In the stomach there was some chyle discovered, not very different in character from the fluid in which the embryo swam. It also contained some white curdled matter, not unlike the mucous sordes which the nurse washes particularly from between the folds of the skin of new-born infants. In the upper part of the intestines there was a small quantity of excrementitious or chylous matter; the lower bowels contained meconium. In the urinary bladder there was urine, and in the gall bladder bile. The intestinum cœcum, that appendix of the colon, was empty as in the adult, and apparently superfluous, not as in the lower animals—the hog, horse, hare—constituting, as it were, another stomach. The omentum, or apron, floated over the intestines at large like a thin and transparent veil or cloud.

The kidneys at this epoch are not yet formed into a smooth and continuous rounded mass, as in the adult, but are compacted of numerous smaller masses, as we see them in the calf and sturgeon, as if there were a renal globule or nipple placed at the extremity of each division of the ureter, from the orifice of which the urine distilled. Over the kidneys two bodies, first observed by Eustachius, are discovered, very abundantly supplied with blood, so that their veins, which anatomists designate as venæ adiposæ, are not much smaller than the emulgents themselves. The liver and spleen, according to their several proportions, are equally full of blood.

I may here observe, by the way, that in every strong and healthy human fœtus we everywhere discover milk; it is particularly abundant in the thymus gland, though it is also found in the pancreas, through the whole of the mesentery, and in certain lacteal veins and glands, as it seems, situated between the divisions of the mesenteric vessels. Moreover, it can be pressed and indeed sometimes flows spontaneously from the breasts of newly-born infants, and nurses imagine that this is beneficial to the infant.

And it clearly appears that this fluid, which abounds in the ovum, is no excrementitious matter thrown off by the embryo, nothing like urine or sweat, because its relative quantity is diminished as the period of parturition approaches, when the fœtus is, of course, larger, and, as it consumes a greater quantity of nutriment, accumulates excrementitious matter more abundantly than it did in the first months of pregnancy. Let it be added, that the bladder is at this time distended with urine. For my own part I have never been able to discover that conduit for the urine, from the bladder to the umbilicus, which anatomists describe under the name of urachus; I have, on the contrary, frequently seen urine escaping by the penis, but never by any urachus, when the bladder was pressed upon with the hand.

So much for what I have observed with reference to the order of the parts in the development of the human fœtus.

In the fourth and last process the parts of the lowest state and order are produced, those, namely, that do not exist as needful to the being or to the maintenance of the individual, but only as defences against external injury, as ornaments, or as weapons of offence.

The outermost part of all, the skin, with its several appendages, cuticle, hair, wool, feathers, scales, shells, claws, hooves, and other items of the same description, may be regarded as the principal means of defence or protection. And it is well devised by Nature, who, indeed, never does aught amiss, that these parts are the last to be engendered, inasmuch as they could never be of use or avail as defences until the animal was born. The common domestic pullet is, therefore, born covered with down only, not with feathers, like certain other birds which have to be speedily prepared for flight, because it has to seek its food on foot, not on the wing, and by active running about hither and thither. In like manner the young of ducks and geese, which feed swimming, have their feathers and wings perfected at a later period than their feet and legs. It is otherwise with swallows, however, which have to fly sooner than to walk, because they feed on the wing.

The down of the pullet begins to appear after the fourteenth day, the fœtus being already perfect in all its parts. When the feathers first show themselves, they are in the guise of points within the skin, but by and by the feathers project, like plants from the ground, increase in length, become unfolded, invest the whole body, and protect it against the inclemencies of the atmosphere.

Feathers differ from quills in form, use, place of growth, and order of production. The pullet is feathered before it has any quills, for the quill-feathers only grow in the wings and tail, and also spring more deeply, from the very lowest part of the integument, or even from the periosteum, and serve essentially as instruments of motion; the feathers again arise superficially from the skin, and are everywhere present as means of protection.

"Nails, hair, horn, and the like," says Aristotle,[1] "are engendered from the skin; whence it happens that they change colour with the skin; for the white and black and particoloured are so in consequence of the colour of the skin whence they arise." In the bird, however, this is not so; for whatever the colour of the feathers, the skin is still never otherwise than of one tint, viz., white. And then the same feather or

[1] On the Generation of Animals, II. 4.

quill is frequently seen of different and often brilliant colours in different parts for the ornament of the creature.

In the human fœtus the skin and all the parts connected with it are in like manner perfected the last of all. In the earlier periods, consequently, we find neither lips, cheeks, external ears, eyelids, nor nose; and the last part to grow together is the upper lip in the course of the middle line of the body.

Man comes into the world naked and unarmed, as if Nature had destined him for a social creature, and ordained him to live under equitable laws and in peace; as if she had desired that he should be guided by reason rather than be driven by force; therefore did she endow him with understanding, and furnish him with hands, that he might himself contrive what was necessary to his clothing and protection. To those animals to which nature has given vast strength, she has also presented weapons in harmony with their powers; to those that are not thus vigorous, she has given ingenuity, cunning, and singular dexterity in avoiding injury.

Ornaments of all kinds, such as tufts, crests, combs, wattles, brilliant plumage, and the like, of which some vain creatures seem not a little proud, to say nothing of such offensive weapons as teeth, horns, spurs, and other implements employed in combat, are more frequently and remarkably conferred upon the male than the female. And it is not uninteresting to remark, that many of these ornaments or weapons are most conspicuous in the male at that epoch when the females come into season, and burn with desire of engendering. And whilst in the young they are still absent, in the aged they also fail as being no longer wanted.

Our common cock, whose pugnacious qualities are well known, so soon as he comes to his strength and is possessed of the faculty of engendering, is distinguished by his spurs, and ornamented with his comb and beautiful feathers, by which he charms his mates to the rites of Venus, and is furnished for the combat with other males, the subject of dispute being no empty or vainglorious matter, but the perpetuation of the stock in this line or in that; as if nature had intended that he who could best defend himself and his, should be preferred to others for the continuance of the kind. And indeed all animals which are better furnished with weapons of offence, and more warlike than others, fall out and fight, either in defence of their young, of their nests or dens, or of their prey; but more than all for the possession of their females. Once vanquished, they yield up possession of these, lay aside their strut and haughty demeanour, and, crestfallen and submissive, they seem to consume with grief; the victor, on the contrary, who has gained possession of the females by his prowess, exults and boastfully proclaims the glory of his conquest.

Nor is this ornamenting anything adventitious and for a season only; it is a lasting and special gift of Nature, who has not been studious to deck out animals, and especially birds only, but has also thrown an infinite variety of beautiful dyes over the lowly and insensate herbs and flowers.

EXERCISE 57. *Of certain paradoxes and problems to be considered in connexion with this subject*

Thus far have we spoken of the order of generation, whereby the differences between those creatures that are engendered by metamorphosis and those that are developed by epigenesis, as well as between those that are said to proceed from a worm and those that arise from an egg, have been made to appear. The latter are partly incorporated from a prepared matter, and are nourished and increased from a certain remaining matter; the former are incorporated from the whole of the matter present; the latter grow and are formed simultaneously, and after their birth continue to wax in size and finally attain maturity; the former increase at once, and from a grub or caterpillar grow into an aurelia, and are then produced, consummately formed, as butterflies, moths, and the like. Wherefore Aristotle, as Fabricius[1] observes: "As he assigns a sort of twofold nature to the egg, and a twofold egg in this kind, so does he assert a twofold action and a twofold animal engendered. For," he proceeds, "from the first eggs, which are the primordia of generation, a worm is constantly produced; *viz.*: from the eggs of flies, ants, bees, silkworms, &c., in which some fluid is contained, and from the whole of which fluid the worm is engendered; but from the second eggs, formed by the worms themselves, butterflies are engendered and disclosed, *viz.*: flying animals contained in a shell, or follicle, or egg, which shell giving way the winged creature escapes; precisely as Aristotle[2] has it where he speaks of the egg of the locust." Finally, whilst the higher animals produced from eggs are perfected by a succession of parts, the lower creatures that arise in this way, or that are formed by metamorphosis, are produced at one effort, as it were,

[1] Fabricius, *op. cit.*, p. 46.
[2] *History of Animals*, v. 28.

and entire. And in the same way are engendered both those creatures that are said to arise spontaneously, by chance or accident, and derive their first matter or take their origin from putrefaction, filth, excrement, dew, or the parts of plants and animals, as well as those that arise congenerately from the semen of animals. Because this is common to all living creatures, *viz.*: that they derive their origin either from semen or eggs, whether this semen have proceeded from others of the same kind, or have come by chance or something else. For what sometimes happens in art occasionally occurs in nature also; those things, namely, take place by chance or accident which otherwise are brought about by art. Of this Aristotle[1] quotes health as an illustration. And the thing is not different as respects the generation, in so far as it is from seed, of certain animals: their semina are either present by accident, or they proceed from an univocal agent of the same kind. For even in fortuitous semina there is an inherent motive principle of generation, which procreates from itself and of itself; and this is the same as that which is found in the semina of congenerative animals,—a power, to wit, of forming a living creature. But of this matter we shall have more to say shortly.

From what has just been said, however, several paradoxes present themselves for consideration. For when we see the cicatricula enlarging in the egg, the colliquament concocted and prepared, and a variety of other particulars all tending, not without foresight, to the development of the embryo, before the first rudiment or the merest particle of this is conspicuous, what should hinder us from believing that the calidum innatum and the vegetative soul of the chick are in existence before the chick itself? For what is competent to produce the effects and acts of life, except their efficient cause and principle, heat, namely, and the faculty of the vegetative soul? Therefore it would seem that the soul was not the act of the organic body possessing life *in potentia;* for we regard the chick with its appropriate form as the consequence of such an act. But where can we suppose the form and vital principle of the chick to inhere save in the chick itself? unless indeed we admitted a separation of forms and conceded a certain metamorphosis.

Now this appears most obviously where the same animal lives, as Aristotle has it, by or under a succession of forms, for example, a caterpillar, a chrysalis, a butterfly. For it is of necessity the same efficient, nutrient, and conservative principle that possesses each of these, although under different forms; unless we allow that there is one vital principle in the youth, another in the man, a third in the aged individual, or maintain that the forms of the grub and caterpillar are the same as those of the silkworm and butterfly. Aristotle has entered very fully into this subject, and we shall ourselves have more to say on it immediately.

It appears further paradoxical to maintain that the blood is produced, and moves to and fro, and is imbued with vital spirits, before any sanguiferous or locomotive organs are in existence. Neither is it less new and unheard-of to assert that sensation and motion belong to the fœtus before the brain is formed; for the fœtus moves, contracting and unfolding itself, when there is nothing more than a little limpid water in the place of the brain.

Moreover, the body is nourished and increases before the organs appropriated to digestion, viz., the stomach and abdominal viscera, are formed. Sanguification, too, which is entitled the second digestion, is perfect before the first, or chylification, which takes place in the stomach, is begun. The excrementitious products of the first and second digestions, namely, excrement in the intestines, urine and bile in the urinary and gall bladder, are contemporaneous with the existence of the concocting organs themselves. Lastly, not only is there a soul or vital principle present in the vegetative part, but even before this there is inherent mind, foresight, and understanding, which from the very commencement to the being and perfect formation of the chick, dispose and order and take up all things requisite, moulding them in the new being, with consummate art, into the form and likeness of its parents.

In reference to this subject of family likeness, we may be permitted to inquire as to the reason why the offspring should at one time bear a stronger resemblance to the father, at another to the mother, and, at a third, to progenitors, both maternal and paternal, farther removed? particularly in cases where at one bout, and at the same moment, several ova are fecundated. And this too is a remarkable fact, that virtues and vices, marks and moles, and even particular dispositions to disease are transmitted by parents to their offspring; and that while some inherit in this way, all do not. Among our poultry some are courageous, and pugnaciously inclined, and will sooner die than yield and flee from an adversary; their descendants, once or twice re-

[1] *Metaphysics*, VII. 9.

moved, however, unless they have come of equally well-bred parents, gradually lose this quality; according to the adage, "the brave are begotten by the brave." In various other species of animals, and particularly in the human family, a certain nobility of race is observed; numerous qualities, in fact, both of mind and body, are derived by hereditary descent.

I have frequently wondered how it should happen that the offspring, mixed in so many particulars of its structure or constitution, with the stamp of both parents so obviously upon it, in so many parts, should still escape all mixture in the organs of generation; that it should so uniformly prove either male or female, so very rarely an hermaphrodite.

Lastly, many things are present before they appear, and some are begun among the very first which are completed among the very last, such as the eyes, the organs of generation, and the beak.

Several doubts and difficulties have thence arisen as to the principality and relative dignity of the several members, in which they who are fond of such things have displayed their ingenuity. Among the number: whether the heart gives life and virtue to the blood; or, rather, the blood to the heart. Whether the blood be extant for the sake of the body as matter, nourishment, and instrument; or, on the contrary, the body and its parts are the cause of the blood, and constituted for the sake of the vital principle which especially inheres in it. In like manner, whether the auricles or the ventricles of the heart are the chief, the auricles being the first to live and pulsate, the last to die. Further, whether the left ventricle, which in man is of greater length, and is also surrounded with thicker and more fleshy walls, and is regarded as the source of the spirits, be hotter, more spiritous, excitable, and excellent, than the right, which contains a larger quantity of blood, and is the last to become unstrung by death; in which the blood of the dying accumulates, congeals, and is deprived of life and spirit; to which, moreover, as to a fountain head, the first umbilical veins bring their blood, and from which they themselves derive their origin.

So much appears from careful observation of the order observed in the production of the parts, and certain other points that follow as deductions from these, and do not a little militate against the commonly received physiological doctrines, viz.: since it is manifest that sensation and motion exist before the brain, all sensation and motion do not proceed from the brain; from our history it is clearly ascertained that sense and movement inhere in the very first drop of blood produced in the egg, before there is a vestige of the body. The first scaffolding or rudiment of the body, too, which we have said is merely mucilaginous, before any of the extremities are visible, and when the brain is nothing more than a limpid fluid, if lightly pricked, will move obscurely, will contract and twist itself like a worm or caterpillar, so that it is very evidently possessed of sensation.

There are yet other arguments deduced from sense and motion whence we should infer that the brain was not so much the first principle of the body, in the way the medical writers maintain, as the heart, agreeably to Aristotle's view.

The motions and actions which physicians style *natural*, because they take place involuntarily, and we can neither prevent nor moderate, accelerate nor retard them by our will, and they therefore do not depend on the brain, still do not occur entirely without causing sensation, but proclaim themselves subject to sense, inasmuch as they are aroused, called forth, and changed thereby. When the heart, for example, is affected with palpitation, tremor, lipothymia, syncope, and with great variety in the extent, rapidity, and order or rhythm of its pulsations, we do not hesitate to ascribe these to morbific causes implicating, deranging its sensation. For whatever by its divers movements strives against irritations and troubles must necessarily be endowed with sensation.

The stomach and bowels, disturbed by the presence of vitiated humours, are affected with ructus, flatus, vomiting, and diarrhœa; and as it lies not in our power either to provoke or to restrain their motions, neither are we aware of any sensation dependent on the brain which should arouse the parts in question to motions of the kind.

It is truly wonderful to observe the effect of taking a solution of antimony, which we neither distinguish by the taste, nor find any inconvenience from, whether in the swallowing or the rejection. Nevertheless there is a certain discriminating sense in the stomach which distinguishes what is hurtful from what is useful, and by which vomiting is induced.

Nay, the flesh itself readily distinguishes a poisoned wound from one that is not poisoned, and on receipt of the former contracts and condenses itself, whereby phlegmonous tumours are produced, as we find in connexion with the stings of bees, gnats, and spiders.

I have myself, for experiment's sake, occasionally pricked my hand with a clean needle, and then having rubbed the same needle on the teeth of a spider, I have pricked my hand in another place. I could not by my simple sensation perceive any difference between the two punctures; nevertheless there was a capacity in the skin to distinguish the one from the other; for the part pricked with the envenomed needle immediately contracted into a tubercle, and by and by became red, and hot, and inflamed, as if it collected and girded itself up for a contest with the poison for its overthrow.

The sensations which accompany affections of the uterus, such as twisting, decubitus, prolapse, ascent, suffocation, &c., and other inconveniences and irritations, do not depend on the brain or on common sensation; yet neither are these to be presumed as happening without all consciousness. For that which is wholly without sense is not seen to be irritated by any means, neither can it be stimulated to motion or action of any kind. Nor have we any other means of distinguishing between an animate and sentient thing and one that is dead and senseless than the motion excited by some other irritating cause or thing, which as it incessantly follows, so does it also argue sensation.

But we shall have an opportunity of speaking further of this matter when we discuss the actions and uses of the brain. Respect for our predecessors and for antiquity at large inclines us to defend their conclusions to the extent that love of truth will allow. Nor do I think it becoming in us to neglect and make little of their labours and conclusions who bore the torch that has lighted us to the shrine of philosophy. I am, therefore, of opinion that we should conclude in this way: we have consciousness in ourselves of five principal senses, by which we judge of external objects; but we do not feel with the same sense by means of which we are conscious that we feel—seeing with our eyes, we still do not know by them that we see, but by another sense or sensitive organ, namely, the internal common sensation or common sensorium, by which we examine those things that reach us through each of the external sensoria, and distinguish that which is white from that which is sweet or hard. Now this sensorium commune to which the species or impressions of all the external instruments of sensation are referred, is obviously the brain, which along with its nerves and the external organs annexed, is held and esteemed to be the adequate instrument of sensation. And this brain is like a sensitive root to which a variety of fibres tend, one of which sees, another hears, a third touches, and a fourth and a fifth smell and taste.

But as there are some actions and motions the government or direction of which is not dependent on the brain, and which are therefore called *natural*, so also is it to be concluded that there is a certain sense or form of touch which is not referred to the common sensorium, nor in any way communicated to the brain, so that we do not perceive by this sense that we feel; but, as happens to those who are deranged in mind, or who are agitated to such a degree by violent passion that they feel no pain, and pay no regard to the impressions made on their senses, so must we believe it to be with this sense, which we therefore distinguish from the proper animal sense. Now such a sense do we observe in zoophytes or plant-animals, in sponges, the sensitive plant, &c.

Wherefore, as many animals are endowed with both sense and motion without having a common sensorium or brain, such as earthworms, caterpillars of various kinds, chrysalides, &c., so also do certain natural actions take place in the embryo and even in ourselves without the agency of the brain, and a certain sensation takes place without consciousness. And as medical writers teach that the natural differ from the animal actions, so by parity of reason does the natural sense of touch differ from the animal sense of touch—it constitutes, in a word, another species of touch; and whilst the one is communicated to the common sensorium, the other is not so communicated.

Further, it is one thing for a muscle to be contracted and moved, and another for it by regulated contractions and relaxations to perform any movement, such as progression or prehension. The muscles or organs of motion, when affected with spasms or convulsions from an irritating cause, are assuredly moved no otherwise than the decapitated cock or hen, which is agitated with many convulsive movements of its legs and wings, but all confused and without a purpose, because the controlling power of the brain has been taken away—common sensation has disappeared, under the controlling influence of which these motions were formerly coordinated to progression by walking or to flight.

We therefore conceive the fact to be that all the natural motions proceed from the power of the heart, and depend on it; the spontaneous motions, however, and those that complete any motion which physicians entitle an animal motion, cannot be performed without the controlling influence of the brain and common sensation. For inasmuch as by this common sensation we are conscious of our perceptions, so also are we conscious that we move, and this whether the motion be regular or otherwise.

We have an excellent example of both of these kinds of motion in respiration. For the lungs, like the heart, are continually carried upwards and downwards by a natural movement, and are excited by any irritation to coughing and more frequent action; but they cannot form and regulate the voice, nor can singing be executed, without the assistance, and in some sort the command, of the sensorium commune.

But these matters will be more fully handled when we come to speak of the actions and uses of the brain, and to consider the vital principle or soul. So much we have thought fit to say by the way, that we might show the respect in which we hold our illustrious teachers, and our anxiety to carry them along with us in our labours.

EXERCISE 58. *Of the nutrition of the chick* IN OVO

That the authority of the ancients is not to be rashly thrown off appears in this: it was formerly current doctrine, though many at the present day, Fabricius[1] among the number, reject it as a delusion and a foolish idea, that the embryo sucked in its mother's womb. This idea nevertheless had Democritus, Epicurus, and Hippocrates for its supporters; and the father of physic contends for it on two principal grounds: "Unless the fœtus sucked," he says,[2] "how should excrements be formed? or how should it know how to suck immediately after it is born?"

Now, whilst in other instances it is customary to swear by the bare statement of this ancient and most distinguished writer, his *ipse dixit* (αὐτὸς ἔφη) sufficing, because he here makes an assertion contrary to the commonly received opinion, Fabricius not only denies the statement, but spurns the arguments in support of his conclusion. We, however, leave it to the judgment of skilful anatomists and learned physicians to say whether our observations on the generation of animals do not proclaim this opinion of Hippocrates to be not merely probable, but even necessary.

All admit that the fœtus *in utero* swims in the midst of an abundance of a watery fluid, which in our history of the egg we have spoken of as the colliquament, this fluid modern authorities

regard as the sweat and excrement of the fœtus, and ascribe as its principal use the protection of the uterus against injury from the fœtus during any violent motion of the mother in running or leaping; and, on the other hand, the defence of the fœtus from injury through contact with neighbouring bones, or an external cause, particularly during the period when its limbs are still delicate and weak.

Fabricius ascribes additional uses to this fluid, viz., "that it may moisten and lubricate all the parts around, and dispose the neck of the uterus to facile and speedy dilatation to the utmost extent; and all this is not less assisted by that thick, white, excrementitious matter of the third digestion, neglected by the ancients, which is unctuous and oily, and further prevents the sweat, which may occasionally be secreted sharp and salt in quality, from excoriating the tender body of the fœtus."[3]

I readily acknowledge all the uses indicated, viz., that the tender fœtus may be secure against all sudden and violent movements of the mother, that he may ride safe in the "bat's wings," as they are called, and, surrounded with an abundance of water, that he may escape coming into contact with his mother's sides, being restrained by the retinacular fluid on either hand: this circumambient fluid must certainly protect the body which floats in its middle from all external injury. But, as in many other instances, my observations compel me here to be of a different opinion from Fabricius. In the first place, I am by no means satisfied that this fluid is the sweat of the fœtus. And then I do not believe that the fluid serves those important purposes in parturition which he indicates; and much less that it is ever so sharp and saline that an unctuous covering was requisite to protect the fœtus from its erosive effects, particularly in those cases where there is already a thick covering of wool, or hair, or feathers. The fluid, in fact, has a pleasant taste, like that of watery milk, so that almost all viviparous animals lap it up, and cleanse their new-born progeny by licking them with their tongues, greedily swallowing the fluid, though none of them was ever seen to touch any of the excrements of their young.

Fabricius spoke of this fluid as saline and acrimonious, because he believed it to be sweat. But what inconvenience, I beseech you, were sweat to the chick, already covered with its feathers?—if indeed anyone ever saw a chicken sweat. Nor do I think he could have said that the use of this fluid in the egg was, by its mois-

---

[1] *De form. fœtu*, pp. 19 and 134.
[2] *De carn. et de nat. pueri.*
[3] *Op. cit.*, p. 137.

tening and lubrifying qualities, to facilitate the birth of the chick; for the drier and older the shell of the egg, the more friable and fragile it becomes. Finally, were it the sweat of the embryo, or fœtus, it ought to be most abundant nearest the period of parturition: the larger the fœtus and the more food it consumes, the more sweat must it necessarily secrete. But shortly before the exclusion of the chick from the egg, namely, about the nineteenth or twentieth day, there is none of the fluid to be seen, because as the chick grows it is gradually taken up; so that if the thing be rightly viewed, the fluid in question ought rather to be regarded as nutriment than as excrement, particularly as he has said that the chick in the egg breathes, and lets its chirping be heard, which it certainly would not do were it surrounded with water.

But all experienced obstetricians know that the watery fluid of the secundines is of no great use either in lubricating the parts or in facilitating the progress of parturition in the way Fabricius would have it. For the parts surrounding the vulva are relaxed of themselves, and by a kind of proper maturity at the full time, without any assistance from the uterine waters; and particularly those that offer the greatest obstacles to the advance of the fœtus, namely, the ossa pubis and the os coccygis, to which the attention of the midwife is especially directed in assisting the woman in labour. For midwives are much less studious to anoint the soft parts with any emollient salves, lest they tear, than careful to pull the os coccygis outwards, a business in which, if the fingers do not suffice, they have recourse to the uterine speculum, applied by the hand of the experienced surgeon, an instrument having three sides or branches, one of which bearing on the os coccygis, the other two on the ossa pubis, the business of distension is effected by force. For the head of the child that is about to be born, when it makes the turn, and is forced downwards, relaxes and opens the os uteri; but coming down he will stick fast, and scarcely be brought forth if he chance to abut upon the point of the os coccygis, and immediately the case is one not without danger both to the child and mother. But nature's intention was obviously to relax and soften all the parts concerned; and the attendant knows that when the uterine orifice is discovered in a soft and lax condition, by the finger introduced, it is an infallible sign that the delivery is at hand even though the waters have not broken. Indeed—and I do not speak without experience—if anything remains in the uterus for expulsion, either after delivery or at any other time, and the uterus makes efforts to get rid of it, the orifice both descends lower and is found soft and relaxed. If the uterine orifice recedes, and is found somewhat hard after delivery, it is a sign of the woman's restoration to health.

Taught by like experience, I assert that the ossa pubis frequently become loosened during labour, their cartilaginous connexion being softened, and the whole hypogastric region enlarged in the most miraculous manner, not, however, by any pouring out of watery fluids, but spontaneously, as ripe fruit gapes that the included seed may find an exit. The degree in which the coccyx may impede delivery, however, is apparent among quadrupeds having tails, which can neither bring forth, nor even discharge the excrement from their bowels, unless the tail be raised; if you but depress the tail with your hand, you prevent the exit of the dung.

Moreover, the most natural labour of all is held to be that in which the fœtus and afterbirth, the waters inclusive, or the ovum, is expelled entire. Now if the membranes have not given way, and the waters have not escaped, it comes to pass that the surrounding parts are more than usually distended and dilated by the labour pains, in consequence, to wit, of the entire and tense state of the membranes, by which it happens that the fœtus is produced more speedily, and with a less amount of effort, although with more suffering to the mother. In cases of this kind we have known women who were suffering much in their travail in consequence of the too great distension, immensely relieved by the rupture of the membranes and the sudden escape of the waters, the laceration being effected either with the nails of the midwife or the use of a pair of forceps.

Experienced midwives are further aware that if the waters come away before the orifice of the uterus is duly dilated, the woman is apt to have a lingering time and a more difficult delivery, contrary to Fabricius's notion of the waters having such paramount influence in softening and lubricating the parts.

Moreover, that the fluid which we have called colliquament is not the sweat of the fœtus is made obvious, both from the history of the egg and of the uterogestation of other animals: it is present before the fœtus is formed in any way, before there is a trace of it to be seen; and whilst it is still extremely small and entirely gelatinous, the quantity of water present is very great, so that it seems plainly impossible that so small a body should produce such a mass of excrementitious fluid.

It happens besides that the ramifications of the umbilical veins are distributed over and terminate upon the membrane which incloses this fluid, precisely as on the membranes of the albumen and yelk of the egg, a circumstance from which, and the thing being viewed as it is in fact, it appears to be clearly proclaimed that this fluid is rather to be regarded as food than as excrement.

To me, therefore, the opinion of Hippocrates appears more probable than that of Fabricius and other anatomists, who look on this liquid as sweat, and believe that it must prove detrimental to the fœtus. I am disposed, I say, to believe that the fluid with which the fœtus is surrounded may serve it for nourishment; that the thinner and purer portions of it, taken up by the umbilical veins, may serve for the constitution and increase of the first formed parts of the embryo; and that from the remainder or the milk, taken into the mouth by suction, passed on to the stomach by the act of deglutition, and there digested or chylified, and finally absorbed by the mesenteric veins, the new being continues to grow and be nourished. I am the more disposed to take this view from certain not impertinent arguments, which I shall proceed to state.

As soon as the embryo acquires a certain degree of perfection it moves its extremities, and begins to prove the actions of the organs destined to locomotion. Now I have seen the chick *in ovo*, surrounded with liquid, opening its mouth, and any fluid that thus gained access to the fauces must needs have been swallowed; for it is certain that whatever passes the root of the tongue and gains the top of the œsophagus, cannot be rejected by any animal with a less effort than that of vomiting. This fact is acted upon every day by veterinary practitioners, who in administering medicated drinks and pills or boluses to cattle, seize the tongue, and having put the article upon its root beyond the protuberant part, the animal cannot do otherwise than swallow it. And if we make the experiment ourselves, we find that a pill carried between the finger and thumb as far as the root of the tongue and there dropped, immediately the action of deglutition is excited, and unless vomiting be produced the pill is taken down. If the embryo swimming in the fluid in question, then, do but open his mouth, it is absolutely necessary that the fluid must reach the

fauces; and if the creature then move other muscles, wherefore should we not believe that he also uses his throat in its appropriate office and swallows the fluid?

It is further quite certain that in the crop of the chick—and the same thing occurs in reference to the stomach of other embryos—there is a certain matter having a colour, taste, and consistence, very similar to that of the liquid mentioned, and some of it in the stomach digested to a certain extent, like coagulated milk; and further, whilst we discover a kind of chyle in the upper intestines, we find the lower bowels full of stercoraceous excrements. In like manner we perceive the large intestines of the fœtuses of viviparous animals to contain excrements of the same description as those that distend them when they feed on milk. In the sheep and other bisulcated animals we even find scybala.

Towards the seventeenth day we find dung very obviously near the anus of the chick; and shortly before the extrusion I have seen the same matter expelled and contained within the membranes. Volcher Coiter, a careful and experienced dissector, states that he has observed the same thing.

Wherefore should we doubt, then, that the fœtus *in utero* sucks, and that chylopoiesis goes on in its stomach, when we find present both the principles and the recrementitious products of digestion?

And then, when we find the bladder both of the bile and the urine full of those excrements of the second digestion, wherefore should we not conclude that the first digestion, or chylopoiesis, has preceded?

The embryo, therefore, seeks for and sucks in nourishment by the mouth; and you will readily believe that he does so if you rip him from his mother's womb and instantly put a finger in his mouth; which Hippocrates thinks he would not seize had he not previously sucked whilst in the womb. For we are accustomed to see young infants trying various motions, making experiments, as it were, approaching everything, moving their limbs, attempting to walk, and uttering sounds, acts all of which when taught by repeated experience, they afterwards come to execute with readiness and precision. But the fœtus so soon as it is born, aye, before it is born, will suck; doubtless as it had done in the uterus long before. For I have found by experience that the child delayed in the birth, and before it has cried or breathed, will seize and suck a finger put into its mouth. A new-born infant, indeed, is more expert at sucking than an adult, or than he is himself if he have but lost the habit for a few days. For the infant does not suck by squeezing the nipple with his lips as we should, and by suction in the common acceptation; he rather seems as if he would swallow the nipple, drawing it wholly into his throat, and with the aid of his tongue and palate, and chewing, as it were, he milks his mother with more art and dexterity than an adult could practise. He therefore appears to have learned that by long custom, and before he saw the light, which we know full well he unlearns by a very brief discontinuance.

These and other observations of the same kind make it extremely probable that the chick *in ovo* is nourished in a twofold manner, namely, by the umbilical and by the mesenteric veins. By the former he imbibes a nourishment that is well nigh perfectly prepared, whence the first-formed parts are engendered and augmented; by the latter he receives chyle for the structure and growth of the other remaining parts.

But the reason is perhaps obscure why the same agent should perform the work of nutrition by means of the same matter in a variety of ways, since nature does nothing in vain. We shall therefore endeavour to explain this.

What is taken up by the umbilical veins is the purer and more limpid part; and the rest of the colliquament in which the fœtus swims is like crude milk, or milk deprived of its purer portion. The purer part does not require any of that ulterior concoction of which the remainder stands in need; and to undergo which it is taken into the stomach, where it is transmuted into chyle. Similar to this is the crude and watery milk which is found in the breasts immediately after parturition. The liquefied albumen of the egg, and the crude or watery milk of the mammæ seem to have in all respects the same colour, taste, and consistence. For the first flow of milk is serous and watery, and women are wont to express water from their breasts before the milk comes white, concocted, and perfect.

Just as the colliquament found in the crop of the chick is a kind of crude milk, whilst the same fluid discovered in the stomach is concocted, white, and curdled; so in viviparous animals, before the milk is concocted in the mammæ, a kind of dew and colliquament makes its appearance there, and the colliquament only puts on the semblance of milk after it has undergone concoction in the stomach. And so it happens, in Aristotle's opinion, that the first and most essential parts are formed out of the purer and thinner portion of the colliquament, and are increased by the remaining more indifferent portion after it has undergone elaboration by a new digestion in the stomach. In the same way are the other less important parts developed and maintained. Thus has nature, like a fond and indulgent mother, been sedulous rather to provide superfluity, than to suffer any scarcity of things necessary. Or it might be said to be in conformity with reason to suppose that the fœtus, now grown more perfect, should also be nourished in a more perfect manner, by the mouth, to wit, and by a more perfect kind of aliment, rendered purer by having undergone the two antecedent digestions and been thereby freed from the two kinds of excrementitious matter. In the beginning and early stages, nourished by the ramifications of the umbilical veins, it leads in some sort the life of a plant; the body is then crude, white, and imperfect; like plants, too, it is motionless and impassive. As soon, however, as it begins by the mouth to partake of the same aliment further elaborated, as if feeling a diviner influence, boasting a higher grade of vegetative existence, the gelatinous mass of the body is changed into flesh, the organs of motion are distinguished, the spirits are perfected, and motion begins; nor is it any longer nourished like a vegetable, by the roots, but, living the life of an animal, it is supported by the mouth.

EXERCISE 59. *Of the uses of the entire egg*

Having now gone through the several changes and processes which must take place in the hen's egg, in order that it may produce a chick, Fabricius proceeds to consider the uses of the egg at large, and of its various parts; nor does he restrict himself to the hen's egg, but condescends upon eggs in general. Among other things he inquires: wherefore some eggs are heterogeneous and composed of different elements; and others are homogeneous and similar? such as the eggs of insects, and those creatures that are engendered from the whole egg, *viz.*, by metamorphosis, and are not engendered from one part of the egg, and nourished by another part.

I have no purpose myself of entering on a general consideration of eggs of all kinds and descriptions; I have not yet given the history of all, but only of the hen's egg; so that I shall here limit myself to a survey of the uses of the common hen's egg, keeping in view the end of all its actions, which is nothing less than the production and completion of a new being, as Fabricius has well and truly said.[1]

Among the points having reference to the whole egg, Fabricius speaks of the form, dimensions, and number of eggs. "The figure of the egg is round," he says,[2] "in order that the mass of the chick may be stowed in the smallest possible space; for the same cause that God made the world round, namely, that it might embrace all things; and it is from this, as Galen conceives, that this figure is always felt to be most agreeable and consonant to nature. Further, as it has no angles exposed to injury from without, it is, therefore, the safest figure, and the one best adapted to effect the exclusion of the chick." It had been well after such a preface to have assigned satisfactory causes why hen's eggs are not spherical, like the eggs of fishes, worms and frogs, but oblong and pointed; to have shown what there is in them which hinders the presumed perfection of figure. Now to me the form of the egg has never appeared to have aught to do with the engenderment of the chick, but to be a mere accident; and to this conclusion I come the rather when I see such diversities in the shape of the eggs of different hens. They vary, in short, in conformity with the variety that obtains among the uteri of different fowls, in which, as in moulds, they receive their form.

Aristotle,[3] indeed, says that the longer-shaped eggs produce females, the rounder males. I have not made any experiments upon this point myself. But Pliny[4] asserts, in opposition to Aristotle, that the rounder eggs produce females, the others males. Now were there any certainty in such statements, either in one way or the other, some hens would always produce males, others always females, inasmuch as the eggs of the same hen are in many instances always of one figure, namely, either much rounded or acutely pointed. Horace[5] thought that the oblong eggs, as being the more perfect and better concocted, and therefore the better flavoured, produced males.

I willingly pass by the reasons alleged by Fabricius for the form of eggs, as being all irrelevant.

The size of an egg appears to bear a proportion to the size of the foetus produced from it;

large hens, too, certainly lay large eggs. The crocodile, however, lays eggs the size of those of the goose; nor does any animal attain to larger dimensions from a smaller beginning. It would seem, too, that the size of the egg and the quantity of matter it contained had some connexion with its fecundity, inasmuch as the very small eggs called centenines are all barren.

The number of eggs serves the same end as abundance of conceptions among viviparous animals—they secure the perpetuity of the species. Nature appears to have been particularly careful in providing a numerous offspring to those animals which, by reason of their pusillanimity or bodily weakness, hardly defend themselves against the attacks of others; she has counterbalanced the shortness of their own lives by the number of their progeny. "Nature," says Pliny,[6] "has made the timid tribes among birds more fruitful than the bold ones." All generation, as it is instituted by nature for the sake of perpetuating species, so does it occur more frequently among those that are shorter-lived and more obnoxious to external injury lest their race should fail. Birds that are of stronger make, that prey upon other creatures, and therefore live more securely and for longer terms scarcely lay more than two eggs once a year. Pigeons, turtle and ring-doves, that lay but a couple of eggs, make up for the smallness of the number by the frequency of laying, for they will produce young as often as ten times in the course of a year. They, therefore, engender greatly although they do not produce many at a time.

EXERCISE 60. *Of the uses of the yelk and albumen*

"An egg," says Fabricius,[7] "properly so called, is composed of many parts, because it is the organ of the engenderer, and Galen everywhere insists on the constitution of an organ as implying multiplicity of parts." But this view leads us to ask whether every egg must not be heterogeneous, seeing that every egg is organic? And every egg, indeed, even that of the fish and insect, appears to be composed of several different parts—membranes, coverings, defences; nor is the included matter by any means without diversity of constitution in different parts.

Fabricius agrees further, and correctly, with Galen, when he says: "Some parts of the egg are the chief instruments of the actions that take place in it, others may be styled necessary —without them no actions could take place;

---

[1] *Loc. cit.*, p. 50.
[2] *De usu part.*, x.
[3] *History of Animals*, VI. 2.
[4] *Hist. nat.*, x. 52.
[5] Pliny, *ibid.*

[6] *Ibid.*
[7] *Op. sup. cit.*, p. 47.

others exist that the action which takes place may be better performed; others, in fine, are destined for the safety and preservation of all of these."[1] But he is mistaken when he says: "If we speak of the prime action, which is the generation of the chick, the chief cause of this is the semen and the chalazæ, these two being the prime cause of the generation of the chick, the semen being the efficient cause, the chalaza the matter only." Now according to the opinion of Aristotle, it must be allowed that that which generates is included in the egg; but Fabricius denies that the semen of the cock is contained in the egg.

Nor does he wander less wide of the mark when he speaks of the chalazæ as the matter from which, by the influence of the semen galli, the chick is incorporated. For the chick is not produced either from one or the other, nor yet from both of the chalazæ, as we have shown in our history. Neither is the generation of the chick effected by metamorphosis, nor by any new form assumed and division effected in the chalazæ, but by epigenesis, in the manner already explained. Nor are the chalazæ especially fecundated by the semen of the male bird, but the cicatricula rather, or the part which we have called the eye of the egg, from which, when it enlarges, the colliquament is produced, in and from which, subsequently, the blood, the veins, and the pulsating vesicles proceed, after which the whole body is gradually formed. Moreover, on his own admission, the semen of the cock never enters the uterus of the hen, and yet it fecundates not only the eggs that are already formed, but others that are yet to be produced.

Fabricius refers the albumen and vitellus to the second action of the egg, which is the nutrition and growth of the chick. "The vitellus and albumen," he says,[2] "are in quantity commensurate with the perfect performance of this action, and with the due development and growth of the chick. The shell and membranes are, therefore, the safety of the whole of the egg as well as the security of its action. But the veins and arteries which carry nourishment are organs without which the action of the egg, in other words, the growth and nutrition of the chick, would not take place." It is uncertain, however, whether the umbilical vessels of the embryo or the veins and arteries of the mother, whence the egg is increased, are here to be understood. For a like reason the uterus and in-

cubation ought to be referred to this last class of actions.

We have to do, then, with the two fluids of the egg, the albumen and the vitellus; for these, before all the other parts, are formed for the use of the embryo, and in them is the second action of the egg especially conspicuous.

The egg of the common hen is of two colours internally, and consists of two fluids, severally distinct, separated by membranes, and in all probability of different natures, and therefore having different ends to serve, inasmuch as they are distinguished by different extensions of the umbilical veins, one of them proceeding to the white, another to the yelk. "The yelk and white of the egg are of opposite natures," says Aristotle,[3] "not only in colour, but also in power. For the yelk is congealed by cold; the white is not congealed, but is rather liquefied; on the contrary, the white is coagulated by heat, the yelk is not coagulated, but remains soft, unless it be overdone, and is more condensed and dried by boiling than by roasting." The vitellus getting heated during incubation, is rendered more moist; for it becomes like melted wax or tallow, whereby it also takes up more room. For as the embryo grows, the albumen is gradually taken up and becomes inspissated; but the yelk, even when the fœtus has attained perfection; appears scarcely to have diminished in size; it is only more diffluent and moist, even when the fœtus begins to have its abdomen closed in.

Aristotle gives the following reason for the diversity: "Since the bird cannot perfect her offspring within herself, she produces it along with the aliment needful to its growth in the egg. Viviparous animals again prepare the food (milk) in another part of their body, namely, the breasts. Now nature has done the same thing in the egg; but otherwise than as is generally presumed, and as Alcmæon Crotoniates states it, for it is not the albumen but the vitellus which is the milk of the egg."[4]

For as the fœtus of a viviparous animal draws its nourishment from the uterus whilst it is connected with its mother, like a plant by its roots from the earth; but after birth, and when it has escaped from the womb, sucks milk from the breast, and thereby continues to wax in size and strength, the chick finds the analogue of both kinds of food in the egg. So that whilst in viviparous animals the uterus exists within the parent, in oviparous the parent may rather be

[1] *Ibid.*, p. 48.
[2] *Ibid.*, p. 48.

[3] *History of Animals*, VII. 2.
[4] *On the Generation of Animals*, III. 2.

said to exist within the uterus (the egg). For the egg is a kind of exposed and detached uterus, and in it are included in some sort vicarious mammæ. The chick in the egg, I say, is first nourished by albumen, but afterwards, when this is consumed, by the yelk or by milk. The umbilical vascular connexion with the albumen, therefore, when this fluid is used up, withers and is interrupted when the abdomen comes to be closed, and before the period of exclusion arrives, so that it leaves no trace of its existence behind it: in viviparous animals, on the contrary, the umbilical cord is permanent in all its parts up to the moment of birth. The other canal that extends to the vitellus, however, is taken up along with this matter into the abdomen, where being stored, it serves for the support of the delicate fœtus until its beak has acquired firmness enough to seize and bruise its food, and its stomach strength sufficient to comminute and digest it; just as the young of the viviparous animal lives upon milk from the mammæ of its mother, until it is provided with teeth by which it can masticate harder food. For the vitellus is as milk to the chick, as has been already said; and the bird's egg, as it stands in lieu both of uterus and mammæ, is furnished with two fluids of different colours, the white and the yelk.

All admit this distinction of fluids. But I, as I have already said, distinguish two albumens in the egg, kept separate by an interposed membrane, the more external of which embraces the other within it, in the same way as the yelk is surrounded by the albumen in general. I have also insisted on the diverse nature of these albumens; distinguished both by situation and their surrounding membranes, they seem in like manner calculated for different uses. Both, however, are there for ends of nutrition, the outermost, as that to which the branches of the umbilical veins are earliest distributed, being first consumed, and then the inner and thicker portion; last of all the vitellus is attacked, and by it is the chick nourished, not only till it escapes from the shell but for some time afterwards.

But upon this point we shall have more to say below, when we come to speak of the manner in which the fœtuses of viviparous animals are developed, and at the same time demonstrate that these all derive their origin from eggs, and live by a twofold albuminous food in the womb. One of these is thinner, and contained within the ovum or conception; the other is obtained by the umbilical vessels from the placenta and uterine cotyledons. The fluid of the ovum resembles a dilute albumen in colour and consistence; it is a sluggish, pellucid liquid, in all respects similar to that which we have called the colliquament of the egg, in which the embryo swims, and on which it feeds by the mouth. The fluid which the fœtus obtains from the uterine placenta by the aid of the umbilical vessels is more dense and mucaginous, like the inspissated albumen. Whence it clearly appears that the fœtus *in utero* is no more nourished by its parent's blood than is the suckling afterwards, or the chick *in ovo;* but that it is nourished by an albuminous matter concocted in the placenta, and not unlike white of egg.

Nor is the contemplation of the Divine Providence less useful than delightful when we see Nature, in her work of evolving the fœtus, furnishing it with sustenance adapted to its varying ages and powers, now more easy, by and by more difficult of digestion. For as the fœtus acquires greater powers of digesting, so is it supplied with food that is successively thicker and harder. And the same thing may be observed in the milk of animals generally: when the young creature first sees the light the milk is thinner and more easy of concoction; but in the course of time, and with increased strength in the suckling, it becomes thicker, and is more abundantly stored with caseous matter. Those flabby and delicate women, therefore, who do not nurse their own children, but give them up to the breast of another, consult their health indifferently; for mercenary nurses being for the major part of more robust and hardy frames, and their milk consequently thicker, more caseous, and difficult of digestion, it frequently happens that milk of this kind given to the infants of such parents, particularly during the time of teething, is not well borne, but gives rise to crudities and diarrhœas, to griping, vomiting, fever, epilepsy, and other formidable diseases of the like nature.

What Fabricius says,[1] and strives to bolster up by certain reasonings, of the chalazæ standing for the matter of the chick, we have already thrown out in our history, and at the same time have made it manifest that the substance of the chick and its first rudiments were produced whilst the chalazæ were still entire and unchanged, and in a totally different situation. Neither is it true, as he states, "that the chalazæ, rendered fruitful by the semen of the cock, stand in the place of seed, and that from them the chick is produced."[2] Nor are the cha-

[1] *Op. cit.,* p. 34.
[2] *Op. cit.,* p. 54.

lazæ, as he will have it, "in colour, substance, and bodily properties so like seed, or bear so strong a resemblance to the embryo in a boiled egg, that we may rightly conceive all the parts designated spermatic to be thence engendered."[1] I am rather of opinion that the fluid which we have called colliquament, or the thinner portion of the albumen liquefied and concocted, is to be regarded as of the nature of seed, and, if the testimony of our eyes is to be credited, as a substitute for it.

The observation of this venerable old man is therefore unnecessary when he says, "As the whole animal body is made up of two substances very different from one another, and even of opposite natures, viz., hot and cold—among the hot parts being included all those that are full of blood and of a red colour; among the cold all those that are exsanguine and white—these two orders of parts doubtless require a different and yet a like nourishment, if it be true that we are nourished by the same things of which we are made. The spermatic, white, and cold parts, therefore, require white and cold nourishment; the sanguineous, red, and hot parts, again, demand nourishment that is red and hot. And so is the cold white of the egg properly held to nourish the cold and white parts of the chick, and the hot and sanguine yelk regarded as a substitute for the hot and purple blood. In this way do all the animal parts obtain nourishment suitable and convenient for them."[2] Now we by no means admit that the two fluids or matters of the egg are there as appropriate means of nourishment for different orders of parts. For we have already said that the heart, lungs, kidneys, liver, spleen, muscles, bones, ligaments, &c., &c., were all alike and indiscriminately white and bloodless on their first formation.

Further, on the preceding view of Fabricius it would follow that the heart, lungs, liver, spleen, &c., were not spermatic parts, did not originate from the seed (which he, however, will by no means allow), inasmuch as they too are by and by nourished by the blood and grow out of it; for every part is both formed and nourished by the same means, and nutrition is nothing more than the substitution of a like matter in the room of that which is lost.

Nor would he find less difficulty in answering the question: how it happens that when the albumen in the egg is all consumed, the cold and white parts, such as the bones, ligaments,

brain, spinal marrow, &c., continue to be nourished and to grow by means of the vitellus? which to these must be nourishment as inappropriate as albumen to the hot, red, and sanguine parts.

Adopting the views commented on, indeed, we should be compelled to admit that the hot and sanguineous parts were the last to be produced: the flesh after the bones; the liver, spleen, and lungs after the ligaments and intestinal canal; and further, that the cold parts of the chick must come together and attain maturity, the white being all the while consumed, and the hot parts be engendered subsequently, when the vitellus fails and ceases from nourishing them; and then it would be certain that all the parts could not take their rise in and be constituted out of the same clear liquid. All such conclusions, however, are refuted by simple ocular inspection.

I add another argument to those already supplied: the eggs of cartilaginous fishes—skates, the dog-fish, &c.—are of two colours; their yelks are of a good deep colour; nevertheless, all the parts of these fishes are white, bloodless, and cold, not even excepting the substance of their liver. On the contrary, I have seen a certain breed of fowls of large size, their feathers lblack, their flesh well supplied with blood, their iver red; yet were the yelks of the eggs of these fowls—fruitful eggs—of the palest shade of yellow, not deeper than the tint of ripe barley straw.

Fabricius, however, seems in these words to retract all he has but just said: "There is one thing to be particularly wondered at both in the yelk and the white, viz., that neither of them being blood, they are still so near to the nature of blood that they in fact differ but very slightly from it—there is but little wanting to constitute either of them blood; so that little labour and a very slight concoction suffice to effect the change. The veins and arteries distributed to the membranes of both the white and yelk are consequently seen replete with blood at all times; the white and yelk nevertheless continuing possessed of their own proper nature, though either, so soon as it is imbibed by the vessels, is changed into blood, so closely do they approach in constitution to this fluid."[3]

But if it be matter of certainty that blood exists no less in the vessels distributed to the albumen than in those sent to the vitellus, and that both of these fluids are so closely allied to blood in their nature, and turn into blood so

[1] Ibid., p. 57.
[2] Ibid., p. 55.
[3] Op. cit., p. 55.

readily; who, I beseech you, will doubt that the blood, and all the parts which are styled sanguineous, are nourished and increased through the albumen as well as the vitellus?

Our author, however, soon contrives a subterfuge from this conclusion: "Although all this be true," he says,[1] "still must we conceive that the matter which is imbibed by the veins from the yelk and white is only blood in the same sense as the chyle in the mesenteric veins, in which nothing but blood is ever seen; now chyle is but the shadow of blood, and is first perfected in the liver; and in like manner the matter taken up by the veins from the white and yellow is only the shadow of blood," &c. Be it so; but hiding under this shadow, he does not answer the question, wherefore the blood and blood-like parts should not, for the reasons cited, be equally well nourished by the albumen as by the vitellus?

Had our author, in like manner, asserted that the hotter parts are rather nourished by that blood which is derived from the vitellus than by that attracted from the albumen, and the colder parts, on the other hand, by that which is derived from the albumen, I should not myself have been much disposed to gainsay him.

There is one consideration in the whole question, however, which is sorely against him; it is this—how is the blood formed in the egg? by what agent is either white or yelk turned into blood whilst the liver is not yet in existence? For in the egg, at all events, he could not say that the blood was transfused from the mother. He says, indeed, "This blood is produced and concocted in the veins rather than in the liver; but it becomes bone, cartilage, flesh, &c. in the parts themselves, where it undergoes exact concoction and assimilation." In this he adds nothing; he neither tells us how or by what means perfect blood is concocted and elaborated in the minute veins both of the albumen and vitellus, the liver, as I have said, not having yet come into existence—not a particle of any part of the body, in fact, having yet been produced by which either concoction or elaboration might be effected. And then, forgetful of what he has previously said, viz., that the hot and hæmatous parts are nourished by the vitellus and the cold and anæmic parts by the albumen, he is plainly in contradiction with himself when he admits that the same blood is turned into bone, cartilage, flesh, and all other parts.

More than this, Fabricius has slipped the greatest difficulty of all, the source of not a

[1] Ibid.

little doubt and debate to the medical mind, viz., how the liver should be the source and artificer of the blood, seeing that this fluid not only exists in the egg before any viscus is formed, but that all medical writers teach that the parenchymata of the viscera are but effusions of blood? Is the work the author of its workman? If the parenchyma of the liver come from the blood, how can it be the cause of the blood?

What follows is of the same likelihood: "There is another reason wherefore the albumen should be separated from the yelk, namely, that the fœtus may swim in it, and be thus supported, lest tending downwards by its own weight, it should incline to one particular part, and dragging, should break the vessels, in preventing which the viscidity and purity of the albumen contribute effectually. For did the fœtus grow amid the yelk, it might readily sink to the bottom, and so cause laceration of that body." Sufficiently jejune! For what, I entreat, can the purity of the albumen contribute to the support of the embryo? Or how should the thinner albumen sustain it better than the thicker and more earthy yelk? Or where the danger, I ask, of its sinking down, when we see that the egg in incubation is always laid on its side, and there is nothing to fear either for the ascent or the descent of the embryo? It is indubitable, indeed, that not only does the embryo of the chick float in the egg, but that the embryo of every animal during its formation floats in the uterus; this however takes place amidst the fluid which we have called colliquament, and neither in the albumen nor vitellus, and we have elsewhere given the reason wherefore this is so.

"Aristotle informs us," says Fabricius, "that the vitellus rises to the blunt end of the egg when the chick is conceived; and this because the animal is incorporated from the chalaza, which adheres to the vitellus; whence the vitellus which was in the middle is drawn towards the upper wider part of the egg, that the chick may be produced where the natural cavity exists, which is so indispensable to its well-being." The chalaza, however, is certainly connected still more intimately with the albumen than with the yelk.

My mode of interpreting the ascent in question is this: the spot or cicatricula conspicuous on the membrana vitelli, expands under the influence of the spirituous colliquament engendered within it, and requiring a larger space, it tends towards the blunt end of the egg. The liquefied portion of the vitellus and albumen, diluted in like manner, and concocted and made more spirituous, swims above the remaining crude parts, just as the inferior particles of water in a vessel, when heated, rise from the bottom to the top, a fact which every medical man must have observed when he had chanced to put a measure of thick and turbid urine into a bath of boiling water, in which case the upper part first becomes clear and transparent. Another example will make this matter still more plain. There is an instrument familiar to almost everybody, made rather for amusement than any useful purpose, nearly full of water, on the surface of which float a number of hollow glass beads which by their lightness and swimming together support a variety of figures, Cupids with bows and quivers, chariots of the sun, centaurs armed, and the like, which would else all sink to the bottom. So also does the eye of the egg, as I have called it, or first colliquament, dilated by the heat of the incubating fowl and genital virtue inherent in the egg, expand, and thereby rendered lighter, rise to the top, when the vitellus, with which it is connected follows. It is because the cicatricula, formerly situated on the side of the vitellus, now tends to rise directly upwards that the thicker albumen is made to give place, and the chalazæ are carried to the sides of the egg.

EXERCISE 61. *Of the uses of the other parts of the egg*

The shell is hard and thick that it may serve as a defence against external injury to the fluids and the chick it includes. It is brittle, nevertheless, particularly towards the blunt end, and as the time of the chick's exclusion draws near, doubtless that the birth may suffer no delay. The shell is porous also; for when an egg, particularly a very recent one, is dressed before the fire, it sweats through its pores. Now these pores are useful for ventilation; they permit the heat of the incubating hen to penetrate more readily, and the chick to have supplies of fresh air; for that it both breathes and chirps in the egg before its exclusion is most certain.

The membranes serve to include the fluids, and therefore are they present in the same number as these, and therefore is the colliquament also invested, as soon as it is produced, with a tunica propria, which Aristotle refers to in these words: "A membrane covered with ramifications of blood-vessels already surrounds the clear liquid,"[1] &c. But the exit of the chick being at hand, and the albumen and colliqua-

[1] *History of Animals*, vi. 3.

ment being entirely consumed, all the membranes, except that which surrounds the vitellus, are dried up and disappear; the membrana vitelli, on the contrary, along with the yelk, is retracted into the peritoneum of the chick and included in the abdomen. Of the membranes two are common to the whole egg, which they surround immediately under the shell; the rest belong, one to the albumen, one to the yelk, one to the colliquament; but all still conduce to the preservation and separation of the parts they surround. The outer of the two common membranes which adheres to the shell is the firmer, that it may take no injury from the shell; the inner one again is smooth and soft, that it may not hurt the fluids; in the same way, therefore, as the meninges of the brain protect it from the roughness of the superincumbent skull. The internal membranes, as I have said, include and keep separate their peculiar fluids, whence they are extremely thin, pellucid, and easily torn.

Fabricius ascribes great eminence and dignity to the chalazæ, regarding them as the parts whence the chick is formed; he, however, leaves the spot or cicatricula connected with the membrana vitelli without any office whatsoever, looking on it merely as the remains of the peduncle whence the vitellus was detached from the vitellarium in the superior uterus of the hen. In his view the vitellus formerly obtained its nourishment either by this peduncle or the vessels passing through it; but when detached, and no longer nourished by the hen, a simple trace of the former connexion and important function alone remains.

I, however, am of opinion that the uses of the chalazæ are no other than those I have assigned them, namely, that they serve as poles to the microcosm of the egg, and are the association of all the membranes convoluted and twisted together, by which not only are the several fluids kept in their places, but also in their distinct relative positions. But I have absolute assurance that the spot or cicatricula in question is of the very highest importance; it is the part in which the calor insitus nestles; where the first spark of the vital principle is kindled; for the sake of which, in a word, the whole of the rest of the fluids and all the membranes of the egg are contrived. But this has been already insisted on above.

Formerly, indeed, I did think with Fabricius that this cicatricula was the remains or trace of the detached peduncle; but I afterwards learned by more accurate observation that this was not the case; that the peduncle, by which the vitellus hangs, was infixed in no such limited space as we find it in apples and plums, and in such a way as would have given rise to a scar on its separation. This peduncle, in short, expands like a tube from the ovary on towards the vitellus, the horizon of which it embraces in a bipartite semicircle, not otherwise than the tunica conjunctiva embraces the eye; and this in suchwise that the superior part of the vitellus, or the hemisphere which regards the ovary, is almost free from any contact or cohesion with the peduncle, in the superior part of the cup or hollow of which nevertheless, but somewhat to the side, the spot or cicatricula in question is placed. The peduncles becoming detached from the vitelli can therefore in no way be said to leave any trace of their attachments behind them. Of the great importance of this spot in generation I have already spoken in the historical portion of my work.

But I have still, always following my old teacher Fabricius as my guide on the way, to treat of the uses of the cavity in the blunt end of the egg.

Fabricius enumerates various conveniences arising from this cavity, according to its dimensions. I shall be brief on the subject: it contains air, and is therefore useful in the ventilation of the egg, assisting the perspiration, refrigeration, and respiration, and finally the chirping of the chick. Whence this cavity, small at first, is larger by and by, and at last becomes of great size, as the several offices mentioned come into play.

Thus far have we spoken of the generation of the egg and chick, and of the uses of the several parts of the egg; and to the type exhibited we have referred the mode of generation of oviparous animals in general. We have still to speak of the generation of viviparous animals, in doing which we shall as before refer all to a single familiarly known species.

EXERCISE 62. *An egg is the common origin of all animals*

"Animals," says Aristotle,[1] "have this in common with vegetables, that some of them arise from seed, others arise spontaneously; for as plants either proceed from the seed of other plants, or spring up spontaneously, having met with some primary condition fit for their evolution, some of them deriving their nourishment from the ground, others arising from and living on other plants; so are some animals engendered

from cognate forms, and others arise spontaneously, no kind of cognate seed having preceded their birth; and whilst some of them are generated from the earth, or putrefying vegetable matter, like so many insects, others are produced in animals themselves and from the excrementitious matters of their parts." Now the whole of these, whether they arise spontaneously, or from others, or in others, or from the parts or excrements of these, have this in common, that they are engendered from some principle adequate to this effect, and from an efficient cause inherent in the same principle. In this way, therefore, the primordium from which and by which they arise is inherent in every animal. Let us entitle this the *primordium vegetale* or *vegetative incipience*, understanding by this a certain corporeal something having life *in potentia;* or a certain something existing *per se*, which is capable of changing into a vegetative form under the agency of an internal principle. Such primordia are the eggs of animals and the seeds of plants; such also are the conceptions of viviparous animals, and the worm, as Aristotle calls it, whence insects proceed: the primordia of different living things consequently differ from one another; and according to their diversities are the modes of generation of animals, which nevertheless all agree in this one respect, that they proceed from the vegetal primordium as from matter endowed with the virtue of an efficient cause, though they differ in respect of the primordium which either bursts forth, as it were, spontaneously and by chance, or shows itself as fruit or seed from something else preceding it. Whence some animals are spoken of as spontaneously produced, others as engendered by parents. And these last are again distinguished by their mode of birth, for some are oviparous, others viviparous, to which Aristotle[2] adds a vermiparous class. But if we take the thing as simple sense proclaims it, there are only two kinds of birth, inasmuch as all animals engender others either *in actu*—virtually, or *in potentia*—potentially. Animals which bring forth in fact and virtually are called viviparous, those that bring forth potentially are oviparous. For every primordium that lives potentially, we, with Fabricius, think ought to be called an egg, and we make no distinction between the worm of Aristotle and an egg, both because to the eye there is no difference, and because the identity is in conformity with reason. For the vegetal primordium which lives potentially is also an animal potentially.

[1] *History of Animals,* v. 1.

[2] *History of Animals,* I. 5.

Nor can the distinction which Aristotle made between the egg and the worm be admitted: for he defines an egg to be that "from part of which an animal is produced";[1] whilst that, he says elsewhere, "which is totally changed, and which does not produce an animal from a part only, is a worm."[2] These bodies, however, agree in this, that they are both inanimate births, and only animals potentially; both, consequently, are eggs.

And then Aristotle himself, whilst he speaks of worms in one place, designates them by the name of eggs in another.[3] Treating of the locust, he says, "its eggs become spoiled in autumn when the season is wet";[4] and again, speaking of the grasshopper, he has these words: "when the little worm has grown in the earth it becomes a matrix of grasshoppers (*tettigometra*)"; and immediately afterwards, "the females are sweeter after coitus, for then they are full of white eggs."

In this very place, indeed, where he distinguishes between an egg and a worm, he adds: "but the whole of this tribe of worms, when they have come to their full size, are changed in some sort into eggs; for their shell or covering hardens, and they become motionless for a season, a circumstance that is plainly to be seen in the vermiculi of bees and wasps, and also in caterpillars."[5] Everyone indeed may observe that the primordia of spiders, silkworms, and the like, are not less to be accounted eggs than those of the crustacea and mollusca, and almost all fishes, which are not actually animals, but are potentially possessed of the faculty of producing them. Since, then, those creatures that produce actually are called viviparous, and those that produce potentially either pass without any general distinguishing title or are called oviparous and particularly as such productions are vegetal primordia, analogous to the seeds of plants, which true eggs must needs be held to be, the conclusion is that all animals are either viviparous or oviparous.

But as there are many species of oviparous animals, so must there also be several species of eggs; for every primordium is not alike fit to receive or assume every variety of animal form indifferently. Though we admit, therefore, that eggs in a general sense do not differ, yet when we find that one is perfect, another imperfect,

it is obvious that they differ essentially from one another. Perfect eggs are such as are completed in the uterus, where they obtain their due dimensions before being extruded; of this kind are the eggs of birds. Imperfect eggs, again, are such as are prematurely excluded before they are of the full size, but increase after they are laid; of this description are the eggs of fishes, crustacea and mollusca; the primordia of insects, which Aristotle entitles worms, are further to be referred to this class, as well as the primordia of those animals that arise spontaneously.

Moreover, although perfect eggs are of two colours, in other words, are composed of albumen and vitellus, some are still only of one hue, and consist of albumen alone. In like manner, of imperfect eggs, some from which a perfect animal proceeds are properly so called; such are the eggs of fishes; others are improperly so styled, they engendering an imperfect animal, namely, a worm, grub, or caterpillar, a kind of mean between a perfect and an imperfect egg, which, in respect of the egg or the primordium itself, is an animal endowed with sense and motion, and nourishing itself; but in respect of a fly, moth or butterfly, whose primordium it is potentially, it is as a creeping egg, and to be reputed as adequate to its own growth; of this description is the caterpillar, which having at length completed its growth is changed into a chrysalis or perfect egg, and ceasing from motion, it is like an egg, an animal potentially.

In the same way, although there are some eggs from the whole of which a perfect animal is produced by metamorphosis, without being nourished by any remains of the substance of the egg, but forthwith finds food for itself abroad, there are others from one part of which the embryo is produced, and from the remainder of which it is nourished—although, I repeat, there are such differences among eggs, still, if we be permitted to conclude on the grounds of sense and analogy, there is no good reason wherefore those that Aristotle calls worms should not be spoken of as eggs; inasmuch as all vegetal principles are not indeed animals actually, but are so potentially, are true animal seeds, analogous to the seeds of vegetables, as we have already demonstrated in the particular instance of the hen's egg. All animals are, therefore, either viviparous or oviparous, inasmuch as they all either produce a living animal in fact, or an egg, rudiment, or primordium, which is an animal potentially.

[1] *On the Generation of Animals*, III. 9.
[2] *History of Animals*, I. 5.
[3] *Ibid.*, v. 29.
[4] *Ibid.*, v. 30.
[5] *On the Generation of Animals*, III. 9.

The generation of all oviparous animals may therefore be referred to that of the hen's egg as a type, or at all events deduced from thence without difficulty, the same things and incidents that have been enumerated in connexion with the common fowl being also encountered in all other oviparous animals whatsoever. The various particulars in which they differ one from another, or in which they agree, either generally, or specifically, or analogically, will be subsequently treated of when we come to speak of the generation of insects and the animals that arise equivocally. For as every generation is a kind of way leading to the attainment of an animal form, as one race of animal is more or less like or unlike another, their constituent parts either agreeing or disagreeing, so does it happen in respect of their mode of generation. For perfect Nature, always harmonious with herself in her works, has instituted similar parts for similar ends and actions: to arrive at the same results, to attain the same forms, she has followed the same path, and has established one and the same method in the business of generation universally.

Wherefore as we still find the same parts in the perfect or two-coloured egg of every bird, so do we also observe the same order and method pursued in the generation and development of their embryos as we have seen in the egg of the common fowl. And so also are the same things to be noted in the eggs of serpents and of reptiles, or oviparous quadrupeds, such as tortoises, frogs, and lizards, from all the perfect two-coloured eggs of which embryos are produced and perfected in the same manner. Nor is the case very different in regard to fishes. But of the manner in which spiders and the crustacea, such as shrimps and crabs, and the mollusca, such as the cuttlefish and calamary, arise from their eggs; of the conditions also upon which worms and grubs first proceed from the eggs of insects, which afterwards change into chrysalides or aurelias, as if they reverted anew to the state of eggs, from which at length emerge flies or butterflies—of the several respects in which these differ in their mode of generation from an egg, from what we have found in the hen's egg, will be matter for remark in the proper place.

Although all eggs consisting of yelk and white are not produced and fecundated in the same manner, but some are made prolific through the intercourse of male and female, and others in some other way (as of fishes); and although there is some difference even in the mode in

which eggs grow, some attaining maturity within the body of the parent, others continuing to be nourished and to grow when extruded, there is still no reason why an embryo should not be developed in the same precise manner in every egg—always understood as perfect—as it is in the egg of the hen. Wherefore the history which has been given of the evolution of the chick from the hen's egg may be regarded as applicable to the generation of all other oviparous animals whatsoever, as well as to the inferences or conclusions which may be deduced from thence.

EXERCISE 63. *Of the generation of viviparous animals*

Thus far have we treated mainly of the generation of oviparous animals; we have still to speak particularly of the other species of generation, the viviparous, to wit, in which many things identical with those we have noticed in oviparous generation will come to be observed. These we have reduced into order, and here at length present for consideration. Even the parts that appear paradoxical and in contradiction with the current views of generation will, I believe, be found entirely in conformity with truth.

Among viviparous animals, man, the most perfect of all creatures, occupies the foremost place; after him come our ordinary domestic animals, of which some are soliped, such as the horse and ass; others bisulcate, as the ox, goat, sheep, deer, and hog; others digitate, such as the dog, cat, rabbit, mouse, and others of the same description; from the modes of whose generation a judgment may be formed of that of all other viviparous animals. Wherefore I shall propose a single genus, by way of general example or type, as we did in the case of the oviparous class; this made familiar to us, will serve as a light or standard, by means of which all the others may be judged of by analogy.

The reasons that led me to select the hen's egg as the measure of eggs in general have been already given: eggs are of little price, and are everywhere to be obtained, conditions that permit repeated study, and enable us cheaply and readily to test the truth of statements made by others.

We have not the same facilities in studying the generation of viviparous animals: we have rarely, if ever, an opportunity of dissecting the human uterus; and then to enter on the subject experimentally in the horse, ox, sheep, goat, and other cattle, would be attended with immense labour and no small expense; dogs, cats, rabbits, and the like, however, will supply those with subjects who are desirous of putting to the test of experiment the matters that are to be delivered by us in this place.

Fabricius of Aquapendente, as if every conception of a viviparous animal were in a certain sense an egg, begins his treatise with the egg as the universal example of generation; and among other reasons for his conclusions assigns this in particular: "Because the study of the egg has the most extensive application, the greater number of animals being engendered from eggs."[1] Now we, at the very outset of our observations, asserted that ALL animals were in some sort produced from eggs. For even on the same grounds, and in the same manner and order in which a chick is engendered and developed from an egg, is the embryo of viviparous animals engendered from a pre-existing conception. Generation in both is one and identical in kind: the origin of either is from an egg, or at least from something that by analogy is held to be so. An egg is, as already said, a conception exposed beyond the body of the parent, whence the embryo is produced; a conception is an egg remaining within the body of the parent until the fœtus has acquired the requisite perfection; in everything else they agree; they are both alike primordially vegetables, potentially they are animals. Wherefore, the same theorems and conclusions, though they may appear paradoxical, which we drew from the history of the egg, turn out to be equally true with regard to the generation of animals generally. For it is an admitted fact that all embryos, even those of man, are procreated from some conception or primordium. Let us, therefore, say that that which is called primordium among things arising spontaneously, and seed among plants, is an egg among oviparous animals, i. e., a certain corporeal substance, from which, through the motions and efficacy of an internal principle, a plant or an animal of one description or another is produced; but the prime conception in viviparous animals is of the same precise nature, a fact which we have found approved both by sense and reason.

What we have already affirmed of the egg, viz., that it was the sperma or seed of animals and analogous to the seeds of plants, we now affirm of the conception, which is indeed the seed of an animal, and therefore also properly called ovum or egg. Because "a true seed," according to Aristotle,[2] "is that which derives its origin from the intercourse of male and female, and possesses the virtues of both; such as is the seed of all vegetables, and of some animals, in which the sexes are not distinct, and is, as that which is first mingled from male and female, a kind of promiscuous conception or animal; for it has those things already that are recognized of both"; i. e., matter adapted to nourish the fœtus, and a plastic or formative and effective virtue. And so in like manner is a conception the fruit of the intercourse of male and female, and the seed of the future embryo; it therefore does not differ from an egg.

"But that which proceeds from the generant is the cause which first obtains the principle of generation (i. e., it is the efficient cause), and ought to be called the geniture,"[3] not the seed, as is commonly done both by the vulgar and philosophers at the present time; because it has not that which is required of both the concurring agents, neither is it analogous to the seeds of plants. But whatever possesses this, and corresponds to the seeds of vegetables, that too is rightly entitled egg and conception.

Further, the definition of an egg, as given by Aristotle, is perfectly applicable to a conception: "An egg," he says, "is that, the principal part of which goes to constitute an animal, the remainder to nourish the animal so constituted."[4] Now the same thing is common to a conception, as shall be made to appear visibly from the dissection of viviparous animals.

Moreover, as the chick is excluded from the egg under the influence of warmth derived from the incubating hen or obtained in any other way, even so is the fœtus produced from the conception in the uterus under the genial warmth of the mother's body. In few words, I say, that what oviparous animals supply by their breast and incubation, viviparous animals afford by their uterus and internal embrace. For the rest, in all that respects the development, the embryo is produced from the conception in the same manner and order as the chick from the egg, with this single difference, that whatever is required for the formation and growth of the chick is present in the egg, whilst the conception, after the formation of the embryo, derives from the uterus of the mother whatever more is requisite to its increase, by which it continues to grow in common with the fœtus. The egg, on the contrary, becomes more and more empty as the chick increases; the nutriment that was laid up in it is diminished;

---

[1] De form. ovi et pulli, 1.
[2] On the Generation of Animals, 1. 18.

[3] Ibid.
[4] History of Animals, 1. 5.

nor does the chick receive aught in the shape of new aliment from the mother; whilst the fœtus of viviparous animals has a continued supply, and when born, moreover, continues to live upon its mother's milk. The eggs of fishes, however, increase through nourishment obtained from without; and insects and crustaceous and molluscous animals have eggs that enlarge after their extrusion. Yet are not these called eggs the less on this account, nor, indeed, are they therefore any the less eggs. In like manner the conception is appropriately designated by the name of ovum or egg, although it requires and procures from without the variety of aliment that is needful to its growth.

Fabricius gives this reason for some animals being oviparous, for all not producing living offspring: "It is," he says, "that eggs detained in the uterus till they had produced their chicks would interfere with the flight of birds, and weigh them down by their weight." Serpents would also be hindered in their alternate zigzag movements by a multitude of eggs in the abdomen. In the body of tortoises, with their hard and girding shell, there is no room for any store or increase of eggs; nor would the abdomen of fishes suffice for the multitude of eggs they must spawn were these to grow to any size. It was, therefore, matter of necessity that those creatures should lay their eggs imperfect. It seems most natural that an animal should retain and cherish its conception in its interior until the fœtus it produces has come to maturity; but Nature sees herself compelled, as it were, occasionally to permit the premature birth of various eggs, and to provide them, without the body of the parent, with the nourishment they require for their complete development. As to everything that refers to the evolution of the fœtus, all animals are engendered from an oviform primordium; I say oviform, not as meaning that it has the precise configuration of an egg, but the nature and constitution of one; this being common in generation, that the vegetal primordium whence the fœtus is produced, including the nature of an egg, corresponding in its proportions to the seed of a plant, pre-exists. In all vegetal primordia, consequently, whether eggs, or having the form of eggs, there are inherent the nature and conditions of an egg, properties which the seeds of plants have in common with the eggs of animals. The primordium of any animal, whatsoever, is therefore called seed and fruit; and in like manner the seed of every plant is spoken of as a kind of conception or egg.

And this is the reason why Aristotle says: "Animals that engender internally have something formed in the fashion of an egg after their first conception: there is a fluid contained within a delicate membrane, like an egg without the shell. And this is the cause why the disorders of the conception, which are apt to occur in the early period, are called discharges."[1] Such a discharge is particularly observed among women when they miscarry in the course of the first or second month. I have repeatedly seen such ova aborted at this time; and such was the one which Hippocrates has described as having been thrown off by the female pipe-player in consequence of a fall.

In the uterus of all animals there is, consequently, present a prime conception or primordium, which, on Aristotle's testimony, "is like an egg surrounded with a membrane from which the shell had been removed."[2] This fact will appear still more plainly from what is about to be said. Meantime let us conclude with the philosopher, "that all living creatures, whether they swim, or walk, or fly, and whether they come into the world with the form of an animal or of an egg, are engendered in the same manner."

EXERCISE 64. *The generation of viviparous animals in general is illustrated from the history of that of the hind and doe, and the reason of this selection*

It was customary with his Serene Majesty, King Charles, after he had come to man's estate, to take the diversion of hunting almost every week, both for the sake of finding relaxation from graver cares, and for his health; the chase was principally the buck and doe, and no prince in the world had greater herds of deer, either wandering in freedom through the wilds and forests, or kept in parks and chases for this purpose. The game during the three summer months was the buck, then fat and in season; and in the autumn and winter, for the same length of time, the doe. This gave me an opportunity of dissecting numbers of these animals almost every day during the whole of the season when they were rutting, taking the male, and falling with young; I had occasion, so often as I desired it, to examine and study all the parts, particularly those dedicated to the offices of generation.

I shall therefore consider the generation of viviparous animals in general, from the particular history of the hind and doe, as the instance most convenient to me; and, as I have done

[1] *On the Generation of Animals*, III. 9.
[2] *History of Animals*, VII. 7.

above, in speaking of oviparous generation, where I have referred everything to the common fowl, so shall I here, in discussing viviparous generation, refer all to the fallow deer and roe. In taking this course, I am not moved by the same reasons as I was in reference to the hen's egg; but because the great prince, whose physician I was, besides taking much pleasure in such inquiries, and not disdaining to bear witness to my discoveries, was pleased in his kindness and munificence to order me an abundant supply of these animals and repeated opportunities of examining their bodies.

I therefore propose to give the history of generation in the hind and doe as I have observed it during a long series of years, and as most familiar to me, believing that from thence something certain in reference to the generation of other viviparous animals may be concluded. In giving a faithful narrative of this history, I shall not abstain in its course from introducing particulars worthy of note that have either been observed accidentally and by the way, or that are the result of particular dissections instituted for the purpose of arriving at conclusions, the subjects of these having been other bisulcated, hoofed, or multungulated animals, or, finally, man himself. We shall give a simple narrative of the series of formations of the fœtus, following the footsteps of nature in the process.

EXERCISE 65. *Of the uterus of the hind and doe*

About to treat of the generation of the hind and doe, our first business will be to speak of the place where it proceeds, or of the uterus, as we have done above, in giving the history of the common fowl, by which all that follows will be more easily and readily understood. And history has this great pre-eminence over fable, that it narrates the events which transpired in certain places at certain times, and therefore leads us to knowledge by a safe and assured way.

Now that we may have a clearer idea of the uterus of the hind, I shall describe both its external and internal structure, following the uterus of the human female as my guide. For man is the most consummate of creatures, and has therefore the genital as well as all other parts in higher perfection than any other animal. The parts of the female uterus consequently present themselves with great distinctness, and by reason of the industry of anatomists in this direction are believed to be particularly well known to us.

We meet with many things in the uterus of deer which we encounter in the uterus of the human female; and we also observe several that differ. In the vulva or os externum we find neither labia, nor clitoris, nor nymphæ, but only two openings, one for the urine, adjacent to the pecten, or os pubis, the other the vagina, lying between the meatus urinarius and the anus. A cuticular or membranous fold, such as we have noted in the hen, stretching downwards from the anus, acts as a velabrum, supplies the place of nymphæ and labia pudendi, and guards against injury from without. This velabrum must be somewhat retracted by the female when she copulates, or at all events must be raised by the penis of the male as it enters the vulva.

The symphysis pubis being divided in deer, and the legs widely separated, the urinary bladder, the vagina which is entered by the penis of the buck, and the cervix uteri, are all seen in their relative situations, not otherwise than they are in women; the ligamenta suspensoria, with the veins, arteries, and testicles, as they are called, also come into sight; the cornua of the uterus in these creatures are also more remarkable than any other part of this organ.

As for the vessels called vasa præparantia and vasa deferentia seu ejaculantia, you will discover nothing of the kind here, nor indeed in any other female animal that I am aware of. The anatomists who believe that women emit a seminal fluid *sub coitu* have been too eager in their search after such vessels; for in some they are not met with at all, and where they do occur they never present themselves with anything of uniformity of character. Wherefore it seems most likely that women do not emit any semen *sub coitu*, which is in conformity as I have said with what the greater number of women state. And although some of warmer temperament shed a fluid in the sexual embrace, still that this is fruitful semen, or is a necessary requisite to conception, I do not believe; for many women conceive without having any emission of the kind, and some even without any kind of pleasurable sensation whatsoever. But of these things more in another place.

The vulva, or vagina uteri, which extends from the os externum to the inner orifice of the uterus, is situated in the hind, as well as in the human female, between the urinary bladder and the intestinum rectum, and corresponds in length, width, and general dimensions, with the penis of the male. When this part is laid open it is found occupied lengthwise by rugæ and furrows, admitting of ready distension, and lubricated with a sluggish fluid. At its bottom we observe a very narrow and small orifice, the commencement of the cervix uteri, by which whatever is propelled outwards from the cavity of the uterus must pass. This is the corresponding orifice to that which medical men assert is so firmly closed and sealed up in the pregnant woman and virgin, that it will not even admit the point of a probe or fine needle.

The os uteri is followed by the cervix or process, which is much longer and rounder than in woman, and also more fibrous, thicker, and nervous; it extends from the bottom of the vagina to the body of the uterus. If this cervix uteri be divided longitudinally, you perceive not only its external orifice at the bottom of the vagina, its surface in close contact, and so firmly agglutinated that not even air blown into the vagina will penetrate the cavity of the uterus, but five other similar constrictions placed in regular order, firmly contracted against the entrance of any foreign body and sealed with gelatinous mucus; just as we find the narrow orifice of the woman's uterus plugged with a yellowish glutinous mass. A like constriction of parts, all firmly closed, and precluding all possibility of entrance, Fabricius has found in the uterine neck of the sheep, sow, and goat. In the deer there are very distinctly five of these constrictions, or so many orifices of the uterus constricted and conglutinated, which may all justly be looked upon as so many barriers against the entrance of anything from without. Such particular care has nature taken, that if the first barrier were forced by any cause or violence, the second should still stand good, and so the third, and the fourth, and the fifth, determined apparently that nothing should enter. A probe pushed from within outwards, however, from the cavity of the uterus towards the vagina, passes through readily. A way had to be left open for the escape of flatus, menstrual blood, and other excreted fluids; but even the smallest and most subtile things, air, for instance, and the seminal fluid are precluded all access from without.

In all animals this uterine orifice is found obstructed or plugged up in the same way as it is wont to be in women, among whom we have sometimes known the outlet so much constricted that the menses, lochia, and other humours were retained in the womb, and became the exciting cause of most severe hysterical symptoms. In such cases it became necessary to contrive a suitable instrument with which the os uteri being opened, the matters that stagnated within were discharged, when all the accidents disappeared. By this contrivance injections could also be thrown into the cavity of the uterus, and by means of these I have cured internal ulcers of the womb, and have occasionally even found a remedy for barrenness.

The cavity of the uterus in the deer is extremely small, and the thickness of its walls not great; the body of the womb in these animals is, in fact, but a kind of vestibule, or ante-room, in the cavity of which a passage opens to the right and left into either cornu.

For the parts are different in almost all animals from what they are in woman, in whom the principal part of the uterus is its body, and the cervix and cornua are mere appendices, that scarcely attract attention. The neck is short; the cornua are slender round processes extending from the fundus uteri like a couple of tubes, which anatomists indeed commonly speak of as the vasa ejaculatoria. In the deer, however, as in all other quadrupeds, except the ape and the solipeds, the chief organ of generation is not the body but the horns of the uterus. In the human female and the solipedia, the uterus is the *place* of conception, in all the rest the conception is perfected in the cornua; and this is the reason why writers so commonly speak of the cornua uteri in the lower animals under the simple name of the uterus, saying that the uterus in certain animals is bipartite, whilst in others it is not, understanding by the word uterus the place in which conception takes place, this in the majority of viviparous and especially of multiparous animals being the cornua, to which, moreover, all the arteries and veins distributed to the organs of generation are sent. We shall, therefore, in treating of the history of generation in the deer employ the words uterus and horns of the uterus promiscuously.

In the human female, as I have said, the two tubes that arise near the cervix uteri and there perforate its cavity have no analogy to the parts generally called cornua, but, on the contrary, in the mind of some anatomists, to the vasa spermatica. By others again they are called the spiramenta uteri—the breathing tubes of the uterus; and by others still they are called the vasa deferentia seu reservantia, as if they were of the same nature as the canals so designated in the male; whilst they in fact correspond to the cornua of the uterus in other animals, as most clearly appears from their situation, connexion, length, perforation, general resemblance, and also office. For as many of the lower animals regularly conceive in the cornua uteri, so do women occasionally carry their conceptions in the cornu, or this tube, as the learned Riolanus[1] has shown from the observations of others, and as we ourselves have found it with our own eyes.

These cornua terminate in a common cavity which, as stated, forms a kind of porch or vestibule to the uterus, and corresponds in the deer to the neck of the womb in women; in the same way as the tubes in question in the human female correspond to the cornua uteri in the deer. Now this name of cornua has been derived from the resemblance of the parts to the horns of an animal; and in the same way as the horns of a goat or ram are ample at the base, arched and protuberant in front, and bent-in behind, so are these horns of the uterus in the hind and doe capacious inferiorly, and taper gradually off superiorly, as they are reflected towards the spine. Further, as the horns of the animal are unequally tuberculated and uneven in front, but smooth behind, so are the horns of the uterus tuberculated, as it were, and uneven, through the presence of cells, something like those of the colon, inferiorly and anteriorly; but superiorly, and on the aspect towards the spine, they are continuous and smooth, and present themselves secured and bound down by a ligamentous band; they at the same time gradually decrease in size like horns. Did one take a piece of empty intestine, such as is used for making sausages, and drawing a tape through it, tied this on one side, he would have it puckered and constricted on that side, and thrown into cells similar to those of the colon on the opposite side. Such is the structure of the cornua of the uterus in the hind and doe. In other animals it is different; for there the cells are either much larger, or they are entirely wanting. The cells of the cornua uteri of the hind and doe, however, are not all of the same size; the first that is met with is much larger than any of the others; and here it is that the conception is generally lodged.

As the uterus, tubes, or cornua, and other parts appertaining in the human female are connected with the pubes, spine, and surrounding structures by the medium of broad and fleshy membranes, by suspensory bands, as it were, which anatomists have designated by the name of bats' wings, because they have found that the uterus suspended in this way resembled a bat with its wings expanded, so also are the cornua uteri, together with the testes [ovaries], on either side, and all the uterine vessels, connected with the neighbouring parts, particularly with the spine, by means of a firm membrane, within the folds of which are suspended all the parts that have been mentioned, and which serves the same office with reference to these uterine structures as the mesentery does to the intestines, and the mesometrium to the uterus of the fowl. In the same way, too, as the mesenteric arteries and veins are distributed to the intestines through the mesentery, are the uterine vessels distributed to the uterus through the membrane in question; in which also certain vessels and glands are perceived on either side, which by anatomists are generally designated the testicles [the ovaries].

The substance of the horns of the uterus in the hind and doe is skinny or fleshy, like the coats of the intestines, and has a few very minute veins ramified over it. This substance you may in anatomical fashion divide into several layers, and note different courses of its component fibres, fitting them to perform the several motions and actions required, retention, namely, and expulsion. I have myself frequently seen these cornua moving like earthworms, or in the manner in which the intestines may at any time be observed, twisting themselves with an undulatory motion, on laying open the abdomen of a recently slaughtered animal, by which they move on the chyle and excrements to inferior portions of the gut, as if they were surrounded and compressed with a ring forced over them, or were stripped between the fingers.

The uterine veins, as in woman, all arise from the vena cava, near the emulgents; the arteries (and this also is common to the deer and the human subject) arise from the crural branches of the descending aorta. And as in the pregnant woman the uterine vessels are relatively larger and more numerous than in any other part of the body, this is likewise the case in the pregnant hind and doe. The arteries, however, contrary to the arrangement in other parts of the body, are much more numerous than the veins; and air blown into them makes its way into the neighbouring veins, although the arteries cannot be inflated in their turn by blowing into the veins. This fact I also find mentioned by Master Riolanus; and it is a cogent argument for the circulation of the blood discovered by me; for he clearly proves that whilst there is a passage from the arteries into the veins, there is none backwards from the veins into the arteries. The arteries are more numerous than the veins, because a large supply of nourishment being required for the fœtus, it is only what is left unused that has to be returned by the latter channels.

[1] *Anthropologia*, II. 34.

In the deer as well as in the sheep, goat, and bisulcate animals generally, we find testicles; but these are mere little glands, which rather correspond in their proportions to the prostate or mesenteric glands, the use of which is to establish divarications for the veins, and to store up a fluid for lubricating the parts, rather than for secreting semen, concocting it into fecundity, and shedding it at the time of intercourse. I am myself especially moved to adopt this opinion, as well by numerous reasons which will be adduced elsewhere, as by the fact that in the rutting season, when the testes of the buck and hart enlarge and are replete with semen, and the cornua of the uterus of the hind and doe are greatly changed, the female testicles, as they are called, whether they be examined before or after intercourse, neither swell nor vary from their usual condition; they show no trace of being of the slightest use either in the business of intercourse or in that of generation.

It is surprising what a quantity of seminal fluid is found in the vesiculæ seminales and testicles of moles and the larger kinds of mice at the season of intercourse; this circumstance corresponds with what we have already noticed in the cock, and the great change perceptible in the organs of generation of both sexes; nevertheless, the glands, which are regarded as the female testes, continue all the while unchanged and without departure from their pristine appearance.

All that has now been said of the uterus and its horns in hinds and does applies in major part to viviparous animals in general, but not to the human female, inasmuch as she conceives in the body of the uterus, but all these, with the exception of the horse and ass, in the horns of the organ; and even the horse and ass, although they appear to carry their fruit in the uterus, still is the *place* of the conception in them rather of the nature of an uterine horn than the uterine body. For the *place* here is not bipartite indeed, but it is oblong, and different from the human uterus both in its situation, connexions, structure, and substance; it bears a greater affinity to the superior uterus or uterine process of the fowl, where the egg grows and becomes surrounded with the albumen, than to the uterus of the woman.

EXERCISE 66. *Of the intercourse of the hind and doe*

So much for the account of the uterus of the female deer, where we have spoken briefly upon all that seemed necessary to the history of generation, *viz.*, the *place* of conception, and the parts instituted for its sake. We have still to speak of the action and office of this *place*, in other words, of intercourse and conception.

The hind and doe admit the male at one and only one particular season of the year, namely, in the middle of September, after the Feast of the Holy Cross; and they bring forth after the middle of June, about the Feast of St. John the Baptist (24th June). They, therefore, go with young about nine months, not eight, as Pliny says;[1] with us, at all events, they produce in the ninth month after they have taken the buck.

At the rutting season the bucks herd with the does; at other times they keep severally apart, the males, particularly the older ones, associating together, and the females and younger males trooping and feeding in company. The rutting season lasts for a whole month, and it begins later if the weather have been dry, earlier if it have been wet. In Spain, as I am informed, the deer are hardly in rut before the beginning of October, wet weather not usually setting in there until this time; but with us the rutting season rarely continues beyond the middle of October.

At this time deer are rendered savage by desire, so that they will attack both dogs and men, although at other seasons they are so timid and peaceable, and immediately betake themselves to flight on the barking of even the smallest dog.

Every male knows all his own females, nor will he suffer any one of them to wander from his herd: with a run he speedily drives back any straggler; he walks jealously from time to time among his wives; looks circumspectly about him, and the careful guardian of his own, he shows himself the watchful sentinel. If a strange doe commit any offence, he does not pursue her very eagerly, but rather suffers her to get away; but if another buck approach he instantly runs to meet him, and gives him battle with his antlers.

The hind and doe are held among the number of the chaster animals; they suffer the addresses of the male reluctantly, who, like the bull, mounts with violence, and unless forced or tired out, they resist him; which disinclination of the females appears also to be the reason of their herding together, and confining themselves to their own males, who are always the older and better armed; for when any strange male approaches them they immediately take to flight, and seek refuge in their own herd, and protection to their chastity, as it seems, from their proper husband.

[1] *Hist. nat.*, VIII. 32.

If a younger male finds a female straying alone, he immediately pursues her, and when she is worn out and unable to fly farther he mounts and forces her to his pleasure.

The males all provide themselves what are called rutting places; that is to say, they dig a trench, or they take their stand upon an acclivity, whither they compel their females to come in turn. The female that is to be leapt stands with her hind feet in the trench prepared for the purpose, stooping or lowering her haunches somewhat, if need be; by which the male is enabled, pressing forward upon her in the same way as a bull, to strike her, in technical language, and finish the business of copulation at one assault.

Old and sturdy bucks have a considerable number of does in their herds, as many as ten, and even fifteen; younger and weaker males have fewer. Keepers say that the doe is sated with two, or at most with three leaps; once she has conceived she admits the male no more.

The lust of the male cools when he has served his females; he becomes shyer, and much leaner; he deserts his herd and roams alone, and feeds greedily to repair his wasted strength, nor does he afterwards approach a female for a whole year.

When the male is capable of intercourse the hair on his throat and neck grows black, and the extremity of the prepuce becomes of the same colour, and stinks abominably. The females take the male but rarely, and only in the night or in dusky places, which are, therefore, always chosen by the males for their connubial pleasures. When two stags engage in battle, as frequently happens, the vanquished yields possession of his females to the victor.

EXERCISE 67. *Of the constitution or change that takes place in the uterus of the deer in the course of the month of September*

We now come to the changes that take place in the genital parts of the female after intercourse, and to the conception itself. In the month of September, then, when the female deer first comes in season, her cornua uteri, uterus, or place of conception, grows somewhat more fleshy and thick, softer also, and more tender. In the interior of either cornu, at that part, namely, which looks drawn together by a band, and is turned towards the spine, we observe, protruding in regular succession, five caruncles, soft warts, or papillæ. The first of these is larger than any of the others, and each in suc-

cession is smaller than the one before it, just as the cornua themselves become smaller and smaller towards their termination. Some of the caruncles grow to the thickness of the largest finger, and look like proud flesh; some are white, others of a deeper red.

From the 26th to the 28th of September, and also subsequently, in the month of October, the uterus becomes thicker, and the carunculæ mentioned come to resemble the nipples of the woman's breast: you might fancy them ready to pour out milk. Having removed their apex that I might examine their internal structure, I found them made up of innumerable white points compacted together, like so many bristles erect, and connected by means of a certain mucous viscidity; compressed between the fore finger and thumb, from the base upwards, a minute drop of blood oozed out from each point, a fact which led me, after further investigation, to conclude that they were entirely made up of the capillary branches of arteries.

During the season of intercourse, therefore, the uterine vessels, particularly the arteries, are observed to be more numerous and of larger size; although the parts called the female testes, as I have said above, are neither larger nor more highly gorged with blood than before, and do not appear to be altered in any way from their former state.

The inner aspect of the uterus or cornua uteri, where it is puckered into cells, is as smooth and soft as the ventricles of the brain, or the glans penis within the prepuce. Nothing, however, can be discovered there—neither the semen of the male, nor aught else having reference to the conception—during the whole of the months of September and October, although I have instituted repeated dissections with a view of examining the conception at this period. The males have been doing their duty all the while; nevertheless, reiterated dissection shows nothing. This is the conclusion to which I have come, after many years of observation. I have only occasionally found the five caruncles so close together that they formed a kind of continuous protuberance into the interior of the uterus. But when, after repeated inspections, I still found nothing more in the uterus, I began to doubt, and to ask myself whether the semen of the male could by any possibility make its way—by attraction or injection—to the seat of the conception? And repeated examination led me to the conclusion that none of the semen whatsoever reached this seat.

EXERCISE 68. *Of what takes place in the month of October*

Repeated dissections performed in the course of the month of October, both before the rutting season was over and after it had passed, never enabled me to discover any blood or semen, or a trace of anything else, either in the body of the uterus or in its cornua. The uterus was only a little larger, and somewhat thicker; and the caruncles were more tumid and florid, and, when strongly pressed with the finger, discharged small drops of blood, much in the manner in which a little watery milk can be squeezed from the nipples of a woman in the fourth month of her pregnancy. In one or two does, indeed, I found a green and ichorous matter, like an abscess, filling the cavity of the uterus, which was preternaturally extenuated; in other respects these animals were healthy, and in as good condition as others which I examined at the same time.

Towards the end of October and beginning of November, the rutting season being now ended, and the females separating themselves from the males, the uterus begins (in some sooner, in others later) to shrink in size, and the walls of its internal cavity, inflated in appearance, to bulge out; for where the cells existed formerly there are now certain globular masses projecting internally, which nearly fill the whole cavity, by which the sides are brought into mutual contact, and almost agglutinated, as it seems, so that there is no interval between them. Even as we have seen the lips of boys who, in robbing a hive, had been stung in the mouth, swollen and enlarged, so that the oral aperture was much contracted, even so does the internal surface of the uterus in the doe enlarge, and become filled with a soft and pulpy substance, like the matter of the brain, that fills its cavity and involves the caruncles, which, though not larger than before, look whiter, and as if they had been steeped in hot water, much as the nurse's nipple appears immediately after the infant has quitted it. And now I have not found it possible by any compression to force blood out of the caruncles as before.

Nothing can be softer, smoother, more delicate, than the inner aspect of the uterus thus raised into tubers. It rivals the ventricles of the brain in softness, so that without the information of the eye we should scarcely perceive by the finger that we were touching anything. When the abdomen is laid open immediately after the death of the animal, I have frequently seen the uterus affected with a wavy and creeping motion, such as is perceived in the lower part of a slug or snail whilst it is moving, as if the uterus were an animal within an animal, and possessed a proper and independent motion. I have frequently observed a movement of the same kind as that just described in the intestines, whilst engaged in vivisections; and indeed such a motion can both be seen and felt in the bodies of dogs and rabbits whilst they are alive and uninjured. I have also observed a corresponding motion in the testes and scrotum of men; and I have even known women upon whom, in their eagerness for offspring, such palpitations have imposed. But whether the uterus in hysterical females, by ascending, descending, and twisting, experiences any such motion or not, I cannot take upon me to declare; and whether the brain, in its actions and conceptions, moves in anything of a similar manner or not, though a point difficult of investigation, I am inclined to look upon as one by no means unworthy of being attempted.

Shortly afterwards, the tubercular elevations of the inner surface of the uterus that have been mentioned begin to shrink; it is as if, losing a quantity of moisture, they became less plump. In some instances, indeed, though rarely, I have observed something like purulent matter adhering to them, such as is usually seen on the surface of wounds and ulcers when they are digested, as it is said, they pour out smooth and homogeneous pus. When I first saw this matter, I doubted whether it was the semen of the male or not, or a substance concocted from its purer portion. But as it was only in exceedingly rare instances that I met with such matter, and as twenty days had then passed since the doe had had any intercourse with the buck, and further, as the matter was not viscid and tenacious, or spumous, such as the seminal fluid presents itself to us, but rather friable, purulent looking, and inclining to yellow, I came to the conclusion that it was the effect of accident, a sweat or exudation in consequence of violent exercise previous to death; just as in a catarrh the thinner defluxion of the nose is by and by changed into a thicker mucus.

Having frequently shown this alteration in the uterus to his majesty the king as the first indication of pregnancy, and satisfied him at the same time that there was nothing in the shape of semen or conception to be found in the cavity of the organ, and he had spoken of this as an extraordinary fact to several about him, a discussion at length arose: the keepers and huntsmen asserted at first that it was but an argument of a tardy conception occasioned by the want of rain. But by and by, when they saw the rutting season pass away, I still continuing to maintain that things were in the same state, they began to say that I was both deceived myself and had misled the king, and that there must of necessity be something of the conception to be found in the uterus. These men, however, when I got them to bring their own eyes to the inquiry, soon gave up the point. The physicians, nevertheless, held it among their ἀδύνατα—their impossibilities—that any conception should ever be formed without the presence of the semen masculinum, or some trace remaining of a fertile intercourse within the cavity of the womb.

That this important question might be the more satisfactorily settled in all time to come, his highness the king ordered about a dozen does to be separated from the bucks towards the beginning of October, and secluded in the inclosure, which is called the course, at Hampton Court, because the animal placed there has no means of escape from the dogs let loose upon it. Now that no one might say the animals thus secluded retained any of the semen received from the last connexions with the male, I dissected several of them before the rutting season had passed, and ascertained that no seminal fluid remained in the uterus, although the others were found to be pregnant in consequence of the preceding intercourse—impregnated by a kind of contagion as it appears—and duly produced their fawns at the proper time.

In the dog, rabbit, and several other animals, I have found nothing in the uterus for several days after intercourse. I therefore regard it as demonstrated that after fertile intercourse among viviparous as well as oviparous animals, there are no remains in the uterus either of the semen of the male or female emitted in the act, nothing produced by any mixture of these two fluids, as medical writers maintain, nothing of the menstrual blood present as "matter" in the way Aristotle will have it; in a word, that there is not necessarily even a trace of the conception to be seen immediately after a fruitful union of the sexes. It is not true, consequently, that in a prolific connexion there must be any prepared matter in the uterus which the semen masculinum, acting as a coagulating agent, should congeal, concoct, and fashion, or bring into a positive generative act, or, by drying its outer surface, include in membranes. Nothing certainly is to be seen within the uterus of the doe

for a great number of days, namely, from the middle of September up to the 12th of November.

It appears, moreover, that all females do not shed seminal fluid into the uterus during intercourse; that there is no trace either of seminal fluid or menstrual blood in the uterus of the hind or doe, and many other viviparous animals. But as to what it is which is shed by women of warmer temperament no less than by men during intercourse, accompanied with failure of the powers and voluptuous sensations; whether it be necessary to fecundation, whether it come from the testes femininæ, and whether it be semen and prolific, is discussed by us elsewhere.

And whilst I speak of these matters, let gentle minds forgive me, if, recalling the irreparable injuries I have suffered, I here give vent to a sigh. This is the cause of my sorrow: whilst in attendance on his majesty the king during our late troubles and more than civil wars, not only with the permission but by command of the Parliament, certain rapacious hands stripped not only my house of all its furniture, but what is subject of far greater regret with me, my enemies abstracted from my museum the fruits of many years of toil. Whence it has come to pass that many observations, particularly on the generation of insects, have perished, with detriment, I venture to say, to the republic of letters.

EXERCISE 69. *Of what takes place in the uterus of the doe during the month of November*

Taught by the experience of many years I can state truly that it is from the 12th to the 14th of November that I first discover anything which belongs to the future offspring in the uterus of the hind.

I remember, indeed, that in the year of grace 1633, the signs of conception, or the commencements of the embryos, made their appearance somewhat earlier; because the weather was then cloudy and wet. In does, too, which have rutted six or seven days sooner than hinds, I have always discovered something of the future fœtus about the 8th or 9th of November. What this is and how it is begun I shall proceed to state.

A little before anything is perceptible, the substance of the uterus or its horns appears less than it was before the animals began to rut, the white caruncles are more flaccid, as I have said, and the protuberances of the internal coat subside somewhat, and are corrugated and look moist. For about the date above mentioned certain mucous filaments like spiders' webs are observed drawn from the extremities, or superior angles of the cornua through the middle of either, and also through the body of the uterus. These filaments becoming conjoined present themselves as a membranous and gelatinous tunic or empty sac. Even as the plexus choroides is extended through the ventricles of the brain, is this oblong sac produced through the whole of either horn and the intervening cavity of the uterus, insinuating itself between the wrinkles of the flabby internal tunic, and sending delicate fibres among the afore-mentioned rounded protuberances, being nearly in the same manner as the pia mater dips between the convolutions of the brain.

Within a day or two this sac becomes filled with a clear, watery, sluggish albuminous matter, and now presents itself as a long-shaped pudding full of fluid. It adheres by its external glutinous matter to the containing walls of the uterus, but so that it is still easily separated from these; for if it be taken hold of cautiously in the strait of the uterus, where it is constricted in its course, it can be drawn entire out of either horn.

The conception arrived at this stage removed entire, presents itself with the figure of a wallet or double pudding; externally, it is covered with a purulent-looking matter; internally, it is smooth, and contains in its cavity a viscid fluid not unlike the thinner white of egg.

This is the conception of the hind and doe in its first stage. And since it has now the nature and state of an egg, and the definition given by Aristotle of an egg is applicable to it, namely: "A body from one part of which an animal is produced, the remainder serving as nourishment to that which is engendered";[1] and further, as it is the primordium of the future fœtus, it is therefore called the ovum, or egg of the animal, in conformity with that passage of the philosopher where he says: "Those animals which engender internally have a certain oviform body produced after the first conception. For a humour is included within a delicate membrane, such as that which you find under the shell in the egg of the hen; wherefore the blightings of conceptions that are apt to take place about this period are called fluxes."[2] This conception, therefore, as we have already said of the egg, is the true sperma or seed, comprising the virtue of both sexes in itself, and is analogous to the seed of the vegetable. So that Aris-

totle, describing the first conception of women, says that it is "covered with a membrane like an egg from which the shell has been removed";[3] such as Hippocrates describes as having been passed by the female pipe-player. And I have myself frequently seen such ova, of the size of pigeons' eggs, and containing no fœtus, discharged by women about the second month after conception; when the ovum was of the size of a pheasant's or hen's egg, the embryo could be made out, the size of the little fingernail, floating within it. But the membrane surrounding the conception has not yet acquired any annexed placenta; neither is it connected with the uterus; there is only at its upper and blunter part a kind of delicate mossy or woolly covering which stands for the rudiments of the future placenta. The inner aspect is smooth and polished, and covered with numerous ramifications of the umbilical vessels. In the third month this ovum exceeds a goose's egg in size, and includes a perfect embryo of the length of two fingers' breadths. In the fourth month it is larger than an ostrich's egg. All these things I have noted in the numerous careful dissections of aborted ova which I have made.

In the way above indicated do the hind and doe, affected by a kind of contagion, finally conceive and produce primordia, of the nature of eggs, or the seeds of plants, or the fruit of trees, although for a whole month and more they had exhibited nothing in the uterus, the conception being perfected about the 18th, at furthest the 21st of November, and having its seat now in the right, now in the left horn, occasionally in both at once. The ovum at this time is full of a colliquate matter, transparent, crystalline, similar to that fluid which in the hen's egg we have called the colliquament or eye, of far greater purity than that fluid in which the embryo by and by floats, and contained within a proper tunic of extreme tenuity, and orbicular in form. In the middle of the ovum, vascular ramifications and the punctum saliens—the first or rudimentary particle of the fœtus—and nothing else, are clearly to be perceived. This is the first genital part, which, once constituted, is not only already possessed by the vegetative, but also by the motive soul; and from this are all the other parts of the fœtus, each in its order, generated, fashioned, disposed, and endowed with life, almost in the same manner as we have described the chick to be produced from the colliquament of the egg.

Both of the humours mentioned are present

[1] History of Animals, i. 5; On the Generation of Animals, ii. 9.
[2] On the Generation of Animals, iii. 9.
[3] History of Animals, vii. 7.

in the conceptions of all viviparous animals, and are regarded by many as the excrements of the fœtus—one the urine, the other the sweat, although neither of them has any unpleasant taste, and they are always and at all periods present in conceptions, even before a particle of the fœtus has been produced.

Of the membranes investing the two fluids, of which there are only two, the outer is called the chorion, the inner the amnion. The chorion includes the whole conception, and extends into either cornu; the amnion swimming in the midst of the liquid of the former, is found in one of the horns only, except in the cases where there is a twin conception, when there is an amnion present in each of them; just as in a twin-fraught egg there are two colliquaments. Where there are two fœtuses consequently, both are contained in one common conception, in one egg, as it were, with its two separate collections of crystalline fluid included. If you incise the external membrane at any point, the more turbid fluid which it contains immediately escapes from either horn of the uterus; but the crystalline liquid in the interior of the amnion does not escape at the same time unless the membrane have been simultaneously implicated.

The vein which is first discerned in the crystalline fluid within the amnion takes its rise from the punctum saliens, and assumes the nature and duty of an umbilical vessel; increasing by degrees it expands into various ramifications distributed through the colliquament, so that it seems certain that the nourishment is in the first instance derived from the colliquament alone in which the fœtus swims.

I have exhibited to his Serene Highness the King, this point still palpitating in the uterus laid open; it was extremely minute indeed, and without the advantage of the sun's light falling upon it from the side, its tremulous motions were not to be perceived.

When the ovum with the colliquament entire was placed in a silver or pewter basin filled with tepid water, the punctum saliens became beautifully distinct to the spectators. In the course of the next ensuing days, a mucilage or jelly, like a tiny worm, and having the shape of a maggot, is found to be added; this is the rudiment of the future body. It is divided into two parts, one of which is the head, the other the trunk, precisely in the same way as we have already seen it in the generation of the chick *in ovo*. The spine, like a keel, is somewhat bent; the head is indifferently made up of three small

vesicles or globules, and swimming in transparent water grows amain, and by degrees assumes its proper shape. There is only this to be observed, that the eye in embryos of oviparous animals is much larger and more conspicuous than that of viviparous animals.

After the 26th of November the fœtus is seen with its body nearly perfect, in one case in the right in another in the left horn of the uterus; in twin cases in both horns.

At this time, too, the male embryo is readily distinguishable from the female by means of the organs of generation. These parts are also very conspicuous in the human embryo, and make their appearance at the same time as the trachea.

Males and females are met with indifferently in the right and left horn of the uterus. I have, however, more frequently found females in the right, males in the left horn; and I have made the same observation in does that carried twins, as well as in the sheep. It is certain, therefore, that the right or left side has no appropriate virtue in conferring sex; neither is the uterus, nor yet the mother herself, the fashioner or framer of the fœtus, any more than the hen is of the pullet in the egg which she incubates. In the same way as the pullet is formed and fashioned in the egg by an internal and inherent agent, is the fœtal form produced from the uterine ovum of the hind and doe.

It is indeed matter of astonishment to find a fœtus formed and perfected within the amnion in so short a space of time after the first appearance of the blood and punctum saliens. On or about the 19th or 20th day of November this punctum first becomes visible; on the 21st the shapeless vermiculus or maggot that is to form the body of the future animal is perceived; and in the course of from six to seven days afterwards a fœtus so perfect in all its parts is seen, that a male can be distinguished from a female by the organs of generation, and the feet are formed, the hooves being cleft, the whole having a mucous consistency and a pale yellowish colour.

The substance of the uterus begins to be extenuated immediately after the appearance of the embryo; contrary to what takes place in the human female, whose uterus grows every day thicker and fleshier with the advancing growth of the fœtus. In the hind and doe, on the other hand, the more the embryo augments the more do the cornua of the uterus assimilate themselves to the intestines; that horn in particular in which the fœtus is contained looks like a bag or pouch, and exceeds the opposite one in dimensions.

The ovum or conception, thus far advanced, and with its included fœtus perfectly distinct, has still contracted no adhesions to its mother's sides: the whole can most readily be withdrawn from the uterus, as I have ascertained with an ovum which contained a fœtus nearly the length of the thumb. It is manifest, therefore, that the fœtus up to this period has been nourished by the albumen alone that is contained within the conception; in the same way as we have ascertained the process to go on within the hen's egg. The mouths of the umbilical veins are lost and obliterated between the albumen and neighbouring humours of the conception and their containing membranes; but nowhere is there as yet any connexion with the uterus, although by these veins alone is nourishment supplied to the embryo. And as in the egg the ramifications of the veins are first sent to the colliquament (in the same way as the roots of trees penetrate the ground) and afterwards take their course to the external tunic called the chorion, whereon, for the sake of the nourishment, they are dispersed in an infinity of ramifications through the albuminous fluid contained within the outer membrane, so have I observed veins in the chorion of a human abortion; and Aristotle also states "that membrane to be crowded with veins."[1]

If the fœtus be single its umbilical vessels are distributed to both horns, and a few twigs are also sent to the intervening body of the uterus; but if the conception be double, one in either horn, each sends its umbilical vessels to its own horn alone; the embryo in the right horn deriving nourishment from the right part of the conception, that in the left from the left portion of the same. In other respects the twin-conception here is precisely similar to the twin-conception of the egg.

Towards the end of November, then, all the parts are clearly and distinctly to be distinguished, and the fœtus is now of the size of a large bean or nutmeg; its occiput is prominent, as in the chick, but its eyes are smaller; the mouth extends from ear to ear, the cheeks and lips, as consisting of membranous parts, being perfected at a very late period. In the fœtuses of all animals, indeed, that of man inclusive, the oral aperture without lips or cheeks is seen stretching from ear to ear; and this is the reason, unless I much mistake, why so many are born with the upper lip divided as it is in the hare

[1] *History of Animals*, VII. 7.

and camel, whence the common name of *hare-lip* for the deformity. In the development of the human fœtus the upper lip only coalesces in the middle line at a very late period.

I have frequently put a fœtus the size of a large bean, swimming in its extremely pure nutritive fluid within the transparent amnion, into a silver basin filled with the clearest water, and have noted these particulars as most worthy of observation: the brain of somewhat greater consistency than white of egg, like milk moderately coagulated, and of an irregular shape, and without any covering of skull, is contained within a general investing membrane. The cerebellum projects in a peak, as in the chick. The conical mass of the heart is of a white colour, and all the other viscera, the liver inclusive, are white and spermatic-looking. The trunk of the umbilical veins arises from the heart, and passing the convexity of the liver, perforates the trunk of the vena portæ, whence, advancing a little and subdividing into a great number of branches, it is distributed to the colliquament and tunica choroidea in innumerable fine filaments. The sides of the body ascend on either hand from the spine, so that the thorax presents itself in the guise of a boat or small vessel, up to the period at which the heart and lungs are included within its area, precisely and in all respects as we have seen it in the development of the chick. The heart, intestines, and other viscera, are very conspicuous, and present themselves as appendages of the body, until the thorax and abdomen being drawn around them, and the roof, as it were, put on the building, they are concealed within the compages of these cavities. At this time the sides both of the thorax and abdomen are white, gelatinous, and apparently identical in structure, save that a number of slender white lines are perceived in the walls of the thorax, as indications of the future ribs, whereby a distinction is here made between the bony and fleshy compages of the cavity.

I have also occasionally observed in conceptions of the sheep, which were sometimes twin, sometimes single, of corresponding age and about a finger's breadth in length, that the form of the embryo resembled a small lizard of the size of a wasp or caterpillar; the spine being curved into a circle, and the head almost in contact with the tail. In the double conceptions both were of the same size, as if produced at once and simultaneously; each floated distinctly within the fluid of its own amnion; but although one lay in the right, the other in the left horn of the uterus, they were still both included in the same double sac or wallet, both belonged to the same ovum, and were surrounded by the same common external fluid. The mouth was large, but the eyes were mere points, so that they could scarcely be seen, very different, therefore, from what occurs among birds. The viscera in these embryos were also pendulous without the body, not yet inclosed within the appropriate cavities. The outer membrane or chorion adhered in no way to the uterus, so that the entire conception was readily removed. Within the substance of the chorion innumerable branches of the umbilical vessels were conspicuous, but having no connexion whatsoever with the walls of the uterus; a circumstance to which allusion has already been made in the case of the deer; the distribution was in fact very much as we have found it on the external tunic of the hen's egg. There were but two humours, and the same number of containing tunics, of which the chorion extending through both cornua, and full of a more turbid fluid, gave general configuration to the ovum or conception. The tunica amnios again is almost invisible, like the tunica arachnoides of the eye, and embraces the crystalline humour in which the embryo floats.

The fluid of the amnion was, in proportion, but a hundredth, or shall I say a thousandth, to that of the chorion; although the crystalline humour of the amnion was still in such quantity that no one could reasonably imagine it to be the sweat of the very small embryo that floated within it. It was, further, extremely limpid, and seemed to be without anything like bad taste or smell. It was, as we have already observed of the deer, in all respects like watery milk, and had none of the obnoxious qualities of an excrement. I add, that if this fluid were of an excrementitious nature it ought to increase in quantity with the growth of the fœtus. But I have found precisely the opposite of this to obtain in the conception of the ewe, so that shortly before she lambs there is scarce a drop of the fluid in question remaining. I am, therefore, rather inclined to regard it as aliment than as excrement.

The internal tunic of the uterus of the ewe is covered with caruncles innumerable, as the heavens are with stars. These are not unlike crabs' eyes, and I have called them by this name; but they are smaller, like pendulous warts, glandular and white, sticking within the coats of the uterus, and somewhat excavated towards the conception; otherwise than in the deer, consequently, in which the caruncles corresponding to these rather project towards the embryo. These caruncles are gorged with blood, and their inner surface, where they regard the conception, is perceived to be beset with black sanguineous points. The umbilical vessels of the embryo were not yet connected with these caruncles, nor did the conception itself adhere to the uterus.

I find nothing of an allantois, of which something has been said as a tunic distinct from the chorion, in the conception of the ewe. At a later period, indeed, when the embryo is larger, when the ovum or conception has contracted adhesions with the uterus, and the umbilical vessels have penetrated the caruncles, the chorion extends farther, and at its extremities on either side, and as it were in a couple of appendices, there is a certain fluid of a yellow colour, which you might call excrementitious, kept separate and distinct.

The human conception scarcely differs in any respect from an egg during the first months of pregnancy. I have observed a clear fluid, like the more liquid white of an egg, to be included within an extremely delicate membrane. At this time the placenta had not yet appeared, and the entire conception was of the size of a pigeon's, or perhaps a pheasant's egg. The embryo itself, of the length of the little finger-nail, and having the form of a small frog, was conspicuous enough. The body was broad, the oral aperture widely cleft, the legs and arms like the stalks of flowers just risen above the ground, the occiput prominent, or rather forming a vesicle appended to the rest of the head, such as we have described the rudiments of the future cerebellum in the chick.

In another human conception of about the fiftieth day, the ovum was as large as a hen's or a turkey's egg. The embryo was as long as a large bean, the head of very large relative dimensions, and dominated by the cerebellum as by a kind of crest. The brain itself was of the consistence of curdled milk. Instead of a cranium there was a coriaceous membrane, in some places cartilaginous, and divided down the forehead to the roots of the nostrils; the face looked like the muzzle of a dog. There were no external ears, nor any nose, yet could the rudiments of the trachea passing down to the lungs, and those of the penis, be detected. The two auricles of the heart presented themselves like eyes, of a black colour.

In the body of a woman who died of fever I found an hermaphrodite embryo nearly of the same size. The pudendum was like that of the rabbit, the labia standing for prepuce, the nymphæ for glans. In the upper part the root of the penis was also apparent, and on either side for the testicle there was the lax skin of the scrotum. The uterus was extremely diminutive, and in figure like that of the ewe or mole, with two horns. And as the prostate glands are situated near the penis of the boy, so were the testicles (ovaries) of visible dimensions, seen adjacent to these cornua. Externally considered, the sex seemed that of the male; internally, however, it was rather that of the female. The uterus of the mother was of great size, having the urinary bladder connected with it as an appendage. In the embryo, on the contrary, the bladder was large with the uterus of very small dimensions attached to it.

All the human ova that have been described above were, like those of the ewe, shaggy externally, and besmeared with a kind of gelatine, or glutinous matter. At this epoch, too, there was neither any placenta apparent, nor any visible connexion with the uterus; neither was there any implantation into the substance of the uterus of the umbilical vessels scattered over the surface of the conception itself.

As in the deer, so in the sheep, goat, and other bisulcated animals, do we find more than one fœtus in the same conception, just as in twin-fraught eggs we find two chicks surrounded by the same albumen. But in the dog, rabbit, hog, and other viviparous animals that produce a considerable number at a litter, the thing is otherwise. In these each fœtus has two humours, these being severally surrounded with their proper membranes.

In the bitch there are a number of knots or constrictions along the whole course of either cornu of the uterus, between each of which the appropriate humours and a single embryo are contained. In the hare and rabbit we observe a number of balls, like the eggs of serpents, so that the horns of the uterus look like a pair of bracelets composed of so many amber beads strung upon a thread. The conception of the hare bears a strong resemblance to an acorn, the placenta embracing the embryo like a cup, and the humours inclosed in their membranes depending like the gland or nut.

EXERCISE 70. *Of the conception of the deer in the course of the month of December*

In the beginning of December the fœtus is seen larger, every way more perfect, and the length of the finger. The heart and other viscera which formerly hung externally are now concealed within the cavities of the body, so that they can no longer be seen without dissection.

The conception, or ovum, by the medium of the five caruncles which we have already spoken of as present in either cornu, is now in connexion with the uterus at an equal number of points; still the union is not so strong but that a very slight rather than a great effort suffices to break it. When the conception is detached, we perceive points or depressions on the surface of the chorion at the places where the adhesions to the uterus had existed, these spots being further covered with a certain viscid and wrinkled matter, as if this had been the bond of union between the mother and the ovum. Thus have we the nature and use of these caruncles made known to us: seen in the first instance as fungi or excrescences growing from the sides of the uterus, they are now recognized in connexion with the conception, as standing instead of the placenta or uterine cake in the human subject, and performing the same office. These caruncles are in fact but as so many nipples, whence the embryo by means of its umbilical vessels receives the nourishment that is supplied by the mother, as shall be clearly shown by what is to follow.

The size and capacity of the uterus, by which name we understand the cornua, or place occupied by the conception, is increased in proportion to the growth of the embryo; in suchwise, however, that the horn in which the fœtus is lodged is larger than the other.

The conception or ovum is single, whether one or several embryos are evolved from it; and it extends, as already said, into both of the horns, so that it presents itself with the shape of a double pudding, or rather of a single pudding having a constriction in its middle. Proceeding rounded and slender from the upper extremity of one of the horns, the conception gradually enlarges, and is produced into that common cavity which in the human female is called the uterus or matrix (because, by conceiving and cherishing her offspring in this place the woman is made a mother); the conception of the deer, passing through a kind of isthmus in the body of the uterus, is narrowed; but by and by, escaping into the other cornu, it there expands at first, but anon contracts again, and finally ends as it began in a tapering extremity. The whole conception, therefore, taken out entire, resembles a wallet filled with water on either side; and hence the chorion is also called allantois, because the conception in the lower animals, such as the deer, looks like an intestine inflated, or stuffed and tied in the middle.

In the embryo anatomized at this period every internal part is seen distinct and perfect; particularly the stomach, intestines, heart, kidneys, and lungs, which, divided into lobes, but having the proper form of the organs, look bloody. The colour of the lungs is deeper than it is in those fœtuses that have breathed, because the lungs, dilated by the act of respiration, assume a whiter tint. And by this indication is it known whether a mother has brought forth a living or dead child; in the former case the colour of the lungs is changed, and the change remains though the infant have died immediately afterwards.

In the female fœtus the testes—improperly so called—are seen situated near the kidneys at the extremities of the cornua uteri on either side; they are relatively of larger size than in the adult, and, like the caruncles of the uterus, look white.

In the stomach of the fœtus there is a watery fluid contained, not unlike that in which it swims, but somewhat more turbid or less transparent. It resembles the milk that begins to be secreted in the breasts of pregnant women about the fourth or fifth month of pregnancy, and may be pressed out of the nipples, or it is like the drink which we call white posset.

In the small intestines there is an abundance of chyle concocted from the same matter; in the colon greenish fæces and scybala begin to appear.

I do not find the urachus perforate; neither do I perceive any difference between the tunica allantoides or allantois, which is said to contain urine, and the chorion. Neither do I detect any urine in the secundines, but only in the bladder, where indeed it is present in large quantity. The bladder, of an oblong form, is situated between the umbilical arteries as they proceed from the bifurcation of the descending aorta.

The liver is rudely sketched and almost shapeless, as if it were a mere accidental part; it looks like a red coloured mass of extravasated blood. The brain, with some pretensions to regularity of outline, is contained within the dura mater. The eyes are concealed under the eyelids, which are as firmly glued together as we find them in puppies for some short time after birth, so that I found it scarcely possible to separate them and open the eyes. The breast-bones and ribs have a certain degree of firmness, and the colour of the muscles changes from white to blood red.

By the great number of dissections which I performed in the course of this month, I was every day confirmed in my opinion that the carunculæ of the uterus perform the office of the placenta; they are at this time found of a reddish colour, turgid, and of the size of walnuts. The conception, which had previously adhered to the caruncles by the medium of mucor or glutinous matter only, now sends the branches of its umbilical vessels into them, as plants send their roots into the ground, by which it is fastened and may be said to grow to the uterus.

About the end of December the fœtus is a span long, and I have seen it moving lustily and kicking; opening and shutting its mouth; the heart, inclosed in the pericardium, when exposed, was found pulsating strongly and visibly; its ventricles, however, were still uniform, of equal amplitude of cavity and thickness of parietes; and each ending in a separate apex, they form together a double-pointed cone. Occasionally, I have seen the fluid contained in the auricles of the heart, which at this time present themselves as ample sacs filled with blood, continuing to pulsate for some short time after the ventricles themselves had left off contracting.

The internal organs, all of which had lately become perfect, were now larger and more conspicuous. The skull was partly cartilaginous, partly osseous. The hooves were yellowish, flexible, and soft, resembling those of the adult animal softened in hot water. The uterine caruncles, of great magnitude and like immense fungi, extended over the whole cavity of the uterus, and plainly performed the office of placentæ, for numerous and ample branches of the umbilical vessels penetrated their substance there to imbibe nutritive matter for the growth of the embryo. As in the fœtus after birth, the chyle is now carried by the mesenteric veins to the porta of the liver.

Where there is a single fœtus the umbilical vessels are distributed to the whole of the carunculæ, both those of the horn where the fœtus is lodged and those of the opposite horn; where there is a pair of embryos formed, the umbilical vessels of each only extend to the caruncles of the horn appropriated to it.

The smaller umbilical veins in tending towards the fœtus, form larger and larger trunks by coalescing, until at length two great canals are formed, which in conjunction pour their blood into the vena cava and vena portæ. But the umbilical arteries, which arise from the division of the descending aorta, form two trunks of small size, not remarkable save for their pulse: proceeding to the boundary of the conception, in other words, to the conjunction of the placenta or carunculæ with the ramifications of the umbilical veins, they first divide into numerous capillary twigs, and then are lost in others that are invisible.

As the extremities of the umbilical veins within the uterus terminate in the caruncles, so the uterine vessels on the outside, which are large and numerous, and bring the blood from the mother towards the uterus, by means of the vessels of the suspensory ligaments, terminate externally on the caruncles. It is to be noted, also, that the internal vessels are almost all veins; the external vessels, again, are in many instances branches of arteries. In the placenta of the woman, if it be carefully examined immediately after delivery, a much larger number of arteries than of veins, and these of larger size, will be found dispersed on every side in innumerable subdivisions to the very edge of the mass. In the same kind of spongy parenchyma of the spleen, the number of the arteries is also greater than that of the veins.

The exterior uterine vessels run to the uterus, as I have said, not to the ovaries (*testiculi*) situated in the suspensory ligament, as some suppose.

I have remarked an admirable instance of the skill of nature, in the bulge or convexity of the caruncles turned towards the conception: a quantity of white and mucilaginous matter is discovered in a number of cavities, cotyledons, or little cups; these are all as full of this matter as we ever see waxen cells full of honey; now this matter, in colour, consistency, and taste, is extremely like white of egg. On tearing the conception away from the caruncles, you will perceive numbers of suckers or capillary branches of the umbilical veins, looking like lengthened filaments, extracted at the same time from every one of the cotyledons and pits, and from amidst their mucilaginous contents; very much as we see the delicate filaments of the roots of herbs following the stem when it is pulled out of the ground.

It is clearly ascertained from this that the extremities of the umbilical vessels are not conjoined by any anastomosis with the extremities of the uterine vessels; that they do not imbibe any blood from them, but that they end and are obliterated in that mucilaginous matter, and from it take up their nourishment, nearly in the same way as at an earlier period they had

sought for aliment from the albuminous humour contained within the membranes of the conception. In the same manner, consequently, as the chick *in ovo* is nourished by the white of the egg through its umbilical vessels, is the fœtus of the hind and doe nourished by a similar albuminous matter laid up in these cells, and not directly from the blood of the mother.

These carunculæ might therefore with propriety be called the uterine liver, or the uterine mammæ, seeing that they are organs adapted for the preparation and concoction of that albuminous aliment, and fitting it for absorption by the veins. In those viviparous animals consequently that have neither caruncles nor placentæ, as the horse and the hog, the fœtus is nourished up to the moment of its birth by fluids contained within the conception or ovum; nor has the ovum in these animals at any time a connexion with the uterus.

From all of what precedes it is manifest that in both the classes of viviparous animals alluded to, those, namely, that are provided with carunculæ or cotyledons, and those that want them, and perhaps in viviparous animals generally, the fœtus *in utero* is not nourished otherwise than the chick *in ovo;* the nutritive matter, the albumen, being of the same identical kind in all. As in the egg the terminations of the umbilical vessels are in the white and yelk, so in the hind and doe, and other animals furnished with uterine cotyledons like them, the final distributions of the umbilical vessels are sent to the humours that are included within the conception or ovum, and to the albumen that is stored in the cotyledons, or cup-like cavities of the carunculæ, where they open and end. And this is further obvious from the fact of the extremities of the umbilical vessels, when they are drawn out of the afore-mentioned mucor, looking completely white; a certain proof that they absorb this mucilage liquefied only, and not blood. The same arrangement may very readily be observed to obtain in the egg.

The human placenta is rendered uneven on its convex surface, and where it adheres to the uterus, by a number of tuberous projections, and it seems indeed to adhere to the uterus by means of these; it is not consequently attached at every point, but at those places only where the vessels pierce it in search of nourishment, and at those where, in consequence of this arrangement, an appearance as if of vessels broken short off is perceived. But whether the extremities of these vessels suck up blood from the uterus, or rather a certain concocted matter of the nature of albumen, as I have described the thing in the hind and doe, I have not yet ascertained.

Finally, that the truth just announced may be still more fully confirmed, it is found that by compressing the uterine caruncles between the fingers, about a spoonful of the nutritive fluid in question may be obtained from each of them, as from a nipple, unmixed with blood, which is not obtained even with forcible pressure. Moreover, the caruncle thus milked and emptied, like a compressed sponge, contracts and becomes flaccid, and is seen to be pierced with a great number of holes. From everything, therefore, it appears that these caruncles are uterine mammæ, or fountains and receptacles of nutritive albumen.

The month of December at an end, the caruncles adhere less firmly to the uterus than before, and a small matter suffices to detach them. The larger the fœtus grows, indeed, the nearer it is to its term, the more readily are the caruncles detached from the uterus, so that, like ripe fruit from the tree, they slip at length from the uterus of themselves, and as if they had formed an original element in the conception.

Separated from the uterus you may perceive in the prints which they leave points pouring out blood; these are the arteries that entered them. But if you now detach the conception from the caruncles, no blood is effused; none escapes, save from the ends of the vessels proceeding from the conception, although it does seem more consonant with reason to suppose that blood should be shed from the caruncles than from the conception when they are forcibly separated. For, as the caruncles or cotyledons have an abundance of uterine branches distributed to them, and they are generally believed to receive blood for the nourishment of the fœtus, we should expect that they would appear replete with blood. Nevertheless, as I have said, they yield no blood either under milking or compression, and the reason of this is that they contain albumen rather than blood, and rather store up than prepare this matter. It seems manifest, therefore, that the fœtus *in utero* is not nourished by its mother's blood, but by this albuminous fluid duly elaborated. It may even be perhaps that the adult animal is not nourished immediately by the blood, but rather by something mixed with the blood, which serves as the ultimate aliment; as may perhaps be more particularly shown in our *Physiology* and particular treatise on the blood.

The truth of that passage of Hippocrates where it said that "those whose acetabula or cotyledons are full of mucor, abort,"[1] has always been suspected by me; for this is no excrementitious matter or cause of miscarriage, but nourishment and a source of life. But Hippocrates, by the word acetabula, perhaps, understood something else than the parts so called in the uterus of the lower animals, for they are wanting in women; nor does the placenta in the human subject contain any collections of albuminous matter in distinct cavities.

Modern medical writers, following the Arabians, speak of three nutritious humours—dew, gluten, and cambium; these Fernelius designates nutritious juices; as if he had wished to imply that the parts of our bodies were not immediately nourished by the blood as ultimate nutriment, but by these secondary juices. The first of them, like dew, bathes all the minutest particles of the body on every side: this fluid, become thicker by an ulterior concoction, and adhering to the parts, is called gluten; finally, altered and assimilated by the proper virtue of the part, it is called cambium.

He who espoused such views might designate the matter which is contained in the cotyledonous cavities of the deer as gluten or nutritious albumen, and maintain that as the ultimate nourishment destined for each of the particular parts of the fœtus it was analogous to the albumen or vitellus of the egg. For as we but lately stated, with Aristotle, that the yelk of the egg was analogous to milk, so do we think it not unreasonable to assert that the matter lodged in the cotyledons, or acetabula of the uterine placenta, stands instead of milk to the fœtus so long as it remains in the uterus; in this way the caruncles approve themselves a kind of internal mammæ, the nutritive matter of which, transferred at the period of parturition to the proper mammæ, there assumes the nature of milk, an arrangement by which the fœtus is seen to be nourished with the same food after it has begun its independent existence, as it was whilst it lodged in the uterus. Between the two-coloured eggs of oviparous animals, consequently, or the eggs that consist of a white and a yelk, and the ova or conceptions of viviparous animals, there is only this difference, that in the former the vitellus (which is a secondary nutritive matter) is prepared within the egg, and at the period of birth, being stored within the abdomen of the young creature, serves it as food;

[1] *On the Nature of Diseases Common to Women;* see also *Aphorisms,* v. 45.

whilst in the latter, the nutritive juice is laid up within acetabula, and after birth is transferred to the mammæ; so that the chick is nourished with milk inclosed in its interior, whilst the fœtus of the viviparous animal draws its nourishment from the breasts of its mother.

In the months of January, February, &c., as nothing new or worthy of note occurs which has not been already mentioned, (more than the growth of the hair, teeth, horns, &c.) but the parts only grow larger without reference to the process of generation, it seems unnecessary to say more upon such points at present.

I have frequently examined the conceptions of sheep during the same intervals. These I find, as in the deer, extending into both horns of the uterus, and presenting the figure of a wallet or double sausage. In several of them I found two fœtuses; in others only one: they were without a trace of wool on the surface, and the eyelids were so closely glued together that they could not be opened; the hooves, however, were present. Where there were two embryos they were contained in the opposite horns of the uterus, and without any regard to sex with reference to the right or left horn, the male being sometimes in the right, sometimes in the left, and the female the same; both, however, were, in every instance, included within one and the same common external membrane or chorion. The extreme ends of this membrane were stained on either hand with a yellow or bilious excrement, and appeared to contain something turbid or excrementitious in their interior.

Many caruncles, or miniature placentas of different sizes, were discovered, and otherwise disposed than in the hind and doe. In the sheep they look like rounded fungi with the footstalks broken off, and are contained in the coats of the uterus; their rounded or convex aspects are turned to the uterus (a circumstance, by the way, common to the cow and sheep), their concave aspects, which are the smooth ones, being turned towards the fœtus. The larger branches of the vessels are also distributed to the concave portion, as in the human placenta. The branches in extension of the umbilical vessels connected with the caruncles, grow pretty firmly into them, so that when I attempted to separate them, the rounded portion was rather torn from the interior of the uterus than from the ovum or conception; different, consequently, from what we observed in the deer, where the chorion was readily detached from the cotyledons of the caruncles, and where the convexity of the caruncle, connected with the

conception, is separable, whilst the concavity, or rather the pedicle or root, is firmly adherent to the uterus. In other respects the function seems to be the same in both cases; in both the same acetabula are discovered, and the same viscid and albuminous mucus can be pressed out in both, as it can also in the cow.

In the conception that contains a single fœtus, the umbilical vessels are distributed to the whole of the caruncles of either horn; but the one in which the fœtus itself is contained, swimming in its crystalline fluid within the amnion, is larger than the other. In the cases where there are two fœtuses present, each has its own separate or appropriate caruncles, and does not send its umbilical vessels in quest of nourishment beyond the cornu in which it is lodged.

In male fœtuses, the testes contained in the scrotum, of large size for the age, hang externally. Female fœtuses, again, have their dugs in the same situation, furnished with nipples like the breasts of women.

In the compound stomach of the fœtus, namely the omasus and abomasus, a clear fluid is discovered, similar to that in which it floats; the two liquids agreeing obviously in smell, taste, and consistency. There is also a quantity of chyle in the upper part of the intestinal tube; in the inferior portion a greenish-coloured excrement and scybala, such as we find when the animal is feeding on grass. The liver is discovered of considerable size, the gall-bladder of an oblong shape, and in some cases empty.

In so far as the order in which the several parts are produced is concerned, we have still found the same rule to be observed in the hind and doe as in the egg, and we believe that the same law obtains among viviparous animals generally.

EXERCISE 71. *Of the innate heat*

As frequent mention is made in the preceding pages of the *calidum innatum*, or innate heat, I have determined to say a few words here, by way of dessert, both on that subject and on the *humidum primigenium*, or radical moisture, to which I am all the more inclined because I observe that many pride themselves upon the use of these terms without, as I apprehend, rightly understanding their meaning. There is, in fact, no occasion for searching after spirits foreign to, or distinct from, the blood; to evoke heat from another source; to bring gods upon the scene, and to encumber philosophy with any fanciful conceits; what we are wont to derive from the stars is in truth produced at home: the blood is the only calidum innatum, or first engendered animal heat; a fact which so clearly appears from our observations on animal reproduction, particularly of the chick from the egg, that it seems superfluous to multiply illustrations.

There is, indeed, nothing in the animal body older or more excellent than the blood; nor are the spirits which are distinguished from the blood at any time found distinct from it; for the blood without heat or spirit is no longer blood, but cruor or gore. "The blood," says Aristotle, "is hot in a certain manner, in that, namely, in virtue of which it exists as blood—just as we speak of hot-water under a single term; as subject, however, and in itself finally, blood is blood, it is not *hot*: so that as blood is in a certain way hot *per se*, so is it also in a certain way not hot *per se*: heat is in its essence or nature, in the same way as whiteness is in the essence of a white man; but where blood is by affection or passion, it is not hot *per se*."[1]

We physicians at this time designate that as spirit which Hippocrates called *impetum faciens*, or moving power; implying by this whatever attempts aught by its own proper effort, and causes motion with rapidity and force, or induces action of any kind; in this sense we are accustomed to speak of spirit of wine, spirit of vitriol, &c. And therefore it is that physicians admit as many spirits as there are principal parts or operations of the body, viz., animal, vital, natural, visual, auditory, concoctive, generative, implanted, influent, &c. &c. But the blood is the first produced and most principal part of the body, endowed with each and all of these virtues, possessed of powers of action beyond all the rest, and therefore, κατ' ἐξοχὴν—in virtue of its pre-eminence, meriting the title of spirit.

Scaliger, Fernelius, and others, giving less regard to the admirable qualities of the blood, have imagined other spirits of an aerial or ethereal nature, or composed of an ethereal or elementary matter, a something more excellent and divine than the innate heat, the immediate instrument of the soul, fitted for all the highest duties. Now their principal motive for this was the consideration that the blood, as composed of elements, could have no power of action beyond these elements or the bodies compounded of them. They have, therefore, feigned or imagined a spirit, different from the ingenerate heat, of celestial origin and nature; a body of perfect simplicity, most subtile, attenuated, mobile, rapid, lucid, ethereal, participant in the qualities of the quintessence. They have not, however, anywhere demonstrated the actual existence of such a spirit, or that it was superior to the elements in its powers of action, or indeed that it could accomplish more than the blood by itself. We, for our own part, who use our simple senses in studying natural things, have been unable anywhere to find anything of the sort. Neither are there any cavities for the production and preservation of such spirits, either in fact or presumed by their authors. Fernelius, indeed, has these words: "He who has not yet completely mastered the matter and state of the ingenerate heat, let him cast an eye upon the structure of the body, and turn to the arteries, and contemplate the sinuses of the heart and the ventricles of the brain. When he observes them empty, containing next to no fluid, and yet feels that he must own such parts not made in vain, or without a design, he will soon, I conceive, be brought to conclude that an extremely subtile aura or vapour fills them during the life of the animal, and which, as being of extreme lightness, vanished insensibly when the creature died. It is for the sake of cherishing this aura that by inspiration we take in air, which not only serves for the refrigeration of the body, by a business that might be otherwise accomplished, but further supplies a kind of nourishment."[2]

But we maintain that so long as an animal lives, the cavities of the heart and the arteries are filled with blood. We further believe the ventricles of the brain to be indifferently fitted for any so excellent office, and that they are rather formed for secreting some excrementitious matter. What shall we say, too, when we find the brain of many animals unfurnished with ventricles? And supposing it were true that any kind of air or vapour was found there, seeing that all nature abhors a vacuum, still it does not seem over probable that it should be of heavenly origin and possessed of such superlative virtues. But what we admire most of all is that a spirit, the native of the skies, and endowed with such admirable qualities, should be nourished by our common and elementary air; especially when we see it maintained that the elements can do nothing that is beyond their natural powers.

It is admitted, moreover, that the spirits are in a perpetual state of flux, and most readily dissipated and corrupted; nor indeed can they endure for an instant unless renovated by due supplies of their appropriate nutriment—they

[1] *On the Parts of Animals*, II. 3.

[2] *Physiologia*, IV. 2.

as much require incessant nourishing as the primum vivens, or first animate atom of the body. What occasion is there, then, I ask, for this extraneous inmate, for this ethereal heat? when the blood is competent to perform all the offices ascribed to it, and the spirits cannot separate from the blood even by a hair's breadth without destruction; without the blood, indeed, the spirits can neither move nor penetrate anywhere as distinct and independent matters. And whether they are engendered and are fed and increased, as some suppose, from the thinner part of the blood, or from the primigenial moisture, as others imagine, all still confess that they are nowhere to be found apart from the blood, but are inseparably connected with it as the aliment that sustains them, even as the flame of a lamp or candle is inseparably connected with the oil or tallow that feeds it. The tenuity, subtilty, mobility, &c. of the spirits, therefore, bring no kind of advantage more than the blood, which it seems they constantly accompany, already possesses. The blood consequently suffices, and is adequate to be the immediate instrument of the soul, inasmuch as it is everywhere present, and moves hither and thither with the greatest rapidity. Nor can it be admitted that there are any other bodies or qualities of a spiritual and incorporeal nature, or any more divine kinds of heat, such as light, as Cæsar Cremoninus,[1] a great adept in the Aristotelian philosophy, strenuously contends against Albertus that there are.

If it be said that these spirits reside in the primigenial moisture as in their ultimate aliment, and flow from thence through the whole body to nourish its several parts, they propound a simple impossibility, viz., that the ingenerate heat, that primigenial element of the body, nourished itself, yet serves for the nourishment of the body at large. Upon such grounds the thing nourished and the thing that nourishes would be one and the same, and itself would both nourish and be nourished; which could in no way be effected; inasmuch as it is by no means probable that the nourishment should ever be mixed with the thing nourished, for things mixed must have equal powers and mutually act on one another; and, according to Aristotle's dictum, "where there is nutrition, there there is no mixture." But as nutrition takes place everywhere, the nutriment is one thing, and that which is nourished by it is another, and it is altogether indispensable that the one pass into the other.

[1] Dictata, VII.

But as it is thought that the spirits, and the ultimate or primigenial aliment, or something else, is contained in animals, which acts in a greater degree than the blood above the forces of the elements, we are not sufficiently informed what is understood by the expression, "acting above the forces of the elements"; neither are Aristotle's words rightly interpreted where he says, "every virtue or faculty of the soul appears to partake of another body more divine than those which are called elements. . . . For there is in every seed a certain something which causes it to be fruitful, viz., what is called heat, and that not fire or any faculty of the kind, but a spirit such as is contained in semen and frothy bodies; and the nature inherent in that spirit is responsive in its proportions to the element of the stars. Wherefore fire engenders no animal; neither is anything seen to be constituted of the dense, or moist, or dry. But the heat of the sun and of animals, and not only that which is stored up in semen, but even that of any excrementitious matter, although diverse in nature, still contains a vital principle. For the rest, it is obvious from this that the heat contained in animals is not fire, neither does it derive its origin from fire."[2] Now I maintain the same things of the innate heat and the blood; I say that they are not fire, and neither do they derive their origin from fire. They rather share the nature of some other, and that a more divine body or substance. They act by no faculty or property of the elements; but as there is a something inherent in the semen which makes it prolific, and as, in producing an animal, it surpasses the power of the elements—as it is a spirit, namely, and the inherent nature of that spirit corresponds to the essence of the stars— so is there a spirit, or certain force, inherent in the blood, acting superiorly to the powers of the elements, very conspicuously displayed in the nutrition and preservation of the several parts of the animal body; and the nature, yea, the soul in this spirit and blood, is identical with the essence of the stars. That the heat of the blood of animals during their lifetime, therefore, is neither fire, nor derived from fire, is manifest, and indeed is clearly demonstrated by our observations.

But that this may be made still more certain let me be permitted to digress a little from my subject, and, in a few words, to show what is meant by the word "spirit," and what by the phrases "superior in action to the forces of the elements," "to have the properties of another

[2] On the Generation of Animals, II. 3.

body, and that more divine than those bodies which are called elements," and "the nature inherent in this spirit which answers to the essence of the stars."

We have already had occasion to say something both of the nature of "spirit" and "the vital principle," and we shall here enter into the subject at greater length. There are three bodies—simple bodies—which seem especially entitled to receive the name, at all events, to perform the office of "spirit," viz., fire, air, and water, each of which, by reason of its ceaseless flux and motion, expressed by the words flame, wind, and flood, appears to have the properties of life, or of some other body. Flame is the flow of fire, wind the flow of air, stream or flood the flow of water. Flame, like an animal, is self-motive, self-nutrient, self-augmentative, and is the symbol of our life. It is therefore that it is so universally brought into requisition in religious ceremonies: it was guarded by priestesses and virgins in the temples of Apollo and Vesta as a sacred thing, and from the remotest antiquity has been held worthy of divine worship by the Persians and other ancient nations; as if God were most conspicuous in flame, and spoke to us from fire as He did to Moses of old. Air is also appropriately spoken of as "spirit," having received the title from the act of respiration. Aristotle himself admits, "that there is a kind of life, and birth, and death of the winds."[1] Finally, we speak of a running stream as "living water."

These three, therefore, inasmuch as they have a kind of life, appear to act superiorly to the forces of the element, and to share in a more divine nature; they were, therefore, placed among the number of the divinities by the heathen. When any excellent work or process appeared, surpassing the powers of the naked elements, it was held as proceeding from some more divine agent. "To act with power superior to the powers of the elements," therefore, and, on that account, "to share in the properties of some more divine thing, which does not derive its origin from the elements," appear to have the same signification.

The blood, in like manner, "acts with powers superior to the powers of the elements" in the fact of its existence, in the forms of primordial and innate heat, in semen and spirit, and its producing all the other parts of the body in succession; proceeding at all times with such foresight and understanding, and with definite ends in view, as if it employed reasoning in its

[1] *On the Generation of Animals*, IV. 10. chapter.

acts. Now this it does not, in so far as it is elementary, and as deriving its origin from fire, but in so far as it is possessed of plastic powers and endowed with the gift of the vegetative soul, as it is the primordial and innate heat, and the immediate and competent instrument of life. Αἷμα, τὸ ζωτικὸν τοῦ ἀνθρώπου: The blood is the living principle of man, says Suidas; and the same thing is true of all animals; an opinion which Virgil seems to have wished to express when he says:

> Una eademque via sanguisque animusque
> sequuntur.
> And by one path the blood and life flowed
> out.

The blood, therefore, by reason of its admirable properties and powers, is "spirit." It is also celestial; for nature, the soul, that which answers to the essence of the stars, is the inmate of the spirit, in other words, it is something analogous to heaven, the instrument of heaven, vicarious of heaven.

In this way all natural bodies fall to be considered under a twofold point of view, viz., either as they are specially regarded, and are comprehended within the limits of their own proper nature, or are viewed as the instruments of some more noble agent and superior power. For as regards their peculiar powers, there is, perhaps, no doubt but that all things subject to generation by birth, and to death and decay, derive their origin from the elements, and perform their offices agreeably to their proper standard; but in so far as they are the instruments of a more excellent agent, and are governed by that, not acting of their own proper nature, but by the regimen of another; therefore is it, therein is it, that they seem to participate with another and more divine body, and to surpass the powers of the ordinary elements.

In the same way, too, is the blood the animal heat, in so far, namely, as it is governed in its actions by the soul; for it is celestial as subservient to heaven; and divine, because it is the instrument of God the great and good. But this we have already spoken of above, where we have shown that male and female were the instruments of the sun, heaven, and Supreme Preserver, when they served for the generation of the more perfect animals.

The inferior world, according to Aristotle, is so continuous and connected with the superior orbits, that all its motions and changes appear to take their rise and to receive direction from thence. In that world, indeed, which the Greeks called Κόσμος from its order and beauty, inferior and corruptible things wait upon superior and incorruptible things; but all are still subservient to the will of the supreme, omnipotent, and eternal Creator.

They, therefore, who think that nothing composed of the elements can show powers of action superior to the forces exercised by these, unless they at the same time partake of some other and more divine body, and on this ground conceive the spirits they evoke as constituted partly of the elements, partly of a certain ethereal and celestial substance—these persons, I say, appear to me to reason indifferently. In the first place you will scarcely find any elementary body which in acting does not exceed its proper powers: air and water, the winds and the ocean, when they waft navies to either India and round this globe, and often by opposite courses, when they grind, bake, dig, pump, saw timber, sustain fire, support some things, overwhelm others, and suffice for an infinite variety of other and most admirable offices—who shall say that they do not surpass the powers of the elements? In like manner what does not fire accomplish? in the kitchen, in the furnace, in the laboratory, softening, hardening, melting, subliming, changing, in an infinite variety of ways! What shall we say of it when we see iron itself produced by its agency?—iron "that breaks the stubborn soil, and shakes the earth with war!"— iron that in the magnet (to which Thales therefore ascribed a soul) attracts other iron, "subdues all other things, and seeks besides I know not what inane," as Pliny[1] says; for the steel needle only rubbed with the loadstone still steadily points to the great cardinal points; and when our clocks constantly indicate the hours of the day and night—shall we not admit that all of these partake of something else, and that of a more divine nature, than the elements? And if in the domain and rule of nature so many excellent operations are daily effected surpassing the powers of the things themselves, what shall we not think possible within the pale and regimen of nature, of which all art is but imitation? And if, as ministers of man, they effect such admirable ends, what, I ask, may we not expect of them, when they are instruments in the hand of God?

We must, therefore, make the distinction and say, that whilst no primary agent or prime efficient produces effects beyond its powers, every instrumental agent may exceed its own

[1] *Hist. nat.* xxxvi. 16.

proper powers in action; for it acts not merely by its own virtue, but by the virtue of a superior efficient.

They, consequently, who refuse such remarkable faculties to the blood, and go to heaven to fetch down I know not what spirits, to which they ascribe these divine virtues, cannot know, or at all events, cannot consider that the process of generation, and even of nutrition, which indeed is a kind of generation, for the sake of which they are so lavish of admirable properties, surpasses the powers of those very spirits themselves, nor of the spirits only, but of the vegetative, aye, even the sensitive, and I will venture to add, the rational soul. Powers, did I say? It far exceeds even any estimate we can form of the rational soul; for the nature of generation, and the order that prevails in it, are truly admirable and divine, beyond all that thought can conceive or understanding comprehend.

That it may, however, more clearly appear that the remarkable virtues which the learned attribute to the spirits and the innate heat belong to the blood alone, besides what has already been spoken of as conspicuous in the egg before any trace of the embryo appears, as well as in the perfect and adult fœtus, the few following observations are made by way of further illustration, and for the sake of the diligent inquirer. The blood considered absolutely and by itself, without the veins, in so far as it is an elementary fluid, and composed of several parts— of thin and serous particles, and of thick and concrete particles called cruor—possesses but few, and these not very obvious virtues. Contained within the veins, however, inasmuch as it is an integral part of the body, and is animated, regenerative, and the immediate instrument and principal seat of the soul, inasmuch, moreover, as it seems to partake of the nature of another more divine body, and is transfused by divine animal heat, it obtains remarkable and most excellent powers, and is analogous to the essence of the stars. In so far as it is spirit, it is the hearth, the Vesta, the household divinity, the innate heat, the sun of the microcosm, the fire of Plato; not because like common fire it lightens, burns, and destroys, but because by a vague and incessant motion it preserves, nourishes, and aggrandizes itself. It further deserves the name of spirit, inasmuch as it is radical moisture, at once the ultimate and the proximate and the primary aliment, more abundant than all the other parts; preparing for and administering to these the same nutriment with which itself is fed, ceaselessly permeating the whole body, cherishing and keeping alive the parts which it has fashioned and added to itself, not otherwise assuredly than the superior stars, the sun and moon especially, in maintaining their own proper orbits, continually vivify the stars that are beneath them.

Since the blood acts, then, with forces superior to the forces of the elements, and exerts its influence through these forces or virtues, and is the instrument of the Great Workman, no one can ever sufficiently extol its admirable, its divine faculties. In the first place, and especially, it is possessed by a soul which is not only vegetative, but sensitive and motive also; it penetrates everywhere and is ubiquitous; abstracted, the soul or the life too is gone, so that the blood does not seem to differ in any respect from the soul or the life itself (*anima*); at all events, it is to be regarded as the substance whose act is the soul or the life. Such, I say, is the soul, which is neither wholly corporeal nor yet wholly incorporeal; which is derived in part from abroad, and is partly produced at home; which in one way is part of the body, but in another way is the beginning and cause of all that is contained in the animal body, viz., nutrition, sense, and motion, and consequently of life and of death alike; for whatever is nourished, is itself vivified, and *vice versa*. In like manner, that which is abundantly nourished increases; what is not sufficiently supplied shrinks; what is perfectly nourished preserves its health; what is not perfectly nourished falls into disease. The blood, therefore, even as the soul, is to be regarded as the cause and author of youth and old age, of sleep and waking, and also of respiration; all the more and especially as the first instrument in natural things contains the internal moving cause within itself. It therefore comes to the same thing, whether we say that the soul and the blood, or the blood with the soul, or the soul with the blood, performs all the acts in the animal organism.

We are too much in the habit, neglecting things, of worshipping specious names. The word blood, signifying a substance, which we have before our eyes, and can touch, has nothing of grandiloquence about it; but before such titles as spirits, and calidum innatum or innate heat, we stand agape. But the mask removed, as the error disappears, so does the idle admiration. The celebrated stone, so much vaunted for its virtues by Pipinus to Migaldus, seems to have filled not only them but also Thuanus, an excellent historian, with wonder and admira-

tion. Let me be allowed to append the riddle: "Lately," says he, "there was brought from the East Indies to our king a stone, which we have seen, wonderfully radiant with light and effulgence, the whole of which, as if burning and in flames, was resplendent with an incredible brilliancy of light. Tossed hither and thither, it filled the ambient air with beams that were scarcely bearable by any eyes. It was also extremely impatient of the earth; if you essayed to cover it, it forthwith and of itself burst forth with violence, and mounted on high. No man could by any art contain or inclose it in any confined place; on the contrary, it appears to delight in free and spacious places. It is of the highest purity, of the greatest brightness, and is without stain or blemish. It has no certain shape, but a shape uncertain and changing every moment. Of the most consummate beauty, it suffers no one to touch it; and if you persist too long or obstinately, it will do you injury, as I have observed it repeatedly to do in no trifling measure. If anything be by chance taken from it by persevering efforts, it is (strange to say) made nothing less thereby. Its custodier adds further, that its virtues and powers are useful in a great variety of ways, and even—especially to kings—indispensably necessary; but these he declines to reveal without being first paid a large reward." The author might have added of this *stone* that it was neither hard nor soft, and exhibited a variety of forms and colours, and had a singular trick of trembling and palpitating, and like an animal—although itself inanimate—consumed a large quantity of food every day for its nutrition or sustenance. Further, that he had heard from men worthy of credit, that this stone had formerly fallen from heaven to earth; that it was the frequent cause of thunder and lightning, and was still occasionally engendered from the solar beams refracted through water.

Who would not admire so remarkable a stone, or believe that it acted with a force superior to the forces of the elements, that it participated in the nature of another body, and possessed an ethereal spirit? especially when he found that it responded in its proportions to the essence of the sun. But with Fernelius[1] for Œdipus, we find the whole enigma resolving itself into "Flame."

In the same way, did I paint the blood under the garb of a fable, and gave it the title of the philosopher's stone, and propose all its wonderful faculties and operations in enigmatical lan-

[1] *De abdit. rer. caus.*, II. 27.

guage, many would doubtless think a great deal of it; they would readily believe that it could act with powers superior to those of the elements, and they would not unwillingly allow it to be possessed of another and more divine body.

EXERCISE 72. *Of the primigenial moisture*

We have now dignified the blood with the title of the innate heat; with like propriety, we believe, that the fluid which we have called the crystalline colliquament, from which the fœtus and its parts primarily and immediately arise, may be designated the radical and primigenial moisture. There is certainly nothing in the generation of animals to which this title can with better right be given.

We call this the radical moisture, because from it arises the first particle of the embryo, the blood, to wit; and all the other posthumous parts arise from it as from a root; and they are procreated and nourished, and grow and are preserved by the same matter.

We also call it primigenial, because it is first engendered in every animal organism, and is, as it were, the foundation of the rest, as may be seen in the egg, in which it presents itself after a brief period of incubation, as the first work of the inherent fecundity and reproductive power.

This fluid is also the most simple, pure, and unadulterated body, in which all the parts of the pullet are present potentially, though none of them are there actually. It appears that nature has conceded to it the same qualities which are usually ascribed to first matter common to all things, viz., that potentially it be capable of assuming all forms, but have itself no form in fact. So the crystalline humour of the eye, in order that it might be susceptible of all colours, is itself colourless; and in like manner are the media or organs of each of the senses destitute of all the other qualities of sensible things: the organs of smelling and hearing, and the air which ministers to them, are without smell and sound; the saliva of the tongue and mouth is also tasteless.

And it is upon this argument that they mainly rely who maintain the possibility of an incorporeal intellect, viz., because it is susceptible of all forms without matter; and as the hand is called the "instrument of instruments," so is the intellect called "the form of forms," being itself immaterial and wholly without form; it is, therefore, said to be possible or potential, but not passible.

This fluid, or one analogous to it, appears also to be the ultimate aliment from which Aristotle taught that the semen, or geniture, as he calls it, is produced.[1] I say the ultimate aliment, called dew by the Arabians, with which all the parts of the body are bathed and moistened. For in the same way as this dew, by ulterior condensation and adhesion, becomes alible gluten and cambium, whence the parts of the body are constituted, so, *mutatis mutandis*, in the commencement of generation and nutrition, from gluten liquefied and rendered thinner is formed the nutritious dew: from the white of the egg is produced the colliquament under discussion, the radical moisture and primigenial dew. The thing indeed is identical in either instance, if any credit be accorded to our observations; and in fact neither philosophers nor physicians deny that an animal is nourished by the same matter out of which it is formed, and is increased by that from which it was engendered. The nutritious dew, therefore, differs from the colliquament or primigenial moisture only in the relation of prior and posterior; the one is concocted and prepared by the parents, the other by the embryo itself, both juices, however, being the proximate and immediate aliment of animals; not indeed "first and second," according to that dictum, "*contraria ex contrariis*," but ultimate, as I have said, and as Aristotle himself admonishes us, according to that other dictum, "*similia ex similibus augeri*," "like is necessarily increased by its like." There is in either fluid a proximate force, in virtue of which, no obstacles intervening, it will pass spontaneously, or by the law of nature, into every part of the animal body.

Such being the state of the question, it is obvious that all controversy about the matter of animals and their nourishment may be settled without difficulty. For as some believe that the semen or matter emitted in intercourse is taken up from every part of the body, so do they derive from this the resemblance of the offspring to the parents. Aristotle has these words: "Against the opinion of the ancients, it may be said that as they avow the semen to be a derivative from all parts else, we believe the semen to be disposed of itself to form every part; and whilst they call it a colliquament, we are rather inclined to regard it as an excrement" (he had, however, said shortly before that he entitled excrement the remains of the nourishment, and colliquament that which is secreted from the growth by a preternatural resolution); "for that which arrives last, and is the excrement of

[1] *On the Generation of Animals*, I. 18; IV. 1.

what is final, is in all probability of the same nature; in the same way as painters have very commonly some remains of colours, which are identical with those they have applied upon their canvass; but anything that is consuming and melting away is corrupt and degenerate. Another argument that the seminal fluid is not a colliquament, but an excrement, is this: that animals of larger growth are less prolific, smaller creatures more fruitful. Now there must be a larger quantity of colliquament in larger than in smaller animals, but less excrement; for as there must be a large consumption of nourishment in a large body, so must there be a small production of excrement. Further, there is no place provided by nature for receiving and storing colliquament; it flows off by the way that is most open to it; but there are receptacles for all the natural excrements—the bowels for the dry excrements, the bladder for the moist; the stomach for matters useful; the genital organs, the uterus, the mammæ for seminal matter —in which several places they collect and run together." After this he goes on by a variety of arguments to prove that the seminal matter from which the fœtus is formed is the same as that which is prepared for the nutrition of the parts at large. As if, should one require some pigment from a painter, he certainly would not go to scrape off what he had already laid on his canvass, but would supply the demand from his store, or from what he had over from his work, which was still of the same nature as that which he might have taken away from his picture. So and in like manner the excrement of the ultimate nutriment, or the remainder of the gluten and dew, is carried to the genital organs and there deposited; and this view is most accordant with the production of eggs by the hen.

The medical writers, too, who hold all the parts to be originally formed from the spermatic fluid, and consequently speak of these under the name of spermatic parts, say that the semen is formed from the ultimate nourishment, which with Aristotle they believe to be the blood, being produced by the virtue of the genital organs, and constituting the "matter" of the fœtus. Now it is obvious enough that the egg is produced by the mother and her ultimate nutriment, the nutritious dew, to wit. That clear part of the egg, therefore, that primigenial, or rather antegenial colliquament, is more truly to be reputed the semen of the cock, although it is not projected in the act of intercourse, but is prepared before intercourse, or is gathered together after this, as happens in many animals,

and as will perhaps be stated more at length by and by, because the geniture of the male, according to Aristotle, coagulates.

When I see, therefore, all the parts formed and increasing from this one moisture, as "matter," and from a primitive root, and the reasons already given combine in persuading us that this ought to be so, I can scarcely refrain from taunting and pushing to extremity the followers of Empedocles and Hippocrates, who believed all similar bodies to be engendered as mixtures by association of the four contrary elements, and to become corrupted by their disjunction; nor should I less spare Democritus and the Epicurean school that succeeded him, who compose all things of congregations of atoms of diverse figure. Because it was an error of theirs in former times, as it is a vulgar error at the present day, to believe that all similar bodies are engendered from diverse or heterogeneous matters. For on this footing, nothing even to the lynx's eye would be similar, one, the same, and continuous; the unity would be apparent only, a kind of congeries or heap—a congregation or collection of extremely small bodies; nor would generation differ in any respect from an aggregation and arrangement of particles.

But neither in the production of animals, nor in the generation of any other "similar" body (whether it were of animal parts, or of plants, stones, minerals, &c.), have I ever been able to observe any congregation of such a kind, or any divers miscibles pre-existing for union in the work of reproduction. For neither, in so far at least as I have had power to perceive, or as reason will carry me, have I ever been able to trace any "similar" parts, such as membranes, flesh, fibres, cartilage, bone, &c., produced in such order, or as co-existent, that from these, as the elements of animal bodies, conjoined organs or limbs, and finally, the entire animal, should be compounded. But, as has been already said, the first rudiment of the body is a mere homogeneous and pulpy jelly, not unlike a concrete mass of spermatic fluid; and from this, under the law of generation, altered, and at the same time split or multifariously divided, as by a divine fiat, from an inorganic an organic mass results; this is made bone, this muscle or nerve, this a receptacle for excrementitious matter, &c.; from a similar a dissimilar is produced; out of one thing of the same nature several of diverse and contrary natures; and all this by no transposition or local movement, as a congregation of similar particles, or a separation of heterogeneous particles is effected under the influence of heat, but rather by the segregation of homogeneous than the union of heterogeneous particles.

And I believe that the same thing takes place in all generation, so that similar bodies have no mixed elements prior to themselves, but rather exist before their elements (these, according to Empedocles and Aristotle, being fire, air, earth, and water; according to chemists, salt, sulphur, and mercury; according to Democritus, certain atoms), as being naturally more perfect than these. There are, I say, both mixed and compound bodies prior to any of the so called elements, into which they are resolved, or in which they end. They are resolved, namely, into these elements according to reason rather than in fact. The so-called elements, therefore, are not prior to those things that are engendered, or that originate, but are posterior rather—they are relics or remainders rather than principles. Neither Aristotle himself nor anyone else has ever demonstrated the separate existence of the elements in the nature of things, or that they were the principles of "similar" bodies.

The philosopher,[1] indeed, when he proceeds to prove that there are elements, still seems uncertain whether the conclusion ought to be that they exist *in esse*, or only *in posse;* he is of opinion that in natural things they are present in power rather than in action; and therefore does he assert, from the division, separation, and solution of things, that there are elements. It is, however, an argument of no great cogency to say that natural bodies are primarily produced or composed of those things into which they are ultimately resolved; for upon this principle some things would come out composed of glass, ashes, and smoke, into which we see them finally

[1] *On the Heavens,* III. 3.

reduced by fire; and as artificial distillation clearly shows that a great variety of vapours and waters of different species can be drawn from so many different bodies, the number of elements would have to be increased to infinity. Nor has any one among the philosophers said that the bodies which, dissolved by art, are held pure and indivisible in their species, are elements of greater simplicity than the air, water, and earth, which we perceive by our senses, which we are familiar with through our eyes.

Nor, to conclude, do we see aught in the shape of miscible matter naturally engendered from fire; and it is perhaps impossible that it should be so, since fire, like that which is alive, is in a perpetual state of fluxion, and seeks for food by which it may be nourished and kept in being; in conformity with the words of Aristotle, that "Fire is only nourished, and is especially remarkable in this."[2] But what is nourished cannot itself be mingled with its nutriment. Whence it follows that it is impossible fire should be miscible. For mixture, according to Aristotle, is the union of altered miscibles, in which one thing is not transformed into another, but two things, severally active and passive, into a third thing. Generation, however, especially generation by metamorphosis, is the distribution of one similar thing having undergone change into several others. Nor are mixed similar bodies said to be generated from the elements, but to be constituted by them in some certain way, solvent forces residing in them at the same time.

These considerations, however, properly belong to the section of *Physiology*, which treats of the elements and temperaments, where it will be our business to speak of them more at large.

[2] *On Generation and Corruption,* II. 8.

THE GREAT IDEAS, *Volumes 2 and 3*